Prototype bridge structures: analysis and design

M. Y. H. Bangash

Thomas Telford

Published by Thomas Telford Publishing, Thomas Telford Limited, 1 Heron Quay, London E14 4JD
URL: http://www.t-telford.co.uk

First published 1999

Distributors for Thomas Telford books are

USA: American Society of Civil Engineers, Publications Sales Department, 345 East 47th Street, New York, NY 10017-2398
Japan: Maruzen Co. Ltd, Book Department, 3–10 Nihonbashi 2-chome, Chuo-ku, Tokyo 103
Australia: DA Books and Journals, 648 Whitehorse Road, Mitcham 3132, Victoria

A catalogue record for this book is available from the British Library

ISBN: 0 7277 2778 8

Typeset in Great Britain by Alden Bookset, Oxford.
Printed and bound in Great Britain by MPG Books Ltd, Bodmin, Cornwall.

Preface

Prototype structures are full-scale structures that belong to facilities that have already been constructed. The bridge structures in this text have been planned, designed and constructed, and they are ready to be serviceable on site. It is necessary to examine and possibly to re-evaluate such structures in detail. Both the pre-design and post-design periods are needed in order thoroughly to assess structural performances for maintaining and preserving the existing facilities, but also to pave the way for the next generation of designing and installing similar bridge structures.

It is a recognized fact that it makes good economic sense to avoid duplication in respect of research and development, the decision-making process, accurate evaluation procedures, efficient repair methods and rational analytical and design criteria. These considerations lead to sound analytical and design techniques. In turn, minimal effect and a reduced economic burden will result if these procedures and techniques are applied to the various constructed facilities of any future prototype bridge structures.

Great effort has been made by the author to highlight all aspects of analysis and design related to prototype bridge structures. The contents of the book have been carefully selected to cover major analytical, numerical and design problems associated with prototype bridge structures. Certain areas could not be presented in this text, but the author has given many references instead and included an extensive bibliography to enable the reader to carry out an in-depth study satisfactorily.

In this book, it has been necessary to dispense with chapters and to replace them with sections. This is because each topic is an entity in itself and needs to be encompassed within a section. One can, therefore, consider this to be a large book comprising a series of mini-books with different titles. A total of seven sections are included in this volume, namely

Section 1. Bridges and their major components
Section 2. Operational research and choice of bridges
Section 3. A review of international codes on bridges
Section 4. Methods of analysis
Section 5. Methods of design

Section 6.   Suspension and cable-stayed bridges
Section 7.   Structural details of some important bridges

Section 1 introduces types of bridge and their components. Here, a vivid approach is adopted, using diagrams, charts and tables to indicate clearly the functional aspects of various bridge components, such as superstructure, substructure, foundations, bearings, railings and bearings-cum-expansion joints. A comparative study and data are included for the reader to make a thorough assessment of various bridge components.

Section 2 is a large section devoted to operational research on bridges. The main theme is to both evaluate and establish a procedure so that a designer can satisfactorily obtain at least a choice for the prototype bridge. Sometimes a tie exists between two choices. In such circumstances, an initial but preliminary design of the two would be needed in order to work out an economic choice. This, of course, involves a number of parameters and factors to be examined, which relate to terrain, soil properties, material properties, vehicular and environmental loading, quantities, costs, etc. A flow chart based on the practical operational indicators is the main prerequisite to such an analysis. Various elimination indicators are available in the flow chart to narrow choice at certain stages. This concept is supported by curves, charts, graphs and tables indicating various parameters and choices in the superstructure, substructure and foundation areas. Costs and inflation factors are incorporated in these charts and graphs, which are flexible and can, therefore, be altered to suit an individual country's requirements, including labour and material costs. The normal operational procedure cannot be affected. During the process, the flow chart provides choices and, later on, minimizes them. The result, at the end, will give a choice for a specific site where the prototype bridge would be recommended. To explain this process, several examples are included to inform the reader of how various case studies can be assessed using the methodology of this operational research. The author has successfully applied this technique in practice and has yielded successful results.

Section 3 gives a thorough review of international codes on bridges. The purpose of this section is to bring various practices to the forefront. The designer now has a clear concept and a useful tool with which to carry out a comparative study of a bridge design. His/Her own evaluation and experience can contribute significantly to the bridge design for a specific country. Where previous experience does not exist, this 'off the shelf' approach can switch over successfully to any new practice, without major hazard and without the necessity to search for objective material.

Section 4 is devoted entirely to the available methods of analysis. The reader is given a choice to suit his/her own skills. All analyses have been compiled successfully in an abridged form without any loss of clarity. Numerous examples are included to justify the requisite analyses.

Section 5 covers methods of design. All types of bridge calculation, based on various codes, are included. Numerous case studies are solved for the reader in order to facilitate understanding of the main theme of a specific code. Among the many important codes examined are the British code, the American code and the Eurocode.

Section 6 is devoted entirely to suspension and cable-stayed bridges and their components. It is a comprehensive section comprising case studies and a litera-ture survey, and covering structural details, material technology, vehicular-cum-environmental loading, analytical/design treatment of cable stays, towers, super-structures, substructures and foundations. Numerous examples based on both codified and 3D finite-element techniques have been included. It is hoped that the reader will benefit from the technical aspects of this subject.

Section 7 covers important structural detailing of prototype bridges. These details can best be understood in conjunction with the details given in other sec-tions. The reader can see how vital these details are for the practical manifesta-tion of all the work carried out in this text. They will be helpful in the arrangement of future programmes of bridge detailing.

To crown all, each section contains numerous analytical and design examples selected on the basis of existing constructed facilities. Examples from both ana-lysis and design have been selected using various practices. This provides the reader with a wide coverage of the international scene. Wherever new codes are operational, such as the Eurocodes, they have received due consideration. This is clear from the contents of the book where such codes give the reader an opportunity to study the comparative analytical and design tools in bridges.

This book is supported by a comprehensive bibliography for those who intend to carry out in-depth study in their individual projects.

The book carries a large Appendix which covers the background analyses and computer subroutines required to execute complicated analyses and designs of prototype structures and their components. With slight adjustments, these can be linked easily to a number of relevant computer packages.

This book will be of use to researchers and practising engineers, designers, technologists, mathematicians and specialists in computer-aided techniques of bridge construction. The major design examples will be beneficial to civil, struc-tural and mechanical engineers who are involved in static and transient load ana-lyses, a comparative study of codified methods and designs, and the preparation of design assignments for individual clients.

The topics covered in this book are within the syllabuses of postgraduate courses at various universities. Both lecturers and students should find the text relevant to their projects and research theses.

This book acts as a technical guide for defence and disaster agencies, research establishments, computer-aided bureaux, construction companies and for those who wish to validate experimental test results and on-site monitoring. Many consultants in bridge design would find this book extremely useful.

M. Y. H. Bangash

Acknowledgements

The author is indebted to many individuals, institutions, organizations and research establishments, mentioned in the book, for helpful discussions and for providing useful practical data and research materials.

The author owes a special debt of gratitude to his family who provided unwavering support, especially T. Bangash for checking some of the hand calculations and Fehmin Bangash for checking the final layout.

I also wish to acknowledge the help given by the following:

Mr Mike Chrimes and his staff, the Institution of Civil Engineers Library, London

Mrs Anita Witten and her staff, the Institution of Structural Engineers Library, London

The American Society of Civil Engineers, New York

The American Concrete Institute, Detroit

The Concrete Society, London

The Royal Institute of British Architects, London

The British Cement Association, UK

Patent Office Library, Chancery Lane, UK

The Home Office, Croydon, Surrey, UK

The Ulster Constabulary, Belfast

The Institution of Chemical Engineers Library, Derby, UK

The MUTO Institute, Tokyo

The Japan Society of Civil Engineers, Tokyo

The Chinese Society of Civil Engineers, Beijing

The Pakistan High Commission, London

The Institution of Mechanical Engineers, London

Der Bauingenieur, Germany

Times Index, Research Publications, Reading, UK

The Ministry of the Environment, UK

The American Association of State Highway and Transportation Officials (AASHTO), California

The Ontario Highways Department, Canada

The European Union Library, Brussels, Belgium

The Asean Countries, Central Library, Korea

Beratende Ingenieure VBI, Hamburg, Germany
Dr Ing Fritz Notzold, Consulting Engineers, Langen, Germany
Transport and Road Research Laboratory, Crowthorne, Berkshire, UK
Flint & Niel, Consulting Engineers, London
Leonhardt, Andra & Partners, Stuttgart, Germany
Swindell Dresseler Corp., Pittsburgh
The Indian Concrete Journal and the Indian Concrete Society, New Dehli
The Punjab Engineering Congress, Lahore, Pakistan
DIANA Analysis, Delft, The Netherlands
Abacus, Manchester
FIP Industriale, SpA, Italy
BBR Systems Ltd, Switzerland
Weidlinger Associates Ltd, New York
Acrow Corporation of America, New Jersey
The D. S. Brown & Co, Baltimore, Ohio, USA
The International Association of Bridge and Structural Engineering
    c/o the Institution of Structural Engineers, London
J. Muller International, San Diego, California, USA
Parsons Brinckerhoff, New York
Yapi Merkezi Inc., Instanbul
Nippon Steel, Tokyo
Takenaka Corporation, Tokyo
Nihon Sekki, Ltd, Tokyo
Hyder Consultants, Surrey, UK
Alan Grant & Partners, Cobham, Surrey, UK
Mott Macdonald, Croydon, Surrey, UK
Gifford & Partners, UK
US Agency for International Development, Washington DC
Civil and Structural Computer Services Ltd, Newtonabbey, Co. Antrim, UK
Taylor Woodrow Construction, Southall, UK

This acknowledgement would be incomplete without praising the enormous help given by the City of London Police and the UK Highways Agency, and the computer bureaux STRUCOM Ltd, London, and the FEA, Kingston, Surrey, UK.

Conversion Tables – I

Imperial units	SI units	Additional
1 in	$= 25.4\,\text{mm}$	
1 in^3	$= 0.003785\,(\text{m}^3)$	
1 ft	$= 30.48\,\text{cm}$	
1 ft^2	$= 0.09290\,(\text{m}^2)$;	$1\,\text{ft}^3 = 0.02832\,(\text{m}^3)$
10 ga	$= 3.57\,\text{mm}$	$1\,\text{cu yard} = 0.765\,(\text{m}^3)$
18 ga	$= 1.27\,\text{mm}$	
1 lb	$= 0.454\,\text{kg}$	
1 ton	$= 9.964\,\text{kN}$	
1 sq ft	$= 929\,(\text{cm})^2$	
1 cubic ft	$= 16.4\,(\text{cm})^3$	
1 psi	$= 6.89\,\text{kPa}$	$= 6895\,\text{Pascal (Pa)}$
20 T/ft^2	$= 1915.2\,\text{kN/m}^2$	
1 lb/sq ft	$= 992.16\,\text{kPa}$	$= 47.88\,\text{Pascal (Pa)}$
1 lb/ft^3	$= 16.02\,\text{kg/m}^3$	
1 ft lb	$= 1.356\,\text{N.m}$	
1 ft/sec	$= 0.3048\,\text{M/s}$	
1 slug	$= 14.59\,\text{kg}$	
1 in lb	$= 0.1129848\,\text{Nm}$	
1 kip/in	$= 175.1268\,\text{kN/m}$	
1 bar	$= 100\,\text{kN/m}^2$	
1 kip	$= 1000\,\text{lb}$	$= 4.448\,\text{kN}$
1 short ton (2000 lb)	$= 0.9072\,\text{Megagram (Mg)}$	

MKS units	SI units
1 Pascal (Pa)	$= 1\,\text{N/m}^2$
1 kgm	$= 9.807\,\text{Nm}$
1 kgf	$= 9.807\,\text{N}$

Temperature in °C (Celsius)

$1°\text{F (Fahrenheit)} = t_\text{f} = \frac{5}{9}\text{K};$ $t_\text{c} = (t_\text{f} - 32)/118$

$1°\text{C}$ $t_\text{f} = 1.8t_\text{c} + 32$

$1\,\text{BTU} = 1055\,\text{J}$

$1 \, \text{m}^2/\text{g}$ $= 1000 \, \text{m}^2/\text{kg}$

$1 \, \text{mm}^2/\text{mg}$ $= 1 \, \text{m}^2/\text{kg}$

$1 \, \text{radian}$ $= 57.296 \, \text{deg}$

$1 \, \text{ft}/\text{sec}$ $= 0.3048 \, \text{m}/\text{sec}$

Conversion Tables – II

Bars
Britain, Europe
Japan, Russia

Bar types (mm)	8	10	12	16	20	25	32	40

USA Canada
South America
Bar types (mm)
denoted by #
or no.

#3	#4	#5	#6	#7	#8	#9	#10	#11	#14	#18
				(22 mm)		(29 mm)		(35 mm)	(43 mm)	(57 mm)

Area (mm^2)

50		113		314		491		804		1257			2581
	78		201		387		645		1006		1452		

Fabric
Fabric reinforcement is manufactured to BS 4483 and to STM requirements. The following are four types of fabric made from hard drawn mild steel wire of $f_y = 485 \, \text{N/mm}^2$ or from cold-worked high-yield bars:

(a) Square mesh fabric: Regular bars of lightweight (A Type). They are used in walls and slabs.

(b) Structural fabric: Main wires 100 mm crs (B Type), cross-wires 200 mm crs.

(c) Long mesh fabric: Main wires 100 mm crs (C Type), cross-wires 400 mm crs.

(d) Wrapping fabric: Lightweight square mesh (D Type) encased conditions for fire resistance; main wire cross-sectional area is 252 mm^2; $f_y = 250 \, \text{N/mm}^2$

Mesh type	Size of wires (mm)		Area (mm^2)		Weight (kg/m^2)
	Main	Cross	Main	Cross	
1. Square mesh (200 × 200) A 393	10	10	3	393	6.16
2. Structural fabric (100 × 200) B 1131	12	8	1131	252	10.90
3. Long mesh fabric (400 × 400) C 785	10	6	785	70.8	6.72
4. Wrapping fabric D49 (100 × 100)	2.5	2.5	49	49	0.76

Contents

Section 3. A review of international codes on bridges: loads and load distribution

PROTOTYPE BRIDGE STRUCTURES

SECTION 1
BRIDGES AND THEIR MAJOR COMPONENTS

1. Bridges and their major components

1.1 General introduction to types of bridge

A bridge is subdivided into (*a*) the superstructure, (*b*) the substructure and (*c*) the foundation. The bridge deck system is the part of the superstructure directly carrying the vehicular loads. It is furnished with balustrades or parapets, crash barriers, highway surfacing, footpaths, traffic islands, railway tracks on ties, expansion joints and drainage systems. The substructure comprises piers, columns or abutments, capping beams and bearings. The foundations consist of reinforced concrete footings, spread foundations, rafts bearing directly on soil or rock and capping slabs supported on piles, wells and caissons. The super-structure of the bridge deck system can be any one or a combination of the following: slabs, coffered slabs, grids, beams, girders, cantilevers, frames, trusses and arches, cables, suspenders and cable-stayed.

Deck surface members may be classified into the three groups which may be of precast, cast-*in situ* and composite construction. They may be of conventional steel reinforcement, partially or fully prestressed or composite construction. The following classified system lists fully the types of bridge constructed in reinforced, prestressed and composite materials.

(*a*) *Slabs*
  (*i*) solid slabs ⎫ supported directly on piers, with or without haunches or
  (*ii*) void slabs ⎭ drop heads;
  (*iii*) coffered slabs – they act like a grid;
  (*iv*) above with beams of reinforced concrete and prestressed concrete (precast or *in situ* beams).

(*b*) *Beams**
  (*i*) longitudinal stringed beams with webs spaced apart and integral with the deck slab;
  (*ii*) longitudinal and transverse beams forming a grid system integral with the deck slab;

(*iii*) inverted longitudinal beams, trusses, and girders, fully or partially integral with the deck;

(*iv*) a single central longitudinal spine beam, T-beam; truss and girder composite or monolithic deck.

Note:

T-beams (precast beam slab deck)

(*a*) T-beam with *in situ* concrete topping;

(*b*) 'tophat' beams with *in situ* concrete topping;

(*c*) continuous beams.

Span range for:

(*a*) precast post-tensioned I-beam 20–35 m;

(*b*) precast post-tensioned T-beam ranges up to 45 m.

(c) **Boxes**

(*i*) A single longitudinal box beam or several box beams with and without cantilevered top flanges comprised of:

(*a*) a double-webbed single unicellular box;

(*b*) twin or multiple unicellular boxes with or without cross-beams or diaphragms.

(d) **Frames (with or without struts)**

These may have members in one or more plane. They may be portal frames (single or multiple), vierendeel girders trestle piers, spill-through abutments and towers for cable-stayed or suspension bridges } Short-span bridges over highways or rivers or flyovers over freeways.

(e) **Arches**

These are classified as:

(*i*) solid arches;

(*ii*) open spandrel arches;

(*iii*) solid spandrel arches;

(*iv*) tied arches;

(*v*) funicular arches;

(*vi*) strut-frame with inclined legs.

(f) **Suspension and cable-stayed bridges**

Suspension bridges with draped cables and vertical or triangulated suspender hangers are adopted for spans exceeding 300 m. *Cable-stayed* bridges are economical over the span range of the order of 100 to 700 m with concrete deck, pylons and frames. For cable-stayed the elevational and transverse arrangments are given below.

(*i*) Elevational arrangement:
single, radiating, harp, fan, star and
combination.
(*ii*) Transverse arrangement:
single plane (vertical – central or eccentric);
double plane (vertical or sloping).

} No: cables single,
double, triple, multiple
or combined.

Figures 1.1 to 1.10 show some typical bridge decks.

Figure 1.1. Typical reinforced concrete decks

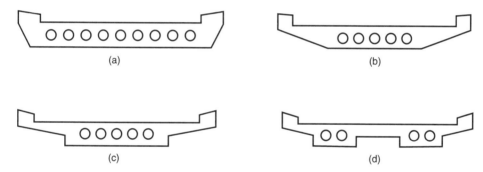

(a)

(b)

(c)

(d)

Figure 1.2. Typical voided decks

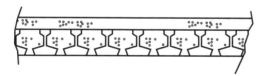

Figure 1.3. Pseudo slab

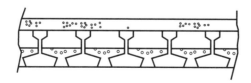

Figure 1.4. Pseudo box

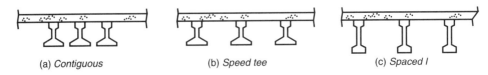

(a) Contiguous   *(b) Speed tee*   *(c) Spaced I*

Figure 1.5. Prestressed concrete beam and slab

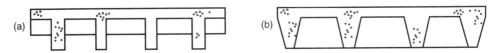

(a)   (b)

Figure 1.6. Reinforced concrete beam and slab

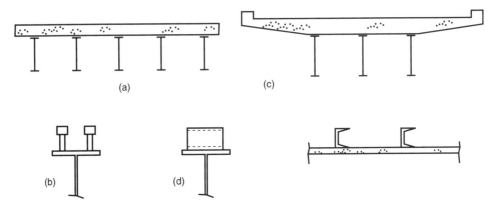

(a)   (c)

(b)   (d)

Figure 1.7. Steel beam and concrete slab

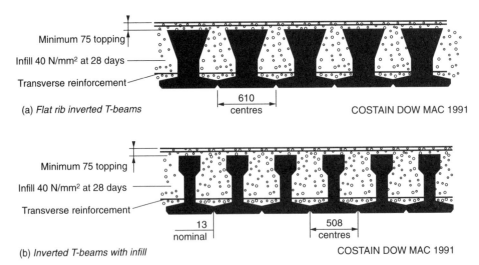

Minimum 75 topping
Infill 40 N/mm² at 28 days
Transverse reinforcement

610 centres

(a) Flat rib inverted T-beams   COSTAIN DOW MAC 1991

Minimum 75 topping
Infill 40 N/mm² at 28 days
Transverse reinforcement

13 nominal   508 centres

(b) Inverted T-beams with infill   COSTAIN DOW MAC 1991

Figure 1.8 (pages 8–10). Bridge deck structural details (courtesy: Cement Association and Concrete Society, UK)

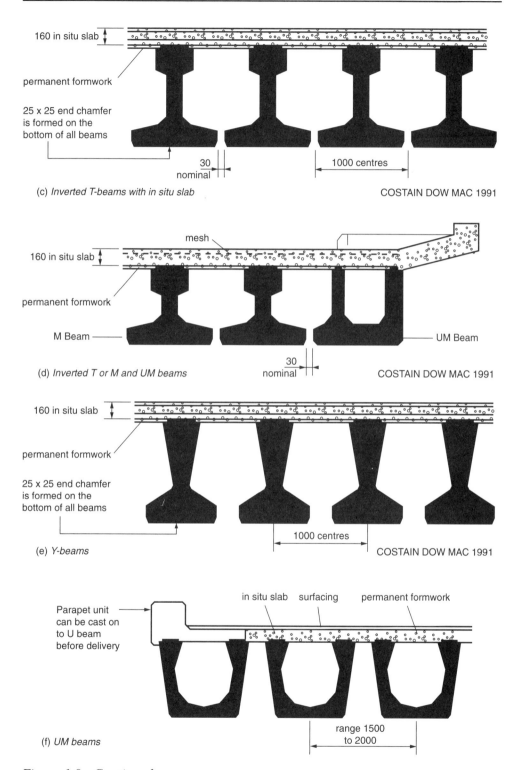

160 in situ slab

permanent formwork

25 x 25 end chamfer is formed on the bottom of all beams

30 nominal

1000 centres

(c) *Inverted T-beams with in situ slab*

COSTAIN DOW MAC 1991

mesh

160 in situ slab

permanent formwork

M Beam

UM Beam

30 nominal

(d) *Inverted T or M and UM beams*

COSTAIN DOW MAC 1991

160 in situ slab

permanent formwork

25 x 25 end chamfer is formed on the bottom of all beams

1000 centres

(e) *Y-beams*

COSTAIN DOW MAC 1991

Parapet unit can be cast on to U beam before delivery

in situ slab   surfacing   permanent formwork

range 1500 to 2000

(f) *UM beams*

Figure 1.8. Continued

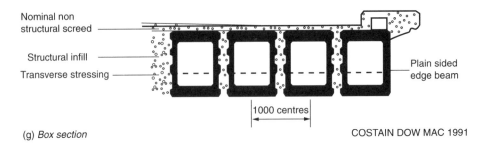

(g) *Box section*   COSTAIN DOW MAC 1991

Figure 1.8. Continued

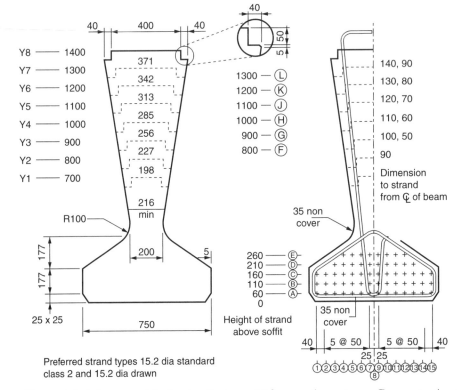

Figure 1.9 (above and facing). Data on Y-beams (courtesy: Concrete Association and Concrete Society, UK)

1.2   Types of load acting on bridges

These are classified as follows:

(*i*)   *Permanent and long-term loads*:
  dead; superimposed; earth pressure and water pressure of excluded or retained water.

(*ii*)   *Transient and variable loads (primary type)*:
  vehicular loading; railway loading; footway loading and cycle loading.

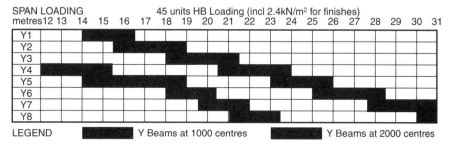

SECTION PROPERTIES   Design self weight per unit volume has been taken as 23.6 kN/m

Section No	Depth mm	Area mm²	Yb mm	Zt mm³ x 10⁶	Zb mm³ x 10⁶	App self weight kN/m
Y1	700	309202	255	24.85	43.40	7.42
Y2	800	339882	299	35.02	58.78	8.14
Y3	900	373444	347	47.88	76.27	8.95
Y4	1000	409890	400	63.53	95.41	9.82
Y5	1100	449220	456	82.06	116.02	10.78
Y6	1200	491433	515	103.58	138.00	11.78
Y7	1300	536530	576	128.15	161.31	12.86
Y8	1400	584708	639	155.98	186.01	14.02

Figure 1.9. Continued

(iii)   *Short-term load*:
erection loads; dynamic and impact loads.
(iv)   *Transient forces*:
braking and traction forces; forces due to accidental skidding and vehicle collision with parapet or with bridge supports.
(v)   *Lurching and nosing by trains.*
(vi)   *Transient forces* due to natural causes:
wind action; flood action and seismic forces.
(vii)   *Environmental effects*:
loads generated due to creep, shrinkage of concrete; prestress parasitic moments or reactions and prestrain and temperature range or gradient.

Relevant codes are consulted for the application of these loads on bridge structures.

1.3 Substructures supporting deck structures
The deck structures are supported directly on:

(a)   mass concrete or masonry gravity abutments;
(b)   closed-end abutments with solid or void walls such as cantilevers, struts or diaphragms;
(c)   counterforted or buttressed walls or combinations;
(d)   open-end or spill-through abutments with trestle beams supported on columns.

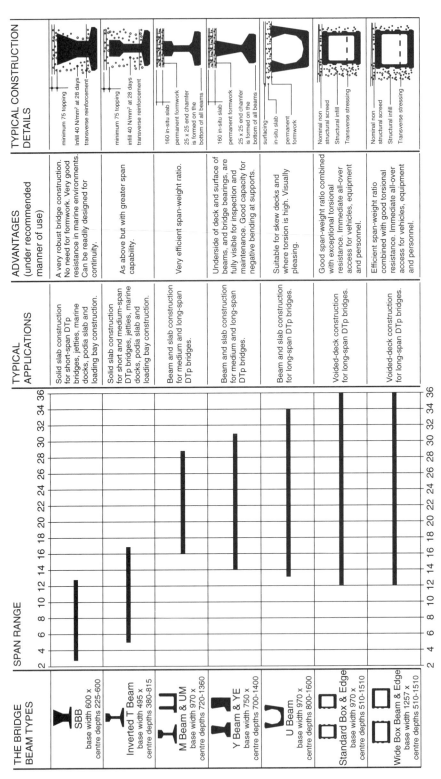

Figure 1.10. Reinforced and prestressed concrete deck systems. The chart gives a guide to the span range of the seven Costain Dow Mac Bridge Beam types for maximum DTp loading, in the recommended manner of use. (The UM and YE beams are used with the M and the Y-beams, respectively.) The final choice of beam and the detailed design will be determined by the relevant performance specification

The intermediate piers can be of the following type:

(*a*) solid or void walls with or without capping beams;
(*b*) single solid or void columns with or without caps;
(*c*) trestles and bents;
(*d*) specially shaped columns, e.g. V-shaped or fork shaped etc.

In most cases bridge bearings are needed to transmit deck loads to substructures and to allow the deck to respond to environmental and vehicle loads.

1.4 Foundations

(*a*) Shallow foundation
These foundations are constructed with or without the help of coffer-dams:
(*i*) Ordinary footings
(*ii*) Raft foundations
(*iii*) Grillage foundations
(*b*) Deep foundation
Bed dry during the process of construction
(*i*) Wooden piles
(*ii*) RC or prestressed concrete piles (precast or cast-*in situ*)
(*iii*) Cast iron piles
(*iv*) Steel piles
(*c*) Deep foundation
Laying under water
(*i*) Box cassions
(*ii*) Cylinder caissons or well foundations of masonry, steel or RC with or without combinations
(*iii*) Caissons with dredging wells
(*iv*) Pneumatic caissons.

1.5 Additional classification of bridges

The bridges are also classified on the basis of usage and these classifications are:

I. Permanent bridges
(*a*) permanent big bridges
(*b*) permanent small bridges
II. Temporary bridges
(*a*) Temporary fixed bridges
(*b*) Movable bridges.

Under I(a), bridges are:

(*i*) *Girder bridges* with various supports and boundary conditions made in steel, concrete, timber and composite. They include solid and cellular construction, plate and truss bridges.

(*ii*)   *Arch bridges, box types* and *suspension* and *cable-stayed bridges*. These are
        considered in greater detail later in Section 6.

Under II(a), bridges are:

  (*i*)   High level causeways
 (*ii*)   Low level causeways
(*iii*)   Metal dips
 (*iv*)   Beam and truss types
  (*v*)   Ramp bridges, trestle and sling bridges.

Under II(b), the movable bridges can be

  (*i*)   Swing bridges
 (*ii*)   Bascule bridges, single or double
(*iii*)   Transverse bridges
 (*iv*)   Transporter bridges
  (*v*)   Lift bridges
 (*vi*)   Flying bridges
(*vii*)   Cut boat bridges.

1.6   Bridge bearings

Bearings are the supporting structures needed to transmit loads from the superstructure to the substructure of the bridge. Their performances are well established and they vary in sizes and capacities to bridge characteristics including
loads and spans.

   The bridge can be rigidly connected to the sole plate and can be made free to
move in a longitudinal direction (expansions and contractions) due to temperature and live load forces.

   British Standard 5400 Part 9 and other codes provide guides on the design of
the component parts of a bearing, dealing with the use of materials, strength
and movement characteristics. The selection of a bearing is determined by the
capacity of a bearing to sustain dead and live or imposed loads in any combination both in serviceability and ultimate limit state conditions for specific bridge
parameters and requirements. Various specifications from the manufacturers are
included.

1.6.1   CCL plain unreinforced pads and strips

CCL plain unreinforced pads and strips are manufactured in 60 IRHD natural
rubber to BS 5400: Part 9: 1983 (see Fig. 1.11). The pads and strips are produced
from moulded rubber sheets 1 metre wide and 3 metres long. Hence, strip can
only be supplied in continuous lengths of up to 3 m long.

   Although any size bearing can be made to order, the more common sizes are
detailed together with their calculated performance. The values listed have been
determined utilizing the design guidelines given in BS 5400: Part 9: 1983.

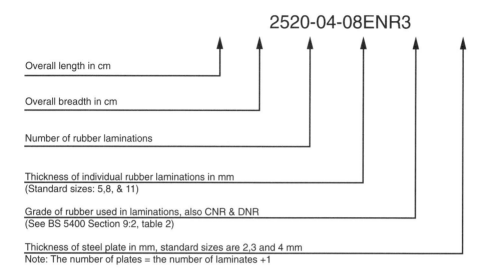

OTHER INFORMATION

Top & bottom cover thickness = 2.5 mm   Side cover thickness = 4.5 mm

TO CALCULATE TOTAL THICKNESS OF BEARING

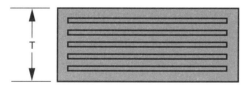

T = Top & bottom cover thickness + total thickness of rubber lamination + total thickness of plates

Example:
Bearing Ref: 2520-04-08ENR3
Number of rubber laminations = 4
Thickness of lamination = 8 mm
Number of plates = 4 + 1 = 5
Thickness of plate = 3 mm

T = (2.5 + 2.5) + (4 x 8) + (5 x 3) = 52 mm

Figure 1.11. CCL Systems' elastomeric bearing reference code

The rubber utilized is checked during its production to ensure close compliance with the British Standard. Whilst certificates of conformity can be issued, no actual testing is carried out on plain rubber unless specifically ordered. CCL does not recommend compression or shear testing plain rubber and suggest only physical property testing.

Tables 1.1 and 1.2 provide data for the strips and pads, respectively.

Table 1.1. CCL plain unreinforced strips

Dimensions (mm)		Load capacity	Rotational capacity	Compressive stiffness	Max shear movement	Shear stiffness	Reference code
l	*t*	*V kN/m*	*rads/100 kN/m*	*K_c kN/mm/m*	*mm*	*K_s kN/mm/m*	
100	12	208	0.01492	200	8.4	7.50	10E12
150	12	468	0.00294	678	8.4	11.25	15E12
200	12	833	0.00093	1607	8.4	15.00	20E12
250	12	1125	0.00038	3139	8.4	18.75	25E12
300	12	1350	0.00018	5425	8.4	22.50	30E12
100	15	166	0.02916	102	10.5	6.00	10E15
150	15	375	0.00576	347	10.5	9.00	15E15
200	15	666	0.00182	823	10.5	12.00	20E15
250	15	1041	0.00074	1607	10.5	15.00	25E15
300	15	1350	0.00036	2777	10.5	18.00	30E15
100	19	131	0.05926	50	13.3	4.74	10E19
150	19	296	0.01170	170	13.3	7.11	15E19
200	19	526	0.00370	404	13.3	9.47	20E19
250	19	822	0.00151	790	13.3	11.84	25E19
300	19	1184	0.00073	1366	13.3	14.21	30E19
100	25	100	0.135	22	17.5	3.60	10E25
150	25	225	0.02666	75	17.5	5.40	15E25
200	25	400	0.00843	177	17.5	7.20	20E25
250	25	625	0.00345	347	17.5	9.00	25E25
300	25	900	0.00166	600	17.5	10.80	30E25

1.6.2 Uplift bearings

True uplift bearings, capable of resisting upward or downward vertical loading while retaining full articulation capability in both modes, are individually designed as an extension of the spherical range (see Fig. 1.12). Three types are produced, fixed (allowing no horizontal movement), free (allowing horizontal movement in either direction), and guided (allowing horizontal movement in one direction only while resisting horizontal forces in the other).

1.6.3 'Hi-Load' roller bearings

Through-hardened rollers of high tensile 'Hi-Load' steel, running on plates of the same material, can carry large vertical loads, with very little resistance to movement.

'Hi-Load' high chromium steel has a tensile strength, in the hardened and tempered condition, of about $1500 \, N/mm^2$. All contact surfaces are finely ground, with a hardness of at least 425 HB, so that a design coefficient of friction of 0.01 is appropriate for single rollers, although still lower values, down to

Table 1.2. CCL plain unreinforced pads: data

Dimensions (mm)			Load capacity $V\,kN$	Rotational capacity rads/100 kN	Compressive stiffness $K_c\,kN/mm$	Max shear movement mm	Shear stiffness $K_s\,kN/mm$	Reference code
l	b	t						
150	200	12	53	0.046	43	8.4	2.250	1520E12
150	300	12	93	0.022	89	8.4	3.375	1530E12
200	300	12	150	0.0087	170	8.4	4.500	2030E12
200	400	12	222	0.0053	279	8.4	6.000	2040E12
250	400	12	320	0.0025	462	8.4	7.500	2540E12
250	500	12	434	0.0017	675	8.4	9.375	2550E12
300	500	12	585	0.0009	1016	8.4	11.250	3050E12
300	600	12	750	0.0007	1380	8.4	13.500	3060E12
400	600	12	1080	0.0003	2597	8.4	18.000	4060E12
150	200	15	42	0.090	22	10.5	1.800	1520E15
150	300	15	75	0.043	45	10.5	2.700	1530E15
200	300	15	120	0.017	87	10.5	3.600	2030E15
200	400	15	177	0.0105	144	10.5	4.800	2040E15
250	400	15	256	0.005	239	10.5	6.000	2540E15
250	500	15	347	0.0034	349	10.5	7.500	2550E15
300	500	15	468	0.0018	528	10.5	9.000	3050E15
300	600	15	600	0.0013	718	10.5	10.800	3060E15
400	600	15	960	0.0005	1361	10.5	14.400	4060E15
150	200	19	33	0.18	11	13.3	1.421	1520E19
150	300	19	59	0.0884	22	13.3	2.131	1530E19
200	300	19	94	0.0347	43	13.3	2.842	2030El9
200	400	19	140	0.0210	71	13.3	3.789	2040El9
250	400	19	202	0.010	118	13.3	4.736	2540El9
250	500	19	274	0.0068	173	13.3	5.921	2550El9
300	500	19	370	0.0037	262	13.3	7.105	3050El9
300	600	19	473	0.0027	357	13.3	8.526	3060El9
400	600	19	757	0.0011	680	13.3	11.368	4060El9
150	200	25	25	0.42	4	17.5	1.080	1520E25
150	300	25	45	0.20	9	17.5	1.620	1530E25
200	300	25	72	0.078	19	17.5	2.160	2030E25
200	400	25	106	0.0479	31	17.5	2.880	2040E25
250	400	25	153	0.0230	52	17.5	3.600	2540E25
250	500	25	208	0.0156	76	17.5	4.500	2550E25
300	500	25	281	0.0086	116	17.5	5.400	3050E25
300	600	25	360	0.0063	158	17.5	6.480	3060E25
400	600	25	576	0.0024	302	17.5	8.640	4060E25

0.0002 are regularly obtained in test. In service, the rollers are surrounded with a grease box, to arrest corrosion and prevent the ingress of dirt and debris.

The impact resistance of 'Hi-Load' steel does not vary significantly in the range $-70°C$ to $200°C$, so these rollers are suitable for use worldwide.

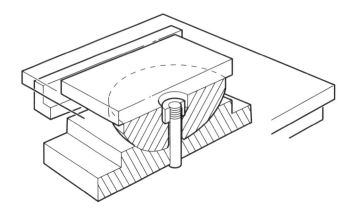

Figure 1.12. Plan of an uplift bearing

Each roller is guided, by means of flanges, which engage on the sides of the contact plates, to prevent skewing and lateral movement, and also to resist lateral forces. In addition, to ensure that the roller does not slide, and to prevent it being displaced by relative rotation between the two contact plates, pinions attached to the ends of the roller engage in racks alongside the plates (Fig. 1.13).

Mild steel distributing plates, Grade 43A to BS 4360, are used as backing to the 'Hi-Load' roller plates, to reduce the contact stress at full vertical load, to less than $20 \, \text{N/mm}^2$ throughout the range.

See Table 1.3 for details of single roller bearings.

1.6.4 Steel linear rocker bearings

Steel linear rocker bearings are manufactured from either high tensile steel to BS 4360 or 'Hi-Load' steel, as described in Section 1.6.3.

The standard design, in steel to BS 4360, consists of a linear rocker on a flat plate, with horizontal fixity being provided by dowels passing from one to the other. Mild steel distributing plates, Grade 43A to BS 4360, are used to reduce the contact stress at full vertical load to less than $20 \, \text{N/mm}^2$ throughout the range (Fig. 1.14).

Steel cylindrical rocker bearings are complementary to the steel roller bearing range, and are normally used to provide longitudinal fixity in the structure (see Table 1.4).

1.6.5 Knuckle bearings

Multiple knuckle bearings are individually designed, in steel to BS 4360, with phosphor bronze brushes on the pin, to suit applications where complete reversals of vertical loading can occur, from downwards to upwards, where very large horizontal forces have to be resisted, or where very large rotations are required about a single axis (Fig. 1.15). Limited horizontal movement capability can be provided along the pin if necessary.

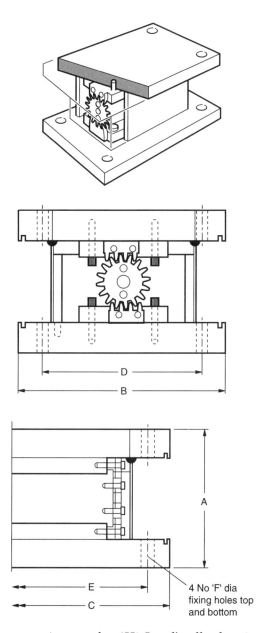

Figure 1.13. Three perspectives on the 'Hi-Load' roller bearing

1.6.6 Guide bearings

In bridges supported entirely on elastomeric bearings, it is often necessary to provide mechanical restraint, to prevent excessive lateral movement of the superstructure.

PSC Guide Bearings have been developed to meet such a requirement, and will resist forces in one horizontal direction, while sliding freely in the other

Table 1.3. Standard 'Hi-Load' single roller bearings (for ±50 movement)

Bearing type	Principal dimensions (mm)						'Working stress' design (kN)	BS.5400: Section 9.1 Design load effects (kN)	
	A	B	C	D	E	F		Serviceability limit state	Ultimate limit state
RM 100	235	490	460	370	340	M24	1 000	1 000	1 300
RM 150	235	490	520	370	400	M24	1 500	1 500	2 000
RM 200	255	490	590	370	470	M24	2 000	2 000	2 500
RM 250	255	490	660	370	540	M24	2 500	2 500	3 300
RM 300	280	490	640	370	520	M24	3 000	3 000	4 000
RM 350	280	490	690	370	570	M24	3 500	3 500	4 600
RM 400	280	490	740	370	620	M24	4 000	4 000	5 300
RM 450	280	490	790	370	670	M24	4 500	4 500	6 000
RM 500	325	530	830	350	650	M42	5 000	5 000	6 600
RM 600	325	530	920	350	740	M42	6 000	6 000	8 000
RM 700	345	530	1000	350	820	M42	7 000	7 000	9 300
RM 800	400	530	980	350	800	M42	8 000	8 000	10 500
RM 900	420	550	1110	320	880	M48	9 000	9 000	12 000
RM 1000	420	550	1180	320	950	M48	10 000	10 000	13 500
RM 1200	550	650	1110	420	880	M48	12 000	12 000	15 000
RM 1400	550	650	1220	420	990	M48	14 000	14 000	18 500
RM 1600	550	650	1320	420	1090	M48	16 000	16 000	21 000

Standard lateral load resistance –
Working stress design or serviceability limit state 250 kN.
Ultimate limit state 300 kN.

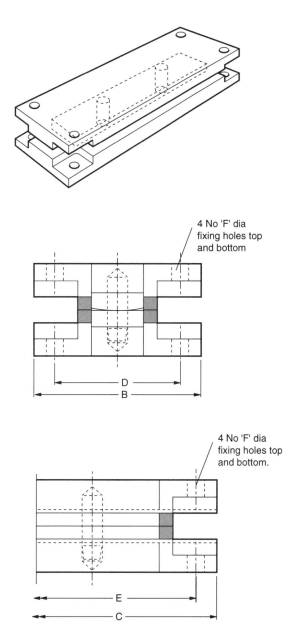

Figure 1.14. Three perspectives on the steel linear rocker bearing

(Fig. 1.16). They will not carry vertical loads, and have a limited capacity for vertical movement, to permit compression and creep to occur in the main support system, and to accept rotation of the superstructure.

The sliding keyway is lined with metal-reinforced PTFE, running on stainless steel, to give a coefficient of friction of 0.03.

Table 1.4. Linear rocker bearings (±0.015 radians rotation capacity)

| Bearign type | Principal dimensions (mm) | | | | | | BS.5400: Section 9.1 Design load effects (kN) | | | | | |
| | | | | | | | 'Working stress' design (kN) | | Serviceability limit state | | Ultimate limit state | |
	A	B	C	D	E	F	Vertical	Resolved horizontal	Vertical	Resolved horizontal	Vertical	Resolved horizontal
PB 100	120	215	335	150	270	M24	1000	400	1000	400	1500	600
PB 150	120	215	410	150	345	M24	1500	400	1500	400	2300	600
PB 200	130	235	505	170	440	M24	2000	400	2000	400	3000	600
PB 250	140	255	575	190	510	M24	2500	400	2500	400	3000	600
PB 300	175	330	610	220	500	M36	3000	900	3000	900	4500	1200
PB 400	175	330	685	220	575	M36	4000	900	4000	900	6000	1200
PB 500	185	350	765	240	655	M36	5000	900	5000	900	7500	1200
PB 600	195	370	865	260	755	M36	6000	900	6000	900	9000	1200
PB 700	205	390	965	280	B55	M36	7000	900	7000	900	10000	1200

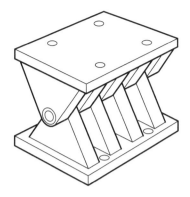

Figure 1.15. Plan of a knuckle bearing

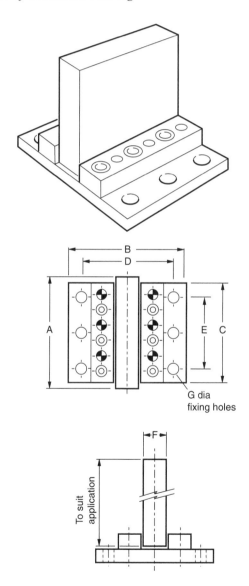

Figure 1.16. Three perspectives on a guide bearing

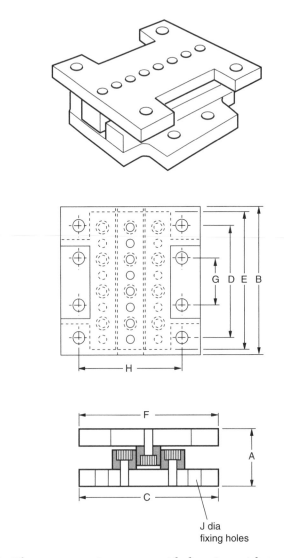

Figure 1.17. Three perspectives on a guide bearing with top plate

1.6.7 Fixed pin bearings

Complementary to the guide bearing range, fixed pin bearings provide complete horizontal restraint, but will not carry vertical loads; they have a limited capacity for vertical movement, and will rotate about any horizontal axis, and also about the centre vertical axis (see Fig. 1.18).

1.6.8 Free sliding pot bearings

Designs are given in Fig. 1.19 and data in Table 1.5.

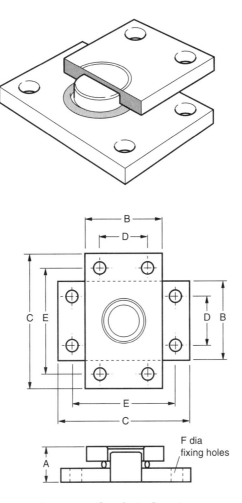

Figure 1.18. Two perspectives on a fixed pin bearing

1.6.9 Removable bearings

Removable bearings can be removed from a structure with minimum of jacking when used in conjunction with cast-in sockets or similar devices.

Tetron D3T: Fixed

Fixed in all directions, free to rotate in all directions (see Fig. 1.20 and Table 1.6).

Tetron D3E: Free sliding

Free sliding in all directions, free to rotate in all directions (see Fig. 1.21 and Table 1.7).

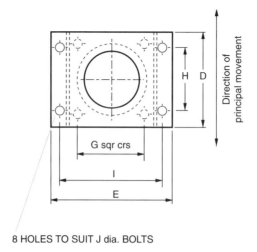

Direction of
principal movement

H D

G sqr crs

I

E

8 HOLES TO SUIT J dia. BOLTS

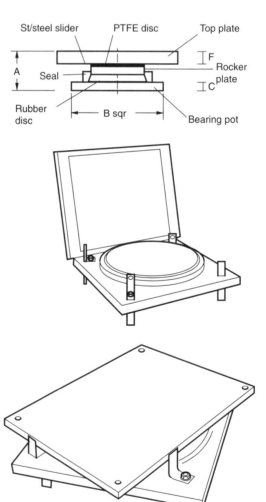

St/steel slider   PTFE disc   Top plate

F
A   Rocker
Seal   C plate

Rubber   B sqr
disc   Bearing pot

Figure 1.19. Four perspectives on a free sliding pot bearing

Table 1.5. Data for free sliding pot bearings

| Bearing code | Principal dimensions (mm) | | | | | | | | | | BS 5400: Section 9.1 Design load effects (kN) | | |
| | | | | | | | | | | | Serviceability limit state | | Ultimate limit state |
	A	B	C	D	E	F	G	H	I	J	Perm. vert.	Total vert.	Vertical
PS50	67	185	15	205	255	17	150	170	220	M12	330	500	660
PS75	74	235	20	235	295	19	190	190	250	M16	500	750	1000
PS100	79	260	20	255	335	24	210	200	290	M16	660	1000	1330
PS125	87	295	25	275	375	27	240	220	320	M20	830	1250	1660
PS150	99	310	30	300	395	29	250	240	340	M20	1000	1500	2000
PS200	104	355	30	345	445	34	300	270	390	M20	1330	2000	2660
PS250	114	385	35	380	485	38	320	300	430	M20	1660	2500	3330
PS300	128	425	40	415	515	43	360	300	460	M20	2000	3000	4000
PS350	129	465	40	460	565	43	400	320	510	M20	2330	3500	4660
PS400	143	490	45	500	605	48	410	340	550	M20	2660	4000	5330
PS500	153	555	50	540	655	53	470	370	600	M20	3330	5000	6660
PS600	168	600	55	610	715	58	500	400	660	M20	4000	6000	8000
PS750	178	670	60	660	765	63	550	440	710	M20	5000	7500	10000
PS1000	198	780	65	780	885	73	650	490	830	M20	6660	10000	13330

These dimensions allow for ±25 mm longitudinal movement and ±10 mm transverse movement. Greater movement will require alteration to the top plate dimensions.

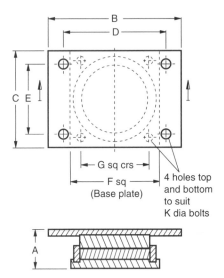

Figure 1.20. The Tetron D3T removable bearing

Table 1.6. Data for Tetron D3T bearings

Bearing type	Principal dimensions (mm)								'Working stress' design (kN)	
									Max. load vertical	Max. load horizontal
	A	B	C	D	E	F	G	K		
D3T 50	58	235	170	195	120	170	130	M12	500	100
D3T 80	75	340	235	280	155	235	175	M20	800	150
D3T 100	80	355	250	295	170	250	190	M20	1 000	150
D3T 125	83	375	270	315	190	270	210	M20	1 250	190
D3T 160	92	395	290	335	210	290	230	M20	1 600	220
D3T 200	97	460	335	385	240	335	260	M20	2 000	250
D3T 250	97	485	360	410	270	360	285	M20	2 500	280
D3T 325	116	575	410	475	280	410	310	M20	3 250	300
D3T 400	127	615	450	515	330	450	350	M24	4 000	360
D3T 500	132	680	515	580	390	515	410	M30	5 000	500
D3T 650	141	770	570	645	420	570	440	M30	6 500	600
D3T 800	156	835	635	710	490	635	510	M30	8 000	650
D3T 1000	175	950	710	805	540	710	560	M30	10 000	700
D3T 1250	179	1015	785	870	620	785	640	M30	12 500	900
D3T 1600	203	1140	870	970	680	870	700	M30	16 000	1000
D3T 2000	203	1260	985	1090	780	985	800	M36	20 000	1300
D3T 2500	232	1425	1100	1220	875	1100	895	M42	25 000	1600
D3T 3000	257	1550	1230	1350	1000	1230	1030	M42	30 000	2000

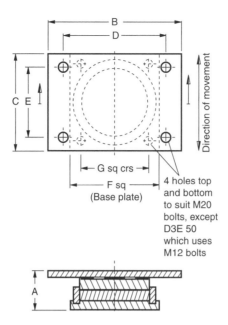

Figure 1.21. The Tetron D3E removable bearing

Table 1.7. Data for Tetron D3E bearings

Bearing type	Principal dimensions (mm)							'Working stress' design (kN)	
								Max. rotation	Max. load vertical
	A	B*	C*	D*	E*	F	G	(Radians)	
D3E 50	60	235	170	195	120	170	130	0.026	500
D3E 80	73	340	235	280	155	235	175	0.026	800
D3E 100	78	355	250	295	170	250	190	0.026	1 000
D3E 125	82	375	270	315	190	270	210	0.026	1 250
D3E 160	86	395	290	335	210	290	230	0.026	1 600
D3E 200	92	460	335	385	240	335	260	0.026	2 000
D3E 250	99	485	360	410	270	360	285	0.024	2 500
D3E 325	112	515	375	455	280	410	310	0.022	3 250
D3E 400	128	555	420	495	330	450	350	0.022	4 000
D3E 500	128	620	465	560	390	515	410	0.020	5 000
D3E 650	137	675	510	615	420	570	440	0.018	6 500
D3E 800	147	740	575	680	490	635	510	0.016	8 000
D3E 1000	162	815	635	755	540	710	560	0.016	10 000
D3E 1250	168	910	700	840	620	785	640	0.014	12 500
D3E 1600	183	1000	780	925	680	870	700	0.012	16 000
D3E 2000	193	1155	875	1055	770	985	800	0.012	20 000
D3E 2500	213	1270	970	1170	865	1100	895	0.012	25 000
D3E 3000	228	1440	1080	1310	950	1230	1030	0.012	30 000

* Dimensions B, C, D and E are for zero movement, and specified movement has to be added to above in increments of 100 mm.

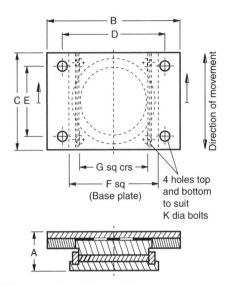

Figure 1.22. The Tetron D3F sliding guided bearing

Table 1.8. Data for Tetron D3F bearings

Bearing type	Principal dimensions (mm)								'Working stress' design (kN)	
									Max. load vertical	Max. load horizontal
	A	*B*	*C* *	*D*	*E* *	*F*	*G*	*K*		
D3F 50	79	260	170	195	120	170	130	M12	500	100
D3F 80	103	345	235	280	155	235	175	M20	800	150
D3F 100	108	360	250	295	170	250	190	M20	1 000	150
D3F 125	117	405	270	315	190	270	210	M20	1 250	190
D3F 160	121	425	290	335	210	290	230	M20	1 600	220
D3F 200	129	475	335	385	240	335	260	M20	2 000	250
D3F 250	129	500	360	410	270	360	235	M20	2 500	280
D3F 325	138	565	410	475	280	410	310	M20	3 250	300
D3F 400	158	605	450	515	330	450	350	M24	4 000	360
D3F 500	158	680	515	580	390	515	410	M30	5 000	500
D3F 650	167	745	570	645	420	570	440	M30	6 500	600
D3F 800	177	810	635	710	490	635	510	M30	8 000	650
D3F 1000	192	905	710	805	540	710	560	M30	10 000	700
D3F 1250	198	970	785	870	620	785	640	M30	12 500	900
D3F 1600	213	1070	870	970	680	870	700	M30	16 000	1000
D3F 2000	227	1215	985	1090	780	985	800	M36	20 000	1300
D3F 2500	267	1360	1100	1220	875	1100	895	M42	25 000	1600
D3F 3000	282	1490	1230	1350	1000	1230	1030	M42	30 000	2000

Rotation as for D3E type
* Dimensions C and E are for zero movement, and specified movement has to be added to above in increments of 1000 mm.

Tetron D3F: Sliding guided
Sliding, guided in one direction, free to rotate in all directions (see Fig. 1.22 and Table 1.8).

Note the following in conjunction with removable bearings:

1 Base contact stress of the bearings illustrated approaches $20 \, \text{N/mm}^2$.
2 Sliding plate dimensions shown are for zero movement. Add to these the amount of sliding required in increments of 100 mm. The bearings may then be described in a code, for example, thus:

3 The height '*A*' is nominal; manufacturing tolerances give a variation of ±3 mm on tabulated figure.

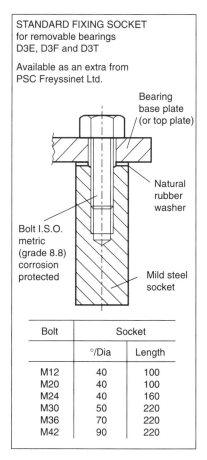

STANDARD FIXING SOCKET
for removable bearings
D3E, D3F and D3T

Available as an extra from
PSC Freyssinet Ltd.

Bearing
base plate
(or top plate)

Natural
rubber
washer

Bolt I.S.O.
metric
(grade 8.8)
corrosion
protected

Mild steel
socket

Bolt	Socket	
	°/Dia	Length
M12	40	100
M20	40	100
M24	40	160
M30	50	220
M36	70	220
M42	90	220

Figure 1.23. Schematic of bolt design for the Tetron bearings

4   The size of fixing bolts listed in the tables (see Fig. 1.23) assumes assistance
    from friction due to the minimum vertical load normally present in service.
5   Larger capacity bearings are available.

Further examples of removable bearings are illustrated in Figs 1.24 and 1.25 with
associated data given in Tables 1.9 and 1.10, respectively.

1.6.10 Glacier standard structural bearings – A series

1.6.10.1 Description
Bearings in this series are designed to support vertical loads of up to 2000 kN
(200 tons) at normal atmospheric temperatures. (Where the environmental temperature exceeds 150°C the bearing may require to be derated.)
   Translation in the plane of movement is maintained at a low frictional resistance by the use of the mating surfaces, polished stainless steel and Glacier DZ.
   Bearings incorporating Glacier DU(B) material as an alternative to Glacier
DZ are available for special applications. Glacier DU(B) is particularly suitable
for installations where severe vibration is a problem.

1.6.10.2 Attachment and movement
The bearings are available as standards with four methods of attachment. Each
bearing is available as a standard offering a number of alternative movements,

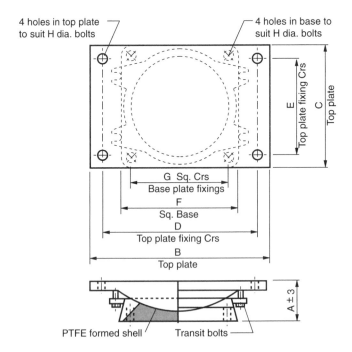

Figure 1.24. The Tetron S3T fixed bearing

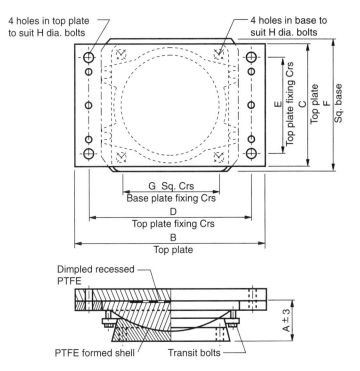

Figure 1.25. The Tetron S3F sliding guided bearing

including constraining in one direction. To give further flexibility the base is available either square or oblong in plan. Bearings are transported with top and base plates fixed together to prevent damage to the working surfaces. This fixing arrangement should be removed before the bearings are required to operate.

Table B1.9. Data for the Tetron S3T fixed bearing

Bearing type	Principal dimensions (mm)							
	A	B	C	D	E	F	G	H
S3T 70	70	400	215	340	145	230	177	M12
S3T 150	100	475	305	410	235	305	254	M20
S3T 250	105	510	360	435	280	375	297	M20
S3T 300	115	570	400	490	310	420	336	M24
S3T 350	130	600	440	515	335	465	364	M24
S3T 400	140	660	485	565	355	500	396	M30
S3T 500	145	685	510	585	375	535	417	M30
S3T 600	155	760	565	640	430	600	463	M30
S3T 750	180	930	660	795	500	705	548	M30
S3T 1000	195	970	710	830	535	755	583	M30
S3T 1200	215	1080	790	925	595	840	654	M30

Table 1.10. Data for the Tetron S3T sliding guided bearing

Bearing type	Principal dimensions (mm)							
	A	B	C	D	E	F	G	H
S3F 70	100	351	270	286	190	230	177	M12
S3F 150	130	497	360	432	280	305	254	M20
S3F 250	135	541	420	476	340	375	297	M20
S3F 300	145	636	460	546	360	420	336	M24
S3F 350	155	680	480	590	400	465	364	M24
S3F 400	170	718	540	628	460	500	396	M24
S3F 500	175	750	570	660	470	535	417	M30
S3F 600	190	814	625	724	525	600	463	M30
S3F 750	225	922	720	832	620	705	548	M30
S3F 1000	240	971	770	881	670	755	583	M30
S3F 1200	265	1055	860	965	760	840	654	M30

1.6.10.3 Support and installation

The bearing support members must provide a uniform support (Fig. 1.26). The compressive bearing stress on the support varies through the range between $6.4\,\mathrm{MN/m^2}$ ($928\,\mathrm{lbf/in^2}$) and $11.3\,\mathrm{MN/m^2}$ ($1638.5\,\mathrm{lbf/in^2}$).

When more than one bearing is installed, the working surfaces of the bearings should, unless intended by special design considerations, be parallel to one another.

1.6.10.4 Bearing selection and part number

Refer to Fig. 1.27 and to the examples below on part number selection. Figure 1.28 covers bearings for some standard applications.

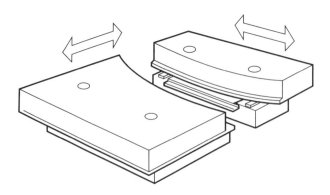

Figure 1.26. Supports for the Glacier standard structural bearing

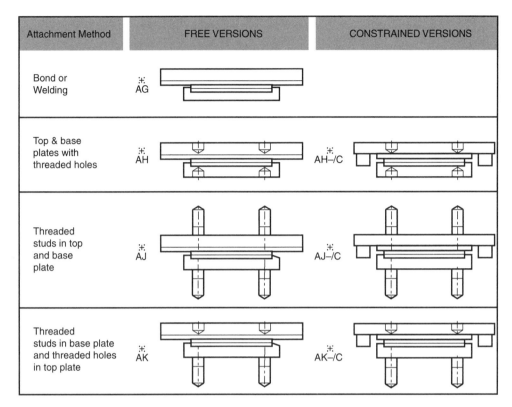

Figure 1.27. Diagram for bearing selection criteria

1   Required load capacity $= 1500\,\text{kN}$ (150 tons)
    Required movements 'X' $= \pm 25\,\text{mm}$
    Required movements 'Y' $= \pm 12.5\,\text{mm}$
    Required attachment $=$ threaded holes in top and base plates
    Dimension 'A' $= 275\,\text{mm}$
    Part No. AH 150/275/50/25
2   Bearing as example 1 but constrained in 'Y' direction
    Part No. AH 150/275/50/C.

1.6.11 AASHTO and LRFD specifications for bearings

This section provides bearing design formulae and a bridge bearing schedule.

(*a*)   *AASHTO*
        Bearing/lineal inch on expansion rockers and rollers should not exceed the
        value determined below:
        (*i*)   Diameters up to 25 inches

$$p = \frac{F_\text{y} - 13\,000}{20\,000}\,(600d) \tag{1.1}$$

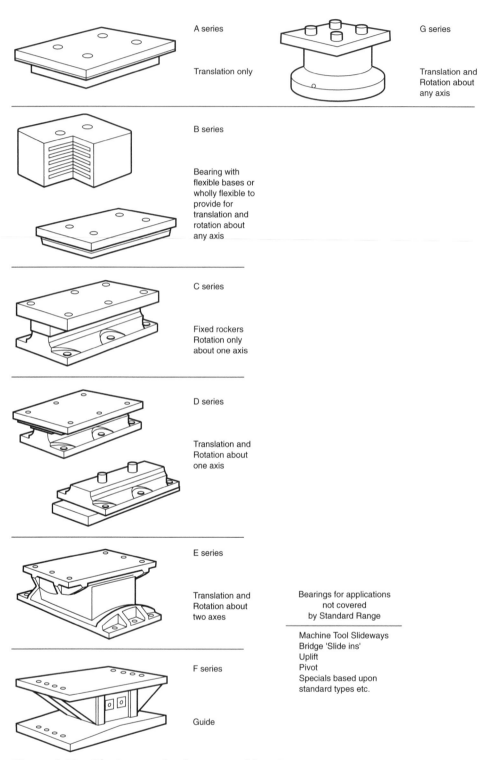

A series

Translation only

G series

Translation and
Rotation about
any axis

B series

Bearing with
flexible bases or
wholly flexible to
provide for
translation and
rotation about
any axis

C series

Fixed rockers
Rotation only
about one axis

D series

Translation and
Rotation about
one axis

E series

Translation and
Rotation about
two axes

Bearings for applications
not covered
by Standard Range

Machine Tool Slideways
Bridge 'Slide ins'
Uplift
Pivot
Specials based upon
standard types etc.

F series

Guide

Figure 1.28. Glacier standard structural bearings

(*ii*)   Diameters 25–125 inches

$$p = \frac{F_y - 13\,000}{20\,000}\,(3000\sqrt{d}) \tag{1.2}$$

where

   p = allowable bearing lb/lineal inch

   d = rocker and roller diameter (in)

   F_y = yield strength in tension in rollers and plates

Bearings may be pot bearings, disk bearings and elastomeric bearings.

(b)   *LRFD*

The bearings are required to resist all factored loads and accommodate the design translations and rotations of the structure θ_u.

θ_u = rotation due to service loads (limit states) + maximum rotation caused by fabrication and installation tolerances + 0.01°

For different bearings, the ratings given in Table 1.11 reflect general judgement and observation as a guidance.

The horizontal forces and moments are developed due to restraints. Horizontal forces are developed due to sliding friction, rolling friction or deformation of a flexible element in the bearing.

   H_u = horizontal force due to friction (sliding)

$$= \mu P_u \tag{1.3}$$

where

   P_u = factored compressive load on bearing

In the case of an elastomeric bearing pad

$$H_u = GA\,\frac{\Delta_u}{h_{rt}} \tag{1.4}$$

where

   G = shear modulus of the elastomeric bearing

   A = plan area of the elastomeric bearing

   Δ_u = factored shear deflection of the elastomeric bearing

   h_{rt} = total elastomeric thickness

The bearing function affects the bridge moment. For a *curved sliding* bearing, the factored moment M_u is given by

$$M_u = \mu P_u R \tag{1.5}$$

Table 1.11. Ratings for different bearing types

Type of bearing	Movement		Rotation			Load capacity		
	Long.	Trans.	Trans.	Long.	Vert.	Vert.	Long.	Trans.
Plain elastomeric pad	S	S	S	S	L	L	L	L
Fibreglass reinforced pad	S	S	S	S	L	L	L	L
Cotton duck reinforced pad	U	U	U	U	U	S	L	L
Steel reinforced elastomeric bearing	S	S	S	S	L	S	L	L
Plane sliding bearing	S	S	U	U	S	S	R	R
Curved sliding spherical bearing	R	R	S	S	S	S	R	R
Curved sliding cylindrical bearing	R	R	S	U	U	S	R	R
Disk bearing	R	R	S	S	L	S	S	R
Double cylindrical bearing	R	R	S	S	U	S	R	R
Pot bearing	R	R	S	S	L	S	S	S
Rocker bearing	S	U	S	U	U	S	R	R
Knuckle bearing	U	U	S	U	U	S	S	R
Single roller bearing	S	U	S	U	U	S	U	R
Multiple roller bearing	S	U	U	U	U	S	U	U

S = suitable

U = unsuitable

L = suitable for limited applications

R = may be suitable, but requires special considerations or additional elements such as sliders or guideways

Long. = longitudinal axis

Trans. = transverse axis

Vert. = vertical axis

where

μ = friction coefficient

R = radius of the curved bearing

The value of M_u for *unconfined elastomeric bearings and pads* bent about an axis parallel to the longer side is given by

$$M_u = 0.5 E_c \left(\frac{\theta_{rL,x}}{h_{rt}} \right) \qquad (1.6)$$

where

E_c = effective plastic modulus in compression

$\theta_{rL,x}$ = relative rotation of the top and bottom surfaces of bearings in radians about the transverse axis under load.

Table 1.12.   LRFD specifications for friction coefficient

| Material | Average bearing stress | | | |
	500 psi	1000 psi	2000 psi	>3000 psi
Unfilled PTFE				
Unlubricated flat sheet	0.16	0.14	0.12	0.08
Lubricated sheet PTFE	0.10	0.09	0.08	0.06
Lubricated dimpled sheet	0.08	0.07	0.06	0.04
Filled PTFE (sheet or woven)	0.20	0.18	0.15	0.10
Woven fabric from PTFE resin	0.10	0.09	0.08	0.06
Woven fabric from PTFE fibre	0.08	0.07	0.05	0.04
and metallic substrate				

The resistance to sliding is controlled by Teflon or tetrafluorethylene since it has a lower value of μ compared to any other material. Based on LRFD, Table 1.12 gives the specification for μ.

Elastomeric bearings

An elastomeric pad consists of:

(*a*)   plain pad
(*b*)   reinforced pad

A parameter relevant to the design is the shape factor for a layer

$$S = \frac{LW}{2t(L+W)} \tag{1.7}$$

where

L = gross length of a rectangular pad parallel to the bridge longitudinal axis in inches

W = load

WL = loaded area

t = thickness of individual layer

Based on AASHTO

The compressive stress σ_c in any layer $\not> \dfrac{GS}{\beta}$ (1.8)

$\not> 1000$ psi for steel reinforced

$\not> 800$ psi for fabric pads

where

G = shear modulus of the elastomer in psi (kN/m^2) at 73°F

β = modifying factor = 1.0 (internal layer and reinforced)

or   = 1.4 for cover layer

or   = 1.8 for plain pads.

Shear deformation

$$T = \text{total elastomeric thickness} \geq 2\Delta_S \tag{1.9}$$

Δ_S = shear deformation in inches

F_S = longitudinal force due to shearing resistance of pad

$$= G \frac{A}{T} \Delta_S \tag{1.10}$$

$$T \not> \frac{L}{5}, \frac{W}{5} \text{ or } \frac{D}{6} \quad \text{smallest value for plain pad} \tag{1.11a}$$

$$\not> \frac{L}{3}, \frac{W}{3} \text{ or } \frac{D}{4} \quad \text{smallest value for reinforced pad} \tag{1.11b}$$

where

D = gross diameter of circular bearings.

Steel girder seated on elastomeric bearings
No stiffening is required for a single web girder symmetric about the vertical minor axis if

$$\frac{b_f}{2t_f} \leq \sqrt{\frac{F_{yg}}{3.4\sigma_c}} \tag{1.12}$$

where

b_f = total flange width

t_f = flange thickness

f_{yg} = yield stress of the girder

σ_c = compressive stress.

LRFD specification (elastomeric bearings)
For steel reinforced, the shear modulus G can be obtained from Table 1.13.

Table 1.13. Shear modulus from the LRFD specification

Hardness (Shore A)	50	60	70
Shear modulus (psi)	95–130	130–200	200–300
at 73°F (MPa)	0.68–0.93	0.93–1.43	1.43–2.14
Creep deflection at 25 years			
instantaneous deflection	25%	35%	45%
k	0.75	0.6	0.55

LRFD limits shear stress–strain in the elastomer. The relationship between shear stress and the applied compressive stress σ_c [σ_{CTL} (total compressive stress); σ_{CLL} = total live load compressive stress] is represented by:

$$\sigma_{CTL} \leq 1600\,\text{psi}$$
$$\sigma_{CTL} \leq 1.66GS$$
$$\sigma_{CLL} \leq 0.66GS$$

For fixed bearings

$$\sigma_{CTL} \leq 1750\,\text{psi}$$
$$\sigma_{CTL} \leq 2GS$$
$$\sigma_{CLL} \leq 1.0GS$$

The maximum shear deformation is limited to $0.10h_t$ where

$$h_t = \text{bearing thickness}$$

For *fibre glass pad* (FGP)

$$\sigma_{CTL} \leq 800\,\text{psi}$$
$$\sigma_{CTL} \leq 1.0GS.$$

A typical bridge bearing schedule is given in Table 1.14.

1.7 Design examples on bearings
Design examples are given on bearings under this section. British and American practices are highlighted.

1.7.1 Example (1.1) British practice
Based on Department of Transport (BE 5175, revised 1990) a concrete hinge is to be designed for subsurface bearing conditions, accommodating a large rotation

Table 1.14. Typical bridge bearing schedule

Bridge name or reference				
Bearing identification mark				
Number off				
Seating material	Upper surface		Epoxy mortar	
	Lower surface		Cement mortar	
Allowable average contact pressure (N/mm²)	Upper face	Serviceability		
		Ultimate		
	Lower face	Serviceability		
		Ultimate		
Design load effects (kN)	Serviceability limit state		max.	
		Vertical	perma-nent	
			min.	
		Transverse		
		Longitudinal		
	Ultimate limit state	Vertical		
		Transverse		
		Longitudinal		
Translation (mm)	Serviceability limit state	Irreversible	Transverse	
			Longitudinal	
		Reversible	Transverse	
			Longitudinal	
	Ultimate limit state	Irreversible	Transverse	
			Longitudinal	
		Reversible	Transverse	
			Longitudinal	

Continued

Table 1.14. Continued

Rotation (radians)	Serviceability limit state	Irreversible	Transverse
			Longitudinal
		Reversible	Transverse
			Longitudinal
	Maximum rate (radians/100 kN)		Transverse
			Longitudinal
Maximum bearing dimensions (mm)	Upper surface		Transverse
			Longitudinal
	Lower surface		Transverse
			Longitudinal
	Overall height		
Tolerable movement of bearing under transient loads (mm)			Vertical
			Transverse
			Longitudinal
Allowable resistance to translation under serviceability limit state (kN)			Transverse
			Longitudinal
Allowable resistance to rotation under serviceability limit state (kN/m)			Transverse
			Longitudinal
Type of fixing required			Upper face
			Lower face

of 0.3°. Ignore a risk of collision and uplift on this hinge and assume at least 2% of the transverse reinforcement in Fig. 1.29 representing such a hinge. Determine the neck zone x_1 (see Fig. 1.30) under a load P (N/mm) of the length of hinge. Assume the notch factor 1.5 and the height of the hinge (net) $= H_e = 120$ mm and $f_{cu} = 50$ N/mm^2; $E_c = 20$ GN/m^2.

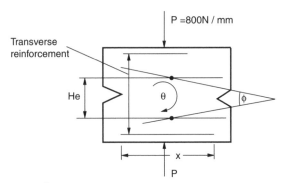

Figure 1.29. Concrete hinge

Elastic parameters

$$\frac{f_{\mathrm{b}}}{\left(\dfrac{x_1}{2}\right)} = \frac{E}{R} = \frac{E\phi}{H_{\mathrm{e}}}$$

$$f_{\mathrm{b}} = \pm\frac{Ex\phi}{2H_{\mathrm{e}}}$$

where for the no tension case

$$\frac{1.5P}{x_1} \geq f_{\mathrm{b}}$$

$$\phi = \phi_{\mathrm{e}} \quad \text{(short term and long term)}$$

$$E\phi_{\mathrm{e}} = E_{\mathrm{c}}\phi_{\mathrm{short}} + \frac{E_{\mathrm{c}}}{2}\,\phi_{\mathrm{long}}$$

$$H_{\mathrm{e}} = 120\,\mathrm{mm}$$

$$f_{\mathrm{b}} = 0.4f_{\mathrm{cu}} = 0.4 \times 50 = 20\,\mathrm{N/mm^2}$$

$$\frac{1.5 \times 800}{20} = x_1 = 60\,\mathrm{mm}$$

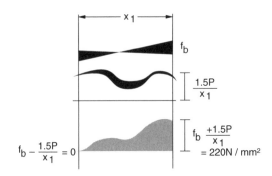

Figure 1.30. Determining neck zone x_1 under load P

If

$$\frac{x_1}{2H_e} \times E\phi_e = f_b$$

or

$$\frac{60}{240} \times 20.0 \times 10^3 \phi_e = 20$$

$$\phi_e = 4 \times 10^{-3}$$

Alternatively $H_e = 125\,\text{mm}$ and from experiment

$$\frac{x_1^2}{380} \leq \frac{P}{E\phi_e}$$

or

$$x_1 \leq \sqrt{\frac{380P}{E\phi_e}}$$

or

$$\frac{380 \times 800}{20 \times 10^3 \phi_e} = (60)^2$$

If

$$\phi_e = 0.004$$

$$x_1 = 60\,\text{mm}$$

$$\phi_e = 0.004$$

1.7.2 Example (1.2) British practice

A reinforced concrete slab bridge with 10 m span is free at one end and fixed at the other. Use the following data:

live load moment $= 225\,\text{kNm}$

$$(\text{dead} + \text{SDL}) = 344\,\text{kNm}$$

$$V = \text{shear/m} = 266.7\,\text{kN}$$

$$I_c = 9401 \times 10^6\,\text{mm}^4$$

$$E_c = 15.4\,\text{kN/mm}$$

$$\text{slab span} = 10\,\text{m}$$

Rubber pads at 2 m, 5 No. Now:

$$H_A = \frac{\text{breaking load}}{\text{notional lane}} = 8\,\text{kN/m of loaded length} + 250\,\text{kN}$$

$$\left.\begin{array}{l}\text{Check for comparable strip bearing}\\ \text{Type 15E25 and pad 30 60E25}\end{array}\right\} \text{CCL type}$$

the shear movement Δ_S is checked against that allowable in each respective bearing.

Based on the CCL System
Concrete

   (a) Shrinkage strain (when concrete poured) $= 250 \times 10^{-6}$

$$\Delta_S = \text{movement due to shrinkage}$$

$$= 250 \times 10^{-6} \times 10\,000 = 2.5\,\text{mm}$$

At the free end

$$\Delta_S = 2.5\,\text{mm}$$

   (b) Thermal expansion and contraction
        [Referring to BD37/88, Fig. (7) and Fig. (8)]:

$$\text{minimum shade air temperature} = -18°\text{C}$$

$$\text{maximum shade air temperature} = +36°\text{C}$$

   [Referring to CL54 (BD37/88), Fig. (9), p. 58, Table 10 (Group 4)]:

$$\text{minimum effective bridge temperature} = -11°\text{C}$$

$$\text{maximum effective bridge temperature} = +36°\text{C}$$

$$\text{total temperature} = 36 + 11 = 47°$$

$$\Delta_{S_{\text{total}}} \text{ (total movement)} = 47 \times 12 \times 10^{-6} \times 10\,000 = 5.64\,\text{mm}$$

At 0°C, contraction occurs when concrete is cast at that temperature

$$\Delta_{Sd} = -2.5 - 11 \times 12 \times 10^{-6} \times 10\,000 = -3.82\,\text{mm}$$

$$\text{max. possible movement at } 0°\text{C} = -2.5 + 36 \times 12 \times 10^{-6} \times 10\,000$$

$$= 1.82\,\text{mm}$$

The bearing could accommodate $\pm 5\,\text{mm}$ as specified.

Rotation

dead (DL) + superimposed (SDL) + live load (LL)

assume live load moments (LL) = 225 kNm

assume (DL + SDL) = 344 kNm

E_c (long term) = 15.4 kN/mm

I_c (second moment of area) = $9401 \times 10^6 \, mm^4$

$$\theta = \frac{FL^2}{24EI} = \frac{M}{3EI}$$

$$\theta_{LL} = \frac{344 \times 10^6}{15.5 \times 9401 \times 10^6} = 2.35 \times 10^{-3}$$

$$\theta_{DL+SDL} = \frac{225 \times 10^6}{3 \times 15.5 \times 9401 \times 10^6} = 5.17 \times 10^{-4} = 0.5$$

$$\theta_{total} = 0.002867 \, radians$$

$$V = \text{shear per metre} = 266.7 \, kN$$

$$\frac{\theta}{100 \, kN} = \frac{0.002867 \times 100}{266.7} = \frac{0.0011}{100 \, kN}$$

For rubber pads at 2 m, 5 No.

Pads (CCL)

$P_{max} = 2 \times 266.7 = 533.7 \, kN$ rotation/100 kN = 0.00055/kN

Bearing type 4317-06-2ENR3.
   30.8 mm maximum shear (allowable).
   535 kN and rotation $\theta = 0.0015$ radians (allowable).

HA loading/notional lane: braking

= 8 kN/m of load length + 250 kN

= 8 × 10 + 250 = 330 kN

load width at serviceability

$$\text{limit state} = 1.0 \times \frac{330}{8} = 41.25 \, kN/m$$

For HB loading, no specific requirement is included, dowels are used and the total shear capacity will be greater than 330 kN. A check is needed; 25⌀ bars as dowels on two sides, adjacent to the pads, are required.

For strip bearing type 15E25

shear stiffness $= 11.25\,\text{kN/mm/m}$

$$\Delta_S = \frac{41.25}{7.20} = 3.67\,\text{mm} < 8.4\,\text{mm maximum}$$

can be allowed as well.
   For the pad:

shear stiffness 30 60E25 $= 6.48\,\text{kN/mm}$

horizontal load $\rightarrow$ per pad $= 2 \times 41.25 = 82.5\,\text{kN}$

$$\Delta_S = \text{shear movement} = \frac{82.5}{6.48} = 12.73\,\text{mm}$$

$$< 17.5\,\text{mm (allowed)}$$

Pads can also be used.

1.7.3 Example (1.3) American practice

Calculate the expansion shoe/plate setting for a two-span bridge (Fig. 1.31).
Each span is 70 ft (21.34 m) and the range of temperatures are 0, 20, 40, 60,
80, 100 and 120°F. The coefficient of expansion is 0.0000065 and the normal temperature is 60°F. Tabulate the results.

Expansion length $= 70\,\text{ft}$

expansion/20°F $= 0.0000065 \times 70 \times 12 \times 20 = 0.109\,\text{in.}$

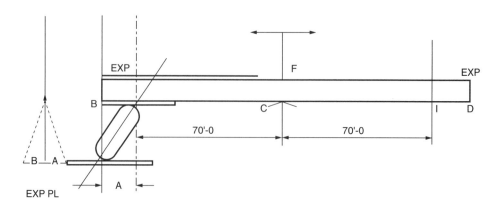

Figure 1.31. Rocker movement in extreme positions

Dimensions at various points are:

	A			B			
0°	20°	40°	60°	80°	100°	120°	Remarks
0.327 $=\frac{5}{16}''$	0.218 $=\frac{3}{16}''$	0.109 $=\frac{1}{8}''$	0 $=0$	0.109 $=\frac{1}{8}''$	0.218 $=\frac{3}{16}''$	0.327 $=\frac{5}{16}''$	Dimensions for A on the pier B

$$\text{expansion}/20°\text{F} = 0.109 \text{ in.}$$

Point D end bend (steel span):

	A			D			
0°	20°	40°	60°	80°	100°	120°	Remarks
0.827 $=\frac{13}{16}''$	0.718 $=\frac{11}{16}''$	0.609 $=\frac{5}{8}''$	0.5 $=\frac{1}{2}''$	0.391 $=\frac{3}{8}''$	0.282 $=\frac{5}{16}''$	0.173 $=\frac{3}{16}''$	Dimensions for A on the bent D

1.7.4 Example (1.4) American practice

A three-span continuous bridge of various span dimensions and boundary conditions is shown in Fig. 1.32. Calculate the expansion plate and rocker settings for the following range of temperatures: 0, 20, 40, 60, 80, 100 and 120°F.

① expansion length = 33.33 ft

$$\text{expansion}/20°\text{F} = 0.0000065 \times 33.33 \times 12 \times 20$$
$$= 0.052 \text{ in.}$$

	0°	20°	40°	60°	80°	100°	120°	Remarks
₵ top shoe to ₵ exp ₤	0.656 $=\frac{11}{16}''$	0.604 $=\frac{5}{8}''$	0.552 $=\frac{9}{16}''$	0.5 $=\frac{1}{2}''$	0.948 $=\frac{7}{16}''$	0.396 $=\frac{3}{8}''$	0.344 $=\frac{3}{8}''$	Starting with with $\frac{1}{2}''$ defl.

② expansion length = 47.33 ft

$$\text{expansion}/20°\text{F} = 0.0000065 \times 47.33 \times 12 \times 20$$
$$= 0.074 \text{ in.}$$

	A				B			
0°	20°	40°	60°	80°	100°	120°	Remarks	
0.222 $=\frac{1}{4}''$	0.148 $=\frac{1}{8}''$	0.074 $=\frac{1}{16}''$	0	0.074 $=\frac{1}{16}''$	0.148 $=\frac{1}{8}''$	0.222 $=\frac{1}{4}''$	Starting with with zero defl.	

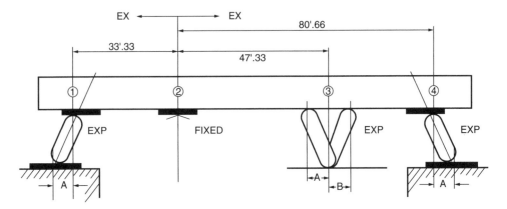

Figure 1.32. A three-span bridge with rockers

③   expansion length $= 80.66\,\text{ft}$

$$\text{expansion}/20°F = 0.0000065 \times 80.66 \times 12 \times 20$$

$$= 0.126\,\text{in.}$$

0°	20°	40°	60°	80°	100°	120°	Remarks
0.878 $= \frac{7''}{8}$	0.752 $= \frac{3''}{4}$	0.626 $= \frac{5''}{8}$	0.5 $= \frac{1''}{2}$	0.374 $= \frac{3''}{8}$	0.248 $= \frac{1''}{4}$	0.122 $= \frac{1''}{8}$	Starting with with $\frac{1''}{2}$ defl.

1.7.5 Example (1.5) American practice

The roller length and diameter together with shoes for a two-span continuous bridge are shown in Fig. 1.33. Check the design when the same setup is adopted for interior and exterior zones having end reactions R_0 as 58 kips and 61.4 kips respectively.

Rocker design

allowable bearing in rocker $= 0.6 \times 13 = 7.8\,\text{kip/in length}$

length of roller $= 12 - 2.625 = 9.375\,\text{in.}$

$$\text{actual bearing on roller} = \frac{58.0}{9.375} = 6.18\,\text{kip/in interior}$$

$$\frac{61.4}{9.375} = 6.55\,\text{kip/in interior}$$

$\left.\right\}$ $< 7.8\,\text{kip/in good}$

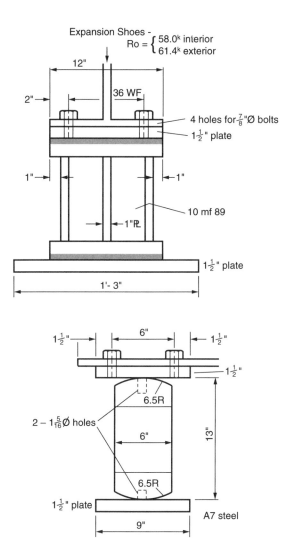

Figure 1.33. Expansion rocker

Use roller length and diameter as shown for interior and exterior top shoe design:

$$p_{\text{int}} = \frac{58.0}{9(12) - 4} = \frac{58.0}{104} = 0.556 \, \text{kip/in}^2$$

$$p_{\text{ext}} = \frac{61.4}{104} = 0.590 \, \text{kip/in}^2$$

$$M_{\text{int}} = 0.556 \times \frac{\overline{4.5}^2}{2} = 5.56 \, \text{kip in}$$

$$M_{\text{ext}} = 0.590 \times \frac{\overline{4.5}^2}{2} = 5.9 \, \text{kip in}$$

$$t = \sqrt{\frac{6M}{f_y}} = \sqrt{\frac{6 \times 5.56}{18}} = 1.36 \, \text{in}$$

$$\left.\begin{array}{l} t_{\text{ext}} = 1.36 \\ t_{\text{int}} = 1.4 \end{array}\right\} \quad \text{adopt } 1\tfrac{1}{2} \text{in throughout}$$

$$\sigma_{\text{c}} = \text{compresssive stress on 10WF89} \leq \frac{61.4}{13.66} = 4.49 \, \text{kip/in}^2 < 18 \, \text{kip/in}^2$$

$$A = 26.19 - 2 \times 0.933 \times 4.275 = 13.66 \, \text{in}^2$$

Masonry plate design

$$\frac{61.4}{15 \times 9} = 0.955 \, \text{kip/in}^2 < 1 \, \text{kip/in}^2 \quad \text{(therefore good)}$$

Use plate thickness $= 1\tfrac{1}{2}$ in.

1.7.6 Example (1.6) American practice

At a pier or bent, the reaction from the bridge is 59.04 kips (262.61 kN). The rocker is to be made of A7 steel. Design the rocker, top shoe and the expansion plate. The plate dimension is (1 ft 6 in)×8 in as shown in Fig. 1.34.

Rocker design

$$\text{length of rocker} = 16 \, \text{in} - 2.63 = 13.37 \, \text{in}$$

$$\frac{59.04}{13.37} = 4.42 \, \text{kip/in.}$$

$$\frac{33\,000 - 13\,000}{20\,000}(0.6)D = 4.42$$

$$D_{\text{req'd}} = \frac{4.42}{0.6} = 7.37$$

$$R_{\text{req'd}} = 3.69 \, \text{in.}$$

Use $R = 3\tfrac{3}{4}$ in, $d = 7\tfrac{1}{2}$ in.

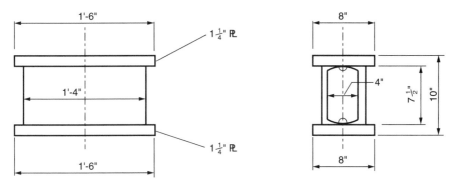

Figure 1.34. Rocker, top shoe and expansion plate design

Top shoe design

$$p = \frac{59.04}{18 \times 8} = \frac{59.04}{144} = 0.41 \text{ kip/in}^2$$

$$M = 0.41 \times \frac{4^2}{2} = 3.28 \text{ kip/in}$$

$$t_{\text{req'd}} = \sqrt{\frac{6M}{f_s}} = \sqrt{\frac{6 \times 3.28}{18}} = \sqrt{\frac{19.68}{18}} = \sqrt{1.093} = 1.046 \text{ in.}$$

Use $1\frac{1}{4}$ in.

Exp ℞ Design

$$\text{base pressure} = \frac{59.04}{18 \times 8} = 0.41 \text{ kip/in}^2$$

Use same t as for the top shoe.

1.7.7 Example (1.7) American practice
A fixed shoe together with a rocker are shown in Fig. 1.35. The reaction on the assembly is 128.28 kips. Design the rocker, top shoe and the fixed shoe. Check the web crippling at the pier at which the bearing rests.

Rocker design

$$\frac{33\,000 - 13\,000}{20\,000}(0.6)D = \frac{128.28}{(12 - 2.625)} = 13.68$$

$$D = \frac{13.68}{0.6} = 22.3 \text{ in.}$$

Use $12''$ R.

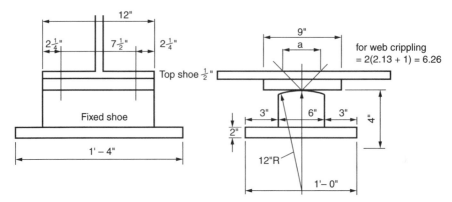

Figure 1.35. A rocker assembly with a fixed shoe plate

Top shoe design

$$p = \frac{128.28}{12 \times 9} = 1.185$$

$$t = \left(\frac{1.185 \times 6 \times \overline{4.5}^2}{2 \times 20\,000}\right)^{1/2} = (3.6)^{1/2} = 1.92 = 2\,\text{in.}$$

Fixed shoe design

$$p = \frac{128.28}{18 \times 12} = 0.668$$

$$M = 0.668 \times \frac{\overline{3}^2}{2} = 3.0$$

$$t = \sqrt{\frac{6 \times 3}{18}} = \sqrt{1.0}$$

Use 2 in minimum.

Note

$$a = 6.3$$
$$K = 1.81$$

as was shown in the calculations

Check web crippling at piers

$$\text{maximum } p = 24 \times 0.625(6.3 \times 2 \times 1.81)$$
$$= 15(9.88) = 14.8 > 128.2\,\text{kip}$$

1.7.8 Example (1.8)   American practice

Figure 1.36 shows an arrangement for the elastomeric pad bearing fixed to a pier. The layer thickness of the pad is $\frac{1}{2}$ in (12 mm). The total load (dead and live) is 355 kips as a bridge reaction on the pier. Use the following data:

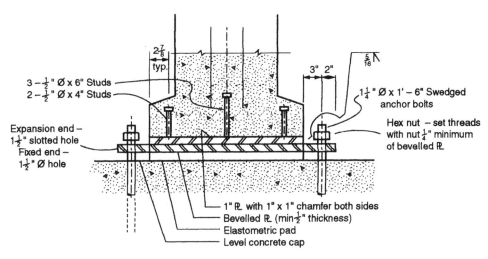

Figure 1.36. Layout of the elastomeric pad bearing (courtesy: AASHTO)

pad area $(9 \times 28 \, \text{in}) = 252 \, \text{in}^2$ each

creep deflection is for 25 years

G = shear modulus = $180 \, \text{kip/in}^2$ for Grade 60

α = expansion coefficient = 0.00006

d = expansion due to creep and shrinkage = $0.027 \, \text{ft}$

Temperature is $60°F$

$$\text{allowable compressive stress} = \frac{\text{density} \times S}{\Delta_S}$$

where

S = shape factor

$$= \frac{A}{(2 \times 0.5(b+d)}$$

$b = 9 \, \text{in}$

$d = 28 \, \text{in}$

Use AASHTO Table 14.3.1 for Δ_S.

The elastomeric pad has the following data for the layout shown in Fig. 1.36.

two pads $\frac{1}{2}$ in (12 mm) thick

$T = 0.5 + 0.5 = 1.0$

$t = 0.5 \, \text{in}$

A = bearing area = $\dfrac{F}{0.8} = \dfrac{355}{0.8} = 444 \, \text{in}^2$

Two pads $9'' \times 28''$ gives area

$$A = 9 \times 28 \times 2 \text{ No.} = 504 \text{ in}^2$$

$$\text{each} = 252 \text{ in}^2$$

$$S = \text{shape factor} = \frac{9 \times 28}{(2 + 0.5(9 + 28))} = 6.8$$

$$\sigma_c = \text{compressive stress} = \frac{F}{A} = \frac{355}{0.504} = 704 \text{ psi}$$

AASHTO Fig. 14.41.213, hardness 60, gives E_c = compressive strain = 3.2% and 4% instantaneous deflection.

$$\text{allowable compressive stress} = \frac{\rho S}{\Delta s_{\text{instantaneous}}}$$

creep deflection 25 years (AASHTO Table 14.3.1) is 3.5

Δ_S instantaneous deflection = $4 \times 0.35 = 1.4\%$

$$\text{allowable compressive stress} = \frac{150 \times 6.8}{1.4} = 729 \text{ psi} > 704 \text{ psi} \quad \text{(allowed)}$$

G = shear modulus (Grade 60) = 180 kip/in^2

temperature = 0 to $60°F$

expansion due to temperature = $0.00006 \times 60 \times 100 = 0.036 \text{ ft}$

expansion due to creep/shrinkage = 0.027 ft

Δ_S (total) = $0.036 + 0.027 = 0.063 \text{ ft} = 0.76 \text{ in}$

$$F_S = \text{shear force} = \frac{EA\Delta_S}{1.0} = \frac{180 \times 252 \times 0.76}{1.0} \times 10^{-3} = 34.5 \text{ kips}$$

1.7.9 Collapse analysis of a bridge bearing (finite element method): British practice

Analysis of bridge bearings

Hyder Consulting contracted FEA to analyse the collapse of fabricated steel 'trestle' bridge bearings, for the M5 road bridge at Avonmouth.

Objective

The objective of the project was to predict the ultimate strength of a variety of bearing structures, both with and without strengthening modifications. The final LUSAS model included geometric, material and contact non-linear effects. A number of initial models was created and used to assess the performance of both shell and solid element idealizations. FEA was provided with experimental data (load–strain measurements) with which to validate the results. This

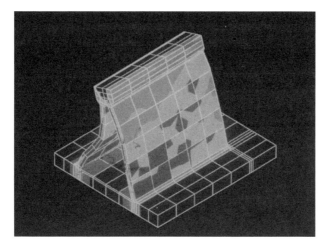

Figure 1.37. Unaveraged stress contours during buckling

allowed the effects of each type of non-linearity to be assessed until good results were obtained for only modest CPU time during analysis. The validated model was then used as the basis for assessment of other similar structures.

Plastic collapse
FEA discovered very close agreement between measured and calculated values of ultimate load. The LUSAS analysis also clearly showed that the failure mode was plastic collapse – elastic buckling occurred at a much higher load (Fig. 1.37).

The results of this work were used by Hyder Consulting to help determine which bearings require strengthening for the additional bridge capacity predicted for the future.

1.8 Expansion and contraction joints
The bridge deck has expansion and contraction joints at suitable positions to cater for the environmental loads. It is customary to see these joints transmit loads to the substructure of the bridge. Various forms of joints are in service and these are:

(a) *Simple joints* with straight edges to the gap.
(b) *Toothed joints* with comb-like interlocking edges, thereby extending the functional range of the simple joint.
(c) *Simple sliding plate joint* with the function of bridging gaps and covering it with a movable plate supported on both edges.
(d) *Elaborate sliding plate joint* with special devices to obviate the gap which develops behind the edge of the movable sliding plate owing to large displacements.

For materials, strength and movement characteristics, a reference is made to various codes and practices prior to selecting any type of joint for a specific project. Products from some manufacturers are included in this section for guidance. They should be tested for various combinations of loads and other bridge requirements and specific parameters.

1.8.1 Joints
The functions of a joint are:

(i)   To allow free movement of the structure due to changes in temperature, elastic shortening and creep both in the longitudinal and transverse directions.

(ii) To provide a good riding quality for traffic passing over the joint and to absorb vehicle load and to transfer loads to substructures.

(iii) To be either waterproof (or to allow the drainage of water from the road surface away from the structure) and to prevent the penetration of solids.

(iv) To be serviceable and require the minimum of maintenance.

(v)   To be resistant to environmental effects and to be replaceable.

Types of Joints
Open joints (10 to 40 mm).

Bridged joints. A mechanical joint, loads transferred across the gap.

Buried joint (5–10 mm). To limit crack width, a bond breaker about 300 mm wide over a joint is necessary. 'Rigiflex' or similar can be recommended.

Joints with rubberised asphalt (5–25 mm). Similar to buried joints except the 300 mm wide section is replaced by rubberised asphalt, giving greater flexibility than mastic asphalt.

For small span bridges (30 m) and multispan bridges up to 150 m, movements can occur between 25 mm and 65 mm and can be best catered for using an elastomer profile, inserted into the joint between the nosing formed in the wearing surface or between the edge constructions of the steel.

In all cases, to ensure a tight seal, three conditions should be fulfilled:

(i)   the flanks of the joint must be clean and flat;

(ii) the elastomer profile must be undamaged; and

(iii) the elastomer profile must be properly glued in place.

The following sections provide illustrations and tables of data for various joints recommended by a number of manufacturers.

1.8.2 Tensa-lastic roadway construction joints
These joints are based on a watertight construction principle and are illustrated in Figs 1.38 and 1.39. Associated specifications are given in Table 1.15.

1.8.3 The 'Britflex' expansion joint
The 'Britflex' expansion joint comprises a flexible profiled neoprene insert located in specially extruded contoured metal rails and a cast *in situ* nosing.

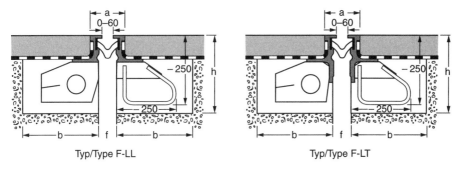

Figure 1.38. Side structures with L-profile, Type F-LL or T-profiles, Type F-LT. Anchoring is either with anchor discs or anchor brackets

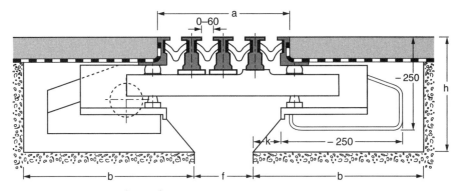

Figure 1.39. Section through supporting zone

The thermal movements of the structure are accommodated by the flexible profiled cellular neoprene insert. The neoprene, which is oven aged and ozone resistant, is located in specially extruded contoured metal rails. All metal components in the 'Britflex' system are zinc sprayed and painted with an anti-corrosive

Table 1.15. Specifications for Tensa-lastic construction joints

Type F-L	Dilation	a			b	f		h	k
	max.	min.	max.			min.	max.		
mm	mm	mm	mm	mm	mm	mm	mm	mm	mm
F-L 60	60	100	160	300	35	95	300	0	
F-L 120	120	184	304	350	60	180	350	30	
F-L 180	180	268	448	460	100	280	400	50	
F-L 240	240	352	592	540	160	400	400	60	
F-L 300	300	436	736	620	230	530	400	78	
F-L 360	360	520	880	700	300	660	400	80	
F L 420	420	604	1024	780	360	780	450	90	
F-L 480	480	688	1168	860	420	900	450	100	

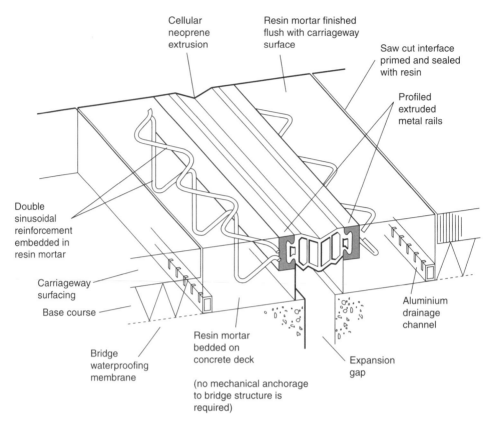

Cellular neoprene extrusion

Resin mortar finished flush with carriageway surface

Saw cut interface primed and sealed with resin

Profiled extruded metal rails

Double sinusoidal reinforcement embedded in resin mortar

Carriageway surfacing

Base course

Bridge waterproofing membrane

Resin mortar bedded on concrete deck

(no mechanical anchorage to bridge structure is required)

Aluminium drainage channel

Expansion gap

Figure 1.40. Principal design features of the 'Britflex' expansion joint

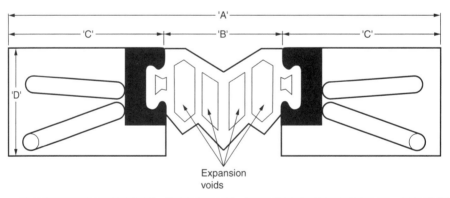

Expansion voids

	BEJ3	BEJ5	BEJ8	BEJ10
'B' (unrestrained width)	55 mm	75 mm	95 mm	125 mm
'C' (minimum dimensions)	100 mm	120 mm	140 mm	160 mm
'D' (minimum dimensions)	55 mm	60 mm	65 mm	70 mm

The cut-out width 'A' and depth 'D' are determined according to requirements subject to agreement with the client.

Figure 1.41. 'Britflex' expansion joint detail of the expansion voids with specifications

coating to prevent corrosion caused by water and salt attack. The cast *in situ* nosing material is based on an advanced technology elastomer. This elastomer is registered with the Department of Transport and complies with the requirements of the Department of Transport's Technical Memoranda BE.3/72.

The profile of the neoprene insert has been designed to adapt to all bridge movements as well as the vertical displacement of the bridge deck relative to abutments or adjacent spans. The system will accommodate up to ±15 mm of vertical movement and a longitudinal or shear movement of up to ±15 mm.

The principal design features of the 'Britflex' expansion joint are detailed in Figs 1.40 and 1.41.

1.8.4 The PSC road joint

The PSC road joint as illustrated by the Freyssi joint is for movement between 25 mm and 75 mm. The joint contains five components (Figs 1.42 and 1.43):

- two malleable iron castings in 0.85 m lengths
- two grooved and galvanised steel cover strips 3.40 metres long
- one continuous elastomeric extrusion clamped betweem the other elements.

The Viajoint PSC-type road joint for small movements of ≤ 20 mm is illustrated in cross-section in Fig. 1.44.

1.8.5 The Zebrajoint

The technical specifications of the Zebrajoint is illustrated in Fig. 1.45. The temperature–expansion relationship is given by Fig. 1.46.

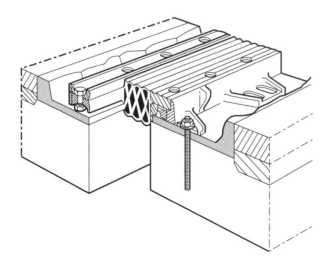

Figure 1.42. The Freyssi PSC-type road joint

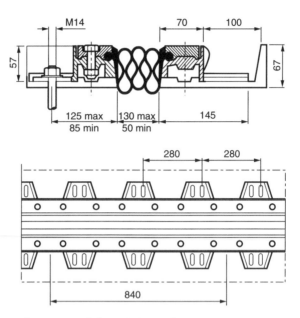

Figure 1.43. Specifications of the PSC road joint

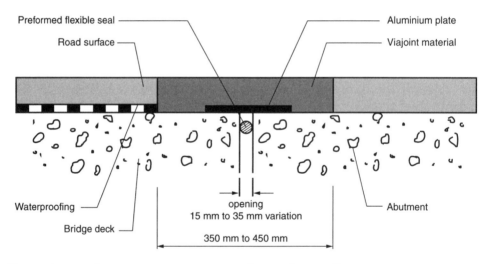

Figure 1.44. The Viajoint PSC-type road joint for small movements

1.8.6 The 'Elast' joint RE

The elastic Robek System unitary joint for bridges carrying general traffic.

This expansion joint is a composite joint with steel edge elements embedded in the elastomeric Roboton material, joining all components firmly and elastically. The joint is installed in the asphalt or concrete surface, ensuring a smooth roadway for maximum driving comfort.

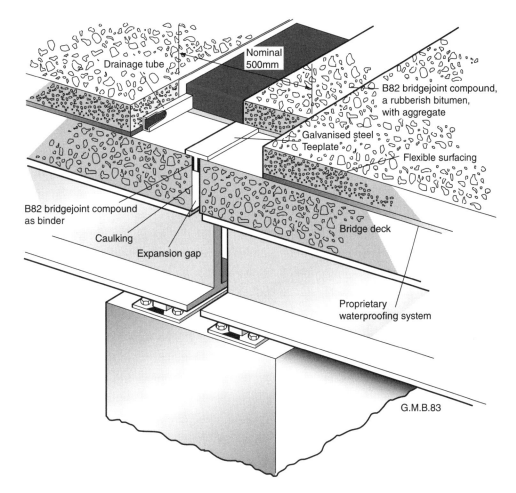

Figure 1.45. Technical specifications for the Zebrajoint

It is for this reason that wear and tear due to snow ploughs and track chains is minimal. (They are absorbed in the wear resistant and shock absorbing characteristics of the joint.)

Construction process
The 'Elast' joint is installed upon completion of all other work. Elastomeric Roboton hardens within a short time so that traffic can pass over 'Elast' joints within a few hours of installation.

The construction process is itemized below and illustrated in Fig. 1.47.

① Asphalting
  The joint aperture is bridged and the asphalt surface laid and compressed without interruption.

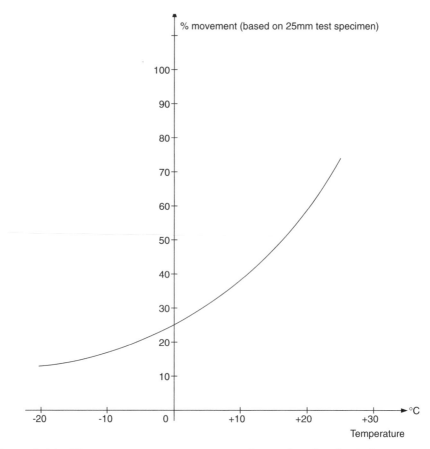

Figure 1.46. The temperature–expansion relationship for the Zebrajoint

② Cutting out
A section the width of the joint is cut out of the asphalt, right down to the concrete base.
③ Preparation
The recess and the edge element is cleaned, prepared and primed.
④ Installation
The elastomeric Roboton is poured and it hardens to give a smooth road surface.
⑤ Clearing
The joint opening is cleaned.
⑥ Anchoring
The locking neoprene profile is fitted.

Weight of the compound joint is approximately 230 kg/m at minimum dimensions.

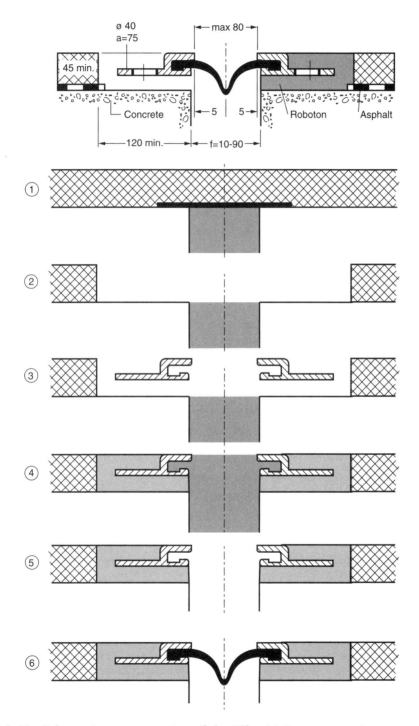

Figure 1.47. Schematic representation of the 'Elast' joint construction process

1.8.7 Heavy duty expansion joint RS

This is the heaviest design of Robek System unitary joints for bridges carrying general traffic.

This expansion joint can cope with wear and tear due to snow ploughs and track chains. Identical heavy-duty edge sections are also used for multi-element modular joints. Anchorages and recesses are reduced in the footway area.

Asphalt roadway RS-A

Heavy-duty beam with anchorages (Fig. 1.48). The edge sections have been standardized for a surface thickness of 7 cm. Surface thicknesses of 10, 12 and 16 cm can also be accommodated, as required.

The weight of the structure is 70 kg/m.

Concrete roadway RS-B

A heavy-duty edge beam without anchorages but using anchoring, thus giving a reduced recess dimension (Fig. 1.49). Weight of the structure is 40 kg/m.

1.8.8 The Honel-161 FS expansion joint

This joint comprises age and weather resisting, removable, continuous, waterproof sealing elements with movements of 80 mm in the longitudinal, 60 mm in the transverse and ±40 mm in the vertical directions. Reaction forces with a closed joint are 400 N/linear metre in compression, with permissible transverse movement of 1800 N/linear metre in shear. The index to be read with Fig. 1.50 is given below.

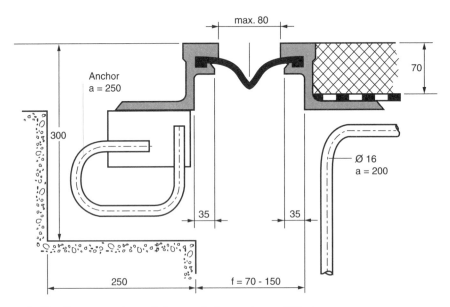

Figure 1.48. Cross-section of the asphalt roadway RS-A

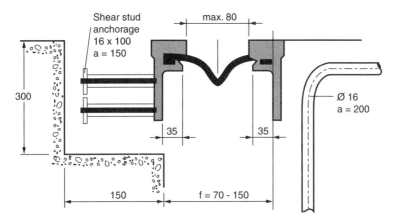

Figure 1.49. Cross-section of the concrete roadway RS-B

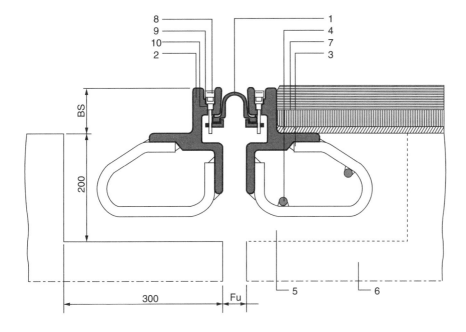

Figure 1.50. The Honel-161 FS expansion joint system

Index:
1 Continuous sealing element
2 Steel edge beam
3 Anchor bars
4 Transverse reinforcing bars
5 Recess
6 Main structure
7 Road surfacing

8 Plastic plug
9 Stainless steel clamping screw
10 Nylon washer

F = Bridge carriageway

G = bridge footpath

Fu = joint gap of main structure

T = main structure

N = shallow construction

H = connection flange for surfacing (+membrane)

S = asphalt

B = concrete surfaced/pre-cast.

1.8.9 The Honel-162/FS expansion joint

This joint comprises age and weather resisting, removable, continuous water-proof sealing elements with longitudinal movement of 160 mm. The index to be read with Figs 1.51 and 1.52 is given below.

Index:
1 Continuous sealing element
2 Steel edge beam
3 Intermediate steel beam
4 Support beam
5 Shockabsorber vertical

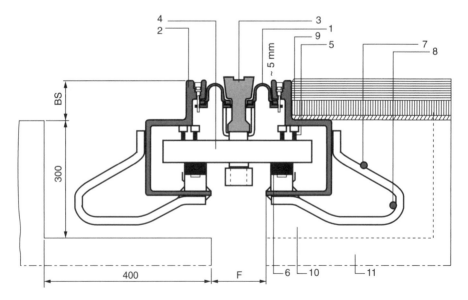

Figure 1.51. The Honel-162/FS expansion joint system

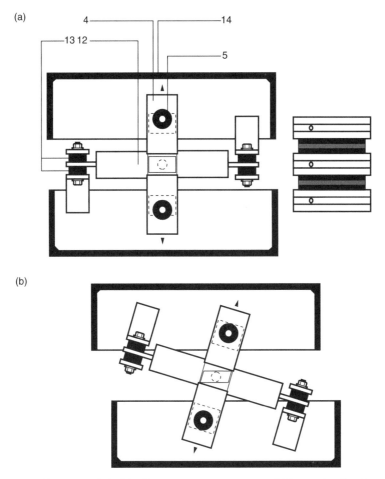

Figure 1.52. The Honel-162/FS expansion joint at 90° to the bridge (a) and oblique to the bridge (b)

 6 Sliding bearing
 7 Anchor spacing
 8 Transverse reinforcing bars
 9 Surfacing and insulation
10 Recess
11 Main structure
12 Control arm
13 Shockabsorber horizontal
14 Box
15 Plastic plug
16 Stainless steel clamping screw
17 Nylon washer
18 Clamping angle

F = carriageway

B = concrete surfaced precast

G = footpath

S = asphalt

1.8.10   The Honel-162N–176N expansion joints

The characteristics of this range of Honel expansion joints are:

(a) Adaptability of all types of construction for movement from 1 to 1600 mm –long lasting, water- and dirt-proof.

(b) Compensation of reactions from hangsliding, settlements, earthquake, etc.

(c) Minimal wear, noiseless, secure surface protection.

(d) Facility for replacement of the securely clamped sealing elements is ensured, even after many years of operation.

(e) Maximal stiffness in longitudinal and transverse direction.

(f) Secure and direct joint to insulation as well as to the total depth of the road surface layer.

(g) Proven design and insertion method in accordance with load standards.

(h) Excellent continuity of road surface and aesthetic appearance.

The index to be read with Fig. 1.53 is given below. Specification data are provided in Table 1.16.

Index:
1   Continuous sealing element
2   Stainless steel clamping screw
3   Clamping angle Alu
4   Steel edge beam
5   Steel edge section
6   Intermediate steel beam
7   Cross member
8   Stainless steel sliding plate
9   Cast iron support frame
10   Cylindrical bearing
11   Control arm
12a   Sliding bearing
12b   Shock absorber vertical
13   Control box
14   Anchor
15   Surface
16   Membrane (insulation)
17   Superstructure

18   Recess area
19   Scaler
20   Support frame

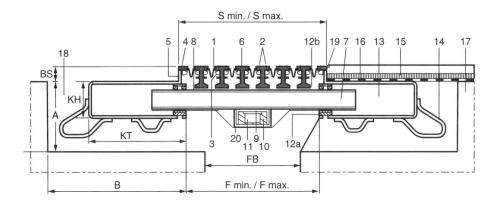

Figure 1.53. The Honel-162N–176N expansion joint system

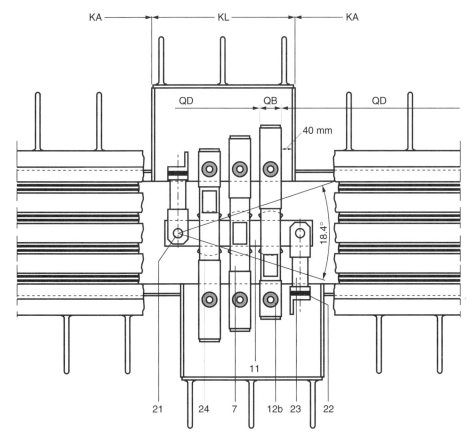

Figure 1.54. The Honel-162N–176N control mechanism

Table 1.16. Specifications for the Honel-162N–176N range of expansion joints

System Honel Type	Movement per seal element maximal			Crossmember distance 1.4 to 2.0 m resulting from load standard	
	Type No.	6	8	10	
	Axis Y:Y	60	80	100	
	Axis X:X	70	60	50	

System Honel Type	Seal-elements Number	Movements Axis Y:Y mm	Movements Axis Y:Y mm	Movements Axis Y:Y mm	Surface thickness in mm BS	Recess dimensions mm A	B	Construction dimensions mm S min	S max	F min	F max	KH	KT	Carriage-way kg	Weight m²
167N	7	420	560	700	Optional	450	850	585	1145	485	1045	270	600		
168N	8	480	640	800	Minimal	450	950	665	1305	565	1205	290	680		
169N	9	540	720	900	50 mm	450	1000	745	1465	645	1365	310	760		
170N	10	600	800	1100	Maximal	500	1100	825	1625	725	1525	320	840		
171N	11	660	880	1100	200 mm	500	1200	905	1785	805	1685	320	920		
172N	12	720	960	1200	Optimal	500	1250	985	1945	885	1845	340	1000		
173N	13	780	1040	1300	Minimal	500	1350	1065	2105	965	2005	350	1080		
174N	14	840	1120	1400	50 mm	500	1400	1145	2265	1045	2165	360	1160		
175N	15	900	1200	1500	Maximal	550	1500	1225	2425	1125	2325	380	1240		
176N	16	960	1280	1600	200 mm	550	1600	1305	2585	1205	2485	380	1320		

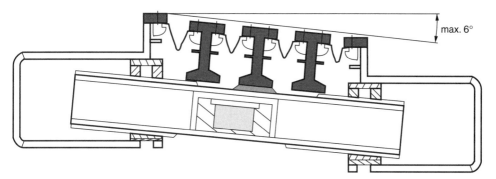

Figure 1.55. Possible rotation of the Honel-162N–176N expansion joint system

The control mechanism for the Honel systems permitting movement in all directions is illustrated in Fig. 1.54. The index is given below. Possible rotation of such expansion joints is represented in Fig. 1.55.

Index:
- 7   Cross member
- 11   Control arm
- 12b Shock absorber vertical
- 21   Pivot pin
- 22   Shock absorber horizontal
- 23   Joint link
- 24   Cylindrical bearing

QB = breadth of cross member

KA = distance between boxes

KL = length of box

QD = distance between cross member concurrent

1.8.11   CCL Systems W80 expansion joint
Dimensions A, B, C and D in Fig. 1.56 vary according to the opening of the joint at the time of installation and during operation.

The spacing between the two rows of tie bolts (dimension C) and final adjustment of the joint (dimension A) is determined on the basis of the data furnished by the Contractor's Engineering Office.

	A	B	C	D
$\Delta\ell \leq 80\,\text{mm}$	$192 \pm \dfrac{\Delta\ell}{2}$	$382 \pm \dfrac{\Delta\ell}{2}$	$268 \pm \dfrac{\Delta\ell}{2}$	$60 \pm \dfrac{\Delta\ell}{2}$

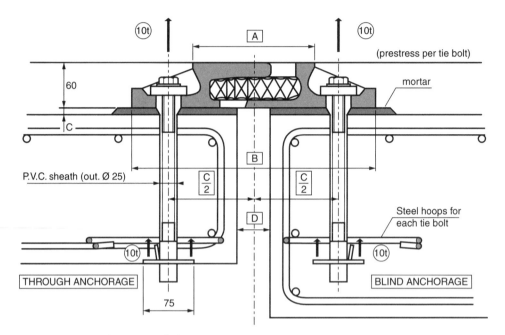

Figure 1.56. Schematic of the CCL Systems W80 expansion joint

The value of $\Delta\ell$ may be increased slightly if non-alignment of the serration tips in the open position is permissible (see Fig. 1.57).

Installation of W type joints
The metal sections are mounted on mortar at a level determined by the planned level of the roadway. Availability in one-metre lengths enables the joint to conform precisely to the particular cross-sectional profile of the roadway. The gap between the serrations, which is determined by temperature conditions, shrinkage, creep and skew, is adjusted prior to tensioning the tie-bolts.

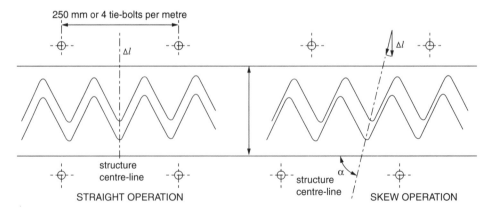

Figure 1.57. $\Delta\ell$ variation in the W80 expansion joint

Figure 1.58. Installation of W type expansion joints

Since road-surfacing operations do not provide a finish conforming perfectly to the cross-sectional or longitudinal profile of roadways, it is recommended that the joints be placed in position after completion of the surfacing. A strip of the surfacing is removed where the joint is to be located and the level of the joint is then adjusted to be flush with the road surface. Porphyrized asphalt, case *in situ* resin concrete, or other material permitting fine adjustment, may be used for filling in.

The diagrams in Fig. 1.58 illustrate an additional drain which is sometimes provided where there is a longitudinal fall on the bridge deck.

Installation of WO S joints

The joint is recessed into the road and is delivered to the site in sections approximately equal in length to the width of a traffic lane (for example 3.50 metres). This allows partial removal without interrupting traffic across the entire width of the roadway.

The recessing trench should be sufficiently large to enable reinforcing bars to be added prior to concreting. The concrete should not be of prestressed quality.

To provide a smoother running surface it is recommended that joints be installed after the roadway has been surfaced. Alignment to the road surface is obtained by means of metal shims spaced at 1 metre intervals which are attached to the metal parts of the joint and supported by the adjacent subsurface. Porphyrized asphalt, cast *in situ* resin concrete, or other such material allowing fine adjustment may be used for filling in (Fig. 1.59).

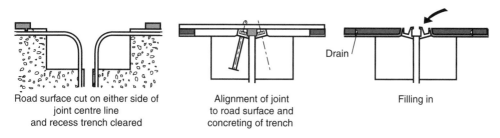

Figure 1.59. Installation of WO S expansion joints

1.9   Parapets, parapet formulae and loads

The function of a parapet is to contain vehicles and/or pedestrians within the bridge width, and to minimize the consequences of an accident.

There are two types of parapet:

(*i*)   rigid concrete
(*ii*)   flexible steel

The former type is shaped so that the wheel of a vehicle in collision runs up the slope and is deflected back and downwards. The latter type absorbs impact forces by yielding.

The British Standard BS 6779 Part 1: 1989 covers parapets for vehicle containment on highways. There is a guidance note from the Department of Transport, UK Memo BE5 which needs to be followed also. In all cases, the end of such a containment shall be connected and shall resist an ultimate tensile force of at least 330 kN. Where sufficient overlap to maintain support for a movement of not less than 100 mm exists, the ultimate tensile

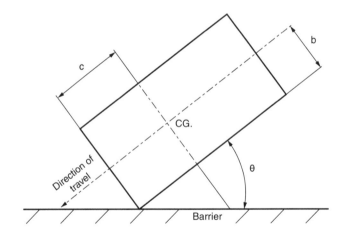

Figure 1.60. Vehicle dimensions and angle of impact diagrams for parapet analysis

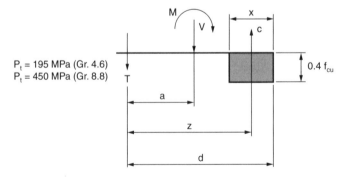

Figure 1.61. Schematic for plastic design approach

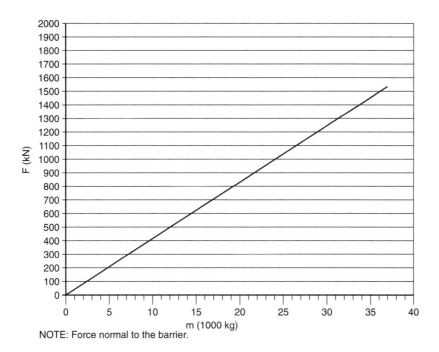

NOTE: Force normal to the barrier.

Figure 1.62. Variation of lateral impact force F with mass of vehicle m (Reference BS 6779, Part 4, 1989)

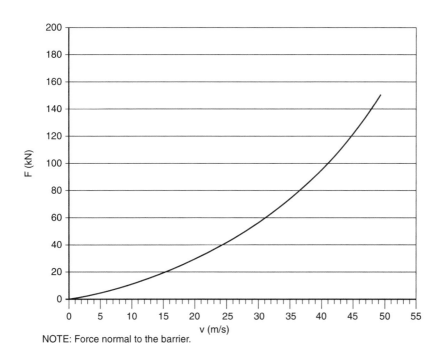

NOTE: Force normal to the barrier.

Figure 1.63. Variation of lateral impact force F with speed of vehicle v (Reference BS 6779, Part 4, 1989)

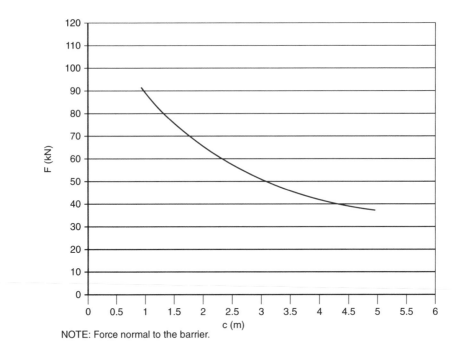

NOTE: Force normal to the barrier.

Figure 1.64. Variation of lateral impact force F with position of centre of gravity c
(Reference BS 6779, Part 4, 1989)

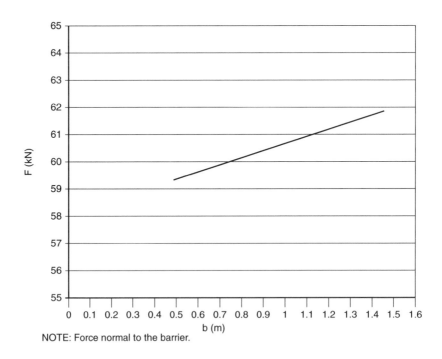

NOTE: Force normal to the barrier.

Figure B1.65. Variation of lateral impact force F with position of centre of gravity b
(Reference BS 6779, Part 4, 1989)

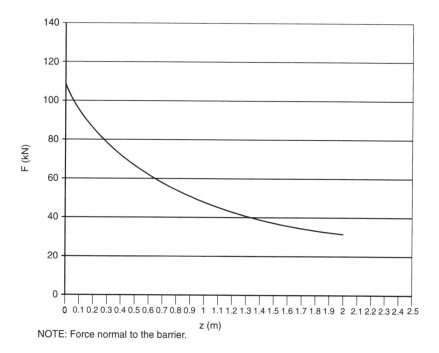

NOTE: Force normal to the barrier.

Figure 1.66. Variation of lateral impact force F with sum of barrier deflection and depth of vehicle crumpling z (Reference BS 6779, Part 4, 1989)

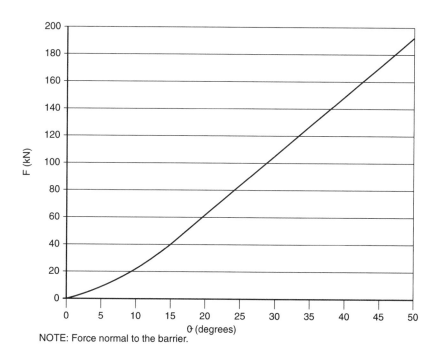

NOTE: Force normal to the barrier.

Figure 1.67. Variation of lateral impact force F with angle of impact θ (Reference BS 6779, Part 1, 1989)

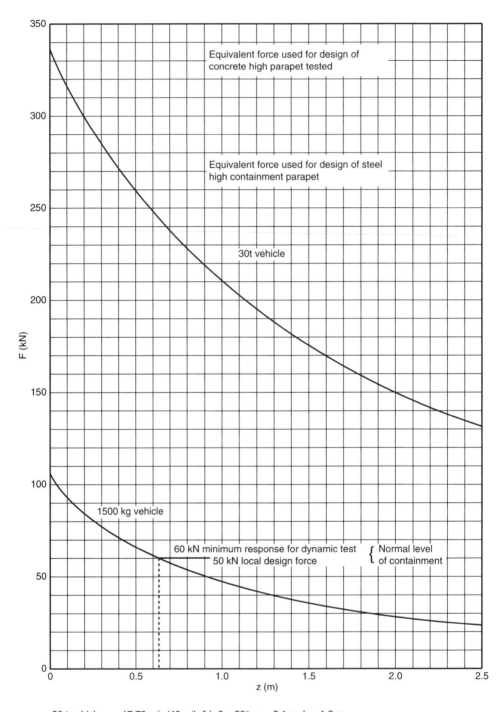

30 t vehicle: v = 17.78 m/s (40 mile/h), θ = 20° , c = 5.1 m, b = 1.2 m
1500 kg vehicle: v = 31.3 m/s (70 mile/h), θ = 20° , c = 2.44 m, b = 0.76 m

Figure 1.68. Theoretical mean lateral impact forces for varying z values for two vehicles

force shall not be less than 50 kN. The minimum height for motorways where pedestrians are excluded shall be 1.25 m. Where pedestrians are included, it shall normally be 1.5 m. The integrity of the parapet and its anchorage/attachment system must be a priority. Where impact is considered, a detailed analysis and design is required. A reference is made to *Impact and explosion: analysis and design* by Bangash (Blackwell Science, 1993).

Section 1.10 and Figs 1.60 to 1.68 give further detailed explanations based on BS 6779. Additional design data on parapets using Department of Transport Memo BE5 are given in Section 1.11.

1.10 Analytical methods for parapets based on BS 6779 Part I, 1989

The mean lateral deceleration of the centre of gravity of the vehicle resulting from an angled impact (see Fig. 1.60) may be approximated by:

$$a = \frac{(v\sin\theta)^2}{2\{c\sin\theta + b(\cos\theta - 1) + z\}} \qquad (1.13)$$

where

$a =$ is the mean lateral deceleration (in m/s^2)

$b =$ is the distance of the centre of gravity of the vehicle from the side (in m)

$c =$ is the distance of the centre of gravity of the vehicle from the front (in m)

$v =$ is the approach velocity (in m/s)

$z =$ is the sum of barrier deflection and depth of vehicle crumpling measured perpendicularly to the face of the barrier (in m)

$\theta =$ is the angle of path of vehicle with barrier at impact (in degrees).

It follows that the mean impact force F (in kN) is obtained from the equation:

$$F = ma = \frac{m(v\sin\theta)^2}{2000\{c\sin\theta + b(\cos\theta - 1) + z\}} \qquad (1.14)$$

where m is the vehicle mass (in kg).

For a car with the data below:

$m = 1500\,\text{kg}$

$v = 31.1\,\text{m/sec (70 miles/hour)}$

$\theta = 20°$

$c = 2.44\,\text{m}$

$$b = 0.76\,\text{m}$$

$$z = 0.64\,\text{m} \quad \text{(minimum)}$$

the impact force F from Eq. 1.14 is 60 kN. Thus, the barrier shall be designed for a 60 kN load dynamically. By the limit state approach, the design resistance $R*$ can then be defined as

$$R* = f\left(\frac{f_k}{\gamma_m}\right) \tag{1.15}$$

where

f_k = characteristic strength of material

γ_m = partial factor for material strength.

Here, f_k is 1.2–1.3.

By the plastic design approach (Fig. 1.61), ΣM about T is given by

$$M + Va + cz = 0 \tag{1.16}$$

Find x by

$$\left(\frac{0.4f_{cu}b}{2}\right)x^2 - (0.4f_{cu}b\,dx) + (M + Va) = 0 \tag{1.17}$$

$$c = 0.4f_{cu}b \tag{1.18}$$

$$T = c - V \tag{1.19}$$

f_t = force/bolt

A_s = area of the bolt = $\dfrac{f_t}{P_t \text{ of a bolt}}$

Choose

$\oslash$ = bolt diameter $\tag{1.20}$

When $\theta = 90°$

$$F(\text{kN}) = \frac{mv^2}{2000z} \tag{1.21}$$

and due to some imbalance of forces, the vehicle will swing around and at the end of the impact will be assumed to be parallel to the parapet. The value of F will be

$$F = \frac{mv^2}{2000(c - b + z)} \tag{1.22}$$

Example:
Vehicle of 30 tons

$$v = 17.78 \, \text{m/sec} \; (40 \, \text{miles/hour})$$

$$b = 1.25 \, \text{m}$$

$$c = 6 \, \text{m from vehicular data}$$

$\theta = 90°$ impact

$z =$	0	0.5	1.0	1.5	2.0
Eq. 1.21	∞	9505	4753	3168	2376
Eq. 1.22	1001	905	827	760	704

Table 1.17. Application and containment requirements for parapets

Parapet group designation	Application	Containment for which designed
P1	Vehicle parapets for bridges carrying motorways or roads to motorway standards* (excluding motorway bridges over railways and high risk locations)	1.5 t vehicle at 113 km/h and 20° angle of impact
P2	Vehicle pedestrian parapets for bridges carrying all purpose roads and for accommodation bridges (excluding bridges over railways and high risk locations). Mesh where pedestrians allowed	1.5 t vehicle at 80 km/h and 20° angle of impact
P4	Pedestrian parapets for use on footbridges and bridges carrying bridleways (excluding bridges over railways)	
P5	Parapets for use over railways (excluding use on bridges at high risk railway locations). Usually follow than P1, solid infill panels	
	(i) On bridges carrying motorways or roads to motorway standards*	As for Group P1
	(ii) On bridges carrying all purpose roads	As for Group P1
	(iii) On footbridges	As for Group P4
P6	High containment vehicle and vehicle pedestrian parapets at high risk locations (excluding accommodation bridges). See Appendix 6 of BE5	30 t vehicle at 64 km/h and 20° angle of impact

(*i*) Where reference * is made to roads to motorway standards, this means roads from which pedestrians, animals, pedal cycles and vehicles drawn by animals are excluded by order.

(*ii*) In addition to their application on bridges, Group P6 parapets are also required for use on other structures close to and alongside railway lines (see Clause 206 and Appendix 6 of BE5).

$\theta = 20°$ impact

$\quad c = 5.1\,\text{m}$

$\quad b = 1.2\,\text{m}$

1.11 Parapet design

Guidance is given in DTp. Memo BE5 for the containment of a vehicle colliding with the parapet at an angle of impact of 20° given in Table 1.17.

Parapets are designated P1, P2, P4, P5 and P6 according to the containment for which they are to be designed as in Table 1.17.

Table 1.18. Design loading for group P4 pedestrian parapets

Parapet construction	Parapet component	Design load	Application	Remarks
Framed construction	Longitudinal member	1400 N/m	Acting separately: in transverse and vertical directions	Where appropriate the strength of the in-filling when acting as a framework may be taken into account, and the design load in the vertical direction shared between longitudinal members
	Post (the greater effect of the following loads)	1400s* N and 700s* N or 1000 N	Acting separately: in transverse direction and in longitudinal direction Acting separately: in transverse and longitudinal directions	Loads to be applied at the level of the longitudinal members which will give the most adverse effect on the post
	Infill panel and fixings	1000 N forces acting on a 70 × 70 mm grid	Loads applied in any position normal to face of the parapet	The contact area of the loads shall be taken as 125 × 125 mm Bracing of large panels may be necessary
	Vertical infill member and fixings	1000 N forces at 700 mm centres	Loads applied in any position or direction normal to the bar	The contact length of the loads shall be taken as 125 mm
Solid construction	N/A	1400 N/m	Acting separately at top of parapet in transverse and vertical directions	

*s = post spacing in metres.

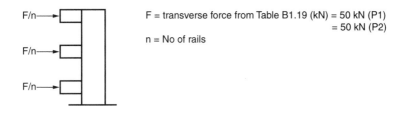

Figure 1.69. Strength requirements for parapet groups P1 and P2

Table 1.19. List of acceptable highway bridge parapets. Vehicle parapet P1

Type	Post spacing mm	Designed by	Unfactored moment at base Nm
1	3000	BACO Contracts Ltd Regal House London Road Twickenham TW1 3QA	31 000
2	3660	British Steel Corporation Tubes Division Corby Northants	30 300
3	3000	High Duty Alloys Extrusion Ltd Lillyhall Workington CA14 4JY	To be revised
4	3660	British Steel Corporation Tubes Division Corby Northants	42 900

Pedestrian parapets (Group P4)

The design loadings are given in Table 1.18, and are ultimate values which should be applied to each longitudinal member – generally 1.4 kN/m.

The post is designed for horizontal loads applied at the levels of the longitudinal members – generally $1.4s$ kN (s = post spacing).

Parapet groups P1 and P2

(1) Strength requirements for *metal* parapets (Fig. 1.69) are given in Clause 106. Rails must be able to resist an *applied movement* of that given in Table 1.19.

(2) Strength requirements for *reinforced concrete* (and reinforced masonry) parapets are given in Clause 107.

The strength is specified as a bending moment per unit length kNm/m, for the various critical sections.

Minimum thickness of RC wall are given as 180 mm for P1 and 150 mm for P2.

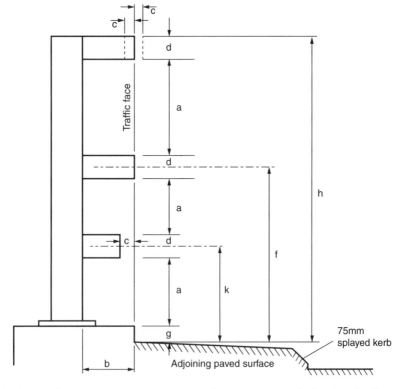

Figure 1.70. Bridges carrying a motorway (motorway underbridges): dimensions of P1 vehicle parapet where height of plinth is less than 700 mm

Table 1.20. Table to Figure 1.70

Dimension	Description	Maximum	Minimum
a.	Clear distance between longitudinal members, or between top of plinth and the longitudinal member above. The dimension is not necessarily constant within the barrier.	300 mm	–
b.	The distance between the traffic face of the parapet and the front face of supporting post at its base, at whatever height the base may be.	–	150 mm
c.	Distance between the front face of a metal longitudinal member, or the top edge of a plinth, and the traffic face of the parapet: (i) Above the main longitudinal member (ii) Below the main longitudinal member (+ = towards the traffic, – = away from traffic)	∓ 25 mm -25 mm	– –
d.	The overall depth of a longitudinal member	–	509mm
f.	The height of the centre line of the 'Main' longitudinal member above the adjoining paved surface.	685 mm	535 mm
g.	Height of plinth, for which this diagram applies, above the adjoining paved surface.	100 mm	50 mm
h.	Height of top of upper longitudinal member above the adjoining paved surface.	–	1000 mm
k.	Height of the centre-line of the lowest longitudinal member, other than the plinth, above the adjoining paved surface.	to comply with 'a'	300 mm

High containment parapets P6
Strength requirements are detailed in Figs 1.70 to 1.75 and Tables 1.20 to 1.23.

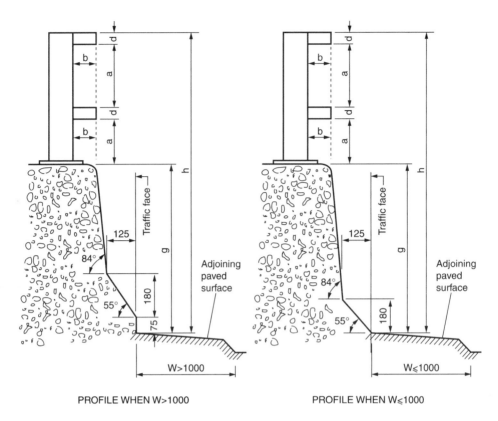

Figure 1.71. Shaped concrete plinth parapets

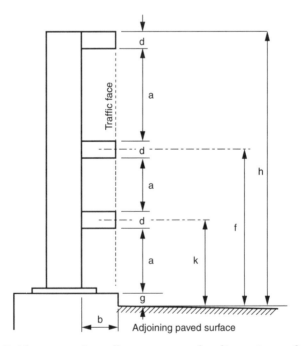

Figure 1.72. Bridges carrying all purpose roads: dimensions of P2 vehicle pedestrian parapet

Table 1.21. Table to Figure 1.71

Dimension	Maximum	Minimum
a	300	
b		100
d		50
g		700 or 800
h		1250 or 1500

Notes
1 All dimensions in mm.
2 *W* is width of adjoining paved surface between kerb and traffic face.
3 Number of longitudinal members to suit overall height required.
4 Infill, shown as dashed lines, required for P2 and P5 applications.
5 Diagrammatic sketches – not to scale.

Table 1.22. Table to Figure 1.72

Dimension	Description	Maximum	Minimum
a.	Clear distance between longitudinal members or between top of plinth and longitudinal member above.	300 mm (400 mm for accommodation bridge parapets only)	–
b.	The distance between the traffic face of the parapet and the front face of a supporting post at its base, at whatever height the base may be.	–	100 mm
d.	Overall depth of the longitudinal member	–	50 mm
f.	Height of the centre-line of the main member above the adjoining paved surface	685 mm	535 mm
g.	Height of the plinth above the adjoining paved surface.	100 mm	50 mm
h.	Height of top of upper longitudinal member above the adjoining paved surface.	–	1000 m
k.	Height of the centre-line of the lowest effective member.	To comply with 'a'	300 mm

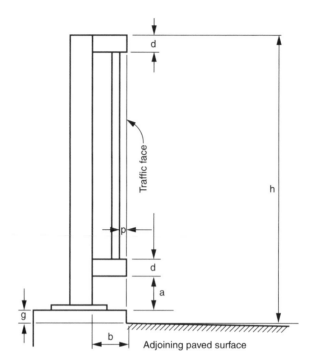

Figure 1.73. Bridges carrying all purpose roads: dimensions of P2 vehicle pedestrian parapet

Table 1.23. Table to Figure 1.73

Dimension	Description	Maximum	Minimum
a.	Clear distance between top of plinth and lower longitudinal member.	100 mm	–
b.	The distance between the traffic face of the parapet and the front face of the supporting post at its base, at whatever height the base may be.	–	100 mm
d.	Overall depth of a longitudinal member.	–	50 mm
g.	Height of plinth above the adjoining paved surface.	100 mm	50 mm
h.	Height of top of upper longitudinal member above the adjoining paved surface.	–	1000 m
p.	Distance between front faces of the vertical infill members and longitudinal members.	50 mm	0 mm

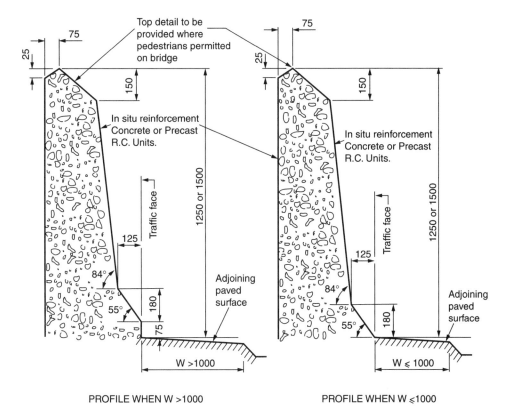

NOTES
1. W is width of adjoining paved surface between kerb and traffic face of parapet.
2. Dimensions are in mm.
3. Diagrammatic sketches - not to scale.

Figure 1.74. Shaped concrete parapets

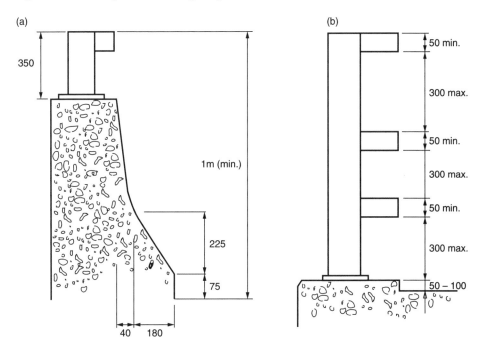

Figure 1.75. Parapet types: (a) rigid; (b) flexible

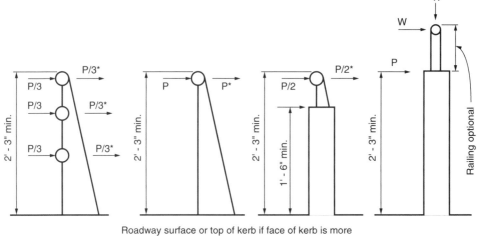

Roadway surface or top of kerb if face of kerb is more
than 6 inches from the face of the rail

Figure 1.76. Scheme of design for traffic railing following US practice

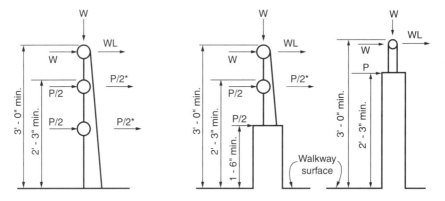

Figure 1.77. Scheme of design for combination railing following US practice

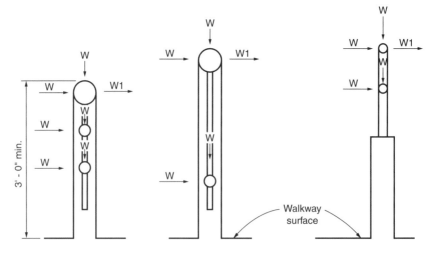

Figure 1.78. Scheme of design for pedestrian railing following US practice

US Practice on parapets (courtesy: California State Highway Officials)
With a simultaneous longitudinal load of half the amount starred in Fig. 1.76, divided among posts along the continuous rail length, the traffic railing design is as shown in Fig. 1.76.

Similarly, designs for the combination railing and pedestrian railing are given, respectively, by Fig. 1.77 and Fig. 1.78.

Note that in Figs 1.76 to 1.78 the following data apply:

$P = 10\,000\,\text{lb}$

$L = $ post spacing for traffic railing

$W = 50\,\text{lb plf}$

$I = $ post spacing for pedestrian railing

Rail load shown left
Post load shown right

SECTION 2
OPERATIONAL RESEARCH
AND CHOICE OF BRIDGES

2. Operational research and choice of bridges

2.1 Introduction

In this section a method is given for narrowing choices of bridge types, leading to the final selection of a bridge. The location and layout of a bridge depends also upon traffic conditions, which are not included in the parameters given. The transportation requirements have a major impact on the choice of a bridge whether it is located in a rural or urban region. The reader shall carry out an independent study in this field since it is not within the scope of this book. Bridge approaches and site investigation are included in the proposed charts and so are the principles of bridges that cross rivers. The sequence of bridge design and a comparison of alternatives are the dominant items of this section. These are solved using standard quantity curves of both substructures and superstructures. The selection of bridge foundations is based generally on the following:

1. choosing the right foundation, and stating the site type
2. the bearing capacity of the ground
   (a) type, nature and strength of the soil and sequences of strata
   (b) nature and magnitude of the loading
   (c) level of the water table and ground-water management
   (d) environment (noise, vibration, pollution, etc.)
   (e) cost economics and quantities.

All selections are clearly supported by tables of design parameters, quantity and cost curves. On the lines suggested in the text, the reader should initially go through the flow chart provided in Section 2.4. Either the choice is narrowed or a single choice is made for the type of bridge needed on a particular site.

The success of this work depends on the correct input. Obviously the unit cost of any item is prone to inflation. Where the work in a particular country is to be carried out, it is necessary to obtain initial information on the material and labour costs of that country. The rate of inflation for the country is also a factor to be reckoned with. The prices must, therefore, be modified and a new cost estimate should be obtained. Examples given in this section will assist the reader in the method and technique of learning this operational research. When the operational research team (ORT) is satisfied and the monetary support is available, the bridge should then be handed over to the design team for thorough design and detailing and to other teams for services.

The entire project is divided into six separate sections:

Section 2.4 – The classification chart	**Section I**
Section 2.5 – General computations	**Section II**
Section 2.6 – Quantity curves and tables for superstructure	**Section III**
Section 2.7 – Quantity curves for substructure	**Section IV**
Section 2.8 – Specification and cost estimates	**Section V**
Section 2.9 – Results from example problems	**Section VI**
Section 2.10 – References	**Section VII**

The various sections are self-explanatory and the interrelation between the several sections is illustrated by means of worked examples.

Section 2.4 (I) – *The classification chart*. This section deals with the classification of various bridges, such as RC slab, culvert, girder, truss, arch, rigid frame, cantilever, cable stayed and suspension bridges. The classification chart is based on a comparative study of both past and present problems.

Regarding the idea behind this chart, it indicates when soil, site, traffic and other pertinent conditions are available from the data and field observations, what systematic preliminary approach should be made in order to obtain conformity within the given requirements, the type of bridge that is most economical. The chart to a great extent solves this problem. In problems where the chart gives 'unsolved comparison' between any two, the matter is referred to other sections dealing with quantity curves and specifications. It is important to note that the term 'unsolved comparison' also means one type of bridge of different material; say, an arch bridge has steel arch, RC arch, and masonry arch. Which one is economical, depends on the quantity curves and the availability of material, labour and transportation. As mentioned in 'The Scope of Research', this chart assumes no responsibility as far as the material availability is concerned and is considered as a constant factor.

To start with, question (1) asks the type of soil and its bearing power or resistance. Chart I answers this by classifying various soil structures on the basis of safe load taken by them. However, if there is any soil structure the condition of which lies in between the existing conditions of Chart I, average values should be assumed, or if by actual observations and field testing, the bearing power of the soil structure is known, this bearing power should be observed in Chart I and under such conditions, regardless of the soil structure indicated on the left side, the chart should be followed along the lines marked by various arrows.

After obtaining this value, the chart gives access to question (2) about the 'Nature of the Site' and having question (1), and Chart I, and question (2), Chart II, in mind, the AH (arrowhead) gives direction to question (3) which means whether or not piers (open or solid) are permissible under the above conditions. This part of the classifications has taken into consideration the problem of erosion that has been observed in past practice. If piers are permissible, then question (4), Chart III, will bring about further limitations so as to give one type of pier. These limitations have also taken into consideration structural stability. On the other hand, if piers are not permissible then AH will give direction to question (5) for the determination of 'End Supports'. Here the idea is whether or not abutments are actually needed. In fact abutments are always needed but it is necessary to establish means of support and certain terms are used which are based on type of construction such as: thrust blocks, wall supports, frames and towers. If the abutments are needed, the AH will give direction to Charts IV and IV(A) for further comparison to reduce to one or a few choices and afterwards give directions to question (6).

After the substructure problem is considered, the question is what type of foundation is necessary for the structure. The blocks representing various 'Cs' will determine whether or not the foundation needed is shallow, deep pile or caisson. The AH will similarly pass through various blocks and charts to give a final type of footing.

Question (7) will decide whether or not the project needs a cofferdam. Question (7), Chart VI, will see to it that the type selected is more economical. If cofferdams are not needed, the AH will give signal to question (8).

Question (8) will indicate the type of bridge superstructure that can be recommended for the project. After giving recommendations for certain types of bridges, the AH will give direction to question (9) to decide whether or not single span or more than one span is necessary. Question (10) brings about limitations for various structures both on single span and more than one span. These limitations in question (10), sections (A) and (B), based on span lengths, have been taken into consideration for further analysis.

When through with question (10) the AH will enter block (6) for comparison among questions (8), (9), and (10). Block (C) will bring about convergence with the help of question (11).

Section 2.5 (II) – *General computations*. This section deals with waterway computations and span versus maximum moments, shears and end reactions for both simple and continuous spans. In some countries, this section is modified for the respective vehicle loads.

As far as waterway computation is concerned both afflux and backwater are considered. Various tables are available to give values such as coefficients, discharge and velocity, etc. All the formulae for the computation of backwater height have been taken from the Iowa State Highway Commission. The value of h_1^* is substituted in the empirical formula that gives the minimum spacing between piers. In this section a relation also exists between velocity and individual span approaches. The formula for minimum width takes care of longitudinal slope, hydraulic depth and silt coefficient.

For preliminary work the tables given in this section are sufficient to give satisfactory results. In case the survey for the actual site gives details of the shape, topography and geology of the area, proper coefficients are established and discharge values are taken to compute the waterway. Apart from waterway computations, tables are given for simple and continuous spans which indicate for the overall span the moments, shears and end reactions and also marked whether truck loading or lane loading governs.

The establishment of continuous spans have the limitation that the main span must not be greater than 1.7 times the end span. This limitation is based on sound economic reasons. It is evident to see why prestressed concrete bridges proved uneconomical in Section 2.9, problem 4 (result). With the help of moments and shears, steel for stem and footing can easily be calculated. Moreover, Tables 2.1 to 2.4 are based on formulae available in Cases I, II, and III.

The author has derived some empirical formulae for prestressed concrete haunched and straight beams, the relation between main and end spans. General cost formula based on economic span length is also derived in this section.

Section 2.6 (III) – *Quantity curves and tables for superstructures.* The tables, charts, and curves given in this section deal with the quantities. For different spans, loads and heights, these curves give quantities for various bridges.

Section 2.7 (IV) – *Quantity curves for substructures.* These curves like those of Section 2.5 give direct quantities for all kinds of substructure, such as piers, abutments, thrust blocks or pedestals, supporting walls wing walls, towers and bents.

Section 2.8 (V) – *Specification and cost estimates.* This section contains unit prices for almost all the items concerning bridge design and construction. These prices take care of various jobs and assume that the structure is open for traffic.

Charts and tables included in this section are quite up to date. The price lists are adjusted to suit the requirement throughout the United States. For a particular country, of course, the price lists can be replaced.

Section 2.9 (VI) – *Results.* The preliminary problems selected are to test the validity of the flow chart and quantity curves. For bridges with extensive data, the technique suggested gives a very economical result. The results given in this section have been compared with the existing bridges and proved to be more economical.

In problem 4, it is assumed that boring or drilling results show the best locations for the piers are C and D.

Note

All tables and prices are given in Imperial units. As enormous effort is required to redraw in metric units, it was decided to provide instead a table of conversion factors. All quantities can be measured in Imperial units and then simply converted to metric units pro rata. The prices of quantities or rates of payment are revised from time to time and are multiplied by a factor F called the multiplying factor or the Inflation Index. Once this factor is known, the accurate price for the bridge type can be assessed easily. This helps in the decision-making stages and choices. The accurate price can then be determined by the completion stage of the bridge and for various structural details and methods of construction. Where vehicular loads differ, they should be accounted for in the case of a job in a particular country. The charts given and the results obtained will provide a firm decision on a bridge choice. Prices will differ finally.

2.2   Conversion factors for the original charts in Imperial units

The following conversion factors are adopted to change Imperial units to metric units.

1 in	25.4 mm
1 ft	0.3048 m or 30.48 cm
1 lb	0.454 kg
1 lb/ft^2	992.16 kPa
1 psi	6.89 kPa
1 ft lb	1.356 Nm
1 in lb	0.1129848 Nm
1 kip/in	175.1268 kN/m
1 lb force	4.448222 N
1 lb/in^2	6.894757 kN/m^2
1 yd^3	0.767 m^3
1 ft^2	0.09290 m^2
1 yd^2	0.8361 m^2
1 ft^3	0.02832 m^3

2.3   Notation for the chart

Note: Conversion factors in 2.2 are considered with SI units; otherwise, other metric units are needed.

A	Natural waterway at the site (ft^2)
A_1	Enlarged area upstream of the bridge (ft^2)
A_2	Flood plain area (ft^2)

A	Cost of one abutment and its foundation
$a_1, a_2, a_3, \ldots$	Divisional areas (ft^2)
a	Artificial waterway (ft^2)
B_1	Clear aggregate width between extreme channel piers (ft)
b_c	Critical width (ft)
C	Coefficient in Kutter's formula
C_1	Coefficient of discharge
C_{RE}	Rehback Pier coefficient
C_S	Cost of superstructure
C'	Total cost
D_1	Distance between the two extreme cross-sections of the river (ft)
d	Normal depth (ft) Intensity of rainfall (in/in)
d_1, d_2	Respective depth (ft)
F_n	Froude number
f	Coefficient of rugosity for river Stress in concrete (lb/in^2)
g	Acceleration (ft/s^2)
H	Total height (ft)
H_{mn}	Minimum specific energy of flow (ft-lb)
h_{ST}	Waterway stage (ft)
h_c	Critical depth (ft)
h	Depth of flow (backwater) (ft)
h_1	Afflux (ft)
h_1^*	Backwater height (ft)
h_n	Depth of uncontracted flow (ft)
I	Moment of inertia (ft^4)
J	Constant
K	Constant of variation
K_1	Constant
L	Any length parameter (ft)
l	Interior span (ft)

l_1	Exterior span (ft)
$(\overline{LW})$	Lineal waterway (ft)
M	Catchment area (acres or ft^2)
M_o	Opening ratio
m	Constant based on Froude number$n$ Number of spans
O	Steel parameter
p	Percentage run-off
P_1	Cost of one pier and foundation
Q	Total discharge (cusecs)
Q_2	Total discharge of flood plain area (cusecs)
R or HMD	Hydraulic mean depth (ft)
S	Longitudinal slope
V	Velocity of approach (ft/s)
V'	Increase in velocity (ft/s)
V_1'	Increase in velocity in the main channel due to flood discharge (ft/s)
V_2	Velocity of flood plain (ft/s)
$V_n = V$	Normal velocity (ft/s)
v_1, v_2, v_3	Velocity in respective divisional areas (ft/s)
w	Live load
w'	Dead load
X, X'	Distances (ft)
ρ	Density of concrete (lbs/ft^3)
$2r^2/y$	Width of the zone
δ_0	Pier shape factor

2.4 The classification chart

Pass through the flow chart given in Fig. 2.1 and proceed to Section 2.5.

The purpose of the flow chart is to select comparatively more economical types of bridge. The problem with given soil, site and loading conditions, is put to this chart. Select these conditions in the chart and pass them along arrow heads through various questions. All possible answers with 'yes' and 'no' are available and they are recorded simultaneously. As these conditions pass through many areas of the charts, the recorded statements will show converging results. The last question will determine the type or a few types for further investigation based on Sections 2.6–2.8.

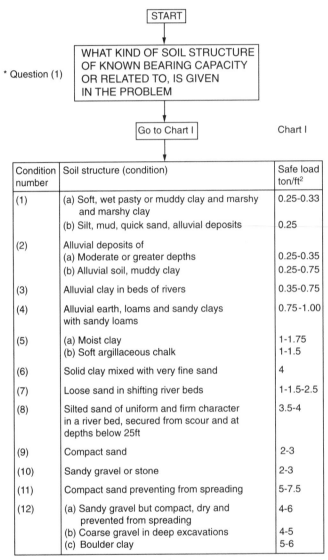

Figure 2.1 (pages 104–119). Classification chart

Question (1) (continued)

(13)	Very firm, compact sand at a depth 20-30ft and compact sandy gravel	6-7
(14)	(a) Firm shale protected from weather and gravel clean	6-8
	(b) Firm shale	6-7
(15)	Compact gravel	7-9
(16)	(a) Clay and sand alternative layers	≮1.5≯3.00
	(b) Unknown layer and variable conditions	≯2.5≮1
(17)	Muram alone or mixed with other soil conditions	4
(18)	Sandy clay at smaller depth over lying shale in sound condition (cracks allowed)	10
(19)	Sandy clay over lying residual deposits of broken bedrock (any stone)	10
(20)	Laminated rock such as slate and schists with layers of alluvial earth loams and sandy loams (often low depth)	35
(21)	(a) Sandstone and clay found interbedded with shale and lime stone and with layer of clay	2.5-9
	(b) Hard stone (sand)	8-12
(22)	Massive bedrock without lamination (granite) (diorite) (gneiss) (traprock) (limestone) (felsite) (cemented conglomerate) (mixture of either of above)	25-100

Go to question (2)

Figure 2.1. (Continued)

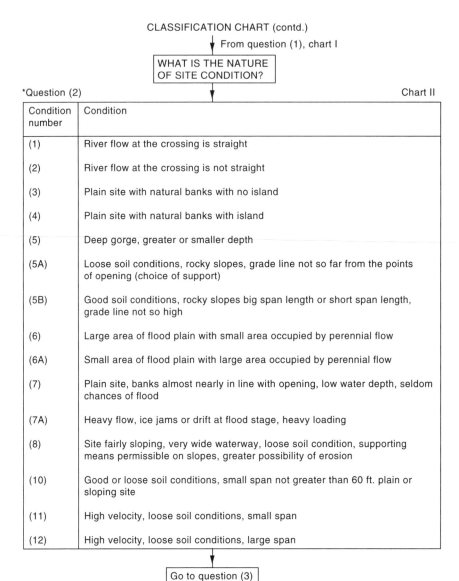

Figure 2.1. (Continued)

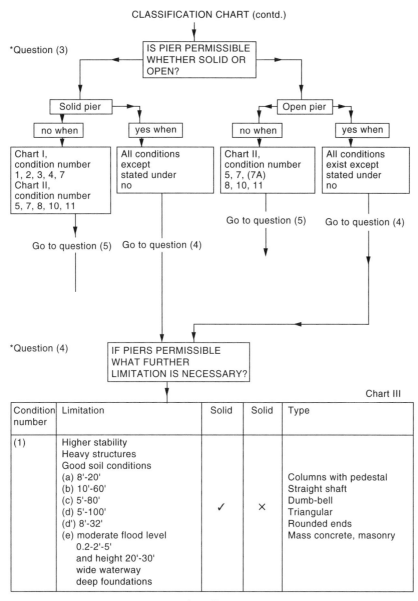

Figure 2.1. (Continued)

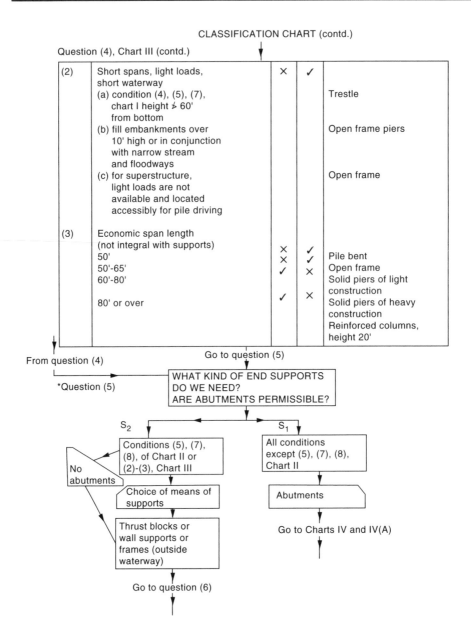

Figure 2.1. (Continued)

CLASSIFICATION CHART (contd.)

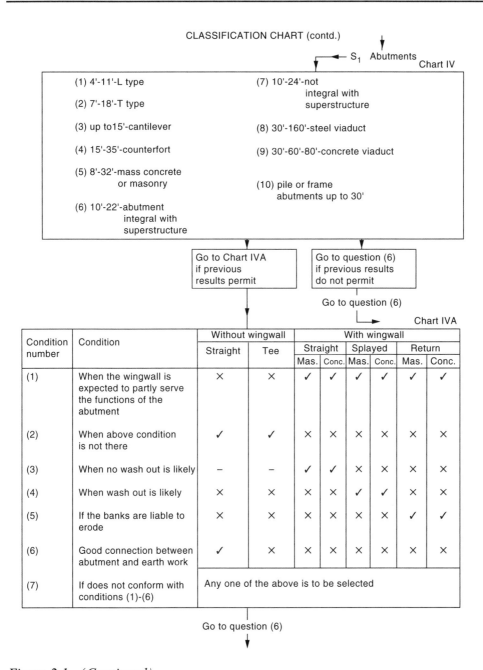

Figure 2.1. (Continued)

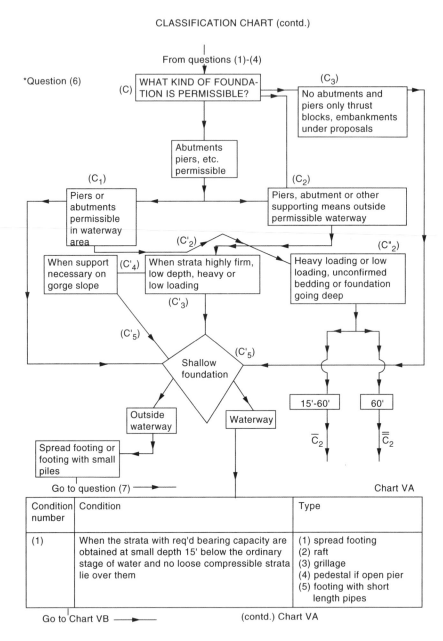

CLASSIFICATION CHART (contd.)

Condition number	Condition	Type
(1)	When the strata with req'd bearing capacity are obtained at small depth 15' below the ordinary stage of water and no loose compressible strata lie over them	(1) spread footing (2) raft (3) grillage (4) pedestal if open pier (5) footing with short length pipes

Go to Chart VB ⟶   (contd.) Chart VA

Figure 2.1. (Continued)

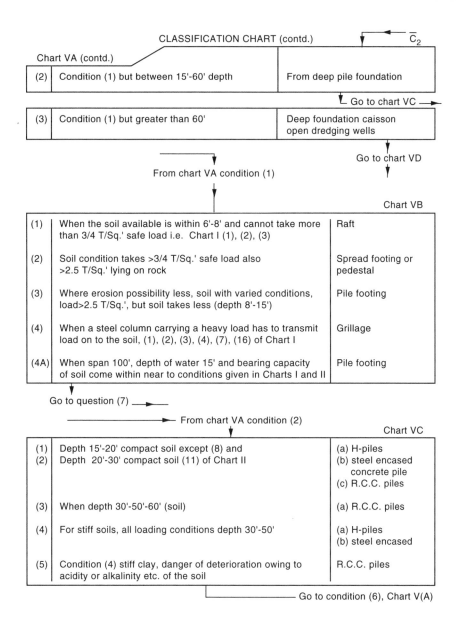

Figure 2.1. (Continued)

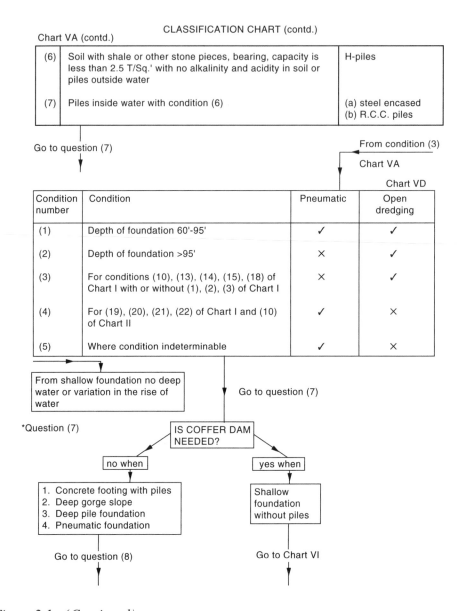

Figure 2.1. (Continued)

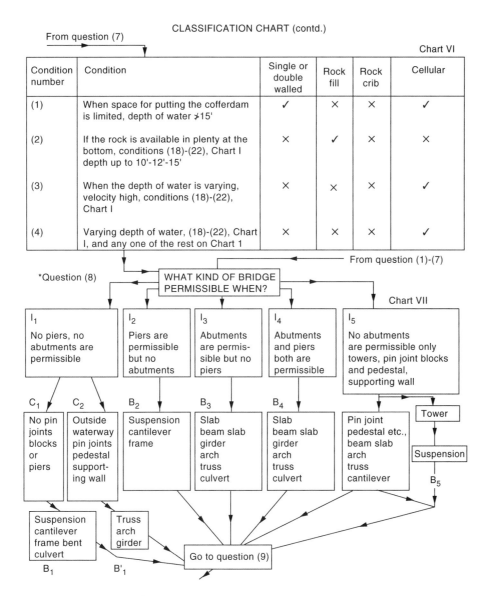

Figure 2.1. (Continued)

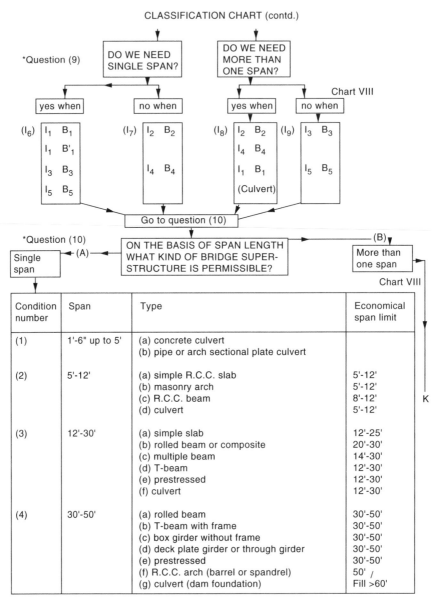

Figure 2.1. (Continued)

CLASSIFICATION CHART (contd.)

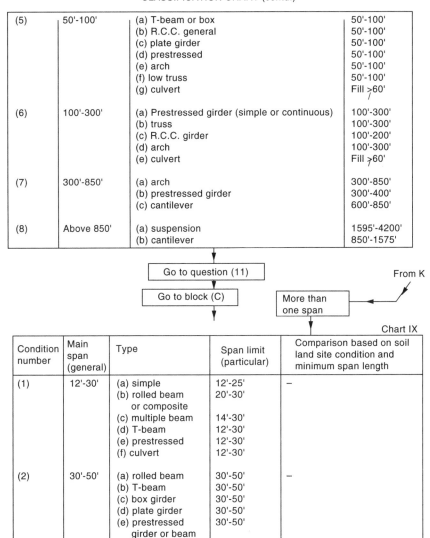

(5)	50'-100'	(a) T-beam or box	50'-100'
		(b) R.C.C. general	50'-100'
		(c) plate girder	50'-100'
		(d) prestressed	50'-100'
		(e) arch	50'-100'
		(f) low truss	50'-100'
		(g) culvert	Fill >60'
(6)	100'-300'	(a) Prestressed girder (simple or continuous)	100'-300'
		(b) truss	100'-300'
		(c) R.C.C. girder	100'-200'
		(d) arch	100'-300'
		(e) culvert	Fill >60'
(7)	300'-850'	(a) arch	300'-850'
		(b) prestressed girder	300'-400'
		(c) cantilever	600'-850'
(8)	Above 850'	(a) suspension	1595'-4200'
		(b) cantilever	850'-1575'

Go to question (11)

Go to block (C)

More than one span

From K

Chart IX

Condition number	Main span (general)	Type	Span limit (particular)	Comparison based on soil land site condition and minimum span length
(1)	12'-30'	(a) simple	12'-25'	–
		(b) rolled beam or composite	20'-30'	
		(c) multiple beam	14'-30'	
		(d) T-beam	12'-30'	
		(e) prestressed	12'-30'	
		(f) culvert	12'-30'	
(2)	30'-50'	(a) rolled beam	30'-50'	–
		(b) T-beam	30'-50'	
		(c) box girder	30'-50'	
		(d) plate girder	30'-50'	
		(e) prestressed girder or beam	30'-50'	
		(f) culvert	30'-50'	

Chart IX (contd.)

Figure 2.1. (Continued)

CLASSIFICATION CHART (contd.)

Chart IX (contd.)

(3)	50'-100'	(a) T-beam or box	50'-100'	(a₁) height 60' 50' mainspan R.C.C. arch 50' mainspan steel arch
		(b) plate girder	50'-100'	(b₁) culvert sectional archplate
		(c) prestressed	50'-100'	
		(d) low truss	50'-100'	
(4)	100'-300'	(a) prestressed girder	100'-300'	(a₂) 100'-200' main span R.C.C. arch
		(b) truss	100'-300'	(b₃) 100'-200' main span steel arch
		(c) R.C.C. girder	100'-200'	(c₃) series of culverts (d₃) (a), (b), (c) of condition (3)
(5)	300'-850'	(a) arch	300'-850'	(a), (b), (c)
		(b) prestressed	300'-400'	(a₂), (b₃), (d₃) of condition (4)
		(c) cantilever	600'-850'	
(6)	Above 850'	(a) suspension	1595'-4200'	(a), (b), (c) of condition (5)
		(b) cantilever	850'-1575'	adopted the same if span length varies within limits

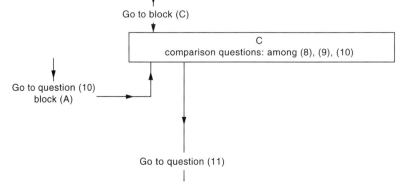

Go to block (C)

```
                              C
              comparison questions: among (8), (9), (10)
```

Go to question (10)
   block (A)

Go to question (11)

Figure 2.1. (Continued)

CLASSIFICATION CHART (contd.)

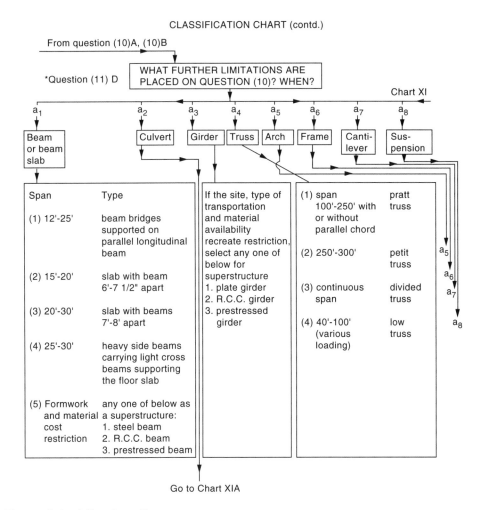

Figure 2.1. (Continued)

CLASSIFICATION CHART (contd.)

From a_2, Chart XI

Chart XIA

Condition	Box type				Arch	Pipe	Sectional plate
	S.B.S.	D.B.S.	S.B.B.S.	D.B.B.S.			
(1) Total waterway 60' or bridge not more than 3-4 span ≮10' catchment 700 acres (up to)	✓	✓	✓	✓	✓	✓	✓
(2) when piers and abutments not permissible	✓	✓	✓	✓	✕	✓	✓
(3) when condition (2) exists (a) area up to 50 Sq. ft.	✓	✕	✕	✕	✕	✓	✓
(b) area up to 75 Sq. ft.	✕	✓	✕	✕	✕	✓	✓
(c) area up to 125 Sq. ft.	✕	✕	✓	✕	✕	✓	✓
(d) area above 125 Sq. ft.	✕	✕	✕	✓	✕	✕	✓
(4) with abutments if above conditions are allowed	✕	✕	✕	✕	✓	✓	✓
(5) For steep banks	✓	✓	✓	✓	✕	✕	✓
(6) height of fill (a) 2'-15'	✓	✓	✓	✓	✓	✓	✓
(b) 15'-30'	✓	✓	✓	✓	✕	✓	✕
(c) 30'-60'	✓	✓	✓	✓	✕	✕	✕

S.B.S. - single box slab; D.B.S. - double box slab; S.B.B.S. - single box beam slab; D.B.B.S. - double box beam slab

Figure 2.1. (Continued)

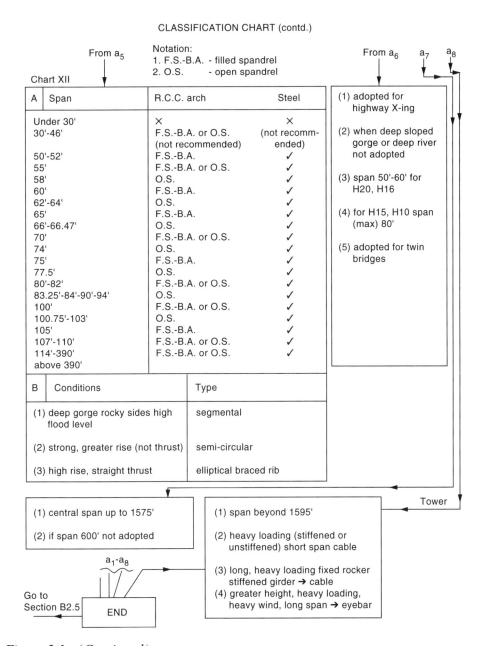

Figure 2.1. (Continued)

2.5   General computation (go to next section)

This is a general section dealing with waterway computation and structural stability. If Section 2.4 suggests more than one span, with the help of this section, economic span lengths are easily determined. Various charts and graphs given in this section simplify waterway computation. Certain formulae for economic span lengths are derived to ease computation in this area. For simple- and continuous-span bridges, for various span ratios, tables are available to give moments, shears and reactions at different points for standard highway loadings. The structure, therefore, passing out of this section will have surety for its stability, good proportions and economic span length.

2.5.1   Waterway computation (I)

Many factors such as the nature of the bed of the river, intensity and distribution of rainfall, discharge, velocity, afflux, backwater and site configuration, etc., decide the waterway dimensions. However, the waterway through the bridge should be sufficient to pass the maximum flood discharge that would ever pass down the river, without increasing the velocity to a dangerous limit and also take into account the carriage of drift, ice, and debris.

Before proceeding with the discussion, it is essential to point out that, in general, the entire stream crossing measured from the high-water line to high-water line clear across the flood plain is composed of three distinct elements: the main channel structure, structural approaches and approach embankments. From an economic standpoint certain limitations are essentially to be imposed on these structures. These limitations are to control the minimum spacing of piers for the main channel spans, minimum length of main channel construction, the length of individual approach spans, the points beyond which an approach embankment may not safely be placed, the type of approach construction and the net vertical clearance. All these are to be considered in the waterway computation.

2.5.2   Discharge and catchment–run-off method (IA)

Several methods are available to compute the waterway when maximum expected flood discharge governs. For operational research like this, the following will give quick results:

(A)   One way of computing the waterway is to divide a river into a convenient number of parts. Two wires 100 ft apart are stretched across and the divisions of the widths of the river are marked on these wires. Mean velocity is measured in each division by the float:

$$Q = a_1 v_1, \; a_2 v_2 \cdots a_n v_n \tag{2.1}$$

Artificial waterway is determined as

$$a = \frac{Q}{V'} \qquad (2.2)$$

where $V' = \sqrt{V^2 + 2gd}$

$$(\overline{LW}) = \frac{a}{d + h_1} \qquad \text{(see Table 2.1)} \qquad (2.3)$$

h_1 is calculated from Merriman's formula or Molesworth formula, whichever is suitable:

$$h_1 = \frac{V^2}{2g} \left[\frac{A}{C_1 a} \frac{A}{A_1} \right] \quad \text{Merriman formula}$$

$$h_1 = \left(\frac{V^2}{58.6} + 0.05 \right) \left[\left(\frac{A}{a} \right)^2 - 1 \right] \quad \text{Molesworth formula}$$

$$C_1 = 0.075 + 0.35 \left(\frac{a}{A} \right) - 0.1 \left(\frac{a}{A} \right)^2$$

(B)   Another way of determining the waterway of major bridges is the catchment–run-off method. In this method the magnitude of the catchment area is computed from one of the run-off formulae:

(a) $$Q = M \times 5280 \times 5280 \times \frac{1}{12 \times 60 \times 60} \times \frac{P}{100} \qquad (2.4)$$

$$a = \frac{Q}{V'} \qquad (2.5)$$

and further calculation is the same as in Eq. (2.1).

(b)   To find HFL, levels along three cross-sections of the river, one mile upstream and one mile downstream are taken. At each cross-section HFL is found verified by flood marks. Then calculate the area of each cross-section up to HFL and adopt the mean value.

Next the value of HMD is found, i.e.

$$\text{HMD} = \frac{\text{area of cross-section}}{\text{wetted perimeter}} \qquad (2.6)$$

for each cross-section and the mean value is adopted.

The slope of water surface is determined by finding the difference of the HFLs at the two extreme cross-sections. Hence

$$S = \frac{\text{total fall}}{D_1} \qquad (2.7)$$

Therefore

$$V = C\sqrt{(\text{HMD})S} \quad \text{Kutter's formula} \qquad (2.8)$$

Table 2.1 (pages 122–124). Maximum run-off for drainage opening designs from various drainage areas (**I**)

Area (square mile)	Discharge (cfs)	Area (square mile)	Discharge (cfs)	Area (square mile)	Discharge (cfs)
0.5	350	4.1	1937	7.8	3057
0.6	417	4.2	1973	7.9	3083
0.7	479	4.3	2008	8.0	3110
0.8	540	4.4	2043	8.1	3137
0.9	598	4.5	2078	8.2	3163
1.0	655	4.6	2113	8.3	3189
1.1	709	4.7	2148	8.4	3216
1.2	753	4.8	2183	8.5	3242
1.3	816	4.9	2219	8.6	3268
1.4	866	5.0	2255	8.7	3294
1.5	914	5.1	2286	8.8	3320
1.6	962	5.2	2316	8.9	3345
1.7	1009	5.3	2347	9.0	3371
1.8	1055	5.4	2377	9.1	3297
2.0	1144	5.6	2437	9.3	3447
2.1	1188	5.7	2466	9.4	3473
2.2	1231	5.8	2496	9.5	3498
2.3	1273	5.9	2525	9.6	3523
2.4	1313	6.0	2555	9.7	3548
2.5	1363	6.1	2584	9.8	3573
2.6	1393	6.2	2612	9.9	3598
2.7	1541	6.3	2641	10	3620
2.8	1469	6.4	2670	11	3870
2.9	1507	6.5	2698	12	4100
3.0	1545	6.6	2727	13	4330
3.1	1581	6.7	2555	14	4560
3.2	1615	6.8	2783	15	4780
3.3	1653	6.9	2811	16	5000
3.4	1689	7.0	2839	17	5210
3.5	1726	7.1	2866	18	5420
3.6	1762	7.2	2894	19	5620
3.7	1798	7.4	2921	20	5820
3.8	1832	7.4	2949	21	6020
3.9	1867	7.5	2976	22	6210
4.0	1902	7.6	3003	23	6400
		7.7	3030	24	6590
25	6780	67	13 310	190	27 150
26	6960	68	13 440	200	28 120
27	7150	69	13 580	210	29 070
28	7330	70	13 710	220	30 010
29	7500	71	13 850	230	30 940
30	7680	72	13 980	240	31 850
31	7860	73	14 110	250	32 750
32	8030	74	14 240	260	33 640
33	8200	75	14 380	270	34 520
34	8370	76	14 510	280	35 390

(Continued)

Table 2.1. (Continued)

Area (square mile)	Discharge (cfs)	Area (square mile)	Discharge (cfs)	Area (square mile)	Discharge (cfs)
35	8530	77	14 460	290	36 250
36	8700	78	14 770	300	37 100
37	8870	79	14 900	310	37 950
38	9030	80	15 020	320	38 780
39	9190	81	15 150	330	39 600
40	9350	82	15 280	340	40 420
41	9510	83	15 410	350	41 230
42	9670	84	15 530	360	42 030
43	9930	85	15 660	370	42 850
44	9980	86	15 790	380	43 620
45	10 140	87	15 910	390	44 400
46	10 290	88	16 040	400	45 170
47	10 440	89	16 160	410	45 940
48	10 690	90	16 280	420	46 700
49	10 740	91	16 410	430	47 460
50	10 890	92	16 530	440	48 220
51	11 040	93	16 650	450	48 960
52	11 190	94	16 780	460	49 700
53	11 340	95	16 900	470	50 440
54	11 480	96	17 020	480	51 170
55	11 630	97	17 140	490	51 900
56	11 770	98	17 260	500	52 620
57	11 920	99	17 380	510	53 340
58	12 060	100	17 500	520	54 050
59	12 200	110	18 680	530	54 760
60	12 340	120	19 830	540	55 470
61	12 480	130	20 950	550	56 170
62	12 620	140	22 030	560	56 860
63	12 760	150	23 090	570	57 560
64	12 900	160	24 140	580	58 240
65	13 040	170	25 160	590	58 930
66	13 170	180	26 160	600	59 160
610	60 290	1400	106 400	5700	278 000
620	60 960	1500	111 600	5800	281 400
630	61 630	1600	116 600	5900	284 700
640	62 300	1700	121 500	6000	288 000
650	62 960	1800	126 400	6100	291 200
660	63 630	1900	131 100	6200	294 500
670	64 280	2000	135 800	6300	297 700
680	64 940	2100	140 400	6400	301 000
690	65 590	2200	145 000	6500	304 200
700	66 240	2300	149 400	6600	307 400
710	66 880	2400	153 900	6700	310 500
720	67 530	2500	158 200	6800	313 700
730	68 170	2600	162 500	6900	316 800
740	68 800	2700	166 800	7000	320 000
750	69 440	2800	171 000	7100	323 100

(Continued)

Table 2.1. (Continued)

Area (square mile)	Discharge (cfs)	Area (square mile)	Discharge (cfs)	Area (square mile)	Discharge (cfs)
760	70 070	2900	175 100	7200	326 200
770	70 700	3000	179 200	7300	329 300
780	71 330	3100	183 300	7400	332 400
790	71 950	3200	187 300	7500	335 400
800	72 570	3300	191 300	7600	338 500
810	73 190	3400	195 300	7700	341 500
820	73 810	3500	199 200	7800	344 500
830	74 420	3600	203 900	7900	347 600
840	75 040	3700	206 900	8000	350 600
850	75 650	3800	210 700	8100	353 600
860	76 250	3900	214 500	8200	356 500
870	76 860	4000	218 200	8300	359 500
880	77 460	4100	221 900	8400	362 500
890	78 060	4200	225 600	8500	365 400
900	78 660	4300	229 300	8600	368 400
910	79 260	4400	232 900	8700	371 300
920	79 850	4500	236 500	8800	374 200
930	80 450	4600	240 100	8900	377 100
940	81 040	4700	243 700	9000	380 000
950	81 620	4800	247 200	9100	382 900
960	82 210	4900	250 700	9200	385 700
970	82 800	5000	254 200	9300	388 600
980	83 380	5100	257 700	9400	391 500
1000	84 500	5300	264 500	9600	397 100
1100	90 200	5400	267 900	9700	400 000
1200	95 800	5500	271 300	9800	402 800
1300	101 200	5600	274 700	9900	405 600
10 000	408 400				
11 000	435 900				
12 000	462 600				
13 000	488 700				
14 000	514 400				
15 000	538 900				
16 000	563 200				
17 000	587 100				
18 000	610 500				
19 000	633 500				
20 000	656 100				
21 000	678 400				
22 000	700 300				
23 000	721 900				
24 000	743 200				
25 000	764 300				
26 000	785 000				
27 000	805 600				
28 000	825 900				
29 000	845 900				

Reference: PDH Bridge Design Manual 1960, page 29.

where

$$C = \frac{41.66 + \dfrac{0.00281}{s} + \dfrac{1.811}{f}}{1 + \left[\left(41.66 + \dfrac{0.00281}{s}\right)\right]\dfrac{f}{\sqrt{HMD}}} \qquad (2.9)$$

(See Table 2.2).

Even Manning's formula can be used for V, i.e.

$$V = \frac{1.486}{f}\sqrt{HMD} \times S^{2/3} \qquad (2.10)$$

Therefore $Q = AV$ will be easily achieved. The rest of the procedure is the same as in Eq. (2.1).

(C) When all factors that influence run-off are not exactly known, a good estimate can usually be made by the Talbot formula:

$$A = C_1 M^{3/4} \quad \text{(see Table 2.3)} \qquad (2.11)$$

$C_1 = \frac{1}{5}$ for flat areas

$\quad = \frac{1}{3}$ for rolling farm land

$\quad = \frac{2}{3}$ for rough, hilly watershed

$\quad = 1$ for steep barren areas

Table 2.2 (below and overleaf). Values of 'C' in Kutter's formula **(II)**

Hydraulic radius	To 1% N 0.030	1% N 0.035	Hydraulic radius	N 0.030	N 0.035
0.1	21.0	17.0	5.1	65.8	57.2
0.2	27.0	22.0	5.2	66.0	57.4
0.3	31.0	25.0	5.3	66.3	57.6
0.4	35.0	29.0	5.4	66.5	57.8
0.5	37.0	31.0	5.5	66.8	58.0
0.6	39.0	33.0	5.6	67.0	58.2
0.7	41.0	34.0	5.7	67.3	58.4
0.8	43.0	35.0	5.8	67.5	58.6
0.9	44.0	36.5	5.9	67.8	58.8
1.0	45.0	38.0	6.0	68.0	59.0
1.1	46.2	39.0	6.1	68.2	59.2
1.2	47.2	40.0	6.2	68.3	59.3
1.3	48.6	41.0	6.3	68.5	59.5
1.4	49.8	42.0	6.4	68.6	59.6
1.5	51.0	43.0	6.5	68.8	59.8
1.6	51.8	43.6	6.6	68.9	59.9
1.7	52.6	44.2	6.7	69.1	60.1
1.8	53.4	44.8	6.8	69.2	60.2
1.9	54.2	45.4	6.9	69.4	60.4

(Continued)

Table 2.2. (*Continued*)

Hydraulic radius	To 1% N 0.030	1% N 0.035	Hydraulic radius	N 0.030	N 0.035
2.0	55.0	46.0	7.0	69.5	60.5
2.1	55.4	46.5	7.1	69.7	60.7
2.2	55.8	47.0	7.2	69.8	60.8
2.3	56.2	47.5	7.3	70.0	61.0
2.4	56.6	48.0	7.4	70.1	61.1
2.5	57.0	48.5	7.5	70.3	61.3
2.6	57.4	49.0	7.6	70.4	61.4
2.7	57.8	49.5	7.7	70.6	61.6
2.8	58.2	50.0	7.8	70.7	61.7
2.9	58.6	50.5	7.9	70.9	61.9
3.0	59.0	51.0	8.0	71.0	62.0
3.1	59.4	51.4	8.1	71.2	62.2
3.2	59.8	51.8	8.2	71.3	62.3
3.3	60.2	52.2	8.3	71.5	62.5
3.4	60.6	52.6	8.4	71.6	62.6
3.5	61.0	53.0	8.5	71.8	62.8
3.6	61.4	53.4	8.6	71.9	62.9
3.7	61.8	53.8	8.7	72.1	63.1
3.8	62.2	54.2	8.8	72.2	63.2
3.9	62.6	54.6	8.9	72.4	63.4
4.0	63.0	55.0	9.0	72.5	63.5
4.1	63.3	55.2	9.1	72.7	63.7
4.2	63.5	55.4	9.2	72.8	63.8
4.3	63.8	55.6	9.3	73.0	64.0
4.4	64.0	55.8	9.3	73.1	64.1
4.5	64.3	56.0	9.5	73.3	64.3
4.6	64.5	56.2	9.6	73.4	64.4
4.7	64.8	56.4	9.7	73.6	64.6
4.8	65.0	56.6	9.8	73.7	64.7
4.9	65.3	56.8	9.9	73.9	64.9
5.0	65.5	57.0	10.0	74.0	65.0

Reference: PDH Bridge Design Manual 1960, page 29.
See Kutter's formula, Eq. (2.9).

Table 2.3 (below and facing). Waterway (ft²) required to drain different acreage M for equivalent rainfall of 1 in/HR. Table is based on Talbot's modified formula for allowing variable rainfall rate. Values of CM 314/4 ft² (**III**)

M (acres)	Flat areas not affected by accumulated snow length several times width C = 1/5	Rolling farm land length of watershed 3 or 4 × width C = 1/3	Rough, hilly watersheds having moderate slopes C = 2/3	Steep, barren watersheds having abrupt slopes C = 1
2	0.08	0.14	0.28	0.42
4	0.14	0.24	0.47	0.71
6	0.19	0.32	0.64	0.96

(*Continued*)

Table 2.3. (Continued)

M (acres)	Flat areas not affected by accumulated snow length several times width $C = 1/5$	Rolling farm land length of watershed 3 or 4 × width $C = 1/3$	Rough, hilly watersheds having moderate slopes $C = 2/3$	Steep, barren watersheds having abrupt slopes $C = 1$
8	0.24	0.40	0.79	1.19
10	0.28	0.47	0.94	1.41
15	0.38	0.63	1.27	1.91
20	0.48	0.79	1.58	2.36
25	0.56	0.93	1.86	2.80
30	0.64	1.07	2.14	3.21
35	0.72	1.20	2.40	3.60
40	0.82	1.33	2.65	3.98
45	0.87	1.45	2.89	4.34
50	0.94	1.57	3.14	4.70
60	1.08	1.80	3.59	5.39
70	1.21	2.02	4.03	6.05
80	1.34	2.23	4.46	6.69
90	1.46	2.43	4.87	7.31
100	1.58	2.63	5.27	7.91
150	2.14	3.57	7.14	10.7
200	2.66	4.43	8.87	13.3
250	3.14	5.24	10.5	15.7
300	3.60	6.00	12	18
350	4.05	6.74	13.5	20.2
400	4.47	7.45	15.9	22.4
450	4.89	8.14	16.3	24.4
500	5.29	8.80	17.6	26.4
600	6.06	10.1	20.2	30.3
700	6.81	11.3	22.7	34.0
800	7.52	12.5	25.1	37.6
900	8.22	13.7	27.4	41.1
1000	8.89	14.8	29.6	44.5
1200	10.2	17.0	34.0	51.0
1400	11.5	19.1	38.1	57.2
1600	12.7	21.1	42.2	63.3
1800	13.8	23.0	46.0	69.1
2000	15.0	24.9	49.8	74.8
2500	17.7	29.5	59.0	88.4
3000	20.3	33.8	67.6	101.4
3500	22.8	37.9	75.8	113.8
4000	25.2	41.9	83.9	125.8
4500	27.5	45.8	91.6	137.5
5000	29.7	49.5	99.1	148.7

Reference: 'Concrete Culverts' & Conduits Portland Cement Association 1961, page 10.

In general, computation will be $A/4 \times$ (rainfall for locality), for example for northern Kansas, equivalent rainfall is $4.6\,\text{in}/HR$, assuming $M = 3000$, $C = 1/3$

$$\frac{CM^{3/4}}{4} = 6$$

$$A = 4.6 \times 6 = 27.6\,\text{ft}^2$$

In order to facilitate the calculations, tables for all conditions are computed below, and these values are based on average conditions, allowing slight deviation which will not affect the overall design.

2.5.3 Backwater (B)

Unless the channel obstruction is very great, the backwater head is relatively small, so that it is not, in most cases, essential to know the backwater effect. However, when the bridge structure is so located as regards adjacent property as to render even a few inches of additional backwater a very serious matter, a backwater consideration is then a matter of necessity. For example, the adjacent dyke or revetment may be topped or railway track flooded or expensive landscaping is inundated by a small amount of water stage. Thus it becomes extremely important to control the length of the main structure and spacing of piers in such a way as to minimize property damage.

Much work has been done on this problem. The Iowa State Highway Department recently conducted experiments on the effect of backwater on the minimum spacing of piers. The theory established and experiments performed gave a number of interesting results. They classified backwater as: (*a*) a contraction backwater; (*b*) resistance backwater. The former is based on energy requirements of a critical flow at the minimum contracted opening and the flow is assumed to have no boundary resistance in a level channel, maintaining the fact that specific energy at all sections is the same.

The latter is based on the fact that flow at the minimum contracted opening is greater than the critical depth and in this case the maximum backwater is mainly governed by the increase of boundary shear.

The relation is established between a *critical depth* and *specific energy* of flow such as

$$h_c = \tfrac{3}{2} H_{\min} \tag{2.12}$$

$$\frac{H}{h_{CB}} = \frac{h}{h_{CB}} + \frac{h_{CB}^2}{2h^2} \quad \text{where } h_{CB} = 3\sqrt{\frac{Q^2}{gB^2}} \tag{2.13}$$

For a critical width considering flow through a contracted channel

$$b_c = \sqrt{\frac{27}{8} \times \frac{Q^2}{gH^3}} \tag{2.14}$$

Considering a resistance backwater condition, an experiment was performed for

$$\dfrac{\text{total maximum depth with backwater}}{\text{depth of uncontracted flow}}$$

$$\left[1 + \dfrac{h_1^*}{h_n}\right]^3 = \dfrac{F_n^2}{2} \dfrac{1}{\dfrac{3}{M_o} \sin\left(\dfrac{\theta}{3} - 30°\right) - 1} \tag{2.15}$$

These relations have been established in the light of the D'Aubuisson Theory; Naglers, Rehback, Yarnell formulae and Kindsvater and Carter laboratory investigations.

The most practical solution to this problem has been put forward by Rehbock by relating maximum backwater to the velocity head of unobstructed flow:

$$h_1^* \propto \text{velocity head of the unobstructed flow} = C_{RE} \dfrac{(V_n)^2}{2g} \tag{2.16}$$

where

$$C_{RE} = [\delta_0 - m(\delta_0 - 1)][0.4m + m^2 + 9m^4][1 + F_n^2]$$

$$m \leq \dfrac{1}{0.97 + \dfrac{21(F_n)^2}{2}} - 0.13$$

$$(F_n)^2 = \dfrac{(V_n)^2}{gL}$$

h_1^* is the most suitable value for the turbulent flow in short pipes or for shooting flow with very high velocities in open channels where $V_n < \sqrt{g + h}$ thus increasing a *critical depth*.

The value of h_1^* is important for the minimum spacing of piers. The relation between the effect of pier obstruction and minimum spacing is expressed by

$$h_1^* = \dfrac{1}{2g}\left[\dfrac{Q^2}{(\delta_0 B_1 h)^2} - V^2\right] \tag{2.17}$$

$$V' = \sqrt{V^2 + 2gh} \quad \therefore \quad \dfrac{Q^2}{(\delta_0 B_1 h)^2} = 2gh_1^* + V^2$$

$$B_1 = \dfrac{Q}{\sqrt{(2gh_1^* + V^2)\delta_0 h}} \tag{2.18}$$

Tables 2.4 and 2.5 consider fundamental values for δ_0 and V.

2.5.4 Approach spans

As mentioned previously, individual approach spans also affect bridge economy. Therefore, investigation regarding the economic approach span is essential.

Table 2.4. Fundamental Values for δ_0 **(IV)**

Rectangular		1.00
Semi-circular		0.90
Elliptical 2:1		0.80
3:1		0.75
2 1/2:1		0.80
Lenticular 3:1		0.70

Table 2.5. Fundamental values for v **(V)**

Type of soil	V ft./s
(1) shallow streams soft silt bottoms	⚡ 1/2
(2) sand bottoms	⚡ 1-1.5
(3) ordinary clay	⚡ 2-3
(4) compact clay	⚡ 5-6
(5) heavy gravel	⚡ 4-7

Apart from the site conditions that affect the nature of the approach span, it is imperative to figure out accurately (to an extent) the approach span considering the flood plain area and other hydraulic dimensions:

Assuming flood plain area $= A_2$

Mean flood velocity $= V_2 = C\sqrt{RS}$

From the Chezy formula $\quad R = 0.47247 \left(\dfrac{Q}{f}\right)^{1/3}$

$$s = \frac{f^{5/3}}{1844(Q)^{1/6}}$$

$$C = 0.8\text{--}0.9$$

where f is taken from Table 2.6.

Table 2.6. Values of f (VA)

No.	Quality	Size (mm)	f
1	Fine	0.2	0.60
2	Sandy silt	0.323	1.00
3	Coarse sand	0.725	1.5
4	Gravel (medium)	7.28	4.75
5	Boulder (medium)	72.5	15

The amount of reduction in the discharge is

$$Q_2 = A_2 V_2 \tag{2.19}$$

The increased velocity in the main channel is therefore equal to

$$V_1 = V + \frac{Q_2}{A} \tag{2.20}$$

The waterway stage in the main channel will be increased by

$$h_{ST} = \frac{1}{2g}\left(V_1'^2 - V^2\right) \tag{2.21}$$

Minimum pier spacing is thus determined by Eq. (2.18).

2.5.5 General cost formulae and economic span length (Section III)

Formula for computing cost of a bridge
Assume the width of the required bridge, including that of footways and the flooring system, is fixed. It is also assumed that for a total length of the bridge, the cost of piers increases as the number of spans, the cost of main girders decreases as the number of spans and the greatest economy is reached when the total cost of the main girders, etc., and the piers is equally divided.

Assuming from Sections 2.5.1–2.5.3 and Eq. (2.3) that the final, economic span is achieved, i.e. $(\overline{LW})$, then

L = total length of the bridge

$$n = \text{number of spans} = \frac{L}{(\overline{LW})} \tag{2.22}$$

Since span, height, dead loads, and live loads are known, the size and cost of one pier can easily be obtained. Let

P_1 = cost of one pier and its foundation

$$C_S = \text{cost of superstructure} = K(\overline{LW})^2 \qquad \text{where } K = \text{constant} \tag{2.23}$$

Since bending moment is proportional to the square of the span, the relation $C_S = K(\overline{LW})^2$ is justifiable.

Let the cost of one abutment and its foundation be fixed at $\bar{A}$

$$C' = \text{total cost} = n[K(\overline{LW})^2] + (n-1)P_1 = 2\bar{A} \tag{2.24}$$

Comparing with Eq. (2.22)

$$C' = \text{total cost}$$

$$= \frac{L}{(\overline{LW})} K(\overline{LW})^2 + \left[\frac{L}{(\overline{LW})} - 1\right] P_1 + 2\bar{A} \tag{2.25}$$

Differentiating with regard to $(\overline{LW})$

$$\frac{dC'}{d(\overline{LW})} = KL - \frac{P_1 L}{(\overline{LW})^2} \qquad \frac{dC'}{d(LW)} = 0 \quad \text{is the minimum condition}$$

Therefore

$$K = \frac{P_1}{(\overline{LW})^2} \quad \text{or} \quad P_1 = K(\overline{LW})^2 = C_S \tag{2.26}$$

Substituting in Eq. (2.24)

$$C' = nK(\overline{LW})^2 + (n-1)K(\overline{LW})^2 + 2\bar{A}$$

$$= (2n-1)K(\overline{LW})^2 2\bar{A} \tag{2.27}$$

C' will give the total cost of the bridge.

Formulae for economic span of prestressed concrete
The following formulae have been derived by the author for various cases given below. (Refer to Tables 2.7 to 2.24 for relevant classifications of data.)

Case I
Continuous beam of constant *cross-section and equal spans*

$$\frac{w'}{w} + \frac{l}{3} = \frac{0.292d(1 + K_1)}{r^2/y}$$

For I-section

$$\frac{r^2}{y} = \frac{d}{4}$$

$$\therefore \quad \frac{w'}{w} + \frac{l}{3} = 1.168(1 + K_1) \tag{2.28}$$

$$l = \text{economic length} \frac{[168.2(1 + K_1) - 48] \times f}{10\rho(1 + K_1)} \tag{2.29}$$

Table 2.7. Symmetrical two-span continuous beam. Constant moment of inertia. AASHTO H20-S16-44 loading (N = 1.0) **(VI)**

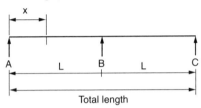

Total length

Total length ft	Exter. span length 'L'	Max. reaction kips		Max. shear kips	Max. moment kip-ft		Impact coefficient		Dist. x ft
		at A	at B	in AB at B	in AB at x	at B	I	VI	
60	30	46.4	63.1	−52.8	231.4	−193.1	.300	.270	10.7
70	35	49.5	65.3	−56.3	288.5	−229.4	.300	.256	14.1
80	40	52.0	66.8	−58.7	358.2	−266.5	.300	.244	16.1
90	45	54.1	67.8	−60.6	429.1	−317.8	.294	.233	18.1
100	50	55.7	68.6	−62.0	500.7	−373.2	.286	.222	20.2
110	55	57.1	70.0	−63.2	572.9	−432.5	.278	.213	22.3
120	60	58.3	74.0	−64.1	645.5	−495.8	.270	.204	24.4
130	65	59.3	78.0	−64.8	718.5	−563.1	.263	.196	26.6
140	70	60.2	82.0	−65.5	791.6	−634.4	.256	.189	28.7
150	75	61.0	86.0	−66.0	865.0	−709.7	.250	.182	30.8
160	80	61.6	90.0	−66.5	938.6	−789.1	.244	.175	33.0
170	85	62.2	94.0	−66.9	1012.3	−872.4	.238	.169	35.1
180	90	62.8	98.0	−67.2	1086.0	−959.7	.233	.164	37.3
190	95	63.2	102.0	−67.5	1159.9	−1051.0	.227	.159	39.4
200	100	63.7	106.0	−67.8	1233.9	−1146.3	.222	.154	41.6
210	105	64.1	110.0	−68.0	1307.9	−1245.6	.217	.149	43.7
220	110	64.4	114.0	−70.0	1382.0	−1349.0	.213	.145	45.9
230	115	64.7	118.0	−72.0	1456.1	−1456.3	.208	.141	48.0
240	120	65.0	122.0	−74.0	1530.3	−1567.6	.204	.137	50.2
Impact		I	VI	I	I	I			
Dead load		0.3750 × wL	1.2500 × wL	−0.6250 × wL	0.0703 × wL²	−0.1250 × wL²			0.3750 × L

Tables for Moments and Shear 2–4.7 AISC 1961.

Span	K_1
2	0
3	0.066
4	0.143
Infinite	0.155

Table 2.8. Symmetrical three-span continuous beam. Constant moment of inertia. AASHTO H20-S16-44 loading (N = 1.0) **(VII)**

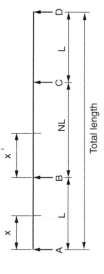

Total length ft	Exter. span length 'L'	Max. reaction kips		Max. shear kips		Max. moment kip-ft			Impact coefficient				Distance ft	
		at A	at B	in AB at B	in BC at B or C	in AB at x	at B	in BC at x'	I	II	III	IV	x	x'
90	30.0	46.2	62.3	−53.0	49.6	228.1	−184.4	179.6	.300	.300	.300	.270	10.6	14.0
105	35.0	49.3	64.7	−56.5	53.1	286.6	−219.5	231.6	.300	.300	.300	.256	12.6	16.0
120	40.0	51.8	66.4	−59.0	55.7	352.4	−254.2	285.9	.300	.300	.300	.244	16.0	18.5
135	45.0	53.9	67.5	−60.8	57.8	422.2	−299.2	342.1	.294	.294	.294	.233	18.0	21.0
150	50.0	55.5	68.4	−62.3	59.4	492.8	−351.1	399.7	.286	.286	.286	.222	20.1	23.5
165	55.0	56.9	69.1	−63.4	60.8	564.0	−406.8	458.2	.278	.278	.278	.213	22.2	26.0
180	60.0	58.1	72.1	−64.3	61.9	635.7	−466.2	517.5	.270	.270	.270	.204	24.2	28.5
195	65.0	59.2	75.9	−65.1	62.8	707.6	−529.3	577.3	.263	.263	.263	.196	26.3	31.0
210	70.0	60.0	79.8	−65.7	63.6	779.9	−596.1	637.6	.256	.256	.256	.189	28.4	33.5
225	75.0	60.8	83.6	−66.2	64.2	852.3	−666.7	698.2	.250	.250	.250	.182	30.5	36.0
240	80.0	61.5	87.4	−66.6	64.8	924.9	−741.0	759.2	.244	.244	.244	.175	32.6	38.5
255	85.0	62.1	91.3	−67.0	65.3	997.6	−819.1	820.3	.238	.238	.238	.169	34.8	41.0
270	90.0	62.6	95.1	−67.4	65.7	1070.5	−900.9	881.7	.233	.233	.233	.164	36.9	43.5
285	95.0	63.1	99.0	−67.7	66.1	1143.4	−986.4	943.2	.227	.227	.227	.159	39.0	46.0
300	100.0	63.6	102.8	−67.9	66.4	1216.5	−1075.6	1004.9	.222	.222	.222	.154	41.1	48.5
315	105.0	64.0	106.6	−68.2	66.7	1289.6	−1168.6	1066.8	.217	.217	.217	.149	43.3	51.0
330	110.0	64.3	110.5	−69.4	67.1	1362.7	−1265.3	1128.7	.213	.213	.213	.145	45.4	53.5
345	115.0	64.6	114.3	−71.4	68.9	1436.0	−1365.8	1190.7	.208	.208	.208	.141	47.5	56.0
360	120.0	64.9	118.2	−73.4	70.8	1509.2	−1469.9	1252.8	.204	.204	.204	.137	49.6	58.5
Impact		I	IV	I	III	I	II	III						
Dead load		0.4000 ×wL	1.1000 ×wL	−0.6000 ×wL	0.5000 ×wL	−0.0800 ×wL	−0.1000 ×wL²	0.0250 ×wL²					0.4000 ×L	0.5000 ×L

inertia. AASHTO H20-S16-44 loading (N = 1.1) **(VIII)**

Total length ft	Exter. span length 'L'	Max. reaction kips at A	Max. reaction kips at B	Max. shear kips in AB at B	Max. shear kips in BC at B or C	Max. moment kip-ft in AB at x	Max. moment kip-ft at B	Max. moment kip-ft in BC at x'	Impact coefficient I	II	III	IV	Distance ft x	Distance ft x'
90	29.0	45.7	62.2	−52.0	51.1	219.1	−185.2	195.6	.300	.300	.300	.269	10.3	14.5
105	33.9	48.8	64.6	−55.7	54.4	275.9	−219.4	250.4	.300	.300	.300	.255	12.2	17.1
120	38.7	51.4	66.2	−58.3	56.9	338.2	−254.0	308.0	.300	.300	.298	.242	15.6	19.8
135	43.5	53.4	67.3	−60.2	58.8	406.2	−302.8	367.4	.297	.293	.289	.231	17.5	22.5
150	48.4	55.2	68.2	−61.7	60.4	475.0	−355.4	428.0	.288	.284	.281	.221	19.5	25.1
165	53.2	56.6	68.8	−62.9	61.6	544.3	−411.8	489.7	.281	.276	.272	.211	21.6	27.8
180	58.1	57.8	72.5	−63.8	62.7	614.2	−472.1	552.0	.273	.269	.265	.202	23.6	30.4
195	62.9	58.9	76.3	−64.6	63.5	684.3	−536.1	614.9	.266	.262	.257	.194	25.6	33.1
210	67.7	59.8	80.2	−65.3	64.2	754.7	−603.9	678.3	.259	.255	.251	.187	27.7	35.8
225	72.6	60.6	84.1	−65.8	64.8	825.3	−675.5	741.9	.253	.248	.244	.180	29.7	38.4
240	77.4	61.2	87.9	−66.3	65.4	896.2	−750.9	805.9	.247	.242	.238	.174	31.8	41.1
255	82.3	61.9	91.8	−66.7	65.8	967.0	−830.1	870.1	.241	.237	.232	.168	33.8	43.7
270	87.1	62.4	95.7	−67.1	66.2	1038.1	−913.2	934.5	.236	.231	.226	.162	35.9	46.4
285	91.9	62.9	99.5	−67.4	66.6	1109.2	−999.9	999.1	.230	.226	.221	.157	38.0	49.1
300	96.8	63.4	103.4	−67.7	66.9	1180.6	−1090.5	1063.3	.225	.221	.216	.152	40.0	51.7
315	101.6	63.8	107.3	−67.9	67.2	1251.8	−1184.9	1128.6	.221	.216	.211	.148	42.1	54.4
330	106.5	64.1	111.2	−63.7	63.5	1323.1	−1283.1	1193.6	.216	.211	.207	.143	44.2	57.1
345	111.3	64.5	115.0	−70.6	70.4	1394.5	−1385.1	1258.6	.212	.207	.202	.139	46.2	59.7
360	116.1	64.8	118.9	−72.6	72.3	1466.0	−1490.9	1323.7	.207	.202	.198	.136	48.3	62.4
Impact		I	IV	I	III	I	II	III						
Dead load		0.3900 ×wL	1.1600 ×wL	−0.6100 ×wL	0.5500 ×wL	0.0761 ×wL²	−0.1100 ×wL²	0.0413 ×wL²					0.3900 ×L	0.5500 ×L

Tables for Moments and Shear 2–4.7 AISC 1961.

Table 2.10. Symmetrical three-span continuous beam. Constant moment of inertia. AASHTO H20-S16-44 loading (N = 1.2) (IX)

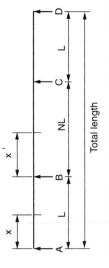

Total length ft	Exter. span length 'L'	Max. reaction kips		Max. shear kips		Max. moment kip-ft			Impact coefficient				Distance ft	
		at A	at B	in AB at B	in BC at B or C	in AB at x	at B	in BC at x'	I	II	III	IV	x	x'
90	28.1	45.1	62.3	−51.1	52.3	210.5	−188.8	209.9	.300	.300	.300	.268	10.0	15.4
105	32.8	48.3	64.6	−54.8	55.5	265.7	−223.7	267.7	.300	.300	.300	.254	11.2	18.2
120	37.5	50.9	66.2	−57.5	57.9	324.6	−258.9	328.2	.300	.300	.294	.241	15.1	21.0
135	42.2	53.0	67.3	−59.6	59.7	390.8	−308.2	390.5	.299	.292	.285	.230	17.0	23.9
150	46.9	54.8	68.2	−61.1	61.2	457.8	−362.0	454.0	.291	.283	.276	.219	19.0	26.7
165	51.6	56.2	69.0	−62.4	62.4	525.4	−419.6	518.5	.283	.275	.268	.210	21.0	29.5
180	56.3	57.5	72.9	−63.4	63.3	593.5	−481.1	583.7	.276	.268	.260	.201	23.0	32.3
195	60.9	58.6	76.8	−64.2	64.1	661.9	−546.5	649.4	.269	.260	.252	.193	24.9	35.1
210	65.6	59.5	80.8	−64.9	64.8	730.5	−615.8	715.5	.262	.254	.245	.186	26.9	37.9
225	70.3	60.3	84.7	−65.5	65.4	799.4	−689.0	782.0	.256	.247	.239	.179	28.9	40.7
240	75.0	61.0	88.6	−66.0	65.9	868.5	−766.1	848.7	.250	.241	.233	.172	30.9	43.5
255	79.7	61.6	92.5	−66.4	66.3	937.7	−847.1	915.7	.244	.235	.227	.166	32.9	46.3
270	84.4	62.2	96.4	−66.8	66.7	1007.0	−932.0	982.9	.239	.230	.221	.161	35.0	49.2
285	89.1	62.7	100.3	−67.1	67.0	1076.4	−1020.8	1050.2	.239	.224	.216	.156	37.0	52.0
300	93.8	63.2	104.2	−67.4	67.3	1145.8	−1113.5	1117.7	.229	.219	.211	.151	39.0	54.8
315	98.4	63.6	108.1	−67.6	67.9	1215.4	−1210.1	1185.3	.224	.214	.206	.146	41.0	57.6
330	103.1	63.9	112.0	−68.1	69.9	1285.0	−1310.6	1252.9	.219	.210	.201	.142	43.0	60.4
345	107.8	64.3	115.9	−70.1	71.9	1354.7	−1414.9	1320.7	.215	.205	.197	.138	45.0	63.2
360	112.5	64.6	119.9	−72.0	73.9	1424.4	−1523.2	1388.6	.211	.201	.192	.134	47.1	66.0
Impact		I	IV	I	III	I	II	III						
Dead load		0.3782 ×wL	1.2218 ×wL	−0.6218 ×wL	0.6000 ×wL	0.0715 ×wL²	−0.1218 ×wL²	0.0582 ×wL²					0.3782 ×L	0.6000 ×L

inertia. AASHTO H20-S16-44 loading (N = 1.3) (X)

Total length ft	Exter. span length 'L'	Max. reaction kips at A	Max. reaction kips at B	Max. shear kips in AB at B	Max. shear kips in BC at B or C	Max. moment kip-ft in AB at x	Max. moment kip-ft at B	Max. moment kip-ft in BC at x'	Impact coefficient I	II	III	IV	Distance ft x	x'
90	27.3	44.7	62.6	−50.4	53.4	202.3	−192.8	223.1	.300	.300	.300	.266	9.7	16.3
105	31.8	47.8	64.8	−54.0	56.4	255.8	−222.3	283.7	.300	.300	.300	.252	11.5	19.3
120	36.4	50.4	66.4	−56.8	58.7	311.5	−264.0	346.9	.300	.300	.290	.240	14.7	22.2
135	40.9	52.6	67.5	−58.9	60.5	376.0	−315.1	411.8	.300	.291	.281	.228	16.6	25.2
150	45.5	54.4	68.3	−60.6	61.9	441.3	−370.3	478.0	.293	.282	.272	.218	18.5	28.1
165	50.0	55.9	69.5	−61.9	63.0	507.3	−429.4	545.0	.286	.274	.263	.208	20.4	31.1
180	54.5	57.2	73.5	−62.9	63.9	573.6	−492.6	612.8	.278	.266	.255	.200	22.3	34.0
195	59.1	58.2	77.4	−63.8	64.6	640.4	−559.8	681.1	.272	.259	.248	.192	24.3	37.0
210	33.6	59.2	81.4	−64.5	65.3	707.3	−631.1	749.8	.265	.252	.241	.184	26.2	39.9
225	68.2	60.0	85.4	−65.1	65.8	774.5	−706.3	818.8	.259	.246	.234	.177	28.2	42.9
240	72.7	60.7	89.3	−65.6	66.3	841.9	−785.6	888.1	.253	.240	.228	.171	30.1	45.8
255	77.3	61.4	93.3	−66.1	66.7	909.4	−868.9	957.6	.247	.234	.222	.165	32.1	48.8
270	81.8	62.0	97.2	−66.5	67.0	977.1	−956.2	1027.3	.242	.228	.216	.160	34.1	51.7
285	86.4	62.5	101.2	−66.8	67.3	1044.8	−1047.6	1097.3	.237	.223	.211	.154	36.0	54.7
300	90.9	62.9	105.2	−67.1	67.6	1112.6	−1142.9	1167.2	.232	.218	.206	.150	38	57.7
315	95.5	63.4	109.1	−67.4	69.3	1180.5	−1242.5	1237.3	.227	.213	.201	.145	40.0	60.6
330	100.0	63.8	113.1	−67.7	71.3	1248.4	−1346.0	1307.5	.222	.208	.196	.141	41.9	63.6
345	104.5	64.1	117.0	−69.6	73.4	1316.4	−1453.4	1377.8	.218	.204	.192	.137	43.9	66.5
360	109.1	64.1	121.0	−71.5	75.4	1364.5	−1564.9	1448.2	.214	.200	.187	.133	45.9	66.5
Impact		I	IV	I	III	I	II	III						
Dead load		0.3645 ×wL	1.2855 ×wL	−0.6355 ×wL	0.6500 ×wL	0.0664 ×wL²	−0.1355 ×wL²	0.0758 ×wL²					0.3645 ×L	0.6500 ×L

Tables for Moments and Shear 204–7 AISC 1961.

Table 2.12. Symmetrical three-span continuous beam. Constant moment of inertia. AASHTO H20-S16-44 loading (N = 1.4) **(XI)**

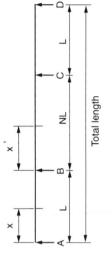

Total length ft	Exter. span length L'	Max. reaction kips at A	Max. reaction kips at B	Max. shear kips in AB at B	Max. shear kips in BC at B or C	Max. moment kip-ft in AB at x	Max. moment kip-ft at B	Max. moment kip-ft in BC at x'	Impact coefficient I	II	III	IV	Distance ft x	x'
90	26.5	44.3	62.9	−49.7	54.3	194.4	−196.9	235.5	.300	.300	.300	.265	9.4	17.1
105	30.9	47.3	65.1	−53.2	57.3	246.4	−233.2	298.5	.300	.300	.297	.251	11.1	20.2
120	35.3	50.0	66.7	−56.1	59.5	300.3	−270.6	364.1	.300	.299	.287	.238	13.0	23.3
135	39.7	52.2	67.8	−58.3	61.1	361.8	−323.2	431.5	.300	.290	.277	.227	16.2	26.4
150	44.1	54.0	68.6	−60.0	62.5	425.5	−380.0	500.1	.296	.281	.268	.217	18.0	29.5
165	48.5	55.5	70.1	−61.3	63.5	489.8	−441.0	569.5	.288	.273	.259	.207	19.9	32.6
180	52.9	56.8	74.1	−62.4	64.4	554.6	−506.1	639.7	.281	.265	.251	.198	21.8	35.6
195	57.4	57.9	78.1	−63.3	65.1	619.7	−575.3	710.3	.274	.258	.244	.190	23.6	38.7
210	61.8	58.9	82.1	−64.1	65.7	685.1	−648.9	781.4	.268	.251	.236	.183	25.6	41.8
225	66.2	59.7	86.1	−64.7	66.2	750.7	−726.6	852.8	.262	.245	.230	.176	27.5	44.9
240	70.6	60.5	90.2	−65.3	66.6	816.4	−808.4	924.4	.256	.238	.223	.170	29.4	48.0
255	75.0	61.1	94.2	−65.7	67.0	882.3	−894.4	996.3	.250	.233	.217	.164	31.3	51.1
270	79.4	61.7	98.2	−66.2	67.3	948.3	−984.6	1068.4	.245	.227	.212	.158	33.2	54.2
285	83.8	62.3	102.2	−66.5	67.6	1014.5	−1079.0	1140.6	.239	.222	.206	.153	35.1	57.3
300	88.2	62.7	106.2	−66.8	68.5	1080.7	−1177.5	1212.9	.234	.217	.201	.148	37.0	60.3
315	92.6	63.2	110.2	−67.1	70.6	1147.0	−1280.2	1285.3	.230	.212	.196	.144	38.9	63.4
330	97.1	63.6	114.2	−67.5	72.7	1213.3	−1387.1	1357.9	.225	.207	.192	.140	40.9	66.5
345	101.5	63.9	118.2	−69.4	74.9	1279.7	−1466.2	1430.5	.221	.203	.187	.136	42.8	69.6
360	105.9	64.3	122.2	−71.2	77.0	1346.2	−1613.5	1503.2	.217	.198	.183	.132	44.7	72.7
Impact		I	IV	I	III	I	II	III						
Dead load		0.3490 ×wL	1.3510 ×wL	−0.6510 ×wL	0.7000 ×wL	0.0609 ×wL²	−0.1510 ×wL²	0.0940 ×wL²					0.3490 ×L	0.7000 ×L

inertia. AASHTO H20-S16-44 loading (N = 1.5) **(XII)**

Total length ft	Exter. span length 'L'	Max. reaction kips		Max. shear kips		Max. moment kip-ft			Impact coefficient				Distance ft	
		at A	at B	in AB at B	in BC at B or C	in AB at x	at B	in BC at x'	I	II	III	IV	x	x'
90	25.7	43.9	63.3	-49.1	55.1	186.8	-201.3	246.8	.300	.300	.300	.264	9.1	17.9
105	30.0	46.8	65.5	-52.4	58.0	237.4	-238.3	312.2	.300	.300	.294	.250	10.8	21.1
120	34.3	49.5	67.0	-55.4	60.1	289.9	-283.7	380.1	.300	.298	.283	.237	12.6	24.3
135	38.6	51.8	68.1	-57.7	61.7	348.2	-333.9	449.8	.300	.289	.273	.226	15.7	27.5
150	42.9	53.8	68.9	-59.4	63.0	410.3	-390.9	520.6	.298	.280	.264	.215	17.5	30.7
165	47.1	55.2	70.7	-60.8	64.0	473.1	-453.9	592.3	.290	.272	.255	.206	19.4	34.0
180	51.4	56.5	74.8	-62.9	64.8	536.3	-521.2	664.6	.283	.264	.247	.197	21.2	37.2
195	55.7	57.6	78.9	-62.9	65.5	599.9	-592.9	737.4	.277	.257	.240	.189	23.0	40.4
210	60.0	58.6	82.9	-63.7	66.1	663.7	-668.9	810.7	.270	.250	.233	.182	24.9	43.6
225	64.3	59.5	87.0	-64.4	66.5	727.7	-749.2	884.3	.264	.243	.226	.175	26.8	46.8
240	68.6	60.2	91.1	-64.9	66.9	791.9	-834.0	958.1	.258	.237	.219	.169	28.6	50.0
255	72.9	60.9	95.1	-65.4	67.3	856.3	-923.0	1032.1	.253	.231	.213	.163	30.5	53.2
270	77.1	61.5	99.2	-65.9	67.6	920.8	-1016.4	1106.4	.247	.226	.208	.157	32.3	56.5
285	81.4	62.0	103.3	-66.2	67.9	985.4	-1114.1	1180.7	.242	.220	.202	.152	34.2	59.7
300	85.7	62.5	107.3	-66.6	69.8	1050.1	-1216.2	1255.2	.237	.215	.197	.147	36.1	62.9
315	90.0	63.0	111.4	-66.9	71.9	1114.8	-1322.7	1329.9	.233	.211	.192	.143	39.0	66.1
330	94.3	63.4	115.5	-67.3	74.1	1179.6	-1433.4	1404.5	.228	.206	.188	.139	39.8	69.3
345	98.6	63.7	119.5	-69.2	76.3	1244.5	-1548.6	1479.3	.224	.201	.183	.135	41.7	72.5
360	102.9	64.1	123.6	-71.1	78.5	1309.4	-1666.0	1554.2	.219	.197	.179	.131	43.6	75.7
Impact		I	IV	I	III	I	II	III						
Dead load		0.3317 ×wL	1.4183 ×wL	-0.6683 ×wL	0.7500 ×wL	0.0550 ×wL²	-0.1682 ×wL²	0.1130 ×wL²					0.3317 ×L	0.7500 ×L

Tables for Moments and Shear 2–4.7 AISC 1961.

Table 2.14. Symmetrical three-span continuous beam. Constant moment of inertia. AASHTO H20-S16-44 loading (N = 1.6) **(XIII)**

Beam diagram: supports A — L — B — C — L — D, with intermediate span NL; distances x and x'; Total length.

Total length ft	Exter. span length 'L'	Max. reaction kips at A	Max. reaction kips at B	Max. shear kips in AB at B	Max. shear kips in BC at B or C	Max. moment kip-ft in AB at x	Max. moment kip-ft at B	Max. moment kip-ft in BC at x'	Impact coefficient I	II	III	IV	Distance ft x	x'
90	25.0	43.5	63.8	−48.5	55.9	179.6	−205.7	257.4	.300	.300	.300	.263	8.8	18.6
105	29.2	46.3	66.0	−51.6	58.6	228.8	−250.3	325.0	.300	.300	.291	.249	10.5	22.0
120	33.3	49.1	67.5	−54.7	60.7	279.9	−304.8	395.0	.300	.297	.280	.236	12.2	25.3
135	37.5	51.3	68.6	−57.1	62.2	335.1	−357.6	466.7	.300	.288	.270	.225	15.3	28.6
150	41.7	53.2	69.3	−58.9	63.4	395.8	−409.1	539.6	.300	.279	.261	.214	17.1	32.0
165	45.8	54.8	71.4	−60.3	64.4	457.0	−467.7	613.4	.293	.271	.252	.205	18.9	35.3
180	50.0	56.2	75.5	−61.5	65.2	518.8	−537.4	687.8	.286	.263	.244	.196	20.7	38.6
195	54.2	57.3	79.6	−62.5	65.8	580.8	−611.6	767.7	.279	.256	.236	.188	22.5	42.0
210	58.3	58.3	83.8	−63.3	66.4	643.2	−690.3	837.9	.273	.249	.229	.181	24.3	45.3
225	62.5	59.2	87.9	−64.0	66.8	705.7	−773.5	913.5	.267	.242	.222	.174	26.1	48.6
240	66.7	60.0	92.0	−64.6	67.2	768.5	−861.3	989.4	.261	.236	.216	.168	27.9	51.9
255	70.8	60.7	96.1	−65.1	67.6	831.4	−953.6	1065.4	.255	.230	.210	.162	29.7	55.3
270	75.0	61.3	100.3	−65.6	67.9	894.4	−1050.7	1141.7	.250	.225	.204	.156	31.6	58.6
285	79.2	61.8	104.4	−66.0	68.7	957.5	−1151.9	1218.1	.245	.219	.199	.151	33.4	62.0
300	83.3	62.3	108.5	−66.3	71.0	1020.7	−1257.8	1294.6	.240	.214	.194	.146	35.2	65.3
315	87.5	62.8	112.6	−66.6	73.2	1083.9	−1368.3	1371.2	.235	.209	.189	.142	37.0	68.6
330	91.7	93.2	116.8	−67.3	75.5	1147.2	−1483.2	1447.9	.231	.205	.184	.138	38.9	72.0
345	95.8	63.6	120.9	−69.2	77.7	1210.6	−1602.7	1524.7	.226	.200	.180	.134	40.7	75.3
360	100.0	63.9	125.0	−71.0	80.0	1274.1	−1726.7	1601.6	.222	.196	.175	.130	42.5	78.6
Impact		I	IV	I	III	I	II	III						
Dead load		0.3126 ×wL	1.4874 ×wL	−0.6874 ×wL	0.8000 ×wL	0.0489 ×wL²	−0.1874 ×wL²	0.1326 ×wL²					0.3126 ×L	0.8000 ×L

inertia. AASHTO H20-S16-44 loading (N = 1.7) **(XIV)**

Total length ft	Exter. span length 'L'	Max. reaction kips at A	at B	Max. shear kips in AB at B	in BC at B or C	Max. moment kip-ft in AB at x	at B	in BC at x'	Impact coefficient I	II	III	IV	Distance ft x	x'
90	24.3	43.1	64.4	−47.9	56.5	172.7	−210.2	267.3	.300	.300	.300	.262	8.5	19.3
105	28.4	45.8	66.6	−50.8	59.2	220.5	−268.2	336.9	.300	.300	.289	.248	10.2	22.8
120	32.4	48.6	68.0	−54.0	61.2	270.3	−325.2	408.9	.300	.296	.278	.235	11.9	26.2
135	36.5	50.9	69.1	−56.5	62.7	322.6	−380.5	482.6	.300	.278	.267	.224	14.9	29.7
150	40.5	52.8	69.8	−58.3	63.8	381.8	−434.4	557.4	.300	.278	.258	.213	16.7	33.1
165	44.6	54.4	72.1	−59.8	64.8	441.6	−487.4	633.1	.295	.270	.249	.204	18.4	36.5
180	48.6	55.8	76.3	−61.1	65.5	501.9	−554.5	709.4	.288	.262	.241	.195	20.2	40.0
195	52.7	57.0	80.4	−62.1	66.1	562.6	−631.4	786.2	.281	.255	.233	.187	21.9	43.4
210	56.8	58.0	84.6	−62.9	66.6	623.5	−713.0	863.3	.275	.248	.226	.180	23.7	46.9
225	60.8	58.9	88.8	−63.6	67.1	684.6	−799.4	940.9	.269	.241	.219	.173	25.4	50.3
240	64.9	59.7	93.0	−64.3	67.5	745.9	−890.4	1018.6	.263	.235	.213	.167	27.2	53.8
255	68.9	60.4	97.2	−64.8	67.8	807.4	−986.2	1096.5	.258	.229	.206	.161	29.0	57.2
270	73.0	61.0	101.4	−65.3	68.1	869.0	−1086.7	1174.6	.253	.224	.201	.155	30.8	60.7
285	77.0	61.6	105.6	−65.7	69.9	930.7	−1191.9	1252.9	.247	.218	.195	.150	32.6	64.1
300	81.1	62.1	109.8	−66.0	72.2	992.4	−1301.9	1331.3	.243	.213	.190	.145	34.3	67.6
315	85.1	62.6	113.9	−66.4	74.5	1054.3	−1416.5	1409.7	.238	.208	.185	.141	36.1	71.0
330	89.2	63.0	118.1	−67.3	76.8	1116.2	−1535.9	1488.5	.233	.204	.181	.137	37.9	74.4
345	93.2	63.4	122.3	−66.2	76.1	1178.2	−1660.0	1567.0	.229	.199	.176	.133	39.7	77.9
360	97.3	63.7	126.5	−71.1	81.4	1240.2	−1788.8	1645.7	.225	.195	.172	.129	41.5	81.3
Impact		I	IV	I	III	I	II	III						
Dead load		0.2918 ×wL	1.5582 ×wL	−0.7082 ×wL	0.8500 ×wL	0.0426 ×wL²	−0.2082 ×wL²	0.1530 ×wL²					0.2918 ×L	0.8500 ×L

Tables for Moments and Shear 2–4.7 AISC 1961.

Table 2.16. Symmetrical four-span continuous beam.
Constant moment of inertia.
AASHTO H20-S16-44 loading ($N = 1.0$)(**XV**)

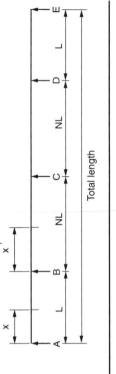

Total length ft	Span length 'L'	Max. reaction kips at A	at B	at C	Max. shear kips in AB at B	in BC at B	in BC at C	Max. moment kip-ft in AB at x	at B	in BC at x'	at C	Impact I	II	NL	III	IV	NL	V	Distance ft x	x'
120	30.0	46.2	62.3	60.5	−53.0	49.4	−49.9	227.9	−183.8	177.8	−171.9	.300	.300	.300	.300	.270	.270	.270	10.7	13.5
140	35.0	49.3	64.7	63.2	−56.5	52.8	−53.3	286.3	−218.8	228.4	−204.0	.300	.300	.300	.300	.256	.256	.256	12.9	15.9
160	40.0	51.8	66.4	65.1	−59.0	55.5	−56.0	352.0	−254.5	281.8	−236.0	.300	.300	.300	.300	.244	.244	.244	16.0	18.4
180	45.0	53.8	67.6	66.4	−60.9	57.6	−58.0	421.7	−303.7	337.2	−277.9	.294	.294	.294	.294	.233	.233	.233	18.1	20.9
200	50.0	55.5	68.4	67.4	−62.3	59.2	−59.7	492.3	−356.8	393.9	−325.9	.286	.286	.286	.286	.222	.222	.222	20.1	23.3
220	55.0	56.9	69.1	68.1	−63.4	60.6	−61.0	563.4	−413.6	451.6	−377.4	.278	.278	.278	.278	.213	.213	.213	22.2	25.8
240	60.0	58.1	73.0	69.9	−64.3	61.7	−62.1	635.0	−474.4	510.1	−432.2	.270	.270	.270	.270	.204	.204	.204	24.3	28.2
260	65.0	59.1	76.9	73.5	−65.8	62.6	−63.0	706.9	−539.0	569.1	−490.5	.263	.263	.263	.263	.196	.196	.196	26.4	30.7
280	70.0	60.0	80.8	77.2	−65.7	63.4	−63.8	779.0	−607.5	628.6	−552.3	.256	.256	.256	.256	.189	.189	.189	28.4	33.2
300	75.0	60.8	84.7	80.9	−66.2	64.1	−64.4	851.4	−679.8	688.5	−617.4	.250	.250	.250	.250	.182	.182	.182	30.6	35.6
320	80.0	61.5	88.6	84.5	−66.7	64.7	−65.0	923.9	−756.0	748.6	−686.0	.244	.244	.244	.244	.175	.175	.175	32.7	38.2
340	85.0	62.1	92.5	88.2	−67.0	65.2	−65.5	996.6	−836.0	809.1	−758.1	.238	.238	.238	.238	.169	.169	.169	34.9	40.6
360	90.0	62.6	96.5	91.8	−67.4	65.6	−65.9	1069.4	−919.9	869.7	−833.5	.233	.233	.233	.233	.164	.164	.164	37.0	43.1
380	95.0	63.1	100.4	95.5	−67.7	66.0	−66.3	1142.3	−1007.0	930.5	−912.4	.227	.227	.227	.227	.159	.159	.159	39.1	45.5
400	100.0	63.6	104.3	99.1	−67.9	66.3	−66.6	1215.3	−1099.2	991.4	−994.7	.222	.222	.222	.222	.154	.154	.154	41.1	48.0
420	105.0	63.9	108.2	102.8	−68.2	66.7	−66.9	1288.3	−1194.7	1052.5	−1080.4	.217	.217	.217	.217	.149	.149	.149	43.2	50.5
440	110.0	64.3	112.1	106.5	−69.7	68.4	−67.2	1361.4	−1294.0	1113.7	−1169.6	.213	.213	.213	.213	.145	.145	.145	45.5	53.0
460	115.0	64.6	116.0	110.1	−71.7	70.4	−68.1	1434.6	−1397.2	1175.0	−1262.2	.208	.208	.208	.208	.141	.141	.141	47.5	55.4
480	120.0	64.9	119.9	113.8	−73.7	72.3	−69.9	1507.7	−1504.2	1236.3	−1358.2	.204	.204	.204	.204	.137	.137	.137	49.6	57.9
Impact		I	IV	V	I	III	III	I	II	III	III								I	III
Dead load		0.3929 ×wL	1.1429 ×wL	0.9286 ×wL	−0.6071 ×wL	0.5357 ×wL	−0.4643 ×wL	0.0772 ×wL²	−0.1071 ×wL²	0.0364 ×wL²	−0.0714 ×wL²								0.3929 ×L	0.5357 ×L

Total length

Table 2.17. Symmetrical four-span continuous beam.
Constant moment of inertia.
AASHTO H20-S16-44 loading (N = 1.1) (XVI)

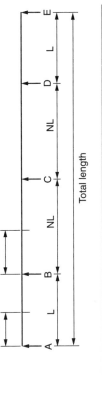

Total length ft	Span length 'L'	Max. reaction kips			Max. shear kips			Max. moment kip-ft				Impact					Distance ft	
		at A	at B	at C	in AB at B	in BC at B	in BC at C	in AB at x	at B	in BC at x'	at C	I	II	III	IV	V	x	x'
120	28.6	45.3	61.9	61.3	-51.6	50.6	-50.8	213.8	-181.7	189.7	-179.9	.300	.300	.300	.270	.266	10.2	14.2
140	33.3	48.5	64.3	63.8	-55.3	54.0	-54.1	269.4	-215.2	243.0	-213.3	.300	.300	.300	.256	.252	12.1	16.8
160	38.1	51.1	66.0	65.5	-58.0	56.5	-56.7	329.6	-251.8	299.1	-248.0	.300	.300	.300	.244	.239	15.3	19.5
180	42.9	53.2	67.2	66.8	-60.0	58.5	-58.7	396.3	-300.3	357.0	-295.8	.294	.294	.290	.233	.228	17.3	22.0
200	47.6	54.9	68.1	67.7	-61.5	60.1	-60.2	463.8	-352.7	416.3	-347.3	.290	.286	.282	.222	.218	19.2	24.7
220	52.4	56.4	68.7	68.4	-62.7	61.4	-61.5	532.0	-408.9	476.5	-402.5	.282	.278	.274	.213	.208	21.3	27.3
240	57.1	57.6	72.5	71.7	-63.7	62.4	-62.6	600.6	-468.8	537.5	-461.5	.275	.270	.266	.204	.199	23.3	29.9
260	61.9	58.6	76.4	75.6	-64.5	63.3	-63.4	669.6	-532.6	599.0	-524.2	.268	.263	.259	.196	.191	25.2	32.5
280	66.7	59.6	80.3	79.4	-65.1	64.0	-64.2	738.8	-600.2	661.0	-590.6	.261	.256	.252	.189	.184	27.2	35.1
300	71.4	60.4	84.2	83.2	-65.7	64.7	-64.8	808.2	-671.5	723.3	-660.7	.255	.250	.246	.182	.177	29.3	37.8
320	76.2	61.1	88.1	87.0	-66.2	65.2	-65.3	877.8	-746.7	786.0	-734.6	.249	.244	.239	.175	.171	31.3	40.3
340	81.0	61.7	91.9	90.8	-66.6	65.7	-65.8	947.6	-825.6	848.8	-812.2	.243	.238	.234	.169	.165	33.4	42.9
360	85.7	62.3	95.8	94.6	-67.0	66.1	-66.2	1017.4	-908.4	911.9	-893.6	.237	.233	.228	.164	.159	35.4	45.6
380	90.5	62.8	99.7	98.4	-67.3	66.5	-66.6	1087.4	-995.0	975.2	-978.6	.232	.227	.223	.159	.154	37.4	48.1
400	95.2	63.2	103.6	102.2	-67.6	66.8	-66.9	1157.4	-1085.3	1038.5	-1067.4	.221	.222	.218	.154	.149	39.5	50.7
420	100.0	63.6	107.4	106.0	-67.8	67.1	-67.2	1227.6	-1179.5	1102.0	-1159.9	.222	.217	.213	.149	.145	41.5	53.3
440	104.8	64.0	111.3	109.9	-68.3	69.0	-67.9	1297.8	-1277.4	1165.7	-1256.2	.218	.213	.208	.145	.141	43.6	55.9
460	109.5	64.3	115.2	113.7	-70.2	71.0	-69.8	1368.0	-1379.2	1229.4	-1356.2	.213	.208	.204	.141	.137	45.5	58.7
480	114.3	64.7	119.1	117.5	-72.1	72.9	-71.7	1438.3	-1484.7	1293.1	-1459.9	.209	.204	.199	.137	.133	47.7	61.2
Impact		I	IV	V	I	III	III	I	II	III	III							
Dead load		0.3859 ×wL	1.1821 ×wL	1.0639 ×wL	-0.6141 ×wL	0.5681 ×wL	-0.5319 ×wL	0.0745 ×wL²	-0.1141 ×wL²	0.0473 ×wL²	-0.0942 ×wL²						0.3859 ×L	0.5681 ×L

Tables for Moments and Shear 2–4.7 AISC 1961.

Table 2.18. Symmetrical four-span continuous beam.
Constant moment of inertia.
AASHTO H20-S16-44 loading (N = 1.2) **(XVII)**

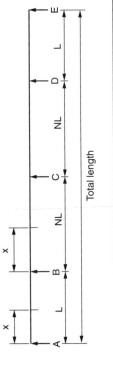

Total length ft	Span length 'L'	Max. reaction kips			Max. shear kips			Max. moment kip-ft				Impact					Distance ft	
		at A	at B	at C	in AB at B	in BC at B	in BC at C	in AB at x	at B	in BC at x'	at C	I	II	III	IV	V	x	x'
120	27.3	44.5	61.8	61.9	−50.2	51.7	−51.6	200.8	−182.7	200.6	−187.1	.300	.300	.300	.270	.263	9.7	17.9
140	31.8	47.7	64.2	64.3	−54.1	54.9	−54.8	253.8	−216.6	256.3	−221.6	.300	.300	.300	.256	.248	11.5	20.6
160	36.4	50.3	65.9	65.9	−56.9	57.4	−57.3	308.4	−251.1	314.7	−261.5	.300	.300	.296	.244	.236	13.9	23.4
180	40.9	52.5	67.1	67.1	−59.1	59.3	−59.2	372.8	−299.6	374.9	−312.2	.300	.294	.287	.233	.224	16.6	26.1
200	45.5	54.3	68.0	67.9	−60.7	60.8	−60.7	437.6	−351.8	436.5	−367.0	.293	.286	.278	.222	.214	18.4	28.8
220	50.0	55.8	68.6	69.5	−62.0	62.0	−61.9	503.0	−407.8	498.9	−425.7	.286	.278	.270	.213	.204	20.3	31.5
240	54.5	57.1	72.3	73.4	−63.0	63.0	−62.9	568.9	−467.6	562.2	−488.5	.273	.270	.263	.204	.195	22.3	34.3
260	59.1	58.2	76.2	77.4	−63.9	63.9	−63.8	635.1	−531.2	625.9	−555.2	.272	.263	.255	.196	.187	24.2	37.0
280	63.6	59.1	80.0	81.3	−64.6	64.6	−64.5	701.6	−598.6	690.1	−626.0	.265	.256	.248	.189	.180	26.2	39.7
300	68.2	59.9	83.9	85.3	−65.2	65.1	−65.1	768.3	−669.8	754.6	−700.8	.259	.250	.242	.182	.173	28.0	42.5
320	72.7	60.7	87.8	89.2	−65.7	65.7	−65.6	835.2	−744.8	819.4	−779.6	.253	.244	.236	.175	.167	30.0	45.2
340	77.3	61.3	91.6	93.2	−66.2	66.1	−66.0	902.3	−823.5	884.5	−862.4	.247	.238	.230	.169	.169	31.9	48.0
360	81.8	61.9	95.5	97.1	−66.6	66.5	−66.4	969.4	−906.1	949.8	−949.2	.242	.233	.224	.164	.156	33.9	50.8
380	86.4	62.4	99.3	101.1	−66.9	66.8	−66.8	1036.7	−992.4	1015.2	−1040.0	.237	.227	.219	.159	.150	35.9	53.5
400	90.9	62.9	103.2	105.0	−67.2	67.1	−67.1	1104.0	−1082.5	1080.7	−1134.8	.232	.222	.214	.154	.146	37.9	56.2
420	95.5	63.3	107.1	109.0	−67.5	67.8	−67.5	1171.5	−1176.5	1146.4	−1233.7	.227	.217	.209	.149	.141	39.8	59.0
440	100.0	63.7	110.9	112.9	−67.7	69.8	−69.5	1238.9	−1274.2	1212.2	−1336.5	.222	.213	.204	.145	.137	41.8	61.6
460	104.5	64.1	114.8	116.9	−69.0	71.7	−71.4	1306.5	−1375.7	1278.1	−1443.4	.218	.208	.200	.141	.133	43.7	64.4
480	109.1	64.4	118.6	120.8	−70.9	73.7	−73.4	1374.1	−1481.0	1344.0	−1554.2	.214	.204	.195	.137	.129	45.6	67.1
Impact		I	IV	V	I	III	III	I	II	III	III							
Dead load		0.3774 ×wL	1.2259 ×wL	1.1934 ×wL	−0.6226 ×wL	0.6033 ×wL	−0.5967 ×wL	0.0712 ×wL²	−0.1226 ×wL²	0.0593 ×wL²	−0.1187 ×wL²						0.3774 ×L	0.6033 ×L

Constant moment of inertia.
AASHTO H20-S16-44 loading (N = 1.3) **(XVIII)**

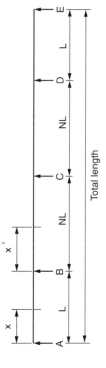

Total length ft	Span length 'L'	Max. reaction kips			Max. shear kips			Max. moment kip-ft				Impact					Distance ft	
		at A	at B	at C	in AB at B	in BC at B	in BC at C	in AB at x	at B	in BC at x'	at C	I	II	III	IV	V	x	x'
120	26.1	43.7	61.9	62.4	-48.8	52.6	-52.2	188.9	-184.4	210.6	-193.5	.300	.300	.300	.270	.259	9.2	18.5
140	30.4	46.9	64.3	64.7	-52.9	55.8	-55.4	239.5	-218.6	268.4	-229.0	.300	.300	.300	.256	.245	11.0	21.4
160	34.8	49.6	66.0	66.2	-55.9	58.2	-57.8	292.0	-252.7	328.9	-274.0	.300	.300	.294	.244	.232	13.0	24.2
180	39.1	51.8	67.2	67.3	-58.2	60.0	-59.6	351.0	-300.8	391.2	-327.5	.300	.294	.284	.233	.221	15.9	27.1
200	43.5	53.7	68.0	68.2	-59.9	61.4	-61.1	413.2	-353.3	454.8	-385.2	.297	.286	.275	.222	.210	17.7	30.0
220	47.8	55.2	68.7	70.8	-61.3	62.6	-62.3	476.1	-409.6	519.3	-447.2	.289	.278	.267	.213	.201	19.6	32.8
240	52.2	56.5	72.3	74.9	-62.4	63.6	-63.2	539.5	-469.7	584.5	-513.5	.282	.270	.259	.204	.192	21.4	35.6
260	56.5	57.7	76.1	79.0	-63.3	64.3	-64.0	603.2	-533.7	650.2	-584.0	.275	.263	.252	.196	.184	23.3	38.5
280	60.9	58.6	80.0	83.1	-64.0	65.0	-64.7	667.1	-601.5	716.4	-658.8	.269	.256	.245	.189	.177	25.1	41.3
300	65.2	59.5	83.8	87.1	-64.7	65.6	-65.3	731.3	-673.1	782.9	-737.9	.263	.250	.238	.182	.170	27.0	44.2
320	69.3	60.3	87.7	91.2	-65.2	66.0	-65.8	795.7	-748.5	849.7	-821.3	.257	.244	.232	.175	.163	28.8	47.0
340	73.9	60.9	91.5	95.3	-65.7	66.5	-66.2	860.3	-827.1	916.7	-908.9	.251	.238	.226	.169	.158	30.8	49.9
360	78.3	61.5	95.4	99.4	-66.1	66.8	-66.6	924.9	-910.7	983.9	-1000.8	.246	.233	.221	.164	.152	32.6	52.7
380	82.6	62.1	99.3	103.4	-66.5	67.2	-66.9	989.7	-997.6	1051.3	-1097.0	.241	.227	.215	.159	.147	34.5	55.7
400	87.0	62.5	103.4	107.5	-66.8	67.4	-67.2	1054.5	-1088.3	1118.8	-1197.4	.236	.222	.210	.154	.142	36.3	58.4
420	91.3	63.0	107.0	111.6	-67.1	68.5	-68.8	1119.4	-1182.8	1186.4	-1302.1	.231	.217	.205	.149	.138	38.3	61.3
440	95.7	63.4	110.8	115.7	-67.4	70.6	-70.8	1184.4	-1281.1	1254.1	-1411.1	.227	.213	.201	.145	.134	40.2	64.1
460	100.0	63.8	114.7	119.7	-68.1	72.6	-72.9	1249.5	-1383.2	1321.9	-1524.4	.222	.208	.196	.141	.130	42.0	67.0
480	104.3	64.1	118.5	123.8	-69.9	74.6	-74.9	1314.6	-1489.2	1389.8	-1641.9	.218	.204	.192	.137	.126	44.0	69.8
Impact		I	IV	V	I	III	III	I	II	III	III							
Dead load		0.3672 ×wL	1.2736 ×wL	1.3185 ×wL	-0.6328 ×wL	0.6407 ×wL	0.6593 ×wL	0.0674 ×wL²	-0.1328 ×wL²	-0.0725 ×wL²	-0.1448 ×wL²						0.3672 ×L	0.6407 ×L

Tables for Moments and Shear 2–4.7 AISC 1961.

Table 2.20. Symmetrical four-span continuous beam. Constant moment of inertia.
AASHTO H20-S16-44 loading ($N = 1.4$) **(XIX)**

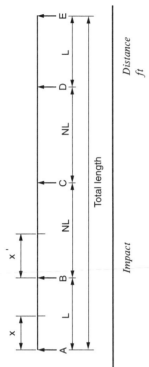

Total length ft	Span length 'L'	Max. reaction kips			Max. shear kips				Max. moment kip-ft				Impact					Distance ft	
		at A	at B	at C	in AB at B	in BC at B	in BC at C	at C	in AB at x	at B	in BC at x'	at C	I	II	III	IV	V	x	x'
120	25.0	42.8	62.1	62.8	-47.5	53.4	-52.8	62.8	177.9	-186.5	219.6	-199.3	.300	.300	.300	.270	.256	8.8	19.1
140	29.2	46.2	64.5	65.0	-51.8	56.5	-55.9	65.0	226.2	-221.1	279.4	-235.8	.300	.300	.300	.256	.242	10.5	22.1
160	33.3	48.9	66.2	66.5	-54.9	58.8	-58.2	66.5	276.6	-256.2	341.8	-285.5	.300	.300	.291	.244	.229	12.3	25.0
180	37.5	51.2	67.4	67.6	-57.3	60.6	-60.0	67.6	330.8	-303.5	405.9	-341.5	.300	.294	.282	.233	.217	15.2	28.0
200	41.7	53.0	68.3	68.3	-59.1	62.0	-61.4	68.3	390.6	-356.6	471.3	-402.1	.300	.286	.273	.222	.207	17.0	31.0
220	45.8	54.6	68.9	72.1	-60.5	63.1	-62.6	72.1	451.1	-413.6	537.6	-467.1	.293	.278	.264	.213	.191	18.8	33.9
240	50.0	56.0	72.3	76.3	-61.7	64.0	-63.5	76.3	512.1	-474.4	604.6	-536.6	.286	.270	.256	.204	.189	20.6	36.9
260	54.2	57.2	76.2	80.5	-62.7	64.8	-64.3	80.5	573.5	-539.1	672.1	-610.7	.279	.263	.249	.196	.181	22.4	39.8
280	58.3	58.2	80.1	84.6	-63.5	65.4	-64.9	84.6	635.1	-607.7	740.1	-689.3	.273	.256	.242	.189	.173	24.1	42.9
300	62.5	59.1	83.9	88.8	-64.2	65.9	-65.5	88.8	697.0	-680.2	808.4	-772.4	.267	.250	.235	.182	.167	25.9	45.8
320	66.7	59.8	87.8	93.0	-64.8	66.4	-66.0	93.0	759.0	-756.5	876.9	-860.0	.261	.244	.229	.175	.160	27.7	48.7
340	70.8	60.5	91.6	97.2	-65.3	66.8	-66.4	97.2	821.2	-836.7	945.7	-952.1	.255	.238	.223	.169	.155	29.5	51.7
360	75.0	61.2	95.5	101.4	-65.7	67.1	-66.8	101.4	883.6	-920.7	1014.7	-1048.8	.250	.233	.217	.164	.149	31.4	54.6
380	79.2	61.7	99.4	105.6	-66.1	67.4	-67.1	105.6	946.0	-1008.7	1083.8	-1149.9	.245	.227	.212	.159	.144	33.2	57.6
400	83.3	62.2	103.2	109.8	-66.5	67.7	-67.9	109.8	1008.5	-1100.5	1153.1	-1255.6	.240	.222	.207	.154	.140	35.0	60.6
420	87.5	62.7	107.1	114.0	-66.8	69.3	-70.0	114.0	1071.1	-1196.2	1222.5	-1365.8	.235	.217	.202	.149	.135	36.8	63.5
440	91.7	63.1	110.9	118.1	-67.0	71.4	-72.1	118.1	1133.8	-1295.7	1292.0	-1480.5	.231	.213	.197	.145	.131	38.6	66.5
460	95.8	63.5	114.8	122.3	-67.4	73.5	-74.2	122.3	1196.5	-1399.2	1361.5	-1599.7	.226	.208	.193	.141	.127	40.5	69.4
480	100.0	63.8	118.7	126.5	-69.2	75.5	-76.3	126.5	1259.3	-1506.5	1431.2	-1723.4	.222	.204	.189	.137	.123	42.2	72.4
Impact		I	IV	V	I	III	III		I	II	III	III							
Dead load		0.3554 ×wL	1.3246 ×wL	1.4401 ×wL	-0.6446 ×wL	0.6800 ×wL	-0.7200 ×wL		0.0631 ×wL²	-0.1446 ×wL²	0.0865 ×wL²	-0.1727 ×wL²						0.3554 ×L	0.6800 ×L

Constant moment of inertia.
AASHTO H20-S16-44 loading (N = 1.5) (XX)

Total length ft	Span length 'L'	Max. reaction kips at A	at B	at C	Max. shear kips in AB at B	in BC at B	in BC at C	Max. moment kip-ft in AB at x	at B	in BC at x'	at C	Impact I	II	III	IV	V	Distance ft x	x'
120	24.0	42.0	62.4	63.2	-46.1	54.1	-53.3	167.6	-193.1	227.9	-204.6	.300	.300	.300	.270	.254	8.4	19.7
140	28.0	45.4	64.9	65.3	-50.6	57.1	-56.3	213.9	-233.1	289.4	-242.6	.300	.300	.299	.256	.239	10.0	22.7
160	32.0	48.2	66.5	66.7	-53.9	59.4	-58.6	262.2	-274.5	353.4	-296.2	.300	.300	.289	.244	.226	11.7	25.8
180	36.0	50.5	67.7	67.7	-56.4	61.1	-60.3	311.4	-321.0	419.3	-354.6	.300	.294	.279	.233	.215	14.0	28.9
200	40.0	52.4	68.6	68.9	-58.3	62.4	-61.7	369.6	-366.8	486.3	-417.7	.300	.286	.270	.222	.204	16.4	31.9
220	44.0	54.1	69.3	73.2	-59.8	63.5	-62.8	427.5	-419.2	554.3	-485.6	.296	.278	.262	.213	.195	18.1	35.0
240	48.0	55.5	72.5	77.5	-61.1	64.4	-63.7	486.7	-481.0	622.9	-558.2	.289	.270	.254	.204	.186	19.8	38.1
260	52.0	56.7	76.4	81.8	-62.1	65.1	-64.5	545.8	-546.8	692.1	-635.5	.282	.263	.246	.196	.178	21.5	41.1
280	56.0	57.7	80.3	86.1	-62.9	65.7	-65.1	605.3	-616.5	761.6	-717.6	.276	.256	.239	.189	.171	23.2	44.2
300	60.0	58.6	84.1	90.4	-63.7	66.2	-65.7	665.0	-690.1	831.5	-804.4	.270	.250	.233	.182	.164	24.9	47.2
320	64.0	59.4	88.0	94.7	-64.3	66.7	-66.1	724.9	-767.7	901.7	-896.0	.265	.244	.226	.175	.158	26.7	50.3
340	68.0	60.1	91.9	99.0	-64.8	67.1	-66.5	784.9	-849.3	972.1	-992.3	.259	.238	.220	.169	.152	28.5	53.4
360	72.0	60.8	95.8	103.3	-65.3	67.4	-66.9	845.0	-934.8	1042.7	-1093.4	.254	.233	.215	.164	.147	30.2	56.4
380	76.0	61.4	99.6	107.5	-65.7	67.7	-67.2	905.3	-1024.2	1113.4	-1199.2	.249	.227	.209	.159	.142	31.9	59.5
400	80.0	61.9	103.5	111.8	-66.1	68.0	-68.9	965.7	-1117.6	1184.3	-1309.8	.244	.222	.204	.154	.137	33.7	62.5
420	84.0	62.4	107.4	116.1	-66.4	70.1	-71.1	1026.1	-1215.0	1255.3	-1425.0	.239	.217	.199	.149	.133	35.5	65.6
440	88.0	62.8	111.3	120.4	-66.7	72.2	-73.2	1086.6	-1316.3	1326.3	-1545.1	.235	.213	.195	.145	.129	37.2	68.6
460	92.0	63.2	115.1	124.7	-67.0	74.3	-75.4	1147.1	-1421.5	1397.5	-1669.9	.230	.208	.190	.141	.125	38.9	71.7
480	96.0	63.5	119.0	129.0	-68.6	76.4	-77.5	1207.7	-1530.7	1468.7	-1799.4	.226	.204	.186	.137	.121	40.7	74.9
Impact		I	IV	V	I	III	III	I	II	III	III							
Dead load		0.3419 ×wL	1.3787 ×wL	1.5588 ×wL	-0.6581 ×wL	-0.7206 ×wL	0.7794 ×wL	0.0585 ×wL²	-0.1581 ×wL²	0.1015 ×wL²	-0.2022 ×wL²						0.3419 ×L	0.7206 ×L

Tables for Moments and Shear 2–4.7 AISC 1961.

Table 2.22. Symmetrical four-span continuous beam.
Constant moment of inertia.
AASHTO H20-S16-44 loading (N = 1.6) **(XXI)**

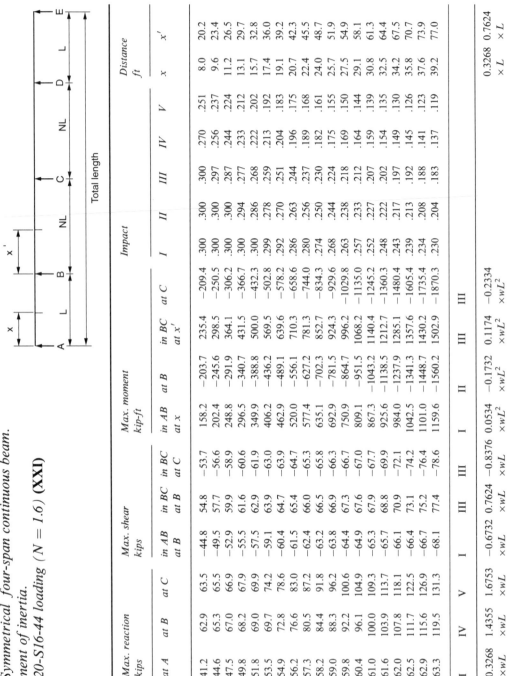

Total length ft	Span length 'L'	Max. reaction kips at A	at B	at C	Max. shear kips in AB at B	in BC at B	in BC at C	Max. moment kip-ft in AB at x	at B	in BC at x'	at C	Impact I	II	III	IV	V	Distance ft x	x'
120	23.1	41.2	62.9	63.5	−44.8	54.8	−53.7	158.2	−203.7	235.4	−209.4	.300	.300	.300	.270	.251	8.0	20.2
140	26.9	44.6	65.3	65.5	−49.5	57.7	−56.6	202.4	−245.6	298.5	−250.5	.300	.300	.297	.256	.237	9.6	23.4
160	30.8	47.5	67.0	66.9	−52.9	59.9	−58.9	248.8	−291.9	364.1	−306.2	.300	.300	.287	.244	.224	11.2	26.5
180	34.6	49.8	68.2	67.9	−55.5	61.6	−60.6	296.5	−340.7	431.5	−366.7	.300	.294	.277	.233	.212	13.1	29.7
200	38.5	51.8	69.0	69.9	−57.5	62.9	−61.9	349.9	−388.8	500.0	−432.3	.300	.286	.268	.222	.202	15.7	32.8
220	42.3	53.5	69.7	74.2	−59.1	63.9	−63.0	406.2	−436.2	569.5	−502.8	.299	.278	.259	.213	.192	17.4	36.0
240	46.2	54.9	72.8	78.6	−60.4	64.7	−63.9	462.9	−489.1	639.6	−578.2	.292	.270	.251	.204	.183	19.1	39.2
260	50.0	56.2	76.6	83.0	−61.5	65.4	−64.7	520.0	−556.1	710.3	−658.6	.286	.263	.244	.196	.175	20.7	42.3
280	53.8	57.3	80.5	87.2	−62.4	66.0	−65.3	577.4	−627.2	781.3	−744.0	.280	.256	.237	.189	.168	22.4	45.5
300	57.7	58.2	84.4	91.8	−63.2	66.5	−65.8	635.1	−702.3	852.7	−834.3	.274	.250	.230	.182	.161	24.0	48.7
320	61.5	59.0	88.3	96.2	−63.8	66.9	−66.3	692.9	−781.5	924.3	−929.6	.268	.244	.224	.175	.155	25.7	51.9
340	65.4	59.8	92.2	100.6	−64.4	67.3	−66.7	750.9	−864.7	996.2	−1029.8	.263	.238	.218	.169	.150	27.5	54.9
360	69.2	60.4	96.1	104.9	−64.9	67.6	−67.0	809.1	−951.5	1068.2	−1135.0	.257	.233	.212	.164	.144	29.1	58.1
380	73.1	61.0	100.0	109.3	−65.3	67.9	−67.7	867.3	−1043.2	1140.4	−1245.2	.252	.227	.207	.159	.139	30.8	61.3
400	76.9	61.6	103.9	113.7	−65.7	68.8	−69.9	925.6	−1138.5	1212.7	−1360.3	.248	.222	.202	.154	.135	32.5	64.4
420	80.8	62.0	107.8	118.1	−66.1	70.9	−72.1	984.0	−1237.9	1285.1	−1480.4	.243	.217	.197	.149	.130	34.2	67.5
440	84.6	62.5	111.7	122.5	−66.4	73.1	−74.2	1042.5	−1341.3	1357.6	−1605.4	.239	.213	.192	.145	.126	35.8	70.7
460	88.5	62.9	115.6	126.9	−66.7	75.2	−76.4	1101.0	−1448.7	1430.2	−1735.4	.234	.208	.188	.141	.123	37.6	73.9
480	92.3	63.3	119.5	131.3	−68.1	77.4	−78.6	1159.6	−1560.2	1502.9	−1870.3	.230	.204	.183	.137	.119	39.2	77.0
Impact		I	IV	V	I	III	III	I	II	III	III							
Dead load		$0.3268 \times wL$	$1.4355 \times wL$	$1.6753 \times wL$	$-0.6732 \times wL$	$0.7624 \times wL$	$-0.8376 \times wL$	$0.0534 \times wL^2$	$-0.1732 \times wL^2$	$0.1174 \times wL^2$	$-0.2334 \times wL^2$						$0.3268 \times L$	$0.7624 \times L$

Table 2.23. Symmetrical four-span continuous beam.
Constant moment of inertia.
AASHTO H20-S16-44 loading (N = 1.7) (XXII)

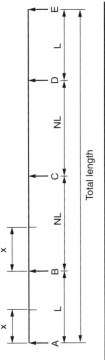

Total length ft	Span length 'L'	Max. reaction kips			Max. shear kips			Max. moment kip-ft				Impact					Distance ft	
		at A	at B	at C	in AB at B	in BC at B	in BC at C	in AB at x	at B	in BC at x'	at C	I	II	III	IV	V	x	x'
120	22.2	40.4	63.4	63.7	−43.4	55.3	−54.2	152.8	−213.8	242.3	−213.8	.300	.300	.300	.270	.249	9.9	20.7
140	25.9	43.9	65.8	65.7	−48.3	58.2	−57.0	191.8	−257.5	306.9	−257.9	.300	.300	.296	.256	.235	9.2	24.0
160	29.6	46.8	67.5	67.1	−51.9	60.3	−59.1	236.3	−308.5	373.9	−315.4	.300	.300	.285	.244	.221	10.8	27.2
180	33.3	49.2	68.7	68.0	−54.6	62.0	−60.8	282.3	−359.5	442.7	−378.0	.300	.294	.275	.233	.210	12.4	30.4
200	37.0	51.2	69.6	70.7	−56.7	63.2	−62.2	331.6	−409.8	512.6	−445.8	.300	.286	.266	.222	.199	15.2	33.7
220	40.7	53.0	70.2	75.2	−58.4	64.2	−63.2	385.9	−459.4	583.4	−518.8	.300	.278	.257	.213	.190	16.8	37.1
240	44.4	54.4	73.1	79.7	−59.8	65.0	−64.1	440.7	−508.4	654.9	−596.9	.295	.270	.249	.204	.181	18.4	40.2
260	48.1	55.7	77.0	84.1	−60.9	65.7	−64.8	495.9	−566.7	726.9	−680.1	.289	.263	.242	.196	.173	20.0	43.4
280	51.9	56.8	80.9	88.6	−61.8	66.3	−65.4	551.4	−639.4	799.3	−768.6	.283	.256	.235	.189	.166	21.6	46.6
300	55.6	57.8	84.8	93.1	−62.6	66.7	−65.9	607.1	−716.1	872.0	−862.2	.277	.250	.228	.182	.159	23.2	49.9
320	59.3	58.6	88.8	97.6	−63.3	67.2	−66.4	663.1	−797.0	945.0	−960.7	.271	.244	.221	.175	.153	24.8	53.2
340	63.0	59.4	92.7	102.0	−63.9	67.5	−66.8	719.1	−882.1	1018.2	−1064.8	.266	.238	.215	.169	.147	26.5	56.4
360	66.7	60.1	96.6	106.5	−64.5	67.8	−67.1	775.4	−971.3	1091.5	−1173.8	.261	.233	.210	.164	.142	28.1	59.6
380	70.4	60.7	100.5	111.0	−64.9	68.1	−68.5	831.7	−1064.7	1165.1	−1288.1	.256	.227	.204	.159	.137	29.7	62.8
400	74.1	61.2	104.5	115.4	−65.3	69.6	−70.7	888.1	−1162.2	1238.7	−1407.4	.251	.222	.199	.154	.133	31.3	66.1
420	77.8	61.7	108.4	119.9	−65.7	71.7	−73.0	944.6	−1263.8	1312.4	−1532.0	.247	.217	.194	.149	.128	33.0	69.3
440	81.5	62.2	112.3	124.4	−66.0.	73.9	−75.2	1001.2	−1369.1	1386.3	−1661.7	.242	.213	.190	.145	.124	34.7	72.5
460	85.2	62.6	116.2	128.9	−66.3	76.1	−77.4	1057.9	−1479.6	1460.2	−1796.5	.238	.208	.185	.141	.121	36.3	75.8
480	88.9	63.0	120.1	133.3	−67.9	78.3	−79.7	1114.6	−1593.6	1534.2	−1936.5	.234	.204	.181	.137	.117	37.9	79.0
Impact		I	IV	V	III	III	III	I	II	III	III							
Dead load		0.3101 ×wL	1.4950 ×wL	1.7899 ×wL	−0.6899 ×wL	0.8051 ×wL	−0.8949 ×wL	0.0481 ×wL²	−0.1899 ×wL²	0.1342 ×wL²	−0.2663 ×wL²						0.3101 ×L	0.8051 ×L

Tables for Moments and Shear 2-4.7 AISC 1961.

Table 2.24. Moments and reactions (thousands of foot pounds and thousands of pounds, respectively). Impact not included; span in feet (**XXIII**)

Span	Moment	End shear and reaction	Span	Moment	End shear and reaction
1	8(b)	32(b)	42	485.3(b)	56.0
2	16(b)	32(b)	44	520.9(b)	56.7
3	24(b)	32(b)	46	556.5(b)	57.3
4	32(b)	32(b)	48	592.1(b)	58.0
5	40(b)	32(b)	50	627.9(b)	58.5(b)
6	48(b)	32(b)	52	663.6(b)	59.1(b)
7	56(b)	32(b)	54	699.3(b)	59.6(b)
8	64(b)	32(b)	56	735.1(b)	60.0(b)
9	72(b)	32(b)	58	770.8(b)	60.4(b)
10	80(b)	32(b)	60	806.5(b)	60.8(b)
11	88(b)	32(b)	62	842.4(b)	61.2(b)
12	96(b)	32(b)	64	878.1(b)	61.5(b)
13	104(b)	32(b)	66	914.0(b)	61.9(b)
14	112(b)	32(b)	68	949.7(b)	62.1(b)
15	120(b)	34.1(b)	70	985.6(b)	62.4(b)
16	128(b)	36(b)	75	1075.1(b)	63.1(b)
17	136(b)	37.7(b)	80	1164.9(b)	63.6(b)
18	144(b)	39.1(b)	85	1254.7(b)	64.1(b)
19	152(b)	40.4(b)	90	1344.4(b)	64.5(b)
20	160(b)	41.6(b)	95	1433.2(b)	64.9(b)
21	168(b)	42.7(b)	100	1524.0(b)	65.3(b)
22	176(b)	43.6(b)	110	1703.6(b)	65.9(b)
23	184(b)	44.5(b)	120	1883.3(b)	66.4(b)
24	192.7(b)	45.3(b)	130	2063.1(b)	67.6
25	207.4(b)	46.1(b)	140	2242.8(b)	70.8
26	222.2(b)	46.8(b)	150	2475.1	74.0
27	237(b)	47.4(b)	160	2768.0	77.2
28	252(b)	48	170	3077.1	80.4
29	267(b)	48.8(b)	180	3402.0	83.6
30	282.1(b)	49.6	190	3743.1	86.8
31	297.3(b)	50.3	200	4100	90.0
32	312.5(b)	51.0	220	4862	96.6
33	327.8(b)	51.6	240	5688	102.8
34	343.5(b)	52.2	260	6578	109.2
35	361.2(b)	52.8	280	7532	115.6
36	378.9(b)	53.3	300	8550	122.0
37	396.6(b)	53.8			
38	414.3(b)	54.3			
39	432.1(b)	54.8			
40	449.8(b)	55.2			

Reference: AASHTO 1957 Design Manual and 1962, p. 273.

Case II
Continuous beam of constant *cross-section and unequal spans*

$$l_1 = 0.81L \tag{2.30}$$

Case III
Spans of variable depth

$$\frac{w'}{w} = \frac{d_1}{d_2} - l \quad \text{(Guyon)}$$

with

$$\frac{d}{l} = \frac{l}{20} \tag{2.31}$$

$l = $ economic length in ft

$$= \frac{\left(\dfrac{d_1}{d_2} - l\right) 14.4}{[\rho]} \tag{2.32}$$

2.6   Quantity curves, tables, and charts for superstructures (Section III)

This section considers the following bridge structures:

III (A)   slab, beam and culvert bridges
III (B)   girder bridges (steel, RC)
III (C)   truss bridges
III (D)   arch bridges
III (E)   suspension and cantilever bridges
III (F)   prestressed concrete bridges.

The information from Sections 2.4 **(I)** and 2.5 **(II)** is passed on to this section for quantitative analysis of the superstructure. For a single superstructure, this section gives direct quantities. If more than one superstructure is to be considered, a result based on comparison should be investigated.

2.6.1   Slab, beam and culvert bridges (steel and RCC concrete) (Section III (A))
The following Figs 2.2–2.8 and Tables 2.25–2.37 provide the necessary data.

Table 2.25. Beam and slab bridges **(Sheet I, Table I)**

	Slab thickness	Rod length in feet	Rods Inches squared	Inches cc	Estimate Steel lbs	Concrete yd^3	Abutment height	
1	6 in	4	$\frac{1}{2}$	10	112	1.5	4	1
2	6 in	6	$\frac{5}{3}$	10	232	2.2	5	2
3	7 ft-6 in	8	$\frac{5}{8}$	8	365	3.7	6	3
4	9 ft	10	$\frac{5}{3}$	7	510	5.5	7	4
5	11 ft	12	$\frac{5}{8}$	6.5	612	8.1	8	5
6	12 ft-5 in	14	$\frac{3}{4}$	7	970	10.8	9	6
7	14 ft-5 in	16	$\frac{3}{4}$	6.5	1160	13.9	10	7
8	16 ft	18	$\frac{3}{4}$	5.5	1540	17.7	11	8
9								9
10	18 ft	20	$\frac{3}{4}$	5	1880	22.2	12	10

Table 2.26. RC beam bridges **(Sheet I, Table II)**

	Span	Side beams Concrete	Rods ft	in^2	Centre beams Concrete	Rods ft	in^2	Estimate Concrete yd^3	Steel lbs	
1	8	12 × 20	2	$\frac{3}{4}$	12 × 6	3	$\frac{3}{4}$	3.8	656	1
2	10	12 × 20	2	$\frac{7}{8}$	12 × 18	3	$\frac{3}{4}$	4.9	850	2
3	12	12 × 20	3	$\frac{7}{8}$	12 × 20	4	$\frac{3}{4}$	6.1	1160	3
4	14	12 × 20	3	$\frac{7}{8}$	12 × 23	4	$\frac{3}{4}$	7.3	1360	4
5	16	12 × 21	3	1	12 × 27	4	$\frac{7}{8}$	8.9	1780	5
6	18	14 × 22	3	1	14 × 28	4	$\frac{7}{8}$	11.2	2000	6
7	20	14 × 25	3	$1\frac{1}{8}$	14 × 32	4	1	18.3	2550	7
8	22	14 × 28	3	$1\frac{1}{8}$	14 × 35	4	1	15.5	2800	8
9	24	14 × 31	4	1	14 × 39	4	$1\frac{1}{8}$	16.2	3350	9
10	26	14 × 34	4	1	14 × 42	4	$1\frac{1}{8}$	20.7	3620	10
11	28	14 × 37	5	1	14 × 46	6	1	23.8	4460	11
12	30	16 × 38	5	1	16 × 46	6	1	28.2	4770	12
13	32	16 × 41	6	1	16 × 50	6	$1\frac{1}{8}$	32.0	5800	13
14	34	16 × 44	6	1	16 × 54	6	$1\frac{1}{8}$	35.7	6200	14
15	36	16 × 48	7	1	16 × 57	8	1	39.8	7600	15

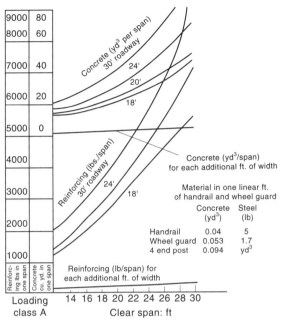

Figure 2.2. Quantity curves for standard RCC slab bridges (without handrails and wheel guards) **(Sheet II)**

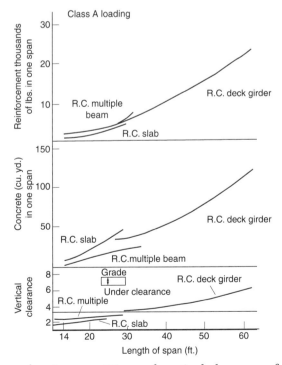

Figure 2.3. Curves showing quantities and vertical clearances for various types of bridges **(Sheet IV)**

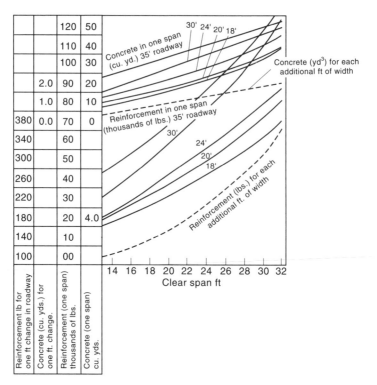

Figure 2.4. Quantity curves for one span of standard multiple beam bridge **(Sheet V (Section VII))**

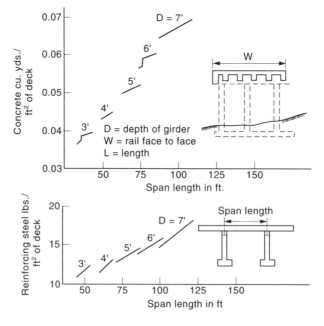

Figure 2.5. Quantity of continuous tee beam superstructure. NOTE: bent caps, sidewalks and kerbs are not included **(Sheet VI)**
For 2 ft-4 in high concrete rail add 4.6 lbs steel reinforcing/ft of railing
For 3 ft high concrete rail add 6.6 lbs steel reinforcing/ft of railing

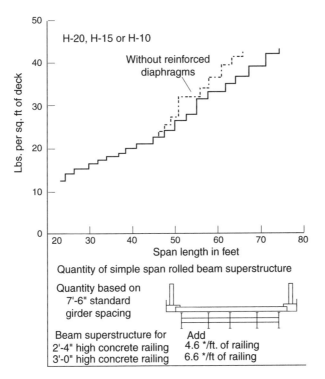

*Figure 2.6. Quantity of simple span rolled-beam superstructure where * indicates lbs of steel reinforcing* (**Sheet III**)

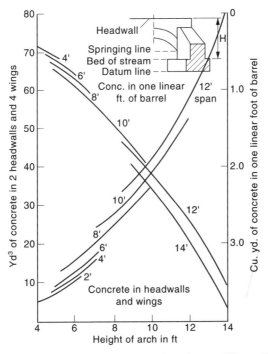

Figure 2.7. Quantity curves for concrete arch culverts (**Sheet IX**)

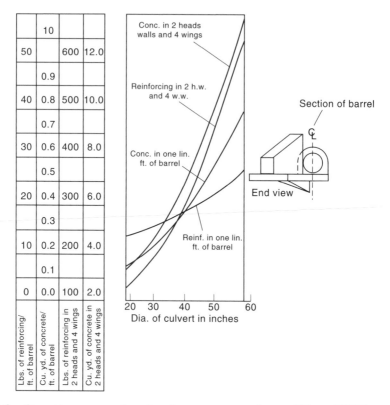

Figure 2.8. Quantity curves for circular concrete culverts (**Sheet XVII**)

Table 2.27. RCC single-box culverts slab construction **(Sheet VII, Table III)**

Slab no.	Width ft	H ft	Area ft²	Two portals		Quantity ft²		Bank height ft					
				C	S	C	S	10	15	20	30	40	50
								Length					
1	2	2	4	1.78		0.19	22	39	54	69	99	129	159
2	2	3	6	3.40		0.23	26	36	51	66	96	126	156
3	3	2	6	3.55		0.28	35	39	54	69	99	129	159
4	3	3	9	4.00		0.34	43	35	50	65	95	125	155
5	3	4	12	4.50	200	0.42	51	32	47	62	92	122	152
6	3	5	15	6	250	0.51	62	29	44	59	89	119	149
7	4	2	8	3.85		0.36	58	38	52	68	98	128	158
8	4	3	12	4.3		0.42	55	35	50	65	95	125	155
9	4	4	16	5.5	250	0.50	65	32	47	62	92	122	152
10	4	5	20	6.8	300	0.89	75	29	44	59	89	119	149
11	4	6	24	8.7	500	0.69	92	26	41	56	86	116	146
12	5	3	15	5	500	0.55	66	34	49	64	94	124	154
13	5	4	20	6.7	600	0.64	75	31	46	61	91	121	151
14	5	5	25	8.5	800	0.74	86	28	43	58	88	118	148
15	5	6	30	10.4	1000	0.79	101	25	40	55	85	115	145
16	5	8	40	13	1600	1.04	132		34	49	79	109	139
17	6	4	24	10	900	0.83	113	31	46	61	91	121	151
18	6	6	36	12.4	1200	0.96	134	25	40	55	85	115	145
19	6	8	48	13.7	1800	1.20	168		34	49	79	109	139
20	6	10	60	15	2200	1.49	216		28	43	73	103	133
21	8	4	32	12	900	1.18	139	30	45	60	90	120	150
22	8	6	48	22	1800	1.33	185		40	55	85	115	145
23	8	8	64	30	2200	1.47	215		34	49	79	109	139
24	8	10	80	43	3200	1.76	265		28	43	73	103	133
25	10	4	40	18	1400	1.71	241	30	45	60	90	120	150
26	10	6	60	28	2200	1.84	266		39	54	84	114	144
27	10	8	80	37	3200	2.07	282		33	48	78	108	138
28	10	10	100	46	4000	2.50	324		27	42	72	102	132
29	10	12	120	57	5000	2.88	381			36	66	96	126
30	12	4	48	23	1800	2.33	327	29	44	59	89	119	149
31	12	6	72	37	2800	2.56	362		38	53	83	113	143
32	12	8	96	52	4000	2.78	378		32	47	77	107	137
33	12	10	120	68	5000	3	412		26	41	65	101	131

C = Concrete, yd^3
S = Steel, pounds
H = Height

Table 2.28. RCC double-box culverts slab construction **(Sheet VII, Table IV)**

Slab no.	Width ft	H ft	Area ft²	Two portals C	Two portals S	Quantity ft² C	Quantity ft² S	Bank height ft 10	15	20	30	40	50
								Length					
1	2	2	8	2.6	0	0.32	51	39	54	66	99	139	159
2	2	3	12	3.9	0	0.38	43	36	51	66	96	126	156
3	3	3	18	4.9	0	0.61	76	35	50	65	95	125	155
4	3	4	24	5.3	200	0.72	89	32	47	62	92	122	152
5	3	5	30	7	250	0.84	104	29	44	59	89	119	149
6	4	3	24	5.5	0	0.82	101	35	50	65	95	125	155
7	4	4	32	6.6	250	0.94	114	32	47	62	92	122	152
8	4	5	40	8	300	1.04	129	29	44	59	89	119	149
9	4	6	48	10	500	1.19	152	26	41	56	86	116	146
10	5	3	30	6.7	600	1.06	123	34	49	64	94	124	154
11	5	4	40	8.2	700	1.21	135	31	46	61	91	121	151
12	5	5	50	9.7	800	1.35	151	28	44	58	88	118	148
13	5	6	60	12.6	1000	1.51	174	25	40	55	85	115	145
14	5	8	80	15	1600	1.79	232		34	49	79	109	139
15	6	4	48	11	900	1.62	206	31	46	61	91	121	151
16	6	6	72	18	1200	1.39	239	25	40	55	85	115	145
17	6	8	96	24	1800	2.20	285		34	49	79	109	139
18	6	10	120	30	2400	2.62	353		28	43	73	103	133
19	8	4	64	14	900	2.35	306	30	45	60	90	120	150
20	8	6	96	20	2000	2.65	338		40	55	85	115	145
21	8	8	128	27	2700	2.95	384		34	49	79	109	139
22	8	10	160	37	3200	3.36	457		28	43	73	103	133
23	10	4	80	15	1450	3.36	462	30	45	60	90	120	150
24	10	6	120	25	2200	3.15	495		39	54	84	114	144
25	10	8	160	37	3200	4.11	522		33	48	78	108	138
26	10	10	200	47	4000	4.7	577		27	42	72	102	132
27	10	12	240	62	5000	5.10	660			36	66	96	126
28	12	4	96	20	1800	4.62	647	29	44	59	89	119	149
29	12	6	144	35	1800	5.08	685		38	53	83	113	143
30	12	8	192	45	4500	5.5	708		32	47	77	107	137
31	12	10	240	62	5000	6.07	759		26	41	71	101	131
32	12	12	288	75	6500	6.55	838			35	65	96	125
33													

C = Concrete, yd³
S = Steel, pounds
H = Height

Table 2.29. RCC single-box culverts: beam and slab construction (**Sheet VIII, Table V**)

Slab no.	Width ft	H ft	Area ft²	Quantity/ft C	Quantity/ft S	Two portals C	Two portals S	Bank height ft 10	15	20	30	40	50
								Length					
1	8	4	32	0.93	177	9.4	1250	27	42	57	87	171	147
2	8	6	46	1.10	206	15.7	2060	27	36	51	81	111	141
3	8	8	64	1.27	240	33.2	3050	27	30	45	75	105	135
4	8	10	80	1.48	278	32	4220	27	30	39	69	99	129
5	10	4	40	1.26	223	13.5	1800	25	40	55	85	115	145
6	10	6	60	1.37	260	21.2	2800	25	34	49	79	109	139
7	10	8	80	1.56	296	30.6	4050	25	28	43	73	103	133
8	10	10	100	1.78	336	40.5	5500	25	28	37	67	97	127
9	10	12	120	2.00	381	53.5	7100	25	28	31	61	91	121
10	12	4	48	1.57	281	16.5	2100	25	40	55	85	115	145
11	12	6	72	1.69	319	25.8	3400	25	34	49	79	109	139
12	12	8	96	1.88	357	31.5	4800	25	28	43	73	103	133
13	12	10	120	2.10	403	52.5	7000	25	28	37	67	97	127
14	12	12	144	2.37	452	64	8500	25	28	31	61	91	121
15	14	6	84	2.35	388	40	5300	25	31	46	76	106	136
16	14	8	112	2.55	456	55	7200	25	25	40	70	100	130
17	14	10	140	2.84	804	72	9600	25	25	34	64	94	124
18	14	12	168	3.03	559	91	12 100	25	25	28	58	88	118
19	16	6	96	2.82	491	49	6500	25	30	45	75	105	135
20	16	8	128	2.98	540	64	8500	25	30	39	69	99	129
21	16	10	160	3.25	589	84	11 100	25	30	33	63	93	123
22	16	12	192	3.5	647	106	14 000	25	30	27	57	87	117
23	18	6	96	3.32	572	60	8000	25	28	43	73	103	133
24	18	8	144	3.47	624	66	8800	25	28	37	63	97	127
25	18	10	180	3.74	677	99	13 100	25	28	31	61	91	121
26	18	12	216	4.02	745	122	16 200	25	28	25	55	85	115
27	20	60	120	3.88	662	71	9400	25	28	43	73	103	133
28	20	8	160	4.05	724	93	12 300	25	28	37	67	97	127
29	20	10	200	4.30	776	177	15 500	25	28	31	61	91	121
30	20	12	240	4.6	842	194	19 160	25	28	25	55	85	115

C = Concrete, yd³
S = Steel, pounds
H = Height

Table 2.30. RCC double-box culvert: beam and slab construction (**Sheet VIII, Table VI**)

P in	Width ft	H ft	Area ft²	Quantity/ft C	Quantity/ft S	Two portals C	Two portals S	Bank height ft 10	15	20	30	40	50
								Length					
15	8	4	64	1.8	320	14.3	1910	27	42	57	87	117	147
15	8	6	96	2.05	348	22.6	3000	27	36	51	81	111	141
15	8	8	128	2.32	383	32.4	4300	27	30	45	75	105	135
15	8	10	160	2.61	433	43	5700	27	30	39	69	99	129
15	10	4	80	2.03	405	20.4	2720	25	40	55	85	115	145
15	10	6	120	2.33	446	31.5	4200	25	34	49	79	109	139
15	10	8	160	2.63	489	43.2	5720	25	28	43	73	103	133
15	10	10	200	2.91	537	53.5	7100	25	28	37	67	97	127
15	10	12	240	3.42	587	72	9500	25	28	31	61	91	121
18	12	4	96	3	510	26	3450	25	40	55	85	112	145
18	12	6	144	3.25	555	38.6	5100	25	34	49	79	109	139
18	12	8	192	3.56	601	53.5	7100	25	28	43	73	103	133
18	12	10	240	3.86	656	73	9700	25	28	37	67	97	127
18	12	12	288	4.21	710	37	11 600	25	28	31	61	91	121
18	14	6	168	4.38	767	54	7200	25	31	46	76	106	136
18	14	8	224	4.71	825	71	9400	25	25	40	70	100	130
18	14	10	280	5	880	91	12100	25	25	34	64	94	124
18	14	12	336	5.38	946	111	14 700	25	25	28	58	88	118
20	16	6	192	5.28	911	72	9600	25	30	45	75	105	135
20	16	8	256	5.51	963	92	12 200	25	30	39	69	99	129
20	16	10	320	5.90	1024	117	15 500	25	30	33	63	93	123
20	16	12	384	6.3	1088	143	19 000	25	30	27	57	87	117
22	18	6	216	6.25	1069	91	12 100	25	28	43	73	103	133
22	18	8	288	6.55	1130	105	13 900	25	28	37	67	97	127
22	18	10	360	6.85	1195	145	19 200	25	28	31	61	91	121
22	18	12	432	7.38	1263	175	23 200	25	28	25	55	85	115
24	20	6	240	7.4	1251	98	13 000	25	28	43	73	103	133
24	20	8	320	7.7	1322	142	18 800	25	28	37	67	97	127
24	20	10	400	8.10	1395	176	33 400	25	28	31	61	91	121
24	20	12	480	8.5	1467	211	28 100	25	28	25	55	85	115

C = Concrete, yd³
S = Steel, pounds
H = Height

Table 2.31. Circular-shaped beams for highway bridges. Minimum gauges for H-20 live load round (**Sheet X**)

Pipe diameter in inches	1–5	6–10	11–15	16–20	21–25	26–30	31–35	36–40	41–45	46–50	51–55	56–60	61–70	71–80	81–90	91–100
60	12	12	12	12	12	10	10	10	10	10	8	8	8	7	5	5
66	12	12	12	12	10	10	10	10	8	8	8	8	8	7	5	5
72	12	12	12	10	10	10	10	8	8	8	8	7	7	5	3	1
78	12	12	12	10	10	10	8	8	8	8	7	7	5	3	1	–
84	10	12	10	10	10	8	8	8	8	7	7	5	5	3	1	–
90	10	12	10	10	8	8	8	7	7	7	5	5	3	1	–	–
96	10	12	10	10	8	8	8	7	7	5	5	5	3	1	–	–
102	10	10	10	8	8	8	7	7	5	5	5	5	1	–	–	–
108	10	10	10	8	8	7	7	5	5	5	5	3	1	–	–	–
114	10	10	10	8	8	7	5	5	5	3	3	1	–	–	–	–
120	8	10	8	8	7	5	5	5	3	3	3	1	–	–	–	–
126	8	10	8	7	7	5	5	3	3	3	1	1	–	–	–	–
132	8	10	8	7	5	5	5	3	3	3	1	1	–	–	–	–
138	8	10	8	7	5	5	3	3	3	1	1	–	–	–	–	–
144	8	8	8	7	5	5	3	3	1	1	–	–	–	–	–	–
150	7	8	7	5	5	3	3	1	1	1	–	–	–	–	–	–
156	7	8	7	5	5	3	3	1	1	–	–	–	–	–	–	–
162	7	8	7	5	3	3	1	1	1	–	–	–	–	–	–	–
168	5	8	5	5	3	1	1	–	–	–	–	–	–	–	–	–
174	5	7	5	3	3	1	1	–	–	–	–	–	–	–	–	–
180	5	7	5	3	3	1	–	–	–	–	–	–	–	–	–	–

Reference: USS AmBridge Sectional Plate p. 8.

*Table 2.32. Circular-shaped beams for highway bridges. Minimum gauges for H-20 live load vertically elongated (**Sheet XI**)*

Pipe diameter in inches	1-5	6-10	11-15	16-20	21-25	26-30	31-35	36-40	41-45	46-50	51-55	56-60	61-70	71-80	81-90	91-100	Maximum height of cover for 1 ga, 6 bolts/ft
60	12	12	12	12	12	12	12	12	12	12	10	10	8	7	5	5	200
66	12	12	12	12	12	12	12	12	12	10	10	8	8	7	5	3	180
72	12	12	12	12	12	12	12	12	10	10	8	8	7	5	3	1	165
78	12	12	12	12	12	12	12	10	10	8	8	8	5	3	1		150
84	12	12	12	12	12	12	12	10	10	8	8	7	5	3	1		140
90	12	12	12	12	12	12	10	10	8	8	7	5	3	1			130
96	12	12	12	12.	12	10	10	10	8	7	7	5	3	1			125
102	12	12	12	12	10	10	10	8	8	7	5	5	1				115
108	12	12	12	10	10	10	10	8	7	5	5	3	1				110
114	10	10	10	10	10	10	8	8	7	5	5	3	1				105
120	10	12	10	10	10	10	8	7	5	5	3	1					100
126	10	12	10	10	10	10	8	7	5	3	3	1					95
132	10	10	10	10	10	8	8	7	5	3	1	1					95
138	10	10	10	10	10	8	7	5	3	3	1						85
144	10	10	10	10	8	8	7	5	3	1	1						80
150	10	10	10	8	8	8	7	5	3	1							80
156	10	10	10	8	8	8	5	3	1	1							75
162	10	10	10	8	8	7	5	3	1								70
168	10	10	10	8	8	7	5	3	1								70
174	8	10	8	8	8	7	5	3	1								65
180	8	10	8	8	8	5	3	1									65

Reference: USS AmBridge Sectional Plate p. 8.

Table 2.33. Elliptical-shaped beams for highway bridges. Sizes and layout details for AmBridge sectional plate pipe–arches (**Sheet XII**)

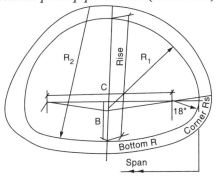

Span (ft-in)	Rise (ft-in)	Area (ft²)	Top	Bottom	Total	B (in)	C (in)	Inside radius R_1	Plate (in) R_2
6-1	4-7	22	11	5	22	21.0	37.1	36.7	76.4
6-4	4-9	24	12	5	23	20.5	40.1	38.1	96.9
6-9	4-11	26	12	6	24	22.0	45.3	41.0	83.5
7-0	5-1	28	13	6	25	21.4	48.2	42.3	104.5
7-3	5-3	31	14	6	26	20.8	51.0	43.5	136.5
7-8	5-5	33	14	7	27	22.4	56.4	46.5	109.9
7-11	5-7	35	15	7	28	21.7	59.2	47.7	138.4
8-2	5-9	38	16	7	29	20.9	61.7	48.9	183.1
8-7	5-11	40	16	8	30	22.7	67.4	51.9	141.3
8-10	6-1	43	17	8	31	21.8	70.0	53.0	179.2
9-4	6-3	46	17	9	32	23.8	75.7	56.2	144.9
9-6	6-5	49	18	9	33	22.9	78.3	57.2	178.2
9-9	6-7	52	19	9	34	21.9	80.6	58.3	228.0
10-3	6-9	55	19	10	35	23.9	86.6	61.5	178.9
10-8	6-11	58	19	11	36	26.2	92.5	64.9	153.2
10-11	7-1	61	20	11	37	25.1	95.0	65.8	180.8
11-5	7-3	64	20	12	38	27.4	100.9	69.4	157.8
11-7	7-5	67	21	12	39	26.3	103.4	70.2	183.4
11-10	7-7	71	22	12	40	25.2	105.7	71.1	217.0
12-4	7-9	74	22	13	41	27.5	111.8	74.7	186.5
12-6	7-11	78	23	13	42	26.3	114.2	75.5	217.4
12-8	8-1	81	24	13	43	25.2	116.4	76.3	258.4
12-10	8-4	85	25		44	25.0	118.4	77.2	315.2
13-5	8-5	89	25	14	45	26.3	124.9	80.7	255.7
13-11	8-7	93	25	11	46	28.9	131.1	84.4	220.8
14-1	8-9	97	26	15	47	27.6	133.3	85.1	254.8
14-3	8-11	101	27	15	48	26.3	135.4	85.9	298.7
14-10	9-1	105	27	16	49	28.9	141.9	89.5	254.9
15-4	9-3	109	27	17	50	31.6	148.1	93.4	226.5
15-6	9-5	113	28	17	51	30.2	150.4	94.0	255.9
15-8	9-7	118	29	17	52	28.8	152.5	94.7	292.5
15-10	9-10	122	30	17	53	27.4	154.5	95.4	339.1
16-5	9-11	126	30	18	54	30.1	161.0	99.2	291.6
16-7	10-1	131	31	18	55	28.7	163.1	99.8	333.8

Reference: USS AmBridge Sectional Plate p. 13.

Table 2.34. Elliptical-shaped beams for highway bridges. Sizes and weights for AmBridge sectional plate pipe–arches **(Sheet XIII)**

Pipe–arch		Number of plates				Total	Approximate weight in pounds per ft							Additional weight per
Span (ft-in)	Rise (ft-in)	3N	5N	6N	7N	'N' required	12 Ga	10 Ga	8 Ga	7 Ga	5 Ga	3 Ga	1 Ga	ft asphalt coat
6-1	4-7	2	2	1	–	22	124	156	187	202	234	265	297	16
6-4	4-9	2	1	2	–	23	129	162	194	210	243	276	309	16
6-9	4-11	2	–	3	–	24	134	168	202	218	252	287	321	17
7-0	5-1	2	–	2	1	25	138	173	209	226	261	297	332	18
7-3	5-3	2	–	1	2	26	147	184	221	240	277	314	351	18
7-8	5-5	2	–	–	3	27	152	190	228	248	286	325	363	19
7-11	5-7	2	3	–	1	28	156	196	236	255	295	336	375	20
8-2	5-9	2	2	1	–	29	163	202	243	263	304	346	386	21
8-7	5-11	1	3	3	–	30	170	213	255	277	320	363	406	21
8-10	6-1	3	2	2	–	31	175	219	262	285	329	374	418	22
9-4	6-3	3	1	3	–	32	179	225	270	293	338	375	430	23
9-6	6-5	3	–	4	0	33	184	231	277	301	347	395	441	23
9-9	6-7	3	0	3	1	34	189	237	285	309	356	406	453	24
10-3	6-9	2	2	2	1	35	194	243	292	316	366	416	465	25
10-8	6-11	2	1	3	1	36	196	249	299	324	375	427	477	26
10-11	7-1	2	1	2	2	37	203	255	306	332	385	437	488	26
11-5	7-3	2	–	3	2	38	207	261	313	340	394	448	500	27
11-7	7-5	2	–	2	3	39	216	271	326	354	408	465	519	28
11-10	7-7	2	2	4	–	40	221	277	334	362	417	476	531	28
12-4	7-9	2	2	3	1	41	226	284	341	370	427	486	543	29
12-6	7-11	2	1	4	1	42	231	290	348	378	436	497	555	30
12-8	8-1	2	–	5	1	43	235	296	356	385	445	507	567	31
12-10	8-4	2	–	4	2	44	240	302	363	393	455	517	578	31
13-5	8-5	2	–	3	3	45	249	312	375	407	470	535	597	32
13-11	8-7	2	3	3	1	46	254	318	383	415	479	546	609	33
14-1	8-9	2	3	2	2	47	258	324	390	423	489	556	621	33
14-3	8-11	2	3	1	3	48	263	330	397	431	498	566	633	34
14-10	9-1	2	2	2	3	49	268	336	404	439	507	576	645	35
15-4	9-3	2	1	3	3	50	273	342	411	447	516	586	657	36
15-6	9-5	2	1	2	4	51	281	353	424	460	531	604	676	36
15-8	9-7	2	2	6	–	52	286	359	431	468	541	644	687	37
15-10	9-10	2	1	7	–	53	291	365	438	476	550	625	699	38
16-5	9-11	2	–	8	–	54	295	371	446	484	559	636	711	38
16-7	10-1	2	–	7	1	55	300	377	453	492	568	646	723	39

Reference: USS AmBridge Sectional Plate p. 15.

Table 2.35. *Arch-shaped beams for highway bridges. Minimum gauges for H-20 and H-15 live loads* (**Sheet XIV**)

Span in ft	H-20 live load Height of cover – ft										H-15 live load Height of cover – ft									
	1	2	3	4	5	6	7	8	9	10	1	2	3	4	5	6	7	8	9	10
4 to 10	12	12	12	12	12	12	12	12	12	12	12	12	12	12	12	12	12	12	12	12
11	10	10	10	12	12	12	12	12	12	12	12	12	12	12	12	12	12	12	12	12
12	10	10	10	12	12	12	12	12	10	10	12	12	12	12	12	12	12	12	12	10
13	8	8	10	12	12	12	12	10	10	8	10	10	12	12	12	12	12	10	10	10
14	7	8	8	10	10	10	10	8	8	8	10	10	10	12	12	12	10	10	8	8
15	5	7	8	10	10	10	10	8	8	7	8	10	10	12	12	10	10	8	8	7
16	5	5	7	8	8	10	8	7	7	5	8	8	8	10	10	10	10	8	7	7
17	3	5	5	7	8	8	8	7	5	3	7	8	8	10	10	10	8	7	7	5
18	3	3	5	7	7	8	7	5	3	3	7	7	7	8	8	8	8	7	5	3
19			3	5	5	7	7	3	3	1	5	5	7	8	8	8	7	5	3	3
20			3	5	5	5	5	3	1		3	5	5	7	8	8	5	5	3	1
21			3	3	5	3	1				3	3	5	5	7	7	5	3	3	
22			1	3	3	3	1					3	3	5	5	7	5	3	1	
23				1	3	1						3	3	5	5	3	1			
24				1	1							1	3	3	5	3	1			
25				1								1	3	3	3					
26												1	1	3	1					
27												1	1	1						
28													1							

Reference: USS AmBridge Sectional Plate p. 20.

Table 2.36. *Arch-shaped beams for highway bridges. Minimum gauges for H-10 live load* (**Sheet XV**)

Span in ft	H-10 live load Height of cover – ft									
	1	2	3	4	5	6	7	8	9	10
4 to 10										
11	12	12	12	12	12	12	12	12	12	12
12	12	12	12	12	12	12	12	12	12	10
13	12	12	12	12	12	12	12	12	10	10
14	12	12	12	12	12	12	12	10	10	8
15	12	12	12	12	12	12	12	10	8	8
16	10	10	12	12	12	12	10	10	8	7
17	10	10	10	12	12	12	10	8	8	7
18	10	10	10	12	10	10	10	8	7	5
19	8	8	10	10	10	10	8	7	5	3
20	8	8	10	10	10	10	8	7	5	3
21	8	8	8	10	10	10	8	5	3	1
22	7	7	8	8	8	8	7	5	3	1
23	5	7	7	8	8	8	7	3	1	
24	3	5	7	7	8	8	5	3	1	
25	1	5	5	7	7	8	5	3	1	
26		5	5	5	5	7	5	3		
27		3	3	5	5	5	5	3	1	
28		1	3	3	3	5	3	1		
29		1	1	3	3	3	3	1		
30			1	1	1	3	1	1		

Reference: USS AmBridge Sectional Plate p. 20.

Table 2.37. Weights for AmBridge sectional plate–arches (**Sheet XVI**)

Arch arc length 'N'	Number of plates				Approximate weight in pounds per foot							Additional weight per ft asphalt coat
	3N	5N	6N	7N	12 Ga	10 Ga	8 Ga	7 Ga	5 Ga	3 Ga	1 Ga	
8	1	1	–	–	46	57	69	75	86	98	109	6
9	1	–	1	–	51	63	76	82	95	108	121	6
10	–	2	–	–	55	69	83	90	104	119	133	7
11	–	1	1	–	60	75	90	98	113	129	145	8
12	–	–	2	–	65	81	98	106	123	140	156	9
13	–	–	1	1	70	87	105	114	132	150	168	9
14	–	–	–	2	78	98	117	128	147	168	187	10
15	–	3	–	–	83	104	125	136	157	178	199	11
16	–	2	1	–	88	110	132	146	166	188	211	11
17	–	2	–	1	92	116	140	152	176	199	223	12
18	–	–	3	–	97	122	147	160	184	209	235	13
19	–	1	–	2	102	128	154	167	194	220	246	13
20	–	–	1	2	107	134	161	175	203	231	258	14
21	–	–	–	3	115	145	173	189	218	249	277	15
22	–	2	2	–	120	151	181	197	227	259	289	16
23	–	1	3	–	125	157	188	205	236	269	301	16
24	–	–	4	–	130	163	196	213	246	279	313	17
25	–	–	3	1	135	169	203	221	255	290	324	18
26	–	–	2	2	139	175	211	228	264	301	336	18
27	–	–	1	3	144	181	218	236	273	311	328	19
28	–	–	–	4	153	191	230	250	288	329	367	20
29	–	3	–	2	158	197	238	258	298	339	379	21
30	–	–	5	–	163	203	245	266	307	349	391	21
31	–	2	–	3	167	209	252	274	316	360	403	22
32	–	–	3	2	172	215	259	282	325	370	415	23
33	–	–	2	3	176	221	267	290	335	381	426	23
34	–	–	1	4	181	227	275	298	344	391	438	24
35	–	–	–	5	189	238	287	311	359	409	457	25
36	–	3	–	3	194	244	294	319	369	419	469	26
37	–	–	5	1	199	250	301	327	378	430	481	26
38	–	2	–	4	204	256	309	335	387	441	493	27
39	–	–	3	3	209	262	216	343	396	451	505	28
40	–	–	2	4	213	268	323	351	406	461	516	28
41	–	–	1	5	218	274	331	359	415	471	528	29
42	–	–	–	6	226	265	343	372	430	489	547	30
43	–	–	6	1	231	291	350	330	439	500	559	31
44	–	–	5	2	236	297	357	388	448	510	571	31
45	–	–	4	3	241	303	365	386	458	521	583	32
46	–	–	3	4	246	309	372	404	367	531	595	33
47	–	–	2	5	250	315	379	412	476	542	606	33
48	–	–	1	6	255	321	386	420	485	552	618	34
49	–	–	–	7	263	331	398	433	500	570	637	35
50	–	–	6	2	268	337	407	441	510	581	649	36
51	–	–	5	3	273	343	414	449	519	591	661	36

(Continued)

Table 2.37. (Continued)

Arch arc length 'N'	Number of plates				Approximate weight in pounds per foot							Additional weight per ft asphalt coat
	3N	5N	6N	7N	12 Ga	10 Ga	8 Ga	7 Ga	5 Ga	3 Ga	1 Ga	
52	–	–	4	4	277	349	421	457	528	601	673	37
53	–	–	3	5	282	355	428	465	537	611	685	38
54	–	–	2	6	287	862	436	473	547	622	696	38
55	–	–	1	7	292	367	443	481	556	632	708	39
56	–	–	–	8	301	378	456	494	572	650	727	40
57	–	–	6	3	305	384	463	502	581	661	739	40
58	–	–	5	4	310	390	470	510	590	671	751	41
59	–	–	4	5	315	396	477	518	599	682	762	42

2.6.2 Girder bridges (steel, RC) (Section III (B))

The following Figs 2.9–2.16 and Tables 2.38–2.40 provide the necessary data.

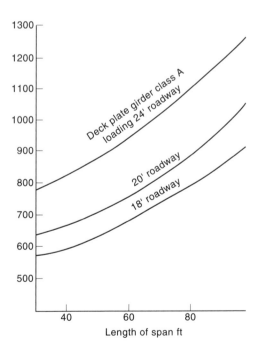

Figure 2.9. Quantity curves for deck-plate girder bridges. Class 'A'-loading concrete deck and rail (**Sheet I (XVIII)**)

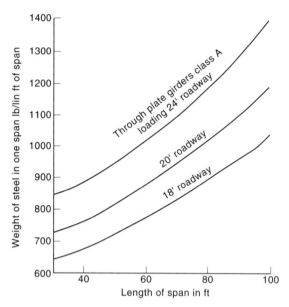

Figure 2.10. Quantity curves for through-plate girder bridges. Class 'A'-loading concrete deck **(Sheet II (XIX))**

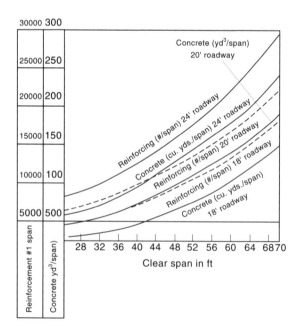

Figure 2.11. Quantity curves for one span of concrete through girder bridges. Superstructure only – Class 'A' loading **(Sheet III (XX))**

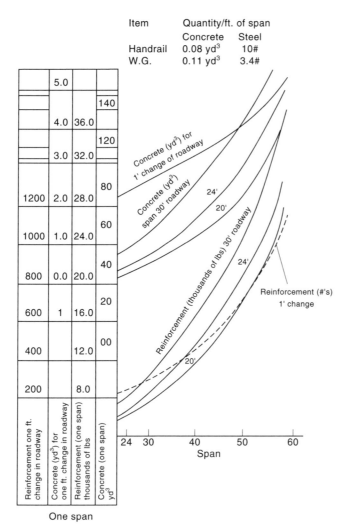

Item	Quantity/ft. of span	
	Concrete	Steel
Handrail	0.08 yd^3	10#
W.G.	0.11 yd^3	3.4#

Figure 2.12. Quantity curves for standard RC deck girder bridges (three girders, superstructure only) **(Sheet IV (XXI))**

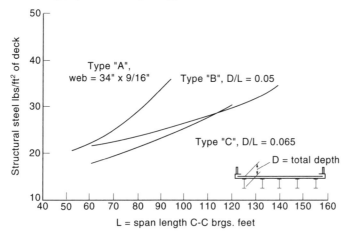

Figure 2.13. Composite beam **(Sheet V (XXII))**

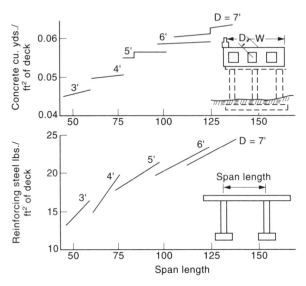

Figure 2.14. Quantity curves for continuous box girder superstructure. Note: bent caps sidewalks and kerbs are not included. For 2 ft-4 in high concrete rail add 4.6# of railing reinforcement per foot. For 3 ft-4 in high concrete rail add 6.6# of railing reinforcement per foot **(Sheet VI (XXIII))**

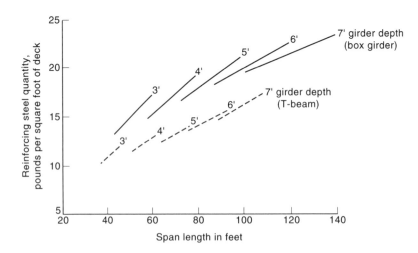

Figure 2.15. Box girder and T-beam **(Sheet VII (XXIV))**

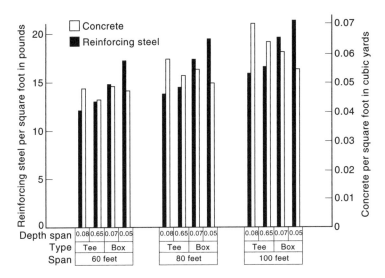

Figure 2.16. Comparative chart for T-beam and box girders **(Sheet VIII (XXV))**

Table 2.38. Standard composite T-beam bridges **(Sheet IX (XXVI))**

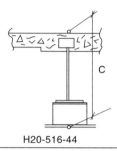

H20-516-44

Roadway 24ft

Span	C	Reinf. lbs	Conc yd³	St. steel lbs
50	$3'\text{-}8\frac{15}{16}''$	7990	36.4	28150
60	$3'\text{-}11\frac{11}{16}''$	9540	43.4	35900
70	$4'\text{-}2\frac{15}{16}''$	11100	50.4	50820
80	$4'\text{-}5\frac{13}{16}''$	12640	57.1	68550
90	$4'\text{-}5\frac{11}{16}''$	14210	65.0	97160
100	$4'\text{-}6\frac{1}{16}''$	15750	72.3	132200

Roadway 28'-0"

Span	C	Reinf. lbs	Conc yd³	St. steel lbs
50	$3'\text{-}11\frac{13}{16}''$	8530	42.0	38060
60	$4'\text{-}3\frac{1}{16}''$	10150	50.0	52410
70	$4'\text{-}6\frac{1}{16}''$	12010	57.5	75150
80	$4'\text{-}5\frac{13}{16}''$	13700	65.3	101880
90	$4'\text{-}6\frac{7}{16}''$	15370	73.2	141260
100	$4'\text{-}6\frac{11}{16}''$	17000	83.0	184540

Table 2.39. Standard riveted PL girder bridges **(Sheet (XXVII))**

Roadway of 24 ft

Span	Depth h	Conc. yd^3	Reinf. lbs	Net weight lbs
90	7 ft–$1\frac{7}{8}$ in	68	12 540	97 350
100	7 ft–$7\frac{1}{8}$ in	76	13 930	116 220
110	8 ft–$3\frac{7}{8}$ in	83	15 330	134 170
120	8 ft–$11\frac{3}{4}$ in	91	16 710	170 220
130	9 ft–$5\frac{7}{8}$ in	98	18 100	202 250
140	9 ft–$11\frac{7}{8}$ in	105	19 480	229 120

Roadway of 28 ft

Span	Depth h	Conc. yd^3	Reinf. lbs	Net weight lbs
90	7 ft–$7\frac{1}{8}$ in	78	17 740	127 600
100	8 ft–$1\frac{1}{4}$ in	87	19 700	148 800
110	8 ft–$9\frac{1}{4}$ in	95	21 670	175 200
120	9 ft–$5\frac{1}{8}$ in	104	23 560	210 400
130	9 ft–$11\frac{1}{8}$ in	112	25 520	243 600
140	10 ft–$5\frac{1}{4}$ in	122	27 470	275 400

Table 2.40. Standard welded PL girder bridges **Sheet XI (XXVIII))**

Roadway of 24 ft

Span	Depth h	Conc. yd^3	Reinf. lbs	Steel weight
90	7 ft–$2\frac{3}{4}$ in	66	12 540	68 690
100	7 ft–$10\frac{3}{4}$ in	73	13 930	83 230
110	8 ft–$6\frac{3}{4}$ in	80	15 330	99 010
120	9 ft–$6\frac{3}{4}$ in	87	16 710	113 960
130	9 ft–$10\frac{3}{3}$ in	94	18 100	145 440
140	10 ft–5 in	101	19 480	171 210

Roadway of 28 ft

Span	Depth h	Conc. yd^3	Reinf. lbs	Steel weight
90	7 ft–$4\frac{3}{4}$ in	76	17 740	92 570
100	7 ft–$10\frac{3}{4}$ in	84	19 700	111 650
110	8 ft–$8\frac{3}{4}$ in	92	21 670	129 240
120	9 ft–$6\frac{3}{4}$ in	101	23 560	150 790
130	9 ft–$10\frac{3}{4}$ in	109	25 520	190 210
140	10 ft–$4\frac{7}{8}$ in	117	27 470	222 000

2.6.3   Truss bridges (steel) (Section III (C))

The following Figs 2.17–2.23 provide the necessary data.

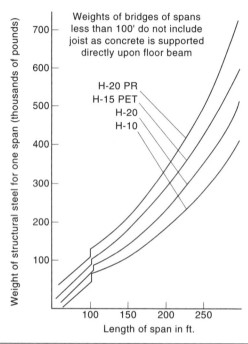

Quantities per foot of span				
	Concrete deck		Wood deck	
	Concrete	Steel	Lumber	Hardware
Handrail	0.08	10.0		
W.G.	0.11	3.4	2.1	0.08
Deck 18' R	0.37	6.4		
Deck 20' R	0.41	7.1		
Deck 24' R	10.48	8.5		
In. ea. add. 1' of width	0.018	3.5		

Figure 2.17. Quantity curves showing weights of steel-deck truss bridges (**Sheet I (XXIX)**)

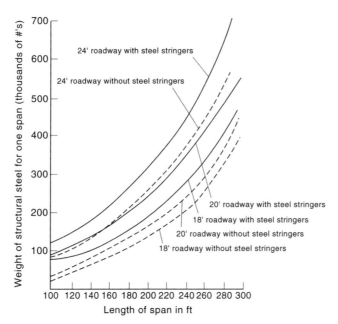

Figure 2.18. Quantity curves for steel through-truss bridges. Class 'A' loading **(Sheet II (XXX))**

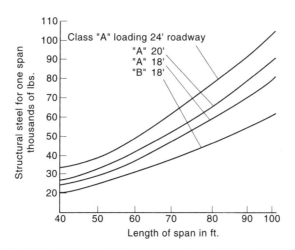

Quantities in deck and handrail (lineal ft.)									
Type	Roadway	Conc. floor		Lumber in FBM				Hardware	
		Conc. yd³	Steel lbs.	Stringer	4" deck	6" deck	4" deck	6" deck	H.R. W.G.
Class "B"	18	–	–	72	108	21	253	470	0.08
Class "A"	18	0.37	64	–	108	"	–	"	0.08
Class "A"	20	0.41	71	–	120	"	–	54.5	–
Class "A"	24	0.48	85	–	168	"	–	655	0.08

Figure 2.19. Quantity curves for steel low-truss bridges **(Sheet III (XXXI))**

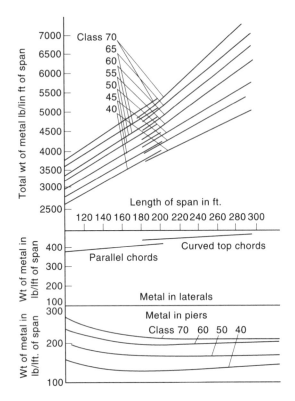

Figure 2.20. Double-track railway through riveted Pratt truss spans **(Sheet IV (XXXII))**

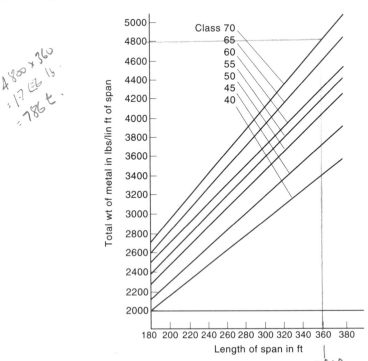

Figure 2.21. Single-track railway through pin-connected Pratt truss **(Sheet V (XXXIII))**

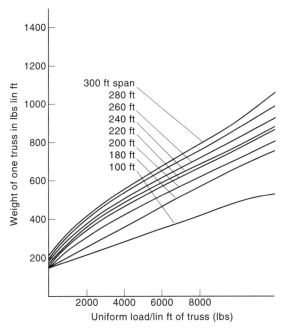

Figure 2.22. Curve showing weights of steel in one truss of riveted through-truss bridges for varying loads and spans **(Sheet VI (XXXIV))**

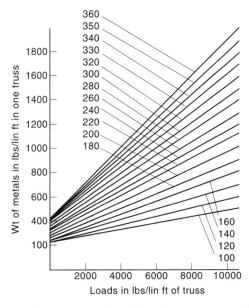

Figure 2.23. Curves showing weights of steel in one truss of steel-deck truss bridges for varying loads and spans. These curves do not include the weight of the floor system **(Sheet VII (XXXV))**

2.6.4   Arch bridges (steel and RCC) (Section III (D))

The following Figs 2.24–2.30 provide the necessary data

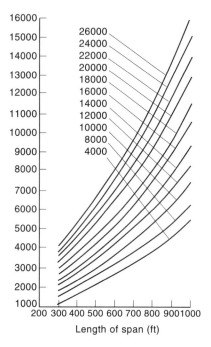

Figure 2.24. Through, pin-connected Petit trusses; metal in one truss **(Sheet VIII (XXXVI))**

Three-hinged arches	Average rise to spare	Detail	Remarks
	0.2 0.225 0.25	Solid rib Braced rib Spandrel braced with hinge above	Grade line approx tangent to the top chord of the crown
Half through	0.225 0.3	Solid rib Braced rib	
High deck	0.25-0.28 0.33-0.38	Solid rib Braced rib	

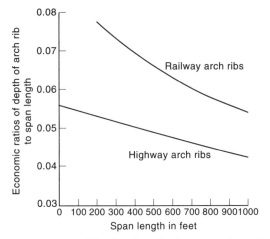

Figure 2.25. Economic ratios of depth of arch rib to span length **(Sheet I (XXXVII))**

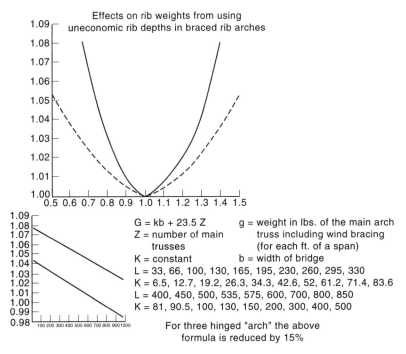

$G = kb + 23.5 Z$ g = weight in lbs. of the main arch
Z = number of main   truss including wind bracing
trusses   (for each ft. of a span)
K = constant   b = width of bridge
L = 33, 66, 100, 130, 165, 195, 230, 260, 295, 330
K = 6.5, 12.7, 19.2, 26.3, 34.3, 42.6, 52, 61.2, 71.4, 83.6
L = 400, 450, 500, 535, 575, 600, 700, 800, 850
K = 81, 90.5, 100, 130, 150, 200, 300, 400, 500

For three hinged "arch" the above
formula is reduced by 15%

Figure 2.26. Ratio of weights of metal in hingeless arches as compared with three-hinged arches for both railway and highway bridges **(Sheet II (XXXVIII))**

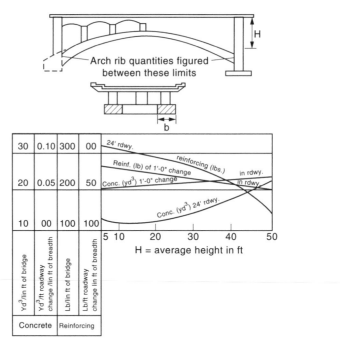

Figure 2.27. Quantities in deck spandrel arches and columns for open-spandrel arch bridges: Class 'A' loading (**Sheet III (XXXIX)**)

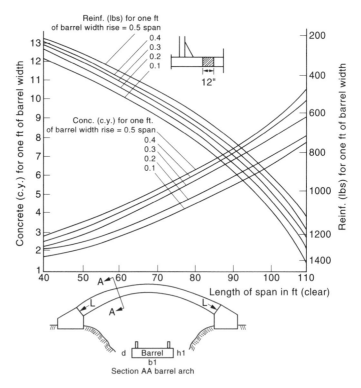

Figure 2.28. Quantity curves for barrel arches with filled spandrels (**Sheet IV (XXXX)**)

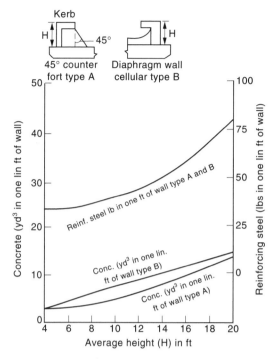

Figure 2.29. Quantity curves for spandrel walls on filled-spandrel arch bridges **(Sheet V (XXXXI))**

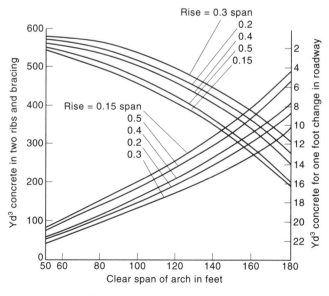

Figure 2.30. Quantities of concrete in two ribs and bracing (open spandrel highway arches): 24 ft clear roadway **(Sheet VI (XXXXII))**

2.6.5 *Suspension and cantilever bridges* (Section III (E))

The following Figs 2.31–2.38 provide the necessary data.

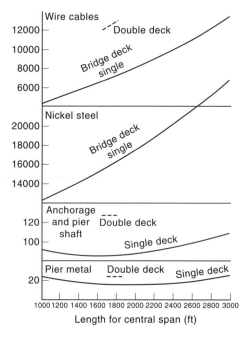

Figure 2.31. Quantities for wire-cable suspension bridges **(Sheet I)**

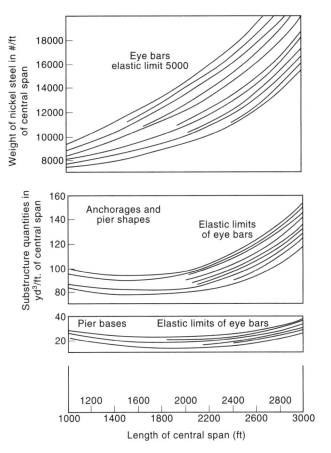

Figure 2.32. Quantities of various metals in eye-bar cable suspension bridges (**Sheet II**)

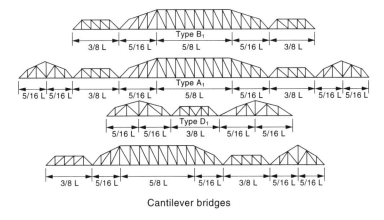

Cantilever bridges

Figure 2.33. Cantilever bridges (**Sheet III**)

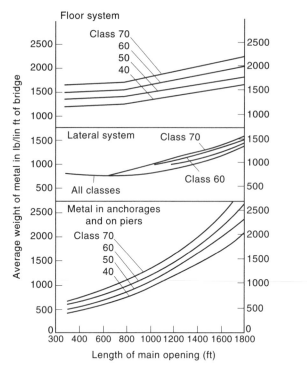

Figure 2.34. Cantilever bridges: Type A (**Sheet IV**)

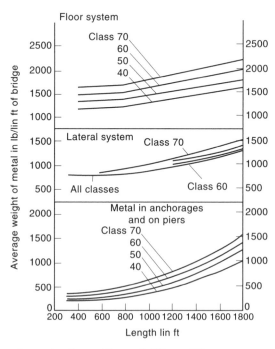

Figure 2.35. Cantilever bridges: Type C (**Sheet V**)

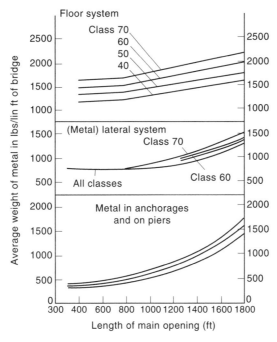

Figure 2.36. Cantilever bridges: Type D **(Sheet VI)**

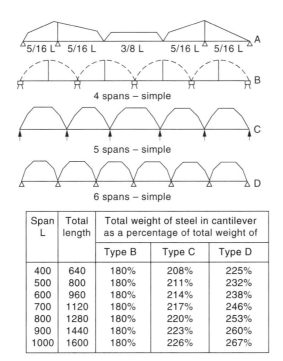

Span L	Total length	Total weight of steel in cantilever as a percentage of total weight of		
		Type B	Type C	Type D
400	640	180%	208%	225%
500	800	180%	211%	232%
600	960	180%	214%	238%
700	1120	180%	217%	246%
800	1280	180%	220%	253%
900	1440	180%	223%	260%
1000	1600	180%	226%	267%

Figure 2.37. Comparison chart for cantilever bridges **(Sheet VII)**

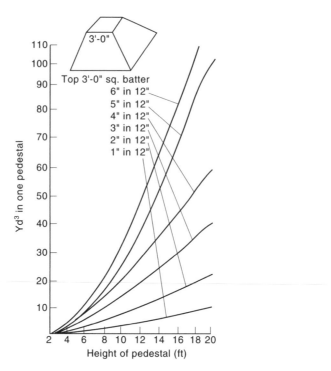

Figure 2.38. Curves showing quantities in square pedestals on sides battered by different amounts on top 3 ft square (**Sheet VII (C)**)

2.6.6 Prestressed concrete bridges (Section III (F))

The following Figs 2.39–2.43 and Tables 2.41–2.43 provide the necessary data.

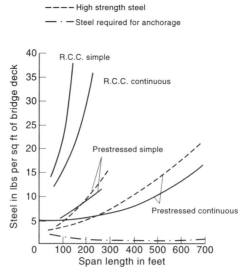

Figure 2.39. Comparative steel requirements per unit area of various bridges depending on the length of span inclusive of deck reinforcement (**Sheet I**)

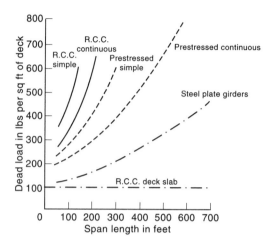

Figure 2.40. Comparative weight per unit area of various bridges depending on the length of span inclusive of deck slab (**Sheet II**)

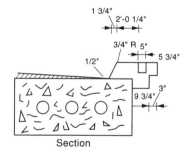

Section

Span ft	Concrete yd³	Reinforcement lbs	Handling weight per 4'-0" unit (tonnes)
25	35.5	2080	7.7
30	48.0	2390	10.7
35	64.0	2840	14.4
40	74.2	3280	16.7
45	96.4	3960	22.1

Figure 2.41. Standard prestressed concrete bridges pretensioned (**Sheet III**)

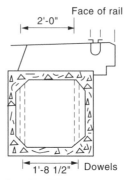

Span ft	Concrete yd^3	Reinforcement lbs	Handling per unit (tonnes)
40	73.3	6620	11.7
50	101.2	8500	16.3
60	136.0	10780	22.2
70	171.1	12820	28.1

Figure 2.42. Standard prestressed concrete box-girder bridges (28 ft roadway) **(Sheet IV)**

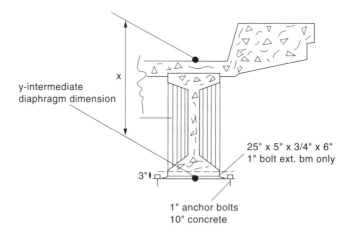

Figure 2.43. Prestressed concrete I-beam bridges (24 ft and 28 ft roadways) for an H20-S16-44 loading. See also Table B2.41 for 24 ft roadway dimensions **(Sheet V (A))**

Table 2.41. Dimensions for 24 ft roadway prestressed concrete I-beam bridge **(Sheet V (A) continued)**

Cast-in-place concrete (pretension beams)

Span	x	y	Concrete yd^3	Reinforcement lbs
24 ft Roadway				
35	2 ft-11$\frac{5}{16}$ in	1 ft-6 in	26.6	5990
40	3 ft-3$\frac{5}{16}$ in	1 ft-8 in	30.2	6760
45	3 ft-7$\frac{5}{16}$ in	1 ft-10 in	33.6	7420
50	3 ft-11$\frac{5}{16}$ in	2 ft-0 in	36.8	8200
60	4 ft-3$\frac{5}{16}$ in	2 ft-0 in	43.5	9640
70	4 ft-7$\frac{5}{16}$ in	2 ft-0 in	50.7	11 300

Slab + curb + diaphragm

Table 2.42. Standard prestressed concrete I-beam bridges (examples of dimensions) **(Sheet V (B))**

Cast-in-place concrete (post-tensioned beams)

Span	x	y	Conc. cy	Reinf. lbs
28 ft Roadway				
35	3 ft-3$\frac{7}{16}$ in	1 ft-10 in	31.2	6880
40	3 ft-3$\frac{7}{16}$ in	2 ft-0 in	35.0	7770
45	3 ft-11$\frac{7}{16}$ in	2 ft-0 in	38.6	8520
50	4 ft-3$\frac{7}{16}$ in	2 ft-2 in	42.4	9410
60	4 ft-7$\frac{7}{16}$ in	2 ft-4 in	50.1	11050
70	5 ft-1$\frac{7}{16}$ in	2 ft-4 in	58.4	12970

Cast-in-place concrete (with post-tension beams)

Span	x	y	Conc. cy	Reinf. lbs
24 ft Roadway				
50	3 ft-11$\frac{5}{16}$ in	2 ft-0 in	38.0	8200
60	4 ft-3$\frac{5}{16}$ in	2 ft-2 in	44.7	9640
70	4 ft-7$\frac{5}{16}$ in	2 ft-2 in	52.5	11 250
80	5 ft-3$\frac{5}{16}$ in	2 ft-6 in	59	12 690
90	5 ft-11$\frac{5}{16}$ in	2 ft-9 in	65.8	14 140
100	6 ft-9$\frac{5}{16}$ in	3 ft-3 in	73.0	15 680
28 ft Roadway				
50	4 ft-3$\frac{7}{16}$ in	2 ft-2 in	43.7	9410
60	4 ft-7$\frac{7}{16}$ in	2 ft-4 in	51.6	11 050
70	5 ft-1$\frac{7}{16}$ in	2 ft-6 in	60.2	12 910
80	5 ft-7$\frac{7}{16}$ in	2 ft-9 in	67.8	14 550
90	6 ft-3$\frac{7}{16}$ in	3 ft-0 in	75.8	16 210
100	7 ft-1$\frac{7}{16}$ in	3 ft-6 in	83.5	17 980

Table 2.43. Standard prestressed concrete I-beam bridges (examples of dimensions) **(Sheet V (C))**

Precast beams (pre-tensioned)

Span (ft)	Concrete		Bearings		Diaphragm rods		Reinf. steel
	One beam	Total	No.	Total wt (lbs)	No.	Total wt (lbs)	
24 ft Roadway							
35	3.0	12.0	8	160	2	220	1560
40	3.8	15.2		160	2		1730
45	4.6	18.4		160	2		1910
50	5.7	22.8		1600	2		2090
60	8.9	35.6		1780	2	220	2300
70	11.4	45.6	8	1980	4	440	2670
28 ft Roadway							
35	3.5	17.5	10	160	2	245	1890
40	4.3	21.5		160		245	2240
45	5.2	26.0		160		245	2330
50	6.2	31.0		2525		245	2420
60	9.4	47.0		2775	2	250	2820
70	12.4	62.0	10	3000	4	500	3260

Precast beams (post-tensioned)

Span (ft)	Concrete		Bearings		Diaphragm rods		Reinf. steel
24 ft Roadway							
50	5.9	23.6	8	1600	2	220	2210
60	7.7	30.8		1780	2	220	2560
70	9.8	39.2		1980	4	440	2980
80	12.8	51.2		2160			3370
90	17.7	70.8		2580			4070
100	22.0	88.0	8	2640	4	440	4540
28 ft Roadway							
50	6.3	31.5	10	2525	2	245	2690
60	8.2	41.0		2775	2	245	3200
70	10.7	53.5		3000	4	495	3770
80	13.5	67.5		3100		500	4300
90	18.3	91.5		3325		505	5290
100	23.0	115.0	10	3400	4	510	5890

2.7 Quantity curves for substructures (Section IV)

For unit costs of various quantities see Section 2.8. However, the information from Sections 2.4–2.6 is passed on to this section for the quantitative analysis of the substructure. As in Section 2.6, it gives direct quantities for a single type. If more than one choice is to be considered, a result based on comparison should be investigated.

The following Figs 2.44–2.73 provide the necessary data.

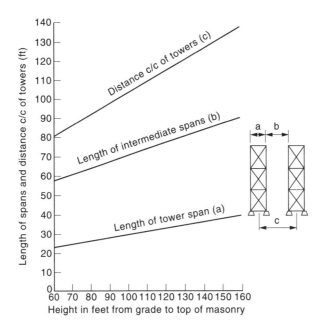

Figure 2.44. Approximate economic span lengths for steel viaducts of various heights (24 ft roadway – concrete deck and railing) **(Sheet I)**

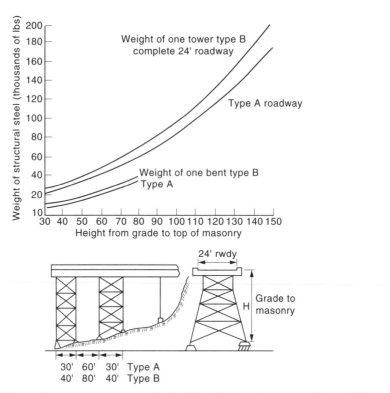

Figure 2.45. Quantity curves: structural steel for viaduct towers and bents **(Sheet II)**

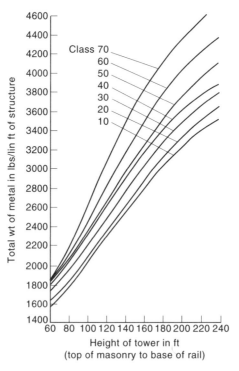

Figure 2.46. Quantity curves for various bridge tower heights **(Sheet III)**

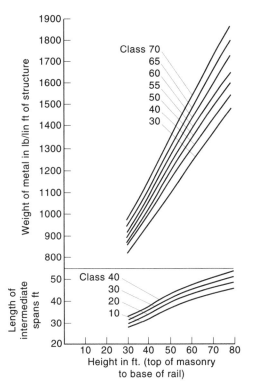

Figure 2.47. Total weight of metal **(Sheet IV)**

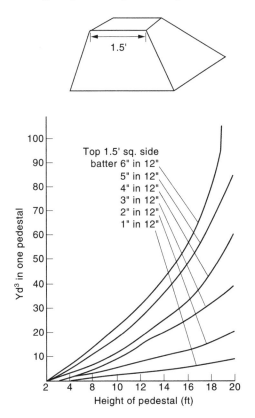

Figure 2.48. Curves showing quantities in square pedestals with sides battered by different amounts. Top is 1.5 ft square **(Sheet V)**

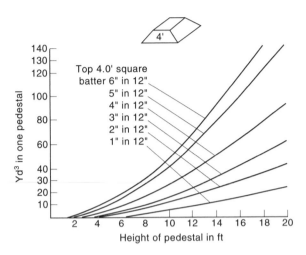

Figure 2.49. Curves showing quantities in square pedestals with sides battered by different amounts. Top is 4 ft square **(Sheet VI)**

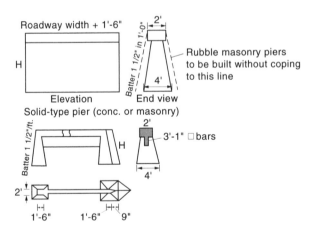

Figure 2.50. Light solid and pedestal-type piers **(Sheet VI)**

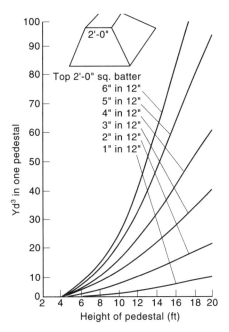

Figure 2.51. Curves showing quantities in square pedestals with sides battered by different amounts. Top is 2 ft square **(Sheet VII (A))**

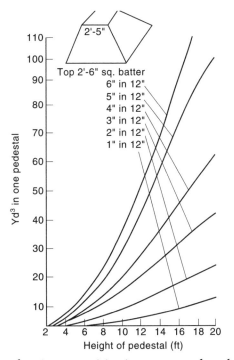

Figure 2.52. Curves showing quantities in square pedestals with sides battered by different amounts. Top is 2 ft-5 in square **(Sheet VII (B))**

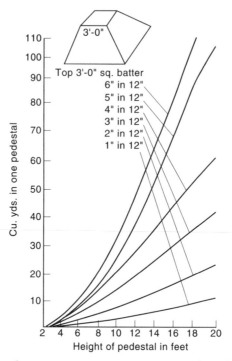

Figure 2.53. Curves showing quantities in square pedestals with sides battered by different amounts. Top is 3 ft square **(Sheet VII (C))**

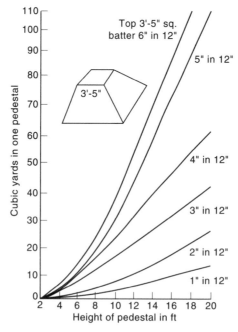

Figure 2.54. Curves showing quantities in square pedestals with sides battered by different amounts. Top is 3 ft-5 in square **(Sheet VII (D))**

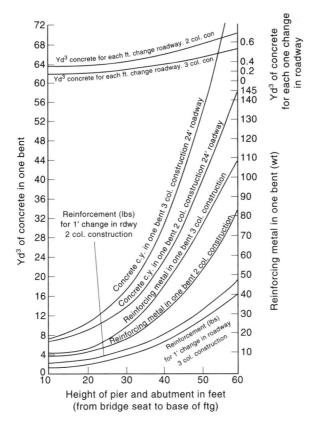

Figure 2.55. Quantity curves for concrete viaduct towers (24 ft roadway initially). Pounds of reinforcing metal for each foot change in roadway **(Sheet VIII)**

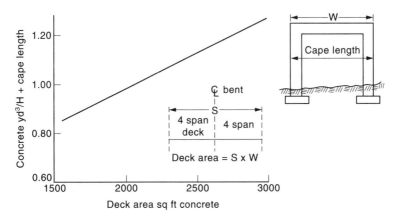

Figure 2.56. Quantity curves for bents: T-beam–box girder–steel beam bridges. Note that quantities are for one bent only cape, columns and footings. To obtain the cubic yards of concrete for bent, multiply the value from the graph by the sum of H + cape length. Reinforcement is 165 lbs/yd³ concrete **(Sheet IX)**

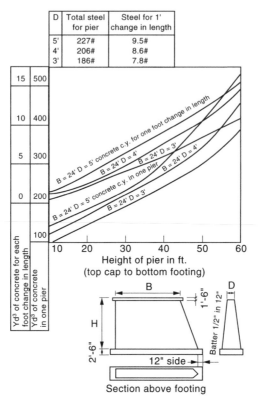

Figure 2.57. Quantity curves for mass-type concrete piers – triangular nose on one end **(Sheet X)**

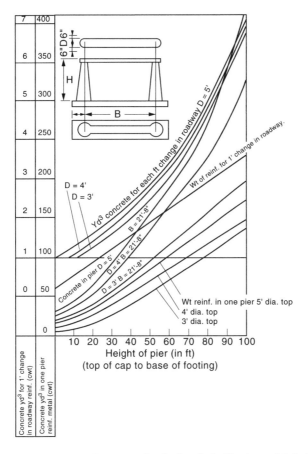

Figure 2.58. Quantity curves for standard dumb-bell piers 21 ft-8 in centre-to-centre shafts (**Sheet XI**)

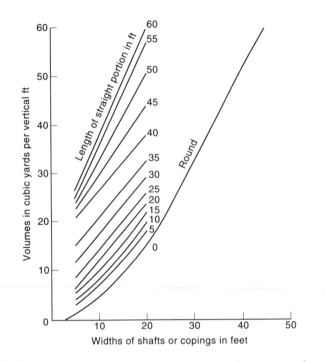

Figure 2.59. Volumes of copings and of shafts of piers with vertical sides **(Sheet XII)**

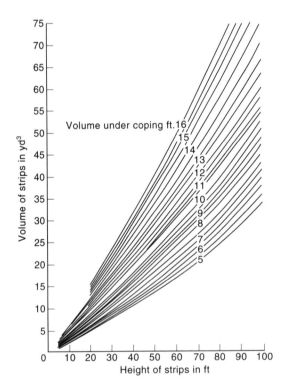

Figure 2.60. Volumes of strips 1′ wide in middle portion of round end piers. Batter $\frac{1}{2}$ *in to 1 ft* **(Sheet XIII)**

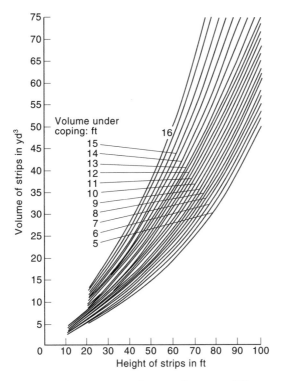

Figure 2.61. Volumes of strips one foot wide in middle portions of round-ended piers. Batter 1 in to 1 ft **(Sheet XIV)**

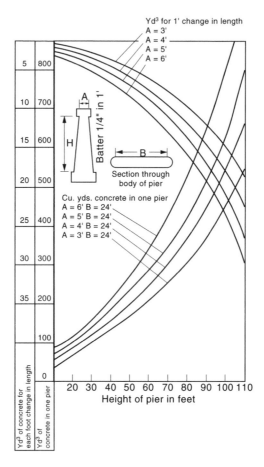

Figure 2.62. Cubical contents of mass piers with rounded ends. Batter $\frac{1}{4}$ in to 1 ft
(Sheet XV)

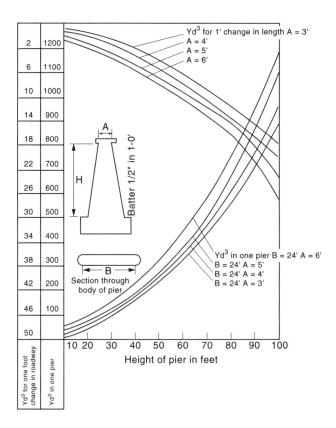

Figure 2.63. Cubical contents of mass piers with rounded ends. Batter $\frac{1}{2}$ in to 1 ft **(Sheet XVI).**

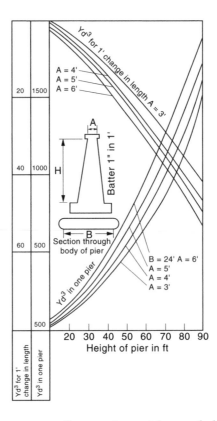

Figure 2.64. Cubical contents of mass piers with rounded ends. Batter 1 in to 1 ft
(Sheet XVII)

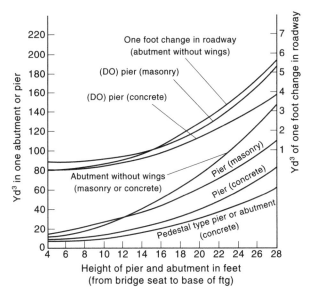

Figure 2.65. Quantity curves – mass concrete and masonry abutments and piers: 20 ft roadway **(Sheet XVIII)**

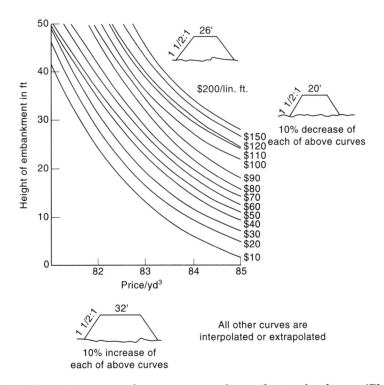

Figure 2.66. Quantity curves showing cost per linear foot embankment **(Sheet XIX)**

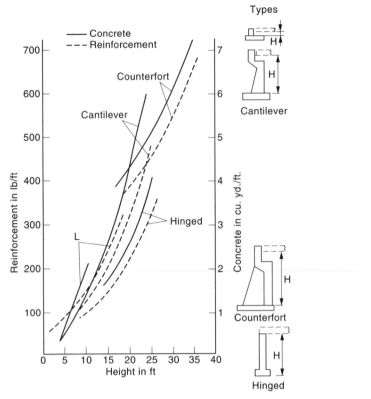

Figure 2.67. Quantity curves for abutments: T and box girders. Note: 1. To obtain the total quantity for an abutment, multiply the values from the graphs by the rail distance for the bridge in feet. 2. Footings and corner stub walls included. 3. Good quantities for spread at pile foundations **(Sheet XX)**

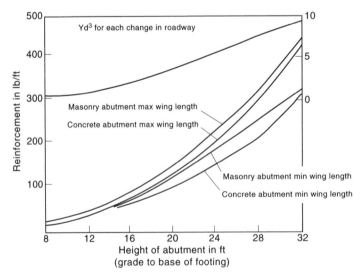

Figure 2.68. Quantity curves for standard mass concrete and masonry abutments (20 ft roadway initially) **(Sheet XXI)**

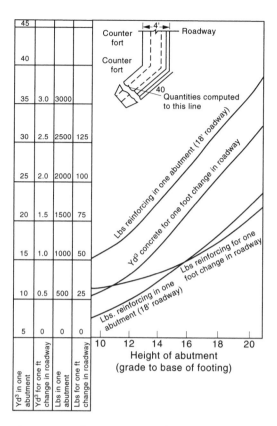

Figure 2.69. Quantity curves for concrete abutment bodies (integral with super-structure) **(Sheet XXII)**

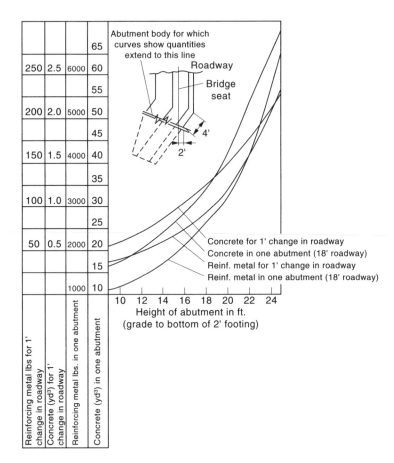

Figure 2.70. Quantity curves for concrete abutment bodies. Abutment not integral with superstructure **(Sheet XXIII)**

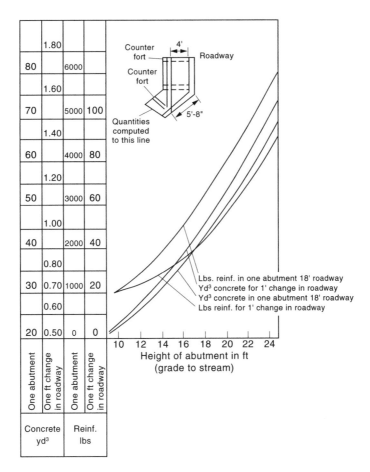

Figure 2.71. Quantity curves for counter-forted abutments with wide bridge seat
(Sheet XXIV)

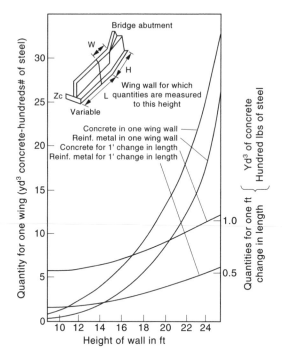

Figure 2.72. Quantity curves for concrete wing walls vertically cantilevered **(Sheet XXV)**

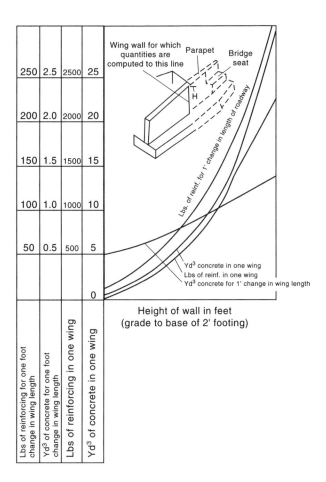

Figure 2.73. Quantity curves for horizontally cantilevered wing walls **(Sheet XXVI)**

2.8   Specifications, cost estimates and standards (Section V)

This section deals with the specifications and unit costs for various materials. To figure out the final cost, various quantities are multiplied with their respective unit costs. For more than one bridge a comparatively low cost will determine the selection.

The following Tables 2.44–2.59 provide the necessary data. Go to Section VI if satisfied or not applicable.

Table 2.44. Concrete – class 'D': RC arches – single spans

Quantity of concrete in yd^3	Price per yd^3
0.1 to 50.0	$80.00
50.1 to 70.0	79.00
70.1 to 90.0	78.00
90.1 to 110.0	77.00
110.1 to 130.0	76.00
130.1 to 150.0	75.00
150.1 to 170.0	74.00
170.1 to 190.0	73.00
190.1 to 212.5	72.00
212.6 to 237.5	71.00
237.6 to 275.0	70.00
275.1 to 325.0	69.00
Over 325.0	68.00
RC arches – multiple spans	$77.00
Bents – walls and columns	$73.00
Concrete foundation seal	$30.00
Class 'D' concrete in structures	
Pipe headwalls including excavation	$90.00
Culverts, retaining walls or steps including excavation	$75.00

Table 2.45. Concrete – class 'E' in footings: Piers (all types except arches) and bents

Quantity of concrete in yd³	Price per yd³
0.1 to 50.0	$69.00
50.1 to 110.0	68.00
110.1 to 170.0	67.00
170.1 to 230.0	66.00
230.1 to 290.0	65.00
290.1 to 350.0	64.00
350.1 to 410.0	63.00
410.1 to 470.0	62.00
470.1 to 550.0	61.00
550.1 to 650.0	60.00
650.1 to 730.0	59.00
Over 750.0	58.00
Abutment, wings, and arch piers	$60.00

Note: Prices should be multiplied by the Inflation Index *F* of a country.

Table 2.46. Concrete – class 'E' above footings: Piers – all types except arches

Quantity of concrete in yd³	Price per yd³
0.1 to 47.5	$74.00
47.6 to 82.5	73.00
82.6 to 125.0	72.00
125.1 to 175.0	71.00
175.1 to 240.0	70 00
240.1 to 320.0	69.00
320.1 to 400.0	68.00
400.1 to 480.0	67.00
480.1 to 560.0	66.00
560.1 to 675.0	65.00
675.1 to 825.0	64.00
825.1 to 975.0	63.00
975.1 to 1125.0	62.00
1125.1 to 1600.0	61.00
Over 1600.0	60.00
Abutments, wings and arch piers	$65.00

Note: Above quantities of concrete are for the entire project and not for individual piers.

Table 2.47. Concrete – class 'F': RC arches – single or multiple spans, $82.00 per yd³

Quantity of concrete in yd³				Price per yd³
Continuous RC slabs	Simple RC girder span(s)	Continuous RC girders	*Steel spans simple or continuous	
	0.1 to 90.0			$85.00
	90.1 to 110.0			84.00
	110.1 to 130.0			83.00
	130.1 to 150.0			82.00
	150.1 to 170.0			81.00
0.1 to 87.5	170.1 to 190.0			80.00
87.6 to 102.5	190.1 to 225.0	0.1 to 425.0		79.00
102.6 to 117.5	225.1 to 275.0	425.1 to 675.0	0.1 to 250.0	78.00
117.6 to 132.5	275.1 to 325.0	675.1 to 925.0	250.1 to 350.0	77.00
132.6 to 147.5	325.1 to 375.0	925.1 to 1175.0	350.1 to 450.0	76.00
147.6 to 162.5	375.1 to 550.0	1175.1 to 1425.0	450.1 to 550.0	75.00
162.6 to 177.5	550.1 to 850.0	1425.1 to 1675.0	550.1 to 650.0	74.00
177.6 to 192.5	Over 850.0	1675.1 to 1950.0	650.1 to 750.0	73.00
192.6 to 250.0		1950.1 to 2250.0	750.1 to 900.0	72.00
250.1 to 350.0		2250.1 to 2550.0	900.1 to 1100.0	71.00
350.1 to 450.0		Over 2550.0	Over 1100.0	70.00
450.1 to 700.0				69.00
Over 700.0				68.00

* Rolled beams or girders with or without RC girder end spans.

Table 2.48. Bridge railings

Type or description	Unit	Unit price × 3
Aluminium		
Single rail – type 1 or 2	lin ft	$ 3.75
Double rail – type 3 or 4	lin ft	5.50
Ornamental – type 5	lin ft	10.00
Ornamental – type 6	lin ft	9.50
Concrete		
Posts, parapet walls and concrete railing	yd³	120.00
Vehicular – solid	lin ft	9.50
Vehicular – open	lin ft	10.00
Pedestrian – solids	lin ft	11.00
Pedestrian – open	lin ft	11.50
Steel		
Single channel	lin ft	4.00
Double channel	lin ft	6.00
Beam guard rail type (exclusive of steel posts)	lin ft	3.00
Beam guard rail type (including steel posts)	lin ft	6.00
Ornamental	lin ft	11.00

Note: Prices should be multiplied by the Inflation Index F of a country.

Table 2.49. Steel and miscellaneous metal

Description	Unit	Unit price × 10
Reinforcing steel		
Less than 50 000 lbs	lb	$0.14
50 000 lbs to 99 999 lbs	lb	0.135
100 000 lbs to 499 999 lbs	lb	0.13
500 000 lbs and more	lb	0.125
Structural steel		
Rolled beams – simple spans	lb	0.15
Rolled beams – continuous spans		
Less than 500 000 lb	lb	0.155
500 000 lbs to 999 999 lbs	lb	0.15
1 000 000 lbs. and more	lb	0.145
Continuous girders – uniform depth	lb	0.17
Continuous girders – variable depth	lb	0.175
Anchor rod	each	5.00
Expansion joints	lb	0.35
Miscellaneous metal		
Bronze plates	lb	2.50
Bearings for concrete spans	lb	0.35
Cast iron	lb	0.60

Note: Prices should be multiplied by the Inflation Index F of a country.

Table 2.50. Excavation and grading

Description	Unit	Unit price
Excavation		
Wet – abutments and wings	yd^3	$10.00
Wet – piers and interior bents	yd^3	16.00
Foundation – dry	yd^3	2.50
Foundation – unclassified	yd^3	4.50
Class 'X'	yd^3	20.00
Class 'Y'	yd^3	4.00
Waterway – use common excavation price	yd^3	see below
Peat – use common excavation price	yd^3	see below
Grading		
Rock excavation	yd^3	2.00
Common excavation		
Quantity in yd^3		
Less than 500	yd^3	1.00
500 to 1099	yd^3	0.95
1100 to 1799	yd^3	0.90
1100 to 2999	yd^3	0.85
3000 to 5999	yd^3	0.80
6000 to 11 999	yd^3	0.75
12 000 to 29 999	yd^3	0.70
30 000 to 99 999	yd^3	0.65
100 000 and more	yd^3	0.60
Special borrow		
Use common excavation plus $0.10 per yd^3		
Grade 'B' special borrow		
Less than 10 000 yd^3	yd^3	2.50
10 000 to 20 000 yd^3	yd^3	2.25
Over 20 000 yd^3	yd^3	2.00

Table 2.51. Sodding and seeding

Description	Unit	Unit price × 3
Sodding		
Less than 5000 yd²	yd²	$ 0.65
5000 yd² and more	yd²	0.60
Mulched seeding		
Less than 1000 yd²	yd²	0.16
1000 yd² to 2999 yd²	yd²	0.15
3000 yd² to 7999 yd²	yd²	0.14
8000 yd² to 40 000 yd²	yd²	0.13
Over 40 000 yd²	yd²	0.12
Plain seeding	acre	100.00

Note: Prices should be multiplied by the Inflation Index F of a country.

Table 2.52. Roadway pavements and surfacing material

Description	Unit	Unit price × 2
Concrete pavements		
8 in Reinforced	yd²	$ 6.00
9 in Reinforced	yd²	7.00
Less than 300 yd²		
300 yd² and more	yd²	6.25
10 in Reinforced	yd²	6.50
6 in Plain concrete – permanent or temp. and conc. base	yd²	5.25
7 in Plain concrete	yd²	5.50
8 in Plain concrete	yd²	5.75
9 in Plain concrete	yd²	6.00
Aggregate material		
Subbase – type 1 or 2	yd³	3.00
Covering aggregate	ton	6.00
Aggregate for compacted aggregate base or surface	ton	3.50
Aggregate for compacted aggregate shoulders	ton	3.50
Aggregate for shoulder drains	ton	7.25
Aggregate for subsurface drains	yd³	5.00
Bituminous material		
Surface – type 'B'	ton	12.00
Bituminous material for prime	ton	60.00
Binder	ton	12.00
Bituminous material applied	ton	55.00
Bitumen coated blended aggregate surface or binder	ton	10.00
Bituminous shoulders	ton	12.00
Hot asphaltic concrete bare or binder	ton	12.00
Bituminous fracture for approaches	ton	10.00
Calcium chloride	ton	90.00

Note: Prices should be multiplied by the Inflation Index F of a country.

Table 2.53. Joints, signs and monuments

Description	Unit	Unit price × 3
Joints		
Pavement contraction	lin ft	$ 1.25
$\frac{1}{2}$ in expansion	lin ft	0.70
1 in expansion	lin ft	1.10
$1\frac{1}{2}$ in expansion	lin ft	1.50
2 in expansion	lin ft	2.00
3 in expansion	lin ft	3.50
Signs		
Warning	each	70.00
3 ft × 4 ft–3 in signs	each	65.00
Standard barricade – type 'A'	each	100.00
Standard barricade – type 'B'	each	90.00
Bridge barrier – temporary	each	65.00
Bridge barrier – temporary	each	75.00
Monuments		
Type 'A'	each	30.00
Type 'B'	each	40.00
Type 'C'	each	30.00
Type 'D'	each	20.00
R/W markers	each	9.00
Bench mark posts	each	40.00

Note: Prices should be multiplied by the Inflation Index *F* of a country.

Table 2.54. Guard rail, fence and slope protection

Description	Unit	Unit price × 10
Guard rail		
Steel beam guard rail – furnish and install	lin ft	$3.00
Steel beam guard rail – install only	lin ft	1.75
Steel beam guard rail – re-set	lin ft	2.50
Guide posts	Each	7.00
R/W Fence		
Farm field type	lin ft	0.85
Chain link type	lin ft	1.60
Slope Protection		
4 in Concrete	yd^2	5.50
5 in Concrete or 12 in hand placed riprap	yd^2	6.00
Revetment or dumped riprap	ton	4.00

Note: Prices should be multiplied by the Inflation Index *F* of a country.

Table 2.55. Sidewalks, kerbs, gutters, and paved side ditches

Description	Unit	Unit price × 3
Sidewalks		
4 in Concrete	yd^2	$4.25
Kerbs		
Concrete kerb and kerb – Type 'B'	lin ft	2.00
Integral conc. kerb and int. conc. kerb type 'B'	lin ft	2.00
Special integral concrete kerb	lin ft	2.50
Bituminous kerb	lin ft	1.75
Concrete centre kerb – all types	lin ft	1.25 × width in feet
Concrete centre kerb – all types	yd^2	11.00
Gutters		
Standard lip gutter	lin ft	2.75
Modified lip gutter	lin ft	2.50
Paved gutter	lin ft	3.00
Paved side ditches		
Type 'A'	lin ft	3.00
Type 'B'	lin ft	3.75
Type 'C'	lin ft	4.50
Type 'D'	lin ft	5.00
Type 'E'	lin ft	5.50
Type 'E'	lin ft	6.25
Type 'G'	lin ft	6.75
Type 'H'	lin ft	7.25

Note: Prices should be multiplied by the Inflation Index *F* of a country.

Table 2.56. Pipe

Diameter inches	Price per linear foot × 8				Diameter inches
	Class 1 BCCM	Class 3	Class 5 CM, C, VC, sewer pipe	Class 7 and drain tile	
4				$1.00	4
6	$ 2.25		$ 2.00	1.25	6
8	2.75		2.50	1.50	8
10	3.25		3.00	2.00	10
12	4.00	$ 4.25	3.75	2.50	12
15	5.00	5.25	4.75	3.00	15
18	6.00	6.50	5.75	3.50	18
24	8.00	8.50	7.50		24
30	11.00	12.00	10.00		30
36	14.00	15.00	13.00		36
42	18.00	19.00	17.00		42
48	22.50	24.00	21.00		48
54	27.50	29.00	26.00		54
60	32.50	34.00	31.00		60
66	38.00	40.00	36.00		66
72	43.50	46.00	41.00		72
78	49.00	52.00	46.00		78
84	55.00	58.00	52.00		84

Pipe arches: Take average of the two dimensions as a diameter and enter the approximate column above using nearest listed diameter.

Perforated pipe: Use above prices with no additional cost.

Cast-iron pipe: Use $1.00 per linear foot per inch of diameter.

Note: Prices should be multiplied by the Inflation Index F of a country.

Table 2.57. Sectional plate pipe

Diameter (inches)	Number of plates	Cost per linear foot BCCM × 5
60	4	$ 52.50
66	4	55.00
72	4	57.50
78	4	60.00
84	4	62.50
90	6	78.00
96	6	81.00
102	6	83.50
108	6	86.00
114	6	88.50
120	6	91.00
126	6	93.50
132	8	109.50
138	8	112.00
144	8	114.50
150	8	117.00
156	8	119.50
162	8	122.00
168	8	124.50
174	10	140.50
180	10	143.00

For sectional plate pipe arches: Take average of two dimensions as diameter and use above table using nearest listed diameter.

Note: Prices should be multiplied by the Inflation Index *F* of a country.

Table 2.58. Drainage structures

Inlets	
Type G, J, K, and M	$225.00 each
Type N	500.00 each
All other types	200.00 each
Catch basins	
Type C, D, E, G. and H	$250.00 each
Type K	400.00 each
Type A and B	450.00 each
Type J	500.00 each
Pipe catch basins	
12 in diameter	$ 80.00 each
15 in diameter	90.00 each
18 in diameter	100.00 each
24 in diameter	120.00 each
Manholes	
Type A	$450.00 each
Type B	350.00 each
Adjusting to grade	50.00 each

Automatic gate valves

Size	Cost in place – each	Size	Cost in place – each
12 in	$ 50.00	42 in	$ 300.00
15 in	60.00	48 in	400.00
18 in	75.00	54 in	500.00
24 in	100.00	60 in	650.00
30 in	150.00	66 in	800.00
36 in	250.00	72 in	1000.00

Spring boxes	
Standard spring box	$225.00 each

Note: Prices should be multiplied by the Inflation Index *F* of a country.

Table 2.59. Removals *(×10)*

Breaking pavement	$0.50 per yd^2
Pavement removal	
Less than 1000 yd^2	1.00 per yd^2
1000 yd^2 to 1999 yd^2	0.90 per yd^2
2000 yd^2 to 7000 yd^2	0.80 per yd^2
Over 7000 yd^2	0.70 per yd^2
Surface removal	1.00 per yd^2
Sidewalk removal	0.73 per yd^2
Kerb removal	0.75 per lin ft
Gutter removal	0.75 per lin ft
Kerb and gutter removal	1.00 per lin ft
Side pitch removal	1.00 per lin ft
Slope wall removal	4.00 per yd^2

Existing structures
These must be estimated individually taking into account the type size, location, equipment required, etc.

Note: Prices should be multiplied by the Inflation Index *F* of a country.

The following estimated unit prices for various items of construction used in bridge construction are current for this section of the United States. These prices were provided by a consulting engineer company based in Pittsburgh, Pennsylvania (see Table 2.60). Unit prices are for the completed items in place, ready for traffic including all materials, equipment, tools, labour, overhead, and profit.

Table 2.60. Consulting engineer unit price estimates

Superstructure (steel structures) × 30	
Structural steel (riveted construction)	
Rolled beams	$0.18 per lb
Built-up girders*	0.24 per lb
Trusses*	0.30 per lb
Cable	0.20 per lb
*For welded construction, add $0.015 per pound	
Concrete deck paving	$75.00 per yd^3
Reinforcement	0.13 per lb
Railing	8.00 to
	10.00 per lin ft
Substructure	
Concrete	
Tremie	$25.00 per yd^3
Footings	45.00 per yd^3
Shafts	65.00 per yd^3
Reinforcements	0.13 per lb
Excavation	
Common	$5.00 per yd^3
Rock	10.00 per yd^3
Wet*	20.00 per yd^3
*Includes cofferdams or dewatering devices	
Piles	
40 ton Cast-in-place concrete	$6.50 per lin ft
60 ton Steel BP	7.50 per lin ft
30 ton Timber	5.00 per lin ft

Note: Prices should be multiplied by the Inflation Index *F* of a country.

These unit prices are for general conditions – actual conditions at a specific bridge site may cause these prices to be altered up or down, as the case may be.

2.8.1   General estimate (the codes of individual countries should be superseded by these items)

(A)   Reinforced concrete versus prestressed concrete
Concrete

Concrete average quantity ratio $\qquad \dfrac{PC}{RC} = 0.5$

Average unit price $\qquad \dfrac{PC}{RC} = 1.2$

Form work
For one cubic yard of PC, two cubic yards of RC are required

Average quantity ratio $\qquad \dfrac{PC}{RC} = 1.12$

Average unit price ratio $\qquad \dfrac{PC}{RC} = 1.4$

False work

$$\dfrac{PC}{RC} = 0.8$$

Steel

Average quantity ratio $\qquad \dfrac{PC}{RC} = 0.20$

Average unit price ratio $\qquad \dfrac{PC}{RC} = 4.2$

Intermediate span
  Endspan
  (a)   for slab spans

$$\text{main span up to 44 ft} \qquad \dfrac{\text{main span}}{1.26}$$

$$\text{main span 44 ft–52 ft} \qquad \dfrac{\text{main span}}{1.31}$$

  (b)   girder spans 44 ft and $\dfrac{\text{main span}}{1.37}$ or 1.4

(B)   Beam, slab, girder and arch
Slab and beams
Form work for slab is measured over the whole area. A portion occupied by beams and girders should not be deducted since the excess area (about 15%)

covers the cost for bevels and fittings around columns. The timber/ft^2 for slab form includes joists of 1/6 ft^3.

Slab form
First erection
    For 100 ft^2 of slab for
        4.5 hrs – carpenter at \$26/hr
        4.5 hrs – 1/6 ft^3 labourer at \$15/hr
        timber 1/6 ft^3
        average timber cost \$100/1000 ft^2
Second erection
        carpenter – 2 hrs
        labourer – 5.5 hrs
        timber – 10%.
Note: These prices are subject to change and to a country's Inflation Index F.

Beams and girders

The measurement is on the basis of the surface area in contact below the slab. This means the area of two sides plus the bottom, and the length is taken from centre to centre of the columns or girders. The timber/ft^2 for beam and girder includes posts and bracing at 1/3 ft^3.

Timber/ft^2 for re-shoring of area of beam (a complete set of shores and braces) 0.15 ft^3.

Timber/ft^2 for re-used form 10%.

Beam and girder
First erection
    For 100 ft^2
        10.5 hrs – carpenter at \$25/hr
        10 – labourer at \$15/hr
        timber – 33.3 ft^3
Subsequent erection
        carpenter – 6.5 hrs
        labourer – 10 hrs
        10% of 33.5 yd^3 – timber
Note: These prices are subject to change and to a country's Inflation Index F.

Culvert

Same as for girders.

Arch

One-half ft^3/ft^2 of area supported by centring 20% in case with piles, silts, wedges, lagging and posts.

For $100\,\text{ft}^3$ of timber – 27 hrs for carpenter and labourer at \$25/hr and \$15/hr, respectively.

(C) Cofferdams

The cost of steel sheet piling in place includes the cost of pile driving equipment and labour. In case the piling is to be salvaged, the additional cost of extracting should be considered. The common practice is driving two piles simultaneously. Tables 2.61–2.63 and Fig. 2.74 provide data based on the code followed by the US Steel Corporation.

Table 2.61. Data for cofferdams based on code of US Steel Corporation

Section number	Width (in)	Web thickness (in)	Weight lbs	
			Per lineal ft of pile	Per sq ft of wall
MP – 101	15	3/8	35	28.0
102	15	1/2	40	32.0
117	15	3/8	38.8	31.0
110	116	31/64	42.7	32.0
112	116	3/8	30.7	23.0
113	116	1/2	37.3	28.0
116	116	3/8	36.0	27.0
115	$19\frac{5}{8}$	3/8	36.0	22.0
27	18	3/8	40.5	27.0
32	21	3/8	56.0	32.0
38	18	3/8	57.0	38.0

Table 2.62. Labour required for installing and removing timber bracing in cofferdams

Size of timber	Crane or derrick	Installing		Removing	
		Fbm/HR	HR/1000 Fbm	Fbm/HR	HR/1000 Fbm
4×4	none	20–50	20–50	250–400	2.5–4
6×6	none	16–40	25–65	200–350	3–5
8×8	none	12–30	35–85	150–300	3.5–6.5
8×8	yes	20–40	25–50	200–350	3–5
10×10	yes	18–35	30–55	175–300	3.5–6
12×12	yes	15–30	35–70	150–250	4–7

Table 2.63. Standard abutment bents (see Fig. B2.74)

X_1	X_2	X_3	Y	Z	B	A	C
2–3	1–3	1–0	2–6	2–3	#6	#4	#4
2–6	1–6	1–0	2–6	2–6	#6	#4	#4
2–$8\frac{1}{2}$	1–6	1–$2\frac{1}{2}$	2–9	2–$8\frac{1}{2}$	#6	#4	#4
2–10	1–6	1–4	3	2–6	#6	#4	#4
3–0	1–6	1–6	3	3	#7	#4	#4
3–0	1–6	1–6	3	3	#8	#5	#4
3–$2\frac{1}{2}$	1–$8\frac{1}{2}$	1–6	3	3	#8	#5	#4

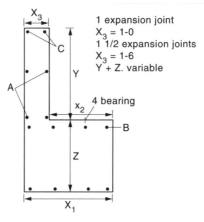

1 expansion joint
$X_3 = 1$-0
1 1/2 expansion joints
$X_3 = 1$-6
$Y + Z$. variable

4 bearing

Figure 2.74. Diagram of cofferdam standard abutment bents

(D) Load on lanes
The lane loading for standard trucks shall be assumed to occupy a width of 10 ft. These loads shall be placed in design traffic lanes having a width of $W(W_k/N)$ where

W_k = Roadway width between kerbs exclusive of median strips
(see Table 2.64)

N = Number of design lanes

W = Width of the design traffic lane

Note: For other codes of practice, individual recommendations should be followed.

Table 2.64. Data used for lane loading

W_k	(in ft)	N
	20–30 inc.	2
over	30–40 inc.	3
over	42–54 inc.	4
over	54–66 inc.	5
over	66–78 inc.	6
over	78–90 inc.	7
over	90–102 inc.	8
over	102–114 inc.	9
over	114–126 inc.	10

Reference: AASHO 1987 and 1995.

2.9   Results from example problems (Section VI)
The design problem and the entire process from Sections 2.4–2.8 are recorded in this section as a final result.

2.9.1   Problem I
1. *Survey information* (see Fig. 2.75).
2. *Data*:
    (*a*)   loading H-20-S-16; 44
    (*b*)   wind load 35 lbs/ft^2; temperature 0–70°F
    (*c*)   24 ft roadway (no skew) crossing river outside populated area
    (*d*)   waterway area at the time of flood 35 000 ft^2
    (*e*)   stream velocity 2.5 ft/s, velocity under bridge $\not> 3$ ft/s
    (*f*)   crossing 2000 ft, end spans 469 ft each, height above HFL 30 ft, not higher
    (*g*)   flux 2 ft with subsoil condition favourable for piling etc.
    (*h*)   non-seismic area.
3. *Further requirements*:
    (*a*)   no navigational requirements (not so high bridge)
    (*b*)   heavy floating material is always carried by the river
    (*c*)   normal weather conditions
    (*d*)   erection, transportation, labour, and material conditions normal
    (*e*)   aesthetic consideration essential.

Classification flow chart for Problem I
Q:1   Chart I   (*i*)   Condition (24) 0.20–0.35T/ft^2
                (*ii*)   Condition (10) 2–3T/ft^2
                Go to Q:2
Q:2   Chart II   (*i*)   Condition (1), (7A) and (8)
                Go to Q:3

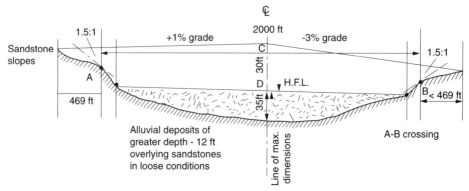

Figure 2.75. Survey data for Problem I

Q:3 No solid and open piers
                Go to Q:4
Q:4 Piers not permissible
                Go to Q:5
Q:5 No abutments
                Go to Q:6
Q:6 C–C$_2$–C$_2'$
                Shallow foundation
                Waterway
                Condition (1) Chart VA
                Type (1), (2), (3), (4), (5)
                Go to Chart VB
                Chart VB   Condition (2)
                Spread footing
                Go to Q:7
Q:7 No cofferdam
                Go to Q:8
Q:8 Chart VII (*i*) Condition I$_1$B$_1$
                Suspension
                Cantilever
                Frame, culvert
                Go to Q:9
Q:9 Condition I$_6$ → (I$_1$B$_1$)
                Single span
                Go to Q:10
Q:10 Span No: (8) Type (*a*) Single choice
                Suspension bridge
                Go to Block C Suspension or cable-stayed adopted
Q:11 D-a8   Condition (3)
                Suspension bridge cable type (see Table 2.65)
                over single span of 2000 ft.

Table 2.65. Summary showing that a suspension bridge is recommended for an accurate design solution to Problem I

Span No.	Quantities/LF	Quantities (total)	Reference and remarks
I(A)	Wt of steel/LF = 18 000#	2938 × 18 000 = 52 884 000#	Section 2.6.5
I(B)	Wt of cable/LF = 8500# (including railing and sidewalks)	2938 × 8500 = 24 973 000#	**(Section III (E))**
(2)	Substructure quantities/LF in yd³ (including anchorages, footing and end span supports)	2000 × 50 = 10 000 yd³	Fig. 2.31 **(Sheet I)**
2(A)	6 in concrete pavements	3917 yd²	Section 2.7 **(Section IV)**

Span No.	Quantities	Rate	Total cost	
I(A)	32 884 000#	$30/#	$ 158 652 000	Section 2.8
I(B)	24 973 000#	$20/#	$ 49 946 000	**(Section V)**
2	100 000 yd³	$45/yd³	$ 4 500 000	Figs 2.42,
2(A)	3917 yd²	$5.25/yd²	$ 20 565	2.43
			$2 538 036 500	**(Sheets 12, 13)**

Note: Prices should be multiplied by the Inflation Index *F* of a country.
Suspension bridge or cable stayed is recommended for accurate design.
Suspension bridge is most favourable, but cable stayed is highly recommended.

2.9.2 Problem II

1. *Survey information* (see Fig. 2.76).
2. *Data*:
   - (*a*) loading H20-S16-44
   - (*b*) wind load 50#/ft²
   - (*c*) 24 ft roadway (10° skew), crossing 450 ft
   - (*d*) waterway area at the time of flood 7000 ft²
   - (*e*) stream velocity at the time of flood, i.e. at HFL, is 3.5 ft/s and velocity at the crossing never exceeds 4 ft/s
   - (*f*) condition unfavourable for excessive formwork
   - (*g*) subsoil conditions favourable for pile or well foundations
   - (*h*) non-seismic area
   - (*k*) temperature 0–70°F
3. *Further requirements*:
   - (*a*) river carries heavy floating material and occasional silt deposition at the crossing
   - (*b*) in winter heavy ice jamming
   - (*c*) erection, transportation and material facilities normal
   - (*d*) aesthetic consideration essential.

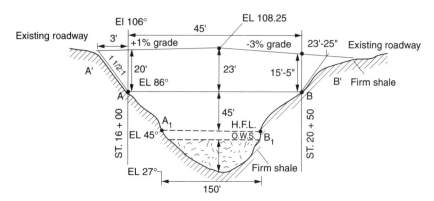

Figure 2.76. Survey data for Problem II

Classification flow chart for Problem II

Start

Q:1 Chart I   Condition (14)(b) 6-7T/ft^2
                Go to Q:2

Q:2 Chart II   Conditions (2), (5), (5A)
                Go to Q:3

Q:3 No solid pier
     No open pier
     Go to Q:5

Q:5 No abutments (other means of support permissible)
     Go to Q:6

Q:6 C–C′–C$_2$–C$_2'$–C$_4'$–C$_5'$
                Shallow foundation outside waterway (on rocky slopes)
                Spread footing or footing with piles
                Go to Q:7

Q:7 No cofferdam
                Go to Q:8

Q:8 I$_1$, C$_1$, B$_1$, Chart VII
                Suspension I$_1$C$_2$B$_1'$
                Cantilever truss
                Frame bent arch
                Culvert girder
                Go to Q:9

Q:9 Chart VIII
                Single span
                I$_6$
                Go to Q:10

Q:10 Section (A) Condition (7)
                800 ft–850 ft
                Arch prestressed cantilever
                Go to Block C

Table 2.66. Summary showing that a steel arch bridge is recommended for an accurate design solution to Problem II

Span No.	Discount for unit quantity	Total quantity	Rate @	Total	Reference and remarks
(1)	Depth of arch $= 0.05 \times 450 = 22.5\,\text{ft}^2$ $g = (90.5)(24) + (23.51)(2)$ $= 2219\#/\text{ft of span}$				Section 2.6.4 **(Section III (D))** Fig. 2.25 **(Sheet I)**
(2)	$g = (2219)(450) = 998\,550\#$	$998\,550\#$			
	$g = \dfrac{(53.25)(998\,550)}{(30' + 23.25')450}$				
	$= 118\,161.75\#$	$\dfrac{118\,116.75\#}{1\,116\,711.75\#}$			
	g total introducing three-hinge, 15% reduction in quantities is considered	$949\,204.99\#$	$\$30/\text{ft}^2$	$\$2\,347\,615$	Fig. 2.26 **(Sheet II)**
(3)	Thrust blocks at A and B 4–3.5 sq block 4 ft high 12:1 6000 #/ft² pressure	$4 \times 5 = 20\,\text{yd}^3$	$\$65/\text{yd}^3$	$\$1300$	Section 2.7 **(Section IV)** Figs 2.51–2.54 **(Sheet VII)**
	Spread footing (5 ft 11 in) (3 ft) Supports @ A′ and B′ @ A → 3 ft high	$4 \times 3.26 = 13.04\,\text{yd}^3$	$\$45/\text{yd}^3$	$\$586.8$	
	Steel walls and shafts at B′–6.5 ft high @ 17 yd³/LF for 24 ft roadway	$17 \times 3 = 51\,\text{yd}^3$ $17 \times 6.5 = 110\,\text{yd}^3$	$\$65/\text{yd}^3$ $\$65/\text{yd}^3$	$\$3315$ $\$7150$	Fig. 2.59 **(Sheet XII)**
(4)	Railing, sidewalks		$\$3/\text{LF}$ $\$7/\text{LF}$	$\$1509.75$ $\$3522.75$	Fig. 2.60 **(Sheet XIII)** Section 2.8
	Total cost estimate			$\$302\,145.90$	**(Section V)**

Note: Prices are subject to change pro rata based on a country's Inflation Index F.

Block C
> Steel arch
> Go to Q:11

Q:11 Above 390 ft Steel arch
> Steel arch bridge is recommended for design (see Table 2.66).

2.9.3 Problem III

1. *Survey information* (see Fig. 2.77).
2. *Data*:
   (a) loading H-10
   (b) wind load 50#/ft²

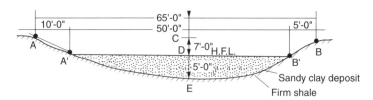

Figure 2.77. Survey data for Problem III

     (c)   24 ft roadway crossing the points in Fig. 2.77 **(Section I)** without any skew

     (d)   waterway area at the time of flood $250\,\text{ft}^2$; discharge 375 cusecs

     (e)   soil conditions are sandy/clay at smaller depths of 3 ft overlying firm shale

     (f)   flux is 1 ft-0 in with velocity $\not> 2\,\text{ft/s}$

     (g)   non-seismic area

     (h)   temperature 0–70°F.

3.   *Further requirements:*

     (a)   no navigational requirements

     (b)   river carries no big and heavy material

     (c)   normal weather conditions

     (d)   erection, transportation, labour, and material conditions normal

     (e)   aesthetic consideration essential.

Classification flow chart for Problem III

Q:1   Chart I   Condition (18) – Safe load $10\,\text{T/ft}^2$

                Go to Q:2

Q:2   Condition (1), (7), (10) Chart II

                Go to Q:3

Q:3   No solid pier

       No open pier

                Go to Q:5

Q:5   No abutments

                Go to Q:6

Q:6 $C–C_3–C'_5$

                Shallow foundation (Waterway)

                Chart VA Condition (1)

                Go to Chart VB

                Spread footing

                Go to Q:7

Q:7   Cofferdam is needed

     Chart VI Condition (4)

                Cellular type

                Go to Q:8

Q:8 I_1, C_1, B_1, Chart VII
              Suspension
              Cantilever
              Frame
              Culvert
              Go to Q:9

Table 2.67. Summary showing that a sectional pipe arch bridge is recommended for an accurate design solution to Problem III

Description	Quantities/LF	Quantities total	Rate @	Total	Reference
Culvert					
10 ft × 8 ft for	Concrete 2.62 yd^3 62.88 yd^3		$75	$4716	Section 2.6 **(Section III)**
24 ft roadway	Steel 489#	11 736#	$0.13	$1525.68	Fig. 2.38 **(Sheet VIII)**
2 portals	Concrete	43.2 yd^3	$75	$3240	Table 2.7
	Steel	5720#	$0.13	$743.60	**(Table VI)**
4 ft Earth fill		243 yd^3	$5	$1170	Section 2.8 **(Section V)**
21.87 ft × 5 ft × 5 ft Triangular earth fill on each side (remaining embankment shape)		97.3 yd^3	$5	$486.50	Figs 2.40 and Figs 2.48–2.50 **(Sheets X, XVIII, XX)**
6 in Plain concrete road pavement		86.6 yd^2	$5.25	$454.65	

Total cost $12 336.48 × *F*

Description	Quantities/LF	Quantities total	Rate @	Total	Reference
Pipe arch					
(12 ft-8 in) × (8 ft-1 in)	2 quantities	17 520#	$03.0	$52 560	
Gauge 8	365# × 2 = 730# or				
24 ft Roadway		114.5/LF × 2		$549 600	Section 2.6 **(Section III)**
4 ft Earth fill yd^3		234 yd^3	$50.0	$1700.0	Figs 2.42–2.44 **(Sheets XII, XIII, XIV)**
Triangular earth fill 19.21 ft × 5 ft on each side of embankment		95.4 yd^3	$35	$3339	Section 2.8 **(Section V)**
6 in Concrete pavement		86.6 yd^2	$15.25	$1363.25	Figs 2.40, 2.45, 2.50 **(Sheets X, XV, XX)**

Total cost $7597.65 × *F*

Note: Prices are subject to change pro rata based on a country's Inflation Index *F*.

Q:9   Chart VIII
                          I$_6$ Block
                          Single span
                          I$_8$ Block
                          More than one span
                          Single span
                          Go to Q:10
Q:10 Section (A)
                          Conditions (4), (5), (6)
                          Culvert
                          Go to Block C
                          Culvert
                          Go to Q:11
Q:11 D-a$_2$ Conditions (2) (3)(d)
         (1)   Box type (double-box beam slab)
         (2)   Sectional plate arch type

Recommended for quantity curves (see Table 2.67).

2.9.4   Problem IV

1. *Survey information* (see Fig. 2.78):
       (*a*)   Average height of piers = 20 ft (up to top of footing)
       (*b*)   From geometry at C + D erosion possibility is less.

2. *Assumptions*
       (*a*)   A–B   Crossing points
       (*b*)   C–D   Are the best survey locations (core boring and drilling results)
                         for placement of piers if any.

3. *Data*:
       (*a*)   loading H20-S-16-44
       (*b*)   wind load 35#/ft^2
       (*c*)   temperature 0–70°F
       (*d*)   24 ft roadway (6° skew)
       (*e*)   waterway area at the time of flood unknown

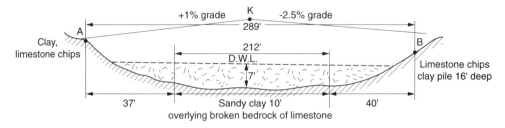

Figure 2.78. Survey data for Problem IV

(*f*) catchment area 10 240 acres or 16 miles^2
(*g*) stream velocity 3.5 ft/s, velocity under bridge $\not> 4$ ft/s
(*h*) subsoil conditions dependent on piling
(*i*) non-seismic area.
4. *Further requirements*:
(*a*) no navigational requirements
(*b*) no danger of ice jamming or heavy floating material carried by the river
(*c*) normal weather conditions
(*d*) erection, transportation, labour and material conditions normal
(*e*) aesthetic consideration essential.

Note that this problem employs aspects of Sections 2.4–2.7 in greater detail.

Classification flow chart for Problem IV
Q:1   Chart I   Conditions (16) and (19) (combinations)
                     Condition (16)   3T/ft^2
                     Condition (19)   10T/ft^2
                     Go to Q:2
Q:2   Chart II   Conditions (1), (3), (5B)
                     Go to Q:3
Q:3   Solid pier or piers permissible go to Q:4
      Open pier or piers permissible go to Q:4
Q:4   Chart III   Condition (3)
                  Solid piers adopted
                  Go to Q:5
Q:5   Abutments permissible
      Chart IV
         Conditions
            (4)   Cantilever
            (5)   Mass concrete or masonry
            (6)   Abutments integral with superstructure
            (7)   Abutments not integral with superstructure
         (10) Pile bent
      Go to Chart 4A
      Chart IVA   Condition (7)
         From site condition
            (5)   Mass concrete or pile bent type if dead load less column
                  reinforcement
               Go to Q:6
Q:6   C–C$_1$ → Shallow foundation in waterway
         Condition (1) → (1)   Spread footing
                         (2)   Raft
                         (3)   Grillage
                         (4)   Footing with short length piles

    Go to Chart VB
      Condition (4A)
        Pile footing adopted
    Go to Q:7

Q:7 No cofferdam
    Go to Q:8

Q:8 Block $I_4 B_4$ Chart VII Slab, beam slab, girder, arch, truss, culvert
                   Go to Q:9

Q:9 Block I_7 Chart VIII
               More than one span
               Go to Q:10

Q:10 More than one span: Block B, Chart X, Condition (4)
      (a) Prestressed girder 100 ft–300 ft
      (b) Truss 100 ft–300 ft
      (c) RCC girder 100 ft–300 ft
      (a_3) 100 ft–200 ft main span RCC arch
      (b_3) 100 ft–200 ft main span steel arch
      (c_2) Series of culverts
      (d_3) $\rightarrow (a)$, (b), (c) of conditions $\boxed{3}$ go to block C
    Comparison shows that following remained for comparison
    (Q:10) (a) Prestressed girder
             (b) Truss
             (a_2), (b_2) RCC arch or steel arch as a main span
             Go to Q:11

Q:11 D-$a_3 \rightarrow$ Condition (3) prestressed girder [of Q:10(a)]
    Chart XI
      D-$a_4 \rightarrow$ Condition (1) Pratt truss
      D-$a_5 \rightarrow$ Block (A)   [of Q:10(b)]
           Between 114 ft–390 ft
           Filled spandrel barrel arch or open spandrel steel arch
           [of Q:10 (a_2), (b_2)]

Summary for quantity curves
(1) Solid pier
(2) Solid concrete abutment (bent type)
(3) Concrete pile footing
(4) Prestressed concrete girder or Pratt truss or RCC or filled spandrel arch or steel arch.

General computation for Problem IV

$$M = 10\,240 \text{ acres} = 16 \text{ miles}^2$$

From Chart VI, Section 2.4:

$$Q = 5000 \text{ cfs}$$

$$a = \frac{Q}{V} = \frac{5000}{4} = 1250 \text{ ft}^2$$

Figure 2.79. Bridge schematic for Problem IV

$$h_1 = \left[\frac{(3.5)^2}{58.6} + 0.05\right]\left[\left(\frac{1875}{1250}\right)^2 - 1\right] = 0.23$$

$$h_1 = 0.23$$

$$d + h_1 = 7 + 0.23 = 7.23$$

$$\text{Linear waterway} = \frac{a}{d + h_1} = \frac{1250}{7.23} = 178$$

$$\text{No. of piers} = \frac{289}{178} = 1.6 = 2 \ (\text{ two piers})$$

Two piers are adopted at 'C' and 'D'   (results from core and drill; see Fig. 2.79)
Total no. spans $= 3$.

Superstructure selections for Problem IV

Four selections of different variations within each have been made based on Sections 2.4 and 2.5. Refer to Sections 2.6 and 2.8 for more details.

First selections

Table 2.68. Central span Pratt truss superstructure end spans steel beam

Span No.	Item	Quantities #/ft	Rate @	Total # quantities	Total cost/Q	Reference
1.	Truss steel		$3.0/#	350 000 #	$105 000	Section 2.6.3
	Concrete	0.48 yd³/ft	$75/yd³	101.76 yd³	$ 7632	**(Section III (C))**
	Reinf.	8.5 #/ft	$0.113 /#	18 020 #	$ 234.26	Fig. 2.18 **(Sheet II)**
						Tables 2.25, 2.26
						(Sheet I)
						(212 ft span)
2.	Beam					
	40 ft span	20 #/ft²	$0.118 #	19 200 #	$ 3456	40 ft span (960 ft²)
	37 ft span	18 #/ft²	$0.118 #	$158 840	$ 2877.12	37 ft span
	77 ft span	0.48 #/ft	$75/yd³	36.96 yd³	$ 2772	Section 2.6.1
	concrete					**(Section III (A))**
						Fig. 2.6
	Reinf. deck	8.5 #/ft	$13/#	645.5#	$ 85 080	**(Sheet III)**
						Prices Section 2.8
						(Section V)
					$207 051.38 $\times F$	**(Table II (A))**

Note: $F =$ Inflation Index pro rata.

Table 2.69. Central span Pratt truss end spans concrete beams superstructure

Span No.	Item	Quantities #/ft	Quantities total	Rate @	Total cost	Reference
1.	Truss steel		350 000 #	$3.0/#	$105 000	Section 2.6.3
	Conc.	@ 0.48 yd^3/ ft	101.76 yd^3	$75/yd^3	$ 7632	**(Section III (C))**
	Reinf.	8.5 #/ft	18 02 #	$13 /#	$ 2342.60	Fig. 2.2
						(Sheet II)
						Tables 2.25, 2.26
						(Sheet I)
						(212 ft span)
2.	Beam					
	40 ft span		55 yd^3	$75	$ 4125	Section 2.6.1
	Conc.					**(Section III (A))**
	Reinf.		10 000 #	$113	$ 1300	Fig. 2.7
	37 ft span					**(Sheet IV)**
	Conc.		50 yd^3	$75	$ 3750	
	Reinf.		8000 #	$113	$ 10 400	
3.	Deck conc.	@ 0.48 yd^3/ft	36.96 yd^3	$75	$ 2772	
	and reinf.	8.5 #/ft	654.5 #	$113	$ 8508	
	for 77 ft				$145 829.60 $\times F$	

Table 2.70. Central span Pratt truss end spans prestressed

Span No.	Item	Quantities #/ft	Quantities total	Rate @	Total cost	Reference
1.	Truss steel		350 000 #	$3.0/#	$105 000	Section 2.6.3
	Conc.	0.48 yd^3/ ft	101.76 yd^3	$75/yd^3	$ 7632	**(Section III (C))**
	Reinf.	8.5 #/ft	18 02 #	$113 /#	$ 2342.60	Fig. 2.2 **(Sheet II)**
						Tables 2.25, 2.26
						(Sheet I)
						(212 ft span)
2.	Beam					
	Prestressed		53 yd^3	$85	$ 4505	50% RCC
	77 ft					Guyon
	(Conc.)					(precast)
	Steel	5 #/ft^2	9240 #	$55	$ 5032	Fig. 2.41
						(Sheet III)
						Section 2.6.6
						(Section III (F))
	Deck conc.	0.48 yd^3/ft	36.96 yd^3/ft	$85	$ 3141.60	(including
					$127 653.20 $\times F$	steel in deck)

Note: F = Inflation Index, could be in millions based on a country's prices.

Second selections

Table 2.71. RCC open or filled spandrel arch mainspan open spandrel steel beam end spans

Span Item No.		Quantities #/ft	Quantities total	Rate @	Total cost	Reference
1.	RCC					Section 2.6.4
	Open spandrel					**(Section III (D))**
	arch					(rise = 3 span)
	Conc.					Figs 2.28, 2.30
	Reinf.		412.2 yd³	$75/yd³	$ 30 915	**(Sheets IV and VI)**
			74 200 #	$113/#	$ 9646.0	(for interpolation)
2.	Beam					
	40 ft span	20 #/ft²	19 200 #	$118/#	$ 3456.0	
	37 ft span	18 #/ft²	15 984 #	$18/#	$ 2877.12	
	77 ft span					
	Conc.	@ 0.48 yd³/ft	39.96 yd³	$75/yd³	$ 2772	Section 2.6.1
						(Section III (A))
						(Fig. 2.6)
						(Sheet III)
	Reinf. (deck)	8.5 #/ft	654.5 #	$113/#		Section 2.6.3
					$ 850.8	**(Section III (C))**
					$ 50 516.92 ×F	(Fig. 2.21)
						(Sheet I)

Table 2.72. Central span → RCC open spandel. End spans → RCC beam or girder

Span Item No.		Quantities #/ft	Quantities total	Rate @	Total cost	Reference
1.	RCC					Section 2.6.4
	Open					**(Section III (D))**
	spandrel					(rise = 3 span)
	arch					Figs 2.28, 2.30
	Conc.		412.2 yd³	$75/yd³	$30 915	**(Sheets IV and VI)**
	Reinf.		74 200 #	$0.13/#	$ 9646.0	(for interpolation)
2.	Beam					
	40 ft span		55 yd³	$75/yd³	$ 4125	As above
	conc.					
	reinf.		10 000#	$0.13/#	$13 000	
	37 ft span		50 yd³	$75/yd³	$ 3750	
	conc.					
	reinf.		8000#	$0.13/#	$10 400	
3.	Deck conc.	@ 0.48 yd³/ft	36.96 yd³	$75/yd³	$ 2772	
	Reinf. (deck)	8.5 #/ft	654.5 #	$113/#	$ 850.8	
					$75 458.80 ×F	

Note: F = Inlfation Index or multiply by price level of a country.

Table 2.73. Central span RCC open spandrel end spans → prestressed beams

Span No.	Item	Quantities $\#/ft$	Quantities total	Rate @	Total cost	Reference
1.	RCC					Section 2.6.4
	Open spandrel					**(Section III (D))**
	arch					(rise = 3 span)
	Conc.					Figs 2.28, 2.30
	Reinf.		412.2 yd^3	$75/yd^3	$30 915	**(Sheets IV and VI)**
			74 200 #	$0.13 /#	$ 9646.0	
2.	Beam					
	prestressed for					
	77 ft span					
	Conc.		53 yd^3	$85/yd^3	$ 4505	Simply supported
						(Guyon) (precast)
	Steel	5#/ft^2	9240#	$9.55/#	$50 820	Section 2.6.6
	Deck conc.	@ 0.48 yd^3/ft	39.96 yd^3	$75/yd^3	$ 2772	**(Section III (F))**
					$98 658.00 × F	Figs 2.39, 2.40
						(Sheets I and II)

Third selections

Table 2.74. Steel arch → central span. Steel beam → end spans

Span No.	Item	Quantities $\#/ft$	Quantities total	Rate @	Total cost	Reference
1.	Steel arch	10 694#/ft	226 712.8 #	$0.13/#	$68 013.84	Section 2.6.4
	Deck conc.	0.48 yd^3/ft	101.76 yd^3	$75/yd^3	$ 7632	**(Section III (D))**
	Reinf.	8.5 #/ft	1802 #	$0.113/#	$ 2342.6	Fig. 2.26
						(Sheet II)
						(15% reduction
						for hinges)
						(Not considered)
2.	Beam					
	40 ft span	20 #/ft^2	19 200#	$0.118/#	$ 3456.0	
	37 ft span	18#/ft^2	15 984#	$18/#	$ 2877.12	
	77 ft span					
	Conc.	@ 0.48 yd^3/ft	36.96 yd^3	$75/yd^3	$ 2772	
	Reinf.	8.5 #/ft	654.5 #	$0.13/#	$ 850.8	
					$87 944.36 × F	

Note: F = Inflation Index or multiply by price level of a country.

Table 2.75. Steel arch → centre span; concrete beam or girder → end spans

Span No.	Item	Quantities #/ft	Quantities total	Rate @	Total cost	Reference
1.	Steel arch	1068.4 #/ft	226 712.8 #	$0.130/#	$ 68 013.84	Section 2.6.4
	Deck conc.	0.48 yd³/ft	101.76 yd³	$75/yd³	$ 7632	**(Section III (D))**
	Steel	8.5 #/ft	1802 #	$0.13 /#	$ 2342.6	Fig. 2.26
						(Sheet II)
2.	Beam					
	40 ft span conc.		55 yd³	$75/yd³	$ 4125	As above
	reinf.		10 000 #	$0.13/#	$ 10 400	
	37 ft span					
	Conc.		50 yd³	$75	$ 3750	
	Reinf.		8000#	$0.13/#	$ 13 000	
	Deck conc.	0.48 yd³/ft	36.96 yd³	$75	$ 2772	
	Reinf.	8.5 #/ft	654.5 #	$0.113	$ 850.8	
					$112 886.24 ×F	

Table 2.76. Steel arch → central span; PR concrete beam → end spans

Span No.	Item	Quantities #/ft	Quantities total	Rate @	Total cost	Reference
1.	Steel arch	1068.4 #/ft	226 712.8 #	$0.130/#	$ 68 013.84	As above
	Deck conc.	0.48 yd³/ft	101.76 yd³	$75/yd³	$ 7632	
	Reinf.	8.5 #/ft	1802 #	$113 /#	$ 2342.6	
2.	Beam or girder (prestressed)					
	77 ft span					
	Conc.		53 yd³	$85/yd³	$ 4505	As above
	Steel.	5 #/ft²	9290 #	$55/#	$ 50 820	
	Deck conc.	0.48 yd³/ft	36.96 yd³	$85/yd³	$ 3141.60	
					$136 455.04 ×F	

Note: F = Inflation Index, could be in millions based on a country's prices.

Fourth selections

Table 2.77. Prestressed concrete (continuous) superstructure

No.	Detailed calculation	Reference
(1)	Concrete thickness $= 30\,\text{in} = 2.5\,\text{ft}$	Section 2.6.6 **(Section III (F))**
	Total volume of concrete $= \dfrac{289 \times 24 \times 2.5}{27 \times 2} = 642.22\,\text{yd}^3$	Figs 2.39, 2.40 **(Sheets I and II)**
	Total steel @ $8.56\,\#/\text{ft}^2 = \dfrac{289 \times 24 \times 8.56}{1 \times 2} = 59\,372.16\,\#$	

(2) Quantity ratios
    Concrete formwork
    Average quantity ratio $= \text{PC}/\text{RC} = 1.12$
    Falsework (etc. included)
  Cost ratios
    Concrete: average unit price ratio $\text{PC}/\text{RC} = 1.2$
    Steel: average unit price ratio $\text{PC}/\text{RC} = 4.2$
    Formwork: average unit price ratio $\text{PC}/\text{RC} = 1.4$
  Calculation for RCC in order to get values for prestressed bridge.

Reference: Section 2.6 **(Section III (F))** **(Sheet II (C))**

Assuming new form work
  (*a*) Slabform
      $100\,\text{ft}^2$ of slabform
        4.5 hrs – carpenter @ $25/hr
        4.5 hrs – labourer @ $15/hr

Reference: Section 2.6 **(Section III (F))** **(Sheet II (C))**

      For $6936\,\text{ft}^2$ of slabform $= \dfrac{6936 \times 11.25}{100} = \$\,780.30$

Reference: Section 2.6 **(Section III (F))** **(Sheet II (C))**

  (*b*) Beam or girder $69.36 \times 675 = \quad 468.18$
      for $100\,\text{ft}^2$ Total $\$1248.48$
        10.5 hrs – carpenter @ $25/hr
        10 hrs – labourer @ $15/hr
      For $6936\,\text{ft}^2$
            $69.36 \times 26.25 = \$1820.70$
            $69.36 \times 15 \quad = \$1040.40$
                Total $\$2861.10$

Cost of timber slab
    Average cost of timber $= \$100/1000\,\text{ft}^2$
    For $6936\,\text{ft}^2$
    Beam and beam $\$693.60$

Reference: Section 2.6 **(Section III (F))** **(Sheet II (C))**

(3) (*a*) Concrete $642.22\,\text{yd}^3$ @ $69/yd^3: $\text{PC}/\text{RC} = 1.2 = \$53\,175.81$
    (*b*) (High tension steel/steel) $59\,372.16\#$: $\text{PC}/\text{RC} = 4.2 = \$32\,404.66$
    (*c*) Formwork $(\text{PC}/\text{RC}) = 1.4 = $ $\$\,\,5753.41$
    (*d*) Assuming a user one (not included) $\$91\,333.88$
Result: RCC arch on central span steel beam on end span with deck slab.

Substructure selections for Problem IV (Table 2.78)
Calculation for pier piles, etc.
Maximum LL reaction for 289 ft span $= 118.3$ K (by interpolation using Section 2.5 for a simple span)
Dead load reaction for $(212\,\text{ft} + 40\,\text{ft span})$

Table 2.78. Substructure selections for Problem IV

Span Type No.	Quantities unit	Quantities total	Rate @	Total amount	Reference
					Section 2.7 **(Section IV)** **(Sheet XX)**
(1) Pier and footing					For 24 ft rdwy c/c rails is always
(a) Reinf.	275 #/ft	19 365 #	\$113/#	\$25 174.5	39 ft 6 in (including
(b) Conc.	3.375 yd^3/ft	266.63 yd^3	\$65/yd^3	\$17 340.95	everything from kerb to kerb) Total height
(c) Piles in pier ftgs (12 ft) long	24 piles	48 piles	\$65 /lin ft	\$ 3724	20 ft + 2 ft 6 in = 22 ft 6 in total quantity is for two piers; diagram for hinge
(2) Bent type abutments	Concrete 7 yd^3	14 yd^3	\$65 yd^3	\$ 910	
	Steel				
	#6 →43 ft	322.5#			
	#4 →43 ft 6 in	57.5#			
	#4 →43 ft	57.5#			
	Stirrup	$\overline{2 \times 437.5\#}$	\$113/#	\$113 714	
(3) Piles 15 ft (average)	6	6 + 6 = 12	\$6.5/lin ft	\$ 1170	Piles 14 in Φ steel encased conc.
(4) Wingwall average	8 yd^3	32 yd^3	\$65/yd^3	\$ 2080	6 ft 6 in c/c (std. 8 ft) max. (long arch spacing 6 ft) (3 rows)
Height 18 ft average length	Reinf. 750#	3000 yd^3	\$113/#	\$ 3900 $\overline{\$168\,013 \times F}$	Abutment single row of piles 6 ft 6 in c/c (stds.) #6 @ $7\frac{3}{4}$ in #4 @ 12 in
		Total cost for bridge \$49 751.20 $\underline{28\,246.14}$ \$77 997.34 $\times F$			Wing wall Section 2.7 Fig. 2.73 **(Section IV)** **(Sheet XXVI)**
	Main span → RCC arch **Side span → steel beam** **Recommended for accurate design**				

Note: $F =$ Inflation Index or multiplying factor, could be in any figure.

Due to superstructure $= \frac{1}{2}(412.2)(27)(0.15) + \frac{1}{2}(19.2) + \frac{1}{2}(36.9 \times 27 \times 0.15)$

$$= 919.15\,\text{K}$$

Due to pier and footing   5 ft thick pier trial   (see Section 2.8)
                           Total height $=$ 22 ft 6 in   **(Section V)**
                           (Bottom off ooting) $\rightarrow$ 2 ft 6 in $\times$ 20 ft   **(Sheet X)**
        Due to this section $= 133.31 \times 27 \times 0.15$
                              $= 539.9\,\text{K}$
            Reaction total $= 1459.09\,\text{K}$ (assuming acting @ ₵ of pier)
        Maximum moment $= 7990\,\text{K}$ (by interpolation of AASHO 1957 Table)
        Restoring moment $= 1459.05 \times 10$
                           $= 14\,590.5$

$\text{FS}\dfrac{14\,590.5}{7900} = 1.86$

Acceptable for piles.
Section is safe (may be adjusted for accurate design; see Fig. 2.80).

Bent type abutment
Standard (PDH) checked against moment
No. piles $= 6$ @ 7 ft 2 in
#6 @ $7\frac{3}{4}$ in spacing
#4

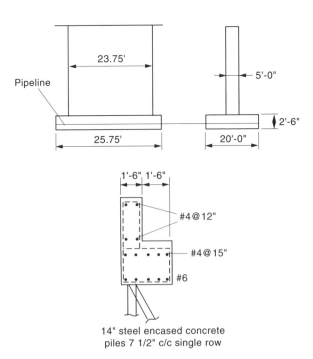

Figure 2.80. Substructure selections for Problem IV

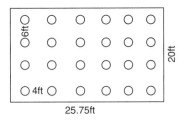

Figure 2.81. Pier pile spacing for Problem IV

Piles for pier

$$\text{No. of piles} = \frac{1459.05 + 3(0.9)(1118.3)}{80}$$

$$= 22 \text{ piles}$$

Four rows of 6 piles take 24 piles

Maximum spacing $= \dfrac{18}{3} = 6\,\text{ft, therefore acceptable.}$

For arch pile spacing $\not> 8\,\text{ft (max.)}$ for others $\not> 10\,\text{ft (max.)}$

Maximum spacing $= \dfrac{23.75}{6} \sim 4\,\text{ft (see Fig. 2.81).}$

SECTION 3
A REVIEW OF INTERNATIONAL CODES ON BRIDGES: LOADS AND LOAD DISTRIBUTION

3. A review of international codes on bridges: loads and load distribution

3.1 Introduction

In this section a brief review and data are included for well-known codes on bridges. An emphasis is placed on loadings and their distribution techniques which vary from one code to another. Examples are included from some codes of the load distribution and its ultimate effects.

The evaluation of the load-carrying capacity of existing and future bridges is an art in itself. Different countries have different bridge codes. The loadings and their distribution do vary. Prior to estimation of the loading, it is necessary to review these codes. In the following section, a brief review of these codes is given.

3.2 A review of international codes and specifications on bridges

A comparative analysis of national bridge codes and standards on external loading and environmental factors is needed. The evaluation of the load-carrying capacity is a vital process in the decision making on the choice of materials, types, analysis, design, maintenance, repair and strengthening or even replacing of bridges.

The evaluation of the safe load and of the load characteristics of bridges is still a matter of engineering judgement. Loads and stress limitations are important subjects that have been discussed for many years by various international organizations and bodies, but so far no satisfactory resolutions have been found. In this section an effort is made to introduce some rational thought to the problem. Against this background, four major conditions are adopted in the review:

(1) As an introduction, present a review of current definitions and classifications of bridge-load characteristics in various countries.
(2) Compare the experience in various countries from the engineering point of view, and review the methods used to assess the structural capacity of existing road bridges.

(3) Use this experience and the research results available in order to describe the problems and the possible ways to solving them.

(4) Define the research studies to be undertaken to determine acceptable methods contributing towards the standardization of bridge–load characteristics and limitations.

National economies require the free flow of traffic and efficient freight movements. In all countries, diversity and individuality have assumed essential characteristics for bridges. This situation has been brought about by several factors such as those enumerated by European countries:

(a) considerable differences in design codes used over the years
(b) changes in motor vehicle regulations
(c) changing design and structural analysis concepts
(d) evolution of the performance of bridge materials
(e) varying maintenance conditions.

In light of this diversity of existing road bridges, two major problems regarding their load-carrying capacity can be identified. These are:

(i) the ability of existing bridges to carry road traffic complying with the prevailing motor vehicle regulations on a long-term basis; and
(ii) the ability of existing bridges, at least of those bridges located along major roads or trunk routes, to carry an acceptable volume of abnormal heavy vehicles at any given time.

Generally bridges suffer from decreasing reliability with time. Such a decrease is expressed in an exponential function of general form $e^{-\lambda_i t}$ where

$t =$ number of years the bridge is in service;

$\lambda_i =$ function for the failure mode and maintenance which is influenced by load intensity and frequency, fatigue, defects, damage and other structural changes.

Reference is made to Fig. 3.1 which was prepared by the European Union on the basis of a number of bridges in service. Four cases were randomly chosen. The starting point is $R(t) \approx 1$ where any bridge is reliable. The load-carrying capacity changes are:

(i) decrease of 17% after 15 years of service due to defective rivets or bolts;
(ii) decrease of 27% after 23 years of service due to defective rivets or bolts;
(iii) 'erratic' decrease of 14% after 40 years of service due to heavy vehicle load (overload);
(iv) decrease of 30% due to a seven-year period without maintenance after 35 years of service.

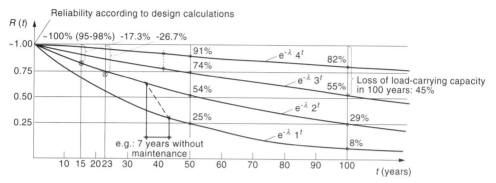

Figure 3.1. Decrease in bridge reliability over the years with regard to load-carrying capacity (reference Highways Agency, UK, and OECD)

The load-carrying capacity is affected and consequently information is needed on bridge rating along the following lines:

(a) the actual behaviour of existing bridges under traffic loads (research, investigations, tests)
(b) data concerning the magnitude, intensity, distribution and frequency of actual commercial traffic loads
(c) the various techniques for assessing the condition of a bridge
(d) the effects of commercial traffic on existing bridges
(e) applied rating systems.

3.3 Freight vehicle characteristics: OECD requirements

The term freight vehicle is normally applied to a vehicle made for transporting goods. Heavy freight vehicles are variously defined. The distribution of the various freight vehicles as percentages of total freight-vehicle traffic varies from country to country. Freight vehicles may be roughly categorized as follows: (see Table 3.1)

(a) vehicles with two axles
(b) vehicles with three or more axles
(c) articulated vehicles with single rear axle
(d) articulated vehicles with tandem or triple rear axles
(e) road trains comprising a vehicle with trailer having single or tandem axles.

Table 3.1. Maximum permissible dimensions and weights of freight vehicles (in metres and metric tonnes)

Parameters	Belgium	Canada	Denmark	Finland	France	Germany	Italy	Japan	Netherlands	Norway	Spain	Sweden	Switzerland	UK	USA*
Maximum permissible dimensions (m)															
Height	4	4.15	4	4	–	4	4	3.8	4	–	4	4	4	4.5	4.1
Width	2.5	2.6	2.5	2.5	2.5	2.5	2.5	2.5	2.5	2.5	2.5	2.5	2.3	2.5	2.6
Length:															
2-axle vehicle	11	11	12	12	11	12	12	12	11	12.4	11	10	10	11	12.2
3-axle vehicle	13	11	12	12	11	12	12	12	11	12.4	12	12	12	11	12.2
articulated vehicle	15	21	15.5	16	15	15	15.5	16.5	15.5	15.5	16.5	16	16	15	16.8
road train	18	21	18	22	18	18	18	25	18	18	18	24	18	18	19.8
Maximum permissible weights or loads (t)															
Single axle	13	10	10	10	13	10	12	10	10	10	13	10	10	10.2	9.1
Tandem axle	20	19.8	16	16	21	16	19	–	16	16	21	16	18	20.3	15.4
2-axle vehicle	19	19	18	16	19	16	18	20	20	20	20		16	16.3	12.7
3-axle vehicle	26	28.1	24	22	26	22	24	20	26	24	26		25	24.4	19.1
Articulated vehicle with 3 axles	38	30	28	26	38	30	–	–	30	28	38		25	24.4	21.8
Articulated vehicle with 4 axles	38	40	38	32	38	36	40	43	36	38	38	28	28	32.5	28.1
Articulated vehicle with 5 axles	38	50	44	36	38	38	44	43	44	39	38	28	28	32.5	34.5
Trailer with 2 axles	20	20	20	20	19	20	24	–	20	20	20	12	12	14.2	–
Trailer with 3 axles	26	30	26	22	26	26	36	–	26	26	26	12	12	24.4	–
Bus with 2 axles	19	20	18	16	19	16	18	20	20	20	20	16	16	16.3	–
Bus with 3 axles	26	25	24	22	26	22	24	20	26	24	26	25	25	16.3	–
Road train	40	63.5	44	42	38	38	44	–	50	42	–	51.4	–	32.5	39.2

Reproduced courtesy of NATO, Brussels.

* Dimensions: AASHTO policy 1974; weights AASHTO.

In the framework of this section the following freight-vehicle characteristics are of special interest:

(*a*)   dimensions (maximum and average) by vehicle category
(*b*)   number of axles and their configuration
(*c*)   gross vehicle weight (GVW)
(*d*)   axle load
(*e*)   parameters characterizing the load transfer to the surfacing.

3.3.1   Dimensions of freight vehicles

A distinction is to be made between maximum permissible dimensions imposed by national motor vehicle regulations and mean values as obtained from traffic surveys based on representative samples of freight vehicles. Data on the maximum dimensions in 14 countries are included in Table 3.1 whereas Table 3.2 presents 'average' dimensions for freight vehicles as obtained through an enquiry made by OECD. The data concern vehicle width and length as well as axle and wheel spacing.

Table 3.2. Average dimensions of freight vehicles.

Category			Width (m)	Length (m)	Axle spacing (m) between				Wheel spacing (m)	
					1st + 2nd	2nd + 3rd	3rd + 4th	4th + 5th	Single	Twin
Vehicle with	2 axles	Light	2.2	6.1	3.3	–	–	–	1.70	1.60
		Medium	2.3	6.8	3.8	–	–	–	1.80	1.74
		Heavy	2.5	7.2	4.1	–	–	–	1.80	1.76
	3 axles		2.5	7.3	3.8	1.3	–	–	2.00	1.84
	4 axles		2.5	9.1	1.4	3.9	1.3	–	1.84	1.90
	Tractor:	Articulated vehicle:								
Articulated vehicle with	2 axles	single	2.4	10.7	3.9	5.6	–	–	1.85	1.80
	3 axles	rear axle	2.5	11.1	3.4	1.3	6.8	–	2.00	1.84
	2 axles	tandem	2.5	14.0	3.3	3.9	1.7	–	1.85	1.80
	2 axles	rear axles	2.5	13.8	3.2	5.3	1.3	1.3	2.00	1.84
	3 axles		2.5	14.3	3.4	1.3	6.1	1.7	1.85	1.80
Trailer (without tractor)	2 axles		2.5	8.5	3.8	–	–	–	1.78	1.80
	3 axles		2.5	8.9	4.7	1.3	–	–	2.05	1.82
	4 axles		2.5	9.8	3.7	1.1	1.1	–	2.05	1.97

The total weight of a freight vehicle and the actual load carried by an axle depend on a number of factors, including the load transported by the vehicle (i.e. fully loaded or empty). In the case of loaded vehicles the front axle load is roughly half that of the rear axle. The weight of an unloaded vehicle is often assumed to be half of the weight of a fully loaded vehicle.

In every case, gross vehicle weights and axle loads must not exceed the national statutory limits (see Table 3.1).

3.3.2 Characterization and classification

A comparative study of the main parameters defining exceptional live loads shows that the limit values above which heavy vehicles are considered exceptional (abnormal) are relatively similar (Tables 3.3 and 3.4). This holds true both for load and dimensional characteristics. Nevertheless such overall tables cannot present all the detailed regulations in force in the different countries. Further work in this area is desirable, taking into account the requirement of international harmonization.

Only a few countries prefer to set an upper limit. The survey conducted by the OECD showed that in Belgium and France a total gross vehicle weight limit of 360 and 400 t, respectively, has been indicated as the maximum upper limit for an exceptional live load.

3.4 Bridge codes and standards

A summary of bridge codes and standards as adopted in various countries is given in Table 3.5. Reduction in loadings, impact factor and comparison of the design calculations and results are the areas that need to be examined. Sections 3.6.1 to 3.6.14 give the bridge codes and standards of various countries. Table 3.6 shows a comparative study of the applied impact factors for various countries assuming spans in metres from 0 to 100 m. Norway, Sweden and the United Kingdom have already included the impact factor in the axle loads.

The codes summarized in Table 3.5 have been compared using a simple span of different dimensions and vehicular loadings in kN/m^2 in Figs 3.2 and 3.3. They indicate a great deal of variation which needs further research and co-ordination to give a future unified code for the international scene.

3.5 Eurocode I on bridges

This is a new code that all European countries have agreed covering common loading, stresses and other design criteria. The code is briefly described in Section 3.5.1.

Table 3.3. Parameters defining exceptional live loads – values above which a heavy freight vehicle is considered 'exceptional'

	Belgium	Canada	Denmark	Finland	France	Germany	Italy	Japan	Netherlands	Norway	Spain	Sweden	Switzerland	U.K.	U.S.A. (7)
Total load (kN)	400	500 to 613(6)	440	420	380	380	440(2)	200	500	420	380	515	280	325	363
Load per axle (kN)	130	82 to 91(6)	100	100	130	100(1)	120	100	100	100	130	100	100	102	91
Load for a group of tandem axles	200	145 to 182(6)	160	160	210	160(1)	190	–	200	160	147 to 200 210(9)	180	180	203	154
Load per wheel (kN)	50	–	50	–	65	–	–	50	50	50	–	50	50	–	45
Load per group of twin wheels (kN)	65	–	65	–	65	–	–	65	50	50	160	160	50	–	–
Contact pressure of tyres (N/mm²)	–	0.9	–	0.9	–	–	0.8	–	–	0.9	0.9	–	–	–	–
Width (m)	2.5	2.59	2.5	2.5	2.5	2.5	2.5	2.5	2.5	2.5	2.5	2.5	2.5	2.5	2.44
Length (m)	18	19.8 to 21.3	15.5(3)	22	18(2)	18	18 (2)	12	18	18	18(2)	24	18	11(4) 15(5)	(8)

(1) Respectively, 130 and 210 kN for Sarre traffic.
(2) Depending on the vehicle.
(3) Semi-trailers.
(4) Non-articulated vehicles.
(5) Articulated vehicles.
(6) According to province.
(7) Interstate highway system.
(8) Varies with bridge formula.
(9) Depending on axle spacings.
Reproduced courtesy of NATO, Brussels.

Table 3.4. Classification of exceptional live loads

	Belgium	Canada	Denmark	Finland	France	Germany	Italy	Japan	Netherlands	Norway	Spain	Sweden	U.K.	U.S.A.
1. Classification of 'exceptional vehicle'	×	No	× (1)	× (2)	×	×	No	×	No	×	×	No	×	×
2. Classification criteria for 'exceptional' heavy vehicles														
total load	×				×	×		×		×	×	×	×	×
axle loads	×					×		×		×	×		×	
overall dimensions	×				×	×		×			×		×	×
types (tractors and semi-trailers, trailers, worksite vehicles, etc.)	×				×	×							×	
reference to standard heavy vehicles	×	×	×										×	
possibility of crossing bridges without prior evaluation of stability (3)	×				×	×		×			×			

(1) Modified NATO military classification.
(2) Unofficial.
(3) Up to the limit of original design limit.
Reproduced courtesy of NATO, Brussels.

Table 3.5 (pages 259–262). Overview of various national codes on bridges – summary

	Belgium	Finland	France C.M. No. 71-155-1971	Germany DIN 1072-1967	United Kingdom BS 5400: Part 2: 1978
Classification of bridges	–	–	3 types: 1st/2nd/3rd	3 types: 60/30/12	–
Uniform distributed load (kN/m²)	4	3	$q = f(L; C; n)$(2)	1st lane: 5/5/4; remaining surface 3/3/3	HA loading (4) Up to 30 m: 30 kN/m of lane Over 30 m: $151(1/L)$ 0.475 kN/m of lane but not less than 9
Loading of convoy type (kN)	320/600	scheme 1: 630 H.S.L. I: 1200(1) H.S.L. II: 800	system Bc: $2 \times (300 \times C_1)$(3) Bt: 320 Br: 100	600/300/120	HB(4) loading: from 1000 up to 1800
Number of axles	5/3	scheme 1: 3 H.S.L. I: 4 H.S.L. II: 4	Bc: 3 Br: 2	3/3/2	HB: 4
Axle distance (m)	$4 \times 4/1.50$–6.00	scheme 1: 2.5–6.0 H.S.L. I: 1.2–8.0 15.0–1.2 H.S.L. II: 1.0–6.0 15.0–1.0	Bc: –4.50–1.50– Bt: –1.35–	–1.50–1.50/ –1.50–1.50/ –3.00	HB: 1.8: 6–26: 1.8 (for basic HB axles arrangement)
Axle load (kN)	$120 - 60 - 40/200$	scheme 1: 210 scheme 2: 260 H.S.L. I: 300 H.S.L. II: 200	Bc: $60 \times C_1$ – $120 \times C_1 - 120 \times C_1$ Bt: 160	200/100/40 – 80	HB: 250 to 450
Wheel load (kN)	$60 - 30 - 20/50$	scheme 1: 105 scheme 2: 130	Bc: $30 \times C_1$ – $60 \times C_1 - 60 \times C_1$ Bt: 80 Br: 100	100/50/20 – 40	HA: 100 (nominal for design) HB: 112.5 (Maxm.)
Contract area wheel $l \times b$ (m²)	0.25 × 0.30 0.10 × 0.30	scheme 1: 0.20 × 0.60 scheme 2: 0.20 × 0.60	Bc: 0.25 × 0.25 Bc: 0.25 × 0.60 Bc: 0.30 × 0.60	0.20 × 0.60/ 0.20 × 0.40/ 0.20 × 0.30	HA: nominal 0.34 m diam. for 100 kN wheel

(Continued)

Table 3.5. (Continued)

	Belgium	Finland	France C.M. No. 71-155-1971	Germany DIN 1072-1967	United Kingdom BS 5400: Part 2: 1978
Max. wheel pressure on surface (N/mm²)	1.0	1.08	1.15	0.833	–
Impact factor	$1+\dfrac{0.4}{1+0.2L}+\dfrac{0.6}{1+4(G/S)}$	–	$1+\dfrac{0.4}{1+0.2L}+\dfrac{0.6}{1+4(P/S)}$	$1.4-0.008L \geq 1$	Included in HA and HB loading
All stresses: $\sigma E = 240$ (N/mm²) tens	150	144	(–)	160	
compr.	150	144		140	
$\sigma E = 360$ tens	240	216	–	240	
compr.	240	216		210	

	Japan	Italy Norme 384 du 14.02.1962	The Netherlands VOSB 1963	Norway and Sweden	Spain code 1972	USA Design standards of 1977
Classification of bridges	2 types: 1st/2nd	2 categories	3 types: 60/45/30	–	–	5 types H10 H15 H20 HS15 HS20 (8)
Uniform distribution load (kN/m²)	L loading (5) 4 (on footways)		$q = f(L; C)$	4	$L \leq 200$ m. / 3	
Loading of convoy type (kN)	T loading = 200/140	differential combinations of 120/180/320/ 615/745	600/450/30	type 1: 630 type 2: 260 = 1 axle	600	90.7–136.1–181.4– 245.0–326.5
Number of axles	T loading = 2	2/2/6/6/6	3/3/3	type 1: 3 type 2: 1	3	H type 2 HS type 3

(Continued)

Table 3.5. (Continued)

	Japan	Italy Norme 384 du 14.02.1962	The Netherlands VOSB 1963	Norway and Sweden	Spain code 1972	USA Design standards of 1977
Axle distance (m)	T loading $= 4$	different	$-1.00-4.00-$ $-1.00-4.00-$ $-1.00-4.00-$	type 1: $- \geq 2.50-\geq 6.00-$	$-1.50-1.50$	H type 4.25 HS type 4.25…9.11
Axle load (kN)	T loading $= 100/70$	max. 190	200/150/100	type 1: 210 type 2: 260	200	H $0.2W - 0.8W$ HS $0.11W - 0.44W$ $- 0.44W$ $W =$ weight
Wheel load (kN)	T loading $= 50/35$		50/37.5/25	type 1: 105 type 2: 130	100	50% of axle load
Contact area wheel $1 \times b\,(\mathrm{m}^2)$	T loading $= 0.2 \times 0.5$		$0.25k \times 0.25/(7)$ $0.1875k \times 0.25/$ $0.125k \times 0.25$	type 1: 0.20×0.60 type 2: 0.20×0.60	0.20×0.60	
Max wheel pressure on surface (N/mm²)	—	0.8	0.8	0.90 (Norway)	0.833	
Impact factor	(6)	$1 + \dfrac{(100 - L)^2}{100(250 - L)}$ $L > 100\,k = 1$	$1 + \dfrac{40}{100 + L}$	type 1: 1.4 type 2: 1.75 is included in the axle loads	—	$1 + \dfrac{50}{3.28L + 125}$ ≤ 1.30
All stresses: $\sigma E = 240$ tens	140	160	160	Norway: 135	—	$0.55\sigma E$ Invent.
compr.	140	160	140	135		$0.75\sigma E$ Operating
(N/mm²) $\sigma E = 360$ tens	210	240	240	215		
compr.	210	240	210	215		

(Continued)

Table 3.5. Footnotes

(1)   Heavy special load.
(2) C = class; n = number of traffic lanes.
(3) C_1 depending on class and number of traffic lanes.
(4)   HA: normal traffic; HB: abnormal vehicle.
(5)

| Class of bridge | Loading | Main loads (up to 5.5 metres in width) | | | Subloads 50% of main loads |
		Line load P (kN/m)	Uniform load, p (kN/m²) L ≤ 80	L > 80	
1	L-20	50	3.5	4.3–L/100 but not less than 3	
2	L-14	70% of those of L-20			

(6)

T loading	20/(50 + L)	
L loading	Steel bridge	20/(50 + L)
	Reinforced concrete bridge	7/(20 + L)
	Prestressed concrete bridge	10/(20 + L)

(7)   The contact area is considered to be proportional to the impact factor.
(8)

| Vehicle type | Uniform load | Concentrated load | |
		Mom.	Shear
H20, HS20	9.4 kN/m	80 kN	116 kN
H15, HS15	7.1 kN/m	60 kN	87 kN
H10	4.7 kN/m	40 kN	58 kN

Table 3.6. Applied impact factors for various countries

L (m)	Germany $1.4-0.008\,L$	France – Belgium Steel $1+\dfrac{0.80}{1+0.2L}$	France – Belgium Concrete $1+\dfrac{0.64}{1+0.2L}$	Italy $1+\dfrac{(100-L)^2}{100(250-L)}$	Netherlands Steel $1+\dfrac{40}{100+L}$	Netherlands Concrete $1+\dfrac{3}{10+L}$	U.S.A. $1+\dfrac{50}{L+125}$ (L in feet) When L is in metres $1+\dfrac{15.24}{L+38}$	Switzerland $1+0.05+\dfrac{L+100}{L+10}$	Japan Steel $1+\dfrac{20}{50+L}$
0	1.40	1.80	1.64	1.40	1.40	1.30	1.30*	1.50	1.40
10	1.32	1.27	1.21	1.34	1.36	1.15	1.30	1.28	1.33
20	1.24	1.16	1.13	1.28	1.33	1.10	1.26	1.20	1.29
30	1.16	1.11	1.09	1.22	1.31	1.08	1.22	1.16	1.25
40	1.08	1.09	1.07	1.17	1.29	1.06	1.20	1.14	1.22
50	1.00	1.07	1.06	1.13	1.27	1.05	1.17	1.13	1.20
60	1.00	1.06	1.05	1.09	1.25	1.04	1.16	1.12	1.18
70	1.00	1.05	1.04	1.05	1.24	1.04	1.14	1.11	1.17
80	1.00	1.05	1.04	1.02	1.22	1.03	1.13	1.10	1.15
90	1.00	1.04	1.03	1.01	1.21	1.03	1.12	1.10	1.14
100	1.00	1.04	1.03	1.00	1.20	1.03	1.11	1.09	1.13

* Maximum value 1.30.
Norway, Sweden and United Kingdom: impact factor included in the axle loads.
Reproduced courtesy of NATO, Brussels.

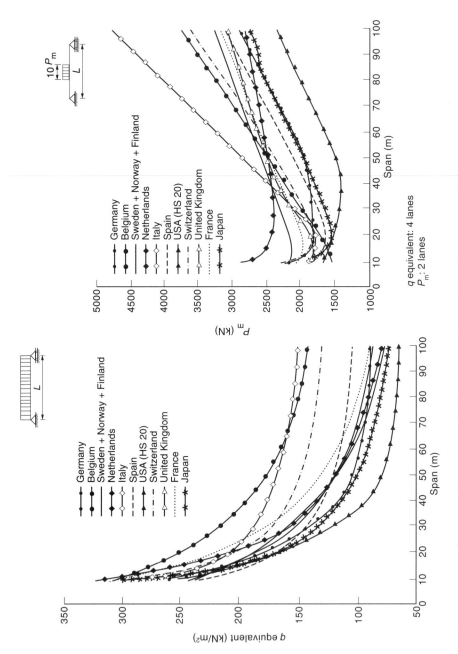

Figure 3.2. Comparison of National Design Calculations – I (reproduced courtesy of OECD and NATO, Brussels)

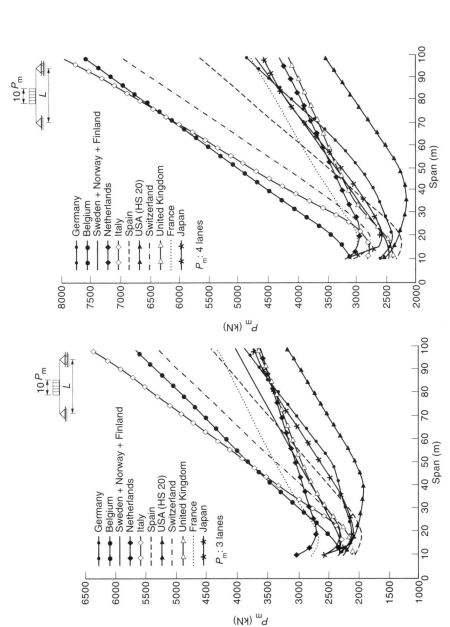

Figure 3.3. Comparison of National Design Calculations – II (reproduced courtesy of OECD and NATO, Brussels)

3.5.1 *Eurocode 1 ENV 1991–3 (1995): design technique*

The basic idea of the Eurocode 1 is to present a unified approach to bridge design in Europe and the draft design document was issued as Volume 3. Before the loading specifications are discussed, the ENV 1991–3 specifies certain notations given as follows:

A = area of rail cross-section

F_T = interaction force due to temperature

F_W^{**} = wind force compatible with railway traffic

F_b = interaction force transferred to the bearings (general)

F_{la} = interaction force due to traction (acceleration)

F_{lb} = interaction force due to braking

F_δ = interaction force due to deflection

G = self-weight (general)

L = length (general)

L_T = expansion length

L_i = influence length

L_Φ = 'determinant' length (length associated with Φ)

Q = rail traffic action (general)

Q_h = horizontal force (general)

N_1 = number of notional lanes

Q_{la} = traction (acceleration) force

Q_{lb} = braking force

Q_r = resulting action (general)

Q_{ik} $(i = 1, 2 \ldots)$ = magnitude of characteristic axle load on notional lane number i

Q_k = characteristic value of an axle load

Q_s = nosing force

Q_t = centrifugal force

Q_v = vertical axle load

Q_{vi} = wheel load

V = speed (km/h)

V_R = resistance of the rail to longitudinal displacement

W = carriageway width including hard shoulder, hard strip, and marking strips

W_1 = width of a notional lane

a = distance between rail supports, length of distributed loads (load models SW)

a_g = horizontal distance to the track centre

b = length of the longitudinal distribution of a load by sleeper and ballast

c = space between distributed loads (load models SW)

c_p = aerodynamic coefficient

d = regular spacing of axles

e = eccentricity of vertical loads, eccentricity of resulting action (on reference plane)

f = reduction factor;
force;
centrifugal force

g = acceleration due to gravity

h = height (general)

h_g = vertical distance from rail level to the underside of a structure

k_1 = train shape coefficient

k_2 = specific factor for slipstream effects on vertical surfaces parallel to the tracks

k_3 = reduction factor for slipstream effects on simple horizontal surfaces adjacent to the track

k_4 = increasing factor of slipstream effects on surfaces enclosing the tracks (horizontal actions)

k_5 = increasing factor of slipstream effects on surfaces enclosing the tracks (vertical actions)

n_0 = natural frequency of the unloaded bridge

q_{Ai} = accidental line load

q_f = footpath loading

q_i = equivalent distributed loads from slipstream effects

q_1 = characteristic value of a vertical UDL

q_{i1} = magnitude of characteristic UDL on notional lane number i

q_v = vertical distributed load

s = gauge

t = twist (changing of cant over 3 m)

u = cant

v = speed in m/s

Greek upper case letters

$\Delta\varphi_{fat}$ = additional dynamic amplification factor for fatigue near expansion joints

Θ = end rotation of structure (general)

$\Phi(\Phi_2, \Phi_3)$ = dynamic factor for railway loads

Greek lower case letters

α = load classification factor;
coefficient for speed

α_{Qi}, α_{qi} = adjustment factors of some load models on lanes
$i\ (i = 1, 2 \ldots)$

α_{qr} = adjustment factor of load models on the remaining area

β_Q = adjustment factor of load model 2

δ = deformation (general); vertical deflection

δ_h = horizontal displacement

$\varphi, \varphi', \varphi''$ = dynamic impact components for actual trains

φ_{fat} = dynamic amplification factor for fatigue

ρ = density

σ = stress

n_1 = number of notional lanes for a road bridge

q_{eq} = equivalent uniformly distributed load for axle loads on embankments

q_{fk} = characteristic vertical uniformly distributed load on footways or footbridges

q_{ik} = magnitude of the characteristic vertical distributed load (load model 1) on notional lane number i $(i = 1, 2 \ldots)$ of a road bridge

q_{rk} = magnitude of the characteristic vertical distributed load on the remaining area of the carriageway (load model 1)

w = carriageway width for a road bridge, including hard shoulders, hard strips and marker strips

w_l = width of a notional lane for a road bridge

Common notation

A_{ref} = reference area for the determination of wind effects

F_W = wind force

F_{Wk} = characteristic wind force

F_{Wn} = nominal wind force

L_s = in general, length of a span

L_{sj} = length of span number j

r = horizontal radius of a carriageway or track centre-line; distance between wheel loads

Q_{flk} = characteristic horizontal force on a footbridge

Q_{fwk} = characteristic value of the concentrated load (wheel load) on a footbridge

Q_{ik} = magnitude of characteristic axle load (load model 1) on notional lane number i $(i = 1, 2 \ldots)$ of a road bridge

Q_{lk} = magnitude of the characteristic longitudinal forces (braking and acceleration forces) on a road bridge

Q_{tk} = magnitude of the characteristic transverse or centrifugal forces on road bridges

Sn (or S) = snow load

T = thermal climatic action

T_k = a group of thermal components, which for many bridges is limited to uniform and gradient components (characteristic value). In other cases more complex groups have to be distinguished (e.g. for railway bridges with continuous welded rails and for bridges with stays)

TS = tandem system for load model 1

UDL = uniformly distributed load for load model 1

gri = group of loads, i is number ($i = 1$ to n)

γ_G = partial factor for permanent actions

γ_Q = partial factor for variable actions

ψ_0 = reduction factor for combination values of loads

ψ_1' = reduction factor for infrequent loads

ψ_1 = reduction factor for frequent loads

ψ_2 = reduction factor for quasi-permanent loads

F_W^* = wind force compatible with road traffic

Q_{ak} = characteristic value of a single axis load (load model 2) for a road bridge.

3.5.2 Loading classes

(1) The actual loads on road bridges result from various categories of vehicles and from pedestrians.
(2) Vehicle traffic may differ between bridges depending on its composition (e.g. percentages of lorries), its density (e.g. average number of vehicles per year), its conditions (e.g. jam frequency), the extreme likely weights of vehicles and their axle loads, and, if relevant, the influence of road signs restricting carrying capacity.
(3) Loads due to the road traffic, consisting of cars, lorries and special vehicles (e.g. for industrial transport), give rise to vertical and horizontal, static and dynamic forces.

3.5.3 Divisions of the carriageway into notional lanes

The widths w_1 of notional lanes on a carriageway and the greatest possible whole (integer) numbering 'n_1' of such lanes on this carriageway are shown in Table 3.7.

Table 3.7. Division of the carriageway into notional lanes

Carriageway width	Number of notional lanes	Width of a notional lane	Width of the remaining area
$w < 5.4$ m	n_1	3 m	$w - 3$ (m)
$5.4 \leq w < 6$	$n_1 = 2$	$w/2$	0
$w \geq 6$	$n_1 = \mathrm{int}(w/3)$	3 m	$w - 3 \times \mathrm{int}(w/3)$

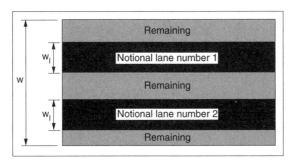

Figure 3.4. Example of lane numbering

Example of calculation

$$\text{carriageway width} = 11\,\text{m}; \qquad n_1 = \mathrm{int}\,\frac{w}{3} = 3$$

$$\text{width of the remaining area} = 11.0 - 3 \times 3 = 2\,\text{m}$$

The location and numbering of a notional lane on a carriageway is chosen on the basis of the loading intensity not the proximity of lanes. The most heavily laden lane is assigned lane number one and the second most intensely loaded, lane number two and so on. The lane giving the most unfavourable effect is the notional lane number 1. The second most unfavourable is lane two. Figure 3.4 shows an example of the lane numbering.

3.5.4 *Vertical loads – characteristic values*

The load models for vertical loads represent the following traffic effects:

> Load model 1. Concentrated and uniformly distributed loads, which cover most of the effects of the traffic of lorries and cars. This model is intended for general and local verifications.
>
> (1) The main loading system consists of two partial systems:
>
>   (*a*) Double-axle concentrated loads (tandem system: TS), each axle having a weight:
>
> $$\alpha_Q Q_k \qquad\qquad (3.1)$$
>
>   where:
>
> α_Q are adjustment factors

Each axle of the tandem model has two identical wheels, the load per wheel being therefore equal to $0.5\alpha_Q Q_k$. The contact surface of each wheel is to be taken as square and of side 0.40 m (see Fig. 3.5).

(b) Uniformly distributed loads (UDL system), having a weight density per square metre:

$$\alpha_q q_k \tag{3.2}$$

where:

α_q are adjustment factors

These loads should be applied only in the unfavourable parts of the influence surface, longitudinally and transversally.

(2) Load model 1 should be applied on each notional lane and on the remaining areas. On notional lane number i, the load magnitudes are referred to as $\alpha_{Qi} Q_{ik}$ and $\alpha_{qi} q_{ik}$. On the remaining areas, the load magnitude is referred to as $\alpha_{qr} q_{rk}$.

(3) Unless otherwise specified, the dynamic amplification is included in the values for Q_{ik} and q_{ik}.

(4) For the assessment of general effects, the tandem systems may be assumed to travel along the axes of the notional lanes.

(5) The values of Q_{ik} and q_{ik} are given in Table 3.8.

The details of load model 1 are illustrated in Fig. 3.5.

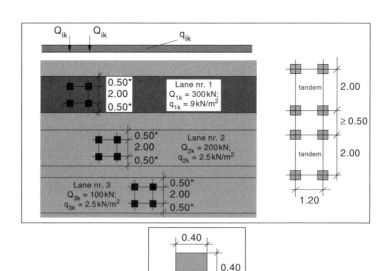

Figure 3.5. Load model 1

Table 3.8. Basic values

Location	Tandem system	UDL system
	Axle loads Q_{ik} (kN)	q_{ik} *(or* q_{rk}*)* (kN/m^2)
Lane number 1	300	9
Lane number 2	200	2.5
Lane number 3	100	2.5
Other lanes	0	2.5
Remaining area (q_{rk})	0	2.5

For general and local effects, the second and third tandem systems are replaced by a tandem system with axial weight $(200\alpha_{Q2} + 100\alpha_{Q3})$ kN or for span lengths greater than 10 m, each tandem system is replaced by a one-axle concentrated load of weight equal to the total weight of the two axles. There is a restriction placed on the axle weight:

Lane 1 → $600\alpha_{Q1}$ kN $\alpha_{Q1} \geq 0.8$

Lane 2 → $400\alpha_{Q2}$ kN

Lane 3 → $200\alpha_{Q3}$ kN

3.5.5 Single axle model (load model 2)

(1) This model consists of a single axle load $\beta_Q Q_{ak}$ with Q_{ak} equal to 400 kN, dynamic amplification included, which should be applied at any location on the carriageway. However, when relevant, only one wheel of $200\beta_Q$ (kN) may be considered. Unless otherwise specified, β_Q is equal to α_{Q1}

(2) Unless it is specified to adopt for the wheels the same contact surface as for load model 1, the contact surface of each wheel is a rectangle of sides 0.35 m and 0.60 m as shown in Fig. 3.6.

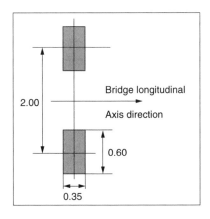

Figure 3.6. Load model 2

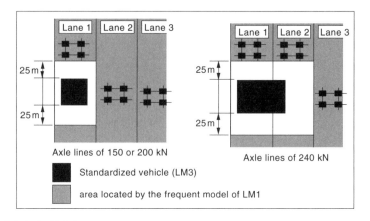

Figure 3.7. Simultaneity of load models 1 and 3

3.5.6 Set of models of special vehicles (load model 3)

When one or more of the standardized models of this set is required by the client to be taken into account, the load values and dimensions should be as described in Annex A of Eurocode 1.

Note 1: For α_{Qi} and α_{qi} factors all equal to one, the effects of the 600/150 standardized model are covered by the effects of the main loading system and do not need to be considered.

Note 2: The client may also specify particular models, especially to cover the effects of exceptional loads with a gross weight exceeding 3600 kN.

Load models 1 and 3 can be combined as shown in Fig. 3.7.

3.5.7 Crowd loading (load model 4)

Crowd loading if relevant, is represented by a nominal load (which includes dynamic amplification). Unless otherwise specified, it should be applied on the relevant parts of the length and width of the road bridge deck, the central reservation being included where relevant. This loading system, intended for general verifications, is associated solely with a transient situation.

3.5.8 Dispersal of concentrated loads

(1) The various concentrated loads to be considered for local verifications, associated with load models 1, 2 and 3, are assumed to be uniformly distributed on their whole contact area.

(2) The dispersal through the pavement and concrete slabs is taken at a spread-to-depth ratio of 1 horizontally to 1 vertically down to the level of the centroid of the structural flange below (Fig. 3.8). The notation and dimensions specifically for railway bridges are given in Fig. 3.9.

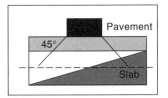

Figure 3.8. Dispersal of concentrated loads

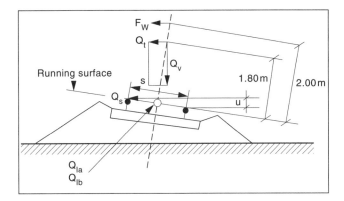

Figure 3.9. Notation and dimensions specifically for railways

3.5.9 Other forces and their components

Along with vertical loads, other loads and forces are acting in combinations as specified by various codes. It was decided to use the symbols of Eurocode 1 as the main symbols and where variations in symbols exist, they should be identified.

The other forces are braking and accelerating forces, centrifugal forces, accidental and collision forces, wind, water and earthquake forces, forces due to temperature effects, earth pressure and forces due to erection. Tables in the code give brief descriptions of these loads. For seismic effects see Section A3 for load computations.

3.6 Design specifications for other countries

Sections 3.6.1 to 3.6.14 below give bridge design specifications for a number of countries. The reader can compare specifications when designing a bridge for a specific country.

3.6.1 Belgium

Classification

Only one type of loading is considered. Bridges are therefore not divided up into classes as a function of their importance or the density of traffic.

Division of the carriageway

On indication of the appropriate authority, the carriageway shall be divided into an integer number of lanes. The lane width shall not be below 2.5 m, although today a width of 4.0 m can be attained.

Loading systems

The loading scheme takes into account, for all lanes, the simultaneous action of:

(*a*)   a uniformly distributed loading of 4 kN/m² (*q*);
(*b*)   a normal vehicle of 320 kN (*Q*) weight, with one axle load of 120 kN, two of 60 kN and two of 40 kN.

The axle loads are interchangeable. The uniformly distributed load shall not be interrupted at the location of the vehicle.

Special heavy vehicle.   As an alternative loading, two schemes are given.

Heavy vehicle type 1:   two groups of 4 axles, each axle load 300 kN, axles spaced 1.7 m from centre to centre (c-t-c), groups spaced 16.1 m c-t-c, and total load 2400 kN.

Heavy vehicle type 2:   Two groups of two axles, each axle load 450 kN, axles spaced 1.8 m (c-t-c), groups spaced 7.8 m (c-t-c), total load 1800 kN.

The appropriate authority decides whether a bridge shall be designed for the normal loading and also for the special heavy vehicle. The type 1 or type 2 heavy vehicle loading shall be considered as being alone on the bridge.

Impact factor

In order to take into account the dynamic effects on bridge members, the live loadings shall be multiplied by a coefficient $K \geq 1$.

$$K = 1 + 0.377 \frac{v}{\sqrt{\alpha \cdot L}} \cdot \sqrt{1 + \frac{2S}{P}}$$

where:

v = maximum allowed speed of vehicles, in km/h ($v_{min} = 60$);

L = length of span of the considered bridge member, in metres;

$\alpha = L/f_s$ where f_s is the static deflection of the member as a result of the dead load, in metres;

S = the live load acting on the member;

P = permanent load acting on the member.

For the purpose of preliminary designs etc., it is allowed to use the formula:

$$K = 1 + \frac{0.4}{1 + 0.2L} + \frac{0.6}{1 + 4(P/S)}$$

3.6.2 *Belgium: new Code*

Classification
In the new draft of the Code, a division of bridges into three classes will be made:

Class A: bridges for normal traffic. Current loadings shall be taken into account when calculating these bridges.

Class B: bridges for heavy traffic. As above; additionally a check shall be made for an exceptional loading (heavy vehicle or dense traffic).

Class C: bridges for light traffic. Calculations shall be made taking into account a lower type of loading.

Division of the carriageway
The carriageway shall be divided into an integer number of traffic lanes, the width of which can vary from 2.5 m to 4.0 m.

Loading systems
For Class A the result of the simultaneous action of the following loads is to be taken into account:

(a) *on the whole surface of the bridge*:   a uniformly distributed loading of 3.5 kN/m horizontal surface;

(b) *for every traffic lane*:   a concentrated unit loading, composed of a pair of axles (tandem), each with an axle load of 150 kN, total weight 300 kN (Q) with an axle spacing of 1.5 m.

Note that the responsible authority is allowed:

to reduce the uniformly distributed lane loading for important bridges (four traffic lanes and a span of more than 100 m);
to request a check of the structure under a uniformly distributed loading of 10 kN/m², while reduced safety factors are admitted (Class B).

Impact factor
The impact coefficient has the value:

$$k = 1 + \frac{0.4}{1 + 0.2L} + \frac{0.6}{1 + 4(P/S)}$$

with

P = the permanent load;

S = the live load;

L = the span of the considered member. In the case of continuous girders, L shall be chosen as the average of all the different spans.

(See also remarks under impact factor of the code for France.)

3.6.3 Finland: Code 197B

Classification

There is a distinction between public and private roads. For the public roads there is no classification.

Division of the carriageway

In any case the number and location of the 3 m wide loaded lanes are chosen so that the determining effect is achieved. The number of loaded lanes is at the most the same as the number of traffic lanes of the road. In special cases (e.g. traffic ramps in the vicinity of road crossings, wide bridges along one-lane roads), the number of loaded lanes is determined separately.

Loading systems

There are three normal load schemes and two special heavy loadings:

load scheme 1 (Fig. 3.10(a)): a three-axle vehicle of 630 kN and a uniformly distributed loading of 3 kN/m^2;
load scheme 2 (Fig. 3.10(b)): one-axle load of 260 kN which consists of two 130 kN wheel loads;
load scheme 3: one 130 kN wheel load;
heavy special load I (Fig. 3.10(c)): a four-axle vehicle of 1200 kN which is composed of two bogies;
heavy special load II (Fig. 3.10(d)): a four-axle vehicle of 800 kN which is composed of two bogies.

Load schemes 1, 2 and 3.* Each part of the structure is dimensioned according to the scheme which is the most critical. Schemes 1 and 2 are supposed to load the bridge surface lengthwise, i.e. along the 3 m wide loaded lane. The wheel loads are located in the centre of the loaded lane and at the most two loaded lanes are calculated for the axle groups. The loaded lanes are placed in a determining position in the cross-section of the carriageway (including shoulders and other surfaces on the level of carriageway).

Special heavy loads. The bridge structures have furthermore to be dimensioned for a special heavy load I or II which, together with the permanent and long lasting loads, are of rare occurrence. The heavy vehicle is presumed to travel in the centre of the carriageway. In this case the largest deviation from the centre-line of the carriageway to the centre-line of the road is to be supposed as:

b	(m)	5	5........8	8........10	≥ 10
e	(m)	0	$0.5xb - 2.5$	1.5	$0.5xb - 3.5$

where the road width b is the summed-up width of the carriageway and other lanes and shoulders on the same level (see Fig. 3.11).

---

* According to 'Preliminary Internordic loading directions for road bridges of 9th December, 1971'.

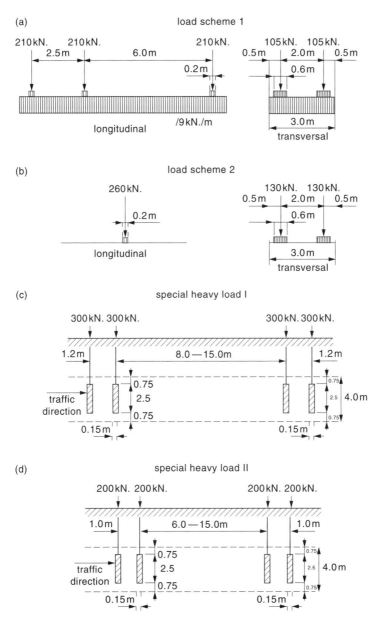

Figure 3.10. (a) Load scheme 1; (b) load scheme 2; (c) special heavy load I; and (d) special heavy load II

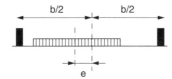

Figure 3.11. Carriageway dimensioning for special heavy loads

Impact factor
The increase caused by impacts is included in the load schemes 1, 2 and 3 and for special heavy loads I and II the impact factor is assumed to be 1.4 (for timber bridges: 1.2).

3.6.4   France: (Circulaire Ministérielle No. 71-155 du 29 Décembre 1971. Fascicule No. 61 – Titre II du Cahier des Prescriptions Communes) (Modified 1989)

Classification
The code distinguishes three bridge classes depending on the width of the carriageway:

Class I: bridges having a carriageway with a width equal to or greater than 7 m.
Class II: bridges with a width of carriageway between 5.50 m and 7 m.
Class III: bridges with a width of carriageway equal to or less than 5.50 m.

Division of the carriageway
The width of the carriageway that can be loaded shall be divided into an integer number of traffic lanes. The width of these lanes shall not be less than 3 m. Carriageways having a width of 5–6 m shall be considered as having two lanes.

Loading systems
Two different and independent types of loading are to be placed on the carriageway:

A: a uniformly distributed load;
B: vehicle or axle loads.

Certain classified routes must allow for the passage of heavy military loads (M80 and M120) or exceptional heavy transports (type D and type E).

Loading system A

$$A(L) = 2.30 + \frac{360}{L + 12} \quad (\text{kN/m}^2)$$

where $L =$ loaded length in metres.
    Depending on the bridge class and the number of loaded lanes, the value of A is to be multiplied by the coefficient a_1 (see Table 3.9).

Table 3.9

Number of loaded lanes		1	2	3	4	≥5
	first	1	1	0.9	0.75	0.7
Bridge class	second	1	0.9	–	–	–
	third	0.9	0.8	–	–	–

The resulting load $A_1 = a_1 A$ is to be multiplied by a coefficient $a_2 = (V_0/V)$, where $V =$ width of lane and $V_0 = 3.5\,\text{m}$ for bridges of the first class, 3.0 m for bridges of the second class, and 2.75 m for bridges of the third class.

The load $A_2 = a_1 \cdot a_2 \cdot A$ obtained in this way is to be placed uniformly over the total width of the considered traffic lanes.

Loading system B
There are three different and independent loading systems that are to be considered for each bridge member.

System Bc (Fig. 3.12(a)) consisting of two vehicles of 300 kN on each lane. Depending on the bridge class and the number of loaded lanes, the value of the vehicle loads is to be multiplied by the coefficient given in Table 3.10.

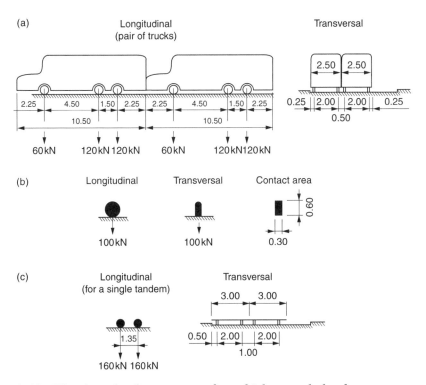

Figure 3.12. The three loading systems for vehicle or axle loads

Table 3.10

Number of loaded lanes		1	2	3	4	≥ 5
	first	1.20	1.10	0.95	0.8	0.7
Bridge class	second	1.00	1.00	–	–	–
	third	1.00	0.8	–	–	–

Table 3.11

Loading system	M80	M120
A track-type vehicle with a total load of	720 kN	1100 kN
Length of a track	4.90 m	6.10 m
Width of a track	0.85 m	1.00 m
Distance between the tracks c.t.c.	2.80 m	3.30 m
Alternative:		
Two axles, each with a load of	220 kN	330 kN
Length of an axle	3.5 m	4.0 m
Distance between the axles c.t.c.	1.5 m	1.80 m

System Br (Fig. B.12(b)) consisting of an isolated wheel load of 100 kN.
System Bt (Fig. 3.12(c)) consisting of a pair of two axles, each 160 kN, on each lane. The distance between axles is 1.35 m and the distance between wheels is 2.0 m. For the second bridge class, the system Bt is to be multiplied by a coefficient 0.9. For the third class the system Bt is not to be considered.
Military loads. See Table 3.11.
Exceptional heavy transports. See Table 3.12.

Impact factor
The impact factor is included in the values of the loading system A. For the loading system B, the value of the impact factor K is given by the following formula:

$$K = 1 + \frac{0.4}{1 + 0.2L} + \frac{0.6}{1 + 4(P/S)}; \quad [1 + \alpha + \beta]$$

Table 3.12

Types	Type D	Type E
Two carriers, each with a total load of	1400 kN	2000 kN
Length of carrier	11.0 m	15 m
Width of carrier	3.3 m	3.3 m
Centre to centre distance of carriers	19 m	33 m

with

P = the permanent load;

S = the live load B;

L = the length of the bridge member in metres.

With sufficient accuracy one can assume that the coefficient β has a value of $0.6\,\alpha$ for concrete structures and a value of α for steel and composite structures. Thus, for concrete structures:

$$K = 1 + \frac{0.64}{1 + 0.2L}$$

and for steel and composite structures:

$$K = 1 + \frac{0.80}{1 + 0.2L}$$

3.6.5 Germany (DIN 1072–1987)
Classification
The code DIN 1072 distinguishes three bridge classes:

Class 60: is applied for bridges on motorways, federal and State (Länder) roads.

Class 30: is applied for bridges on county roads, community roads, city roads, and service roads in rural areas for heavy traffic. One axle load of 130 kN is to be applied for cross-beams with a centre to centre distance of ≤ 2 m and for longitudinal girders as well as for slabs with a span of ≤ 7 m.

Class 12: is applied for bridges on roads for light traffic (rural areas mostly).

Division of the carriageway
The carriageway shall be divided into a principal traffic lane of 3 m width, and normal lanes for the rest. The principal lane must be chosen at the most critical position for the considered element of the structure.

Loading systems
For the principal lane:

a heavy vehicle (Q); and
a uniformly distributed loading (q_1) in front and behind this vehicle.

For the other lanes:

a uniformly distributed loading q_2.

The values of Q, q_1 and q_2 are given in Table 3.13.

Table 3.13

Class	Heavy vehicle type				Distributed load	
	Total load Q (kN)	Axle load (kN)	Wheel load (kN)	Distance between axles (m)	q_1 (kN/m^2)	q_2 (kN/m^2)
60	600	200	100	$-1.50-1.50-$	5	3
30	300	100	50	$-1.50-1.50-$	5	3
12	120	40/80	20/40	$-3.0-$	4	3

Impact factor

The traffic loadings on the principal lane have to be multiplied by an impact factor k, the value of which varies between 1.4 and 1:

$k = 1.4 - 0.008L \geq 1$ where

$L =$ length of span of bridge member (stringer, cross-girder, main girder) in metres.

3.6.6 Italy (Code 384 of 14.2.1982)

Classification

The code distinguishes two bridge classes: Class I routes subjected to both civil and military traffic; Class II country roads destined for civil vehicles only.

Division of the carriageway

The carriageway is divided into an integer number of traffic lanes the width of which varies between 3 and 3.5 m, in accordance with the design load schemes as indicated below. In the transverse direction, the design loads are placed at locations that are the most unfavourable.

Loading systems

Different loading systems are to be considered (see Fig. 3.13).

Scheme 1: an unrestricted train of vehicles, each with a load of 120 kN.
Scheme 2: a single rolling machine of 180 kN.
Scheme 3: pedestrians densely crowded – 4 kN/m².
Scheme 4: an unrestricted train of military loads of 615 kN.
Scheme 5: an unrestricted train of military loads of 320 kN.
Scheme 6: a single military load of 745 kN.

The width of the surface covered by the schemes is 3.0 m for Schemes 1 and 2 and 3.5 m for Schemes 4, 5 and 6.

Civil loads

Scheme 1: unrestricted train of trucks of 120 kN

Scheme 2: single rolling machine of 180 kN

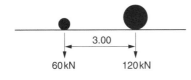

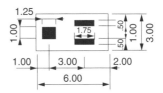

Military loads

Scheme 4: unrestricted train of military loads of 615 kN

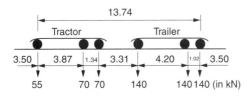

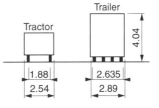

Scheme 5: unrestricted train of military loads of 320 kN

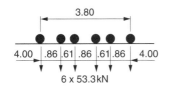

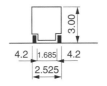

Scheme 6: single military load of 745 kN

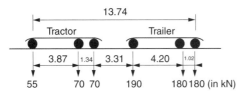

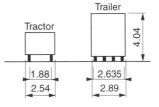

Figure 3.13. The different loading systems of Schemes 1, 2, 4, 5 and 6

Schemes to be adopted for the calculation of the bridges:

Class I: The most unfavourable of the Schemes 4, 5 and 6 together with one
           or more vehicle trains (Scheme 1) and a load of $4\,kN/m^2$ on the
           side-walks (Scheme 3).

Class II: The most unfavourable of the following conditions: one or more
           vehicle trains (Scheme 1) and a load of $4\,kN/m^2$ on the side-
           walks (Scheme 3);
           one or more rolling machines (Scheme 2) together with the load of
           $4\,kN/m^2$ (Scheme 3) on the side-walks.

Impact factor
For spans with a length $L < 100\,m$:

$$K = 1 + \frac{(100 - L)^2}{100 \times (250 - L)}$$

For the spans with a length $L \geq 100\,m$, $K = 1$.

   L represents for the main bridge members the distance between bearings and
for the other members the length of the span concerned.

3.6.7   United Kingdom (British Standard No. 5400: Part 2: 1978 'Steel, concrete and composite bridges' – specification for loads)

Classification
The loading representing normal traffic is not varied. The axle loads in the
nominal four-axle abnormal vehicle unit (used for design) may vary between
$250\,kN$ and $450\,kN$.

Division of the carriageway
For design purposes, the carriageway shall be divided into notional traffic lanes,
the width of which shall be not less than 2.3 m nor more than 3.8 m.

Loading systems
There are two types of loadings:

(a) *Type HA loading* (normal traffic)
     Formula design loading for bridges. It consists of a uniformly distributed
     lane loading, together with one knife-edge load.

(b) *Type HB loading* (abnormal vehicle)
     Exceptional design loading for bridges. A bridge is calculated for the
     type HA loading and checked for HB loading, which represents abnor-
     mally heavy vehicles. When considering the effects of this loading a
     reduced partial load factor is applied to the HB load and the coexistent
     HA loading.

Type HA loading
- Two carriageway lanes shall always be considered as occupied by full HA loading (100 per cent).
- All other lanes shall be considered as occupied by one-third of the full lane loading (33 1/3%).

Type HB loading
- The HB load may be in any position, occupying one lane or straddling two. No other loading shall be considered in the 25 m length at each end of the vehicle.
- HA loading shall be applied to two lanes – either the remainder of the lane occupied by the HB vehicle plus an adjacent lane, or the remainder of the two lanes straddled by the HB vehicle, or the remainder of one straddled lane plus an adjacent lane.
- All other lanes shall be loaded to 1/3 HA load.

Load values
The type HA loading consists of (*a*) and (*b*), or (*c*) namely:

(*a*)   A uniformly distributed lane loading. For loaded lengths up to 30 m, the value shall be 30 kN/m of notional lane. For greater length (*L*) it shall be $151 \times (1/L)^{0.475}$, but not less than 9 kN/m of notional lane (see Fig. 3.14).

(*b*)   One knife-edge load (axle load) of 120 kN, uniformly distributed across the width of the notional traffic lane (see Table 3.14).

(*c*)   A single nominal wheel load, as an alternative to (*a*) + (*b*). The load shall be 100 kN and distributed over an area of 0.34 m² or a square of 0.30 m sides. The HA wheel load is applied to members supporting small areas of roadway, where the proportion of the distributed load and knife-edge load which would otherwise be allocated to it is small.

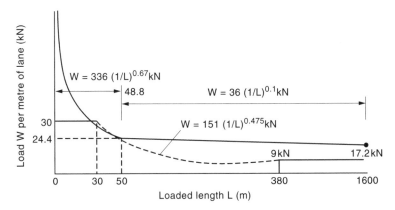

Figure 3.14. Loading curve for HA uniformly distributed lane loading. Assuming a concrete deck, note that the notional lane width is 3.65 m and that HA loading for a loaded length of 20 m is 45.14 kN/m of lane without the use of HB loading

Table 3.14. Uniformly distributed lane loading applied in conjunction with knife-edge load of 120 kN

Load length m	Load kN/m	Load length m	Load kN/m	Load length m	Load kN/m
Up to 30	30.0	73	19.7	160	13.6
32	29.1	76	19.3	170	13.2
34	28.3	79	18.9	180	12.8
36	27.5	82	18.6	190	12.5
38	26.8	85	18.3	200	12.2
40	26.2	90	17.8	210	11.9
42	25.6	95	17.4	220	11.7
44	25.0	100	16.9	230	11.4
46	24.5	105	16.6	240	11.2
49	23.8	110	16.2	255	10.9
52	23.1	115	15.9	270	10.6
55	22.5	120	15.5	285	10.3
58	21.9	125	15.2	300	10.1
61	21.4	130	15.0	320	9.8
64	20.9	135	14.7	340	9.5
67	20.5	140	14.4	360	9.2
70	20.1	145	14.2	380 and	9.0
		150	14.0	above	

The type HB loading is a unit loading representing a single abnormally heavy vehicle (Fig. 3.15). The loading is composed of four-axle loads, each with a weight expressed in units (1 unit = 10 kN). The number of units of HB loading normally required is 45 units (450 kN per axle). Detailed illustrations are given in Fig. 3.16.

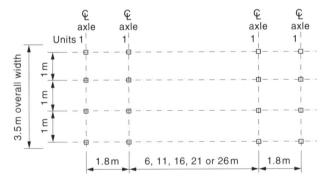

Figure 3.15. HB unit loading. Note that the loading is composed of four-axle loads and that 37.5 units of HB is equivalent to an axle load of 375 kN. Therefore, the loading per wheel is 93.75 kN. The other HB units are calculated similarly

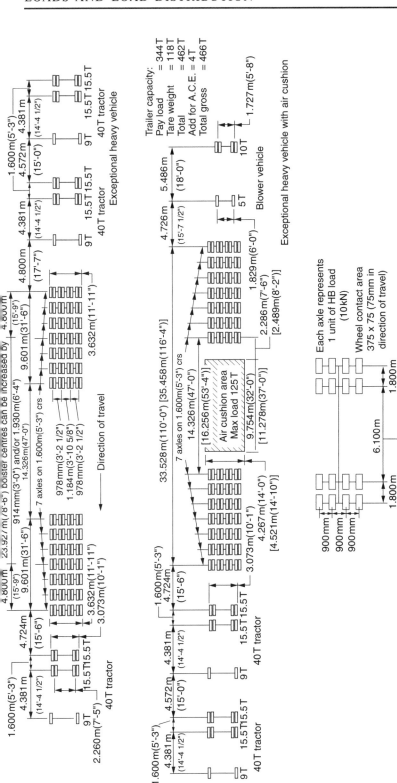

Figure 3.16. HB unit loading repesenting a single abnormally heavy vehicle. The abnormal loading stipulated in BS 153 is applied to most public highway bridges in the UK: 45 units on motorway under-bridges, 37½ units on bridges for principal roads and 30 units on bridges for other roads.

Some bridges are checked for special heavy vehicles which can range up to 466 tonnes gross weight. Where this is needed the gross weight and trailer dimensions are stated by the authority requiring this special facility on a given route.

The vehicles illustrated are by way of example only

Table 3.15. Minimum effective bridge temperature (reference BS 5400 and BD 37/88)

Minimum shade air temperature	Minimum effective bridge temperature		
	Type of superstructure		
	Groups 1 and 2	Group 3	Group 4
°C	°C	°C	°C
−24	−28	−19	−14
−23	−27	−18	−13
−22	−26	−18	−13
−21	−25	−17	−12
−20	−23	−17	−12
−19	−22	−16	−11
−18	−21	−15	−11
−17	−20	−15	−10
−16	−19	−14	−10
−15	−18	−13	−9
−14	−17	−12	−9
−13	−16	−11	−8
−12	−15	−10	−7
−11	−14	−10	−6
−10	−12	−9	−6
−9	−11	−8	−5
−8	−10	−7	−4
−7	−9	−6	−3
−6	−8	−5	−3
−5	−7	−4	−2

Table 3.16. Maximum effective bridge temperature (reference BS 5400 and BD 37/88)

Maximum shade air temperature	Maximum effective bridge temperature		
	Type of superstructure		
	Groups 1 and 2	Group 3	Group 4
°C	°C	°C	°C
24	40	31	27
25	41	32	28
26	41	33	29
27	42	34	29
28	42	34	30
29	43	35	31
30	44	36	32
31	44	36	32
32	44	37	33
33	45	37	33
34	45	38	34
35	46	39	35
36	46	39	36
37	46	40	36
38	47	40	37

Note: See Fig. 3.17 for different types of superstructure.

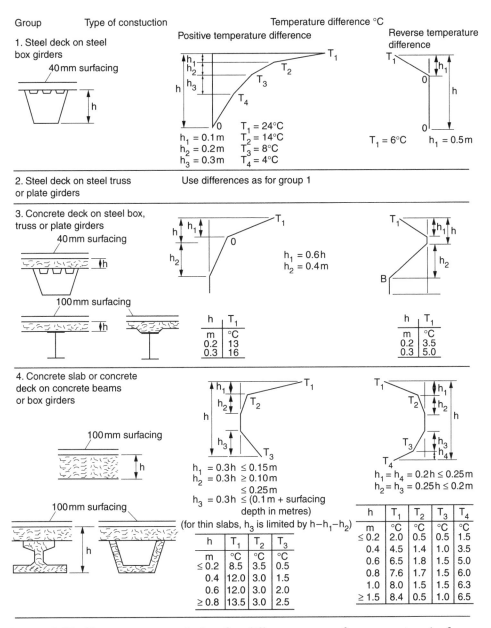

Figure 3.17. Temperature variation for different types of construction (reference BS 5400 and BD 37/88)

Impact factor

An impact factor of 1.25 is taken into account in the HA loading. No impact factor is used with the HB loading.

Classification of loads

The loads applied to a structure are regarded as either permanent or transient.

(a) *Permanent loads.* For the purposes of this standard, dead loads, super-imposed dead loads and loads due to filling material shall be regarded as permanent loads.

(i) *Loading effects not due to external action.* Loads deriving from the nature of the structural material, its manufacture or the circumstances of its fabrication are dealt with in the appropriate parts of this standard. Where they occur they shall be regarded as permanent loads.

(ii) *Settlement.* The effect of differential settlement of supports shall be regarded as a permanent load where there is reason to believe that this will take place, and no special provision has been made to remedy the effect.

(b) *Transient loads.* For the purposes of this standard all loads other than permanent ones shall be considered transient.

The maximum effects of certain transient loads do not coexist with the maximum effects of certain others. The reduced effects that can coexist are specified in the relevant clauses.

Combinations of loads

Three principal and two secondary combinations of loads are specified: values of γ_{fL} for each load for each combination in which it is considered are given in the relevant clauses and also summarized in Table 3.17.

(a) *Combination 1.* For highway and foot/cycle track bridges, the loads to be considered are the permanent loads, together with the appropriate primary live loads, and, for railway bridges, the permanent loads, together with the appropriate primary and secondary live loads.

(b) *Combination 2.* For all bridges, the loads to be considered are the loads in combination 1, together with those due to wind and, where erection is being considered, temporary erection loads.

(c) *Combination 3.* For all bridges, the loads to be considered are the loads in combination 1, together with those arising from restraint due to the effects of temperature range and difference, and, where erection is being considered, temporary erection loads.

(d) *Combination 4.* Combination 4 does not apply to railway bridges except for vehicle collision loading on bridge supports. For highway

Table 3.17 (pages 293–295). Loads to be taken in each combination with appropriate γ_{fL} (ULS: ultimate limit state; SLS: serviceability limit state)

Clause number	Load	Limit state	γ_{fL} to be considered in combination				
			1	2	3	4	5
5.1	Dead						
	steel	ULS*	1.05	1.05	1.05	1.05	1.05
		SLS	1.00	1.00	1.00	1.00	1.00
	concrete	ULS*	1.15	1.15	1.15	1.15	1.15
		SLS	1.00	1.00	1.00	1.00	1.00
5.2	Superimposed dead						
	deck surfacing	ULS†	1.75	1.75	1.75	1.75	1.75
		SLS†	1.20	1.20	1.20	1.20	1.20
	other loads	ULS	1.20	1.20	1.20	1.20	1.20
		SLS	1.00	1.00	1.00	1.00	1.00
5.1.2.2 and 5.2.2.2	Reduced load factor for dead and superimposed dead load where this has a more severe total effect	ULS	1.00	1.00	1.00	1.00	1.00
5.3	Wind						
	during erection	ULS		1.10			
		SLS		1.00			
	with dead plus superimposed dead load only, and for members primarily resisting wind loads	ULS		1.40			
		SLS		1.00			
	with dead plus superimposed dead plus other appropriate combination 2 loads	ULS		1.10			
		SLS		1.00			
	relieving effect of wind	ULS		1.00			
		SLS		1.00			
5.4	Temperature						
	restraint to movement, except frictional	ULS			1.30		
		SLS			1.00		
	frictional bearing restraint	ULS				1.30	
		SLS				1.00	
	effect of temperature difference	ULS			1.00		
		SLS			0.80		
5.6	Differential settlement	ULS	1.20	1.20	1.20	1.20	1.20
		SLS	1.00	1.00	1.00	1.00	1.00
5.7	Exceptional loads		to be assessed and agreed between the engineer and the appropriate authority				
5.8	Earth pressure retained fill and/or live load						
	vertical loads	ULS	1.20	1.20	1.20	1.20	1.20
		SLS	1.00	1.00	1.00	1.00	1.00
	non-vertical loads	ULS	1.50	1.50	1.50	1.50	1.50
		SLS	1.00	1.00	1.00	1.00	1.00
	relieving effect	ULS	1.00	1.00	1.00	1.00	1.00

(Continued)

Table 3.17. (Continued)

Clause number	Load	Limit state	γ_{fL} to be considered in combination				
			1	2	3	4	5
5.9	Erection						
	temporary loads	ULS		1.15	1.15		
		SLS		1.00	1.00		
6.2	Highway bridges live loading						
	HA alone	ULS	1.50	1.25	1.25		
		SLS	1.20	1.00	1.00		
6.3	HA with HB or HB alone	ULS	1.30	1.10	1.10		
		SLS	1.10	1.00	1.00		
6.5	footway and cycle track loading	ULS	1.50	1.25	1.25		
		SLS	1.00	1.00	1.00		
6.6	accidental wheel loading[‡]	ULS	1.50				
		SLS	1.20				
6.7.1	Loads due to vehicle collision with parapets and associated primary live load						
	Local effects						
	parapet load low and normal	ULS¶				1.50	
	containment	SLS¶				1.20	
	high containment	ULS¶				1.40	
		SLS¶				1.15	
	Associated primary live load						
	low, normal and high	ULS¶				1.30	
	containment	SLS¶				1.10	
6.7.2	*Global effects*						
	parapet load						
	Massive structures						
	bridge superstructures and non-elastomeric bearings	ULS¶				1.25	
	bridge substructures and wing and retaining walls	ULS¶				1.00	
	elastomeric bearings	SLS¶				1.00	
	Light structures						
	bridge superstructures and non-elastomeric bearings	ULS¶				1.40	
	bridge substructures and wing and retaining walls	ULS¶				1.40	
	elastomeric bearings	SLS ¶				1.00	
	Associated primary live load: massive and light structures						
	bridge superstructures, non-elastomeric bearings, bridge substructures and wing and retaining walls	ULS¶				1.25	
	elastomeric bearings	SLS¶				1.00	

(Continued)

Table 3.17. (Continued)

Clause number	Load	Limit state	γ_{fL} to be considered in combination				
			1	2	3	4	5
6.8	Vehicle collision loads on bridge supports and superstructures						
	Effects on all elements excepting non-elastomeric	ULS¶				1.50	
	Effects on non-elastomeric bearings	SLS¶				1.00	
6.9	Centrifugal load and associated primary live load	ULS¶				1.50	
		SLS¶				1.00	
6.10	Longitudinal load						
	HA and associated primary live load	ULS¶				1.25	
		SLS¶				1.00	
	HB and associated primary live load	ULS¶				1.10	
		SLS¶				1.00	
6.11	Accidental skidding load and associated primary live load	ULS¶				1.25	
		SLS¶				1.00	
7	Foot/cycle track bridges						
	live load and effects due to parapet load	ULS	1.50	1.25	1.25		
		SLS	1.00	1.00	1.00		
	vehicle collision loads on supports and superstructures§	ULS				1.50	
8	Railway bridges						
	type RU and RL primary and secondary live loading	ULS	1.40	1.20	1.20		
		SLS	1.10	1.00	1.00		

* γ_{fL} shall be increased to at least 1.10 and 1.20 for steel and concrete, respectively, to compensate for inaccuracies when dead loads are not accurately assessed.

† γ_{fL} may be reduced to 1.2 and 1.0 for the ULS and SLS, respectively, subject to approval of the appropriate authority.

‡ Accidental wheel loading shall not be considered as acting with any other primary live loads.

§ This is the only secondary live load to be considered for foot/cycle track bridges.

¶ Each secondary live load shall be considered separately together with the other combination 4 loads as appropriate.

NOTE: For loads arising from creep and shrinkage, or from welding and lack of fit, see Parts 3, 4 and 5 of the standard, as appropriate

bridges, the loads to be considered are the permanent loads and the secondary live loads, together with the appropriate primary live loads associated with them. Secondary live loads shall be considered separately and are not required to be combined. Each shall be taken with its appropriate associated primary live load.

For foot/cycle track bridges, the only secondary live loads to be considered are the vehicle collision loads on bridge supports and superstructures.

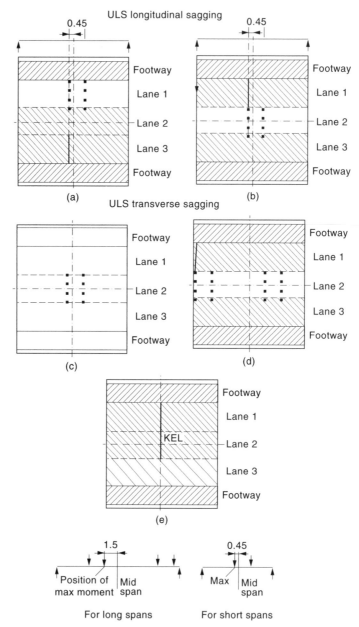

Figure 3.18. *Ultimate limit state behaviour*

(e) *Combination 5.* For all bridges, the loads to be considered are the permanent loads, together with the loads due to friction at bearings.*

---

* Where a member is required to resist the loads due to temperature restraint within the structure and to frictional restraint of temperature-induced movement at bearings, the sum of these effects shall be considered. An example is the abutment anchorage of a continuous structure where temperature movement is accommodated by flexure of piers in some spans and by roller bearings in others.

Application of loads
Each element and structure shall be examined under the effects of loads that can coexist in each combination.

(a)   *Selection to cause most adverse effect.**   Design loads shall be selected and applied in such a way that the most adverse total effect is caused in the element or structure under consideration.

(b)   *Removal of superimposed dead load.*   Consideration shall be given to the possibility that the removal of superimposed dead load from part of the structure may diminish its relieving effect. In so doing the adverse effects of live load on the elements of the structure being examined may be modified to the extent that the removal of the superimposed dead load justifies this.

(c)   *Live load.*   Live load shall not be considered to act on relieving areas except in the case of wind on live load when the presence of light traffic is necessary to generate the wind load.

(d)   *Wind on relieving areas.*   Design loads due to wind on relieving areas shall be modified (see Table 3.17).

Overturning
The stability of the superstructure and its parts against overturning shall be considered for the ultimate limit state (ULS).

(a)   *Restoring moment.*   The least restoring moment due to the unfactored nominal loads shall be greater than the greatest overturning moment due to the design loads (i.e. γ_{fL} for the ultimate limit state $\times$ the effects of the nominal loads).

(b)   *Removal of loads.*   The requirements relating to the possible removal of superimposed dead load shall also be taken into account in considering overturning.

Foundation pressures, sliding on foundations, loads on piles, etc.
In the design of foundations, the dead load, the superimposed dead load and loads due to filling material shall be regarded as permanent loads and all live loads, temperature effects and wind loads shall be regarded as transient loads, except in certain circumstances such as a mainline railway bridge outside a busy terminal where it may be necessary to assess a proportion of live load as being permanent.

The design of foundations including consideration of overturning shall be based on the principles set out in BS 8004 using load combinations as given in this Part.

---

* It is expected that experience in the use of this standard will enable users to identify those load cases and combinations (as in the case of BS 153) which govern design provisions, and it is only those load cases and combinations which need to be established for use in practice (see also Fig. 3.18).

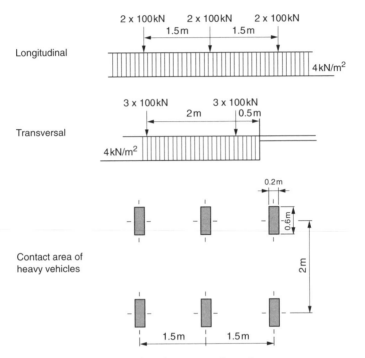

Figure 3.19. Loading system for the Spanish code

3.6.8 Spain

General
The code adopted the standard of the 600 kN heavy vehicle together with a uniform loading of 4 kN/m². The impact factor is included in these loads.

The code is applicable to bridges of span less than 125 m.

Loading system
A heavy vehicle of 600 kN together with a uniform loading of 4 kN/m² is considered (see Fig. 3.19). Load factors and safety factors to be used in the design are fixed factors.

3.6.9 The Netherlands (Norm NEN 1008 – VOSB 1983 for steel bridges)

Classification
Bridges can be divided into three classes as a function of the type of traffic:

Class 60: a bridge on a principal route where an exceptionally heavy vehicle cannot be diverted.

Class 45: a bridge on a principal route; there is the possibility to divert exceptionally heavy vehicles to a route with bridges of class 60.

Class 30: a bridge not suited for carrying heavy vehicles.

Table 3.18. Summary of loadings

Uniformly distributed loading			Vehicle loading*		
Class	(q) per m²	max load per lane (m²)	(Q) total	Load per axle	Load per wheel
60	4 kN	12 kN	600 kN	200 kN	50 kN
45	3 kN	9 kN	450 kN	150 kN	37.5 kN
30	2 kN	6 kN	300 kN	100 kN	25 kN

* The vehicle has three axles spaced, respectively, 1 m and 4 m. The width of the vehicle is 2.5 m.

Division of the carriageway

The number of traffic lanes on the bridge has to match with that on the adjacent road section (e.g. in towns). The carriageway on the bridge shall be divided into an integer number of traffic lanes of 3.0 m width.

Loading systems

The simultaneous action of the following loadings shall be taken into account:

(a) a uniformly distributed loading q over the whole surface of the bridge (kN/m^2);

(b) a vehicle load Q (kN) moving on a traffic lane.

The number of vehicles in the transverse direction is limited to two. In the case where two vehicles are taken into account, all the live loads shall be reduced by 20%. The vehicles are situated in the centre of the traffic lanes concerned. The uniformly distributed loading (Table 3.18) shall not be interrupted on the spot where the vehicles are situated and its value per traffic lane is limited to $3q$ (kN/m^2). The value of the live loads shall be multiplied by a reduction coefficient k_2, which is a function of the span.

Impact factor k_1 and reduction coefficient k_2

Loadings are multiplied by two coefficients, k_1 and k_2, which make allowance for the dynamic effect and a reduction of the loadings in relation to the span L (in metres):

$$k_1 = 1 + \frac{40}{100 + L} \qquad k_2 = 0.6 + \frac{40}{100 + L}$$

For concrete bridges an impact factor of:

$$k_1 = 1 + \frac{3}{10 + L}$$

shall be applied.

3.6.10   Norway and Sweden (According to 'Preliminary Internordic loading directions for road bridges' of 9.12.1971)

Classification

The loading prescriptions do not vary as a function of the importance of the road, hence there is only one type of loading.

Division of the carriageway

The carriageway shall be divided into a whole number of lanes, the width of which is constant and equal to 3.0 m.

Loading systems (see also Finland)

One or two lanes

 Equivalent load, type 1.   A uniformly distributed lane load $p = 9 \, \text{kN/m}$ ($= 3 \, \text{kN/m}^2$) together with an axle group of $3 \times 210 \, \text{kN}$ (spaced $\geq 2.5 \, \text{m}$ and $\geq 6.0 \, \text{m}$).

 Equivalent load, type 2.   Axle load of 260 kN placed symmetrically in the loaded lanes of the bridge. (Maximum: two fully loaded lanes.)

 Equivalent load, type 3.   A wheel load of 130 kN placed anywhere in the free area of the carriageway, the centre of the wheel having a minimum distance to the guardrail or other obstacles of 0.5 m.

 Sidewalks and bicycle lanes, separated from the carriageway, are loaded by $p = 4 \, \text{kN/m}^2$ or alternatively by $p = 2 \, \text{kN/m}$, when the equivalent loadings of the carriageway are simultaneously applied.

Three or more lanes

 Only two lanes, i.e. those lanes where loads act in the most unfavourable way, are loaded according to types 1, 2 and 3. Additional lanes are loaded by a p of 9 kN/m.

 The above-mentioned loadings are valid for bridges up to a span of 200 m. For bridges of greater span and ferry bridges, special regulations are adopted.

Impact factor

An impact factor also taking care of uneven weight distribution and varying from 1.4 (in the case of the equivalent load of type 1) to 1.75 for the equivalent load, type 2, is included in the axle loads.

3.6.11   Australia (NAASRA, 1989)

The association of state, territory and federal road and traffic authorities in Australia was established in 1989 to replace NAASRA (National Association of Australian State Road). The Australian bridge design specifications are outlined in the '92 Austroads' standard. According to this document, 'All road bridges shall be designed for the effects of the T44 truck loading, the L44 lane loading, and the appropriate fatigue loading.'

 T44 truck loading represents a hypothetical truck with five axles. The front axle exerts a load of 48 kN, and the other four axles exert a load of 96 kN each.

 The arrangement of such a truck is shown in Fig. 3.20.

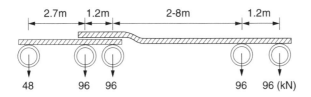

Figure 3.20. Arrangement of T44 truck loading

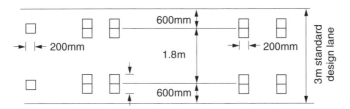

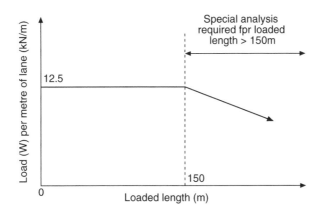

Figure 3.21. Uniformly distributed L44 lane loading

The L44 lane loading consists of a uniformly distributed load, of 12.5 kN/m of the loaded length, together with a concentrated load of 150 kN (Fig. 3.21).

The concentrated load is not intended to represent a heavy axle, but is merely an analytical device to simulate bending and shearing effects caused by an actual vehicle loading.

The L44 lane loading arrangement
The HLP is a modular platform that comprises sixteen rows of axles with 8 tyres per axle spaced at 1.8 m centres.

There are two types of HLP, HLP 400, and HLP 320. The total load per axle of HLP 400 is 250 kN and the total load per axle of HLP 320 is 200 kN, distributed equally among all wheels (Fig. 3.22).

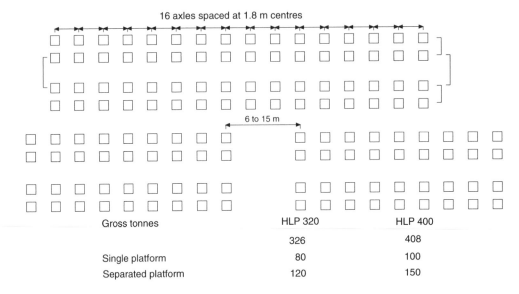

Figure 3.22. Load distribution per axle for HLP 400 and HLP 320

Load application

T44 truck and L44 lane load, are considered to occupy one standard design lane of 3 m width.

The number of standard design lanes, n, is given by:

$n = b/3.1$ (rounded down to nearest integer)

where b = carriageway width in metres between kerbs.

When a number of standard design lanes is loaded, the load factors shown in Table 3.19 must be applied to all T44 truck or L44 lane loadings, but not applied to HLP loadings.

Impact loading

$$I = 50/(L + 125)$$

where

I = impact fraction (maximum 30%);

L = length in feet of the portion of the span that is loaded.

Table 3.19. Load factors

No. of standard design lanes	1	2	3	4	5	6
Modification factor	1	0.9	0.8	0.7	0.6	0.55

3.6.12. Indian IRC loading, 1989

Class 70 R loading

IRC Class 70 R loading consists of a tracked vehicle of 700 kN or a wheeled vehicle of total load 1000 kN (Fig. 3.23).

The track is 4.87 m, the nose to tail length of the vehicle is 7.92 m and the specified minimum spacing between successive vehicles is 30 m. The wheeled vehicle is 15.22 m long and has seven axles with the loads totalling 1000 kN. A bogie loading of 400 kN is also specified with wheel loads of 100 kN each. The details of Class 70 R loading are shown in Fig. 3.24.

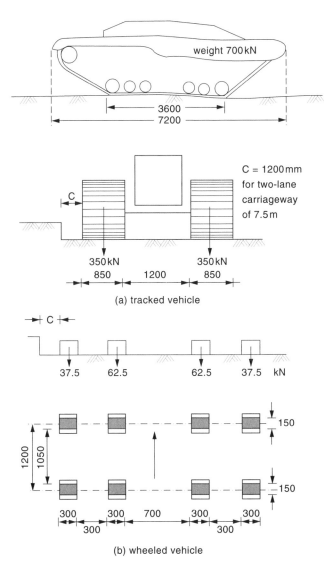

Figure 3.23. Class 70R loading arrangement (detailed)

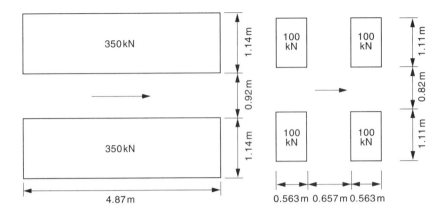

Figure 3.24. Class 70R loading arrangement (Tracked vehicle and bogie axle types)

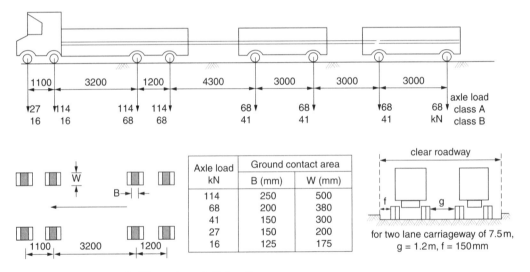

Figure 3.25. IRC Class A and B loadings

IRC Class A loading

IRC Class A loading consists of a wheel load train comprising a truck with trailers of specified axle spacing and loads as detailed in Fig. 3.24. This type of loading is adopted on all roads on which permanent bridges and culverts are constructed.

IRC Class B loading

Class B loading comprises a truck and trailers similar to that of class A loading but with lesser intensity of wheel loads. The axle loads of class B loading is also shown in Fig. 3.25. This type of loading is adopted for temporary structures and timber bridges.

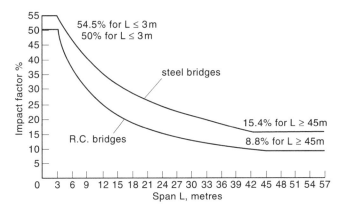

Figure 3.26. Impact percentages for highway bridges

Impact factors
The impact factors can be directly obtained from the curves given in Fig. 3.26.

IRC Class AA or 70 R loading
    For spans less than 9 m:
   (a) For tracked vehicle – 25% for spans up to 5 m linearly reduced to 10%
       for span of 9 m.
   (b) For wheeled vehicle – 25%

    For spans of 9 m or more:
   (a) For tracked vehicle – for RC bridges, 10% up to a span of 40 m and in
       accordance with Fig. 3.26 for spans exceeding 40 m. For steel bridges,
       10% for all spans.
   (b) For wheeled vehicle – For RC bridges, 25% for spans up to 12 m and in
       accordance with Fig. 3.26 for spans exceeding 12 m. For steel bridges,
       25% for spans up to 23 m and as per Fig. 3.26 for spans exceeding 23 m.

Table 3.20. Loadings

Class of bridge	Loading	Main loads (up to 5.5 metres in width)			Sub-loads
		Line load $P(kN/m)$	Uniform load, p (kN/m^2)		
			$L \leq 80$	$L > 80$	
1st	L-20	50	3.5	$4.3 - L$ but not less than 3.0	50% of main loads
2nd	L-14	70% of those of L-20			

3.6.13   Japan (Specifications for Highway Bridges Part 1. Common specifications, 1972) (Revised 1985)

Classification
The code distinguishes two bridge classes according to its design live load:
   Class 1:   a bridge designed by a design vehicle load of 200 kN.
   Class 2:   a bridge designed by a design live load of 140 kN.

Division of the carriageway
See Table 3.20.

Loading system
The design live loads, assuming vehicle loads are divided into the following two loadings:

   (*a*)   *L* loadings (combined load of a uniformly distributed load and a linear load);
   (*b*)   *T* loadings (truck wheel loads).

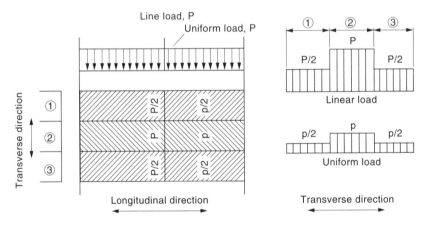

Figure 3.27. L Loadings (maximum stress)

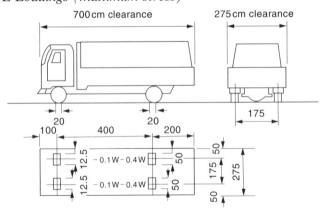

Figure 3.28. T loadings

L loadings are used for designing main girders or main structures, and T loadings for slabs and floor systems.

(a) *L loadings*

On the roadway, the L loadings consisting of a linear load P and the uniform load p defined as 'main loads' in Table 3.20, are placed on the area up to 5.5 m in width of the roadway, and $P/2$ and $p/2$, defined as "sub-loads" in this Table are placed on the remaining area of the roadway, as illustrated in Fig. 3.27, so as to produce the maximum stress.

(b) *T loadings*

The T loadings shown, in Fig. 3.28 and Table 3.21, are placed on the roadway. In the longitudinal direction of a bridge, generally only one T loading is placed, and in the transverse direction, an arbitrary number of T loadings is placed so as to produce the maximum stress.

Impact factor

The impact factor is given as functions of the loadings and spans of members as shown in Table 3.22.

Table 3.21. T loading

Class of bridge	Loading	Gross weight W (ton)	Weight of a front wheel 0.1W (kg)	Weight of a rear wheel 0.4W (kg)	Width of a front wheel b_1(cm)	Width of a rear wheel b_2 (cm)	Length of contact area of a wheel on the road surface a (cm)
1st	T-20	20	2000	8000	12.5	50	20
2nd	T-14	14	1400	5600	12.5	50	20

Table 3.22. Impact factor

Kind of bridge	Impact fraction i	Type of loadings to be applied
Steel bridge	$\dfrac{20}{50 + L}$	T loadings and L loadings
Reinforced concrete bridge	$\dfrac{20}{50 + L}$	T loadings
	$\dfrac{7}{20 + L}$	L loadings
Prestressed concrete bridge	$\dfrac{20}{50 + L}$	T loadings
	$\dfrac{10}{25 + L}$	L loadings

3.6.14 Canada (OHBDC)

The Ontario Highway Bridge Design Code (OHBDC), known as the Ontario design loading, specifies that highway live load should model the following:

1. heavy wheel load
2. heavy axle load in a design lane
3. one heavy vehicle in a design lane
4. multiple presence of vehicles in a design lane
5. simultaneous presence of vehicles in more than one lane.

In the light of the above criteria the highway live load system has two components, the truck and the lane load.

Truck loading

The truck loading is an idealized load in the form of a truck with five axles of two wheels each. The two lines of axles are spaced at 1.8 m centres, and there are many possible different axle weights and spacing.

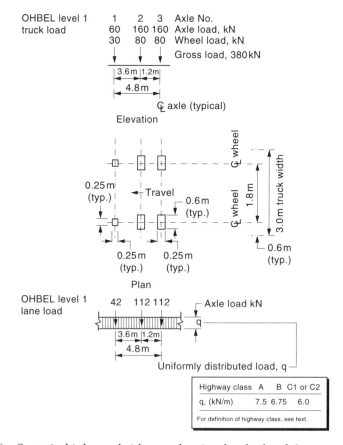

Figure 3.29. Ontario highway bridge evaluation loads, level 1

The front row of wheels has a contact area equal to that of a square of 0.25 m sides, where as the other four rows have a contact area of $0.6 \times 0.25 \, \text{m}^2$.

Evaluation level 1
Evaluation level 1 consists of the OHBD truck without the 4th and the 5th axles, in combination with OHBD lane load reduced to 75% (see Fig. 3.29).

Evaluation level 2
The OHBD truck and lane load is applied with the 5th axle of the truck omitted, and the lane load reduced to 90% (see Fig. 3.30).

Evaluation level 3
Evaluation level 3 is the OHBD design load which is the usual Ontario bridge design load (see Fig. 3.31).

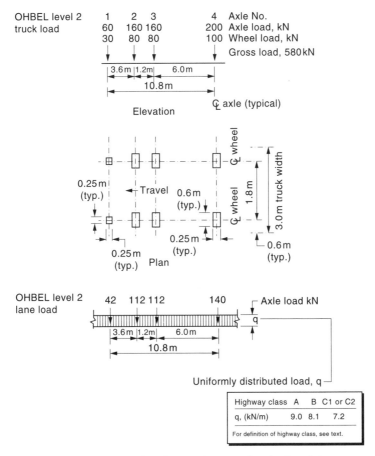

Figure 3.30. Ontario highway bridge evaluation loads, level 2

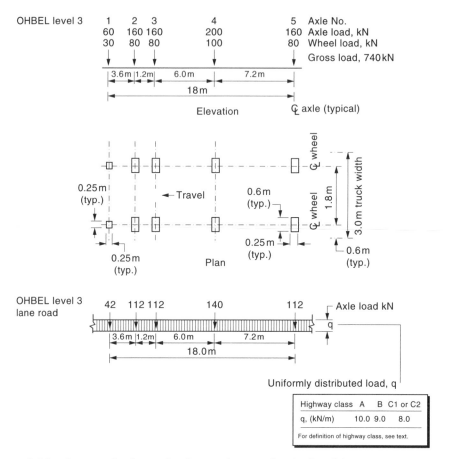

Figure 3.31. Ontario highway bridge evaluation loads, level 3

Controlled vehicle loads

Evaluation for controlled vehicles shall be carried out using wheel loads, axle spacing and other appropriate dimensions available from actual measurements or from available drawings of the loaded vehicle. The requirements of Clause 2–4.3.1.3 of the code shall not apply in determining the total live load effect. The assumed position and direction of the vehicle and the simultaneous applica- tion of other live loads shall be in accordance with the controls imposed.

Classification of highways

Class A highways are roads with an average daily traffic (ADT) of:

truck traffic > 1000 or   traffic > 4000.

Class B highways are roads with an ADT of:

$250 <$ truck traffic < 1000 or

$1000 <$ traffic ≤ 4000.

Class C1 highways are roads with an ADT of:

$50 <$ truck traffic ≤ 250 or

$100 <$ traffic ≤ 1000.

Class C2 highways are roads with an ADT of:

truck traffic ≤ 50 or

traffic ≤ 100.

Design lanes
The specified number of design lanes according to the OHBD is given in Table 3.23.

Normal traffic
The number of loaded lanes shall be determined according to the current or intended use of the bridge. Where the traffic lanes are clearly designated on the bridge, these lanes shall be used as design lanes.

The modification factor for multiple lane loading shall be as given in Table 3.24. The modification factor shall not apply where the simplified method of analysis as given in Clause 3–7 of the code is used.

Controlled vehicle with normal traffic
The modification factors for multiple lanes loaded given in Table 3.24 shall not apply to the load due to the controlled vehicle itself, but shall apply to the normal traffic loads in the other loaded lanes. The lane containing the controlled vehicle shall be included in determining the number of loaded lanes.

Table 3.23. OHBD design lanes

Width (m)	<6	6–10	10–13.5	13.5–17.5	17.5–20.5	20.5–24	24–27.5	over 27.5
N	1	2	3	4	5	6	7	8

Table B3.24. Modification factor for multiple lane loading

Number of lanes loaded	Highway class		
	A	B	C1 and C2
1	1.00	1.00	1.00
2	0.90	0.90	0.85
3	0.80	0.80	0.70
4	0.70	0.70	–
5	0.60	–	–
6 or more	0.55	–	–

Table 3.25. Dynamic load allowance (DLA) modification factor for evaluation levels 1, 2 and 3

	Scale-down factor F	Evaluation level		
		1	2	3
DLA for 1 or 2 axles	F > 0.95	1.00	1.00	1.00
	0.6 ≤ F ≤ 0.95	1.10	1.10	1.10
	F < 0.6	1.25	1.25	1.25
DLA for 3 or more axles	F > 0.95	1.00	1.00	1.00
	0.6 ≤ F ≤ 0.95	1.25	1.10	1.10
	F < 0.6	1.60	1.25	1.25

Other loads
Where the evaluation is to be carried out for other loads, these loads shall be as specified in Section 2 of the code.

Half-through trusses shall also be evaluated for the loads specified in Clause B6.13.3.5 of the code.

Dynamic load allowance
Subject to the provisions of Clauses B6.2.6.1 and B6.2.6.2 of the code, the dynamic load allowance shall be applied as specified in Section 2 of the code unless otherwise approved (see Table 3.25).

3.6.15 United States (Standard Specifications for Highway Bridges 'American Association of State Highway Officials') 1996 16th edition

Classification
Two systems of loadings are provided: H and HS.

Division of the carriageway
The lane loading or standard truck shall be assumed to occupy a width of 10 feet (3.048 m). These loads shall be placed in 12-ft (3.658 m) wide design traffic lanes spaced across the entire bridge roadway width in numbers and positions required to produce the maximum stress in the member under consideration. Roadway width shall be the distance between kerbs. Fractional parts of design lanes shall not be used. Roadway widths from 20 to 24 feet (6.096 to 7.815 m) shall have two design lanes each equal to one-half the roadway width. The lane loading or standard trucks having a 10-ft (3.048 m) width shall be assumed to occupy any position within their individual design traffic lane, which will produce the maximum stress.

Loading systems
H loadings [Fig. 3.32(a)] consist of a two-axle truck or the corresponding lane loading. (Three classes H20, H15 and H10.) *HS loadings* [Fig. 3.32(b)] consist

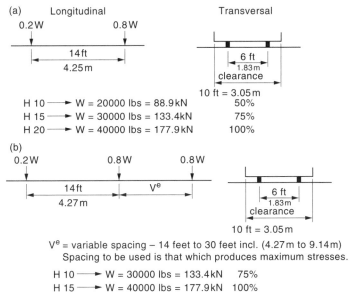

Figure 3.32. Loading systems: (a) H loadings; (b) HS loadings

of a semi-trailer combination or of the corresponding lane loading. (Two classes HS20 and HS15.)

Bridges supporting Interstate highways shall be designed for HS20 loading or an alternate military loading [two axles of 4 feet (1.219 m) apart with each axle weighing 24 000 pounds (108 kN)], whichever produces the greatest stress.

Corresponding lane loading for H20 and HS20 is a uniform load 640 lb per linear foot of load lane, i.e. 9.4 kN per linear metre together with a concentrated load of:

18 000 lb = 80 kN for the moment;

26 000 lb = 116 kN for shear.

For H15 and HS15, 75% of this loading is taken and for H10 50% of this loading is used.

As regards the *reduction in load intensity*, i.e. where maximum stresses are produced in any member by loading any number of traffic lanes simultaneously, the following percentages of the resultant live load stresses shall be used in view of improbable coincident maximum loading:

	Per cent
One or two lanes	100
Three lanes	90
Four lanes or more	75

The reduction in intensity of floor beam loads shall be determined as in the case of main trusses or girders, using the width of roadway which must be loaded to produce maximum stresses in the floor beam.

Referring to the standard HS and H trucks (Fig. 3.33), the lane loading is the same for both the H20-44, loading and the HS20-44 loading (Fig. 3.34).

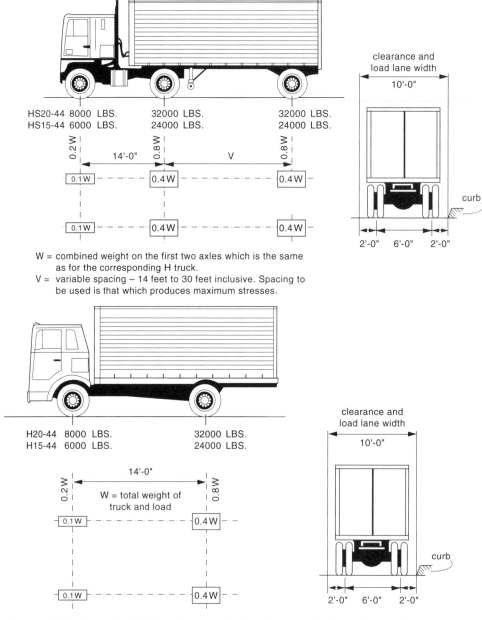

Figure 3.33. Standard HS and H trucks (AASHTO highway bridge design 3.10.1)

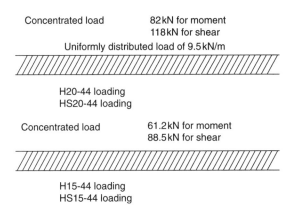

Figure 3.34. AASHTO lane loading

The HS20-44, and HS15-44 comprise of a truck and trailer with a total load of 326 kN, and 245 kN, respectively. The load per axle of these trucks is shown in Table 3.26.

Impact factor
For superstructures the live load stresses produced by H or HS loadings shall be increased with an impact factor, allowing for dynamic, vibratory and impact effects. The amount of this allowance is expressed as a fraction of live load stresses, and shall be determined by the formula:

$$I = \frac{50}{L + 125}; \quad \text{when } L \text{ is in metres} \qquad I = \frac{15.24}{L + 38}$$

in which

I = impact fraction (maximum 30%);

L = length in feet of the portion of the span which is loaded to produce maximum stress.

Combinations of loads
The following groups represent various combinations of loads and forces to which a structure may be subjected. Each component of the structure, or the foundation on which it rests, shall be proportioned to withstand safely all

Table 3.26. Load per axle

Loading	Front axle	Mid. axle	Rear axle	Total
HS20-44	36 kN	145 kN	145 kN	326 kN
HS15-44	27 kN	109 kN	109 kN	245 kN

Table 3.27 (below and facing). Coefficients γ and β

Col. No.	1	2	3	3A	4	5	6	7	8	9	10	11	12	13	14
Group	γ	β factors													%
		D	$(L+I)_n$	$(L+I)_p$	CF	E	B	SF	W	WL	LF	$R+S+T$	EQ	ICE	
Service load															
I	1.0	1	1	0	1	β_E	1	1	0	0	0	0	0	0	100
IA	1.0	1	2	0	0	0	0	0	0	0	0	0	0	0	150
IB	1.0	1	0	1	1	β_E	1	1	0	0	0	0	0	0	†
II	1.0	1	0	0	0	1	1	1	1	0	0	0	0	0	125
III	1.0	1	1	0	1	β_E	1	1	0.3	1	1	0	0	0	125
IV	1.0	1	1	0	1	β_E	1	1	0	0	0	1	0	0	125
V	1.0	1	0	0	1	1	1	1	1	0	0	1	0	0	140
VI	1.0	1	1	0	1	β_E	1	1	0.3	1	1	1	0	0	140
VII	1.0	1	0	0	1	1	1	1	0	0	0	0	1	0	133
VIII	1.0	1	1	0	0	1	1	1	0	0	0	0	0	1	140
IX	1.0	1	0	0	0	1	1	1	1	0	0	0	0	1	150
X	1.0	1	1	0	0	β_E	0	0	0	0	0	0	0	0	100 Culvert
Load factor design															
I	1.3	β_D	1.67*	0	1.0	β_E	1	1	0	0	0	0	0	0	Not applicable
IA	1.3	β_D	2.20	0	0	0	0	0	0	0	0	0	0	0	
IB	1.3	β_D	0	1	1.0	β_E	1	1	0	0	0	0	0	0	
II	1.3	β_D	0	0	0	β_E	1	1	1	0	0	0	0	0	
III	1.3	β_D	1	0	1	β_E	1	1	0.3	1	1	0	0	0	
IV	1.3	β_D	1	0	1	β_E	1	1	0	0	0	1	0	0	
V	1.25	β_D	0	0	0	β_E	1	1	1	0	0	1	0	0	
VI	1.25	β_D	1	0	1	β_E	1	1	0.3	1	1	1	0	0	
VII	1.3	β_D	0	0	0	β_E	1	1	0	0	0	0	1	0	
VIII	1.3	β_D	1	0	1	β_E	1	1	0	0	0	0	0	1	
IX	1.20	β_D	0	0	0	β_E	1	1	1	0	0	0	0	1	
X	1.30	1	1.67	0	0	β_E	0	0	0	0	0	0	0	0	Culvert

$(L + I)_n$ – live load plus impact for AASHTO Highway H or HS loading.

$(L + I)_p$ – live load plus impact consistent with the overload criteria of the operation agency.

* 1.25 may be used for design of outside roadway beam when combination of sidewalk live load as well as traffic live load plus impact governs the design but the capacity of the section should not be less than required for highway traffic live load only using a beta factor of 1.67. 1.00 may be used for design of deck slab with combination of loads as described in Article 3.24.2.2 of the code.

†Percentage $= \dfrac{\text{maximum unit stress (operating rating)}}{\text{allowable basic unit stress}} \times 100$

For service load design

% (Column 14) percentage of basic unit stress

No increase in allowable unit stresses shall be permitted for members or connections carrying wind loads only.

$\beta_E = 1.00$ for vertical and lateral loads on all other structures

For culvert loading specifications.

$\beta_E = 1.0$ and 0.5 for lateral loads on rigid frames (check both loadings to see which one governs).

For load factor design

$\beta_E = 1.3$ for lateral earth pressure for retaining walls and rigid frames excluding rigid culverts. For lateral at-rest earth pressures, $\beta_E = 1.15$

$\beta_E = 0.5$ for lateral earth pressure when checking positive moments in rigid frames.

$\beta_E = 1.0$ for vertical earth pressure.

$\beta_D = 0.75$ when checking member for minimum axial load and maximum moment or maximum eccentricity (for column design).

$\beta_D = 1.0$ when checking member for maximum axial load and minimum moment (for column design).

$\beta_D = 1.0$ for flexural and tension members.

$\beta_E = 1.0$ for rigid culverts.

$\beta_E = 1.5$ for flexible culverts.

For Group X loading (culverts) the β_E factor shall be applied to vertical and horizontal loads.

group combinations of these forces that are applicable to the particular site or type. Group loading combinations for service load design and load factor design are given by:

$$\text{Group } (N) = \gamma [\beta_D \cdot D + \beta_L (L + I) + \beta_C CF + \beta_E E + \beta_B B$$

$$+ \beta_S SF + \beta_W W + \beta_{WL} WL + \beta_L \cdot LF + \beta_R (R + S + T)$$

$$+ \beta_{EQ} EQ + \beta_{ICE} ICE] \tag{3.3}$$

where,

N = group number

γ = load factor, see Table 3.27

β = coefficient, see Table 3.27

D = dead load

L = live load

I = live load impact

E = earth pressure

B = buoyancy

W = wind load on structure

WL = wind load on live load – 100 pounds per linear foot

LF = longitudinal force from live load

CF = centrifugal force

R = rib shortening

S = shrinkage

T = temperature

EQ = earthquake

SF = stream flow pressure

ICE = ice pressure.

For service load design, the percentage of the basic unit stress for the various groups is given in Table 3.27.

The loads and forces in each group shall be taken as appropriate from Articles 3.3 to 3.21 of the code. The maximum section required shall be used.

For load factor design, the gamma and beta factors given in Table 3.27 shall be used for designing structural members and foundations by the load factor concept.

Distribution of loads for bending moment in spread box girders
Interior beams
The live load bending moment for each interior beam in a spread box beam superstructure shall be determined by applying to the beam the fraction (DF) of the wheel load (both front and rear) determined by the following equation:

$$DF = \frac{2N_L}{N_B} + k\frac{S}{L} \tag{3.4}$$

where:

N_L = number of design traffic lanes

N_B = number of beams ($4 \le N_B \le 10$);

S = beam spacing in feet ($6.57 \le S \le 11.00$);

L = span length in feet;

$k = 0.07W - N_L(0.10N_L - 0.26) - 0.20N_B - 012;$ \hfill (3.5)

W = numeric value of the roadway width between curbs expressed in feet ($32 \le W \le 66$).

Exterior beams
The live load bending moment in the exterior beams shall be determined by applying to the beams the reaction of the wheel loads obtained by assuming the flooring to act as a simple span (of length S) between beams, but shall not be less than $2N_L/N_B$.

The live load bending moment for each section shall be determined by applying to the beam the fraction of a wheel load (both front and rear) determined by the following equation

$$\text{load fraction} = \frac{S}{D} \tag{3.6}$$

where:

S = width of precast member;

$D = (5.75 - 0.5N_L) + 0.7N_L(1 - 0.2C)^2 \quad \text{when } C \ge 5;$ \hfill (3.7)

$D = (5.75 - 0.5N_L) \quad \text{when } C > 5;$ \hfill (3.8)

N_L = number of traffic lanes;

$C = K(W/L);$ \hfill (3.9)

where:

W = overall width of bridge measured perpendicular to the longitudinal girders in feet;

L = span length measured parallel to longitudinal wind girders in feet; for girders with cast-in-place end diaphragms, use the length between end diaphragms;

$K = \{(1+\mu)I/J\}^{1/2};$

I = moment of inertia;

J = Saint–Venant torsion constant; and

μ = Poisson's ratio for girders.

In lieu of more exact methods, 'J' may be estimated using the following equation:

$$J = \sum\{(1/3)bt^3(1 - 0.630t/b)\}$$

where:

b = the length of each rectangular component within the section;

t = the thickness of each rectangular component within the section.

Table 3.28. Distribution of wheel loads in transverse beams

Kind of floor	Fraction of wheel load to each floor beam
Plank[a,b]	$\dfrac{S}{4}$
Nail laminated[c] or glued laminated[e], 4 inches in thickness, or multiple layer[d] floors more than 5 inches thick	$\dfrac{S}{4.5}$
Nail laminated[c] or glued laminated[e], 6 inches or more in thickness	$\dfrac{S^f}{5}$
Concrete	$\dfrac{S^f}{6}$
Steel grid (less than 4 inches thick)	$\dfrac{S}{4.5}$
Steel grid (4 inches or more)	$\dfrac{S^f}{6}$
Steel bridge corrugated plank (2 inches minimum depth)	$\dfrac{S}{5.5}$

S = spacing of floor beams in feet.
[a-e] For footnotes a through e, see Table 3.29.
[f] If S exceeds denominator, the load on the beam shall be the reaction of the wheels loads assuming the flooring between beams to act as a simple beam

If the value of $\sqrt{I/J}$ exceeds 5.0, the live load distribution should be determined using a more precise method, such as the Articulated Plate Theory or Grillage Analysis.

For a detailed analysis of wheel loading, refer to Tables 3.28 and 3.29.

Truck loads
Under the following formulas for distribution of loads on cantilever slabs, the slab is designed to support the load independently of the effects of any edge support along the end of the cantilever. The distribution given includes the effect of wheels on parallel elements.

Case A – reinforcement perpendicular to traffic
Each wheel on the element perpendicular to traffic shall be distributed over a width according to the following formula:

$$E = 0.8X + 3.75 \tag{3.10}$$

The moment per foot of slab shall be $(P/E)\,X$ foot-pounds, in which X is the distance in feet from load to point of support.

Case B – reinforcement parallel to traffic
The distribution width for each wheel load on the element parallel to traffic shall be as follows:

$$E = 0.35X + 3.2, \quad \text{but shall not exceed 7.0 ft} \tag{3.11}$$

The moment per foot of slab shall be $(P/E)\,X$ foot-pounds.

Railing loads
Railing loads shall be applied in accordance with Article 2.7 of the code. The effective length of slab resisting post loadings shall be equal to $E = 0.8X + 3.75$ feet where no parapet is used and equal to $E = 0.8X + 5.0$ feet where a parapet is used, where X is the distance in feet from the centre of the post to the point under investigation. Railing and wheel loads shall not be applied simultaneously.

Forces from superstructure
The transverse and longitudinal forces transmitted by the superstructure to the substructure for various angles of wind direction shall be as set forth in Table 3.30. The skew angle is measured from the perpendicular to the longitudinal axis and the assumed wind direction shall be that which produces the maximum stress in the substructure. The transverse and longitudinal forces shall be applied simultaneously at the elevation of the centre of gravity of the exposed area of the superstructure.

The loads listed above shall be used in Group II and Group V loadings as given in Article 3.22 of the code.

Table 3.29. Distribution of wheel loads in longitudinal beams

Kind of floor	Bridge designed for one traffic lane	Bridge designed for two or more traffic lanes
Timber:[a]		
Plank[b]	$S/4.0$	$S/3.75$
Nail laminated[c]		
4″ thick or multiple layer[d]		
floors over 5″ thick	$S/4.5$	$S/4.0$
Nail laminated[c]		
6″ or more thick	$S/50$	$S/4.25$
	If S exceeds 5′	If S exceeds 6.5′
	use footnote f	use footnote f
Glued laminated[e]		
Panels on glued laminated stringers		
4″ thick	$S/4.5$	$S/4.0$
6″ or more thick	$S/6.0$	$S/5.0$
	If S exceeds 6′	If S exceeds 7′
	use footnote f	use footnote f
On steel stringers		
4″ thick	$S/4.5$	$S/4.0$
6″ or more thick	$S/5.25$	$S/4.5$
	If S exceeds 5.5′	If S exceeds 7'
	use footnote f	use footnote f
Concrete:		
On steel I-Beam stringers[g] and		
prestressed concrete girders	$S/7.0$	$S/5.5$
	If S exceeds 10′	If S exceeds 14′
	use footnote f	use footnote f
On concrete T-beams	$S/6.5$	$S/6.0$
	If S exceeds 6′	If S exceeds 10′
	use footnote f	use footnote f
On timber stringers	$S/6.0$	$S/5.0$
	If S exceeds 6′	If S exceeds 10′
	use footnote f	use footnote f
Concrete box girders[h]	$S/8.0$	$S/7.0$
	If S exceeds 12′	If S exceeds 16′
	use footnote f	use footnote f
On steel box girders	See Article 10.39.2	
On prestressed concrete spread		
box beams	See Article 3.28	
Steel grid:		
(less than 4″ thick)	$S/4.5$	$S/4.0$
(4″ or more)	$S/6.0$	$S/5.0$
	If S exceeds 6′	If S exceeds 10.5′
	use footnote f	use footnote f
Steel bridge		
Corrugated plank[i]		
(2″ minimum depth)	$S/5.5$	$S/4.5$

Table 3.30

	Trusses		Girders	
Skew angle of wind	Lateral load	Longitudinal load	Lateral load	Longitudinal load
Degrees	PSF	PSF	PSF	PSF
0	75	0	50	0
15	70	12	44	6
30	65	28	41	12
45	47	41	33	16
60	24	50	17	19

For Group III and Group VI loadings, these loads may be reduced by 70% and a load per linear foot added as a wind load on a moving live load, as given in Table 3.31.

This load shall be applied at a point 6 ft above the deck.

For the usual girder and slab bridges having maximum span lengths of 125 ft, the following wind loading may be used in lieu of the more precise loading specified above

W   (wind load on structure)
    50 pounds per square foot, transverse
    12 pounds per square foot, longitudinal
    Both forces shall be applied simultaneously

WL (wind load on live load)
    100 pounds per linear foot, transverse
    40 pounds per linear foot, longitudinal
    Both forces shall be applied simultaneously.

Table 3.31

Skew angle of wind	Lateral load	Longitudinal load
Degrees	lb/ft	lb/ft
0	100	0
15	88	12
30	82	24
45	66	32
60	34	38

3.7   Examples on load distribution – vehicular and environmental

3.7.1   Example (3.1)   British practice

The local effects for the wheel load on deck slabs are determined by Westergaard's equations. Stating briefly the method and giving relevant equations concerning HA single wheel loads and for multiple HB loading, the results must give moments in the x and y-directions as shown in Fig. 3.35.

Moments due to a point load P_1 at mid-span

When $\nu = 0$, P_1 is at mid-span of the slab; the principal moments are given in simplified form by

$$M_{\text{ox}} = \frac{P_1 s}{2.32s + 8c} \tag{3.12}$$

$$M_{\text{oy}} = M_{\text{ox}} - 0.0676P_1$$

where $P_1 =$ applied wheel load in kN and $c =$ effective diameter of loaded area; for the abnormal wheel load, $c = 190\,\text{mm} + 2t$, t being the thickness (mm) of the non-structural surfacing on the slab.

Increase in moment under P_1 due to load P_3

The increase in M_{ox} due to P_3 is given by

$$\text{increase in } M_{\text{ox}} = \frac{100}{1 + 10(y/s)^2}\ \% \tag{3.13}$$

it being assumed that $P_3 = P_1$. Hence, for the abnormal load, with axles at 1800 mm centres, since $y = 1800$, the increases are dependent on the spacing of the main beams. Westergaard showed that, for $y/s > 0.5$, the increase in M_{ox} due to P_3 becomes negative; since y/s will always be greater than 0.5

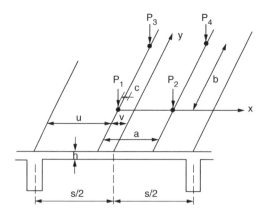

Figure 3.35. Local effects of wheel loads

when the standard beams are being used, there is no need for an equation giving the increase in M_{oy} due to P_3.

Moments due to P_1 and P_2 distance a apart
The maximum moments, which occur under P_1, are given by

$$M_x = M_{ox} + 0.21072P \log\left(\frac{\cot(\pi a/4s)}{2}\right) \tag{3.14}$$

$$M_y = M_{oy} = 0.21072P \log\left(\frac{\cot(\pi a/4s)}{2}\right) \tag{3.15}$$

To achieve these moments, $\nu = a/4$ and, if $a > 0.5903s$, the second term in the above equations becomes negative. Hence, the maximum moments are produced when P_1 acts alone at the centre of the span.

Moments due to four equal loads P at P_1, P_2, P_3 and P_4
The moments at point $P_1(-a/4, 0)$ due to the loads at P_3 and P_4 show

$$\left.\begin{matrix}M_x\\M_y\end{matrix}\right\} = 0.10536P \log\frac{A^2}{B_3 B_4} \pm 0.10625\,\frac{Pb}{s}\sinh\frac{\pi b}{s}\left(\frac{1}{B_3}+\frac{1}{B_4}-\frac{2}{A}\right) \tag{3.16}$$

$$M_{xy} = -0.10625\,\frac{Pb}{s}\,\frac{\sin\dfrac{\pi a}{s}}{B_4} \tag{3.17}$$

where

$$A = \cosh\frac{\pi b}{s} + \cos\frac{\pi a}{2s}$$

$$B_3 = \cosh\frac{\pi b}{s} - 1$$

$$B_4 = \cosh\frac{\pi b}{s} - \cos\frac{\pi a}{s}$$

Effect of encastré supports
The effect of encastring the supports can be shown to be given by

$$M'_{ox} = M_{ox}(0.83783 - 0.5592c/s)$$

where M'_{ox} is the moment under P_1 when the supports are fully encastré.

It should be noted that the support conditions do not significantly affect the moments in the y-direction since the analysis is for an infinitely wide slab.

Design moments due to wheel loads
Depending on the spacing of the beams, either two or four wheel loads will create the maximum values of M_{ox} and M_{oy}; the equations above enable both loading conditions to be considered.

Application to HA and HB loadings

$$P_1, P_2, P_3, P_4 = P \qquad \text{HA}$$

(i)   the slab is simply supported;
(ii) the Poisson's ratio is 0.15.

Equations given for *HA loading* will be

$$M_x = 0.21072P \left(\log \frac{s}{c_1} + 0.4825 \right) \tag{3.18}$$

where

$$c_1 = 2(\sqrt{0.4c^2 + h^2} - 0.675h) \tag{3.19}$$

$$M_y = M_x - 0.676P \tag{3.20}$$

For HB loading when $s < 1.7$, i.e. $s < 1.7$ m for HB wheels on a transverse spanning slab, the worst-case situation is where one wheel is at mid-span, i.e., $\nu = 0$. P_3 is to increase the value of M_x by

$$\frac{100}{1 + 10(b/s)^2} \, (\%); \qquad b > 1.8 \, \text{m for HB}$$

provided $b > 0.5s$ for HB.

P_3 will, however, reduce M_y. It is safe to use $M_y = M_x - 0.676P$. If $s > 1.7a$, the worst case is $\nu = a/4$.

The maximum moments occur under P_1

Simple span
$$\begin{cases} M_x = 0.2107P \left(\log \frac{s}{c_1} + 0.4825 \right) + 0.2107P \log \left\{ \frac{\cot}{2} \frac{\pi a}{4s} \right\} \tag{3.21} \\[4mm] M_y = M_x - 0.0676P + 0.2107P \log \left\{ \frac{\cot}{2} \frac{\pi a}{4s} \right\} \tag{3.22} \end{cases}$$

If $s > 3$ m for HB loading consider the third wheel

Encastré span
$$\begin{cases} M_x = 0.2107P \left(\log \frac{s}{c_1} + 0.4825 \right) - 0.07P \tag{3.23} \\[4mm] M_y = 0.2107P \left(\log \frac{s}{c_1} + 0.4825 \right) - 0.1065P \tag{3.24} \end{cases}$$

3.7.2   Example (3.2)   British practice

A slab bridge has a span of 18.33 m and a carriageway of 11.0 m, calculate the HA and KEL (knife-edge load) effects. If the same bridge is of a slab/beam deck and the beams are at 1.29 m centres, calculate the HA and KEL effects and find the variations.

(a) Lane loading = 9.786 kN. For 11 m carriageway, the number of lanes is three each of 3.66 m width.

$$\text{HA loading/m}^2 = 9.786 \times 0.1 = 0.9786 \,\text{kN}$$

$$\text{KEL} = 39.4 \,\text{kN/m}$$

(b)

$$\text{Lane loading} = 9.786 \,\text{kN}$$

$$\text{lane width} = 3.66 \,\text{m}$$

$$\text{HA loading} = 9.786/3.66 = 2.674 \,\text{kN/m}^2$$

$$\text{Loading due to KEL} = 39.4/3.66 = 10.765 \,\text{kN}$$

Loading on beams (half lane width)

$$2.674 \times \frac{3.66}{2} = 4.9 \,\text{kN} \quad \text{as a UDL}$$

$$10.765 \times \frac{3.66}{2} = 19.7 \,\text{kN} \quad \text{as a knife-edge load}$$

Variations:

$$\text{UDL HA type} = 1.6954 \,\text{kN/m}^2 \quad \text{more in case } (b)$$

$$\text{KEL} = 28.635 \,\text{kN/m} \quad \text{in case } (a).$$

3.7.3 Example (3.3) British practice

Calculate the contact circle diameter for the HA, HB 45 units and HB 25 units for a simple span of a slab bridge of fully loaded length 15 m. The diameter at the neutral axis must have a spread/depth of 1 : 2 and through concrete at 1 : 1 down to the neutral axis. Consider HA and HB loads to have square contact areas.

$$\text{span} = 15 \,\text{m}$$

$$\text{HA loading} = 30 \,\text{kN/m}$$

$$\text{notional single lane} = 3.725 \,\text{m wide}$$

$$\text{intensity} = 30/3.725 = 8.05 \,\text{kN/m}^2$$

$$\text{KEL} = 120 \,\text{kN/notional lane}$$

$$\text{intensity} = 120/3.725 = 32.2 \,\text{kN/m}^2$$

$$\text{wheel load} = 100 \,\text{kN with a circular area of } 0.34 \,\text{m}^2$$

$$\text{HB loading} = 45 \,\text{units}$$

$$\text{axle spacing} = 6 \,\text{m (shortest).}$$

Circular contact area with an effective pressure $= 1.1 \, \text{N/mm}^2$.

HB 45 units:

$$\text{load per axle} = 450 \, \text{kN}$$

$$\text{contact circle diameter} = \sqrt{\frac{450}{4} \times 1000 \times 4 \times \frac{1}{1.1\pi}} = 360 \, \text{mm}$$

HB 25 units:

$$\text{load per axle} = 125 \, \text{kN}$$

$$\text{load per wheel} = 62.5$$

$$\text{contact circle diameter} = \sqrt{\frac{62.5 \times 1000 \times 4}{1.1\pi}} \bigg/ 1000 = 0.27 \, \text{m}$$

Diameter of the contact circle at the neutral axis

$$= 360 + 10.0 + 90 \times 10^{-3} = 1.36 \rightarrow \text{HB 45}$$

$$270 + 10.0 + 90 \times 10^{-3} = 1.27 \rightarrow \text{HB 25}$$

$$340 + 10.0 + 90 \times 10^{3} = 1.34 \rightarrow \text{HA}.$$

3.7.4 Example (3.4) British practice

Calculate loads and load distribution for 30 units HB in nearside lane plus one-third of HA loading in the farside lane. The girder bridge span is 27 m in steel. Combine these loads with DL + services + walkway liveloads. Calculate the worst possible bending moment. Using the following data and see Fig. 3.36:

$$\text{DL} + \text{sevices} + \text{walkway} = 1039.5 \, \text{kN}$$

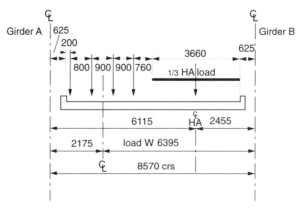

Note all dimensions are in mm

Figure 3.36. Load distribution: one-third HA and HB

Girder 'A' is the design criterion
  HB loading:

$$\text{axle loads} - 30 \text{ units} = 300\,\text{kN}$$

$$\text{effective axle loads to girder A} = 300 \times \frac{6395}{8570}$$

$$= 224\,\text{kN}$$

Total loads
  $\frac{1}{3}$ *HA loading:*

$$\text{lane load UDL} = \tfrac{1}{3}[27 \times 30] = 270\,\text{kN}$$

$$\text{lane load KEL} = \tfrac{1}{3}[120] = 40\,\text{kN}$$

$$\therefore \quad \text{EFF UDL to girder A} = 270 \times \frac{2455}{8570} = 77.3\,\text{kN}$$

$$\text{EFF KEL to girder A} = 40 \times \left[\frac{2455}{8570}\right] = 11.5\,\text{kN} \quad \text{Total}$$

Maximum bending moment
From the design criterion above, and referring to Fig. 3.37, $\frac{1}{3}$ HA KEL [11.5 kN]
and HB axles [4 @ 224 kN]:

$$RL = \frac{1}{27}\,[224(7.125 + 8.925 + 15.025 + 16.825) + 11.5(15.025)]$$

$$= 403.8\,\text{kN}$$

$$M_{xx} = 403.8 \times 11.975 - 224 \times 1.8 \qquad\qquad = 4432.2\,\text{kN/m}$$

$$M_{xx} \text{ due to } \tfrac{1}{3}\text{ HA (WDL)} = \frac{77.3 \times 27}{8} \qquad\qquad = 260.9\,\text{kN/m}$$

$$M_{xx} \text{ due to DL/services/walkway LL} \simeq \frac{1039.5 \times 27}{8} = 3508.3\,\text{kN/m}$$

$$\text{Total BM at x–x} = 8201.4\,\text{kN/m}$$

$$\therefore \quad \text{maximum axial force} = \frac{8201.4}{3} = +2733.8\,\text{kN}$$

$400 \times 200 \,\square\, 12.5$ GL: 50C

$$f_{ac} = \frac{2733.8 \times 10}{143} = 191\,\text{N/mm}^2$$

$$p_{ac} = 175 + 25\% = 219\,\text{N/mm}^2$$

Fatigue life satisfactory. Adopt $400 \times 200 \,\square\, 12.5$; GR: 50C RHS top chord.

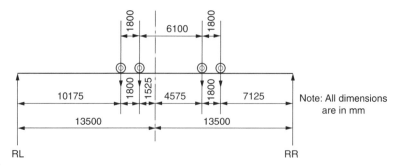

Figure 3.37. Maximum bending moment

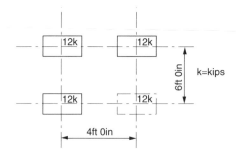

Figure 3.38. Illustration of US military loading

3.7.5 Example (3.5) American practice

The United States military loading is shown in Fig. 3.38 and governs for certain smaller spans over H20–S16 loading. Compute moments, end shears/reactions and centre-line shears for the following spans:

spans 11 ft to 44 ft   (3.35 m to 13.5 m)

Mark the spans where H20–S16 governs over the military loading (Table 3.32) and note:

1 kip = 4.448 kN;   1 ft kip = 1.356 kN/m.

3.7.6 Example (3.6) American practice

A simple span of 21.34 m. The load distribution is given on the span identified by P in Fig. 3.39. The value of P for the 3S2 vehicle wheel is 3.632 ton, $S =$ the stringer spacing and is 2.3876 ft. Determine the moment M_p for the bridge using the following data for the dead load interior beam:

slab = 1.0923 ton/metre

haunch = 0.0744

distributed* = 0.3601

Table 3.32. Data for Example (3.5)

Span (ft)	Moment (ft kips)	End shear and end reactions (kips)	℄ shear
11	88.36	39.27	15.27
12	97,75	40.00	16.00
13	111.69	40.62	16.62
14	123.43	41.14	17.14
15	135.20	41.60	17.60
16	147.00	42.00	18.00
17	158.82	42.35	18.35
18	170.67	42.67	18.67
19	182.53	42.95	18.95
20	194.40	43.20	19.20
21	206.29	43.43	19.43
22	218.18	43.64	19.64
23	230.09		19.83
24	242.00	↓ H20–S16-44	20.00
25	253.92		20.16
26	265.85		20.31
27	277.78		20.44
28	289.71		20.57
29	301.66		20.69
30	313.60		20.80
31	325.55		20.90
32	337.50		21.00
33	349.45		21.09
34	361.41		21.18
35	373.37		21.26
36	385.53		21.34
37	397.30		21.41
38			21.48
39			21.54
40	↓ H20–S16-44		21.60
42			21.71
44			21.82

↓ H20

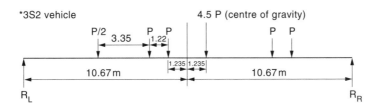

Figure 3.39. Example (3.6): 3S2 vehicle loading for a steel beam bridge

beam $= 0.4464$

details $= 0.0327$

$\Sigma = 2.0059$ ton/metre

FWL $= 1.424$,   i.e. fraction of wheel load

$$I = \text{impact} = \frac{50}{L + 125} \quad (L \text{ in ft})$$

$f_{\text{perm}} = 0.75 f_y$

Calculate the rating for working stress, serviceability, inventory and operating cases:

value of R_L (critical wheel point) $= \dfrac{45P(10.67 - 1.235)}{21.34}$

$$M_P = R_L(10.67 - 1.235) - 1.22P - (3.35 + 1.22)\frac{P}{2} \qquad (3.25)$$

FWL (fraction of wheel load) to a stringer or beam $= \dfrac{S}{1.676}$

$$= \frac{2.3876}{1.676}$$

$$= 1.424$$

$$I = \text{impact} = \frac{15.24}{L + 38}$$

$$= 0.256$$

$$L = 21.34 \text{ m}$$

in Imperial units

$$I = \frac{50}{L + 125} \quad (L \text{ in ft})$$

$P = 3.632$ tons (wheel)

$\dfrac{16}{2} = 8000 \text{ lb}$

Live load moment for the 3S2 vehicle:

$= \text{load} \times \text{distribution factor} \times \text{impact} \times \text{distance to the load centre}$

$= 3.632 \times 1.424(1 + 0.256) \times \text{Eq. (3.25) terms}$

$= 99.20$ ton m   (1 American ton $= 1000$ lb)

$$= 3281 \text{ ft lb}$$

$$= 3.281 \text{ ft kip} =$$

$$M_g = \text{deadload moment} = \frac{\omega l^2}{8} = \frac{2.0059(21.34)^2}{8}$$

$f_{\text{perm}} = \text{permissible stress (inventory)} = 114.2 \text{ ton m}$

$$= 0.55 f_y = 20\,000 \text{ psi } (1406 \text{ kg/cm}^2) = 138 \text{ MN/m}^2$$

S_x (using 36 WF 300) $=$ section modulus

$$= 1110 \text{ m}^3 \ (18\,190 \text{ cm}^3)$$

$$\text{WF} = \text{wide flange}$$

$$M_{\text{perm}} = f_{\text{perm}} S_x = 255.8 \text{ ton m}$$

Working stress

$$\frac{M_{\text{perm}} - M_g}{M} \leftarrow \text{rating factor RF}$$

$$= \frac{255.8 - 114.2}{99.2} = 1.427 \text{ inventory}$$

Operating

$$f_{\text{perm}} = 0.75 f_y; \qquad f_y = 36\,000 \text{ psi}$$

$$= 0.75 \times 36\,000 = 27\,000 \text{ psi} = 1898 \text{ kg/cm}^2$$

$$M_{\text{perm}} = 1898 \times 18\,190 = 34\,524\,620 \text{ kg cm} = 345.2 \text{ ton m}$$

$$\text{RF} = \frac{345.2 - 114.2}{99.2} = 2.329 \quad \text{operating}$$

Load factor method

$$Z_x = 1260(2.54)^3 = 20\,648 \text{ cm}^3$$

$$S_x = 1110(2.54)^3 = 18\,190 \text{ cm}^3$$

$$f_y Z_x = 522.6 \text{ ton m}$$

$$f_y S_x = 460.4 \text{ ton m}$$

$$\text{RF} = (f_y Z - 1.3 M_g) \Big/ \left\{ 1.3 \left(\frac{5}{3}\right) (LL + I) \right\}$$

$$= \frac{522.6 - 1.3(114.2)}{1.3 \times \frac{5}{3} \times 99.20} = 1.741 \quad \text{(inventory)}$$

$$\text{RF} = (0.8 f_y S - M_g) \Big/ \frac{5}{3} (LL + I) = 1.537 \quad \text{(serviceability)}$$

Strength

$$RF = (f_y Z - 1.3 M_g)/\{1.3(LL + I)\} = 2.901 \quad \text{(operating)}$$

$$RF = (0.8 f_y S - M_g)/(LL + I) = 2.562 \quad \text{(serviceability)}.$$

3.7.7 Example (3.7) British practice

Figure 3.40 shows the prestressed-concrete box beam bridge deck. Determine lanes, HA and HB loading distribution. Calculate respective moments and shear forces according to BS 5400. Use the relevant data from the code (Table 3.33) and a simple span of 60 m.

Bending moment
Referring to Fig. 3.41:

$$R_a + R_b = 866.8 \, \text{kN}$$

Taking moment about a:

$$216.7[1.8 + 7.8 + 9.6] - 60.R_b = 0$$

Therefore:

$$R_a = 797.5 \, \text{kN}$$
$$R_b = 69.3 \, \text{kN}$$

Therefore the most severe case is from HA + KEL:

$$= 1251 \, \text{kN}$$

For HB maximum SF: 1251 kN
Maximum bending moment for HA + KEL:

$$= 8870 + 3260.5$$
$$= 12\,130.4 \, \text{kNm}$$

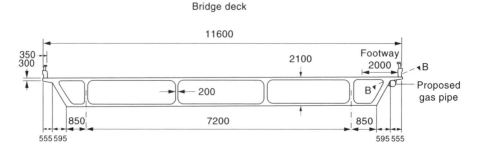

Bridge deck

Note: all dimensions are in mm

Figure 3.40. Prestressed-concrete box beam bridge deck cross-section

Table 3.33. BS 5400 data for Example (3.7)

Lanes
Width of carriageway = 7600 mm
No. of notional lanes = 2
Therefore width of one lane:

$$= \frac{7600}{3} = 3800 \, \text{mm}$$

Width of central reserve = 600 mm

Width of one lane = $3800 - \dfrac{600}{2}$

$$= 3500 \, \text{mm}$$

Lane 1:
3500 mm
Lane 2:
3500 mm

HA loading
For type HA uniformly distributed load:
up to 60 m loaded length = 21.4 kN/m
For a unit box beam, i.e. 2.60 m
HA = (21.4/2.917) × 2.60
$\qquad$ = 19.07 kN/m

HA:
19.07 kN/m

HB loading
Min units is 25
One unit = 10 kN per axle (2.5 kN per wheel)
Dimension of HB vehicles = 1.8 m
between axles
For unit box beam, i.e. 2.60 m:

$$\text{HB} = \frac{(10 \times 35)}{3} \times 2.60 = 216.7 \, \text{kN}$$

HB:
216.7 kN

KEL (knife-edge loading)
The KEL per notional lanes shall be
taken as 120 kN

$$\text{KEL} = \frac{120 \times 2.60}{2.917} = 106.9 \, \text{kN}$$

KEL:
106.9 kN

Dimension of HB vehicles:

$\qquad$ 1.8 m, 6 m, 1.8 m

HB loading (see Fig. 3.42)

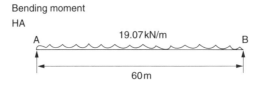

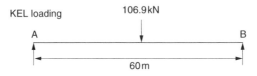

Figure 3.41. Example (3.7): bending moment

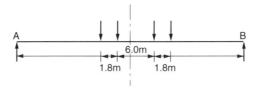

Figure 3.42. Example (3.7): HB loading

Taking moment about a:

$$216.7[27.2 + 29 + 35 + 36.8] - 60.R_b = 0$$

$$R_b = 454.7\,\text{kN}$$

$$R_a = 412.1\,\text{kN}$$

$$M = 412.1(32) - 216.7(4.8) - 216.7(3.0)$$

$$= 11\,496.9\,\text{kNm}$$

Therefore the most severe case is from HA + KEL loading:

where HA + KEL = 12 130.4 kNm.

Maximum BM: 12 130.4 kNm

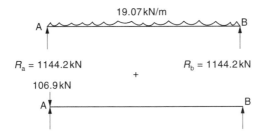

Figure 3.43. Example (3.7): Shear force

Shear force
HA + KEL loading (Fig. 3.43):
Therefore maximum shear force at a:

$$= 1144.2 + 106.9 \, \text{kN}$$
$$= 1251 \, \text{kN}$$

Maximum SF: 1251 kN.

3.7.8 Example (3.8) American practice
Determine the centre of gravity of load to create maximum bending moment.
Compute live load plus impact moment and range of shears HS 20-44 truck.
The span is 45 ft (13.716 m). Referring to Figs 3.44 and 3.45:

P (3.44)	x (ft)	$P \times$ ft kip
16 K	0	0
16 K	14	224
4 K	28	112
Σ 36 K		Σ 336 ft kips

$$x_1 = \frac{336}{36} = 9.33 \, \text{ft}$$

$$x = 14 - x_1 = 4.67 \, \text{ft} \ (4 \, \text{ft} \ 8 \, \text{in})$$

$$\Sigma M_A = 0$$

$$4 \times 6.167 + 16 \times 20.167 + 16 \times 34.167 - R_B \times 45 = 0$$

$$R_B = 19.867 \, \text{kips}; \qquad R_A = 36 - 19.867 = 16.133 \, \text{kips}$$

$$\text{Maximum LL moment} = M_{LL} = M_{max} = R_A(20.167) - 4(14)$$

$$= 269.35 \, \text{ft kip}$$

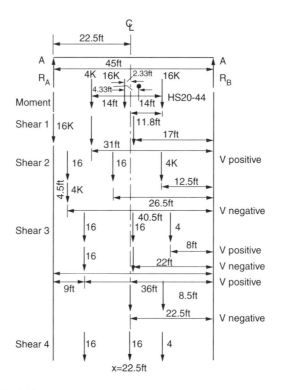

Figure 3.44. HS20-44 locations

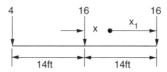

Figure 3.45. Example (3.8): values for P

Impact + wheel load distribution

$$I = \frac{50}{L + 125} = 0.29 \qquad I_e = 1.29$$

$$M_{LL+I} = 269.35 \times 1.45 \times 1.29 = 503.83 \text{ ft kip}$$

Shear ① $x = 0 + V$

$$+V = 1.75\left(16^K \times \frac{45'}{45'}\right) + 1.45\left(16^K \times 4^K \frac{31'}{45'} + \frac{17'}{45'}\right) = 46.17 \text{ kips}$$

$$I \text{ impact} = \frac{50}{125 + 45} = 0.29$$

$$+V_{x=0} = 1.29 \times 46.17 = 59.56 \, \text{kips}$$

$$-V_{x=0} = 0 \quad \text{negative shear}$$

$$\text{at } x = 0$$

Total shear $= 59.56 + 0 = 59.56 \, \text{kips}$

Shear ②: similar calculations are carried out $x = 4.5 \, \text{ft}$

$$+V + \text{impact} = 46.99 \, \text{kips}$$

$$-V = -0.75 \, \text{kips}$$

$$V_{\text{total}} = 47.74 \, \text{kips}$$

Shear ③: $x = 9.0 \, \text{ft}$

$$+V = 40.21 \, \text{kips} \qquad -V = -2.35 \, \text{kips} \quad \text{(impact included)}$$

$$V_{\text{total}} = 42.56 \, \text{kips}$$

Shear ④:

$$+V + \text{impact} = 20.78 \, \text{kips}$$

$$-V \text{ (impact included)} = -19.35 \, \text{kips}$$

$$V_{\text{total}} = 40.13 \, \text{kips}$$

3.7.9   Example (3.9)   British practice

A beam/slab bridge is subjected to HB 45 units loading. The spacings of the beams (Fig. 3.46) are 1.53 m centres. Position the load on the deck in such a way that it produces maximum longitudinal bending moment on the beam marked ① in Fig. 3.46:

$4P = 450 \, \text{kN}$. Hence $P = 112.5 \, \text{kN}$

The load on beam ① $= 112.5 + 2 \times \dfrac{0.53}{1.53} \times 112.5 = 190.44 \, \text{kN}.$

The position of the load is shown in Fig. 3.47.
   Dimensions are clarified in the diagram:

$$109.44(2.88 + 4.68 + 10.68 + 12.48) = R_1 \times 18.33$$

$$R_1 = 319.2 \, \text{kN}$$

$$R_2 = 130.8 \, \text{kN}$$

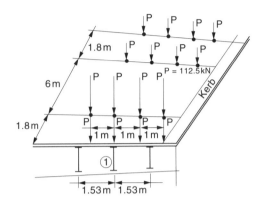

Figure 3.46. Steel/concrete composite deck

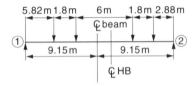

Figure 3.47. Position of HB loading [Example (3.9)]

The moment at the centre of the beam ①

$$= M_{\text{₵ beam}}(\text{max}) = 319.2 \times 9.15 - 190.44(1.53 + 3.33)$$

$$= 1995 \, \text{kNm}$$

The longitudinal member sustains $M = 1995 \, \text{kNm}$.

3.7.10 Example (3.10) British practice

A concrete-slab deck bridge is shown in Fig. 3.48. On the 16 m side the slab is supported by a concrete beam 750 mm wide and 700 mm deep. The slab spans 16 m and is simply supported along the 20 m edge. Distribute the load effectively

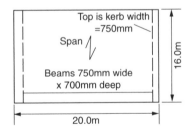

Figure 3.48. Slab/beam deck [Example (3.10)]

and calculate the maximum longitudinal bending moment. For HB loading, the deck should be divided into eight sections with nine reference stations. Use the following data:

$$\text{HA loading} = 0.98 \, \text{kN/m}^2$$

$$\text{KEL} = 39.4 \, \text{kN/m}$$

$$\text{HB (45 units), wheel load} = 112.5 \, \text{kN}$$

$$\text{axle spacing} = 0.92 \, \text{m}$$

$$\text{spaced} = 1.8 : 6.0 : 1.8 \, \text{m}$$

$$\text{load due to surfacing} = \gamma_f D_L = 2 \, \text{kN/m}^2$$

$$\rho = \text{density of concrete} = 23.6 \, \text{kN/m}^3$$

For HB loading, data from the Guyon–Massonnet–Bares method is given in Table 3.34 for the load distribution parameters:

$\alpha = $ slab torsional parameter $= 1.0$

$$\theta = \text{flexural parameter} = \frac{b}{2a} \left(\frac{i}{j} \right)^{1/4}$$

Determine stresses due to these loads. Compare the results. Ignore torsional calculations.

(a) *HA loading* full width of the deck

$$M = \text{moment/unit width}$$

$$\frac{0.98 \times 16^2}{8} + \frac{39.4 \times 16}{4} = 31.36 + 157.6$$

$$= 188.96 \, \text{kN m} \approx 189 \, \text{kN m}$$

$$\text{moment due to surfacing} = \frac{2 \times 16^2}{8} = 64 \, \text{kN m}$$

$$\text{slab weight} = 23.6 \times 0.7 = 16.52 \, \text{kN m}$$

$$\text{moment due to self weight} = \frac{16.52 \times 16^2}{8} = 528.64 \, \text{kN m}$$

$$\text{total bending moment} = 797.89 \, \text{kN m}$$

Stresses:

$$\text{HA loading} = \frac{M}{Z} = \frac{189}{0.0817} = 2313 \, \text{kN m}^2$$

$$Z = \frac{(0.7)^2}{6} \times 1 = 0.0817 \, \text{m}^3$$

Table 3.34 (below and facing). Values of K for different positions

$y_e\rightarrow$ ↓	$-b$	$-3b/4$	$-b/2$	$-b/4$	0	$b/4$	$b/2$	$3b/4$	b
K_1									
0	+0.6259	+0.7738	+0.9802	+1.2308	+1.3641	+1.2308	+0.9802	+0.7738	+0.6259
$b/4$	+0.3923	+0.5089	+0.6812	+0.9313	+1.2308	+1.4371	+1.3426	+1.1547	+0.9971
$b/2$	+0.2516	+0.3389	+0.4720	+0.6812	+0.9802	+1.3426	+1.6305	+1.6381	+1.5588
$3b/4$	+0.1695	+0.2358	+0.3369	+0.5089	+0.7738	+1.1547	+1.6381	+2.1023	+2.3534
b	+0.1177	+0.1695	+0.2516	+0.3923	+0.6259	+0.9971	+1.5588	+2.3534	+3.3539
$\theta = 0.90$ **K_0**									
0	-0.4715	+0.2749	+1.0436	+1.7771	+2.1592	+1.7771	+1.0436	+0.2749	-0.4715
$b/4$	-0.5493	-0.0646	+0.4700	+1.1070	+1.7771	+2.1334	+1.7309	+0.9565	+0.1129
$b/2$	-0.4042	-0.1851	+0.0792	+0.4700	+1.0436	+1.7309	+2.1980	+2.0203	+1.5843
$3b/4$	-0.1919	-0.2028	-0.1851	-0.0646	+0.2749	+0.9565	+2.0203	+3.2519	+4.2579
b	+0.0299	-0.1919	-0.4042	-0.5493	-0.4715	+0.1129	+1.5843	+4.2579	+8.0034
$\theta = 0.90$ **K_1**									
0	+0.5452	+0.7119	+0.9631	+1.2903	+1.5028	+1.2903	+0.9631	+0.7119	+0.5452
$b/4$	+0.3155	+0.4335	+0.6224	+0.9184	+1.2903	+1.5534	+1.3996	+1.1380	+0.9359
$b/2$	+0.1864	+0.2663	+0.3987	+0.6224	+0.9631	+1.3996	+1.7493	+1.7094	+1.5677
$3b/4$	+0.1166	+0.1722	+0.2663	+0.4335	+0.7119	+1.1380	+1.7094	+2.2658	+2.5180
b	+0.0762	+0.1166	+0.1864	+0.3155	+0.5452	+0.9359	+1.5677	+2.5180	+3.7710
$\theta = 1.00$ **K_0**									
0	-0.6044	+0.1715	+1.0080	+1.8775	+2.3663	+1.8775	+1.0080	+0.1715	-0.6044
$b/4$	-0.5391	-0.1183	+0.3824	+1.0658	+1.8775	+2.3492	+1.8265	+0.8567	-0.1726
$b/2$	-0.3181	-0.1774	+0.0184	+0.3824	+1.0080	+1.8285	+2.3729	+2.0116	+1.2940
$3b/4$	-0.0796	-0.1402	-0.1774	-0.1183	+0.1715	+0.8587	+2.0116	+3.3546	+4.3335
b	+0.1460	-0.0796	-0.3161	-0.5391	-0.6044	-0.1726	+1.2940	+4.3335	+8.8915
K_1									
0	+0.4688	+0.6482	+0.9410	+1.3499	+1.6320	+1.3499	+0.9410	+0.6482	+0.4688
$b/4$	+0.2506	+0.3657	+0.5652	+0.8985	+1.3499	+1.6081	+1.4523	+1.1105	+0.8667
$b/2$	+0.1363	+0.2070	+0.3342	+0.5652	+0.0410	+1.4523	+1.8696	+1.7679	+1.5557
$3b/4$	+0.0789	+0.1240	+0.2070	+0.3856	+0.6482	+1.1105	+1.7679	+2.4213	+2.6605
b	+0.0484	+0.0789	+0.1363	+0.2506	+0.4688	+0.8667	+1.5557	+2.6605	+4.1892

(Continued)

Table 3.34. (Continued)

$y_e \rightarrow$	$-b$	$-3b/4$	$-b/2$	$-b/4$	0	$b/4$	$b/2$	$3b/4$	b
$\theta = 1.10$									
K_0									
0	−0.6652	+0.0880	+0.9531	+1.9518	+2.5621	+1.9518	+0.9531	+0.0880	−0.6652
$b/4$	−0.4770	−0.1515	+0.2842	+0.9925	+1.9518	+2.5643	+1.9180	+0.7675	−0.4129
$b/2$	−0.2209	−0.1626	−0.0403	+0.2842	+0.9531	+1.9180	+2.5717	+2.0089	+0.9824
$3b/4$	−0.0097	−0.0936	−0.1626	−0.1515	+0.0880	+0.7675	+2.0089	+3.4539	+4.3474
b	+0.1709	−0.0097	−0.2209	−0.4770	−0.6652	−0.4129	+0.9824	+4.3474	+9.7780
K_1									
0	+0.3985	+0.5848	+0.9142	+1.4075	+1.7691	+1.4075	+0.9142	+0.5848	+0.3985
$b/4$	+0.1969	+0.3055	+0.5103	+0.8771	+1.4075	+1.8095	+1.5003	+1.0740	+0.7931
$b/2$	+0.0985	+0.1593	+0.2783	+0.5103	+0.9142	+1.5003	+1.9915	+1.8145	+1.5263
$3b/4$	+0.0527	+0.0882	+0.1593	+0.3055	+0.5848	+1.0740	+1.8145	+2.5695	+2.7813
b	+0.0303	+0.0527	+0.0985	+0.1969	+0.3985	+0.7931	+1.5263	+2.7813	+4.6078
$\theta = 1.20$									
K_0									
0	−0.6677	+0.0199	+0.8805	+2.0050	−2.7541	+2.0050	+0.8805	+0.0199	−0.6677
$b/4$	−0.3856	−0.1685	+0.1841	+0.8977	+2.0050	+2.7777	+1.9987	+0.6851	−0.6038
$b/2$	−0.1417	−0.1424	−0.0900	+0.1841	+0.8805	+1.9987	+2.7876	+2.0114	+0.6620
$3b/4$	+0.0279	−0.0594	−0.1424	−0.1685	+0.0199	+0.6851	+2.0114	+3.5547	+4.3049
b	+0.1439	+0.0279	−0.1317	−0.3856	−0.6677	−0.6038	+0.8620	+4.3049	+10.6646
K_1									
0	+0.3352	+0.5233	+0.8834	+1.4614	+1.9124	+1.4614	+0.8834	+0.5233	+0.3352
$b/4$	+0.1533	+0.2534	+0.4582	+0.8520	+1.4614	+1.9468	+1.5432	+1.0306	+0.7182
$b/2$	+0.0706	+0.1217	+0.2304	+0.458	+0.8834	+1.5432	+2.1156	+1.8501	+1.4827
$3b/4$	+0.0348	+0.0621	+0.1217	+0.2534	+0.5233	+1.0306	+1.8501	+2.7114	+2.8817
b	+0.0188	+0.0348	+0.0706	+0.1533	+0.3352	+0.7182	+1.4827	+2.8817	+5.0268

(This table is extracted from *Analysis of Beam Grids and Orthotropic Plates by the Guyon–Massonnet–Bares method* by R. Bares and C. Massonnet published by Crosby Lockwood & Son Ltd., English Edition, 1968. Permission for reproduction is acknowledged in the preface)

Due to surfacing and self-weight

$$= \frac{64.0 + 528.64}{0.0817} = 7254\,\text{kN/m}^2$$

(b)   *HB loading (Fig. 3.49)*

$$\text{section size} = \frac{20}{8} = 2.5\,\text{m}$$

$$\theta = \frac{20/2}{2 \times 16} = 0.625$$

$$4P = 4 \times 112.5 = 450.0\,\text{kN at reference stations below:}$$

b	$3b/4$	$b/2$	$b/4$	0	$-b/4$	$-b/2$	$-3b/4$	$-b$	
①	②	③	④	⑤	⑥	⑦	⑧	⑨	section reference station

↓ $4P$ acting position

K_1 distribution factor

11	10	9	8	7	8	9	10	11	
2.0	1.8	1.47	1.14	0.88	0.65	0.50	0.39	0.3	K_1

$K_{1\text{max}}$ at $b = 2.0$

$$M_x = M_x(\text{average}) \times K \times 1.1$$

$$R_A = \frac{4 \times 112.5}{20} \times 4 \times \frac{6.5}{16}$$

$$= 0.325 \times 112.5$$

$$= 36.5625\,\text{kN}$$

$$M_{\text{max}} = M_{x\,\text{average}} \times K_1 \times 1.11$$

$$M_{\text{max}} = K_1 \times 1.1 \times \left(0.325 \times 112.5 \times 6.5 - \frac{450}{20} \times 1.80\right)$$

$$= (237.656 - 40.5) \times 2 \times 1.1$$

$$= 433.74\,\text{kNm/m width}$$

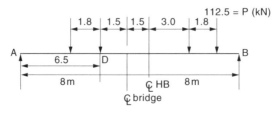

Figure 3.49. HB loading position [Example (B3.10)]

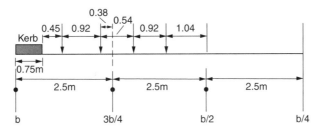

Figure 3.50. Reactions at reference stations

Using Table 3.34 (Guyon–Massonnet–Bares), reactions at reference stations
(Fig. 3.50 and Table 3.35) can be considered

axle spacing $= 0.92\,\text{m}$

$$\frac{b}{2} = \frac{0.54}{2.5} \times P + \left(\frac{2.054}{2.5}\right) P = 0.800P$$

$$\frac{3b}{4} = \left(\underbrace{\frac{1.04}{2.5} + \frac{1.96}{2.5}}_{\text{right-hand side}} + \underbrace{\frac{2.12}{2.5} + \frac{1.2}{2.5}}_{\text{left-hand side}}\right) P = 2.529P$$

$$b = \left(\frac{1.3}{2.5} + \frac{0.38}{2.5}\right) P = 0.672P$$

Table 3.35. Reference station results for HB loading

Ref station		Load at								
		$-b$	$-3b/4$	$-b/2$	$-b/4$	0	$b/4$	$b/2$	$3b/4$	b
0		0.78	0.87	0.98	1.13	1.2	1.13	0.98	0.87	0.78
$b/4$		0.57	0.65	0.79	0.95	1.12	1.25	1.22	1.14	1.08
$b/2$		0.41	0.50	0.62	0.79	0.99	1.22	1.42	1.47	1.48
$3b/4$		0.32	0.40	0.51	0.67	0.87	1.14	1.48	1.78	2.0
b	λ	0.25	0.3	0.42	0.56	0.77	1.08	1.48	2.0	2.52
0	0									K_1
$b/4$	0									0
$b/2$	0.8									0
				$\lambda(b/2)(b/2) = 0.8 \times 1.48$						$= 1.183$
$3b/4$	2.529									≈ 5.06
b	0.672				0.672×2.52					$= 1.682$

for $P = 1$

total $= \quad 0.8$
$\quad \quad \quad + 2.529$
$\quad \quad \quad + \underline{0.672}$
$\quad \quad \quad \quad 4.001$

$\quad \quad = 4 \quad$ QED, i.e. $4P$

$$\sum \lambda K_1 = 0 + 0 + 1.183 + 5.06 + 1.682 = 7.925$$

$$\sum \lambda \frac{K_1}{4} = \frac{7.925}{4} = 1.98125$$

Comparison: $K_1 = 2.0$ from approximate analysis. Detailed analysis $K_1 = 1.98125$. The above calculations are retained and HB $<$ HA, i.e. HA governs.

3.7.11 Example (3.11) OHBDC Canadian practice

Determine load distribution, moments and shears and reactions at end and at 0.1, 0.2, 0.3, 0.4, and 0.5 span for a bridge span of 25 m for a Class A highway.

The cross-section is shown in Fig. 3.51: shoulder width $= 2.0$ m; lane width $= 3.75$ m.

The deck consists of five prestressed concrete beams, supporting a 225 mm span, of the type CPCI 1400.

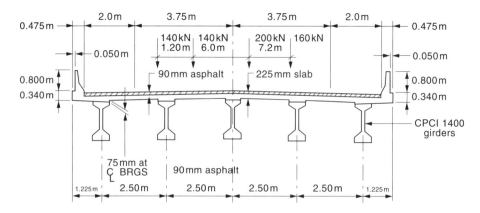

Figure 3.51. A cross-section of a roadway (courtesy Ontario Highway Department)

Tabulate the factored shears at 0, 0.1, 0.2, 0.3, 0.4 and 0.5 L for vehicle loading, CPCI girders, slab, barriers and asphalt. Partial factors for

$$\text{factors}\begin{cases} \text{live load} & = 1.4 \\ \text{girder} & = 1.1 \\ \text{slab} & = 1.2 \\ \text{barriers} & = 1.2 \\ \text{asphalt} & = 1.5 \end{cases}$$

Typical vehicular loadings of OHBDC are shown in Fig. 3.51.

Moments and shears (Fig. 3.52)
End

$$R_A \times 25 = 640 \times 18.89$$

$$R_A = 483.58\,\text{kN} = \text{max shear}$$

Maximum moment at the load centre

$$483.58 \times 6.11 - 140 \times 7.2 - 140 \times 6 = 1106.7\,\text{kN m}.$$

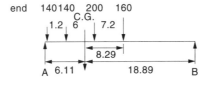

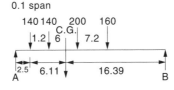

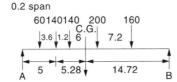

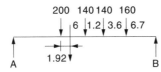

Figure 3.52 (above and overleaf). Moments and shears for different spans and load positions

(a)   *0.1 span* $= 0.1 \times 25 = 2.5\,\mathrm{m}$

$$R_\mathrm{A} = 640 \times \frac{16.39}{25} = 419.58\,\mathrm{kN}$$

$$= \mathrm{shear}$$

(b)   *0.2 span* $= 5\,\mathrm{m}$

$$\mathrm{max\ shear} = 412.16 - 60$$

$$= 352.16\,\mathrm{kN}$$

$$\mathrm{moment} = 412.16 \times 5 - 60 \times 3.6$$

$$= 1845\,\mathrm{kN\,m}$$

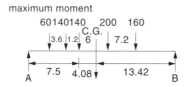

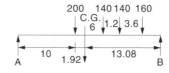

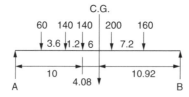

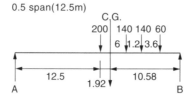

Figure 3.52. Continued

(c)   0.3 *span* = 7.5 m
For maximum effect 160 kN axle neglected

$$R_A = 278.16 \, kN = max \ shear$$

$$= \frac{13.42}{25} \times 700 = 375.76 \, kN$$

max shear at 7.5 m = 375.76 − 140 − 60

$$= 175.76 \, kN$$

max moment = 375.76 × 7.5 − 60 × 4.8

$$- 140 \times 1.2$$

$$= 2362 \, kN \, m$$

(d)   0.4L = 10.0 m span

$$R_A = 224.16 = max \ shear$$

160 kN axle neglected

$$R_A = \frac{10.92}{25} \times 700 = 305.76 \, kN$$

shear = 305.76 − 200

$$= 105.76 \, kN$$

max moment at 10.0 m span

$$= 305.76 \times 10 - 60 \times 4.8 - 140 \times 1.2$$

$$= 2601.6$$

(e)   0.5L = 12.5 m span

160 kN axle neglected.

max shear = R_A = 170.16 kN

Shear consistent with maximum applied live load moment

$$R_A = 292.88 \, kN$$

shear = 292.88 − 60 − 140

$$= 92.88 \, kN$$

For a summary of Example (3.11), refer to Table 3.36.

Table 3.36. Factored shear for vehicle loading, girder, slab, barrier, and asphalt

	Live Load	Girder	Slab	Barrier
End	$0.676 \times 483.58 \times 1.4 = 458$ kN	1.1×126.49 $= 139.139$	1.2×181.3 $= 217.56$	1.2×28.58 $= 34.296$
0.1 L	$0.676 \times 419.58 \times 1.4 = 397$ kN	1.1×101.19 $= 111.309$	1.2×144.90 $= 173.88$	1.2×22.86 $= 27.552$
0.2 L	$0.676 \times 352.60 \times 1.4 = 334$ kN	1.1×75.89 $= 83.479$	1.2×108.68 $= 130.416$	1.2×17.15 $= 20.58$
0.3 L	$0.676 \times 278.16 \times 1.4 = 263$ kN	1.1×50.60 $= 55.66$	1.2×72.45 $= 86.94$	1.2×11.43 $= 13.716$
0.4 L	$0.676 \times 224.16 \times 1.4 = 212$ kN	1.1×25.30 $= 27.83$	1.2×36.20 $= 43.44$	1.2×5.72 $= 6.864$
0.5 L	$0.676 \times 170.16 \times 1.4 = 161$ kN	0	0	0

Asphalt

End	0.1 L	0.2 L	0.3 L	0.4 L	0.5 L
1.5×60.81 $= 91.215$ $\sum 940.21$ kN	1.5×48.65 $= 72.975$ $\sum 682.713$ kN	1.5×36.49 $= 54.735$ $\sum 623.21$ kN	1.5×24.33 $= 36.495$ $\sum 955.796$ kN	1.5×12.16 $= 18.24$ $\sum 308.374$ kN	0 $\sum 161$ kN

3.7.12 Example (3.12) British practice

A slab bridge 1 m deep with 100 mm surfacing is reinforced with 40 mm diameter bars at 150 c/c (8378 mm^2) at an effective depth of 940 mm.

Calculate the stresses in the section due to a positive temperature difference for the following cases:

(*i*)   uncracked section;
(*ii*) cracked section.

Use the following data:

(*a*) Adopt Department of Environment Standard BD 37/88.
(*b*) Divide the bridge depth from top: ① 150 mm, ② 400 mm, ③ 800 mm, ④ 1000 mm on the lines suggested in the code. Assume 1 mm wide strip.
(*c*) The forces at these depths shall be computed as

$$F_i = A_i E_C \beta_L T_i \qquad E_C = 30 \text{ kN/mm}^2 \qquad A_i = \text{gross area at } i$$

where i (in this case) $= 4$. $T =$ temperature: at top $= 13.5°$C; at bottom $= 2.5°$C. $\beta_L =$ thermal expansion; $\beta_L = 12 \times 10^{-6}/°$C

(*d*) $f_L =$ partial safety factor for $T = 0.8$ for *combination* 3 loading at serviceability limit state (SLS).

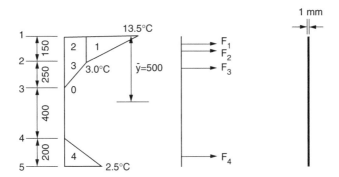

Figure 3.53. Temperature distribution [Example (3.12)]

(e) Stresses are calculated according to the following expression

$$\sigma = (-E\beta_L T + \sum F/A + \sum (y - \bar{y}/I) \times M$$

Take $E_S = 200 \, \text{kN/mm}^2$

Temperature distribution on the lines suggested is illustrated in Fig. 3.53:

Gross area for 1 mm wide strip

$$A = 1 \, \text{mm} \times 1000 \, \text{mm}$$

$$I(\text{gross}) = \frac{1 \times 1000^3}{12} = 83.34$$

$$T_1 = 0.8 \times 13.5 = 10.8°C$$
$$T_2 = 0.8 \times 3.0 = 2.4°C$$
$$T_3 = 0.8 \times 2.5 = 2.0°C$$

Forces

$$F_1 = \tfrac{1}{2} \times 150 \times 30 \times 12 \times 10^{-6}(10.8 - 2.4) = 0.227 \, \text{kN}$$

$$F_2 = 1 \times 150 \times 30 \times 12 \times 10^{-6} \times 2.4 = 0.13 \, \text{kN}$$

$$F_3 = \tfrac{1}{2} \times 1 \times 250 \times 30 \times 12 \times 10^{-6} \times 2.4 = 108 \, \text{kN}$$

$$F_4 = \tfrac{1}{2} \times 1 \times 200 \times 30 \times 12 \times 10^{-6} \times 2.0 = 0.072 \, \text{kN}$$

The centroid of areas from the top $= \bar{y} = 500 \, \text{mm}$.

Moments (Table 3.37)

   (i)   *Uncracked section*

$$\sigma_1 = -30 \times 10^3 (12 \times 10^{-6})(10.8) + \frac{0.537 \times 10^3}{1000 \times 1}$$

$$+ \frac{-155 \times 10^6 (0-500)}{83 \times 10^6 \times 10^3}$$

$$= -3.89 + 0.537 + 0.933$$

$$= -2.42\,\text{N/mm}^2 \quad \leftarrow \text{compressive}$$

Similarly

$$\sigma_2 = 0.86 + 0.537 + 0.654 = 0.331\,\text{N/mm}^2 \quad \text{tensile} \rightarrow$$

$$\sigma_3 = 0 + 0.537 + 0.187 = 0.724\,\text{N/mm}^2 \quad \text{tensile} \rightarrow$$

$$\sigma_4 = 0 + 0.537 - 0.560 = -0.023\,\text{N/mm}^2 \quad \leftarrow \text{compressive}$$

$$\sigma_5 = -0.72 + 0.537 - 0.933 = -1.116\,\text{N/mm}^2 \quad \leftarrow \text{compressive}$$

   (ii)   *Cracked section*
      Concrete having a transformed section:

$$\frac{E_S}{E_C} = \frac{200}{30} = 6.67$$

$$\frac{\sigma_e A_S'}{bd} = 0$$

$$\frac{A_S}{\text{mm width}} = 8.5\,\text{mm}^2$$

$$A_S \text{ transformed} = \alpha A_S' = 56.695\,\text{mm}^2$$

Table 3.37

Area zone	F_i (kN)	y from top mm	$y - \bar{y}$ (distance from N–A)	$M = F_i(y - \bar{y})\,kN \times 10^{-3}$
1	0.227	50	−450	−102.15
2	0.130	75	−425	−55.25
3	0.108	233.3	−266.7	−28.80
4	0.072	933.3	+433.3	+31.2
	$\sum F = 0.537$			$\sum M = -155 \times 10^{-3}$

Using **BS 8110** chart

$$\frac{\bar{y}}{d} = 0.30$$

$$\bar{y} = 0.30 \times 940$$

$$= 282$$

From chart

$$\frac{I}{bd^3} = 0.0415$$

Therefore $I = 0.0451 \times 1 \times (940)^3 = 34.47 \times 10^6 \, \text{mm}^4$

$$A_{\text{transf}} = 1 \times 282 + 56.695$$

$$= 338.695 \quad \text{or} \quad 338 \, \text{mm}^2$$

In this case T_4 is an added effect which is the temperature at the reinforcement level. The new temperature distribution is set out below (see
Fig. 3.54):

$$T_4 = \frac{2.5°\text{C}}{200} \times 150 = 1.875°\text{C}$$

$$T_{\bar{y}} = (400 - 282)\frac{2.4}{250} = 1.33°\text{C}$$

$$F_1 = 0.227 \, \text{kN}$$

$$F_2 = 0.130 \, \text{kN}$$

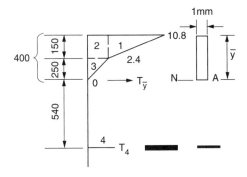

Figure 3.54. New temperature distribution

Table 3.38. Forces and moments [Example (3.12)]

Zone	F_i (kN)	y (mm)	$y - \bar{y}$	M (kN) $\times 10^{-3}$
1	0.227	50	−451	−102.400
2	0.130	75	−216	−28.080
3	0.084	70	−221	−18.564
4	0.0383	940	649	+24.857
	$\sum F_i = 0.4793$ kN			$\sum M = 124.187 \times 10^{-3}$ kN

$$F_3 = \tfrac{1}{2}(282 - 150)(2.4 + 1.133) \times 1 \times 30 \times 12 \times 10^{-6}$$
$$= 0.084 \, \text{kN}$$

$$F_4 = 56.695(T_4 = 1.875) \times 30 \times 12 \times 10^{-6}$$
$$= 0.0383 \, \text{kN}$$

The forces and moments, assuming new values, are given in Table 3.38.
Calculations for new stresses for the cracked section are as follows:

$$\sigma_1 = -3.89 + \frac{0.4793 \times 10^3}{338 \times 1} + \frac{-124.187(0 - 282) \times 10^6}{34.47 \times 10^6 \times 10^3}$$
$$= -3.89 + 1.418 + 1.016 = -1.456 \, \text{N/mm}^2$$

$$\sigma_2 = -0.86 + 1.418 + \frac{-124.187(150 - 282) \times 10^6}{34.47 \times 10^6 \times 10^3}$$
$$= -0.86 + 1.418 + 0.0476 = 1.034 \, \text{N/mm}^2$$

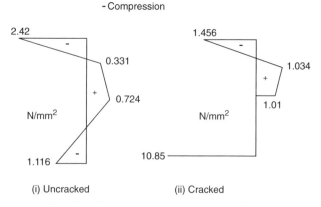

Figure 3.55. Temperature distribution – a comparative study

$$\sigma_3 = -0.36(1.133) + 1.418 - 0$$

$$= -0.408 + 1.418 = 1.01\,\text{N/mm}^2$$

$$\sigma_4 = \left[-0.36 \times 1.875 + 1.418 + \frac{-124.187(940 - 282) \times 10^6}{34.47 \times 10^6 \times 10^3} \right](\alpha_e = 6.67)$$

$$= (-0.675 + 1.418 - 2.37)6.67$$

$$= -10.85\,\text{N/mm}^2$$

Comparative results of the temperature distribution for the uncracked and cracked situations are given in Fig. 3.55.

SECTION 4
METHODS OF ANALYSIS

4. Methods of analysis

4.1 Methods of analysis – superstructures and substructures

4.1.1 Introduction

In this section, methods of analysis are given for both the superstructures and the substructures of bridges. Specialized bridges such as suspension and cable-stayed bridges are not included in this section. They are given under a special section in this text (Section 6). Here, methods of analysis include flexibility and stiffness methods, influence line techniques, grillage methods, finite difference methods and finite element methods. No dynamic analysis is included in this section to cater for wind, seismic and vehicle load–bridge deck interactions. Nevertheless, dynamic analyses given in other sections in the text can be applied. The Appendix gives a summary of the analysis where finite element (static and dynamic) analysis is required for more complicated problems. Analytical examples are given for both superstructures and substructures of bridges. Tables are included for quick solutions of the substructure problems. Where columns and bents/frames are used to support bridge decks, analyses and analytical problems are included for instability cases of these substructures. Bearings are included elsewhere (5.6) which may require changes due to specific loads transferred through them.

4.2 Methods of analysis – superstructures

4.2.1 Flexibility method of analysis

The structure is made to statically determinate specifications. Calculate statical moments, shears and axial effects etc. Remove the loads on the bridge deck and apply indeterminate reactions one by one and draw flexibility diagrams. The final diagrams are drawn by algebraically adding all quantities along the ordinates of indeterminacy or other specified locations. The determinate moment, for example, is m_0 and various other indeterminates are $x_1, x_2, x_3 \ldots x_n$. The final moment is

$$M = m_0 + m_1 x_1 + m_2 x_2 + \cdots m_n x_n \tag{4.1}$$

where m_1 to m_n are moments from the redundant reactions that are similar for axial effects

$$N = N_0 + N_1 X_1 + N_2 X_2 + \cdots N_n X_n \tag{4.2}$$

Other effects such as shear torsion can be represented in the same way. All are algebraically added in the form

$$f_{ik} = \underbrace{\int_s m_i m_k \frac{\mathrm{d}s}{EI}}_{\text{bending}} + \underbrace{\int_s n_i n_k \frac{\mathrm{d}s}{EA}}_{\text{direct force}} + \lambda \underbrace{\int_s \frac{v_i v_k \,\mathrm{d}s}{GA}}_{\text{shear}} + \underbrace{\int_s \frac{m_{ti} m_{tk} \,\mathrm{d}s}{GI_t}}_{\text{torsion}} \qquad (4.3)$$

where it has a variable section.

The component of the bridge is divided into several points and moment I is integrated within the established points:

$$\left.\begin{array}{ll}
\text{for bending} & \mathrm{d}s^{\mathrm{I}} = \dfrac{I_c}{I}\,\mathrm{d}s \\[2mm]
\text{for direct force} & \mathrm{d}s^{\mathrm{II}} = \dfrac{I_c}{A}\,\mathrm{d}s \\[2mm]
\text{for shear force} & \mathrm{d}s^{\mathrm{III}} = \dfrac{EI_c}{GA} \\[2mm]
\text{for torsional moment} & \mathrm{d}s^{\mathrm{IV}} = \dfrac{EI_c}{GI_t}
\end{array}\right\} \qquad (4.4)$$

4.2.1.1 Example (4.1)

A two-span prestressed concrete bridge (Fig. 4.1) has a post-tensioned girder of constant EI. It is stressed with a straight cable of 1000 kN. The eccentricity of the cable is 180 mm. Determine the indeterminate moment M due to prestress over the intermediate support. The losses are ignored and assume EI constant.

Using Table 4.1:

$$f_{11} = \int \frac{m_1 m_0}{EI}\,\mathrm{d}s$$

$$= 2 \times \tfrac{1}{3} \times 10 EI$$

$$= \frac{20}{3} EI$$

$$EID_{10} = \tfrac{1}{2} lik + \tfrac{1}{2} lik$$

$$= -\tfrac{1}{2} \times 10 \times 1 \times 180 - \tfrac{1}{2} \times 10 \times 1 \times 180$$

$$= -180 \times 10 EI$$

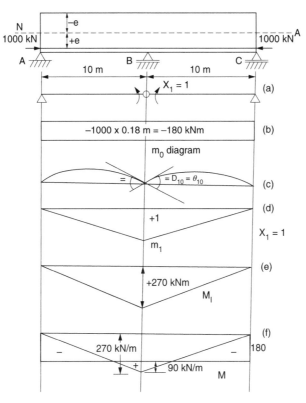

Figure 4.1. A two-span prestressed concrete beam with various flexibility diagrams

$$X_1 f_{11} + D_{10} = 0$$

$$X_1 = -\frac{D_{10}}{f_{11}}$$

$$= -\left(\frac{-180 \times 10}{\left(\frac{20}{3}\right)}\right)$$

$$= 270 \, \text{kNm}$$

$$M = m_0 + m_1 X_1$$

At *B*:

$$M = -180 + 1 \times 270$$

$$= 90 \, \text{kNm}$$

Table 4.1. Flexibility coefficients

$\int M_i M_k\,ds$	κ (uniform)	κ (triangle)	$K_1 \mid K_2$	K_m	κ (parabola)	κ (parabola)	κ $(\alpha l,\ \beta)$
①	lik	$\frac{1}{2}lik$	$\frac{1}{2}li(k_1+k_2)$	$\frac{2}{3}lik_m$	$\frac{2}{3}lik$	$\frac{1}{3}lik$	$\frac{1}{2}lik$
②	$\frac{1}{2}lik$	$\frac{1}{3}lik$	$\frac{1}{6}li(k_1+2k_2)$	$\frac{1}{3}lik_m$	$\frac{5}{12}lik$	$\frac{1}{4}lik$	$\frac{1}{6}l(1+\alpha)ik$
③	$\frac{1}{2}lik$	$\frac{1}{6}lik$	$\frac{1}{6}li(2k_1+k_2)$	$\frac{1}{3}lik_m$	$\frac{1}{4}lik$	$\frac{1}{12}lik$	$\frac{1}{6}l(1+\beta)ik$
④	$\frac{1}{2}l(i_1+i_2)k$	$\frac{1}{6}l(i_1+2i_2)k$	$\frac{1}{6}l(2i_1k_1+i_1k_2+i_2k_1+2i_2k_2)$	$\frac{1}{3}l(i_1+i_2)k_m$	$\frac{1}{12}l(3i_1+5i_2)k$	$\frac{1}{12}l(i_1+3i_2)k$	$\frac{1}{6}lk((1+\beta)i_1+(1+\alpha)i_2)$
⑤	$\frac{2}{3}li_mk$	$\frac{1}{3}li_mk$	$\frac{1}{3}li_m(k_1+k_2)$	$\frac{8}{15}li_mk_m$	$\frac{7}{15}li_mk$	$\frac{1}{5}li_mk$	$\frac{1}{3}l(1+\alpha\beta)i_mk$
⑥	$\frac{2}{3}lik$	$\frac{5}{12}lik$	$\frac{1}{12}li(3k_1+5k_2)$	$\frac{7}{15}lik_m$	$\frac{8}{15}lik$	$\frac{3}{10}lik$	$\frac{1}{12}l(5-\beta-\beta^2)ik$
⑦	$\frac{2}{3}lik$	$\frac{1}{4}lik$	$\frac{1}{12}li(5k_1+3k_2)$	$\frac{7}{15}lik_m$	$\frac{11}{30}lik$	$\frac{2}{15}lik$	$\frac{1}{12}l(5-\alpha-\alpha^2)ik$
⑧	$\frac{1}{3}lik$	$\frac{1}{4}lik$	$\frac{1}{12}li(k_1+3k_2)$	$\frac{1}{5}lik_m$	$\frac{3}{10}lik$	$\frac{1}{5}lik$	$\frac{1}{12}l(1+\alpha+\alpha^2)ik$
⑨	$\frac{1}{3}lik$	$\frac{1}{3}lik$	$\frac{1}{12}li(3k_1+k_2)$	$\frac{1}{5}lik_m$	$\frac{2}{15}lik$	$\frac{1}{30}lik$	$\frac{1}{12}l(1+\beta+\beta^2)ik$
⑩	$\frac{1}{2}l(1+\alpha)ik$	$\frac{1}{6}l(1+\alpha)ik$	$\frac{1}{6}li((1+\beta)k_1+(1+\alpha)k_2)$	$\frac{1}{3}l(1+\alpha\beta)ik_m$	$\frac{1}{12}l(5-\beta-\beta^2)ik$	$\frac{1}{12}l(1+\alpha+\alpha^2)ik$	$\frac{1}{3}lik$
lk^2	$\frac{1}{3}lk^2$	$\frac{1}{3}lk^2$	$\frac{1}{3}l(k_1^2+k_2^2+k_1k_2)$	$\frac{8}{15}lk_m^2$	$\frac{8}{15}lk^2$	$\frac{1}{5}lk^2$	$\frac{1}{3}lk^2$

A Simpson rule is adopted for the integration process:

$$\text{area under curve} = \frac{L}{3}(y_1 + 4y_2 + y_3) \tag{4.5}$$

where y_1, y_2, y_3 are the ordinates between two equal spaces L. The product integral can be easily obtained by using Table 4.1. This will ease the job of evaluating various moments and forces. The flexibility matrix for n indeterminacies is given as

$$\begin{bmatrix} f_{11} & f_{12} & \cdots & f_{1n} \\ f_{21} & f_{22} & \cdots & f_{2n} \\ \vdots & \vdots & & \vdots \\ f_{n1} & f_{n2} & \cdots & f_{nn} \end{bmatrix} \begin{Bmatrix} X_1 \\ X_2 \\ \vdots \\ X_n \end{Bmatrix} = - \begin{Bmatrix} D_{10} \\ D_{20} \\ \vdots \\ D_{n0} \end{Bmatrix} \tag{4.6}$$

$$[f] \times \{X\} = -\{D\} \tag{4.6a}$$

The Ds are displacements for statically determinate assumed structure and Xs are indeterminate quantities obtained by matrix $[f]$. In the analysis a choice is given either to find moments first or reactions first. All other quantities are determined subsequently.

4.2.1.2 Example (4.2)

A culvert shown in Fig. 4.2 with constant cross-section is loaded with a portion of HA loading occurring on the top CD. Assuming $q = 2\,\text{kN/m}$, $L = 10\,\text{m}$ and h is 5 m, calculate moments at A, B, C and D. Ignore the soil around it and treat the moments above the surface while the interior of the culvert is used as a bypass. Use the flexibility method for E, I constant, the elastic centre method is adopted, where

$$e = \frac{h}{2} = \frac{5}{2} = 2.5$$

Various flexibility diagrams are drawn, indicating various flexibility coefficients. Using Table 4.1:

$$m_0 \text{ (at C, D, A and B)} = \frac{qL^2}{8} = 25\,\text{kNm}$$

$$f_{11} = (10 \times 1 \times 1) + 2(5 \times 1 \times 1) = 30$$

$$f_{22} = 2(5 \times 5 \times 5) + \frac{2}{3} \times 5 \times 5 \times 5 \times 2 = \frac{1250}{3}$$

$$f_{33} = 2 \times 10 \times 2.5^2 + \frac{4}{3} \times 2.5 \times 2.5^2 = 145.8$$

$$f_{21} = f_{12} = 0; \qquad f_{13} = f_{31} = 0; \qquad f_{23} = f_{32} = 0$$

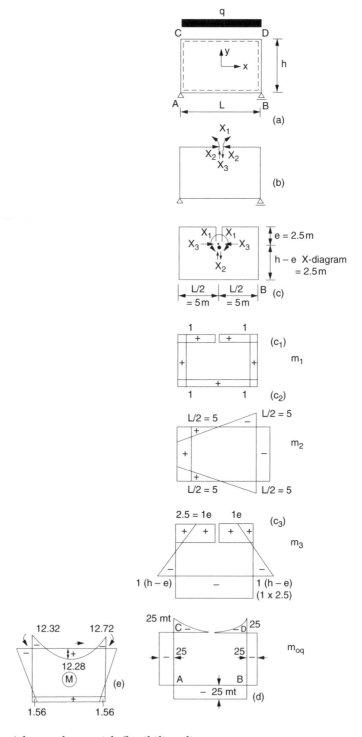

Figure 4.2. A box culvert with flexibility diagrams

$$D_{10} = \int \frac{m_1 m_0}{EI} \, ds = -\frac{2}{3} \times 5 \times 25 \times 1 - 2 \times 5 \times 25 \times 1 - 10 \times 25 \times 1$$

$$= -\frac{7}{6} \times 250 = \frac{1750}{6}$$

$$D_{20} = 0$$

$$D_{30} = 10 \times 2.5 \times 25 - \frac{10}{3} \times 2.5 \times 25 = \frac{1250}{3}$$

$$X_1 = -\frac{D_{10}}{f_{11}} = 19.42 \, \text{kNm}$$

$$X_2 = 0; \qquad X_3 = -\frac{D_{30}}{f_{33}} = -2.85 \, \text{kN}$$

$$M = m_0 + m_1 X_1 + m_2 X_2 + m_3 X_3$$

$$M_C = -12.72 \, \text{kNm}$$

$$M_D = -12.72 \, \text{kNm}$$

$$M_A = +1.56 \, \text{kNm} = M_B$$

4.2.2 Arch bridges using the flexibility method

For long spans, arch bridges are sometimes the most economical since deep sections in girder bridges can be avoided. A typical example for certain arch bridges with pinned supports can be examined by putting one end on rollers. The moments, like simple beam moments, can be written as

$$M_{\text{max}} = \frac{qL^2}{8}; \qquad V = \frac{qL}{2} \tag{4.7}$$

and N, the axial force is 0 (Fig. 4.2(b)). The shear force, as in Fig. 4.2(c), is:

$$S = V = \frac{qL}{2} \cos \phi; \qquad N = \frac{qL}{2} \sin \phi \tag{4.8}$$

Usually

$$\frac{h}{L} \geq \frac{1}{6} \text{ to } \frac{1}{7}$$

$$S = V \cos \phi - H \sin \phi \tag{4.9}$$

$$T = N = V \sin \phi + H \cos \phi \tag{4.10}$$

4.2.2.1 Flexibility of parabolic arches pinned at supports

The parabolic arch bridge is carrying a uniformly distributed load (Fig. 4.3):

m_0 = bending moment

$$= \tfrac{1}{2}qx(L - x) \qquad (4.11)$$

$$X_1 = 1 \quad \text{at} \quad A$$

The moment m_1 at any point at distance $x = -1h$. The flexibility equations are:

$$X_1 = -\frac{D_{10}}{f_{11}}$$

$$f_{11} = \int \frac{m_1^2 \, ds}{EI} + \int \frac{1}{EA} \, n_1^2 \, ds + \frac{T}{GJ} \int T_1 T_0 \, ds \qquad (4.12)$$

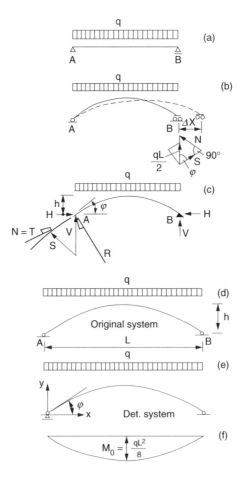

Figure 4.3 (above and facing). Flexibility of arch bridges

But

$$ds = \frac{dx}{\cos \phi}$$

Now, f_{11}, D_{10} in terms of I_c (2nd moment of area at the centre) can be written as

$$EI_c f_{11} = \int m_1^2 \frac{I_c}{I} \frac{dx}{\cos \phi} + \int n_1^2 \frac{I_c}{I} \frac{dx}{\cos \phi} \tag{4.13}$$

$$EI_c D_{10} = \int m_1 m_0 \frac{I_c}{I} \frac{dx}{\cos \phi} + \int n_1 n_0 \frac{I_c}{A} \frac{dx}{\cos \phi} \tag{4.14}$$

$$n_0 = -V_A \sin \phi$$

$$n_1 = -1 \cos \phi \tag{4.15}$$

If ϕ is small,

$$\sin \phi - 0 \qquad \cos \phi = 1 \tag{4.16}$$

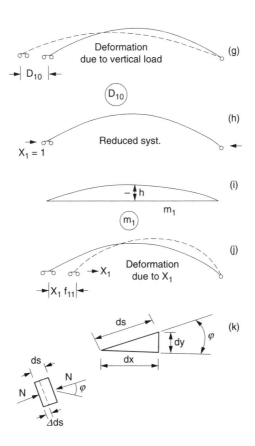

Figure 4.3. Continued

The above equations can be reduced to

$$\int n_1 n_0 \frac{I_c}{A} \frac{dx}{\cos \phi} = 0 \tag{4.17}$$

$$\int n_1^2 \frac{I_c}{A} \frac{dx}{\cos \phi} = \int \frac{I_c}{A} \frac{dx}{\cos \phi} \tag{4.18}$$

If

$$I = \frac{I_c}{\cos \phi} \tag{4.19}$$

$$A_c = A \cos \phi \tag{4.20}$$

The above equations reduce to

$$EI_c f_{11} = \int m_1^2 \, dx + \frac{I_c}{A_c} \, dx \tag{4.21}$$

$$EI_c D_{10} = \int m_1 m_0 \, dx \tag{4.22}$$

$$X_1 = -EI_c \frac{D_{10}}{EI_c}$$

The moment

$$M = m_0 + m_1 X_1 = m_0 - X_1(y) \tag{4.23}$$
$$N = n_0 + n_1 X_1 = n_0 - X_1 \cos \phi \tag{4.24}$$
$$V = v_0 + v_1 X_1 = v_0 - X_1 \sin \phi \tag{4.25}$$

4.2.2.2 Parabolic arches supported at different levels
Figure 4.4 shows such an arch of a bridge.

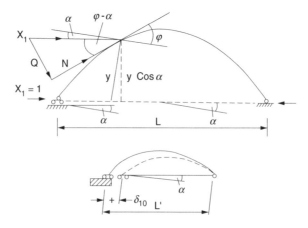

Figure 4.4. Parabolic arches at different levels and positions

The final equations for Ms, Ns, and Vs are written as

$$M = m_0 + m_1 X_1 = m_0 - X_1 y \cos \alpha \tag{4.26}$$

$$N = n_0 + n_1 X_1 = n_0 - X_1 \cos(\phi - \alpha) \tag{4.27}$$

$$V = v_0 + v_1 X_1 = v_0 - X_1 \sin(\phi - \alpha) \tag{4.28}$$

where

$$m_1 = -y \cos \alpha \qquad n_1 = -\cos(\phi - \alpha) \tag{4.29}$$

$$f_{11} = \int \frac{m_1^2 \, ds}{EI} + \int \frac{n_1^2 \, ds}{EA} \tag{4.30}$$

or

$$EIf_{11} = \cos^2 \alpha \int y^2 \frac{ds}{I} + \int \cos^2(\phi - \alpha) \frac{ds}{A} \tag{4.31}$$

4.2.2.3 Cases
(i) *Shrinkage and temperature analysis*
Assuming the supports at different levels, D_{10} will then depend on the increase or decrease of the arch length

$$ED_{1t} = -\alpha_t t L \times E \quad \text{(temperature)} \tag{4.32}$$

$$ED_{1s} = -E_s LE \quad \text{(shrinkage)} \tag{4.33}$$

m_0, n_0 are zero in this case, $-$ sign decreases. If $+$ sign is attached, this means increase in a quantity.
(ii) *Tied arch* (at hinge level)

$$Ef_{11} = \cos^2 \alpha \int y \frac{ds}{I} + \int \cos^2(\phi - \alpha) \frac{ds}{A} + \frac{E_{\text{rib}}}{E_{\text{tie}}} \cdot \frac{L}{A_{\text{tie}}} \tag{4.34}$$

(iii) *Displacement of abutments*
L receives changes ΔL along the hinges

$$\delta_{10} = D_{10} = D_{1A} = \Delta L \qquad ED_{1A} = E\Delta L \tag{4.35}$$

$$m_0 = 0 \qquad n_0 = 0 \tag{4.36}$$

4.2.2.4 Example (4.3)
A parabolic arch bridge is loaded uniformly in its plane projection by HA loading only which is applied at $20 \, \text{kN/m}$. Using the flexibility method, calculate

moments, shear and axial forces for the arch shown in Fig. 4.5. Use the following data:

(a) $I = I_c \sec \phi$

$A = \text{rib area} = 100 \, \text{m}^2$

$\dfrac{I_c}{A_c} = 0.04 \, \text{m}^2$

Equation of the parabola

$y = c(L - x)$

$c = \dfrac{h}{(0.5L)^2}$

(b) Temperature rise $= 30°\text{C}$

$\alpha_t = 10^{-5}$ $E = 30 \times 10^6 \, \text{kN/m}^2$

Additional effects

Case (c):   if the HA portion of loading is over half the span
Case (d):   if the knife-edge load is $10 \, \text{kN}$ on the span as a shared load concentrated

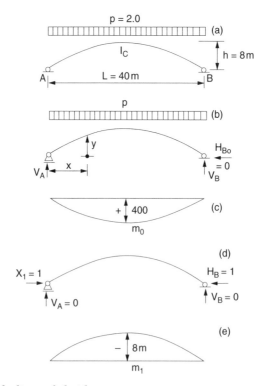

Figure 4.5. Parabolic arch bridge

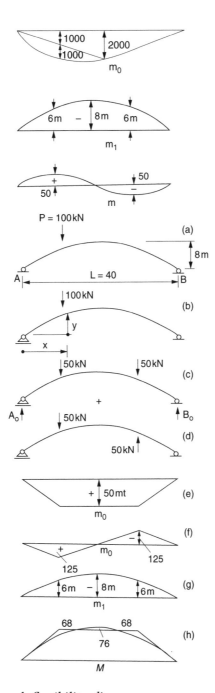

Figure 4.6. Parabolic arch flexibility diagrams

Flexibility diagrams are shown in Fig. 4.6:

$$C = 0.02$$

$$y = 0.02(40 - x)$$

$$m_{0x} = \tfrac{1}{2}qx(L - x)$$

$$m_{0(L/4=10)} = 3000 \, \text{kNm} \qquad m_{1(L/4)} = -1 \times 6 = -6$$

$$m_{0(L/2=20)} = 4000 \, \text{kNm} \qquad m_{1(L/4)} = -1 \times 8 = -8$$

$$X_1 = -\frac{EI_c}{EI}\frac{D_{10}}{\delta_{11}} = 500 \, \text{kN}$$

Taking into account n_1, $EI_c f_{11}$ is increased by an amount of 1.6

$$M_{(L/4=10)} = m_0 + m_1 x_1 = 3000 - 6(500) = 0$$

$$M_{(L/2=20)} = m_0 + m_1 x_1 = 4000 - 8(500) = 0$$

$$V_x = \text{shear} = V_A \cos\phi - qx\cos\phi$$

$$y = 0.02(40x - x^2)$$

$$\frac{dy}{dx} = \tan\phi = \text{slope} = 0.02(40 - 2x)$$

At $x = 0$, the springing level

$$\frac{dy}{dx} = 0.8 \quad \text{or} \quad \phi = 38.67°$$

$$\sin\phi = 0.625 \qquad \cos\phi = 0.781$$

At $x = L/4$, when $\phi = 21.8°$

$$\sin\phi = 0.3714 \qquad \cos\phi = 0.9285$$

$$V_x \text{ (at } x = 0) = 0$$

$$V_{x=L/4} = 0$$

$$N_x \text{ (at } x = 0) = -V_A \sin\phi - H\cos\phi + qx\sin\phi$$

$$= -635 \quad \text{kN (compressive)}$$

$$N_{x=L/4} = -538.3 \, \text{kN (compressive)}$$

$$D_{1t} = -\alpha_t t L = -12 \times 10^{-3} \, \text{m}$$

$$EI_c = 30 \times 10^6 (4)(10^{-4}) = 120 \times 10^2 \, \text{m}^2 \, \text{kN}$$

$$EI_c D_{1t} = EI_c D_{10} = -144 \, \text{m}^3 \, \text{kN}$$

$$X_{1t} = \frac{EI_cD_{10}}{EI_cf_{11}} = 0.1055 \, \text{kN}$$

$$M = m_0 + m_1x_1 \qquad\qquad m_{1(L/2)} = 8$$

$$= 0 + 8 \times 0.1055$$

$$= -0.844 \, \text{kNm}$$

(c) Load half-way on arch UDL HA loading only

$$V_A = 300 \, \text{kN} \qquad V_B = 100 \, \text{kN}$$

$$m_{0(x=10)} = 2000 \, \text{kNm} \qquad m_{1(10)} = -6$$

$$m_{0(x=20)} = 2000 \, \text{kNm} \qquad m_{1(20)} = -8$$

$$EI_cD_{10} = -\tfrac{8}{15} \times 40(16000) = -341\,333.34$$

$$EI_cf_{11} = \tfrac{8}{15} \times 2560 = 1365.334$$

$$X_1 = -EI_cD_{10}/EI_cf_{11} = 250 \, \text{kN}$$

$$M_{x(10m)} = +500 \, \text{kNm}$$

$$M_{x(30m)} = -500 \, \text{kNm}$$

$$M_{x(20m)} = 0$$

(d) The bridge arch with a knife-edge load as its share

$$EI_cD_{10} = 98\,334 \, \text{m}^3 \, \text{kN}$$

$$EI_cf_{11} = 64.64/3 = 21.5467$$

$$X_1 = H = 72 \, \text{kN}$$

$$M_{(x \neq 10m)} = +68 \, \text{kNm}$$

$$M_{(x=20m)} = -76 \, \text{kNm}$$

4.2.3 Arches with fixed ends

Various flexibility diagrams are shown in Fig. 4.7. Since, due to fixity, there are three unknowns X_1, X_2 and X_3, the best method is to use the elastic centre method. In this method the elastic centre is established by introducing rigid arms and the redundants. X_1, X_2 and X_3 are applied as shown in Fig. 4.7(c)–(e).
The flexibility relation is established as

$$\begin{bmatrix} f_{11} & f_{12} & f_{13} \\ f_{21} & f_{22} & f_{23} \\ f_{31} & f_{32} & f_{33} \end{bmatrix} \begin{Bmatrix} X_1 \\ X_2 \\ X_3 \end{Bmatrix} = - \begin{Bmatrix} D_{10} \\ D_{20} \\ D_{30} \end{Bmatrix} \qquad (4.37)$$

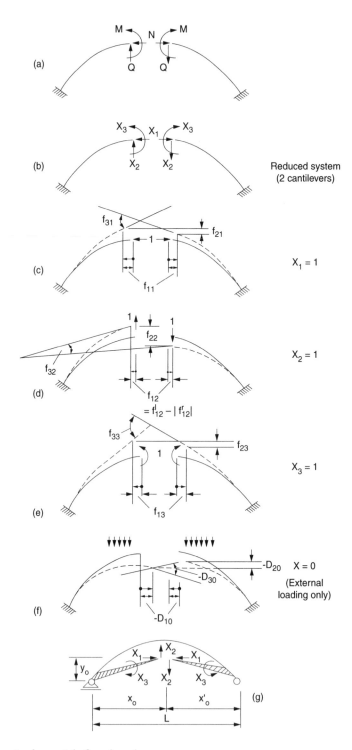

Figure 4.7. Arches with fixed ends

The moments, shear and axial forces are written as:

at any point X

$$M_x = m_{x0} + m_{x1}X_1 + m_{x2}X_2 + m_{x3}X_3 \tag{4.38}$$

$$V_x = v_{x0} + v_{x1}X_1 + v_{x2}X_2 + v_{x3}X_3 \tag{4.39}$$

$$N_x = n_{x0} + n_{x1}X_1 + n_{x2}X_2 + n_{x3}X_3 \tag{4.40}$$

since

$$i \neq k$$

$$\delta_{ik} = 0 \tag{4.41}$$

$$f_{12} = f_{21} = 0$$
$$f_{13} = f_{31} = 0 \tag{4.42}$$
$$f_{32} = f_{23} = 0$$

$$X_1 = -\frac{D_{10}}{f_{11}}$$

$$X_2 = -\frac{D_{20}}{f_{22}} \tag{4.43}$$

$$X_3 = -\frac{D_{30}}{f_{33}}$$

4.2.3.1   Supports at different levels

The elastic centre method can still be applied. Figure 4.8 shows such an arrangement and flexibility diagrams are drawn in a similar manner.

Due to X_1

$$m_1 = -y\cos\theta \tag{4.44}$$

$$n_1 = -\cos(\gamma - \theta) \tag{4.45}$$

Due to X_2

$$m_2 = -x\cos\theta \tag{4.46}$$

$$n_2 = -\sin\gamma \tag{4.47}$$

Due to X_3

$$m_3 = +1 \tag{4.48}$$

$$n_3 = 0 \tag{4.49}$$

$$f_{12} = f_{21} = 0$$

$$f_{13} = f_{31} = 0$$

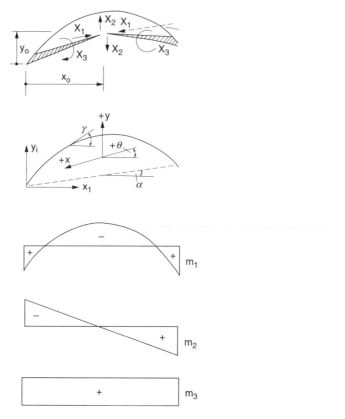

Figure 4.8. Supports at different levels

Elastic centre

$$x_0 = \frac{\int x_1 \dfrac{ds}{I}}{\int \dfrac{ds}{I}} \tag{4.50}$$

$$y_0 = \frac{\int y_1 \dfrac{ds}{I}}{\int \dfrac{ds}{I}} \tag{4.51}$$

$$\int xy \, \frac{ds}{I} = 0$$

It is easy to find $\tan\theta$

$$\tan\theta = \frac{f(y_1 - y_0)(x_0 - x_1)\dfrac{ds}{I}}{\int (x_0 - x_1)^2 \dfrac{ds}{I}} \tag{4.52}$$

$$EIf_{11} = \int m_1^2 \frac{ds}{I} + \frac{n_1^2\, ds}{A}$$

$$= \cos^2 \theta \int y^2 \frac{ds}{I} + \int \cos^2(\gamma - \theta) \frac{ds}{A} \qquad (4.53)$$

$$EIf_{22} = \cos^2 \theta \int \frac{x^2\, ds}{I} + \int \sin^2 \gamma \frac{ds}{A} \qquad (4.54)$$

$$EIf_{33} = \int \frac{ds}{I} \qquad (4.55)$$

For the external load

$$ED_{i0} = \int m_i m_0 \frac{ds}{I} + \int n_i n_0 \frac{ds}{I} \qquad (4.56)$$

$$ED_{10} = -\cos \theta \int m_0 \frac{y\, ds}{I} - \int n_0 \cos(\gamma - \theta) \frac{ds}{A} \qquad (4.57)$$

$$ED_{20} = -\cos \theta \int m_0 \frac{x\, ds}{I} - \int n_0 \sin \gamma \frac{ds}{A} \qquad (4.58)$$

$$ED_{30} = + \int m_0 \frac{ds}{I} \qquad (4.59)$$

Note that the above equations are modified by making $\theta = 0$ for fixed-ended symmetrical arches.

For support at different levels

$$M = m_0 + m_1 X_1 + m_2 X_2 + m_3 X_3$$

$$= m_0 - y \cos \theta X_1 - x \cos \theta X_2 + X_3 \qquad (4.60)$$

$$N = n_0 + n_1 X_1 + n_2 X_2 + n_3 X_3$$

$$= n_0 - \cos(\gamma - \theta) X_1 - X_2 \sin \gamma \qquad (4.61)$$

$$M = m_0 + m_1 X_1 + m_2 X_2 + m_3 X_3$$

4.2.3.2 Temperature and shrinkage in fixed arches supports at different levels

Without the bridge deck loading (Fig. 4.9):

$$D_{10} = D_{20} = D_{30} = 0 \qquad (4.62)$$

$$D = \text{displacement}$$

and slope at the elastic centre O

$$D_{10} = \varepsilon L \frac{\cos \alpha}{\cos \theta} \qquad (4.63)$$

$$D_{20} = -\varepsilon L(\sin \alpha - \cos \alpha \tan \theta) \qquad (4.64)$$

$$D_{30} = 0$$

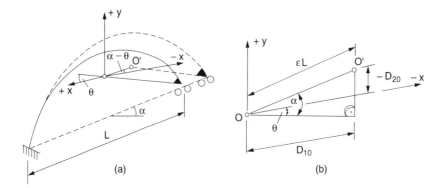

Figure 4.9. Temperature and shrinkage effects

Note that for a symmetrical arch $\alpha = \theta = 0$ in the above equations.

For unsymmetrical arches:

$$\text{temperature range } \alpha = \theta + \alpha t$$

$$\text{shrinkage} = -\varepsilon s$$

where s is shrinkage and t is temperature. Thus:

$$X_{1t} = \frac{ED_{1t}}{Ef_{11}}$$

or

$$X_{1s} = -\frac{ED_{1s}}{Ef_{11}} \tag{4.65}$$

The stress resultants are then:

$$M_t = -X_{1t}y\cos\theta \quad \text{or} \quad M_s = -X_{1s}y\cos\theta \tag{4.66}$$
$$N_t = -X_{1t}\cos(\gamma - \theta) \quad N_s = -X_{1s}\cos(\gamma - \theta) \tag{4.67}$$

4.2.3.3 Example (4.4)

The arch in Example (4.3) is now fixed and a symmetrical HA UDL part of the load is again 20 kN/m. Using the flexibility method and the application of the elastic centre method, calculate moments, shear and axial forces of the arch. Use the data given in Example (4.3):

$$I_c = I\cos\gamma$$

Various flexibility diagrams are drawn in Fig. 4.10

$$f_{12} = f_{23} = 0$$

$$y_0 \int dx = \frac{4h}{L^2}\int x(L - x)\,dx \quad \text{(parabola)}$$

or

$$y_0 L = \frac{4h}{L^2}\left(\frac{L^3}{2} - \frac{L^3}{3}\right)$$

or

$$y_0 = \tfrac{2}{3}h = \tfrac{2}{3} \times 8 = \tfrac{16}{3} = 5.33\,\mathrm{m}$$

$$m_0 = -20\left(\frac{L}{2}\right)^2 /2 = -4000\,\mathrm{kNm}$$

$$f_{11} = \int m_1^2\,\mathrm{d}x$$

$$= 40(\tfrac{16}{3} \times \tfrac{16}{3} - 2\tfrac{16}{3} \times 8 \times \tfrac{2}{3} + \tfrac{8}{15} \times 8 \times 8) = 227.56$$

$$f_{22} = \int m_2^2\,\mathrm{d}s = 16 \times 10^4$$

$$f_{33} = 40$$

$$D_{10} = 9481.5$$

$$D_{20} = 0$$

$$D_{30} = -53\,333$$

$$X_1 = -500\,\mathrm{kN}$$

$$X_2 = 0$$

$$X_3 = 1333\,\mathrm{kNm}$$

At C,

$$M_C = -50 \times 500 + 0 + 2500 = 0$$

At A,

$$M_A = 0$$

$$V_C = 0$$

$$N_C = 0 - 500 \times 1 + 0 = -500\,\mathrm{kN}$$

$$V_A = 0$$

$$N_A = -640\,\mathrm{kN}$$

when

$$\gamma = 38.67° \qquad \cos\gamma = 0.781 \qquad \sin\gamma = 0.625$$

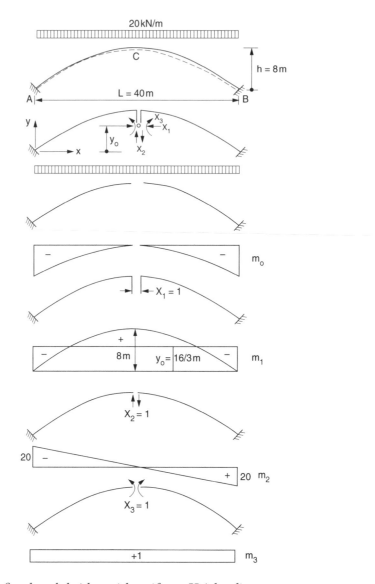

Figure 4.10. A fixed arch bridge with uniform HA loading

4.3 Influence lines for girders of variable cross-section

The bending moments and shear forces at various sections of a continuous girder can be evaluated by using an influence lines technique. The live loads are suitably positioned on the influence lines so that maximum bending moments and shear forces are developed at any section.

Figures 4.11 to 4.14 have been developed by the Portland Cement Association, USA in which various graphs show the parameters needed for drawing influence lines subject to various boundary conditions.

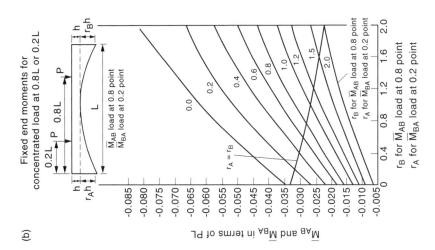

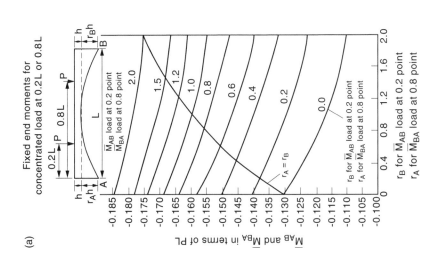

Figure 4.11 (pages 381–383). Influence line for girders of variable sections – I (Portland Cement Association, USA)

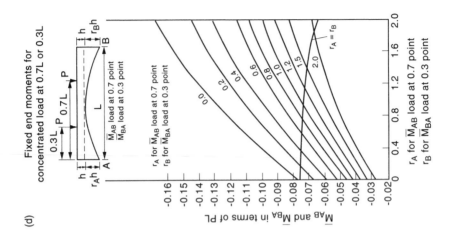

(d)

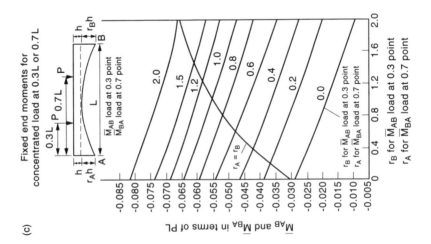

(c)

Figure 4.11. Continued

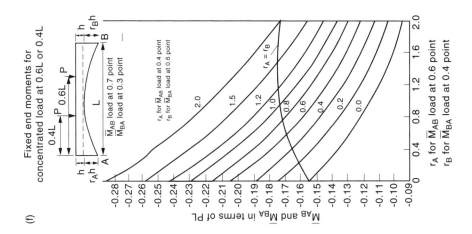

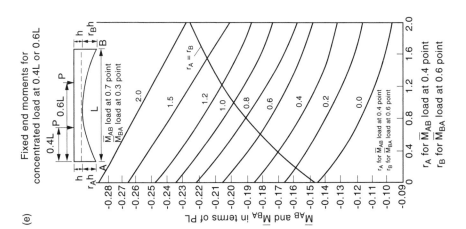

Figure 4.11. Continued

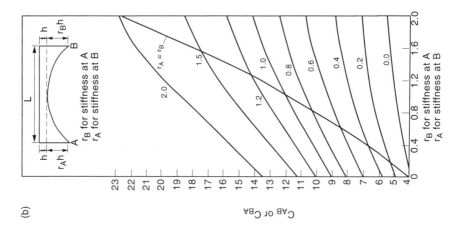

(b)

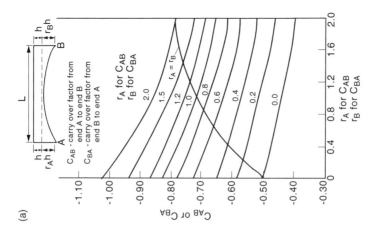

(a)

Figure 4.12 (pages 384–385). Influence lines for girders of variable sections – II (Portland Cement Association, USA)

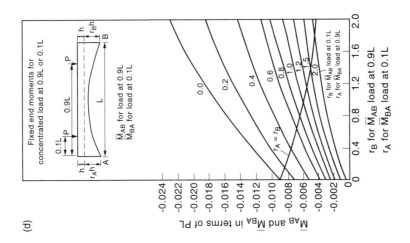

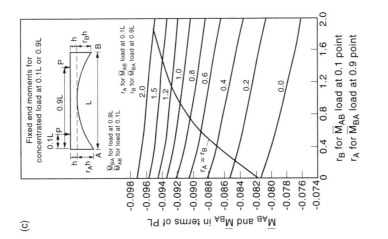

Figure 4.12. Continued

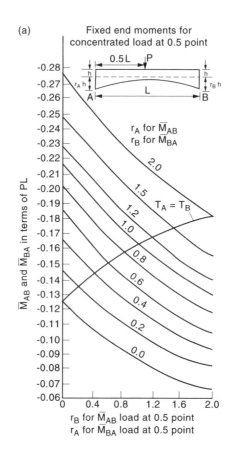

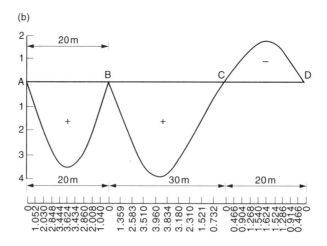

Figure 4.13 (above and facing). Influence lines for girders of variable sections –
III (Portland Cement Association, USA)

Procedure

(a) For a continuous girder ABCD, AB and CD are the exterior spans and the interior span is denoted by BC. C_{AB}, C_{BA}, C_{BC} and C_{CB} are the carry-over factors (Fig. 4.12).

(b) The distribution factors D_{BA}, D_{BC}, D_{CB} etc. are given by

$$D = \frac{K}{\sum K} = \frac{KEI_c}{L} \bigg/ \sum \frac{KEI_c}{L} \qquad (4.68)$$

where

K = stiffness of the joint at end members K_{AB}, K_{BA}

L = length

I_c = second moment of area at centre

E = Young's modulus

(c) The fixed end moments $\bar{M}_{AB}$ and $\bar{M}_{BA}$ etc. are found for different positions of loads.

(d)
$$M_1 = \bar{M}_{BA} - C_{AB}\bar{M}_{AB}$$
$$M_2 = \bar{M}_{BC} - C_{CB}\bar{M}_{CB}$$
$$M_3 = \bar{M}_{CD} - C_{DC}\bar{M}_{DC}$$
$$U = C_{BC} \cdot C_{CB} \cdot D_{BC} \cdot D_{CB} \qquad (4.69)$$

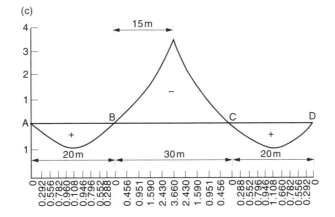

Figure 4.13. Continued

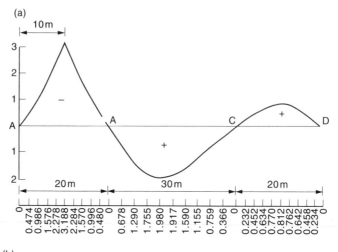

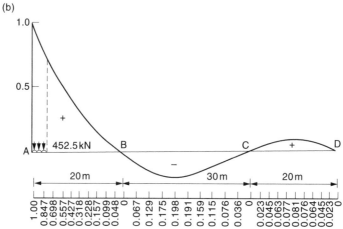

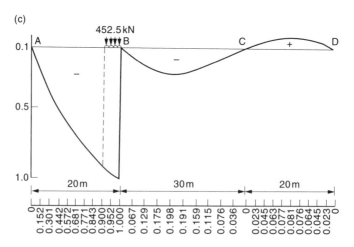

Figure 4.14. Influence lines for girders of variable sections – IV (Portland Cement Association, USA)

The load in span AB is:

$$M_B = \left[\frac{(1 - D_{BA} - U)}{(1 - U)} \right] M_1 \tag{4.70}$$

$$M_C = \left[\frac{V}{(1 - U)} \right] M_1 \tag{4.71}$$

Load in span BC is:

$$M_B = \left[\frac{(D_{BA} - \bar{M}_{BC} - W\bar{M}_{CB})}{(1 - U)} \right] \tag{4.72}$$

$$M_C = \left[\frac{(D_{CD}\bar{M}_{CD} - V\bar{M}_{BC})}{(1 - U)} \right] \tag{4.73}$$

Load in span CD is:

$$M_B = \left[\frac{W}{(1 - U)} \right] M_3 \tag{4.74}$$

$$M_C = \left[\frac{(1 - D_{CD} - U)}{(1 - U)} \right] M_3 \tag{4.75}$$

The influence line for a bending moment at B due to a limit load can be drawn.

The bending moment at point P at a distance xL (Fig. 4.15) can now be written as

$$M_P = M_B + \left(\frac{M_B}{L} \right) (xL) \tag{4.76}$$

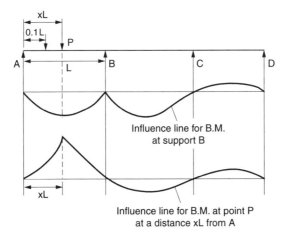

Figure 4.15. Influence line for bending moment at support B

The influence for shear is obtained as

$$\left[\frac{M + (M_C - M_B)}{L}\right]$$ (4.77)

where

M_C = influence line ordinate at support C

M = shear ordinate

Table 4.2 shows coefficients for bending moments at the support B.

Figures 4.13 and 4.14 indicate various influence lines. In order to compute the maximum values of bending moments and shear forces, the loads from any code given in Section B3 can be positioned. The graphs are equally useful for computing moments and shears due to self weight of the girder and dead load.

4.3.1 Analysis of girder having a box section – Bangash method

The analysis of a continuous box girder with variable cross-section is divided into the following two main categories:

(a)   Equations based on the flexibility concept for influence lines for bending moments, shears and reactions at supports and at regular intervals in spans of a longitudinal elevation of a girder. These influence lines are directly obtained as the deflection lines resulting from unit relative rotation or vertical translation at any section or from a unit displacement at the support. While determining these influence lines, it is assumed that the girder has a constant uniform width.

(b)   Where the girder has a variable trapezoidal cross-section, independent equations based on the flexibility concept are developed, with special emphasis on a double-cell type. This concept can be extended to the multi-cell types by increasing the storage in the program. Here ordinates for bending moments are first computed at any requisite point and then equations for deflection influence lines are solved for a unit load at a cross-section and a unit torsional moment at support. For design purposes, maximum values of moments, reactions, shears and deflections are obtained by placing specified loads in the critical zones of influence lines obtained from the two categories.

To sum up, this method is a mixture of the flexibility and influence lines methods.

4.3.1.1 Influence lines for longitudinal elevation

Figure 4.16(a) shows a continuous girder. Diagrams for moments and rotations are plotted both due to applied load and unit arbitrary moments X_1, X_2, etc. on a released structure. It is assumed that the width of the girder is constant and the intrados follows the line of a quadratic parabola, the apex of which is at the end

Table 4.2. Coefficients for bending moments at the support B

Beam diagram: spans A–B–C–D with lengths L_1, L_2, L_3; unit loads $\alpha L_1\,|\,1\text{ kN}$, $\alpha L_2\,|\,1\text{ kN}$, $\alpha L_3\,|\,1\text{ kN}$.

M_{AB}	$\bar{M}_{BA}$ (L_1)	M_1	$\bar{M}_{BC}$	$\bar{M}_{CB}$ (L_2)	$\bar{M}_{CD}$	$\bar{M}_{DC}$ (L_3)	M_3	Load in span AB M_B	Load in span BC M_B	Load in span CD M_B
$-0.0755L$	$-0.0230L$	$-0.0990L$	$-0.0950L$	$-0.0040L$	$-0.0970L$	$-0.0010L$	$-0.0980L$	$-0.0526L_1$	$-0.0453L_2$	
	$+0.0233L_3$	$-0.1100L$	$-0.0800L$	$-0.1910L$	$-0.1740L$	$-0.0200L$	$-0.1840L$	$-0.0060L$	$-0.1900L$	$-0.0160L$
	$-0.1015L_1$	$-0.0861L_2$	$+0.0452L_3$	$-0.1120L$	$-0.1550L$	$-0.2680L$	$-0.2220L$	$-0.0550L$	$-0.2500L$	$-0.0380L$
$-0.2660L$	$-0.1424L_1$	$-0.1170L_2$	$+0.0634L_3$	$-0.0950L$	$-0.2250L$	$-0.3240L$	$-0.2250L$	$-0.1120L$	$-0.2850L$	$-0.0660L$
$-0.3220L$	$-0.1722L_1$	$-0.1320L_2$	$+0.0770L_3$	$-0.0660L$	$-0.2750L$	$-0.3410L$	$-0.1810L$	$-0.1810L$	$-0.2750L$	$-0.0950L$
$-0.3410L$	$-0.1812L_1$	$-0.1278L_2$	$+0.0812L_3$	$-0.0380L$	$-0.2850L$	$-0.3230L$	$-0.1120L$	$-0.2250L$	$-0.2550L$	$-0.1150L$
$-0.3200L$	$-0.1717L_1$	$-0.1060L_2$	$+0.0762L_3$	$-0.0180L$	$-0.2510L$	$-0.2690L$	$-0.0550L$	$-0.2220L$	$-0.1550L$	$-0.1100L$
$-0.2700L$	$-0.1430L_1$	$-0.0770L_2$	$+0.0643L_3$	$-0.0052L$	$-0.1840L$	$-0.190L$	$-0.0200L$	$-0.1740L$	$-0.0820L$	$-0.0755L$
$-0.1920L$	$-0.1004L_1$	$-0.0507L_2$	$+0.0457L_3$	$-0.0010L$	$-0.0970L$	$-0.0980L$	$-0.0040L$	$-0.0950L$	$-0.0230L$	
$-0.0980L$	$-0.0520L_1$	$-0.0244L_2$	$+0.0233L_3$							

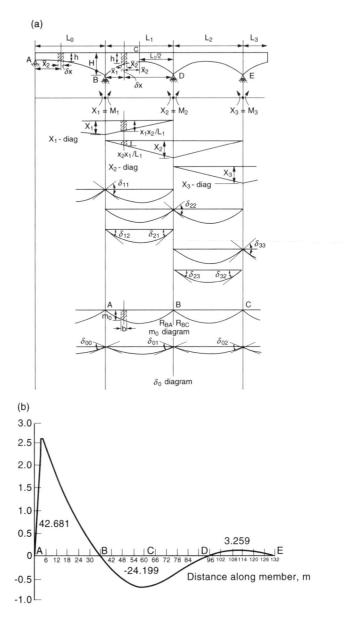

Figure 4.16 (pages 392–395). Flexibility method and influence line mixed method

support for end spans and at the centre for the interior spans. An elemental area $h \cdot \delta_x$ is chosen at a distance $\bar{x}_2$ from the apex at C then the depth at mid section of the elemental area in span BD is given by

$$h = h_c + h_x = h_c + \frac{(H - h_c)\bar{x}_2^2}{\left(\dfrac{L_1}{2}\right)^2} \tag{4.78}$$

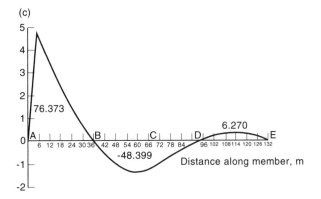

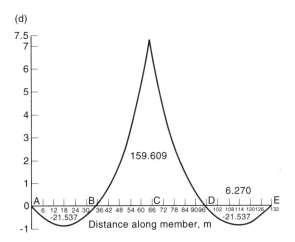

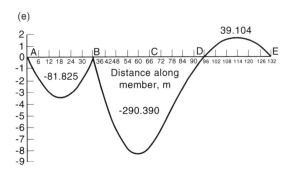

Figure 4.16. Continued

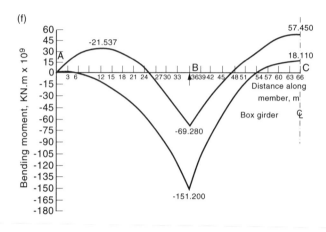

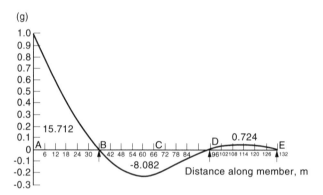

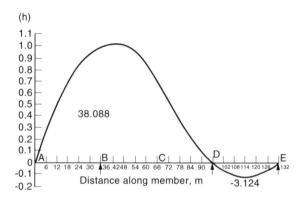

Figure 4.16. Continued

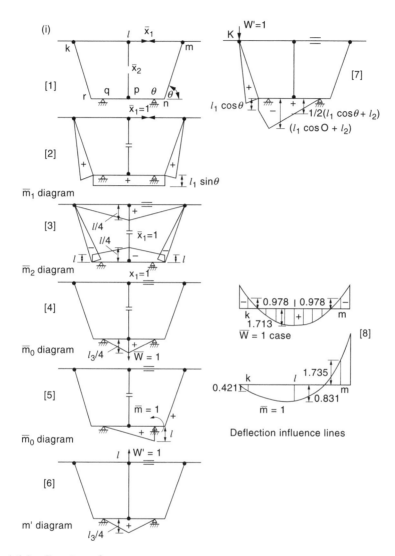

Figure 4.16. Continued

Using the same coordinates the depth h at any adjacent span is then

$$h = h_c + 4\frac{(H - h_c)}{(L_1)^2}\left(\frac{L_1}{2} - \bar{x}_2\right)^2 \tag{4.79}$$

Hence the elastic length

$$\delta L = \frac{\delta x}{\left\{h_c + \dfrac{(H - h_c)\bar{x}_2^2}{\left(\dfrac{L_1}{2}\right)}\right\}^3} \tag{4.80}$$

If m_0 is the moment produced in a primary structure due to external loading, the relative rotation of δ at a support is calculated from the moment diagrams in the span contributed from the two adjacent spans on each side of a support. For example δ_{01} at D is computed as:

$$\delta_{01} = \frac{1}{L_1} \sum_{B}^{D} m_0 \delta L \cdot \bar{x}_1 + \frac{1}{L_2} \sum_{E}^{D} m_0 \delta L \cdot \bar{x}_2 \tag{4.81}$$

All other values of δ are computed in a similar manner in a primary structure by adjusting the relevant parameters.

Next the relative rotation is determined corresponding to moments m_1, m_2, m_3, etc. resulting from the continuity moments at the supports X_1, X_2, X_3, etc. as are shown in Fig. 4.16(a). For example for span L_1 the rotation at D, $d\delta_{11}$, due to element δ_x is

$$d\delta_{11} = \left(\frac{x_1}{L_1}\right)^2 \cdot \delta L \cdot X_2 \tag{4.82}$$

Therefore the total contribution from the span BD and DE is summed up as

$$\delta_{11_{(BD)}} = \sum_{B}^{D} d\delta_{11} = \frac{X_2}{(L_1)^2} \sum_{B}^{D} \bar{x}_1^2 \cdot \delta L + \frac{X}{(L_1)^2} \sum_{B}^{D} \bar{x}_1 \bar{x}_2$$

$$= \left(\frac{X_2}{L_1}\right)^2 I_{X_1} + \frac{X_1}{(L_1)^2} \cdot I_{X_1 X_2} \tag{4.83}$$

$$\delta_{11_{(DE)}} = \sum_{D}^{E} d\delta_{11} = \frac{X_2}{(L_1)^2} \sum_{D}^{E} \bar{x}_2^2 \cdot \delta L + \frac{X_2}{(L_2)^2} \sum_{D}^{E} (\bar{x}_1 \bar{x}_2) \delta L$$

$$= \frac{X_2}{(L_1)^2} I_{x_2} + \frac{X_2}{(L_2)^2} I_{X_1 X_2} \tag{4.84}$$

Hence

$$\delta_{11} = \delta_{11_{(BD)}} + \delta_{11_{(DE)}} = \text{reaction} \tag{4.85}$$

In this way all other values of δ are computed by collecting terms from the respective diagrams in adjacent spans. If the structure has n redundants, the flexibility matrix for n unknowns are:

$$
\begin{bmatrix} X_1 \\ X_2 \\ X_3 \\ \vdots \\ X_n \end{bmatrix}
\begin{bmatrix}
\delta_{11} & \delta_{12} & \delta_{13} \ldots \delta_{1n} \\
\delta_{21} & \delta_{22} & \delta_{23} \ldots \delta_{2n} \\
\delta_{31} & \delta_{32} & \delta_{33} \ldots \delta_{3n} \\
\vdots & & \vdots \\
\delta_{n1} & \delta_{n2} & \delta_{n3} \ldots \delta_{nn}
\end{bmatrix}
= -
\begin{bmatrix} \delta_{10} \\ \delta_{20} \\ \delta_{30} \\ \vdots \\ \delta_{n0} \end{bmatrix}
\tag{4.86}
$$

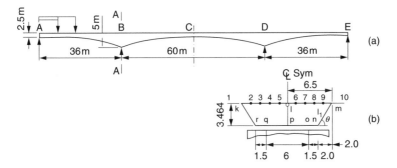

Figure 4.17. (a) Elevation of a box girder. (b) Cross-section of a double-cell box

or

$$X = -F^{-1}\Delta$$

Influence lines for bending moment at an internal support are determined by making Eq. (4.85) equal to 1 for that support only. Influence lines for bending moment at any other section are computed from

$$m = m_0 + \frac{1}{\delta_x}[X_1\bar{x}_2 + X_2\bar{x}_1 + \cdots] \qquad (4.87)$$

Similarly influence lines for shear at any section are given by

$$\nu = \nu_0 + \frac{1}{\delta_x}[X_2 - X_1 \pm \cdots] \qquad (4.88)$$

As an example a three-span continuous bridge shown in Fig. 4.17 is investigated. The bridge is subject to the following load usually adopted for British railway bridges:

Applied dead load (tracks, ballast, hand rails, parapets)   60.44 kN/m.
Live load BS 5400 RB loading speed   6 rev/sec.
For 60 m span load/track = 569 tons (English)

$$2 \text{ track equivalent UDL} = \frac{2 \times 569 \times 9.964}{60} \text{ kN/m}$$

$$= 190 \text{ kN/m}$$

For 36 m span load/track = 392 tons

$$\text{equivalent UDL} \frac{= 2 \times 392 \times 9.964}{36}$$

$$= 218 \text{ kN/m}$$

Table 4.3 indicates the properties of the sections at discrete points of the bridge from its support A and is used throughout for solving Eqs (4.78)–(4.87) in order to obtain bending moments and reaction influence lines. The value of elemental

Table 4.3. Properties of sections

Distance from support A (m)	Depth (m)	Cross-sectional area (m²)	I (m⁴)	z = 2I/h (m³)
3	2.517	6.206	5.176	4.113
6	2.569	6.279	5.450	4.243
9	2.656	6.400	5.928	4.464
12	2.778	6.571	6.638	4.779
15	2.934	6.790	7.619	5.194
18	3.125	7.057	8.932	5.716
21	3.351	7.373	10.652	6.357
24	3.511	7.597	11.983	6.826
27	3.906	8.150	15.691	8.034
30	4.236	8.612	19.275	9.089
33	4.601	9.128	23.787	10.340
36	5.000	9.682	29.415	11.766
39	4.525	9.017	22.798	10.076
42	4.100	8.420	17.743	8.655
45	3.725	7.897	13.916	7.471
48	3.400	7.442	11.049	6.499
51	3.125	7.057	8.391	5.370
54	2.900	6.742	7.398	5.102
57	2.275	6.497	6.324	4.641
60	2.600	6.322	5.618	4.321
63	2.525	6.217	5.218	4.133
66	2.500	6.182	5.088	4.070

length δ_x is therefore maintained at 3 m throughout the bridge. A computer program MASTER-IAN written in FORTRAN 77 solves the above equations in the given order (see flow chart given in Fig. 4.18). Figures 4.16(b) and (c) show influence lines for bending moment at points 3 m and 6 m from the support A, respectively. Figure 4.16(d) shows bending moment at the centre of the girder giving a peak value at C. Figure 4.16(e) gives the bending moment influence line at the support B. From the output the net areas under the influence lines are computed and the above diagrams indicate values of these areas. A typical bending moment envelope diagram is shown in Fig. 4.16(f) when the bridge is subject to the above-mentioned specified loadings. The curves in Fig. 4.16(f) give bending moment influence lines.

4.3.1.2 Influence lines for transverse section

Here the transverse section is divided at deck level into a series of discrete points. It is assumed that the deck slab is less rigidly connected to the diaphragm and the trapezoidal part. This assumption simplifies the analysis without losing accuracy in the results. The double-cell box section of Fig. 4.17(b) is supported at

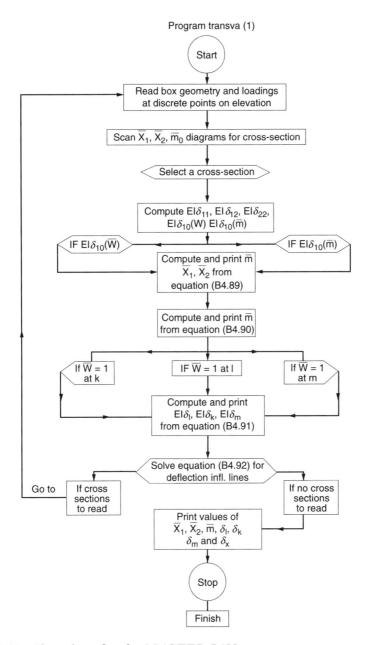

Figure 4.18. Flow chart for the MASTER-IAN program

bearing points q and 0. In this case an attempt is made to compute moments at all rigid points of the box and also influence line ordinates for deflection when a unit load or unit moment is applied at any support.

If $\bar{X}_1$ and $\bar{X}_2$ in Fig. 4.16(i) [1] are the redundant axial forces in the deck and the cell wall then they introduce moments in the box as shown in Fig. 4.16(i) [1] and [2]. Next the structure is analysed as a primary structure with a unit load applied at the centre of $q0$ due to lp and also a unit moment at 0 (Fig. 4.16(i) [3] to [5]). The moments due to these loading cases are then superimposed on the moment diagrams due to $\bar{X}_1$ and $\bar{X}_2$.

$EI\delta$ values are computed from the above figures and the formal equations assume the following form:

$$\bar{X}_1\delta_{11} + \bar{X}_2\delta_{12} = -\delta_{10}$$
$$\bar{X}_1\delta_{21} + X_2\delta_{22} = -\delta_{20}$$

(4.89a)

or

$$\bar{X}_1 = \frac{-\delta_{10}\delta_{22} + \delta_{20}\delta_{12}}{\delta_{11}\delta_{22} - \delta_{12}^2}$$
$$\bar{X}_2 = \frac{-\delta_{11}\delta_{20} + \delta_{21}\delta_{10}}{\delta_{11}\delta_{22} - \delta_{12}^2}$$

(4.89b)

For both cases of unit load or unit moment the final moments at points in a box can now easily be determined from Eq. (4.90):

$$\bar{m} = \bar{m}_0 + \bar{X}_1\bar{m}_1 + \bar{X}_2\bar{m}_2$$

(B4.90)

If the unit load is applied at l and k or m, the moment diagrams are shown in Fig. 4.16(i) [6] and [7]. Calling these moments m', $EI\delta$, the values of deflection at these points l, m or k can be evaluated from the following relationship

$$EI_c\delta_{l,k,m} = \int \bar{m}\frac{m'}{I}\,ds$$

(4.91)

Influence lines for deflection at all other intermediate points are determined by solving Equation (4.92):

$$EI_c\delta_X = EI_c\delta_{k,l}\left(1 - \frac{x}{L}\right) + EI_c\delta_{k,m}\frac{x}{L} + P\frac{L^2}{6}W_D$$

(4.92)

Table 4.4. Typical output for a section at B or D

Case/quantity	$\bar{W} = 1$	$\bar{m} = 1$
$\bar{X}_1$	−0.0482	−0.0376
$\bar{X}_2$	+0.0944	+0.0500
$\bar{m}_1$	+0.3060	+0.1625
$\bar{m}_n = \bar{m}_2$	−0.2614	−0.1810
$\bar{m}_q = \bar{m}_0$	−0.3320	−0.2185
$\bar{m}_p$	+1.0270	+0.2065
$\bar{m}_{0(left)}$	—	+0.7815

Values of $\bar{m}$ from Table 4.4 are substituted into Eq. (4.91) for the final values of deflections at points l, k and m. It is assumed that EI is constant throughout. Should EI differ in different zones of the section, the above equations are simply modified in the ratio of I/I_c.

When the final deflections are computed at l, k, m, deflection ordinates at intermediate points are evaluated by solving Eq. (4.92). Figure 4.16(i) [8] shows deflection influence lines for both $\bar{W}$ and $\bar{m}$ cases for a given section. In the first two terms δ is for a typical span.

Such $EI\delta_k(\quad) + EI_c\delta_l(\quad)$ are for intermediate points in a kl span. W_D is a term equal to

$$\left[\frac{x}{L} - \left(\frac{x}{L}\right)^3\right] \tag{4.93}$$

giving the relationship between the load at a point and a moment at that point in a specific span such as kl.

4.3.2 Computer program MASTER-IAN

4.3.2.1 Input sequence

The computer is written in FORTRAN IV language for ICL 1902A. The input cards are arranged according to the following format:

Format (5F6, 0, 212)
Columns 1–6 length of span AB to two decimal places (SI)
Columns 7–12 length of span BD to two decimal places (S2)
Columns 13–18 depth of girder at A to two decimal places (DA)
Columns 19–24 depth of girder B to two decimal places (DB)
Columns 25–30 depth of girder C to two decimal places (DC)
Columns 31–32 number of elements of length in span AB and DE (N1)
Columns 33–34 number of elements of length in span BD (N2).

4.3.2.2 Nomenclature

X_1, X_2 = arbitrary moments at specified releases at continuous supports

$\bar{X}_1, \bar{X}_2$ = redundant forces in a box section

h_c = depth of a girder at the centre of a span

H = depth of a girder at any support

L_0, L_1 = effective span lengths between supports

δL = elemental length

δ = deflection or rotations

$\bar{W}$ = unit load on a primary structure of a box section

$\bar{m}_0$ = unit moment or rotation at support in a primary structure in a box section

$I_{x_{1,2}}$ = moment of inertia at sections

$I_{x_1 x_2}$ = product of inertia

F = flexibility matrix

Δ = displacement matrix

m = influence lines for moments in a longitudinal elevation

ν = influence lines for shear in a longitudinal elevation

Computer symbols

$$D_1, D_2 = \text{elemental lengths}$$

$$DA, DB = \text{depth at } A, B \text{ etc.}$$

$$AI(1), BI(1) = \text{influence lines for reactions}$$

$$A(\text{I}), \ldots, BMI \ldots = \text{influence lines for bending moments}$$

The following shows the complete program listings and source code for program MASTER-IAN.

4.3.2.3   Program listings (Program MASTER-IAN)

```
JOB F-PC GIRDER.ELSRC036,BANGASH
                             RUN BY GEORGE 2/MK9B ON 16/10/72 AT 12.28
THFORTRUN
* * **



FORTRAN COMPILATION BY #XFAE MK 4D            DATE 16/10/72 TIME – 12/28/15



    LIST (LP)
    PROGRAM (HOPE)
    INPUT 1=CRO
    OUTPUT 2=LP7
    INPUT 3=TR0
    OUTPUT 4=TP7
    TRACE 2
    END
```

```
        MASTER IAN
        DIMENSION PM(132)
        DIMENSION A(36),B(60),C(36),AI(132),BI(132)
        DIMENSION EDA(36),EDB(60),EDC(36),PA(36),PB(60),PC(36)
C       ANALYSIS OF 3-SPAN CONTINUOUS BEAM WITH VARIABLE DEPTH
C       INFLUENCE LINE FOR BRIDGES WITH PARABOLIC SOFFIT
C
C       READ DATA
        READ(1,1) S1,S2,DA,DB,DC,N1,N2
1       FORMAT(5F6.1,2I2)
        S3=S1
        AAI=0
C       COMPUTE ELASTIC LENGTH, ELA M OF I SPAN AB
        XN1=N1
        D1=S1/XN1
        DS1=D1/2
        DO 10 I=1,N1
        D=DA+((DB-DA)/(S1*S1))*DS1**2
        G=12/(5.87*D**3-4.47*(D-0.6)**3)
        EDA(I)=D1*G
        AAI=AAI+EDA(I)*DS1**2
10      DS1 =DS1+DT
C       COMPUTE ELA LENGTH, ELAM OF I AND PRODUCT OF I SPAN BD
        XN2=N2
        D2=SZ/XN2
        DS2=D2/2.
        S4=S2/2.
        BBI=O
        BDI=O.
        DO 11 I=1, N2
        IF(S4-DS2)14,14,12
12      XL=S4-DS2
        GO TO 13
14      XL=DS2-S4
13      XM=DS2
        D=DC+(4.*(DB-DC)/(S2*S2))*XL*XL
        EDA(I)=D2*G
        BBI=BBI+EDB(I)*XM*XM
        BDI=BDI+EDB(I)*XM*(S2-XM)
11      DS2=DS2+D2
C       COMPUTE MB MD TO PRODUCE UNIT REL ROT AT B
        XN=AAI/(S1*S1)+BBI/(S2*S2)
        XO=BDI/(S2*S2)
        BM1 =XN/(XN*XN-XO*XO)
        BM3=XO/(XN*XN-XO*XO)
C       COMPUTE ELA LOADS ON SPAN AB
        DS1 =D1/2.
        DO 15 I=1,N1
        PA(I)=BM1/S1*DS1*EDA(I)
15      DS1 =DS1+D1
C       COMPUTE ILO ON SPAN AB
```

```
          DS1=D1/2.
          XN=S1-DS1
          SUM=0
          DO 16 I=1,N1
          SUM=SUM+PA(I)*XN
      16  XN=XN-D1
          XX=SUM/S1
          WRITE(2,2)
2          FORMAT(1H1////30X,42HANALYSIS OF 3-SPAN CONTINUOUS BEAM OF,
          121H OF VARIABLE DEPTH//103X,13H** Y BANGASH///////5X,
          21OHDIS FROM A,5X,19HILO FOR MOMENT AT B/6X,8H(METRES),12X,
          37HSPAN AB/)
          XN=3.
          DO 17 I=3,36,3
          SUM=0.
          DS1=D1/2.
          DO 18 J=1,N1
          IF(XN-DS1)19,19,20
      19  XP=0.
          GO TO 21
      20  XP=XN-DS1
      21  SUM=SUM+PA(J)*XP
      18  DS1=DS1+D1
          A(I)=SUM-XK*XN
          WRITE(2,3)XN,A(I)
3          FORMAT(F13.3,F19.3)
      17  XN=XN+3.
C          COMPUTE ELA LOADS ON SPAN BD
          DS2=D2/2.
          XN=DS2
          DO 22 I=1,N2
          PB(1)=(BM1*(S2-XN)-BM3*XN)*EDB(I)/S2
      22  XN=XN+D2
C          COMPUTE ILO ON SPAN BD
          XN=S2-DS2
          SUM=0.
          DO 23 I=1,N2
          SUM=SUM+PB(I)*XN
      23  XN=XN-D2
          XK=SUM/S2
          WRITE(2,4)
4          FORMAT(///5X,10HDIS FROM B,5X,19HILO FOR MOMENT AT B/6X,
          18H (METRES),12X,7HSPAN BD/)
          XN=3.
          DO 24 I=3,60,3
          SUM=0.
          DS2=D2/2.
          DO 25 J=1, N2
          IF(XN-DS2)26,26,27
      26  XP=0.
          GO TO 28
      27  XP =XN-DS2
```

```
   28  SUM=SUM+PB(J)*XP
   25  DS2=DS2+D2
       B(I)=SUM-XK*XN
       WRITE(2,3)XN,B(I)
   24  XN=XN+3
C      COMPUTE ELA LOADS ON SPAN DE
       J=N1
       DO 29 I=1,N1
       EDC(I)=EDA(J)
   29  J=J-1
       D S3=S3-D1/2.
       DO 30 I=1,N1
       PC(I)=BM3/S3*DS3*EDC(I)
   30  DS3=DS3-D1
C      COMPUTE ILO ON SPAN DE
       DS1 =D1/2.
       XN=S3-DS1
       SUM=0.
       DO 31 I=1,N1
       SUM=SUM*PC(I)*XN
   31  XN=XN-D1
       XK=SUM/S3
       WRITE(2,6)
6      FORMAT(///5X,10HDIS FROM D,5X,19HILO FOR MOMENT A1 B/6X,
       18H(METRES),12X,7HSPAN DE/)
       XN=3.
       DO 32 I=3,36,3
       SUM=0.
       DS3=D1/2.
       DO 33 J=1,N1
       IF(XN-DS3)34,34,35
   34  XP=0.
       GO TO 36
   35  XP=XN-DS3
   36  SUM=SUM+PC(J)*XP
   33  DS3=DS3+D1
       C(I)=XK*XN-SUM
       WRITE(2,3)XN*C(I)
   32  XN=XN+3.
C      COMPUTE ILO FOR REACTIONS
       WRITE(2,8)
8      FORMAT(///5X,10HDIS FROM A,5X,21HILO FOR REACTION AT A,5X,
       121HILO FOR REACTION AT 8/8H(METRES)/)
       DS1=3.
       DO 38 I=3,129,3
   39  I*(DS1-S1)40,41,42
   40  J=DS1
       AI(I)=(A(J)*(S1-DS1))/S1
       K=S3-J
       BI(I)=(C(K)+(S1+S2-DS1)-AI(I)*(S1+S2))/S2
       WRITE(2,9)DS1,AI(I),BI(I)
9      FORMAT(F13.3,F20.3,F26.3)
```

```
       GO TO 38
41     AI(I)=0.
       BI(I)=1.
       GO TO 38
42     IF(DS1-(S1,S2))43,44,45
43     J=DS1-S1
       AI(I)=B(J)/S1
       K=S2-J
       BI(I)=(B(K)+(S1+S2-DSI)-AI(I)*(S1+S2)/S2
       WRITE(2,9)DS1,AI(I),BI(I)
       GO TO 38
44     AI(I)=0.
       BI(I)=0.
       GO TO 38
45     J=DS1-(S1+S2)
       AI(I)=C(J)/S1
       K=SI-J
       BI(I)=(A(K)-AI(I)*(S1+S2))/S2
       WRITE(2,9)DS1,AI(I),BI(I)
38     DS1=DS1+3.
       IF(132.-DS1)46,47,47
46     GO TO 39
C      COMPUTE ILO FOR BENDING MOMENT AT ANY POINT P
47     DS4=3.
       DO 48 K=3,66,3
       SUM=0.
49     WRITE(2,100)
100    FORMAT(///5X,20HDIS OF NODE P FROM A,5X,10HDIS FROM A,5X,
       119HILO FOR MOMENT AT P,6X,4HAREA/11X,8H(METRES),12X,8H(METRES)/)
       DS1=3.
       DO 50 I=3,129,3
60     IF(DS4-S1)51,51,52
51     IF(DS4-DS1)53,53,54
53     BM4=AI(I)*DS4
       GO TO 55
54     BM4=AI(I)*DS4-(DS4-DS1)
       GO TO 55
52     IF(DS4-DS1)56,56,57
56     BM4=(AI(I)*DS4)+(BI(I)*(DS4-S1))
       GO TO 55
57     BM4=(AI(I)*DS4)+(BI(I)*(DS4-S1))-(DS4-DS1)
55     SUM=SUM+BM4
       XN3=SUM*3.
       WRITE(2,101)DS4,DS1,BM4,XN3
101    FORMAT(F18.3,2F20.3,F17.3)
50     DS1=DS1+3
       IF(132.-DS1)58,58,59
59     GO TO 51
58     CONTINUE
48     DS4=DS4+3.
       IF(96.-DS4)61,62,62
61     GO TO 49
```

```
  62   WRITE(2,102)
 102   FORMAT(/////50X,20H** END OF RUN **)
       STOP
       END
```

END OF SEGMENT, LENGTH 1391, NAME IAN

4.4 Grillage analysis

The bridge deck is approximately represented by a grillage of interconnected beams under loads. The top of these beams has a slab. The method involves the idealization of the deck as a plane or three-dimensional gridwork of discrete interconnected beams. At the joints of such a grillage a normal form of restraint to movement is applied which represents support conditions such as fixity, discrete columns, elastic foundation, etc. A tapered member, if any, can be represented by a member with a dummy joint or by making several steps in the member. A curved member is usually approximated by a series of short straight members. Where bridge deck slabs are stiffened by beams (U-type) and boxes, the longitudinal grillage beams, boxes etc., should coincide with individual webs. Generally for a top slab in the transverse direction, the transverse stiffening members (beams, boxes etc.) should then be positioned. At intermediate positions the spacings shall, generally, be 1.5 times the longitudinal spacings.

Two methods of analysis are proposed: The direct stiffness method and the flexibility method.

Figure 4.19 shows typical layouts of grids. A typical bridge gridwork (grillage) is analysed using the flexibility method in Example (4.5). If the bridge grid is extensive in all directions, a similar method is employed by connecting individual grids and providing boundary conditions for the true representation of various continuities and nodes.

4.4.1 Example (4.5)

A symmetric beam gridwork is shown with a load P at B' in Fig. 4.20(a), and the corresponding released structure is shown in Fig. 4.20(b). Determine the redundants X_1 to X_4. Calculate moments and reactions. Draw the final bending moment diagram indicating principal values. Take $EI = GJ$.

Solution

For a grillage under load Fig. 4.21(a) to (e) give various flexibility diagrams.

The statics are described by:

$$R_{A0} + R_{B0} + R_{D0} = P$$

$$R_{B0} = 2R_{D0} = 4R_{A0}$$

$$2R_{A0} = -R_{D0}$$

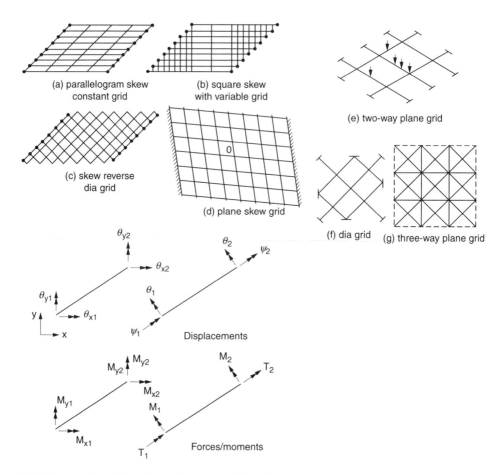

(a) parallelogram skew constant grid

(b) square skew with variable grid

(c) skew reverse dia grid

(d) plane skew grid

(e) two-way plane grid

(f) dia grid   (g) three-way plane grid

Displacements

Forces/moments

(h) Displacements and forces/moments - representative views

Figure 4.19. Simple two-dimensional grids

$$R_{D0} = \tfrac{2}{5}P$$

$$R_{A0} = -\tfrac{1}{5}P$$

$$R_{B0} = \tfrac{4}{5}P$$

$$f_{ii} = \int \frac{m_i^2}{EI}\, ds + \frac{(T_i)^2}{GJ}\, ds$$

$$f_{ij} = \int \frac{m_i m_j}{EI}\, ds + \int \frac{T_i T_j}{GJ}\, ds$$

$$f_{11} = 2L\left(\frac{1}{GJ} + \frac{1}{EI}\right)$$

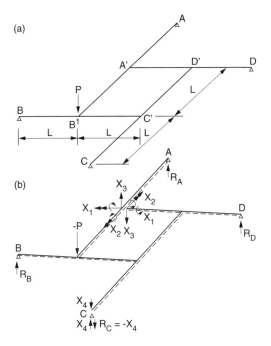

Figure 4.20. (a) A symmetric beam grid. (b) Stress resultants

$$f_{22} = 2L \left(\frac{1}{GJ} + \frac{1}{EI} \right)$$

$$f_{33} = 2L^3 \left(\frac{1}{GJ} + \frac{2}{3EI} \right)$$

$$f_{44} = 5L^3 \left(\frac{1}{GJ} + \frac{1}{EI} \right)$$

$$f_{34} = f_{43} = -L^3 \left(\frac{1}{GJ} + \frac{2}{3EI} \right)$$

$$f_{12} = 0 = f_{21}$$

$$f_{13} = -L^2 \left(\frac{1}{GJ} + \frac{1}{EI} \right) = f_{31}$$

$$f_{24} = -L^2 \left(\frac{1}{GJ} + \frac{1}{EI} \right) = f_{42}$$

$$f_{14} = 2L^2 \left(\frac{1}{GJ} + \frac{1}{EI} \right) = f_{41}$$

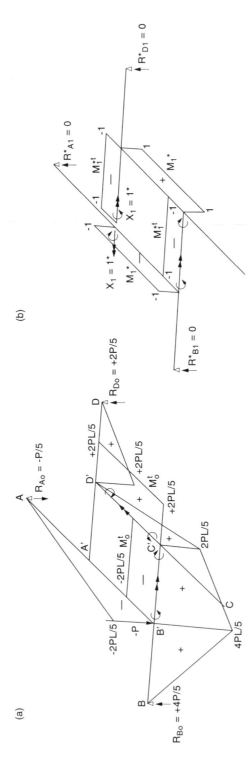

Figure 4.21 (above and facing). Flexibility diagrams for Example (B4.5). (a) Due to applied load on static structure values m_0. Diagram involving m_0^t (torsion), n_0 (axial). (b) Values f_{11}. Diagram for involving m_1 and m_1^t, n_1 or s_1. (c) Values f_{22}. Diagram involving m_2, m_2^t, n_2. (d) Values f_{33}. Diagram involving m_3, m_3^t, n_3 or s_3. (e) Values f_{44}. Diagram involving m_4, m_4^t, n_4 or s_4

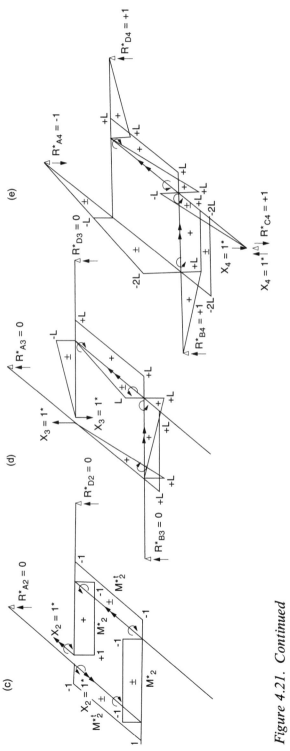

Figure 4.21. Continued

$$f_{23} = f_{32} = -L^2 \left(\frac{1}{GK} + \frac{1}{EI} \right)$$

$$D_{10} = PL^3 \left(\frac{2}{5GJ} + \frac{1}{2EI} \right)$$

$$D_{20} = -\frac{PL^3}{5} \left(\frac{2}{3GJ} + \frac{3}{EI} \right)$$

$$D_{30} = -\frac{PL^3}{30EI}$$

$$D_{40} = PL^3 \left(\frac{6}{5GJ} + \frac{5}{3EI} \right)$$

When $EI = GK$ and L/EI cancels on both sides, the following relation

$$[f]\{X\} = -\{\delta_0\}$$

reduces to

$$
\begin{bmatrix}
40 & 0 & -20L & 40L \\
0 & 4 & -2L & -2L \\
-60L & -60L & 100L^2 & -50L^2 \\
60L & -30L & -25L^2 & 150L^2
\end{bmatrix}
\begin{Bmatrix}
X_1 \\
X_2 \\
X_3 \\
X_4
\end{Bmatrix}
=
\begin{Bmatrix}
-9PL \\
PL \\
PL^2 \\
-43PL^2
\end{Bmatrix}
$$

Solution gives

$$X_1 = \frac{13}{880} PL$$

$$X_2 = \frac{4}{55} PL$$

$$X_3 = \frac{-101}{1320} P$$

$$X_4 = \frac{-367}{1320} P$$

$$R_A = R_{A0} + X_4 R_{A4}^* = \frac{-P}{5} + \frac{367P}{1320} = \frac{103}{1320} P$$

Similarly

$$R_B = R_{B0} + X_4 R_{B4}^* = \frac{4P}{5} - \frac{367P}{1320} = \frac{684P}{1320}$$

$$R_C = \frac{367P}{1320}$$

$$R_D = \frac{161P}{1320}$$

$$M = m_0 + m_1X_1 + m_2X_2 + m_3X_3 + m_4X_4$$

$$T = T_0 + T_1X_1 + T_2X_2 + T_3X_3 + T_4X_4$$

$$\left.\begin{array}{l} M_{A'-E} = -\dfrac{PL}{5} - X_4L = \dfrac{103PL}{1320} = R_AL \\[3mm] M_{A'+E} = -\dfrac{PL}{5} - X_1 - X_4L = \dfrac{167}{2640}\,PL \\[3mm] M_{B'} = -\dfrac{2PL}{5} - X_1 + X_1L - 2X_4L = \dfrac{171}{2640}\,PL \\[3mm] T_{(A'B')} = X_2 = \dfrac{4PL}{55} \end{array}\right\} \text{Member AA'B'}$$

$$\left.\begin{array}{l} M_{B'-E} = R_{B'}L = \dfrac{689}{1320}\,PL \\[3mm] M_{B'+E} = \dfrac{4PL}{5} - X_2 + X_4L = -\dfrac{26PL}{1320} \\[3mm] M_C = \dfrac{2PL}{5} - X_2X_3L + X_4L = \dfrac{-26}{1320}\,PL \\[3mm] T_{(B'C')} = \dfrac{-2PL}{5} - X_1 + X_3L - X_4(2L) \end{array}\right\} \text{Member BB'C}$$

$$\left.\begin{array}{l} M_{C'-E'} = R_CL = \dfrac{367}{1320}\,PL \\[3mm] M_{C'+E} = +\dfrac{2PL}{5} + X_1 - X_3L + X_4L = \dfrac{563}{2640}\,PL \\[3mm] M_{D'} = X_1 + 0 = \dfrac{13PL}{880} \\[3mm] T_{(C'D')} = \dfrac{2PL}{5} - X_2 + X_3L + X_4L = -\dfrac{72PL}{2640} \end{array}\right\} \text{Member CC'D}$$

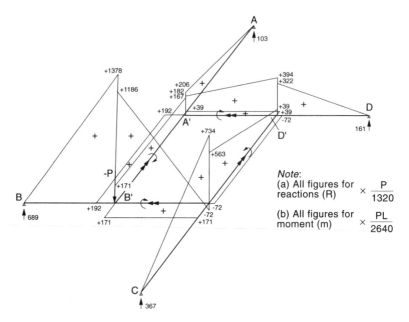

Figure 4.22. Final moment diagram with end reactions shown

$$M_{D'-E} = R_D L = \frac{161PL}{1320}$$

$$M_{D'+E} = X_2 - X_3 L + \frac{197}{1320} PL$$

$$M_{A'} = X_2 = \frac{4PL}{55}$$

$$T_{(D'A')} = -X_1 = \frac{13PL}{880}$$

Member DD'A

Figure 4.22 shows M and R values and the final bending moment diagram.

4.4.2 Grillage involving stiffness method

The *stiffness approach* of a plane grid representing a bridge deck. The coordinate axes are chosen such that the z-axis is normal to the x and y axes. The element of the grillage has three independent displacements as shown in Figure 4.23. Two of these rotations are θ_x and θ_y about the x and y axes and the third is a translation w in the z-direction. In deriving the stiffness matrix $[K]$, take

θ = rotation due to bending $\rightarrow$ double headed arrow $\twoheadrightarrow$ normal

ψ = torsional rotation along the axis of the member

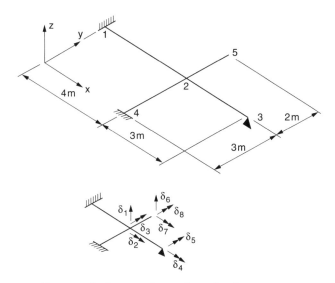

Figure 4.23. A grillage with three independent displacements

The force–displacement relation is given by

$$
\begin{bmatrix} F_{z1} \\ M_1 \\ F_{z2} \\ M_2 \end{bmatrix} = \frac{EI}{L(1+\bar{G})} \begin{bmatrix} \dfrac{12}{L^2} & -\dfrac{6}{L} & -\dfrac{12}{L^2} & -\dfrac{6}{L} \\ & 4+\bar{G} & \dfrac{6}{L} & 2-\bar{G} \\ & \text{symmetric} & \dfrac{12}{L^2} & \dfrac{6}{L} \\ & & & 4+\bar{G} \end{bmatrix} \begin{bmatrix} w_1 \\ \theta_1 \\ w_2 \\ \theta_2 \end{bmatrix}
\tag{4.94}
$$

where

F_{z1}, F_{z2} = shear forces at the ends 1 and 2

w_1, w_2 = translations in the z-direction at the ends 1 and 2

M_1, M_2 = bending moments at the ends 1 and 2

θ_1, θ_2 = bending rotations at ends 1 and 2

L = member length

$\bar{G} = \dfrac{12EI_{\gamma}}{GAL^2}$ a factor to allow for shear deformation effects

In grillages, in addition to bending and shear, torsion is at the ends in particular such as ψ_1 and ψ_2 at ends 1 and 2. Net twist is $(\psi_2 - \psi_1)$ and the rate of twist is $(\psi_2 - \psi_1)/L$.

Torque at $2 = T_2 = GJ(\psi_2 - \psi_1)/L$ while at 1 the torque is $T_1 = -T_2$ such that

$$\begin{bmatrix} T_1 \\ T_2 \end{bmatrix} = \frac{GJ}{L} \begin{bmatrix} 1 & -1 \\ -1 & 1 \end{bmatrix} \begin{bmatrix} \psi_1 \\ \psi_2 \end{bmatrix} \tag{4.95}$$

where

G = shear modulus

J = torsional inertia

L = length

Resolving the rotation vector along the x and y axes to a member along the axis and normal to it, the following relations are obtained

$$\psi_1 = \theta_{x1}\ell + \theta_{y1}m \quad \text{and} \quad \psi_2 = \theta_{x2}\ell + \theta_{y2}m$$
$$\theta_1 = -\theta_{x1}m + \theta_{y1}\ell \quad \text{and} \quad \theta_2 = -\theta_{x2}m + \theta_{y2}\ell \tag{4.96}$$

where ℓ and m are the direction cosines of the line 1–2.

In the same way the bending and twisting moments are considered and are resolved along the x and y axes:

$$M_{x1} = T_1\ell - M_1 m \quad \text{and} \quad M_{x2} = T_2\ell - M_2 m$$
$$M_{y1} = T_1 m - M_1 \ell \quad \text{and} \quad M_{y2} = T_2 m - M_2 \ell \tag{4.96a}$$

The above equations are substituted into the stiffness matrix $[K]$.

For a 2-D rigid jointed grillage

$$
\begin{bmatrix} F_{z1} \\ M_{x1} \\ M_{y1} \\ F_{z2} \\ M_{x2} \\ M_{y2} \end{bmatrix}
= \frac{EI}{L(1+\bar{G})}
\begin{bmatrix}
\dfrac{12}{L^2} & \dfrac{6m}{L} & \dfrac{-6\ell}{L} \\[2mm]
 & (4+\bar{G})m^2 + G'\ell^2 & -(4+\beta-G')\ell m \\[2mm]
 & & (4+\bar{G})\ell^2 + G'm^2 \\[2mm]
 & \text{symmetric} &
\end{bmatrix}
$$

$$\{F\} \hspace{6cm} [K]$$

$$\begin{bmatrix} \dfrac{-12}{L^2} & \dfrac{6m}{L} & \dfrac{-6\ell}{L} \\[2mm] \dfrac{-6m}{L} & (2-\bar{G})m^2 - G'\ell^2 & -(2-\bar{G}+G')\ell m \\[2mm] \dfrac{6\ell}{L} & -(2-\bar{G}+G')\ell m & (2-\bar{G})\ell^2 - G'm^2 \\[2mm] \dfrac{12}{L^2} & \dfrac{-6m}{L} & \dfrac{6\ell}{L} \\[2mm] & (4+\bar{G})m^2 + G'\ell^2 & -(4+\bar{G}-G')\ell m \\[2mm] & & (4+\bar{G})\ell^2 + G'm^2 \end{bmatrix} \begin{bmatrix} w_1 \\ \theta_{x1} \\ \theta_{y1} \\ w_2 \\ \theta_{x2} \\ \theta_{y2} \end{bmatrix}$$

$$\times \{\Delta\}$$

$$(4.97)$$

$$\bar{G} = \frac{12EI\gamma}{GAL^2}$$

$$G' = \frac{GJ}{EI}(1+\bar{G})$$

To ignore shear deformation effects set $G' = 0$. Then forces at nodes are related as

$$F = K \cdot \Delta \tag{4.98}$$

A typical example (4.6) gives a thorough explanation of this process. Where the grid is extensive in all directions, members, joints, parameters and boundary conditions will increase.

4.4.2.1 Derivation for a four-element grid
Degree of freedom (DOF) coordinates: $= 3 \times \sum$ joints$-\sum$ restraints co-ordinates:

Node freedoms

Node	w	θ_x	θ_y
1	0	0	0
2	d_1	d_2	d_3
3	0	d_4	d_5
4	0	0	0
5	d_6	d_7	d_8

Coordinates of joints

Node	x	y
1	0	3
2	4	3
3	7	3
4	4	0
5	4	5

Joints 1 and 4 are suppressed, only vertical translation at 3 exists. Thus:

$$DOF = 15 - 7 = 8$$

The next process is to define which joint for which member and hence direction cosines are needed

$$l = \frac{x_2 - x_1}{L}$$

$$m = \frac{(y_2 - y_1)}{L}$$

Member parallel to x-axis

$$l = 1 \qquad m = 0$$

Member parallel to y-axis

$$l = 0 \qquad m = 1$$

Hence the following classification is formed

Elements

Element	End 1	End 2	ℓ	m
1	1	2	1	0
2	2	3	1	0
3	4	2	0	1
4	2	5	0	1

The fixed end moments at the ends are in the X and Y directions and they are:

$$M_{x1} = T_1\ell - M_1 m \qquad M_{y1} = T_1 m + M_1 \ell$$

$$M_{x2} = T_2\ell - M_2 m \qquad M_{y2} = T_2 m + M_2 \ell$$

Loads, if specified, are the following forces (see Fig. 4.23) and can be summed up in the direction of δ_s:

$$\sum F_1$$
$$\sum F_2$$
$$\sum F_3$$
$$\sum F_4 = 0$$
$$\sum F_6 = 0$$
$$\sum F_5$$

These are in matrix $\{F\}$ of Eq. (4.97). The $[K]$ matrix is written substituting various values. The moments due to displacements are computed as:

$$M_1 = \frac{EI}{L(1+\bar{G})} \left\{ (4+\bar{G})\theta_1 + (2-\bar{G})\theta_2 - \frac{6}{L}(w_2 - w_1) \right\}$$

$$M_2 = \frac{EI}{L(1+\bar{G})} \left\{ (2-\bar{G})\theta_1 + (4+\bar{G})\theta_2 - \frac{6}{L}(w_2 - w_1) \right\}$$

$$T_1 = -T_2 = -\frac{GL}{L}(\psi_2 - \psi_1)$$

where

$$\theta_1 = -\theta_{x1}m + \theta_{y1}\ell \qquad \psi_1 = \theta_{x1}\ell + \theta_{y1}m$$
$$\theta_2 = -\theta_{x2}m + \theta_{y2}\ell \qquad \psi_2 = \theta_{x2}\ell + \theta_{y2}m$$

4.4.2.2   Example (4.6)

A bridge grillage scheme is shown in Fig. 4.24. The overall load is 200 kN/m in both directions along the grillage beams. Using the following data, analyse this gridwork:

$$I_{girder} = 41\,667 \times 10^{-6}\,\text{m}^4$$

$$J = 29\,167 \times 10^{-6}\,\text{m}^4$$

$$E = 14.5 \times 10^6\,\text{kN/m}^2$$

$$\bar{G} = 0.165$$

$$A = 0.5\,\text{m}^2$$

$$G' = 1.2$$

$$L = 4\,\text{m}$$

$$G = 6.4 \times 10^5\,\text{kN/m}^2$$

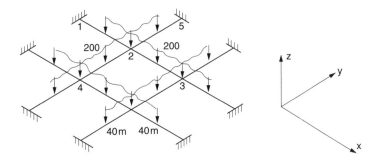

Figure 4.24. A grillage system under loads

Assume the grid and its loading are symmetrical and thus ignore the shear deformations in members. Analyse one-quarter of the grillage with suitable boundary
conditions.

Elements, nodal freedoms and their coordinates are tabulated below

Degrees of freedom

Node	x	y	θ_x	θ_y	ω	ℓ	m	Ends	
1	0	2	0	0	0	1	0	1–2	element 1
2	4	2	δ_2	δ_2	δ_1	1	0	2–3	element 2
3	6	2	δ_2	0	δ_3	0	1	2–5	element 3
4	4	0	0	δ_2	δ_3	0	1	4–2	element 4
5	4	6	0	0	0				

Contribution of forces and displacement
Explanation of the data
1 and 2 and opposite 4 and 0 displace vertically 2 and 3 and opposite
rotate about their own axes with no torsional forces and are equal (Fig. 4.25).
Hence θ_x at 2 and 3 are equal. For joints 3 and 4:

$$\theta_x = 0 \quad \text{at } 4$$
$$\theta_y = 0 \quad \text{at } 3$$

At joint 2 θ_x and θ_y are identical.
$\bar{G} = 0$, i.e. shear deformations are zero.

The direction cosines ℓ and m as tabulated provide a force–displacement
relation for each element:

Element 1

$$\begin{Bmatrix} F_{z2} \\ F_{x2} \\ F_{y2} \end{Bmatrix} = 10^2 \begin{bmatrix} 1095 & 0 & 2190 \\ 0 & 465 & 0 \\ 2190 & 0 & 5840 \end{bmatrix} \begin{Bmatrix} \delta_{z2} \\ \delta_{x2} \\ \delta_{y2} \end{Bmatrix}$$

Element 2

$$\begin{Bmatrix} F_{x1} \\ M_{x1} \\ M_{y1} \\ F_{z2} \\ M_{x2} \end{Bmatrix} = 10^2 \begin{bmatrix} 8750 & 0 & -8750 & -8750 & 0 \\ 0 & 927 & 0 & 0 & -927 \\ -8750 & 0 & 11\,700 & 8750 & 0 \\ -8750 & 0 & 8750 & 8750 & 0 \\ 0 & -927 & 0 & 0 & 927 \end{bmatrix} \begin{Bmatrix} \delta_{z1} \\ \delta_{x1} \\ \delta_{y1} \\ \delta_{z2} \\ \delta_{x2} \end{Bmatrix}$$

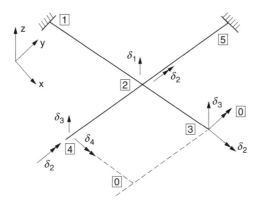

Figure 4.25. Displacements for the grillage in Fig. B4.24

Element 3

$$\begin{Bmatrix} F_{z1} \\ M_{x1} \\ M_{y1} \end{Bmatrix} = 10^2 \begin{bmatrix} 1095 & 2190 & 0 \\ 2190 & 5840 & 0 \\ 0 & 0 & 465 \end{bmatrix} \begin{Bmatrix} \delta_{z1} \\ \delta_{x1} \\ \delta_{y1} \end{Bmatrix}$$

Element 4

$$\begin{Bmatrix} F_{z1} \\ M_{y1} \\ F_{z2} \\ M_{x2} \\ M_{y2} \end{Bmatrix} = 10^2 \begin{bmatrix} 8750 & 0 & -8750 & 8750 & 0 \\ 0 & 927 & 0 & 0 & -927 \\ 8750 & 0 & 8750 & -8750 & 0 \\ 8750 & 0 & -8750 & 11\,670 & 0 \\ 0 & 927 & 0 & 0 & 927 \end{bmatrix} \begin{Bmatrix} \delta_{z1} \\ \delta_{y1} \\ \delta_{z1} \\ \delta_{x2} \\ \delta_{y2} \end{Bmatrix}$$

Assemble these matrices in the normal way.

The fixed moments are at Elements 1 to 4 as laid out below:

Element	$M_{\text{at end } 1}$ kN/m	$M_{\text{at end } 2}$ kN/m
1	−267	+267
2	−67	+67
3	−267	+267
4	−67	+67

Restraining forces at each joint are obtained by summing the appropriate forces from the elements meeting at the joint. Therefore:

$$\sum F_1 = -1200\,\text{kN}$$

$$\sum M_2 = -400\,\text{kNm}$$

$$\sum M_3 = -400\,\text{kNm}$$

Displacements δ_1, δ_2, δ_3 (m)
These are described by

$$\begin{Bmatrix} \delta_1 \\ \delta_2 \\ \delta_3 \end{Bmatrix} = - \begin{Bmatrix} +0.0140 \\ -0.0031 \\ +0.0175 \end{Bmatrix}$$

The stress resultants induced by these displacements are classified as follows:

Elements	M_1	M_2	T_2	T_1	(kNm)
1	−2081.00	−1118.00	153.50	−153.50	
2	763.95	−1164.00	0	0	
3	1118.00	2081.00	−153.50	+153.50	
4	1164.00	−763.95	0	0	

Final stress resultants = fixed end results + results from displacements and these values are classified below. The final bending moment diagram is given in Fig. 4.26.

Elements	M_1	M_2	T_2	T_1	(kNm)
1	−2348.00	−851.00	153.50	−153.50	
2	+695.95	−1097.00	0	0	
3	851.00	2348.00	−153.50	+153.50	
4	+1097.00	−696.95	0	0	

4.4.3 Grillage with cellular and multicellular decks

The modes of deformation and internal forces are affected when the grillage has a cellular deck. The deck can be approximately analysed if the cells are stiffened with diaphragms or cross-bracings at frequent intervals. It is sensible to consider

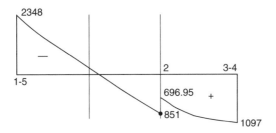

Figure 4.26. The final bending moment diagram for Example (4.6)

shear and torsional loadings because the shape can distort. The shear flexibility in the grillage produces the distortion behaviour of the cells. The modes of structural action are:

(a) longitudinal bending
(b) transverse bending
(c) torsion
(d) distortion

In (a) the deck is assumed to be cut longitudinally between webs into a number of I-beams and bending stresses are computed as if it were made up of such beams. The shear flow for each I-beam (longitudinally) can be evaluated. In (b) *transverse bending* as shown in Fig. 4.27 covers both top and bottom flexures in unison about the neutral axis at the level of their common centre of gravity. The second moment of area in this case, I_t, is computed as

$$I_t = (h_1^2 d_1 + h_2^2 d_2) = \frac{h^2 d_1 d_2}{(d_1 + d_2)} \quad \text{(per unit length)} \tag{4.99}$$

Where the diaphragm is included, this value of I should be added.

Torsion stated in (c) is applied to cellular decks where it describes the shear forces and deformation induced by twisting the deck without any distorting cross-section. There is a network of shear flows around the slabs and up and

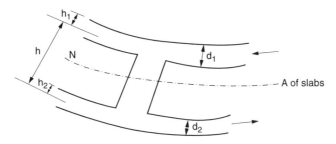

Figure 4.27. Transverse bending

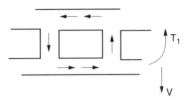

Figure 4.28. Shear and torque diagram

down the web. The total torque on a cross-section is made up partly from the torques in the longitudinal members and partly from the opposed shear forces on the two sides of the deck (Fig. 4.28).

The torsional constant is represented by C and is given by

$$C = (h_1^2 d_1 + h_2^2 d_2) = \frac{2h^2 d_1 d_2}{(d_1 + d_2)} \quad \text{(per unit width of cell)} \tag{4.100}$$

This constant is equal to one-half the St. Venant torsion constant.

If

$$h = 1.325\,\mathrm{m}$$

$$d_1 = 0.2\,\mathrm{m}$$

$$d_2 = 0.15\,\mathrm{m}$$

$$C = 0.30\,\mathrm{m^4/m}$$

$C =$ torsion constant for a width of cell of 3.30 m is

$$\frac{3.30}{2} \times 0.3 = 0.495$$

Assuming the web thickness is 0.45:

$$\text{area of the web} = 0.495 \times 1.325 = 0.656\,\mathrm{m^2}$$

4.4.3.1 Example (4.7)

The MOT/C&CA standard M7 beam is in a pseudo-box construction (Fig. 4.29(a)). Its idealized version is given in Fig. 4.29(b). The torsional inertia $\bar{C}$ is defined as

$$\bar{C} = \frac{4A^2}{\oint \dfrac{ds}{E}}$$

where

$A =$ area inside the medium line of the concrete walls

$\oint \dfrac{ds}{t} =$ the sum of the lengths of the sides around the median line each divided by the appropriate wall thickness

The thickness of the bottom *in situ* concrete is taken as the maximum thickness.

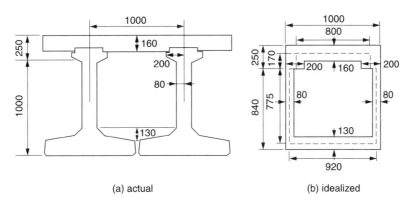

(a) actual   (b) idealized

Figure 4.29. Inverted T-sections as a pseudo-box

It is assumed that the actual section through the deck [Fig. 4.29(a)] can be idealized in the form shown in Fig. 4.29(b). The stiffness of the side struts is taken as the stiffness of the length of the beam which they replace, i.e. half the length of beam in any section goes to each side. The side struts are now replaced by continuous side walls of equivalent stiffness and are used to calculate the torsional inertia.

$$t^* = \frac{E}{G} \times 1 \Big/ \left[\frac{ab^2}{12I_{b2}} + \frac{a^2 b}{48} \left(\frac{1}{I_{s1}} + \frac{1}{I_{s2}} \right) \right]$$

where

t^* = thickness of the equivalent continuous side wall

I_{s1} = bending inertia of the top slab

I_{s2} = bending inertia of the bottom slab

I_{b2} = bending inertia of the equivalent length of longitudinal beam about the z axis

a = spacing of the longitudinal beams

b = distance between the neutral axis of the top slab and the neutral axis of the bottom slab

Cónsider a 2000 mm transverse section (Fig. 4.30) as a slice through a pseudo slab deck of the same beam. Calculate the torsional inertia $\bar{C}$ and evaluate the difference between case I and case II.

Case I

$$A = 170 \times 800 + 775 \times 920 = 0.849 \times 10^6 \, \text{mm}^2$$

$$\oint \frac{\mathrm{d}s}{t} = \frac{170}{200} \times 2 + \frac{775}{80} \times 2 + \frac{800}{160} + \frac{920}{130} = 33.15$$

$$C = \frac{4 \times (0.849 \times 10^6)^2}{33.15} = 86.97 \times 10^9 \, \text{mm}^4$$

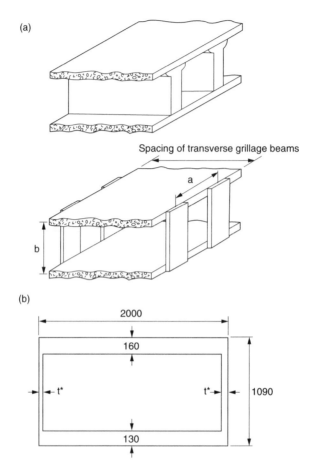

Figure 4.30. (a) Transverse slice through a voided deck. (b) Equivalent box section for a lattice girder

Case II

$$a = 1000 \, \text{mm}$$

$$b = 945 \, \text{mm}$$

$$\text{width of section} = 2000 \, \text{mm}$$

$$I_{s1} = \frac{2000 \times 160^3}{12}$$

$$= 0.683 \times 10^9 \, \text{mm}^4$$

$$I_{s2} = \frac{2000 \times 130^3}{12}$$

$$= 0.366 \times 10^9 \, \text{mm}^4$$

To calculate I_{b2}, a weighted mean of the web and the thickened portion at the top of the web are taken. The thickened section is taken as 300 mm, i.e. its minimum thickness:

$$\text{length of web between faces of } in\ situ \text{ concrete} = 800\,\text{mm}$$

$$\text{length of thickened section (300 mm thick)} = 90\,\text{mm}$$

$$\text{length of web (160 mm thick)} = 710\,\text{mm}$$

$$I_{b2} = \frac{1000 \times 300^3}{12} \times \frac{90}{800} + \frac{1000 \times 160^3}{12} \times \frac{710}{800}$$

$$= 0.556 \times 10^9 \,\text{mm}^4$$

$$t^* = 2(1 + 0.15)\bigg/ \left[\frac{1000 \times 945^2}{12 \times 0.556 \times 10^9} + \frac{1000^2 \times 945}{48} \right.$$

$$\left. \times \left(\frac{1}{0.683} \times 10^{-9} + \frac{1}{0.366} \times 10^{-9} \right) \right] = 10.58\,\text{mm}$$

This is the equivalent thickness of one side; the other side will be identical:

$$A = 945 \times (2000 - 10.58)$$

$$= 1.88 \times 10^6\,\text{mm}^2$$

$$\frac{\mathrm{d}s}{t} = \frac{945}{10.58} \times 2 + \frac{1989.4}{160} + \frac{1989.4}{130}$$

$$= 206.4$$

$$C = \frac{4 \times 1.88^2 \times 10^{12}}{206.4}$$

$$= 68.5 \times 10^9\,\text{mm}^4$$

The difference between Cases I and II is:

$$(89.97 - 68.5) \times 10^9\,\text{mm}^4 = 18.47 \times 10^9\,\text{mm}^4$$

4.4.4   Finite difference method of a bridge deck

4.4.4.1   Introduction

For a simple bridge deck, the use of a Fourier sine series can be successfully applied. Where more complex boundary conditions are encountered, the method becomes more difficult. A numerical analysis is therefore needed. The finite difference method has been used for bridge decks. In this method, the deck is divided into grid points. Both the equations and boundary conditions are then expressed in terms of the unknowns resulting from the grid points. Simultaneous equations are developed and are then solved for deflections at grid nodes. These deflections are then used to determine the moments and shears of the grid points. The number of equations depends on the sophisticated mesh and the accuracy of the results is based on the refinement of such a mesh.

The bridge deck can be

(a)   a right bridge deck
(b)   a skewed bridge deck

Such bridges can be isotropic and orthotropic.
The governing equations are:

Orthotropic deck

$$D_x \frac{\partial^4 \omega}{\partial x^4} + 2H \frac{\partial^4 \omega}{\partial x^2 \partial y^2} + D_y \frac{\partial^4 \omega}{y^4} = q(x, y) \qquad (4.101a)$$

Isotropic deck

$$\frac{\partial^4 \omega}{\partial x^4} + 2 \frac{\partial^4 \omega}{\partial x^2 \partial y^2} + \frac{\partial^4 \omega}{\partial y^4} = \frac{q}{D} \qquad (4.101b)$$

$$D_x, D_y = D$$

$$H = 1$$

where D is the stiffness.

The finite difference method is illustrated in Fig. 4.31 and developed later in Examples (4.8) to (4.19).

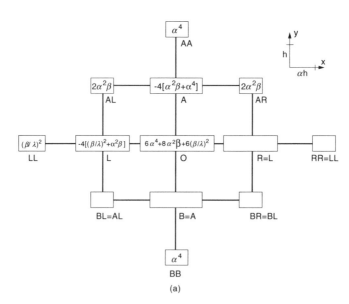

(a)

Figure 4.31 (pages 428–431). Finite difference method of a bridge deck. (a) Orthotropic deck. (b) Isotropic deck. (c) Load near simple support (orthotropic). (d) Load near simple support (isotropic). (e) Load near free edge (orthotropic). (f) Load near free edge (isotropic). (g) Load near corner and free edge (isotropic). (h) Load near corner of fixed and free edge (orthotropic). (i) Load near simple edge (isotropic). (j) Finite difference pattern

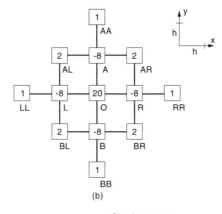

(b)

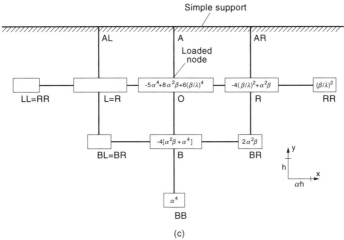

(c)

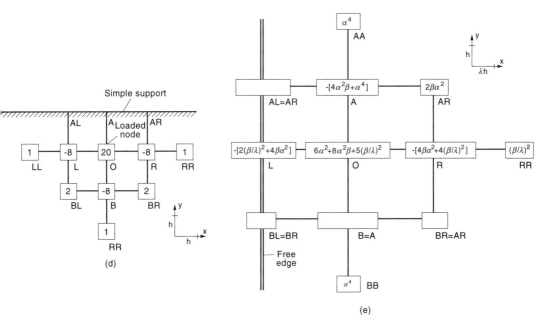

(d)

(e)

Figure 4.31. Continued

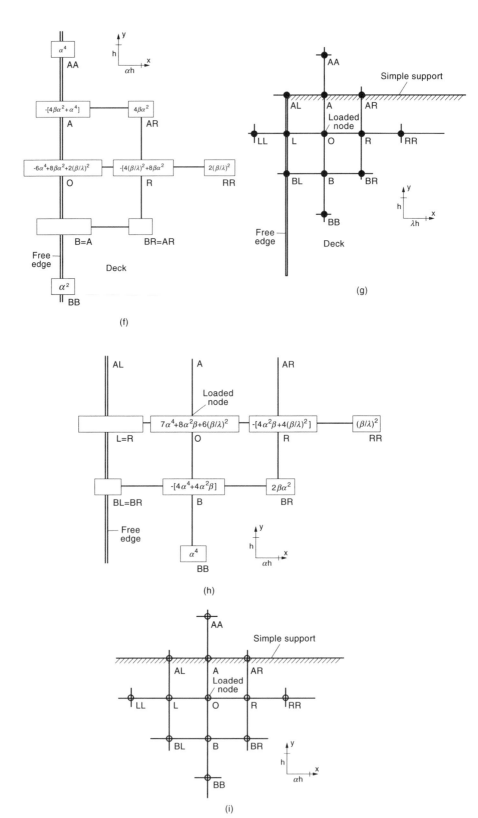

Figure 4.31. Continued

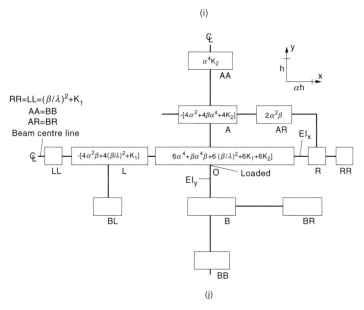

Figure 4.31. Continued

Based on Fig. 4.31

$$\omega_x = \omega_y = \omega \tag{4.102}$$

ω_x, ω_y beams

ω slab

$$\underbrace{q_x + q_y}_{\text{beam}} + \underbrace{q}_{\text{slab}} = q_{\text{total}} \tag{4.103}$$

The following equation is derived for the central node O, loaded

$$\frac{(\alpha h)^4}{D_y}\left(\frac{EI_x}{h}\right)\left(\frac{\partial^4 \omega}{\partial x^4}\right) + \frac{(\partial h)^4}{D_y}\left(\frac{EI_y}{\alpha h}\right)\left(\frac{\partial^4 \omega}{\partial y^4}\right)$$

$$= q \frac{\alpha^4 h^4}{D_y} \tag{4.104}$$

If

$$K_1 = \frac{EI_x}{hD_y} \quad \text{and} \quad K_2 = \frac{EI_y \alpha^3}{RD_y} \tag{4.105}$$

and the values of $\partial^4 w/\partial y^4$ and $\partial^4 w/\partial x^4$ at O are substituted, the global finite difference equation emerges

$$\omega_0 \left[6\alpha^4 + 8\alpha^2\beta + 6\left(\frac{\beta}{\lambda}\right)^2 + 6K_1 + 6K_2 \right] - 4(\omega_r + \omega_\ell)$$

$$\left[\alpha^2\beta + \left(\frac{\beta}{\lambda}\right)^2 + 4K_1 \right] + (\omega_{hh} + \omega_{bb})[\alpha^4 + K_2]$$

$$+ (\omega_{hr} + \omega_{br} + \omega_{h\ell} + \omega_{b\ell})[2\alpha^2\beta] = q\,\frac{\alpha^4 h^4}{D_y} \qquad (4.106)$$

The finite difference pattern is shown in Fig. 4.31(j).

Similarly other patterns can be obtained with and without the participation of either beams or slabs.

Examples (4.10) to (4.19) give other cases.

For the orthotropic deck, Eq. (4.101) can now be written as:

$$\frac{D_x}{\alpha^4 h^4}\,(\omega_{rr} - 4\omega_r + 6\omega_0 + 4\omega_\ell + \omega_{\ell\ell})$$

$$+ \frac{2H}{\alpha^4 h^4}\,(\omega_{br} - 2\omega_b + \omega_{b\ell} - 2\omega_r + 4\omega_0 + 2\omega_\ell + \omega_{hr} - 2\omega_h + \omega_{h\ell})$$

$$+ \frac{D_y}{h^4}\,(\omega_{hh} - 4\omega_h + 6\omega_0 - 4\omega_b + \omega_{bb})$$

$$= q(x, y) \qquad (4.107)$$

Now denoting

$$\lambda = \frac{H}{\sqrt{D_y D_y}}$$

$$\beta = \frac{H}{D_y}$$

Equation (4.107) is simplified as

$$\omega_0 \left[6\alpha^4 + 8\alpha^2\beta + 6\left(\frac{\beta}{\lambda}\right)^2 \right] - 4(\omega_r + \omega_\ell)\left[\left(\frac{\beta}{\lambda}\right)^2 + \alpha^2\beta \right]$$

$$- 4(\omega_h + \omega_b)[\alpha^2\beta + \alpha^4] + (\omega_{rr} + \omega_{\ell\ell})\left[\left(\frac{\beta}{\lambda}\right)^2 \right]$$

$$+ (\omega_{hh} + \omega_{bb})\alpha^4 + (\omega_{hr} + \omega_{br} + \omega_{h\ell} + \omega_{b\ell})2\alpha^2\beta$$

$$= q\,\frac{\alpha^4 h^4}{D_y} \qquad (4.108)$$

Where the deck is isotropic $D_x = D_y = H = D$, and λ and $\beta = 1$. The spaces are equal $h \times h$ when

$$D + \frac{Et^3}{12(1 - \nu^2)} \tag{4.109}$$

where t, E and ν are defined elsewhere.

Figure 4.31 gives a comparative grid for both orthotropic and isotropic decks.

4.4.4.2 Boundary conditions and cases
(a) Simply supported edge (Fig. 4.31(i))
The load is at node O. At point A $M_y = 0$ and $\partial^2 w/\partial x^2 = 0$:

$$M_y = -D_y \frac{\partial^2 w}{\partial y^2} = 0 \tag{4.110}$$

$$M_y = -\frac{D_y}{h^2} (w_{hh} + w_0) = 0 \tag{4.111}$$

The governing equation for node O is:

$$\left(\frac{\beta}{\lambda}\right)^2 [w_{rr} - 4w_r + 6w_0 - 4w_\ell + w_{\ell\ell}]$$

$$+ 2\beta\alpha^2[w_{br} - 2w_b + w_{b\ell} - 2w_r + 4w_0 - 2w_1] + \alpha^2[5w_0 - 4w_b + w_{bb}]$$

$$= q\, \frac{\alpha^2 h^2}{D_y} \tag{4.112}$$

The finite difference pattern is indicated in Fig. 4.31.

The pattern is changed when it is *isotropic* and when the mesh has equal spacing h. This is shown in Fig. 4.31(a).

The pattern is the same as discussed above and thus proves the validity of the orthotropic equations.

(b) Fixed support
Figure 4.31(i) is taken again and the support is fixed. The slope at A is $\partial w/\partial y$. The additional boundary condition is to omit deflection w_{aa}:

$$\left(\frac{\partial w}{\partial y}\right)_{\text{at A}} = \frac{1}{2h} (w_{hh} - w_0) = 0 \tag{4.113}$$

At the loaded point O,

$$w_0 = \left[7\alpha^4 + 8\alpha^2\beta + 6\left(\frac{\beta}{\lambda}\right)^2\right] \tag{4.114}$$

For an *isotropic* deck with equal spaces on the grid the centre pattern turns out to be $21w_0$.

The slope at point O is now with points B and BB and are in the deck:

$$\left(\frac{\partial w}{\partial y_0}\right) = \frac{1}{6h}\left[2w_h + 3w_h - 6w_b + w_{bb}\right] \tag{4.115}$$

$$w_{hh} = \left(3w_0 - \frac{w_b}{2}\right) \tag{4.116}$$

(c) Free edge

If the free edge is parallel to the y-axis when the node O is loaded, the value of $w_{\ell\ell}$ is eliminated. The deflection terms can be finally obtained as

$$w_0\left[6\alpha^4 + 8\alpha^2\beta + 5\left(\frac{\beta}{\lambda}\right)^2\right] - w_r\left[4\beta\alpha^2 + 4\left(\frac{\beta}{\lambda}\right)^2\right] - w_\ell\left[2\left(\frac{\beta}{\lambda}\right)^2 + 4\beta\alpha^2\right]$$

$$- 4(w_h + w_b)[\alpha^2\beta + \alpha^4] + w_{rr}\left(\frac{\beta}{\lambda}\right)^2 + (w_{hh} + w_{bb})\alpha^4$$

$$+ (w_{hr} + w_{br} + w_{h\ell} + w_{b\ell})2\alpha^2\beta$$

$$= q\,\frac{\alpha^4 h^4}{D_y} \tag{4.117}$$

A combination of such boundaries in the form of equations can be solved. The ∇-operator charts for cases such as Fig. 4.31(a) to (j) can give assistance in formulating such equations.

(d) Deck with intersecting beams

The presence of intersecting beams below the slab presents a special boundary condition. The deck can be transformed into an orthotropic plate of equivalent rigidities D_x, D_y, and $2H$. On the other hand, the slab and beams can be separate structural elements and in the analysis they can be made compatible by satisfying a set of boundary conditions such as

(*i*)   beams and deck slab have identical deflections,
(*ii*) beams have no torsional rigidity, and
(*iii*) horizontal forces causing shears are zero between the slab and the beam.

4.4.4.3   Example (4.8)

The method of finite difference replaces the plate differential equations, and expressions defining the boundary conditions with equivalent difference equations. The solution of the plate bending thus reduces to simultaneous equations for nodal points within the deck. If the deck differential equations from

Eqs (4.125) to (4.131) are considered, determine expression in finite difference form for first to fourth derivatives with fully developed operator '∇' sketches. How are the errors computed? For the plate analysis, the concentrated loads are needed. Determine equivalent concentrated loads at node points when

(a) the load is distributed
(b) the load is trapezoidal
(c) the load is two-degree parabolic.

Solution
General derivation of plate equations using finite difference coefficient (Fig. 4.32):

(1) First derivative:

$$\left(\frac{d\omega}{dx}\right)_i = \frac{1}{2h}\left(\omega_{i+1} - \omega_{i-1}\right) \tag{4.118}$$

Equation (4.118) suggests the slope of the curve is constant between $i-1$ to $i+1$ in the ω–x relation (Fig. 4.32).

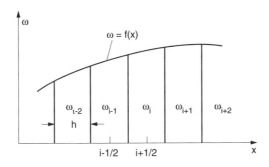

Figure 4.32. The ω–x relationship and finite difference coefficients for Example (4.8)

(2) Second derivative:

$$\left(\frac{d^2\omega}{dx^2}\right)_i = \frac{1}{h}\left[\left(\frac{d\omega}{dx}\right)_{i+\frac{1}{2}} - \left(\frac{d\omega}{dx}\right)_{i-\frac{1}{2}}\right] \tag{4.119}$$

$$\left(\frac{d\omega}{dx}\right)_{i+\frac{1}{2}} = \frac{1}{h}\left(\omega_{i+1} - \omega_i\right) \tag{4.120}$$

$$\left(\frac{d\omega}{dx}\right)_{i-\frac{1}{2}} = \frac{1}{h}\left(\omega_i - \omega_{i-1}\right) \tag{4.121}$$

Combining (4.120) and (4.121)

$$\left(\frac{d^2\omega}{dx^2}\right)_i = \frac{1}{h^2}\left(\omega_{i+1} - 2\omega_i + \omega_{i-1}\right) \tag{4.122}$$

Bending moment is proportional to this derivative.

(3) Third derivative:
This derivative is related to shear force

$$\left(\frac{d^3\omega}{dx^3}\right)_i = \frac{1}{2h}\left[\left(\frac{d^2\omega}{dx^2}\right)_{i+1} - \left(\frac{d^2\omega}{dx^2}\right)_{i-1}\right] \tag{4.123}$$

Substituting the values from the second derivatives (Eq. (4.122) into Eq. (4.123))

$$\left(\frac{d^3\omega}{dx^3}\right) = \frac{1}{2h^3}\left[\omega_{1+2} - 2\omega_{i+1} + 2\omega_{i-1} - \omega_{i-2}\right] \tag{4.124}$$

(4) Fourth derivative:

$$\left(\frac{d^4\omega}{dx^4}\right)_i = \frac{1}{h^4}\left[\omega_{i+2} - 4\omega_{i+1} + 6\omega_i - 4\omega_{i-1} + \omega_{i-2}\right] \tag{4.125}$$

Similarly if h is different from k

$$\nabla^2\omega \approx \frac{1}{h^2}\left(\omega_1 - 2\omega_0 + \omega_3\right) + \frac{1}{k^2}\left(\omega_2 - 2\omega_0 + \omega_4\right)$$

For all others, the following coefficients (see Fig. 4.33) are given:

(5) $$\frac{\partial^3\omega}{\partial x\,\partial y} = \frac{1}{2h^3}\left(\omega_5 - \omega_6 - 2\omega_1 + 2\omega_3 + \omega_8 - \omega_7\right) \tag{4.126}$$

(6) $$\text{moment} = \frac{h^2}{D}\left(-M_x\right) \tag{4.127}$$

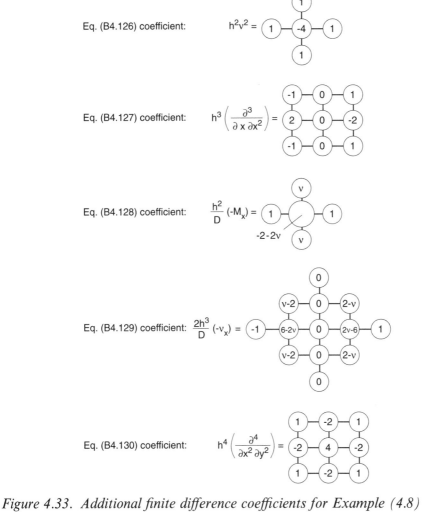

Figure 4.33. Additional finite difference coefficients for Example (4.8)

(7) $\quad \text{shear} = \dfrac{2h^3}{D}\,(-Q_x)$ $\qquad\qquad\qquad\qquad$ (4.128)

(8) $\quad \dfrac{\partial^4 \omega}{\partial x^2\,\partial y^2} = \dfrac{1}{h^4}\,[\omega_5 + \omega_6 + \omega_7 + \omega_8 + 4\omega_0 - 2(\omega_1 + \omega_2 + \omega_3 + \omega_4)]$

$\qquad\qquad\qquad\qquad\qquad\qquad\qquad\qquad\qquad\qquad\qquad\qquad$ (4.129)

(9) $\quad \dfrac{\partial \omega}{\partial x^4\,\partial y^4} = \dfrac{1}{h^4}\,[\omega_9 + \omega_{10} + \omega_{11} + \omega_{12} + 2(\omega_5 + \omega_6 + \omega_7 + \omega_8)$

$\qquad\qquad\qquad\qquad - 8(\omega_1 + \omega_2 + \omega_3 + \omega_4) + 20\omega_0]$

$\qquad\qquad = \dfrac{q}{D}$ $\qquad\qquad\qquad\qquad\qquad\qquad\qquad\qquad$ (4.130)

In general terms the finite difference mesh for plates with x–y axes at boundaries can be interpreted in the following way.

The distance h is the same (Fig. 4.34) on both sides of a grid along the x- and y-directions. The second and fourth derivatives along the x-direction are written as

$$\left(\frac{\partial^2 w}{\partial x^2}\right)_{i,j} \approx \nabla^2 w_{i,j} = \{(w_{i+h,j} - 2w_{i,j} + w_{i-h,j})\} \frac{1}{h^2} \tag{4.131}$$

$$\left(\frac{\partial^4 w}{\partial x^4}\right)_{i,j} \approx \nabla^4 w_{i,j} = \{(w_{i+2h,j} - 4w_{i+h,j} + 6w_{i,j} - 4w_{i-h,j} + w_{i-2h,j})\} \frac{1}{h^4} \tag{4.132}$$

Similarly the second and the fourth derivatives with respect to the y-direction (x fixed and moving along y) are:

$$\left(\frac{\partial^4 w}{\partial y^2}\right)_{i,j} = \{(w_{i,j+h} - 2w_{i,j} + w_{i,j-h})\} \frac{1}{h^2} \tag{4.133}$$

$$\left(\frac{\partial^4 w}{\partial y^4}\right)_{i,j} = \{(w_{i,j+2h} - 4w_{i,j+h} + 6w_{i,j} - 4w_{i,j-h} + w_{i,j-2h})\} \frac{1}{h^4} \tag{4.134}$$

The cross-derivatives with respect to x and y can be written as

$$\left(\frac{\partial^4 w}{\partial x^2 \partial y^2}\right)_{i,j} = \frac{\partial^2}{\partial x^2}\left(\frac{\partial^2 w}{\partial y^2}\right)_{i,j}$$

$$\approx \frac{1}{h^2}\left[\left(\frac{\partial^2 w}{\partial y^2}\right)_{i+h,j} - 2\left(\frac{\partial^2 w}{\partial y^2}\right)_{i,j} + \left(\frac{\partial^2 w}{\partial y^2}\right)_{i-h,j}\right] \tag{4.135}$$

$$\approx \frac{1}{h^4}[(w_{i+h,j+h} - 2w_{i+h,j} + w_{i+h,j-h})$$

$$- 2(w_{i,j+h} - 2w_{i,j} + w_{i,j-h})$$

$$+ (w_{i-h,j+h} - 2w_{i-h,j} + w_{i-h,j-h})] \tag{4.136}$$

Errors in finite difference expressions

Taylor's expansion of the functions of w about x gives:

$$w(x_{i+1}) = w(x_i) + w'(x_i)\frac{h}{1!} + w''(x_i)\frac{h^2}{2!} + w'''(x_i)\frac{h^3}{3!} + \cdots \tag{4.137}$$

$$w(x_{i-1}) = w(x_i) - w'(x_i)\frac{h}{1!} + w''(x_i)\frac{h^2}{2!} - w'''(x_i)\frac{h^3}{3!} + \cdots \tag{4.138}$$

Note that 1! means 1 factorial $= 1 \times 1 = 1$.

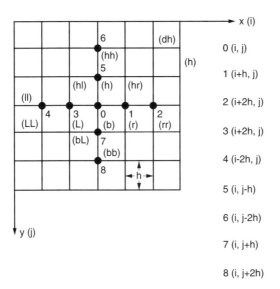

Figure 4.34. A finite difference grid

Substituting for $\omega(x_i)$ in Eq. (4.137) gives

$$\omega(x_{i+1}) - \omega(x_{i-1}) = 2h\omega'(x_i) + \frac{2h^3}{3!}\omega'''(x_i) + \cdots \tag{4.139}$$

or

$$\omega'(x_i) = \frac{1}{2h}\left[\omega(x_{i+1}) - \omega(x_{i-1})\right] - \frac{h^3}{3!}\omega'''(x_i) - \frac{h^4}{5!}\omega^V(x_i) \tag{4.140}$$

The errors 'e' in the derivatives are:

   e_1 = errors in the first derivatives:

$$-\frac{h^3}{3!}\omega'''(x_i) - \frac{h^4}{5!}\omega^{IV}(x_i) - \cdots \tag{4.141}$$

   e_2 = errors in the second derivatives:

$$-\frac{2h^2}{4!}\omega^{IV}(x_i) - \frac{2h^4}{6!}\omega^{VI}(x_i) - \cdots \tag{4.142}$$

   e_3 = errors in the third derivatives:

$$-\frac{h^2}{4!}\omega^{IV}(x_i) - \cdots \tag{4.143}$$

   e_4 = errors in the fourth derivatives:

$$-\frac{h^2}{6!}\omega^{VI}(x_i) - \cdots \tag{4.144}$$

Equivalent concentrated loads

The equivalent concentrated loads at node points are illustrated in Fig. 4.35 for Example (4.8).

(a)   Distributed load (see Fig. 4.35).

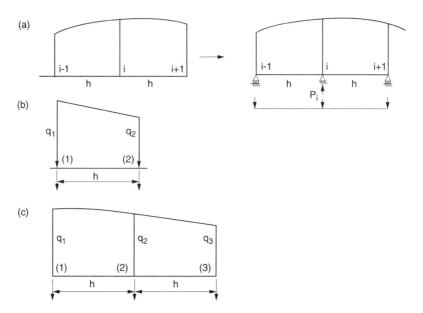

Figure 4.35. Equivalent concentrated loads

(b)   Trapezoidal load (Fig. 4.35):

$${}^1\!\downarrow \text{At}(1)\ \frac{h}{6}\ (2q_1 + q_2)$$

$$\text{At}(2)\ \frac{h}{6}\ (q_1 + 2q_2)\ \downarrow^2$$

(c)   Two-degree parabola (Fig. 4.35):

$${}^1\!\downarrow \text{At}(1)\ \frac{h}{24}\ (7q_1 + 6q_2 - q_3)$$

$$\text{At}(2)^2 \downarrow \frac{h}{12}\ (q_1 + 10q_2 - q_3)$$

$$\frac{h}{24}\ (7q_3 + 6q_2 - q_1)\ \downarrow^3$$

If the spacing 'h' from the x and y coordinates is not the same (say along the x-axis h is αh) then h is taken along the y-axis.

4.4.4.4 Example (4.9)

A 1.5 m simply supported square deck is arbitrarily divided into four equal meshes as shown in Fig. 4.36. Given that $\nabla^2(\nabla^2 w) = q/D$ show that when using the finite difference method the following is valid:

$$\nabla^2(w_i) = \frac{1}{0.5625}\,(w_a + w_b + w_r + w_\ell - 4w_i)$$

where

$\quad w = $ displacement at a particular node

$\quad q = 10\,\text{kN/m}^2$ on the plate

$$D = \frac{Et^3}{\{12(1-\nu^2)\}}$$

$\quad E = 200 \times 10^6\,\text{kN/m}^2$

$\quad t = $ plate thickness $= 75\,\text{mm}$

$\quad \nu = $ Poisson's ratio $= 0.3$

Calculate deflection at the node 'i'.

Solution

A simply supported square plate with 2×2 mesh subjected to uniform load:

$$\frac{\partial w}{\partial x}\bigg]_{i,r} = \frac{w_r - w_i}{h}$$

$$\frac{\partial w}{\partial x}\bigg]_{i,\ell} = \frac{w_i - w_\ell}{h}$$

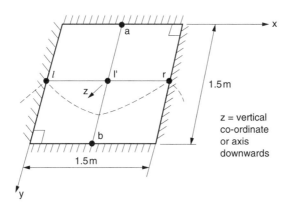

Figure 4.36. A square deck

$$\frac{\partial^2 w}{\partial x^2}\Big]_i = \frac{\dfrac{\partial w}{\partial x}\Big]_{i,r} - \dfrac{\partial w}{\partial x}\Big]}{h}$$

$$\frac{\partial^2 w}{\partial x^2}\Big]_i = \frac{\dfrac{w_r - w_i}{h} - \dfrac{w_i - w_\ell}{h}}{h}$$

$$= \frac{w_r - 2w_i + w_\ell}{h^2}$$

Similarly:

$$\frac{\partial^2 w}{\partial y^2} = \frac{w_a - 2w_i + w_b}{h^2}$$

$$\nabla^2 w = \frac{1}{h^2}\left[w_a + w_b + w_r + w_\ell - 4w_i\right]$$

$$(h = 0.75\,\text{m})$$

Boundary conditions are:

$$\nabla^2(w) = 0$$

i.e., $\nabla^2(w_a)$, $\nabla^2(w_b)$, $\nabla^2(w_\ell)$, $\nabla^2(w_r)$ are zeros; w_a, w_b, w_ℓ, w_r are zeros.

$$\nabla^2 \phi = [\phi_a + \phi_b + \phi_\ell + \phi_r - 4\phi_i] \times 1/h^2 = q$$
$$\qquad\quad \underset{0}{\|} \quad \underset{0}{\|} \quad \underset{0}{\|} \quad \underset{0}{\|}$$

$$= 0.075\,\text{m}$$

$$q = \text{load} = 10\,\text{kN/m}^2$$

$$\nabla^2(\phi) = -\frac{4\phi_i}{h^2} = q$$

$$\phi_i = \frac{-10(75)^2}{4} = -1.40625$$

$$\nabla^2(w_i) = \frac{\phi_i}{D} = -\frac{4w_i}{h^2}$$

$$D = \frac{200 \times 10^6 (0.075)^3}{12(1 - 0.3^2)} = 77.253$$

$$-\frac{-1.40625}{77.253} = \frac{-4w_i}{0.5625}$$

$$w_i = 0.0025598\,\text{m} \approx 0.0026\,\text{m}$$

$$= 2.6\,\text{mm deflection}$$

4.4.4.5 Example (4.10)

Calculate the maximum deflection of a steel deck subjected to a distributed load in the form of a triangular prism as shown in Fig. 4.37. Owing to symmetry a two-stage solution based on finite difference is adopted. Assume

$$q = 20 \, \text{kN/m}^2$$

$$a = 1 \, \text{m}$$

$$\nu = 0.3$$

$$t = 0.05 \, \text{m}$$

$$E = 200 \times 10^6 \, \text{kN/m}^2$$

Solution

A simple plate subjected to a distributed load in the form of a triangular prism. Grid nodes are defined in Fig. 4.37. Using the technique adopted in Example (4.8):

$$2\phi_2 - 2\phi_3 - 4\phi_1 = -q \, \frac{a^2}{16}$$

$$\phi_1 + 2\phi_4 - 4\phi_2 = -q \, \frac{a^2}{16}$$

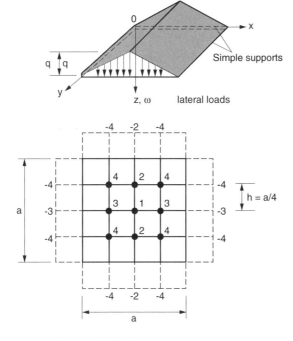

Figure 4.37. *A rectangular steel deck*

$$\phi_1 + 2\phi_4 - 4\phi_3 = -\frac{q}{2}\frac{a^2}{16}$$

$$\phi_2 + \phi_3 - 4\phi_4 = -\frac{q}{16}\frac{a^2}{16}$$

Solving the above equation, the values of ϕ_1 to ϕ_4 are obtained

$$\phi_1 = \frac{14qa^4}{256}$$

$$\phi_2 = \frac{11qa^4}{256}$$

$$\phi_3 = \frac{9qa^2}{256}$$

$$\phi_4 = \frac{7qa^2}{256}$$

Deflections at node points are given by:

$$\frac{16}{a^2}(2w_2 + 2w_3 - 4w_1) = -\frac{14}{256}\bar{K}$$

$$\frac{16}{a^2}(w_1 + 2w_4 - 4w_2) = -\frac{11}{256}\bar{K}$$

$$\frac{16}{a^2}(w_1 + 2w_4 - 4w_3) = -\frac{9}{256}\bar{K}$$

$$\frac{16}{a^2}(w_2 + w_3 - 4w_4) = -\frac{7}{256}\bar{K}$$

where

$$\bar{K} = \frac{qa^4}{D}$$

$$D = \frac{Et^3}{12(1-\nu)} = 228.94$$

Solving the above equations in w either by matrix method or by other means

$$w_1 = 0.002928\bar{K} \times 10^3$$

$$= 0.256\,\text{mm (max)}$$

$$w_2 = 0.002137\bar{K} \times 10^3$$

$$= 0.187\,\text{mm}$$

$$\omega_3 = 0.00202\bar{K} \times 10^3$$

$$= 0.176\,\text{mm}$$

$$\omega_4 = 0.00198\bar{K} \times 10^3$$

$$= 0.173\,\text{mm}$$

$$\bar{K} = \frac{qa^4}{D} = 0.08736$$

4.4.4.6 Example (4.11)

Sketch the difference operator diagram for moments M_x and M_y in a square bridge deck.

Assume a square deck with three edges simply supported with the fourth one free, as shown in Fig. 4.38, is subjected to a uniformly distributed load of $q = 4\,\text{kN/m}^2$. Determine M_x at node 6 and M_y at nodes 2 and 6. Calculate, using the same plate, ω, M_x, M_y at nodes 2 and 6, respectively, when the plate mesh scheme is 20×20. Adopt for the first part of the problem the following data:

4×4 mesh:

$$\{\omega\} = \begin{cases} 0.6941 & 0.9670 & 0.5603 & 0.7823 & 0.4312 & 0.6005 & 0.2501 & 0.3467 \\ ① & ② & ③ & ④ & ⑤ & ⑥ & ⑦ & ⑧ \end{cases}$$

$$t = \text{thickness} = 0.012\,\text{m}$$

$$D = \text{plate stiffness} = 34.56$$

$$\nu = 0.3$$

$$E = 200\,\text{GN/m}^2$$

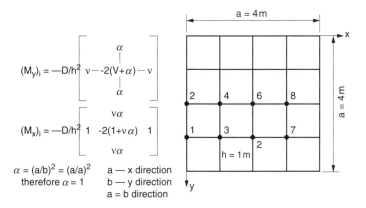

$$(M_y)_i = -D/h^2 \begin{bmatrix} & \alpha & \\ \nu & -2(V+\alpha) & \nu \\ & \alpha & \end{bmatrix}$$

$$(M_x)_i = -D/h^2 \begin{bmatrix} & \nu\alpha & \\ 1 & -2(1+\nu\alpha) & 1 \\ & \nu\alpha & \end{bmatrix}$$

$\alpha = (a/b)^2 = (a/a)^2$ a — x direction
therefore $\alpha = 1$ b — y direction
  a = b direction

Figure 4.38. A simply supported square deck

Solution
A steel deck with mixed boundaries and subjected to a uniform load.

(a)   For expressions describing $(M_y)_i$ and $(M_x)_i$, refer to Fig. 4.38.

(b) $M_{y2}(\text{free end}) = -D\left(\dfrac{\partial^2 w}{\partial y^2} + \nu\,\dfrac{\partial^2 w}{\partial x^2}\right)$

$$= \frac{-D(1 - \nu^2)}{a^2}\,(2w_1 + w_2)$$

$$= 34.56\,\frac{(1 - 0.3^2)}{(1)^2}\,(2 \times 0.6941 - 2 \times 0.9670)$$

$$= 17.165\,\text{kNm/m}$$

$$M_{x6} = 0.0374q(a)^2 = 0.0374 \times 4(4)^2 = 2.3936\,\text{kNm/m}$$

$$M_{y6} = 0.0777q(a)^2 = 0.0777 \times 4 \times (4)^2 = 4.9728\,\text{kNm/m}$$

(c)   For a 20×20 mesh:

$$h = \frac{a}{20} = \frac{4}{20} = \frac{1}{5}$$

The deck is divided into 20 squares and equations are solved:
(1)   Finite difference

$$w_2 = 0.1404q\,\frac{a^2}{E}$$

$$M_{y2} = 0.112qa^2$$

$$M_{x6} = 0.039qa^2$$

$$M_{y6} = 0.084qa^2$$

(2)   Classical method

$$w_2 = 0.1500q\,\frac{a^2}{E}$$

$$M_{y2} = 0.119qa^2$$

$$M_{x6} = 0.042qa^2$$

$$M_{y6} = 0.094qa^2$$

Note that $q = 4\,\text{kN/m}^2$ and $a = 4\,\text{m}$.

4.4.4.7 Example (4.12)

A deck plate of constant thickness (20 mm) is placed symmetrically on two simple supports with its central planes vertical and loaded with a total load of 400 kN (services duct) uniformly distributed over the central area of its upper surface as shown in Fig. 4.39. Derive a set of simultaneous equations in functions ϕ and express them in a matrix form.

Derive the values of stress functions (biharmonic equations) at nodes 1, 2, 3 and 4. The equations themselves are left unsolved.

Solution

A plate supported on two plates is loaded uniformly over its central area.

Boundary conditions

$$\phi = 0 \quad \text{at A, D, E}$$

AH:

$$\phi_A = 0 \qquad \sigma'_{xx} = 0$$

$$\phi = 0 \quad \text{for all } y$$

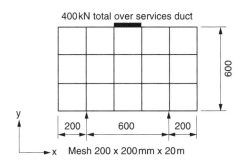

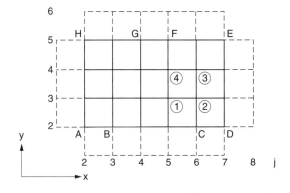

Figure 4.39. A rectangular plate with finite difference mesh

DE:

$$\phi_D = 0 \qquad \sigma'_{xx} = 0$$

$$\phi = 0 \quad \text{for all } y$$

HE:

$$\phi_H = \phi_E = 0 \qquad \sigma'_{yy} = \frac{\partial^2 \phi}{\partial x^2}$$

$$\omega = \frac{d^2 M}{dx^2}$$

GF:

$$\sigma_{yy} = \frac{400 \times 10^3}{200 \times 20} = 100 \, \text{N/mm}^2$$

$$\phi_{5,3} = \phi_{5,6} = 2 \times 10^6$$

$$\phi_{5,4} = \phi_{5,5} = 4 \times 10^6$$

For an analogous beam simply supported:

$$\phi_{2,2} = \phi_{2,7} = 0$$

$$\phi_{2,3} = \phi_{2,4} = \phi_{2,6} = 2 \times 10^6$$

Shear stress is assumed zero on all boundaries.

AD and HE:

$$T_{yx} = -\frac{\partial}{\partial x}\left(\frac{\partial \phi}{\partial y}\right) = 0$$

hence

$$\frac{\partial \phi}{\partial y} = \text{constant} \quad (\text{at A})$$

and

$$D_3 \frac{\partial \phi}{\partial y} = 0 \quad \text{for all } x$$

$$\therefore \quad \phi_{i,j} = \phi_{3,j} \qquad \phi_{6,j} = \phi_{4,j}$$

Similarly for all points on AH

$$\frac{\partial \phi}{\partial x} = 10^4$$

since AH and ED have

$$T_{xy} = -\frac{\partial}{\partial y}\left(\frac{\partial \phi}{\partial x}\right) = 0$$

and

$$\frac{\partial \phi}{\partial x} = \text{constant}$$

$$\phi_{i,3} = \phi_{i,1} + 400 \times 10^4$$

$$\phi_{i,1} = \phi_{i,3} - 4 \times 10^6$$

In this same context (Fig. 4.40):

$$\frac{\partial \phi}{\partial x} = 10^{-4} \quad \text{for all points on DE}$$

$$\phi_{i,8} = \phi_{i,6} - 4 \times 10^6$$

Nodes

① $20\phi_1 - 8(\phi_1 + 2 \times 10^6 + \phi_2 + \phi_4) + 2(2 \times 10^6 + 2 \times 10^6 + \phi_3 + \phi_4)$

$\qquad + \phi_2 + \phi_1 + 0 + 4 \times 10^6 = 0$

$\qquad$ or $\quad 13\phi_1 - 7\phi_2 + 2\phi_3 - 6\phi_4 = 4 \times 10^6$ $\qquad\qquad$ (4.145)

② $20\phi_1 - 8(\phi_1 + 2 \times 10^6 + 0 + \phi_3) + 2(2 \times 10^6 + 0 + 0 + \phi_4)$

$\qquad + \phi_2 + (\phi_2 - 4 \times 10^6) + 2 \times 10^6 + \phi_1 = 0$

$\qquad$ or $\quad -7\phi_1 - 22\phi_2 - 8\phi_3 + 2\phi_4 = 14 \times 10^6$ $\qquad\qquad$ (4.146)

③ $20\phi_3 - 8(\phi_4 + \phi_2 + 0 + 2 \times 10^6) + 2(\phi_1 + 0 + 0 + 4 \times 10^6)$

$\qquad + 2 \times 10^6 + (\phi_3 - 4 \times 10^6) + \phi_3 + \phi_4 = 0$

$\qquad$ or $\quad 2\phi_1 - 8\phi_2 + 22\phi_3 - 7\phi_4 = 10 \times 10^6$ $\qquad\qquad$ (4.147)

④ $20\phi_4 - 8(\phi_4 + \phi_1 + \phi_3 + 4 \times 10^6) + 2(\phi_1 + \phi_2 + 2 \times 10^6 + 4 \times 10^6)$

$\qquad + \phi_3 + 2 \times 10^6 + 0 + \phi_4 = 0$

$\qquad$ or $\quad -6\phi_1 + 2\phi_2 - 7\phi_3 + 13\phi_4 = 18 \times 10^6$ $\qquad\qquad$ (4.148)

Figure 4.40. Node loading in Example (4.12)

ϕ relations without solution are given by:

$$
\begin{bmatrix}
13 & -7 & 2 & -6 \\
-7 & 22 & -8 & 2 \\
2 & -8 & 22 & -7 \\
-6 & 2 & -7 & 13
\end{bmatrix}
\begin{bmatrix}
\phi_1 \\
\phi_2 \\
\phi_3 \\
\phi_4
\end{bmatrix}
=
\begin{bmatrix}
4 \\
14 \\
10 \\
18
\end{bmatrix}
\times 10^6
$$

4.4.4.8 Example (4.13)

A square deck is subjected to a uniformly distributed load '*q*' placed at the centre as shown in Fig. 4.41. Using the operator ∇ method of the finite difference method, calculate displacements at nodes 1, 2 and 3, adopting the following information.

A steel deck simply supported on all sides and subjected to:

$$q = 10\,\text{kN/m}^2$$

$$E = 200 \times 10^6\,\text{kN/m}^2$$

$$t = 0.075\,\text{m}$$

Poisson ratio $\nu = 0.3$

$$L = 8.0\,\text{m}$$

$$L = 2.5\,\text{m}$$

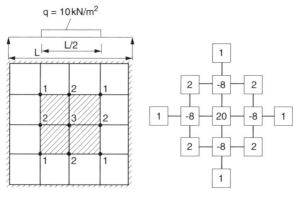

Figure 4.41. A square deck loaded with uniform load at the centre over a half plate

Solution

A simple plate loaded in its central area (q/unit area over central area, side $L/2$).

Negative fictitious

$$-\omega_1 \bullet \quad \bullet\omega_1 \quad \bullet\omega_2 \quad \bullet\omega_1 \quad \bullet-\omega_1$$

main grid $\quad -\omega_2\bullet \quad \bullet\omega_2 \quad \bullet\omega_3 \quad \bullet\omega_2 \quad \bullet-\omega_2$

$$-\omega_3\bullet \quad \bullet\omega_1 \quad \bullet\omega_2 \quad \bullet\omega_1 \quad \bullet-\omega_3$$

$$-\omega_3 \bullet \quad -\omega_2 \bullet \quad -\omega_1 \bullet$$

load at ② $= \frac{1}{2}q$

load at ① $= \frac{1}{4}q$

load at ③ $= q$

The next approach is to develop the operator technique.

For the ω_1-operator [see Fig. 4.42(a)]:

$$\{2\omega_3 - 16\omega_2 + (20 + 1 + 1)\omega_1\} \times 4 - 1 - 1 = 4(2\omega_3 - 16\omega_2 + 20\omega_1)$$

For the ω_2-operator [see Fig. 4.42(b)]:

$$- 8\omega_3 + 20(2\{-8\omega_3 + (20 + 2 + 2)\omega_2 - 16\omega_1\} \times 4$$
$$= (-8\omega_3 + 24\omega_2 - 16\omega_1) \times 4$$

For the ω_3-operator [see Fig. 4.42(c)]:

$$\{20\omega_3 + 4(-8\omega_2) + 4(2\omega_1) + 0(4\omega_1)\} = (20\omega_3 - 32\omega_2 + 8\omega_1 + 0) \times 1$$

$$D = 77.253$$

$$h = \frac{a}{4}$$

$$\begin{bmatrix} +80 & -64 & +8 \\ -64 & +96 & -32 \\ +8 & -32 & +20 \end{bmatrix} \begin{Bmatrix} \omega_1 \\ \omega_2 \\ \omega_3 \end{Bmatrix} = \begin{Bmatrix} \frac{1}{2} \\ \frac{1}{2} \\ 1 \end{Bmatrix}$$

$$D = \frac{Et^3}{12(1 - \nu_2)} = 7726.6484$$

$$L = 8\,\text{m}$$

$$\begin{Bmatrix} \omega_1 \\ \omega_2 \\ \omega_3 \end{Bmatrix} = \begin{Bmatrix} 0.00101 \\ 0.00146 \\ 0.00214 \end{Bmatrix} \times \frac{qL^4}{D} \times 10^3 = \begin{Bmatrix} 5.107 \\ 7.382 \\ 10.821 \end{Bmatrix} \quad \text{(mm)}$$

(a) For ω_1-operator

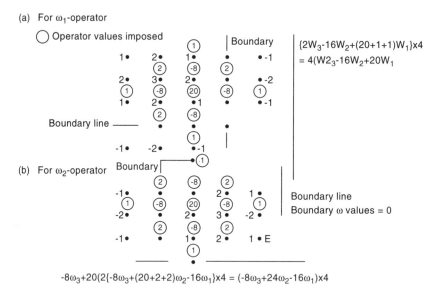

(b) For ω_2-operator

$-8\omega_3+20(2\{-8\omega_3+(20+2+2)\omega_2-16\omega_1\}x4 = (-8\omega_3+24\omega_2-16\omega_1)x4$

(c) For ω_3-operator

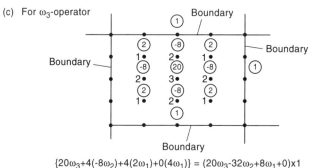

$\{20\omega_3+4(-8\omega_2)+4(2\omega_1)+0(4\omega_1)\} = (20\omega_3-32\omega_2+8\omega_1+0)x1$

Figure 4.42. Developing the operator technique for Example (4.13)

4.4.4.9 Example (4.14)

Calculate the deflection, bending moment and end reactions of a continuous bridge resting on an elastic foundation between supports with stiffness $K = 0.1024$ where $h = L/4$ as shown in Fig. 4.43. Assume EI is constant.

Solution

A plate strip on an elastic foundation following the procedure outlined earlier using the ∇-operator:

$$\omega_1 = 1.928q\,\frac{h^4}{EI} = \omega_3$$

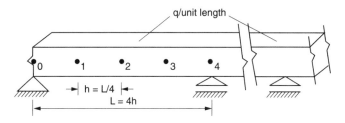

Figure 4.43. A continuous deck

or

$$\omega_1 = \omega_3 = 0.00753q\,\frac{L^4}{EI}$$

$$\omega_2 = 2.692q\,\frac{h^4}{EI} = \omega_4$$

or

$$\omega_2 = \omega_4 = 0.0105q\,\frac{L^4}{EI}$$

At points ① and ②

$$M_1 = -\frac{EI}{h^4}\,q\,\frac{h^4}{EI}\,(0 - 2 \times 1.928 + 2.692) = 1.164qh^4 = 0.0728qL^2$$

$$M_2 = -\frac{EI}{h^4}\,q\,\frac{h^4}{EI}\,(1.928 - 2 \times 2.692 + 1.928) = 1.528h = 0.0955qL^2$$

$$R_0 = \text{reaction at O} = \frac{EI}{h^3}\,(2\omega_1 - \omega_2) = R_0 - Q_0$$

$$R_0 = R_4 = 0.416qL$$

$$Q_0 = \frac{qh}{2} = \frac{qL}{8}$$

Based on six-nodes within a distance L

$$h = \frac{L}{6}$$

Following the above techniques:

$$\omega_1 = \omega_3 = 0.00732q\,\frac{L^4}{EI}$$

$$\omega_2 = 0.0102q\,\frac{L^4}{EI}$$

$$M_1 = M_3 = 0.0745qL^2$$

$$M_2 = 0.0978qL^2$$

$$R_0 = 0.414qL$$

4.4.4.10 Example (4.15)

A rectangular deck with a mesh of $a/2$ adopted is shown in Fig. 4.44. Determine the warping displacements, shear forces or stresses at the node points. From the classic solution, the maximum shear stress τ_{max} is $0.986Ga\theta$. Calculate the percentage error of the maximum shear stress using the finite difference method. If the same deck has a 1×3 mesh scheme as shown in Fig. 4.45, calculate warping displacements and shear forces or stresses. Take $G\theta$ and EI as constant.

Solution

Warping displacements and shear forces in a rectangular deck.

At the axis of symmetry, the warping displacements are zero:

$$T_{yz} = 0 = T_{xz}$$

At ②

$$\omega_3 + \omega_A - 4\omega_2 = 0 \tag{4.149}$$

$$T_{yz} = G\left(x\theta + \frac{\partial\omega}{\partial y}\right)$$

$$
\begin{array}{ccc}
 & \bullet 1 & \\
1\bullet & \bullet{-4} & \bullet 1 \\
 & \bullet 1 &
\end{array}
$$

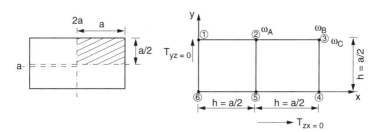

Figure 4.44. A rectangular deck with a coarse mesh

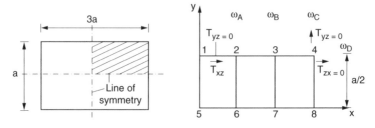

Figure 4.45. A 3 × 1 rectangular mesh scheme

$$x = \frac{a}{2}$$

$$\frac{\partial w}{\partial y} = \frac{w_A - w_5}{2h} = \frac{w_A}{a}$$

$$0 = G\left(0.5a\theta + \frac{w_A}{a}\right)$$

$$\therefore \quad w_A = -0.5a^2\theta$$

At ③

$$w_a + w_B + w_2 + 4w_3 = 0 \tag{4.150}$$

$$T_{yz} = G\left(x\theta + \frac{\partial w}{\partial y}\right)$$

$$x = a$$

$$h = \frac{a}{2}$$

$$\frac{\partial w}{\partial y} = \frac{w_B - w_4}{2h} = \frac{w_B}{a} \quad (\text{where } w_4 = 0)$$

$$w_B = -a^2\theta$$

Now $T_{xz} = 0$

$$0 = G\left(-0.5a\theta + \frac{w_C}{a} + \frac{w_2}{a}\right)$$

$$w_C = 0.5a^2\theta + w_2 \tag{4.151}$$

Substituting w_A, w_B and w_C in Eqs (4.149) and (4.150), the values of w_2 and w_3 are solved and are given below:

$$w_2 = 0.139a^2\theta$$

$$w_3 = 1.056a^2\theta$$

At ①

$$T_{yz} = 0$$

$$T_{xz} = G\left(-y\theta + \frac{\partial w}{\partial x}\right)$$

$$y = \frac{a}{2}$$

$$h = \frac{a}{2}$$

$$\frac{\partial w}{\partial x} = \frac{w_2 - (-w_2)}{2h} = \frac{2w_2}{a} = 2(0.139a^2\theta) \times \frac{1}{a}$$

$$\therefore \quad T_{xz} = G(-0.5a\theta + 0.278a\theta) = -0.222Ga\theta$$

At ②

$$T_{yz} = 0$$

$$T_{xz} = G\left(-y\theta + \frac{\partial w}{\partial x}\right)$$

$$y = \frac{a}{2}$$

$$\frac{\partial w}{\partial x} = \frac{w_3 - w_1}{2h} = \frac{1.056a^2\theta}{2\frac{a}{2}} = 1.056a\theta$$

$$T_{xz} = G(-0.5a\theta + 1.056a\theta) = -0.556Ga\theta$$

At ③

$$T_{yz} = 0 = T_{xz}$$

At ④

$$T_{zx} = 0$$

$$T_{yz} = G\left(x\theta + \frac{\partial w}{\partial y}\right)$$

$$x = a + 0.5a$$

$$y = \frac{a}{2} = \frac{h}{2}$$

$$\frac{\partial w}{\partial y} = \frac{w_3 - (-w_3)}{2h} = \frac{2w_3}{2\frac{a}{2}} = \frac{2(1.056a^2\theta)}{a}$$

$$T_{yz} = G(a\theta + 2.112a\theta) = 3.112Ga\theta$$

Similarly, the same method is applied for node points ⑤ and ⑥.
   At ⑥

$$T_{yz} = 0 = T_{xz}$$

Note that percentage error for the maximum shear stress $\tau_{\max}$ between the finite difference and classical solutions (closed form) is around 56%. If the mesh is narrowed to $a/50$ the error is reduced to 1%.

By increasing the mesh to 3×1, and by using the same nodal points and finite difference operator ∇, a similar procedure is followed.

Again ①–⑤ and ⑤–⑧ warping is zero.

At ②

$$w_3 + w_A - 4w_2 = 0 \tag{4.152}$$

At ③

$$w_B + w_4 + w_2 - 4w_3 = 0 \tag{4.153}$$

At ④

$$w_D + w_C + w_B - 4w_4 = 0 \tag{4.154}$$

At ②

$$T_{yz} = 0$$

$$T_{yz} = G \left(x\theta + \frac{\partial w}{\partial y} \right)$$

$$x = 2$$

$$\frac{\partial w}{\partial y} = w_A = \frac{w_6}{2h} = \frac{w_A}{a} \quad \text{(where } w_6 = 0\text{)}$$

After substitution

$$w_A = -\frac{a^2}{2}\theta$$

At ③

$$T_{yz} = 0$$

$$x = a$$

$$h = \frac{a}{2}$$

$$\frac{\partial w}{\partial y} = \frac{w_B - w_7}{2h} = \frac{w_B}{a}$$

$$w_B = -a^2\theta$$

At ④

$$x = 1.5a$$

$$T_{yz} = 0$$

$$\frac{\partial w}{\partial y} = \frac{w_C - w_B}{h} = -\frac{w_C}{a}$$

$$0 = G\left(1.5a\theta + \frac{w_C}{a}\right)$$

$$w_C = -1.5a^2\theta$$

$$T_{zx} = 0$$

$$T_{zx} = G\left(-y\theta + \frac{\partial w}{\partial x}\right)$$

$$y = \frac{a}{2}$$

$$\frac{\partial w}{\partial x} = \frac{w_D - w_3}{2h} = \frac{w_D - w_3}{a}$$

$$0 = G\left(-\frac{a}{2}\theta + \frac{w_D - w_3}{a}\right)$$

$$w_D = \frac{a^2\theta}{2} + w_3$$

Substituting w_A, w_B, w_C into Eqs (4.152) to (4.154):

$$w_2 = -0.23077a^2\theta$$
$$w_3 = -0.42308a^2\theta$$
$$w_4 = -0.46154a^2\theta$$

At ①

$$T_{yz} = 0 \quad \text{but } T_{xz} \neq 0 = G\left(-y\theta + \frac{\partial w}{\partial x}\right) = G\left(-\frac{a}{2}\theta + \frac{2w_2}{a}\right)$$

$$T_{zx} = -0.9615Ga\theta$$

At ②

$$T_{yz} = 0$$

$$T_{zx} = G\left(-0.5a\theta + \frac{w_3}{a}\right) = -0.92308Ga\theta$$

At ③

$$T_{yz} = 0 \quad \text{but } T_{xz} \neq 0$$

$$T_{xz} = -0.70377Ga\theta$$

At ④

$$T_{yz} = 0 = T_{zx}$$

At ⑤

$$T_{yz} = 0 = T_{zx}$$

At ⑥

$$T_{xz} = 0$$

$$T_{yx} = G\left(x\theta + \frac{\partial w}{\partial y}\right) = G(0.5a\theta - 0.4615a\theta) = 0.03846Ga\theta$$

At ⑦

$$T_{zx} = 0$$

$$T_{yz} = G\left(x\theta + \frac{\partial w}{\partial y}\right) \qquad x = a$$

$$= G(a\theta - 0.84616a\theta) = 0.15384Ga\theta$$

At ⑧

$$T_{zx} = 0$$

$$T_{yz} = G\left(x\theta + \frac{\partial w}{\partial y}\right)$$

$$x = 1.5a$$

$$h = \frac{a}{2}$$

$$\frac{\partial w}{\partial y} = 2(-0.41654a^2\theta) \times \frac{1}{a}$$

$$T_{yz} = 0.577Ga\theta$$

4.4.4.11   Example (4.16)

A simply supported square skew deck with a triangular mesh is shown in Fig. 4.46. The Cartesian and the triangular coordinates are related by the following expressions:

$$x = \xi_1 + \xi_2 \cos\theta_1 + \xi_3 \cos\theta_2$$

$$y = \xi_2 \sin\theta_1 + \xi_3 \sin\theta_2$$

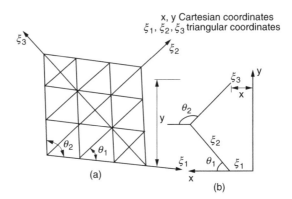

Figure 4.46. A square-shaped skewed deck

If the decxk is subjected to a uniformly distributed load 'q', then $\nabla^2(\nabla^2 w) = q$. From this, calculate:

(*a*)   the second partial derivative of deflection 'w'
(*b*)   the value of $\nabla^2(w)$

Take $\theta_1 = 60°$, $\theta_2 = 120°$ and EI and deck thickness to be constant.

Solution
A simply supported skew square deck with triangular mesh:

$$x = \xi_1 + \xi_2 \cos\theta_1 + \xi_3 \cos\theta_2 \quad (a)$$

$$y = \xi_2 \sin\theta_1 + \xi_3 \sin\theta_2 \quad (b)$$

(4.155)

$$\frac{\partial x}{\partial \xi_1} = 1 \qquad \frac{\partial x}{\partial \xi_2} = \cos\theta_1 \qquad \frac{\partial x}{\partial \xi_3} = \cos\theta_2 \quad (a)$$

$$\frac{\partial y}{\partial \xi_1} = 0 \qquad \frac{\partial y}{\partial \xi_2} = \sin\theta_1 \qquad \frac{\partial y}{\partial \xi_3} = \sin\theta_2 \quad (b)$$

(4.156)

Using the chain rule for defining $w(\xi_1, \xi_2, \xi_3)$ and its derivatives:

$$\frac{\partial w}{\partial \xi_1} = \frac{\partial w}{\partial x} \times \frac{\partial x}{\partial \xi_1} + \frac{\partial w}{\partial y} \times \frac{\partial y}{\partial \xi_1} = \frac{\partial w}{\partial x} \quad (a)$$

$$\frac{\partial w}{\partial \xi_2} = \frac{\partial w}{\partial x} \cos\theta_1 + \frac{\partial w}{\partial y} \sin\theta_1 \quad (b)$$

(4.157)

Similarly for the third ordinate:

$$\frac{\partial w}{\partial \xi_3} = \frac{\partial w}{\partial x} \cos\theta_2 + \frac{\partial w}{\partial y} \sin\theta_2 \quad (c)$$

The second partial derivative $\partial^2 w/\partial \xi^2$ etc. are computed and the following matrix relations are established

$$\left\{ \begin{array}{c} \dfrac{\partial^2 w}{\partial \xi_1^2} \\[2mm] \dfrac{\partial^2 w}{\partial \xi_2^2} \\[2mm] \dfrac{\partial^2 w}{\partial \xi_3^2} \end{array} \right\} \left[\begin{array}{ccc} 1 & 0 & 0 \\ \cos^2 \theta_1 & 2\sin \theta_1 \cos \theta_1 & \sin^2 \theta_1 \\ \cos^2 \theta_2 & 2\sin \theta_2 \cos \theta_2 & \sin^2 \theta_2 \end{array} \right\} \left\{ \begin{array}{c} \dfrac{\partial^2 w}{\partial x^2} \\[2mm] \dfrac{\partial^2 w}{\partial x\,\partial y} \\[2mm] \dfrac{\partial^2 w}{\partial y^2} \end{array} \right\} \qquad (4.158)$$

First of Eq. (4.158) into second and third and eliminating $\partial^2 w/\partial x\,\partial y$, the following relations are obtained:

$$\frac{\partial^2 w}{\partial y^2} = \bar{N}\left[2\,\frac{\partial^2 w}{\partial \xi_1^2}\cos \theta_1 \cos \theta_2 \sin(\theta_2 - \theta_1) - \frac{\partial^2 w}{\partial \xi_2^2}\sin 2\theta_2 + \frac{\partial^2 w}{\partial \xi_3^2}\sin 2\theta_1 \right] \qquad (4.159)$$

where

$$\bar{N} = \tfrac{1}{2}\sin \theta_1 \sin \theta_2 \sin(\theta_2 - \theta_1)$$

Hence

$$\nabla^2(w) = \frac{\partial^2 w}{\partial x^2} + \frac{\partial^2 w}{\partial y^2} = \frac{\partial^2 w}{\partial \xi_1^2} + \frac{\partial^2 w}{\partial y^2}$$

$$= \bar{N}\left[\frac{\partial^2 w}{\partial \xi_1^2}\sin 2(\theta_2 - \theta_1) - \frac{\partial^2 w}{\partial \xi_2^2}\sin 2\theta_2 + \frac{\partial^2 w}{\partial \xi_3^2}\sin 2\theta_1 \right]$$

When $\theta_1 = 60°$, $\theta_2 = 120°$

$$\nabla^2 w = \frac{2}{3}\left[\frac{\partial^2 w}{\partial \xi_1^2} + \frac{\partial^2 w}{\partial \xi_2^2} + \frac{\partial^2 w}{\partial \xi_3^2} \right]$$

Operator $\tfrac{3}{2}h^2\nabla$ is represented in Fig. 4.47.

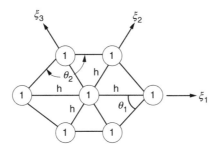

Figure 4.47. Calculated operator for Example (4.16)

4.4.4.12 Example (4.17)

A portion of deck with curved boundaries of irregular type is shown in Fig. 4.48. A triangular curved mesh with square mesh of a mixed type can represent the finite difference scheme especially at node zero, ⓪, where the ∇^2-operator does not apply. Assuming the region surrounding this node can be expressed as

$$w(x, y) = w_0 + a_1 x + a_2 y + a_3 x^2 + a_4 y^2 \tag{4.160}$$

establish the finite difference representation.

Solution

A deck with a curved boundary containing nodes 1, 2, 3, 4.
  Expressions

$$w_1 = w_0 + a_2 h_1 + a_4 h_1^2$$

$$w_2 = w_0 + a_1 h + a_3 h^2$$

$$w_3 = w_0 + a_2 h + a_4 h^2$$

$$w_4 = w_0 + a_1 h_4 + a_3 h_4^2$$

After solving, the four coefficients are given below:

$$a_1 = \frac{h^2 \bar{w} + h_4^2 w'}{L_1} \qquad a_3 = \frac{h \bar{w} - h_4 w'}{L_1}$$

$$a_2 = \frac{h^2 w'' + h_1^2 w'''}{L_2} \qquad a_4 = \frac{h w'' - h_1 w'''}{L_2} \tag{4.161}$$

where

$$\bar{w} = (w_4 - w_0) \qquad w' = (w_0 - w_2) \qquad L_1 = h_1 h_4 (h + h_4)$$

$$w'' = (w_1 - w_0) \qquad w''' = (w_0 - w_3) \qquad L_2 = h h_1 (h + h_1)$$

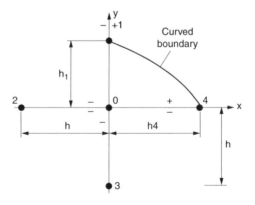

Figure 4.48. A portion of a curved deck

At point 0 $(x = 0; \ y = 0)$, Eq. (4.160) for $\omega(x, y)$ gives

$$\left(\frac{\partial^2 \omega}{\partial x^2}\right) = 2a_3 \qquad \left(\frac{\partial^2 \omega}{\partial y^2}\right) = 2a_4 \tag{4.162}$$

Substituting Eq. (4.161) into Eq. (4.162) and adding resulting equations, the $\nabla^2 \omega$ operator is written as

$$h^2 \left(\frac{\partial^2 \omega}{\partial x^2} + \frac{\partial^2 \omega}{\partial y^2}\right) \approx \frac{2\omega_1}{U_1(1 + U_1)} + \frac{2\omega_2}{1 + U_4} + \frac{2\omega_4}{U_4(1 + U_4)}$$

$$- \left(\frac{2}{U_1} + \frac{2}{U_4}\right)\omega_0 \tag{4.163}$$

in which $U_i = h_i/h$, $i = 1, 4$ and

$$h^2 \nabla^2 (\omega)_0 \approx d_1 \omega_1 + d_2 \omega_2 + d_3 \omega_3 + d_4 \omega_4 - (d_5 + d_6)\omega_0 \tag{4.164}$$

$$\bullet d_4$$

$$h^2 \nabla^2 \omega \qquad d_3 \bullet \quad \overset{\bullet}{\underset{-(d_5 + d_6)}{}} \quad \bullet d_1$$

$$\bullet d_2$$

If h_i, $i = 1, 2, 3, 4 < h$

$$h^2 \nabla^2 \omega \approx \frac{2\omega_1}{U_1(U_1 + U_3)} + \frac{2\omega_2}{U_2(U_2 + U_4)} + \frac{2\omega_3}{U_3(U_1 + U_3)} + \frac{2\omega_4}{U_4(U_2 + U_4)}$$

$$- \left(\frac{2}{U_1 U_3} + \frac{2}{U_2 U_4}\right)\omega_0 \tag{4.165}$$

The only difference is in certain coefficients.

4.4.4.13 Example (4.18)

Draw the operator diagram (∇-operator) for a circular shaped, curved deck in bending as shown in Fig. 4.49. The polar coordinates in terms of (r, θ) are given where r is the radius and θ is the angle subtended.

Solution

Polar coordinates $-\nabla$-operator:

$$\nabla^2 \omega = \frac{\partial^2 \omega}{\partial r^2} + \frac{1}{r}\frac{\partial \omega}{\partial r} + \frac{1}{r^2}\frac{\partial^2 \omega}{\partial \theta^2}$$

$$\frac{\partial^2 \omega}{\partial r^2} \approx \frac{1}{h^2}(\omega_2 - 2\omega_0 + \omega_4)$$

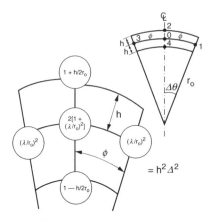

Figure 4.49. A circular-shaped curved deck

$$\frac{\partial \omega}{\partial r} \approx \frac{1}{2h}(\omega_2 - \omega_4)$$

$$\frac{\partial^2 \omega}{\partial \theta^2} \approx \frac{1}{\phi^2}(-2\omega_0 + \omega_1 + \omega_3)$$

where $h = \nabla r$; $\phi = \Delta\theta$; using relationship $\lambda = h/\phi$, the $h^2\nabla^2$ can be given as:

at ② $1 + \dfrac{h}{2r_0}$

at ③ $\left(\dfrac{\lambda}{r_0}\right)^2 = ①$

at ⓪ $= 2\left[1 + \left(\dfrac{\lambda}{r_0}\right)^2\right]$

at ④ $= 1 - \dfrac{h}{2r_0}$

The finite difference version is shown.

4.5 Dynamic relaxation method

Dynamic relaxation is applied to bridge problems. The bridge is analysed assuming that it vibrates freely in a viscous medium by adding inertia and viscous damping terms to the static equilibrium equation. The equation assumes a dynamic form and it is solved by an iterative procedure such that the bridge and its components achieve a steady state condition. While deriving such equations, consideration is given separately to:

(i) the motion of any component, due to internal forces and imposed body forces;

(ii) the motion maintaining an elastic relation between forces and displacements.

A typical model of such a system is given in Fig. 4.50. The viscous damping force is:

$$F = -c\dot{\omega} \qquad (4.166)$$

where

$\omega =$ displacement

$\dot{\omega} = \dfrac{d\omega}{dt}$

$\quad =$ velocity

$c =$ viscous damping coefficient

The equation of motion is written as

$$m\ddot{\omega} + c\dot{\omega} + k\omega = 0 \qquad (4.167)$$

where

$\ddot{\omega} =$ acceleration $= \dfrac{d^2\omega}{dt^2}$

$k =$ stiffness

If this equation is established, the next procedure is to ascertain what type of bridge it is? If the deck is idealized as an orthotropic plate type, then with the knowledge of the finite difference methods discussed in Section 4.4 a corresponding static equilibrium equation is written. For the orthotropic plate type, the equation is written as

$$\frac{\partial^2 M_x}{\partial x^2} - \frac{\partial^2 M_{xy}}{\partial x\,\partial y} + \frac{\partial^2 M_{yx}}{\partial x\,\partial y} + \frac{\partial^2 M_y}{\partial y^2} = q(x,y) \qquad (4.168)$$

In a three-dimensional treatment, if required, the z term will appear.

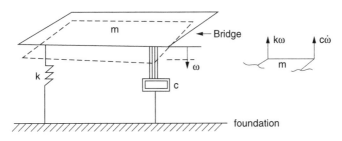

Figure 4.50. Free vibration with viscous damping

Note from Eq. (4.168) that

$q(x, y)$ = transverse load in the two-dimensional situation

M_x, M_y = bending moments in the x and y directions

M_{xy}, M_{yx} = the twisting moments

such that

$$M_x = -\left[D_x \frac{\partial^2 \omega}{\partial x^2} + D_1 \frac{\partial^2 \omega}{\partial y^2}\right] \qquad (4.169)$$

$$M_y = -\left[D_y \frac{\partial^2 \omega}{\partial y^2} + D_2 \frac{\partial^2 \omega}{\partial x^2}\right] \qquad (4.170)$$

$$M_{xy} = -D_{xy} \frac{\partial^2 \omega}{\partial x \, \partial y} \qquad (4.171)$$

$$M_{yx} = -D_{yx} \frac{\partial^2 \omega}{\partial x \, \partial y} \qquad (4.172)$$

where D values are the elastic rigidities of the deck.

The equations are then summed up as

$$m\ddot{\omega} + c\dot{\omega} + \frac{\partial^2 M_x}{\partial x^2} + \frac{\partial^2 M_{xy}}{\partial x \, \partial y} + \frac{\partial^2 M_{yx}}{\partial x \, \partial y} + \frac{\partial^2 M_y}{\partial y^2} + k\omega = q(x, y) \qquad (4.173)$$

After rearrangement, the equation will give velocities. If the time increment is Δt, the displacement found by integrating velocities over the time increment Δt are obtained in terms of velocities and moments. The displacements are substituted into the moment equations so that preparation is made for the next step of the integration. This technique is described in detail in the Appendix.

4.5.1 Boundary conditions

At each step of the calculation, boundary conditions for the bridge deck must be satisfied. These boundary conditions are variable. A few examples are given so that the reader can follow the complex conditions.

(a) Internal supports
In any computer analysis, inputs can be arranged by specifying zero displacements for rigid supports. Where settlement occurs, they should be included. Where piers, abutments and columns appear, their stiffness should be included.

(b) External supports
Here, if the boundary conditions apply, zero displacements and zero moments are included. Parallel to any axis, they should be examined. In this situation, $\omega = 0$ and $M_x = 0$ at all nodes along the edge parallel to the y-axis.

(c) Free edges

Zero normal moment and supplemented shear force are the two most important conditions that need to be looked at.

For edges parallel to the x-axis

$$M_y = 0 \tag{4.174}$$

$$\frac{\partial M_y}{\partial y} + \frac{\partial M_{yx}}{\partial x} - \frac{\partial M_{xy}}{\partial x} = 0 \tag{4.175}$$

In principle, the central difference forms of these equations are easily solved. Looking at a bridge deck interlaced with finite difference mesh and time, the bending moments (Fig. 4.51) are written as

$$(M_x)_{oo} = \frac{D_x}{(\alpha h)^2} [w_\ell - 2w_{oo} + w_r] + \frac{D_1}{h^2} [w_h - 2w_{oo} + w_b] \tag{4.176}$$

$$(M_y)_{oo} = \frac{D_y}{h^2} [w_h - 2w_{oo} + w_b] + \frac{D_2}{(\alpha h)^2} [w_\ell - 2w_{oo} + w_r] \tag{4.177}$$

$$(M_{xy}) \text{ at node oo} = \frac{D_{xy}}{\alpha h^2} (w_{br} - w_b - w_r + w_{oo}) \tag{B4.178}$$

Similar equations are devised for $\partial^2 M_{xy}/(\partial x\, \partial y)$. Greater accuracy is maintained if all parameters such as w, M_x, M_y, M_{xy} and M_{yx} all occur at one instant in time while the velocities $\dot{w}$ occur at $\Delta t/2$. Referring to the Appendix for the nth step iteration, the velocities $\dot{w}_b$ and $\dot{w}_h$ for $y = $ constant are obtained before and after moment curvature and equations of motions are satisfied. The final equation is then written as

$$\frac{m}{\Delta t} (\dot{w}_h - \dot{w}_b) + \frac{c}{2} (\dot{w}_h + \dot{w}_b) + \frac{\partial^2 M_x}{\partial x^2} + \frac{\partial^2 M_{xy}}{\partial x\, \partial y} + \frac{\partial^2 M_{yx}}{\partial x\, \partial y}$$

$$+ kw - q(x, y) = 0 \tag{4.179}$$

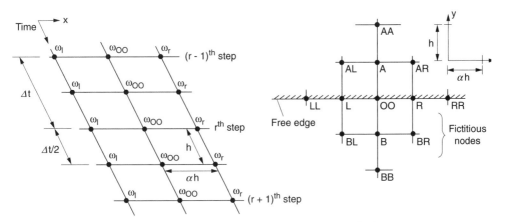

Figure 4.51. Dynamic relation mesh scheme for a bridge deck

In the non-dimensional situation, the viscous damping coefficient, for ease of solution, is written as

$$\phi = \frac{c\Delta t}{m} \quad \text{(critical damping)} \tag{4.180}$$

In order to give an explicit expression for $\dot{\omega}_h$, a rearrangment of Eq. (4.179) is necessary in order to produce a compact solution:

$$\dot{\omega}_h = \left(\frac{2-\phi}{2+\phi}\right)\ddot{\omega}_b$$

$$-\frac{2(\Delta t)}{m}\left[\frac{\partial^2 M_x}{\partial x^2} - \frac{\partial M_{yx}}{\partial x\,\partial y} + \frac{\partial^2 M_{xy}}{\partial x\,\partial y} + \frac{\partial^2 M_y}{\partial y^2} + k\omega - (x,y)\right] \tag{4.180a}$$

In reality, the success of dynamic relaxation is based on the proper choice of

(*i*) time increment 'Δt'
(*ii*) pseudo-mass 'm'
(*iii*) viscous damping coefficient 'c'

A reference is made to the dynamic analysis part of the Appendix for the choices of these parameters and elements. In bridges $\Delta t = 1$ is a normal choice. The condition for mass M is such that

$$M = \|k\| \tag{4.181}$$

where

$k =$ stiffness matrix

$\|k\| =$ the norm of k (greatest column or row sum of moduli of coefficients)

In order to look at the value of 'c', the best choice is to relate it to critical damping at time interval Δt.

At the centre, the nodal displacement is ω_0, then

$$\omega_0 = \frac{c}{2m} = \frac{\phi}{2\Delta t} \quad \text{(smaller value for efficiency)} \tag{4.182}$$

The damping factor will vary with mesh size as

$$\frac{1}{\left[\left(\frac{1}{\alpha h}\right)^2 + \left(\frac{1}{h}\right)^2\right]} \tag{4.183}$$

The oscillation of the bridge deck will settle down in the dynamic relation process within 1 or 2% of the static value. The number of iterations N to reach this stage of oscillation is given by

$$N = \frac{6\pi}{\phi} \tag{4.184}$$

It is concluded that dynamic analysis of the finite difference form of analysis is the dynamic relaxation approach with an iteration process.

4.6 Incremental collapse analysis
4.6.1 Introduction
The scope of this section encompasses a theoretical analysis based on the incremental collapse mechanism as a numerical technique. The grids of composite bridges are assumed to be continuous across supports of fixed elevation. The equations developed do not include the effects due to torsion and dynamic plasticity. However, these equations will be modified later on to include such effects.

The present analysis is flexible and can take spans with any boundary conditions or rigidities. Apart from dead load, slow but heavy vehicular loading moving from point to point across the bridge is also included. Again, the vehicular loading can be replaced by UDL or patched loading representing some kind of dynamic loads. A numerical example is included in order to explain the use of these equations.

4.6.2 Problem description and analytical equations
4.6.2.1 Composite bridges
Slab is divided into rectangular meshes and the longitudinal grid lines must be in line with longitudinal beams as shown in Fig. 4.52. Several plastic hinge mechanisms for spans must be examined; the one that gives the lowest load

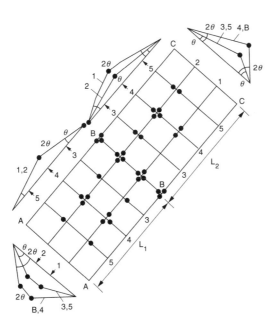

Figure 4.52. Plane grid: wheel loads only. AB span Mech I; BC span Mech II. Note that they can be interchanged as they produce the same order of collapse

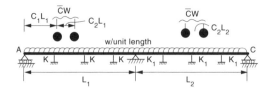

Figure 4.53. Beam grid

is chosen – the value of $\bar{K}\bar{M}_\mathrm{p}/C_3L_3$. This kind of optimization can easily be carried out by computer: $\bar{K} = 2$ for the sample grid/line. Figure 4.53 shows a continuous span ABC loaded with dead and imposed vehicular loadings. The grid points are assumed to be supported on springs K_1 or K. If $L_1 = L$, then $K_1 = K = \bar{K}\bar{M}_\mathrm{p}/C_3L_3$ (Fig. 4.54). For the sample grid $\bar{K} = 4$.

The analysis involves the algebraic sum of residual moments to maximum elastic moments at several nodal or grid points in simple or continuous structures. These moments are then equated to full plastic moments. The resulting equilibrium equations will give several possible collapse loads. The minimum value of such loads will then be considered as the final collapse load.

4.6.2.2 Symbols

$L_{1,2} = $ spans of main members

$C_3L_3 = $ spacings of main members across span

$M_\mathrm{p} = $ full plastic moment

$\bar{M}_\mathrm{p} = $ plastic moment from grid across span

$\bar{C}W = $ vehicular loading

$w = $ dead load/unit length

$C_1 = $ distance from the origin to the nearest load

$C_2 = $ spacings between any two loads

(For single concentrated, $C_2 = 0$)

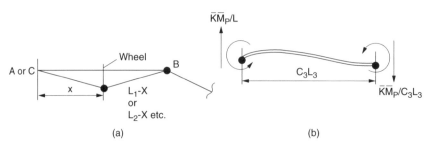

Figure 4.54. Cross grid: typical mechanisms

$K, K_1, \ldots = $ spring stiffness

$\quad\quad M_{ej} = $ maximum elastic moment at any zone of failure

$\quad\quad M_R = $ residual moment at any zone of failure.

4.6.3 Main analysis

$$M_p = M_e + M_R \tag{4.185}$$

Case A
Dead load alone

$$M_x = \frac{wL_{1,2}^2}{8}\bar{S} - \frac{4.125\bar{M}_p}{C_3L_3}\cdot x \quad \text{for } 0 \le x \le \frac{L_{1,2}}{4} \tag{4.186}$$

$$M_x = \frac{wL_{1,2}^2}{8}\bar{S} - \frac{\bar{M}_pL_{1,2}}{8}\left[\frac{x}{L_{1,2}} + \frac{8}{C_3L_3}\right] \quad \text{for } \frac{L_{1,2}}{4} \le x \le \frac{L_{1,2}}{2} \tag{4.187}$$

$$M_x = \frac{wL_{1,2}^2}{8}\bar{S} + \frac{3\bar{M}_p}{C_3L_3}[1.291x - L_{1,2}] \quad \text{for } \frac{L_{1,2}}{2} \le x \le \frac{3L_{1,2}}{4} \tag{4.188}$$

$$M_x = \frac{wL_{1,2}^2\bar{S}}{8} + \frac{6\bar{M}_p}{C_3L_3}[1.3125x - L_{1,2}] \quad \text{for } \frac{3L_{1,2}}{4} \le x \le L_{1,2} \tag{4.189}$$

Case B
Vehicular loading

$$M_x = \frac{P_x}{8}\bar{S}_1 \quad \text{for } 0 \le x \le C_1L_{1,2} \tag{4.190}$$

$$M_x = \frac{P_x}{8}\bar{S}_1 + \frac{C_1}{2}\cdot WL_{1,2} \quad \text{for } C_1L_{1,2} \le x \le (C_1 + C_2)L_{1,2} \tag{4.191}$$

$$M_x = \frac{P_x}{8}\cdot\bar{S}_1 + \frac{W}{2}L_{1,2}(2C_1 + C_2)$$

$$\text{for } (C_1 + C_2)L_{1,2} \le x \le L_{1,2} \tag{4.192}$$

where

$$\bar{S} = 3\left(\frac{x}{L}\right) + 4\left(\frac{x}{L}\right)^2 \tag{4.193}$$

$$\bar{S}_1 = 3C_1^2C_2 + 3C_1C_2^2 + 2C_1^3 + C_2^3 - 5(2C_1 + C_2)$$

$$C_1 = \frac{-C_2 + \sqrt{1.334 - C_2^2}}{2}$$

Plastic moment formula (non-dimensional)

$$\frac{wL_{1,2}^2}{2M_p}[C_1 - C_1^2] - \frac{\bar{M}_p L_{1,2}}{M_p C_3 L_3}(1 + 2C_1)$$

$$+ \frac{WL_{1,2}}{8M_p}\bar{S}_1 + \frac{C_1}{2}\left(\frac{4}{3} - C_2^2\right) = 1 + C_1 \qquad (4.194)$$

$$M_e = \frac{wL_{1,2}^2}{8}[3C_1 - 4C_1^2] - \frac{\bar{M}_p \cdot L_{1,2}}{C_3 L_3}\left[\frac{C_1}{8} + 1\right] \qquad (4.195)$$

Numerical example

$$w = 15\,\text{kN/m from beam and slab}$$

$$C_2 = 0.1 \quad \text{for } K_1 = K_2 \ldots \bar{K} = 4$$

$$C_3 = \frac{1}{8}$$

$$\bar{M}_p = 410\,\text{kNm} \quad \text{(computed)}$$

$$M_p = 5100\,\text{kNm}$$

W is obtained from Eq. (4.194) by substituting the above values. Results are plotted and $W = 2197\,\text{kN}$ at 8.8 m is the collapse load and its point of application, i.e. failure zone, is 8.8 m from the left support as shown in Fig. 4.55.

Thus this will determine what type of vehicles are permitted to cross a typical bridge or what sizes of bridge components are necessary for typical vehicular loadings.

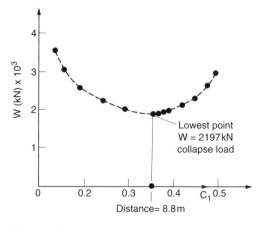

Figure 4.55. $W - C_1$ graph

4.7 Finite element analysis of bridge decks

The finite element method employs an assemblage of discrete two- or three-dimensional members. The elements are connected at nodal points which possess an appropriate number of degrees of freedom. The Appendix indicates many shapes of element. Material properties, often more than one, can be incorporated which will truly represent various components of the bridge deck. Static and dynamic problems can be easily tackled by this single method, thus making it the most powerful technique.

The bridge is idealized as an assemblage of discrete parts, known as elements. The next stage is to evaluate the element properties. This is followed by the structural analysis of the element assemblage. Forces, stresses, moments, displacements, strains, etc. are calculated. Where a computer program is interactive, those results are plotted which will show the exact behaviour of various components of the bridge.

Again, the purpose of the analysis using finite element methods has to be clearly established. Where dynamic problems are investigated, the results must provide displacements, velocities, accelerations, frequencies, etc. Where plasticity and material/geometrical non-linearity is to be investigated, the analysis should be thoroughly justified. Material failure criteria must be included together with the solution and acceleration procedures. A convergence criterion should be established. The Appendix gives a thorough study of the finite element method. A reference is made to various techniques. Normally, suitable graphical techniques are associated with any finite element program package. These are to be used to interpret meaningful results. Typical finite element meshes for bridge decks are shown in Figs 4.56 to 4.61.

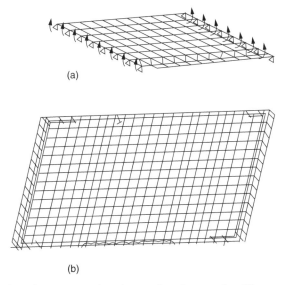

(a)

(b)

Figure 4.56. Finite element mesh scheme for the steel grillage

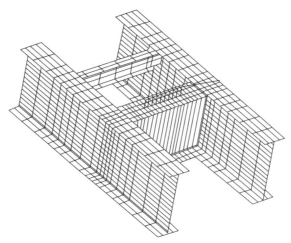

Figure 4.57. Steel girder bridge with cross-beams

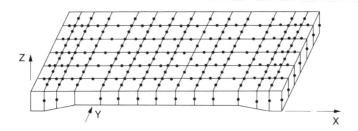

Figure 4.58. Finite element mesh scheme for the deck slab

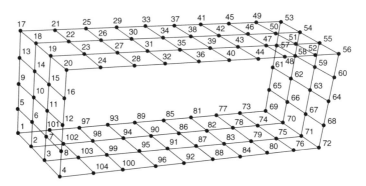

Figure 4.59. Finite element mesh scheme of a box culvert

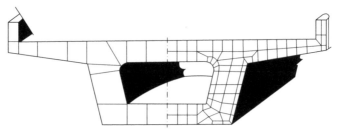

Figure 4.60. Finite element mesh scheme for a 3-D box girder

Figure 4.61. Finite element mesh (FEA) of a box girder

4.8 The finite strip method (Professor Cheung method)

This is a hybrid method which combines series of solutions for orthotropic plates with the finite element method. Both slabs and cellular decks can be analysed. The deck is divided into discrete longitudinal strips spanning between supports. Simple displacement interpolation functions may be used to represent displacement fields within and between individual strips. The total potential of a strip (strain energy + potential energy) is evaluated. Simulating boundary conditions, the total energy of the deck is evaluated from the sum of the values for the individual strips. The principle of minimum potential energy is applied in order to obtain particular harmonics. In reality it is a 'direct stiffness harmonic analysis'. The reader is directed to the relevant bibliography for an in-depth study. Here the work of various researchers is summarized.

4.8.1 Summary of the analysis

Figures 4.62 and 4.63 show the bridge deck is divided into series of strips for a simply supported deck. The displacement polynomial of the third degree is written as

$$
\omega(x,y) = \sum_{n=1}^{\infty} \left[\left(1 - \frac{3y^2}{b^2} + \frac{2y^3}{b^3} \right) \omega_{in} + \left(y - \frac{2y^2}{b} + \frac{y^2}{b^2} \right) \theta_{in} \right.
$$

$$
\left. + \left(\frac{3y^2}{b^2} - \frac{2y^3}{b^3} \right) \omega_{jn} + \left(\frac{y^3}{b^2} - \frac{y^2}{b} \right) \theta_{jn} \right] \sin \frac{n\pi x}{L} \qquad (4.196)
$$

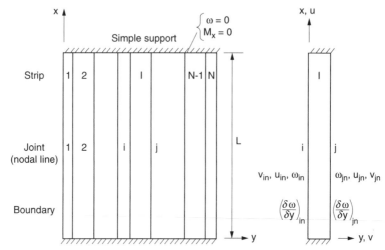

Figure 4.62. Finite strip method

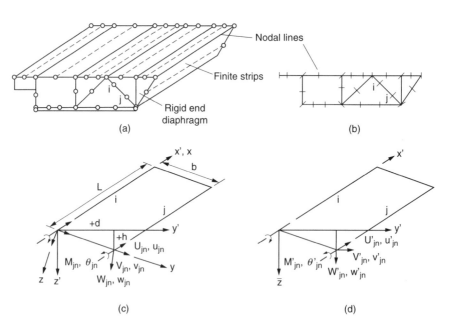

*Figure 4.63. Local and global forces and displacements. (a) Division of box deck.
(b) Division of cross-section. (c) Local forces and displacements. (d) Global
forces and displacements (courtesy: Professor Cheung, University of Hong Kong
(1996))*

where displacement amplitudes are given as

$$w_i = \sum_{n=1}^{\infty} w_{in} \sin \frac{n\pi x}{L}$$

$$\theta_i = \sum_{n=1}^{\infty} \theta_{in} \sin \frac{n\pi x}{L} \quad \text{etc.} \tag{4.197}$$

The total potential for the strip I is given by

$$U_T = U_s + U_p \tag{4.198}$$

Where strain energy U_s and potential energy U_p are written as

$$U_s = \frac{1}{2} \int_0^L \int_0^b \left(-M_x \frac{\partial^2 w}{\partial x^2} - M_y \frac{\partial^2 w}{\partial y^2} + 2M_{xy} \frac{\partial^2 w}{\partial x\, y} \right) dx\, dy \tag{4.199}$$

$(q^I(x, y) = \text{loading on strip})$

$$U_p = -\int_0^L \int_0^b q^I(x, y) w\, , dx\, dy \tag{4.200}$$

$$U_T = \frac{1}{2} \int_0^L \int_0^b \{M\}^T \{\phi^I\}\, dx\, dy$$

$$\qquad - \int_0^L \int_0^b q^I(x, y) \{w_{bn}^I\} [C_b^I]^T \sin \alpha_n x\, dx\, dy \tag{4.201}$$

For the orthotropic plate deck:

$$\{M\} = \left\{ \begin{array}{c} M_x \\ M_y \\ M_{xy} \end{array} \right\} = \begin{bmatrix} D_x & D_1 & 0 \\ D_2 & D_y & 0 \\ 0 & 0 & \dfrac{D_{xy}}{2} \end{bmatrix} \left\{ \begin{array}{c} -\dfrac{\partial^2 w}{\partial x^2} \\[2mm] -\dfrac{\partial^2 w}{\partial y^2} \\[2mm] 2\dfrac{\partial^2 w}{\partial x\, \partial y} \end{array} \right\} = [D_b^I]\{\phi^I\} \tag{4.202}$$

where

$$w_{bn}^I = \left\{ \begin{array}{c} w_{in} \\ \theta_{in} \\ w_{jn} \\ \theta_{jn} \end{array} \right\}$$

$$[C_b^I] = \begin{Bmatrix} C_{0i} \\ C_{1i} \\ C_{0j} \\ C_{1j} \end{Bmatrix} \tag{4.203}$$

For a particular harmonic

$$\sum_{I=1}^{N} \int_0^L \int_0^b [B_{bn}^I]^T [D_b^I][B_{bn}^I] \, dx \, dy \{w_{bn}^I\}$$

$$= \int_0^L \int_0^b [C_b^I]^T q^I(x, y) \, dx \, dy \tag{4.204}$$

or

$$\sum_{I=0}^{N} [k_{bn}^I]\{w_{bn}^I\} = \{F_{bn}^I\}$$

A set of simultaneous linear equations relates the unknown nodal line displacement amplitude $\{w_{bn}\}$ to the applied loading $q(x, y)$. The same work can be extended to a 3-D analysis.

The curvature $\{\phi^I\}$ is given by

$$\{\phi^I\} = \sum_{n=1}^{\infty} [B_{bn}^I \{w_{bn}^I\}] \tag{4.205}$$

Total discrete strips are summed up for the deck as

$$\sum_{I=1}^{N} \left[\sum_{n=1}^{\infty} \right] \int_0^L \int_0^b [B_{bn}^I]^T [D_b^I][B_{bn}^I] \, dx \, dy \{w_{bn}^I\}$$

$$- \sum_{n=1}^{\infty} \int_0^L \int_0^b [C_b^I]^T q^I(x, y) \sin \alpha_n x \tag{4.206}$$

$\{\phi^I\}$ is given by Eq. (4.205) when

$$[B_{bn}^I] = \begin{bmatrix} (\alpha_n^2 C_{0j} \sin \alpha_n x)(\alpha_n^2 C_{1j} \sin \alpha_n x)(\alpha_n^2 C_{0j} \sin \alpha_n N)(\alpha_n^2 C_{1j} \sin \alpha_n x) \\ (-C_{0i}'' \sin \alpha_n x)(-C_{1i}'' \sin \alpha_n x)(-C_{0j} \sin \alpha_n x)(-C_{1j} \sin \alpha_n x) \\ (\alpha_n C_{0i}' \cos \alpha_n x)(\alpha_n C_{1i}' \cos \alpha_n x)(\alpha_n C_{0j}' \cos \alpha_n x)(\alpha_n C_{1j}' \cos \alpha_n x) \end{bmatrix}$$

$$\tag{4.207}$$

$$C' = \frac{dC}{dy} \quad \text{and} \quad C'' = \frac{d^2C}{dy^2}$$

The stiffness and load matrices are given in Tables 4.5 to 4.8.

Table 4.5. Force matrices for strip in bending with in-plane forces (with one ANL)

(1) Concentrated load

$$\{F_n\} = \left\{ \begin{array}{c} 1 - \dfrac{3y_0^2}{b^2} + 2\,\dfrac{y_0^3}{b^3} \\[2ex] y_0 - \dfrac{2y_0^2}{b} + \dfrac{y_0^3}{b^2} \\[2ex] \dfrac{3y_0^2}{b^2} - \dfrac{2y_0^3}{b^3} \\[2ex] \dfrac{y_0^3}{b^2} - \dfrac{y_0^2}{b} \end{array} \right\} P \sin \alpha_n x_0$$

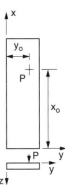

(2) Patch load

$$\{F_n\} = \left\{ \begin{array}{c} (y_2 - y_1) - \dfrac{(y_2 - y_1)^3}{b^2} + \dfrac{(y_2 - y_1)^4}{2b^3} \\[2ex] \dfrac{(y_2 - y_1)^2}{2} - \dfrac{2(y_2 - y_1)^3}{3b} + \dfrac{(y_2 - y_1)^4}{4b^2} \\[2ex] \dfrac{(y_2 - y_1)^3}{b^2} - \dfrac{(y_2 - y_1)^4}{2b^3} \\[2ex] \dfrac{(y_2 - y_1)^4}{4b^2} - \dfrac{(y_2 - y_1)^3}{3b} \end{array} \right\} \dfrac{q}{\alpha_n} (\cos \alpha_n x_1 - \cos \alpha_n x_2)$$

$$k_1 = \frac{7}{6}\frac{L}{b} A + \frac{1}{15} Lb\alpha_n^2 D$$

$$k_2 = \frac{1}{4} L\alpha_n C - \frac{1}{4} L\alpha_n D$$

$$k_3 = -\frac{4}{3}\frac{L}{b} A + \frac{1}{30} Lb\alpha_n^2 D$$

$$k_4 = \frac{1}{3} L\alpha_n C + \frac{1}{3} L\alpha_n D$$

$$k_5 = \frac{1}{6}\frac{L}{b} A - \frac{1}{60} Lb\alpha_n^2 D$$

$$k_6 = -\frac{1}{12} L\alpha_n C - \frac{1}{12} L\alpha_n D$$

$$k_7 = \frac{1}{15} Lb\alpha_n^2 B + \frac{7}{6}\frac{L}{b} D$$

$$k_8 = -k_4$$

$$k_9 = \frac{1}{30} Lb\alpha_n^2 B - \frac{4}{3}\frac{L}{b} D$$

Continued

Table 4.5. *Continued*

$$k_{10} = -\frac{1}{60} Lb\alpha_n^2 B \frac{1}{6}\frac{L}{b} D$$

$$k_{11} = \frac{8}{3}\frac{L}{b} A + \frac{4}{15} Lb\alpha_n^2 D$$

$$k_{12} = \frac{4}{15} Lb\alpha_n^2 B + \frac{8}{3}\frac{L}{b} D$$

where

$$A = \frac{E_y}{1 - \nu_x\nu_y}$$

$$B = \frac{E_x}{1 - \nu_x\nu_y}$$

$$C = \nu_y A = \nu_x B$$

$$D = G_{xy}$$

Table 4.6. *Stiffness matrix for strip in bending*

Third-order polynomial

$$[k_n] = \begin{bmatrix} k_1 & \text{symmetrical} & & \\ k_3 & k_2 & & \\ k_4 & k_5 & k_1 & \\ k_5 & k_6 & k_3 & k_2 \end{bmatrix}$$

where

$$k_1 = 6\frac{LD_y}{b^3} + \frac{13}{70} Lb\alpha_n^4 D_x + \frac{6}{5}\frac{L}{b}\alpha_n^2 D_{xy} + \frac{6}{5}\frac{L}{b}\alpha_n^2 D_1$$

$$k_2 = 2\frac{LD_y}{b} + \frac{1}{210} Lb^3\alpha_n^4 D_x + \frac{2}{15} Lb\alpha_n^2 D_{xy} + \frac{2}{15} Lb\alpha_n^2 D_1$$

$$k_3 = 3\frac{LD_y}{b^2} + \frac{11}{420} Lb^2\alpha_n^4 D_x + \frac{1}{10} L\alpha_n^2 D_{xy} + \frac{3}{5} L\alpha_n^2 D_1$$

$$k_4 = 6\frac{LD_y}{b^3} + \frac{9}{140} Lb\alpha_n^4 D_x - \frac{6}{5} L\alpha_n^2 D_{xy} - \frac{6}{5} L\frac{\alpha_n^2}{b} D_1$$

$$k_5 = -3\frac{LD_y}{b^2} + \frac{13}{840} Lb^2\alpha_n^4 D_x - \frac{1}{10} L\alpha_n^2 D_{xy} - \frac{9}{10}\alpha_n^2 D_1$$

$$k_6 = \frac{L}{b} D_y - \frac{1}{280} Lb^3\alpha_n^4 D_x - \frac{1}{30} Lb\alpha_n^2 D_{xy} - \frac{1}{30} Lb\alpha_n^2 D_1$$

Continued

Table 4.6. Continued

With one auxiliary nodal line

$$[k_n] = \begin{bmatrix} k_1 & & & & & \\ k_2 & k_7 & & & & \\ k_3 & k_8 & k_{11} & \text{symmetrical} & & \\ k_4 & k_9 & 0 & k_{12} & & \\ k_5 & -k_6 & k_3 & -k_4 & k_1 & \\ k_6 & k_{10} & -k_8 & k_9 & -k_2 & k_7 \end{bmatrix}$$

where

$$k_1 = \frac{5092}{70} \frac{LD_y}{b^3} + \frac{523}{6930} Lb\alpha_n^4 D_x + \frac{278}{105} \frac{L}{b} \alpha_n^2 D_{xy} + \frac{278}{210} \frac{L}{b} \alpha_n^2 D_1$$

$$k_2 = \frac{1138}{70} \frac{LD_y}{b^2} + \frac{19}{4620} Lb^2\alpha_n^4 D_x + \frac{13}{210} L\alpha_n^2 D_{xy} + \frac{59}{210} L\alpha_n^2 D_1$$

$$k_3 = -\frac{512}{10} \frac{LD_y}{b^3} + \frac{4}{126} Lb^2\alpha_n^4 D_x - \frac{256}{105} \frac{L}{b} \alpha_n^2 D_{xy} - \frac{256}{210} \frac{L}{b} \alpha_n^2 D_1$$

$$k_4 = \frac{384}{14} \frac{LD_y}{b^2} - \frac{8}{1386} Lb^2\alpha_n^4 D_x + \frac{8}{21} L\alpha_n^2 D_{xy} + \frac{4}{21} L\alpha_n^2 D_1$$

$$k_5 = -\frac{1508}{70} \frac{LD_y}{b^3} + \frac{131}{13\,860} Lb\alpha_n^4 D_x - \frac{22}{105} \frac{L}{b} \alpha_n^2 D_{xy} - \frac{22}{210} \frac{L}{b} \alpha_n^2 D_1$$

$$k_6 = \frac{242}{70} \frac{LD_y}{b^2} - \frac{29}{27\,720} Lb^2\alpha_n^4 D_x - \frac{1}{70} L\alpha_n^2 D_{xy} - \frac{1}{140} L\alpha_n^2 D_1$$

$$k_7 = \frac{166}{35} \frac{LD_y}{b} + \frac{1}{3465} Lb^3\alpha_n^4 D_x + \frac{2}{45} Lb\alpha_n^2 D_{xy} + \frac{1}{45} Lb\alpha_n^2 D_1$$

$$k_8 = -\frac{64}{5} \frac{LD_y}{b^2} + \frac{1}{315} Lb^2\alpha_n^4 D_x - \frac{8}{105} L\alpha_n^2 D_{xy} - \frac{4}{105} L\alpha_n^2 D_1$$

$$k_9 = \frac{32}{7} \frac{LD_y}{b} - \frac{1}{2310} Lb^3\alpha_n^4 D_x - \frac{4}{315} Lb\alpha_n^2 D_{xy} - \frac{2}{315} Lb\alpha_n^2 D_1$$

$$k_{10} = \frac{19}{35} \frac{LD_y}{b} - \frac{1}{9240} Lb^3\alpha_n^4 D_x - \frac{1}{126} Lb\alpha_n^2 D_{xy} - \frac{1}{252} Lb\alpha_n^2 D_1$$

$$k_{11} = \frac{512}{5} \frac{LD_y}{b^3} + \frac{64}{315} Lb\alpha_n^4 D_x + \frac{512}{105} \frac{L}{b} \alpha_n^2 D_{xy} + \frac{256}{210} \frac{L}{b} \alpha_n^2 D_1$$

$$k_{12} = \frac{128}{7} \frac{LD_y}{b} + \frac{16}{3465} Lb^3\alpha_n^4 D_x + \frac{128}{315} Lb\alpha_n^2 D_{xy} + \frac{64}{315} Lb\alpha_n^2 D_1$$

Table 4.7. Force matrices for strip with one ANL

(1) Concentrated load

$$
\{F_{bn}^I\} = \begin{Bmatrix}
1 - 23\,\dfrac{y_0^2}{b^2} + 66\,\dfrac{y_0^3}{b^3} - 68\,\dfrac{y_0^4}{b^4} + 24\,\dfrac{y_0^5}{b^5} \\[2mm]
y_0 - 6\,\dfrac{y_0^2}{b} + 13\,\dfrac{y_0^3}{b^2} - 12\,\dfrac{y_0^4}{b^3} + 4\,\dfrac{y_0^5}{b^4} \\[2mm]
16\,\dfrac{y_0^2}{b^2} - 32\,\dfrac{y_0^3}{b^3} + 16\,\dfrac{y_0^4}{b^4} \\[2mm]
-8\,\dfrac{y_0^2}{b} + 32\,\dfrac{y_0^3}{b^2} - 40\,\dfrac{y_0^4}{b^3} + 16\,\dfrac{y_0^5}{b^4} \\[2mm]
7\,\dfrac{y_0^2}{b^2} - 34\,\dfrac{y_0^3}{b^3} + 52\,\dfrac{y_0^4}{b^4} - 24\,\dfrac{y_0^5}{b^5} \\[2mm]
-\dfrac{y_0^2}{b} + 5\,\dfrac{y_0^3}{b^2} - 8\,\dfrac{y_0^4}{b^3} + 4\,\dfrac{y_0^5}{b^4}
\end{Bmatrix}
$$

(2) Patch load

$$
\{F_{bn}^I\} = \begin{Bmatrix}
\bar{y} - 23\,\dfrac{\bar{y}^3}{3b^2} + \dfrac{33}{2}\,\dfrac{\bar{y}^4}{b^3} + \dfrac{68}{5}\,\dfrac{\bar{y}^5}{b^4} + 4\,\dfrac{\bar{y}^6}{b^5} \\[2mm]
\dfrac{\bar{y}^2}{2} - \dfrac{2\bar{y}^3}{b} + \dfrac{13}{4}\,\dfrac{\bar{y}^4}{b^2} - \dfrac{12}{5}\,\dfrac{\bar{y}^5}{b^3} + \dfrac{2}{3}\,\dfrac{\bar{y}^6}{b^4} \\[2mm]
\dfrac{16\bar{y}^3}{3b^2} - 8\,\dfrac{\bar{y}^4}{b^3} + \dfrac{16}{5}\,\dfrac{\bar{y}^5}{b^4} \\[2mm]
-\dfrac{8}{3}\,\dfrac{\bar{y}^3}{b} + 8\,\dfrac{\bar{y}^4}{b^2} - \dfrac{8\bar{y}^5}{b^3} + \dfrac{8}{3}\,\dfrac{\bar{y}^6}{b^4} \\[2mm]
\dfrac{7}{3}\,\dfrac{\bar{y}^3}{b^2} - \dfrac{17}{2}\,\dfrac{\bar{y}^4}{b^3} + \dfrac{52}{5}\,\dfrac{\bar{y}^5}{b^4} - \dfrac{4\bar{y}^6}{b^5} \\[2mm]
-\dfrac{\bar{y}^3}{3b} + \dfrac{5}{4}\,\dfrac{\bar{y}^4}{b^2} - \dfrac{8}{5}\,\dfrac{\bar{y}^5}{b^3} + \dfrac{2}{3}\,\dfrac{\bar{y}^6}{b^4}
\end{Bmatrix} \dfrac{q}{\alpha_n}\,(\cos\alpha_n x_i - \cos\alpha_n x_j)
$$

where

$$\bar{y}^m = y_j^m - y_i^m$$

A typical example illustrates the finite strip method for a cellular bridge deck with local and global forces and displacements. Appropriate direction cosines are used for determining the local force system $\{F_n\}_L$ and the global force system $\{F_n\}_G$:

$$\underbrace{\{F_n\}_L}_{[K_n]\{\omega_n\}} = [R]^T \underbrace{\{F_n'\}_G}_{[K_n']\{\omega_n'\}} \tag{4.208}$$

$$R] = \begin{bmatrix} [R_i] & [0] \\ [0] & [R_j] \end{bmatrix}$$

Table 4.8. In-plane forces

(1) Concentrated load in y direction

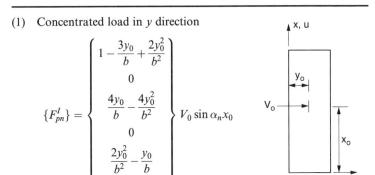

$$\{F_{pn}^I\} = \left\{\begin{array}{c} 1 - \dfrac{3y_0}{b} + \dfrac{2y_0^2}{b^2} \\[2mm] 0 \\[2mm] \dfrac{4y_0}{b} - \dfrac{4y_0^2}{b^2} \\[2mm] 0 \\[2mm] \dfrac{2y_0^2}{b^2} - \dfrac{y_0}{b} \\[2mm] 0 \end{array}\right\} V_0 \sin \alpha_n x_0$$

(2) Concentrated load in x direction

$$\{F_{pn}^I\} = \left\{\begin{array}{c} 0 \\[2mm] 1 - \dfrac{3y_0}{b} + 2\dfrac{y_0^2}{b^2} \\[2mm] 0 \\[2mm] \dfrac{4y_0}{b} - \dfrac{4y_0^2}{b^2} \\[2mm] 0 \\[2mm] -\dfrac{y_0}{b} + \dfrac{2y_0^2}{b^2} \end{array}\right\} U_0 \cos \alpha_n x_0$$

$$[R_i] = [R_j] = \begin{bmatrix} \dfrac{d}{b} & 0 & -\dfrac{h}{b} & 0 \\[2mm] 0 & 1 & 0 & 0 \\[2mm] \dfrac{h}{b} & 0 & \dfrac{d}{b} & 0 \\[2mm] 0 & 0 & 0 & 1 \end{bmatrix} \tag{4.209}$$

where $[R]$ is the matrix for the direction cosines; d and h are horizontal and vertical projections.

4.9 Methods of analysis – substructures
4.9.1 Introduction
The substructure is a supporting structure to the superstructure and its bearings. Its function is to transmit loads to the foundation. The major components of such structures are

- abutments
- piers or structures

An abutment supports an end span. It also resists, where possible, soil pressures from an embankment with and without vehicle loads from the roadway leading to the bridge. Typical substructure arrangements are shown in Fig. 4.64.

Piers

Piers are almost universally constructed of reinforced concrete. The three main types are:

(*i*)   leaf or plate/slab
(*ii*) portal
(*iii*) column or stanchions

(a)   Leaf

This is the simplest type of pier, which is essentially a reinforced concrete wall. It can be either pinned or fixed at the top or bottom, depending upon the chosen articulation for the bridge. Figure 4.64(a) shows such a leaf.

(b)   Portal

Portal frames are pleasing to the eye, especially if they incorporate cantilever sections at the ends. They are pinned and fixed to the foundations. They can be vertical or tapering legs as shown in Fig. 4.64(b).

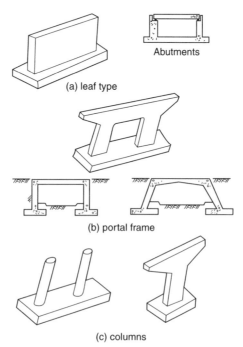

Figure 4.64. Types of pier

Columns or stanchions

Columns may be circular or rectangular in section (hollow or solid), and are ideal where maximum visibility is required. Columns are best used either singly or in pairs, and are particularly graceful in deep crossings.

Open or braced steel stanchions have been employed to replace solid concrete piers. Figure 4.64(c) shows two types of column supports.

These structures are analysed as independent walls, portals and columns. Any method described in the analysis of the bridge deck can be employed here for the abutments and piers. More details are given later in a special section on *Method of Design* giving case studies.

A flexibility method and frame formulae tables are very popular among designers. In this section these two methods have been given priority. In addition a stability analysis in some cases is needed to check the stability of portal frames and columns.

4.9.2 Analytical formulae

4.9.2.1   *Case A.   Moments of the two columns – piers fixed at the top of the footing*
(Note that the rotation of joint sign convention is $+\curvearrowright$ $\curvearrowleft(-)$.)

Consider a single portal (Fig. 4.65)

$$n = \frac{I_{AB}}{I_{AD}} \times \frac{h}{\ell} \qquad (4.210)$$

For PDH the width of columns and beams is the same, thus:

$$n = \frac{(h_b)^3}{(h_c)^3} \times \frac{h}{\ell}$$

h_b = overall depth of concrete in cap beam

h_c = overall dimension of column in the plane of the bent

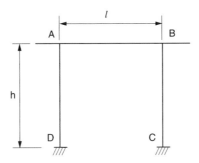

Figure 4.65. A single portal

Coefficients used:

$$\alpha = \frac{1}{n+2} \qquad \beta = \frac{n}{n+2} \qquad \gamma = \frac{1}{6n+1} \tag{4.211}$$

$$\delta = \frac{6n}{6n+1} \qquad \varepsilon = \frac{2n}{(n+2)(3n+2)} \qquad \theta = \frac{1}{(n+2)(3n+2)} \tag{4.212}$$

Note that $\varepsilon + \theta$ to be used only in double-bents.

In the formulas given below, the absolute values of the unbalanced moments of the fixed-end moments are to be substituted.

Considering Fig. 4.66(a)

$$|FEM|_{CANT} > |FEM|_{BEAM}$$

$$M_U = \text{unbalanced moment}$$

$$M = |FEM|_{CANT} - |FEM|_{BEAM}$$

$$M_{AB} = -M_{BA} = +FEM_{BEAM} + \beta M \tag{4.213}$$

$$M_{AD} = -M_{BC} = +2\alpha M \tag{4.214}$$

$$M_{DA} = -M_{CB} = +\alpha M \tag{4.215}$$

4.9.2.2   Case B.   Loads not symmetrical about centre-line of bent. Sidesway included
(*a*)   Based on Fig. 4.66(b):

$$M_{AB} = +FEM_{BEAM} + \frac{M}{2}(1 + \beta - \gamma) - \frac{M'}{2}(\beta - \delta) \tag{4.216}$$

$$M_{BA} = -FEM_{BEAM} - \frac{M}{2}(\beta - \delta) + \frac{M'}{2}(1 + \beta - \gamma) \tag{4.217}$$

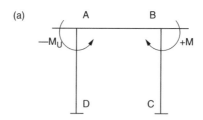

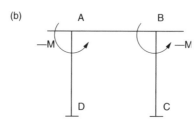

Figure 4.66. Single portal rotations: (a) piers fixed at top of footing; (b) unsymmetrical with sidesway included

$$M_{AD} = +\frac{M}{2}(1 - \beta + \gamma) + \frac{M'}{2}(\beta - \delta) \tag{4.218}$$

$$M_{BC} = +\frac{M}{2}(\beta - \delta) + \frac{M'}{2}(1 - \beta + \gamma) \tag{4.219}$$

$$M_{DA} = +\frac{M}{2}(\alpha - \gamma) - \frac{M'}{2}(\alpha + \gamma) \tag{4.220}$$

$$M_{CB} = -\frac{M}{2}(\alpha + \gamma) + \frac{M'}{2}(\alpha - \gamma) \tag{4.221}$$

$$M_{AB} = +\text{FEM}_{\text{BEAM}} + M(\beta + \varepsilon) + M'(\varepsilon) \tag{4.222}$$

$$M_{BA} = +\text{FEM}_{\text{BEAM}} + M(\varepsilon) + M'(\beta + \varepsilon) \tag{4.223}$$

$$M_{AD} = +2M(\varepsilon + \theta) - M'(\varepsilon) \tag{4.224}$$

$$M_{BC} = -M(\varepsilon) + 2M'(\varepsilon + \theta) \tag{4.225}$$

$$M_{DA} = \frac{M_{AD}}{2}$$

$$M_{CB} = \frac{M_{BC}}{2}$$

(b) Based on Fig. 4.67:

$$M_{AB} = +\text{FEM}_{\text{BEAM}} + M(\beta + \varepsilon) + M'(\varepsilon) \tag{4.226}$$

$$M_{BA} = -\text{FEM}_{\text{BEAM}} + M(\varepsilon) - M'(\beta + \varepsilon) \tag{4.227}$$

$$M_{AD} = +2M(\varepsilon + \theta) + M'(\varepsilon) \tag{4.228}$$

$$M_{BC} = -M(\varepsilon) - 2M'(\varepsilon + \theta) \tag{4.229}$$

$$M_{DA} = \frac{M_{AD}}{2}$$

$$M_{CB} = \frac{M_{BC}}{2} \tag{4.230}$$

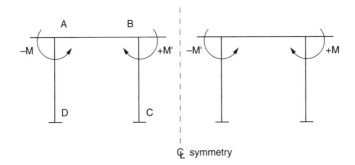

Figure 4.67. Twin portal pier double bent

4.9.2.3 Case C.   Live load – single-bent pier

In general, only two positions of live load need to be investigated (Fig. 4.68): (a) with live load as close as possible to the centre-line to obtain maximum moment at the centre-line of the cap beam; and (b) as eccentric as possible to obtain maximum moment at the top of columns and maximum sidesway in the structure.

(a)   *Symmetrical loads about centre-line of pier*

$$\left.\begin{array}{l} M_{AB} = -M_{BA} = +\text{FEM}_{\text{BEAM}} - \beta M \\[2mm] M_{AD} = -M_{BC} = -2\alpha M \\[2mm] M_{DA} = -M_{CB} = -\alpha M \end{array}\right\} \tag{4.231}$$

(b)   *Maximum eccentricity of live load. Sidesway included*

$$M_{AB} = +\text{FEM}_{\text{BEAM}} - \frac{M_1}{2}(1 + \beta - \gamma) - \frac{M_1'}{2}(\beta - \delta) \tag{4.232}$$

$$M_{BA} = -\text{FEM}_{\text{BEAM}} + \frac{M_1}{2}(\beta - \delta) + \frac{M_1'}{2}(1 + \beta - \delta) \tag{4.233}$$

$$M_{BC} = -\frac{M_1}{2}(\beta - \delta) + \frac{M_1'}{2}(1 - \beta + \gamma) \tag{4.234}$$

$$M_{AD} = -\frac{M_1}{2}(1 - \beta + \gamma) + \frac{M_1'}{2}(\beta - \delta) \tag{4.235}$$

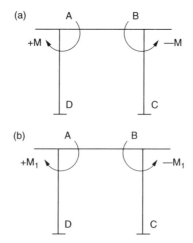

Figure 4.68. A single portal under live load: (a) symmetric case; (b) unsymmetric case

$$M_{CB} = +\frac{M_1}{2}(\alpha + \gamma) + \frac{M_1'}{2}(\alpha - \gamma) \qquad (4.236)$$

$$M_{DA} = -\frac{M_1}{2}(\alpha - \gamma) - \frac{M_1'}{2}(\alpha + \gamma) \qquad (4.237)$$

4.9.2.4   Case D.   Live load – double-bent piers with superstructure preventing differential sidesway

In general, three positions of live load need be investigated.

(a) Loads symmetrical about centre-line of a bent causing maximum moment at centre-line of cap beam

Although the loads are placed symmetrical about the centre-line of bent ①
(Fig. 4.69), the reactions will not be symmetrical because of the continuity in
the deck slab. Both bents will be subjected to sidesway motion since the superstructure prevents any differential sidesway between the two bents. For most
cases, the effect of sidesway can be neglected. The solution for the case in
which it is desired to include the sidesway corrections can be obtained either
by moment distribution or by combining the solution already given, taking
into account that each one of the bents will take half the total sidesway present.

Solution neglecting sidesway (Fig. 4.70):

$$M_{AB} = +\text{FEM}_{\text{BEAM}} - M(\beta + \varepsilon) + M'(\varepsilon) \qquad (4.238)$$

$$M_{BA} = -\text{FEM}_{\text{BEAM}} - M(\varepsilon) + M'(\beta + \varepsilon) \qquad (4.239)$$

$$M_{AD} = -2M(\varepsilon + \theta) - M'(\varepsilon) \qquad (4.240)$$

$$M_{BC} = +M(\varepsilon) + 2M'(\varepsilon + \theta) \qquad (4.241)$$

$$M_{DA} = \frac{M_{AD}}{2}$$

$$M_{CB} = \frac{M_{BC}}{2} \qquad (4.241a)$$

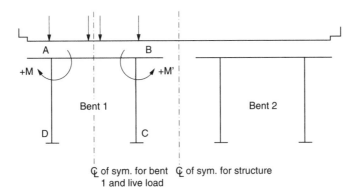

Figure 4.69. Double bent – live load case (a)

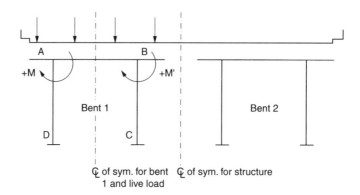

Figure 4.70. Double bent – live load case (b)

(b) *Loads symmetrical about centre-line of bent ① with one truck or lane load as close as possible to the kerb (2 ft normal)*

The same consideration regarding sidesway and reactions can be made for this case as in Case D(a).

Solution neglecting sidesway (Fig. 4.70):

$$M_{AB} = +\text{FEM}_{\text{BEAM}} - M(\beta - \varepsilon) - M'(\varepsilon) \qquad (4.242)$$

$$M_{BA} = -\text{FEM}_{\text{BEAM}} - M(\varepsilon) - M'(\beta + \varepsilon) \qquad (4.243)$$

$$M_{AD} = -2M(\varepsilon + \theta) + M'(\varepsilon) \qquad (4.244)$$

$$M_{BC} = +M(\varepsilon) - 2M'(\varepsilon + \theta) \qquad (4.245)$$

$$M_{DA} = \frac{M_{AD}}{2}$$

$$M_{CB} = \frac{M_{BC}}{2} \qquad (4.245a)$$

(c) *Live load symmetrical about centre-line of stringer supported by interior cantilever*

For this case the horizontal shear at the top of the columns in bent ① is of opposite sign to the one in bent ② (Fig. 4.71), therefore the net shear causing sidesway has an even smaller value than in Case D(a) and D(b) and can be neglected.

The formulae are the same as in Case D(b).

4.9.2.5 Wind

For all practical purposes, the wind on the substructure and the frame effect under the reactions from each one of the stringers, can be neglected. The effect of the eccentricity of the wind force will be taken into account to decrease or increase the reaction in the columns (Fig. 4.72).

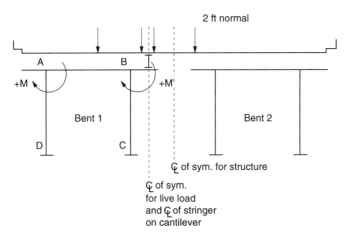

Figure 4.71. Double bent – live load case (c)

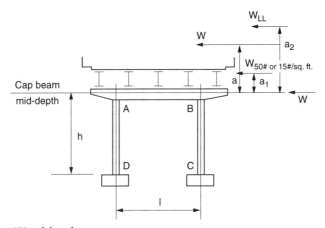

Figure 4.72. Wind load

The general equation is:

$$(\Delta \text{ reaction})_A = -(\Delta \text{ reaction})_B = \frac{W \times a}{\ell} \tag{4.246}$$

where

$\quad W$ = wind on dead load and/or wind on live load

$\quad a$ = distance from centre-line of cap beam to line of action of W

$$M_{AD} = M_{BC} = -Wh \times \frac{\delta}{4}$$

$$M_{CB} = M_{DA} = -Wh\left(\frac{\delta}{4} + \frac{\gamma}{2}\right)$$

$$M_{AB} = -M_{AD}$$

$$M_{BA} = -M_{BC}$$

4.9.2.6 Shrinkage
Referring to Fig. 4.73:

$$M = \frac{6EI\Delta}{h^2}$$

in which

$$\Delta = \frac{\ell}{2} \times 0.0002 = 0.0001 \times \ell$$

$$\therefore \quad M = 21.6 \times \frac{b_c(h_c)^3}{h^2} \times \ell$$

(for Class 'A' concrete) in ft kips substituting all values in feet, where b_c = width of columns and h_c = overall dimension of column in the plane of the bent:

$$M_{AB} = -M_{BA} = -\beta M$$

$$M_{AD} = -M_{BC} = +\beta M$$

$$M_{DA} = -M_{CB} = +M(1 - \alpha)$$

4.9.2.7 Example (4.19)   British practice
A bridge bent is subjected to reactions from an HA-type loading in the form shown in Fig. 4.74. A 6 m walkway is provided at position C with a worst case loading of 100 kN at the tip of the cantilever. The HA loading calculated for the portal or bent is 10 kN/m with 100 kN as a knife-edge load. Using the flexibility method draw the final bending moment diagram indicating various values.

Take E to be constant, $I_1 = I_3$, and $I_2 = 2I_1$:

$$f_{11} = \frac{1}{3}(10)(10)^2 + \frac{20(10)^2}{2} + \frac{10(10)^2}{3} = \frac{5000}{3}$$

$$m_{0(KEL)} = \frac{Pab}{2} = 375 \text{ kNm}$$

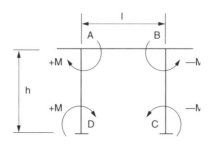

Figure 4.73. Moments due to shrinkage

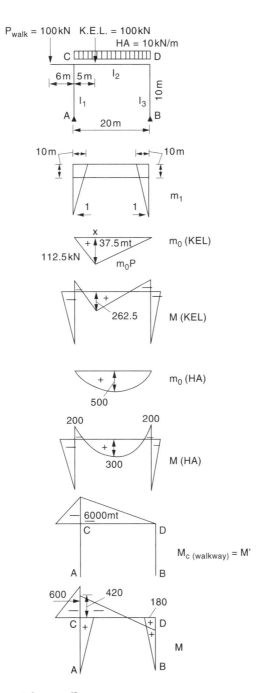

Figure 4.74. A bent with a walkway

$$D_{10_{(KEL)}} = \frac{1}{2} \times \frac{20}{2} \times 375 \times 10 = 18\,750\,\text{kNm}^3$$

$$X_1 = \frac{-D_{10_{(KEL)}}}{f_{11}} = -11.25\,\text{kN}$$

$$M_C = M_D = 0 + m_1 X_1 = 0 + (-112.5) = -112.5\,\text{kNm}$$

$$M_{x_{(KEL)}} = +262.5\,\text{kNm}$$

$$m_{0_{(HA)}} = \frac{100 \times 20^2}{8} = 500\,\text{kNm}$$

$$D_{10_{(HA)}} = \frac{2}{3} \times \frac{20}{2} \times 500 \times 10 = \frac{10^5}{3}$$

$$X_1 = -\frac{10^5}{3}$$

$$M_C = M_D = 0 + m_1 X_1 = 0 + 100(-2) = -200\,\text{kNm}$$

$$M_{xm} = 500 - 200 = 300\,\text{kNm}$$

$$M_{C_{(walkway)}} = M'_C = 100 \times 6 = -600\,\text{kNm}$$

$$D'_{10} = -20 \times 10 \times \frac{600}{2} \times 2 = -3 \times 10^4\,\text{kNm}$$

$$X_1 = +18\,\text{kN}$$

$$M_C = -420\,\text{kNm}$$

$$M_D = +180\,\text{kNm}$$

4.9.3 Analytical examples

4.9.3.1 Example (4.20)

A V-type portal supports a load of 100 kN from the deck of a bridge. The wind load of 20 kN/m acts horizontally on this portal as shown in Fig. 4.75. Using the flexibility method of analysis, draw bending moment diagrams for both loadings separately. Take EI as constant and calculate final moments:

$$f_{11} = \int \frac{m_1^2\,ds}{EI} = 2 \times 4 \times 1 \times 1 + 2(3.36) \times 1 \times 1 = 14.92$$

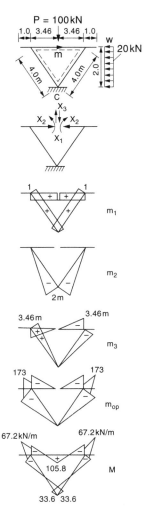

Figure 4.75. Loading and wind load on a V-type portal support

Similarly:

$$f_{22} = 10.67$$

$$f_{33} = 59.82$$

$$f_{12} = -8$$

$$f_{13} = f_{31} = 0$$

$$f_{23} = f_{32} = 0$$

(i)   For the 100 kN load

$$D_{10} = \int \frac{m_1 m_0}{EI}\, ds = -1292$$

$$D_{20} = +462$$

$$D_{30} = 0$$

$$\begin{bmatrix} f_{11} & f_{12} & f_{13} \\ f_{21} & f_{22} & f_{23} \\ f_{31} & f_{32} & f_{33} \end{bmatrix} \begin{Bmatrix} X_1 \\ X_2 \\ X_3 \end{Bmatrix} = -\begin{Bmatrix} -1292 \\ +462 \\ 0 \end{Bmatrix}$$

The matrix reduces to

$$\begin{bmatrix} f_{11} & f_{12} \\ f_{21} & f_{22} \end{bmatrix} \begin{Bmatrix} X_1 \\ X_2 \end{Bmatrix} = -\begin{Bmatrix} 1292 \\ +462 \end{Bmatrix}$$

or

$$\begin{bmatrix} 14.92 & -8 \\ -8 & 10.67 \end{bmatrix} \begin{Bmatrix} X_1 \\ X_2 \end{Bmatrix} = \begin{Bmatrix} 1292 \\ -462 \end{Bmatrix}$$

$$X_1 = 105.8 \text{ Knm}$$

$$X_2 = 36.1 \text{ kN}$$

$$M = m_0 + m_1 X_1 + m_2 X_2 + m_3 X_3$$

$$M_A = -173 + 105.8 + 0 + 0 = -67.2 \text{ kNm}$$

$$M_B = -67.2 \text{ kNm}$$

$$M_C = +33.6 \text{ kNm}$$

$$M_m = 0 + 105.8 + 0 + 0 = -67.2 \text{ kNm}$$

(ii)   Wind load of 20 kN/m

$$D_{10} = \int \frac{m_1 m_0}{EI}\, ds = -\frac{1}{3} \times 4 \times 1 \times 4 \times 10 = -53.3$$

$$D_{20} = 80$$

$$D_{30} = 46.0$$

$$\{f\} = \begin{bmatrix} 14.92 & -8 & 0 \\ -8 & 10.67 & 0 \\ 0 & 0 & 59.2 \end{bmatrix} \begin{Bmatrix} X_1 \\ X_2 \\ X_3 \end{Bmatrix} = -\begin{Bmatrix} -53.3 \\ +80.0 \\ +46.0 \end{Bmatrix}$$

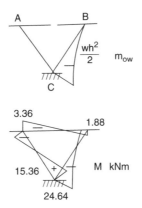

Figure 4.76. Combination of loadings for Example (4.20)

$$X_1 = -0.74 \, \text{kNm}$$

$$X_2 = -8.05 \, \text{kNm}$$

$$X_3 = -0.76 \, \text{kNm}$$

$$M = m_0 + m_1 X_1 + m_2 X_2 + m_3 X_3$$

$$M_A = -3.36 \, \text{kNm}$$

$$M_B = 1.88 \, \text{kNm}$$

$$M_C(\text{right}) = -24.6 \, \text{kNm}$$

$$M_C(\text{left}) = 15.36 \, \text{kNm}$$

The two cases can be combined (Fig. 4.76) so that the final results are obtained:

$$M_A = -67.2 - 0.36 = -70/56 \, \text{kNm}$$

$$M_B = -67.2 + 1.88 = -65.72 \, \text{kNm}$$

$$M_C = +33.6 + 15.36 \, \text{right} = 48.96 \, \text{kNm}$$

$$+ \, 33.6 - 24.64 \, \text{left} = 8.96 \, \text{kNm}$$

$$M_m = +105.8 + 0 = 105.80 \, \text{kNm}$$

4.9.3.2 Example (4.21)

A bent or a portal frame with variable second moment of area forms a substructure for a bridge crossing a motorway. During erection this substructure is subjected to heavy wind of $2 \, \text{kN/m}$ on the area shown in Fig. 4.77. Using the flexibility method of analysis, estimate various reactions which may be algebraically added to the ones existing when the bridge deck was placed. Take the wind load 'w' acting horizontally, $I_C = 1000 \, \text{dm}^4$ and E for concrete as constant. The leg on either side is divided as shown below.

Locations	$I \, (\text{dm}^4) \times 10^3$	$A \, (\text{dm})$
0	0.042875	3.5
1	0.080200	4.3125
2	0.13461	5.125
3	0.20932	5.938
4	0.30754	6.750
5	0.43251	7.563
6	0.58752	8.375
7	0.77552	9.188
8	1.00000	10.00
9	1.26409	10.813
10	1.57101	11.625

The legs are pinned and the structure of the bent is statically indeterminate to one degree. From the m_1 diagram in Fig. 4.77:

$$X_1 = 1 \quad \text{at } \mathbf{B}$$

The equation is therefore

$$X_1 = \frac{-D_{10}}{f_{11}}$$

$$M_D = 1 \times 5 = 5 \, \text{kNm} = M_C$$

I_C/I can now be determined:

$$H_A = H_B = 2 \times 5 = 10 \, \text{kN (negative)}$$

$$V_A = \frac{-2 \times 5 \times 5}{2 \times 5} = \frac{-10 \times 5}{2 \times 10} = -2.5 \, \text{kN}$$

$$M_C = \frac{-2 \times 5^2}{2} = -25 \, \text{kNm}$$

$$M_D = -10 \times 5 = -50 \, \text{kNm}$$

Calculations at 10 nodal points are summarized in Table 4.9.

$$I_C f_{11} = 2 \left[\frac{0.5 \, \text{m}}{3} \, 359.929 \, \text{m}^2 \right] + 10 \times 5 \times 5 \, \text{m}^3$$
$$\text{(beam)}$$

$$= 119.976 + 250 = 369.976 \, \text{m}^3$$

$$f' = f \, dx$$

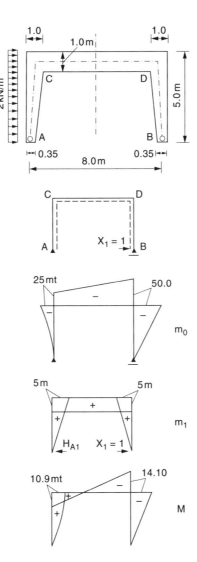

Figure 4.77. Bridge bent of variable cross-section

$$I_C D_{10} = -\frac{1}{2}\, 10\,\mathrm{m} \times 5\,\mathrm{m}\,(25 + 50)\,\mathrm{mkN} - \frac{0.5\,\mathrm{m}}{3}\, 1091.032\,\mathrm{m}^2\mathrm{kN}$$

$$- \frac{0.5\,\mathrm{m}}{3}\, 3599.290\,\mathrm{m}^2\mathrm{kN}$$

$$= -1875\,\mathrm{m}^3\mathrm{kN}\ (\text{beam}) - 181.84\,\mathrm{m}^3\mathrm{kN}\ (\text{left column})$$

$$- 599.88\,\mathrm{m}^3\mathrm{kN}\ (\text{right column})$$

$$I_C D_{21} = -2656.72\,\mathrm{m}^3\mathrm{kN}$$

Table 4.9. Summary of calculations at 10 nodes of a bridge bent of variable cross-section

1	2	3	4	5	6	7	8	9	10	11	12	13
P_{ts}	$I\ (dm^4)$	I_C/I	f	$(I_C/I)f$	$M_1\ (m)$	$M_1\ (m)$	$M_1^2(m^2)$	$(I_C/I)f\,M_1^2$ (m^2)	$M_0\ (mt)$ left col	$(I_C/I)f\,M_0M_1$ (m^2t)	$M_0\ (mt)$ right col	$(I_C/I)f\,M_0M_1$ (m^2t)
0	42.875	23.324	1	23.324	0	0	0	0	0	0	0	0
1	80.202	12.469	4	49.876	0.5	0.5	0.25	12.469	0.25	6.235	5	124.690
2	134.608	7.429	2	14.858	1.0	1.0	1.00	14.858	1.0	14.858	10	148.580
3	209.320	4.777	4	19.108	1.5	1.5	2.25	42.993	2.25	64.490	15	429.930
4	307.543	3.252	2	6.504	2.0	2.0	4	26.016	4.0	52.032	20	260.160
5	432.510	2.312	4	9.248	2.5	2.5	6.25	57.800	6.25	144.500	25	578.000
6	587.518	1.702	2	3.404	3.0	3.0	9	30.636	9.0	91.908	30	306.360
7	775.518	1.289	4	5.156	3.5	3.5	12.25	63.161	12.25	221.064	35	631.610
8	1000.000	1.000	2	2.000	4.0	4.0	16.00	32.000	16.0	128.000	40	320.000
9	1264.090	0.791	4	3.164	4.5	4.5	20.25	64.071	20.25	288.320	45	640.710
10	1571.009	0.637	1	0.637	5.0	5.0	25	15.925	25	79.625	50	159.250
								Σ 359.929		Σ 1091.032		Σ 3599.290

$$X_1 = \frac{2656.72}{369.976} = 7.18\,\text{kN}$$

$$M_C = 7.18 \times 5 - 25 = 10.90\,\text{kNm}$$

$$M_D = 35.0 - 50.0 = -14.10\,\text{kNm}$$

4.10   Stability of bridge piers
4.10.1   Piers without sway

The bending moment at any section x (Fig. 4.78) from a nodal point is given as

$$\frac{-EI\,\mathrm{d}^2 y}{\mathrm{d}x^2} = k - kx\frac{1+c}{\ell} + Py \tag{4.247}$$

$$y = A\cos\alpha x + B\sin\alpha x - \frac{k}{P} + kx\frac{1+c}{PL} \tag{4.248}$$

where $\alpha = \sqrt{P/EI}$.

At the end, condition $\mathrm{d}y/\mathrm{d}x = 0$ at $x = \ell$, $y = 0$, $x = 0$:

$$c = \frac{\alpha\ell - (\sin\alpha\ell)}{(\sin\alpha\ell - \alpha\ell\cos\alpha\ell)} \tag{4.249}$$

When $\mathrm{d}y/\mathrm{d}x = 1$ at $x = 0$:

$$k = \frac{\alpha EI(1 - \alpha\ell\cos\alpha\ell)}{2(\tan\alpha\ell/2 - \alpha\ell/2)} \tag{4.250}$$

Tables are available for stability functions such as:

$$q = \frac{K\ell}{EI} \qquad r = qc \qquad \rho = \frac{P}{P_E} = \frac{\alpha^2\ell^2}{\pi^2}; \qquad P_E = \frac{\pi^2 EI}{\ell^2} \tag{4.251}$$

where

$$P_E = \text{Euler}, \qquad P = \text{compressive or tensile load}$$

Where the end is hinged

$$k' = k(1 - c^2) \tag{B4.252}$$

$$q' = \frac{k'\ell}{EI}$$

Table 4.10 gives various values for these parameters.

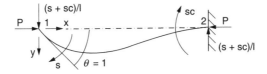

Figure 4.78. Member 1–2

Table 4.10 (below and facing). Stability functions for frames without sway

ρ	q	r	q'	t
4.0	$-\infty$	∞	0.00	∞
3.9	-78.33	78.57	0.49	24.77
3.8	-38.17	38.65	0.96	12.61
3.7	-24.68	25.39	1.42	8.555
3.6	-17.87	18.79	1.89	6.523
3.5	-13.72	14.85	2.35	5.309
3.4	-10.91	12.24	2.83	4.497
3.3	-8.86	10.40	3.33	3.916
3.2	-7.30	9.02	3.86	3.480
3.1	-6.05	7.96	4.42	3.141
3.0	-5.03	7.12	5.05	2.868
2.9	-4.18	6.44	5.77	2.646
2.8	-3.44	5.88	6.61	2.460
2.7	-2.81	5.42	7.63	2.302
2.6	-2.25	5.02	8.95	2.167
2.5	-1.75	4.68	10.75	2.049
2.4	-1.30	4.38	13.47	1.946
2.3	-0.89	4.13	18.19	1.855
2.2	-0.52	3.90	28.78	1.774
2.1	-0.18	3.70	77.83	1.702
2.0	0.14	3.53	-86.86	1.636
1.9	0.44	3.37	-25.35	1.577
1.8	0.72	3.22	-13.78	1.522
1.7	0.98	3.10	-8.83	1.473
1.6	1.22	2.98	-6.03	1.427
1.5	1.46	2.87	-4.22	1.385
1.4	1.68	2.78	-2.92	1.346
1.3	1.89	2.69	-1.94	1.310
1.2	2.09	2.61	-1.17	1.277
1.1	2.28	2.54	-0.53	1.245
1.0	2.47	2.47	0.00	1.216
0.9	2.65	2.41	0.46	1.188
0.8	2.82	2.35	0.86	1.162
0.7	2.98	2.29	1.22	1.138
0.6	3.14	2.24	1.54	1.115
0.5	3.29	2.19	1.83	1.093
0.4	3.44	2.15	2.10	1.073
0.3	3.59	2.11	2.35	1.053
0.2	3.73	2.07	2.58	1.035
0.1	3.87	2.03	2.80	1.017
0.0	4.00	2.00	3.00	1.000
-0.2	4.26	1.94	3.37	0.969
-0.4	4.50	1.88	3.71	0.940
-0.6	4.74	1.83	4.03	0.913
-0.8	4.96	1.79	4.31	0.889
-1.0	5.17	1.75	4.58	0.867

Continued

Table 4.10. Continued

ρ	q	r	q'	t
−1.5	5.68	1.67	5.19	0.817
−2.0	6.15	1.60	5.73	0.775
−2.5	6.58	1.54	6.22	0.738
−3.0	6.99	1.50	6.67	0.707
−3.5	7.37	1.46	7.08	0.679
−4.0	7.74	1.43	7.47	0.655
−5.0	8.42	1.38	8.18	0.612
−7.0	9.62	1.30	9.45	0.549
−9.0	10.69	1.26	10.52	0.502

(Courtesy: *Stability of Frames* by Chandler)

Where additional loading is placed laterally when the ends are fixed as well as loading from wind effects etc., the bending moment is likewise written as:

$$-\frac{EI\,d^2y}{dx^2} = -M^F + \frac{Wx}{2} - \frac{Wx^2}{2\ell} + Py \tag{4.253}$$

The general solution (Fig. 4.79) is written as

$$y = A\cos\alpha x + B\sin\alpha x + \frac{M^F}{P} + \frac{W(x^2 - x\ell - 2/\alpha^2)}{2P\ell} \tag{4.254}$$

Boundary conditions at the ends are:

$$y = 0 \text{ at } x = 0 \qquad \frac{dy}{dx} = 0 \text{ at } x = \frac{\ell}{2}$$

$$M^F = \frac{W(2 - \alpha\ell\cot\alpha\ell/2)}{2\alpha^2\ell}$$

$$= t\frac{W\ell}{12}$$

$$t = \frac{6}{q+r} \tag{4.255}$$

where t is the magnification factor.

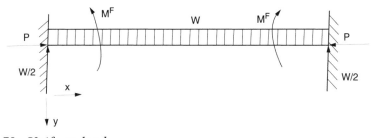

Figure 4.79. Uniform load

4.10.2 Piers subject to sways

Where the piers are not laterally restrained, there is a possibility of piers becoming unstable by swaying on one or the other sides. The effects are substantial.

Figure 4.80 shows the sway effect of piers.

The sway moment produced in member $1 - 2$ is given by

$$M_{12}^F = M_{21}^F = k(1+c)\frac{x}{\ell} = \frac{Q\ell}{2} \tag{4.256}$$

where $Q =$ shear force.

The increase of lateral displacement mx ($m =$ magnification factor) and the sway moments are

$$M_{12}^F = M_{21}^F = k(1+c)\frac{mx}{\ell} \tag{4.257}$$

The lateral displacement of an axially loaded member subjected to Q is

$$\delta = mx = \frac{mQ\ell^2}{2k(1+c)} \tag{4.258}$$

The moment at 1 for the axially loaded member is

$$M_{12}^F + M_{21}^F = Pmx + Q\ell$$

$$= 2k(1+c)\frac{mx}{\ell} \tag{4.259}$$

Hence

$$Pmx\ell = 2k(1+c)x(m-1) = \frac{\rho\pi^2 EImx}{\ell} \tag{4.260}$$

For the hinged condition:

$$m' = \frac{q'}{(q'-\rho\pi^2)} \qquad k' = k - mxk\frac{(1+c)}{\ell} \tag{4.261}$$

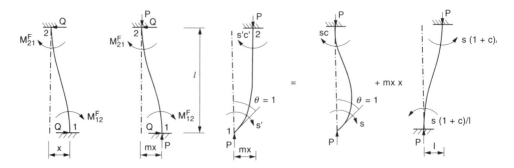

Figure 4.80. Piers under sway effects

$$c'k' = ck - mk\frac{(1+c)}{2} = \frac{nEI}{\ell} \tag{4.262}$$

$$c'k' = ck - mk\frac{(1+c)}{2} = \frac{\theta EI}{\ell} \tag{4.263}$$

$$c' = \theta/n$$

Values for m, n, θ are tabulated in Table 4.11.

4.10.3 Example (4.22)
A two-pier frame is a substructure to a bridge (Fig. 4.81). Determine load P at which elastic instability occurs. Assume all members have EI constant, and no sway is expected. Use Table 4.10.

At Joint 2:

$$k_2 = k_{23} + k_{21}$$

$$= \frac{2EI}{2\ell} + q'_{21}\frac{EI}{\ell}$$

At critical load, from Table 4.10:

$$k_2 = 0$$

$$q'_{21} = 1$$

$$\rho_{21} = 1.8$$

$$P_{cr} = 1.18P_E$$

4.10.4 Example (4.23)
If a third pier exists in Example (4.22) and is needed for structural reasons and is placed at the centre a further load P is applied. Determine the critical load at which the elastic instability occurs from Fig. 4.82. Assume displacements at the far end columns are the same.

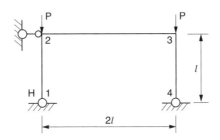

Figure 4.81. Single bent

Table 4.11. Stability functions for frames with sway

ρ	m	n	o	n'
1.50	−1.41	4.51	5.93	−3.28
1.40	−1.82	5.73	6.83	−2.41
1.30	−2.50	7.60	8.40	−1.69
1.20	−3.85	11.13	11.65	−1.06
1.10	−7.90	21.32	21.57	−0.51
1.02	−40.33	101.47	101.51	−0.20
1.00	∞	∞	∞	0.00
0.98	40.73	−98.47	−98.51	0.20
0.95	16.41	−38.41	−38.53	0.24
0.90	8.31	−18.33	−18.57	0.48
0.85	5.60	−11.58	−11.93	0.72
0.80	4.25	−8.16	−8.63	0.97
0.75	3.44	−6.08	−6.66	1.22
0.70	2.90	−4.67	−5.35	1.48
0.65	2.51	−3.63	−4.43	1.77
0.60	2.22	−2.84	−3.74	2.08
0.55	2.00	−2.21	−3.21	2.46
0.50	1.82	−1.69	−2.79	2.92
0.45	1.67	−1.25	−2.45	3.54
0.40	1.55	−0.88	−2.17	4.50
0.35	1.44	−0.55	−1.94	6.28
0.30	1.35	−0.26	−1.74	11.39
0.27	1.30	−0.10	−1.64	26.46
0.25	1.27	0.00	−1.57	∞
0.23	1.24	0.10	−1.51	−23.45
0.20	1.21	0.24	−1.43	−8.40
0.15	1.15	0.45	−1.30	−3.29
0.10	1.09	0.65	−1.19	−1.53
0.05	1.04	0.83	−1.09	−0.59
0.00	1.00	1.00	−1.00	0.00
−0.10	0.93	1.31	−0.85	0.75
−0.20	0.86	1.59	−0.73	1.25
−0.40	0.76	2.06	−0.56	1.91
−0.60	0.69	2.47	−0.43	2.40
−0.80	0.63	2.83	−0.34	2.79
−1.00	0.58	3.15	−0.27	3.13
−1.20	0.55	3.45	−0.22	3.43
−1.40	0.51	3.72	−0.18	3.71
−1.60	0.49	3.98	−0.15	3.97
−1.80	0.46	4.22	−0.13	4.21
−2.00	0.44	4.44	−0.11	4.44
−2.50	0.40	4.97	−0.07	4.97
−3.00	0.36	5.44	−0.05	5.44
−3.50	0.34	5.88	−0.03	5.88
−4.00	0.32	6.28	−0.02	6.28

(Courtesy: *Stability of Frames* by Chandler)

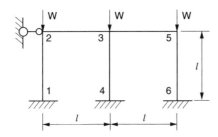

Figure 4.82. Double bent

Instability at Joints 2 and 3 are needed from symmetry. Moments M_{23}, M_{32}, M_{21}, M_{34}, M_{35}, M_{53} are important and should be investigated. The following matrices are established based on stiffnesses:

$$\begin{bmatrix} M_{23} \\ M_{32} \end{bmatrix} = EI \begin{bmatrix} \dfrac{4}{\ell} & \dfrac{2}{\ell} \\ \dfrac{2}{\ell} & \dfrac{4}{\ell} \end{bmatrix} \begin{Bmatrix} \theta_2 \\ \theta_3 \end{Bmatrix}$$

$$\begin{bmatrix} M_{35} \\ M_{53} \end{bmatrix} = E \begin{bmatrix} \dfrac{4}{\ell} & \dfrac{2}{\ell} \\ \dfrac{2}{\ell} & \dfrac{4}{\ell} \end{bmatrix} \begin{Bmatrix} \theta_3 \\ \theta_3 = \theta_5 \end{Bmatrix}$$

$$M_{21} = \frac{qEI\theta_2}{\ell}$$

$$M_{34} = \frac{qEI\theta_3}{\ell}$$

$$P = k \cdot \theta$$

$$\begin{Bmatrix} P_2 \\ P_3 \end{Bmatrix} = \frac{EI}{\ell} \begin{bmatrix} 4+q & 2 \\ 4 & 8+q \end{bmatrix} \begin{Bmatrix} \theta_2 \\ \theta_3 \end{Bmatrix}$$

When $k = 0$, i.e. stiffness at Joint is 0 when critical load versus instability occurs

$$\rho = 2.65$$

$$P_{cr} = 2.65 P_E$$

If P is known from $\pi^2 EI/\ell$, then P_{cr} is established. Assume

$$\ell = 6.4 \, \text{m}$$

$$E = 200 \, \text{GN/m}^2$$

$$I = 0.04 \, \text{m}^4$$

$$P_{cr} = 2.65 \left(\frac{\pi^2 200 \times 0.04}{6.4} \right) = 12.347 \, \text{GN}$$

This is the value at which the instability occurs. The loads acting on the pier column must always be less than this value of $P_{cr} = 12.347 \, \text{GN}$.

4.10.5 Example (4.24)

A two-pier structure supports a slab deck. The load W occurs uniformly on the two-pier substructural system. The supports are pinned to the bases. Calculate the load W at which elastic instability occurs using Fig. 4.83. Take EI to be constant and use Table 4.10. No sway occurs.

Joint 2 is considered:

$$k_2 = k_{21} + k_{23}$$

$$= \left\{ q'_{21} + \frac{q_{23} - r_{23}}{2} \right\} \frac{EI}{\ell} \tag{4.264}$$

Equating external and internal moments at Joint 2

$$k_2 \theta_2 - t_{23} \frac{W\ell}{6} \tag{4.265}$$

$$P_{23} = H = EI\theta_2 q'_{21}/\ell^2$$

Finally dividing by $\pi^2 EI/\ell^2$, the following equation is obtained:

$$\rho_{23} \left\{ q'_{21} + \frac{(q_{23} - r_{23})}{2} \right\} - \frac{4q'_{21} t_{23} \rho_{21}}{3} = 0 \tag{4.266}$$

Various values of ρ_{23}, $(q_{23} - r_{23})$, t_{23}, ρ_{21} and q'_{21} are tested. A plot of ρ_{21} and ρ_{23} is made such that $\rho_{21}/\rho_{23} = 0$ at the origin. The values are:

$$\rho_{23} = 0.4, \, 0.8, \, 1.0, \, 1.2$$

$$\rho_{21} = 0.36, \, 0.59, \, 0.61, \, 0.59\}$$

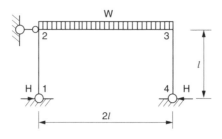

Figure 4.83. A bent under uniform bridge load

$$q'_{21} = 2.2, \ 1.58, \ 1.49$$

$$t_{23} = 1.073, \ 1.162, \ 1.216, \ 1.277$$

$$\frac{W_{\text{cr}}}{P_{\text{E}}} = 1.234$$

For the example with the concentrated loads at the joint:

$$\frac{W_{\text{cr}}}{P_{\text{E}}} = \frac{P_{\text{cr}}}{P_{\text{E}}} = 1.18$$

4.10.6 Example (4.25)

A two-pier substructure shown in Fig. 4.81 is not laterally restrained and is subjected to sway. Assuming EI is constant, determine the value of P at which the elastic instability occurs. Compare the two cases.
Joint 2 is still considered:

$$k_2 = k_{23} + k_{21}$$

$$= \frac{6EI}{2\ell} + n'_{21} \frac{EI}{\ell}$$

At critical load, $k_2 = 0$

$$n'_{21} = -3 \qquad \rho_{21} = 0.142$$

$$P_{\text{cr}} = 0.142 P_{\text{E}}$$

Assume $L = 6.4\,\text{m}$, $E = 200\,\text{GN/m}^2$; $I = 0.04\,\text{m}^4$, then:

$$P_{\text{cr}} = 0.142\pi^2 \times \frac{200 \times 0.04}{6.4} = 0.662\,\text{GN}$$

$$P_{\text{cr}}(\text{without sway}) = P_{\text{cr}} = 1.18 P_{\text{E}}$$

$$= 5.50\,\text{GN}$$

It is important to provide lateral restraint in this case so that the elastic stability is enhanced from 0.662 GN to 5.50 GN.

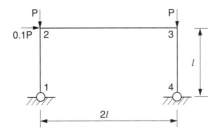

Figure 4.84. A bent with loads and sway

4.10.7 Example (4.26)

If the pier substructure given in Example (4.24) is now subjected to a $0.1P$ horizontal braking force (Fig. 4.84), determine the critical load P_{cr} at which the elastic instability occurs. Take EI as constant.

Using Table 4.11 for the analysis:

$$\left\{ \begin{array}{c} M_{21} \\ \ell Q_{21} \end{array} \right\} = \frac{EI}{\ell} \begin{bmatrix} q'_{21} & -q'_{21} \\ -q'_{21} & q'_{21} \\ & m'_{21} \end{bmatrix} \times \left\{ \begin{array}{c} \theta_2 \\ \dfrac{x_2}{\ell} \end{array} \right\} \tag{4.267}$$

$$\left\{ \begin{array}{c} M_{23} \\ M_{32} \end{array} \right\} = \frac{EI}{2\ell} \begin{bmatrix} q_{23} & r_{23} \\ r_{23} & q_{23} \end{bmatrix} \left\{ \begin{array}{c} \theta_2 \\ \theta_3 \end{array} \right\} \tag{4.268}$$

$$\left\{ \begin{array}{c} M_{34} \\ \ell Q_{34} \end{array} \right\} = \frac{EI}{\ell} \begin{bmatrix} q'_{34} & -q'_{34} \\ -q'_{34} & q'_{34} \\ & m'_{34} \end{bmatrix} \left\{ \begin{array}{c} \theta_3 \\ \dfrac{x_2}{\ell} \end{array} \right\} \tag{4.269}$$

Relevant terms are collected thus:

$$\left\{ \begin{array}{c} P_2 \\ P_3 \\ \ell P_{x2} + \ell P_{x3} \end{array} \right\} = \left\{ \begin{array}{c} 0 \\ 0 \\ 0.1PL \end{array} \right\} \frac{EI}{P} \begin{bmatrix} q'_{21} + \dfrac{q_{23}}{2} & \dfrac{r_{23}}{2} & -q'_{21} \\ \dfrac{r_{23}}{2} & \left(q'_{34} + \dfrac{q_{23}}{2} \right) & -q'_{34} \\ -q'_{21} & -q'_{34} & (j'_{21} + j'_{34}) \end{bmatrix}$$

$$\times \left\{ \begin{array}{c} \theta_2 \\ \theta_3 \\ \dfrac{x_2}{\ell} \end{array} \right\} \tag{4.270}$$

where

$$B'_{21} = \frac{q'_{21}}{m'_{21}}$$

$$B'_{34} = \frac{q'_{34}}{m'_{34}}$$

$$P_{23} = Q_{34}$$

$$P_{34} = P + \frac{(M_{23} + M_{32})}{2\ell}$$

Again several random values are chosen and a plot of P_{21} against rotation θ_2 in radians gives the following random values:

$$\frac{P}{P_E} = 0.04 \qquad \frac{P}{P_E} = 0.08 \qquad \frac{P}{P_E} = 0.12 \qquad \frac{P}{P_E} = 0.13$$

$$\rho_{23} = 0.0078 \qquad 0.0139 \qquad -0.0089 \qquad -0.0788$$

$$\rho_{34} = 0.0427 \qquad 0.887 \qquad 0.1541 \qquad 0.1908$$

$$\frac{\theta_2}{\text{(rads)}} = 0.009 \qquad 0.0290 \qquad 1.144 \qquad 2.048$$

$$\frac{P_{cr}}{P_E} = 0.142$$

is the lowest value interpolated.

4.11 Vehicle bashing of bridges and ship collision with piers

Vehicle bashing of road bridges is sometimes due to low rise and not enough signs on display for drivers. Vehicles with greater heights and lengths bash bridges with greater impacts. A special analysis is needed for such impacts on a bridge. A reference is made to Bangash for detailed analysis and design studies for impact.

The problem is one of risk to road and rail users alike since a number of worrying accidents specifically at road over rail bridges has occurred. The head-room is generally not more than 15 ft-6 in (4.73 m). Where the headroom is more, the chances of an accident are very remote. The standard container size of 8 ft (2.44 m) high, 8 ft (2.44m) wide and 20 ft (6.1 m) long will encounter problems where the headroom is less. These containers have increased dimensions and their width and height do present potential accident problems. It is estimated that, in general, the number of accidents/year/country is in the range of 70 to 130. New bridges must have a height of 20 ft (6.1 m) at least where a possible rail/road crossing is established. A proper analysis (dynamic) is needed to evaluate various structural components under a bashing impact load.

In some cases front buffer/sacrificial beams etc. are needed to protect the bridge facade. A bridge raising and road lowering is another possibility for avoiding impactive loads. A wide range of publicity is the real answer on such locations. For flat-span bridges on all roads or for any other structure, the following provides a useful guide:

Flat bridges: headroom not less than	15 ft-6 in (4.73 m)
Arch bridges: headroom not less than	12 ft (3.66 m)
Over turnpike: headroom not less than	16 ft (4.88 m)
Private carriage road: headroom not less than	14 ft (4.27 m)

In most circumstances the impact on a bridge by a vehicle can be avoided easily. However, it is difficult to prevent ship collision with bridge piers. Bangash has given design analysis for such an impact whether square on straight or occurring at an inclination. Table 4.12 gives a brief overview of ship/tanker collisions against bridge piers. The impact mechanics under consideration are both external and internal. The external mechanics may be categorized on the basis of the influence of the surrounding water and the calculation of the impact

Table 4.12. Ship impact on substructures

If

$$\mu' \le \frac{1}{\tan \alpha} \quad \text{otherwise set} \quad \mu = \frac{1}{\tan \alpha} \quad \text{(see Fig. 4.85)}$$

for v_N normal to the pier

$$= v \sin \alpha \to 0$$

i_N = impact pulse normal to the wall

$$= \frac{I_N}{v m_1 (1.05)}$$

$$= \frac{\sin \alpha}{A + B + C\left(\dfrac{1.05}{0.3}\right)}$$

where

$$A = \sin^2 \alpha$$

$$B = \mu' \sin \alpha \cos \alpha$$

$$C = \cos^2 \alpha - \mu' \sin \alpha \cos \alpha$$

$E_{k,h}$ = leftover energy

$$= \tfrac{1}{2}(1.05)v_{lh}^2 + \tfrac{1}{2}(0.3)m_1 v_{qh}^2$$

where

$$v_{lh} = v - i_N v(\sin \alpha \mu' \cos \alpha)$$

$$v_{q,h} = -i_N v \frac{\cos \alpha - \mu \sin \alpha}{0.286}$$

$$\eta = \text{collision energy} = 1 - E_{k,h}$$

where

$$E_{k,h} = \left(1 - i_N \frac{\sin \alpha \mu' \cos \alpha}{1.05}\right)^2 + 0.286 i_N^2 \left(\frac{\cos \alpha - \mu \sin \alpha}{0.3}\right)^2$$

$$F_{av} = \text{average impact} = \frac{\Delta E}{L_S} \quad \text{(see Fig. 4.86)}$$

$$F_{max} \approx 0.88\sqrt{dwt} \pm 50\%$$

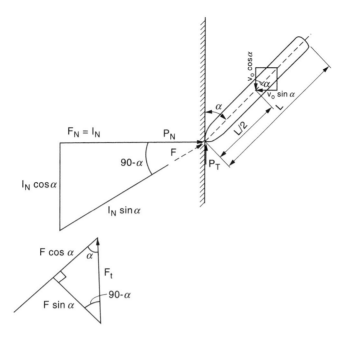

Figure 4.85. Schematic of ship collision angles

energy is not possible without knowing the impact forces by means of the principles of maintenance of energy, impulse and torsion. The important aspect is the introduction of the hydrodynamic supplementary mass which increases with ship acceleration and impact duration. In Western countries and Japan, the value of impact is around $1.8 \times$ ship mass.

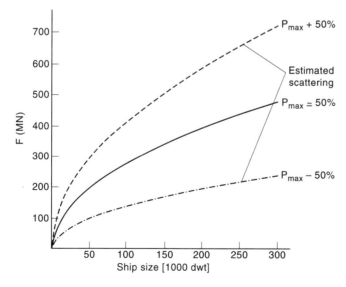

Figure 4.86. Approximate impact force versus ship size

Internal impact mechanics are dependent upon the deformation resistance of the structural elements hitting each other during the impact. The impact force is a function of the ship length L_s which is damaged and the pier. The impact force F is related to the damage length L_s and energy E. For a right-angle collision, the Minorsky formula for ship–ship collision when one of the ships is stationary is generally adopted:

$$\text{transmitted energy} = \Delta_E = \frac{\mu}{\mu H} \frac{m_1 v_1^2}{2}$$

$$\Delta_W = aR + b \quad \text{(see Fig. 4.87)} \tag{4.271}$$

where

$$\mu = \frac{m_2}{m_1}$$

Δ_W = the energy absorbed in damage area = Δ_E

$\dfrac{m_1 v_1^2}{2}$ = kinetic energy of the striking ship = Δ_E

a = constant = $47\,\text{MNm/m}^3$

b = $32\,\text{MNm}$

R = volume of the steel deformed where damage occurred

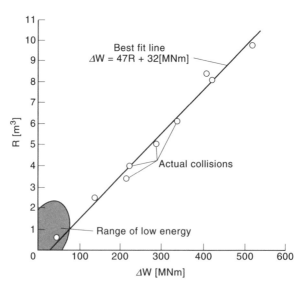

Figure 4.87. Relation between absorbed energy ΔW and deformed steel volume R for collisions between two ships

The kinetic energy (KE) for a straightforward movement:

$$\mathrm{KE} = \frac{1}{2} \frac{m_1 + \Delta m}{m_1} m_1 v^2 \tag{4.272}$$

where

$$m_1 = \text{ship mass}$$

$$\frac{m_1 + \Delta m}{m_1} = \text{hydrodynamic access with } \Delta m \text{ hydrodynamic supplementary mass}$$

In order to avoid rotation and translation, it is recommended to reduce the ship's mass by

$$m_{\text{reduced}} = \frac{1.5 m_1 \times CG^2}{CG^2 + r^2} \tag{4.273}$$

$$r = \text{mass radius of inertia}$$

$$CG = \text{ship's centre of gravity}$$

If $CG = L/4$ and $r = L/2$

where

$$L = \text{ship length}$$

$$m_{\text{reduced}} = \frac{1.5 m_1 \times \left(\dfrac{L}{4}\right)^2}{\left(\dfrac{L}{4}\right)^2 \times \left(\dfrac{L}{2}\right)^2} = \frac{6 m_1}{L^2} \tag{4.274}$$

For approximate cases:

$$m_{\text{reduced}} = 0.3 m_1$$

Referring to Table 4.12, if the impact angle is α and μ' is the friction between the ship and the pier, then:

$$F = \mu' P_{\mathrm{N}}$$

$$\mu' = 0.15 \quad \text{for steel to steel}$$

$$= 0.35 \quad \text{for steel to concrete}$$

$$= 0.65 \quad \text{for steel to wood}$$

The collision energy η is plotted against the angle of collision α in Fig. 4.88.

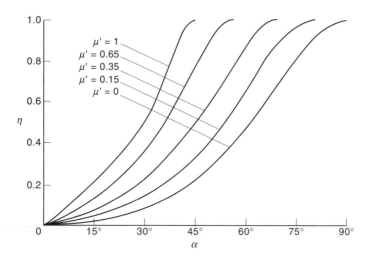

Figure 4.88. Impact/collision energy versus ship impact inclination

4.11.1 Example (4.27)

A ship of 45 000 tons displacement collides with a pier made of concrete. Because of the impact, assume the ship's bow is flattened over a length $L_S = 3.0$ m. Duration is 0.1–0.2 sec of the maximum impact and the velocity of the ship $= 3$ m/sec.

Check the example with the German code for railways which stipulates a load of 30 MN for piers for barges with 1800 tons displacement and a speed of 5.8 m/sec.

Calculate for the damage length L_S.

(a) The 45 000 ton displacement gives dead weight tonnage:

$$\text{dwt} = \frac{45\,000}{1.1842} \approx 38\,000$$

$$\text{impact force } F_{max} = 0.88\sqrt{\text{dwt}} \times \pm 1.5 = \begin{matrix} +258\,\text{MN} \\ -86\,\text{MN} \end{matrix}$$

$$\text{The average impact force } F = \tfrac{1}{2}F_{max}, \text{ i.e. } \begin{matrix} +129\,\text{MN} \\ -43\,\text{MN} \end{matrix}$$

$$\text{KE} = \tfrac{1}{2}mv^2(1.05) = \tfrac{1}{2} \times 45\,\text{MN} \times (3)^2 \times 1.05 = 212.625\,\text{MNm}$$

$$L_S = \text{damage length} = \frac{212.625}{129 \pm 43}$$

$$= 2.47 \quad \text{maximum in metres against actual damage} \\ \text{length of 3.0 m}$$

(b)
$$\mathrm{dwt} = \frac{18\,000}{1.1842} = 1520$$

$$F_{\mathrm{max}} = 0.88\sqrt{1520} \times 1.5 = 51.463\,\mathrm{MN}$$

$$\text{average impact force} = \frac{51.463}{2} = 25.73\,\mathrm{MN}$$

The German code gives 30 MN. Now:

$$\mathrm{KE} = 32.8\,\mathrm{MNm}$$

$$L_{\mathrm{S}} = 2.5\,\mathrm{m}$$

The results are comparable.

4.12 Section summary

Figures 4.89 to 4.92 and Table 4.13 give shapes of substructure with and without sloping members. All of these can be subjected to ship impact and vehicular loads. A number of static and dynamic analyses is given in the text which can be used to analyse piers and abutments. The Appendix will play a significant part in supporting such analyses.

A typical shape of bridge pier is given in Fig. 4.93 and can be analysed using such analyses. Using the finite element method, the reinforcements in the finite element mesh can be idealized as line or barelments placed on top of or within the body of the solid element.

The simulation technique is given in detail in the following publications:

References

1. Bangash. M.Y.H. *Concrete and Concrete Structures – Numerical Modelling and Applications*, Thomas Telford, London, 2000 (in press).
2. Bangash, M.Y.H. *Impact and Explosion – Analysis and Design*, Blackwell, Oxford, 1993.

Appendix: Summary of analysis where finite element analysis is used for more complex problems

Kvaerner Technology Ltd is one of a consortium of companies designing the New Tagus Crossing in Lisbon, Portugal. It used the extensive solid modelling capabilities of the LUSAS *Bridge* analysis system from FEA Ltd for analysing reinforced concrete diaphragms on the 6.5 km long central viaduct section of the crossing (Fig. 4.94).

Viaduct construction
Each 77 m long viaduct span unit consists of 8 precast box sections that are assembled, prestressed and concreted together before floating out and jacking into position onto piers initially on temporary supports. Once adjoining spans are in place, continuity prestress tendons are fixed through the diaphragm

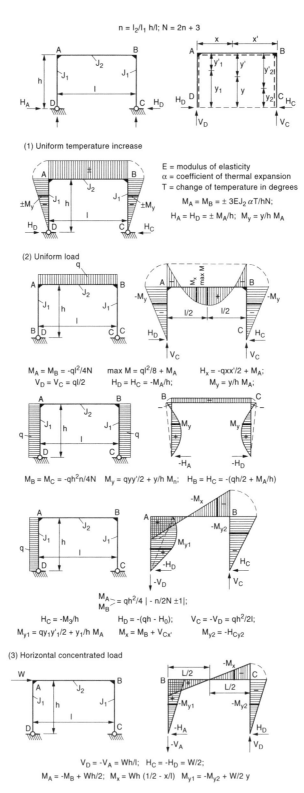

$n = I_2/I_1 \cdot h/l$; $N = 2n + 3$

(1) Uniform temperature increase

E = modulus of elasticity
α = coefficient of thermal expansion
T = change of temperature in degrees

$$M_A = M_B = \pm\, 3EJ_2\,\alpha T/hN;$$
$$H_A = H_D = \pm\, M_A/h; \quad M_y = y/h\, M_A$$

(2) Uniform load

$$M_A = M_B = -ql^2/4N \qquad \max M = ql^2/8 + M_A \qquad H_x = -qxx'/2 + M_A;$$
$$V_D = V_C = ql/2 \qquad H_D = H_C = -M_A/h; \qquad M_y = y/h\, M_A;$$

$$M_B = M_C = -qh^2n/4N \quad M_y = qyy'/2 + y/h\, M_n; \quad H_B = H_C = -(qh/2 + M_A/h)$$

$$\frac{M_A}{M_B} = qh^2/4\,|\,-\,n/2N \pm 1|;$$

$$H_C = -M_3/h \qquad H_D = -(qh - H_0); \qquad V_C = -V_D = qh^2/2l;$$
$$M_{y1} = qy_1y'_1/2 + y_1/h\, M_A \qquad M_x = M_B + V_{Cx'} \qquad M_{y2} = -H_{Cy2}$$

(3) Horizontal concentrated load

$$V_D = -V_A = Wh/l; \quad H_C = -H_D = W/2;$$
$$M_A = -M_B + Wh/2; \quad M_x = Wh\,(1/2 - x/l) \quad M_{y1} = -M_{y2} + W/2\, y$$

Figure 4.89. Symmetrical rectangular two-hinged frame

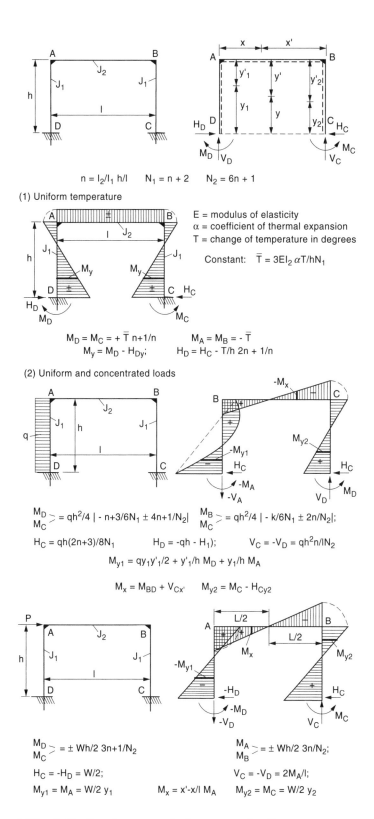

$$n = l_2/l_1 \cdot h/l \qquad N_1 = n + 2 \qquad N_2 = 6n + 1$$

(1) Uniform temperature

E = modulus of elasticity
α = coefficient of thermal expansion
T = change of temperature in degrees

Constant: $\overline{T} = 3EI_2 \, \alpha T/hN_1$

$$M_D = M_C = + \overline{T} \cdot n+1/n \qquad M_A = M_B = - \overline{T}$$
$$M_y = M_D - H_D y; \qquad H_D = H_C - T/h \cdot 2n + 1/n$$

(2) Uniform and concentrated loads

$$\begin{matrix} M_D \\ M_C \end{matrix} = qh^2/4 \mid - n+3/6N_1 \pm 4n+1/N_2 \mid \qquad \begin{matrix} M_B \\ M_C \end{matrix} = qh^2/4 \mid - k/6N_1 \pm 2n/N_2 \mid;$$

$$H_C = qh(2n+3)/8N_1 \qquad H_D = -qh - H_1); \qquad V_C = -V_D = qh^2n/lN_2$$

$$M_{y1} = qy_1 y'_1/2 + y'_1/h \cdot M_D + y_1/h \cdot M_A$$

$$M_x = M_{BD} + V_C x' \qquad M_{y2} = M_C - H_C y_2$$

$$\begin{matrix} M_D \\ M_C \end{matrix} = \pm Wh/2 \cdot 3n+1/N_2 \qquad\qquad \begin{matrix} M_A \\ M_B \end{matrix} = \pm Wh/2 \cdot 3n/N_2;$$

$$H_C = -H_D = W/2; \qquad\qquad V_C = -V_D = 2M_A/l;$$

$$M_{y1} = M_A = W/2 \cdot y_1 \qquad M_x = x'-x/l \cdot M_A \qquad M_{y2} = M_C = W/2 \cdot y_2$$

Figure 4.90. Fully fixed symmetrical rectangular frame

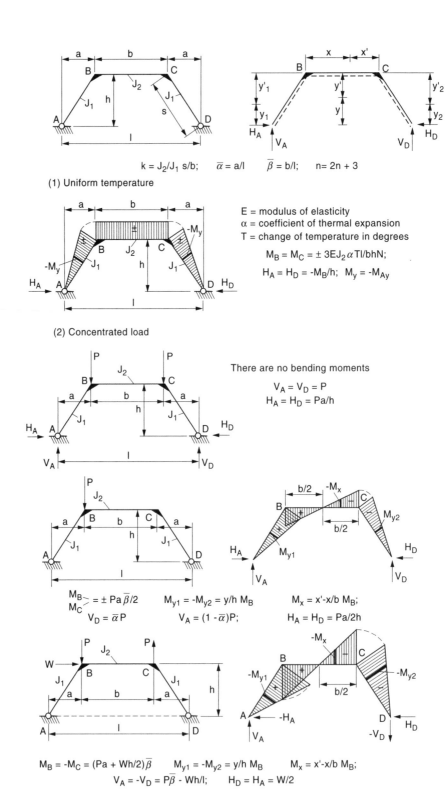

$k = J_2/J_1 \, s/b; \qquad \bar{\alpha} = a/l \qquad \bar{\beta} = b/l; \qquad n = 2n + 3$

(1) Uniform temperature

E = modulus of elasticity
α = coefficient of thermal expansion
T = change of temperature in degrees

$$M_B = M_C = \pm \, 3EJ_2 \alpha \, Tl/bhN;$$
$$H_A = H_D = -M_B/h; \quad M_y = -M_{Ay}$$

(2) Concentrated load

There are no bending moments

$$V_A = V_D = P$$
$$H_A = H_D = Pa/h$$

$$M_B \atop M_C = \pm \, Pa \, \bar{\beta}/2 \qquad M_{y1} = -M_{y2} = y/h \, M_B \qquad M_x = x'{-}x/b \, M_B;$$
$$V_D = \bar{\alpha} \, P \qquad V_A = (1 - \bar{\alpha})P; \qquad H_A = H_D = Pa/2h$$

$$M_B = -M_C = (Pa + Wh/2)\bar{\beta} \qquad M_{y1} = -M_{y2} = y/h \, M_B \qquad M_x = x'{-}x/b \, M_B;$$
$$V_A = -V_D = P\bar{\beta} - Wh/l; \qquad H_D = H_A = W/2$$

Figure 4.91. Symmetrical two-hinged, trapezoidal rigid frame

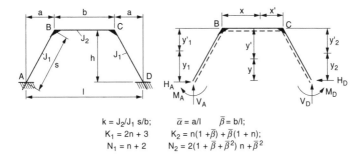

$$k = J_2/J_1 \, s/b; \qquad \bar{\alpha} = a/l \qquad \bar{\beta} = b/l;$$
$$K_1 = 2n + 3 \qquad K_2 = n(1 + \bar{\beta}) + \bar{\beta}(1 + n);$$
$$N_1 = n + 2 \qquad N_2 = 2(1 + \bar{\beta} + \bar{\beta}^2) n + \bar{\beta}^2$$

(1) Uniform temperature

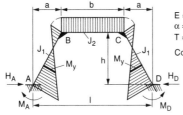

E = modulus of elasticity
α = coefficient of thermal expansion
T = change of temperature in degrees

Constant: $\bar{T} = \pm 3EJ_1 l \, \varepsilon t / sh N_1$

$$M_A = M_D = +\bar{T}(n+1) \qquad M_B = M_C = -\bar{T}k; \qquad V_A = V_D = 0$$
$$H_A = H_D = M_A - M_B/h; \qquad M_y = y'/h \, M_A + y/h \, M_B$$

(2) Concentrated loads

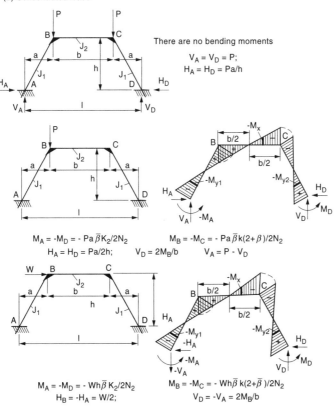

There are no bending moments

$$V_A = V_D = P;$$
$$H_A = H_D = Pa/h$$

$$M_A = -M_D = - Pa\bar{\beta}K_2/2N_2 \qquad M_B = -M_C = - Pa\bar{\beta}k(2+\bar{\beta})/2N_2$$
$$H_A = H_D = Pa/2h; \qquad V_D = 2M_B/b \qquad V_A = P - V_D$$

$$M_A = -M_D = - Wh\bar{\beta}K_2/2N_2 \qquad M_B = -M_C = - Wh\bar{\beta}k(2+\bar{\beta})/2N_2$$
$$H_B = -H_A = W/2; \qquad V_D = -V_A = 2M_B/b$$

Figure 4.92. Symmetrical hingeless, trapezoidal rigid frame

Table 4.13 (below and facing). A single portal with overhangs on both sides

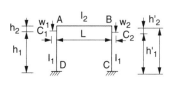

$$n = \frac{I_2}{I_1} \cdot \frac{h}{L} \qquad u = 3 + 2n \qquad u_1 = 2 + n \qquad u_2 = 1 + 6n$$

$$\alpha = \frac{h_1}{h} \qquad \beta = \frac{h_2}{h} \qquad \gamma = \frac{h_1'}{h} \qquad \eta = \frac{h_2'}{h}$$

$$\Phi = (\sec \varnothing - \mathrm{tg}\,\varnothing)^2 \qquad m_1 = W_1 \cdot e_1 \qquad m_2 = W_2 \cdot e_2$$

Wheel load (IL method) 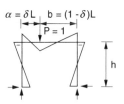 $\alpha = \delta L \quad b = (1-\delta)L$	$M_D = \frac{L}{2} \cdot \frac{\delta(1-\delta)[5n - 1 + 2\delta u_1]}{u_1 \cdot u_2}$ $\qquad V_D = \frac{(1-\delta)(\delta - 2\delta^2 + u_2)}{u_2}$ $M_C = \frac{L}{2} \cdot \frac{\delta(1-\delta)(3 + 7n - 2\delta u_1)}{u_1 \cdot u_2}$ $\qquad V_C = \frac{\delta \cdot (3\delta - 2\delta^2 + 6n)}{u_2}$ $M_B = M_D - H_D \cdot h \qquad H_A = H_D = \frac{3\delta(1-\delta) \cdot L}{2h \cdot u_1}$ $M_C = M_C - H_D \cdot h$ $M_{max} = M_D - H_D \cdot h + V_A \cdot \delta \cdot L$ $a = \delta L$

$M_D = \frac{L}{2} \cdot \frac{\delta(1-\delta)[5n - 1 + 2\delta u_1]}{u_1 \cdot u_2}$

$V_D = \frac{(1-\delta)(\delta - 2\delta^2 + u_2)}{u_2}$

$M_C = \frac{L}{2} \cdot \frac{\delta(1-\delta)(3 + 7n - 2\delta u_1)}{u_1 \cdot u_2}$

$V_C = \frac{\delta \cdot (3\delta - 2\delta^2 + 6n)}{u_2}$

$M_B = M_D - H_D \cdot h$

$H_A = H_D = \frac{3\delta(1-\delta) \cdot L}{2h \cdot u_1}$

$M_C = M_C - H_D \cdot h$

$M_{max} = M_D - H_D \cdot h + V_A \cdot \delta \cdot L$
$a = \delta L$

Wheel load (approx. formula for M_{max})

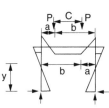

$M_{A,D} = \frac{Pab}{L}\left(\frac{5n + u_1 - 1}{u_1 \cdot u_2}\right)$

$H_{D,C} = \frac{3P \cdot a \cdot b}{h \cdot L \cdot u_1}$

$M_y = M_D - H_D y$

$V_{D,C} = P$

$M_{max} = M_D - H_D \cdot h + P \cdot a$

Load W_2 transmit from neighbour span

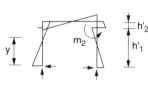

$M_{DC} = \frac{m_2}{2}\left\{\frac{1}{u_1}[K(\lambda^2 + 2\eta^2)\right.$
$\left. + 3\eta^2 - (K+1)]\right.$
$\left. \mp \left(1 - \frac{6K\lambda}{u_2}\right)\right\}$

$H_{DC} = -\frac{m_2}{2h}\left\{1 - \frac{1}{u_1}\right.$
$\left. \times [3n(\lambda^2 + \eta^2) + 3\eta^2\right.$
$\left. - 2n - 1]\right\}$

$M_{AB} = -\frac{Km_2}{2}\left[\frac{1}{u_1}(2\lambda^2 + \eta^2 - 1)\right.$
$\left. \mp \frac{6\lambda}{u_2}\right]$

$V_{DC} = \pm\frac{1}{L}(M_C - M_D)$

Continued

Table 4.13. Continued

Brake force	$M_{DC} = \mp \dfrac{T_B}{2} \cdot \dfrac{1+3n}{u_2}$	$H_{DC} = \mp \dfrac{T_B}{2}$
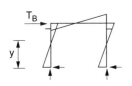	$M_{AB} = \pm \dfrac{T_B}{2} \cdot \dfrac{3n}{u_2}$	$V_{DC} = \mp \dfrac{3\,Thn}{u_2 L}$
	$M_y = M_D + \dfrac{T_B}{2} \cdot y$	

Change of temperature	α = heat transfer coefficient	$H_A = H_D$
	T = temperature differential	$= \dfrac{3EI_2 \alpha T}{h^2} \cdot \dfrac{2n+1}{u_1 n}$
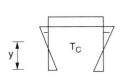	E = modulus of elasticity	
	$M_{AB} = -\dfrac{3EI_2}{hu_1} \cdot \alpha_t \cdot t^*$	$V_D = V_C = 0$
	$M_{DC} = \dfrac{n+1}{n} \cdot \dfrac{3EI_2 \alpha_t \cdot t}{hu_1}$	
	$M_y = M_D - H_y$	

Earth pressure	$M_A = -\dfrac{q_0 h^2}{120}\left(2 - \dfrac{12+7n}{u_1} - \dfrac{15n}{u_2}\right)$	$H_D = \dfrac{q_0 \cdot h}{40} \cdot \dfrac{4+3n}{u_1}$
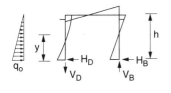	$M_B = M_C - H_B \cdot h$	$H_D = H_D - \dfrac{q_0 h}{2}$
	$M_C = \dfrac{q_0 h^2}{120}\left(\dfrac{12+7K}{u_1} - \dfrac{15K}{u_2}\right)$	$V_{DC} = \mp \dfrac{q_0 \cdot h^2 \cdot n}{4L \cdot u_2}$
	$M_{A,B} = -\dfrac{q_0 h^2 n}{40}\left(\dfrac{2}{3u_1} \mp \dfrac{5}{u_2}\right)$	
	$M_y = M_D + \left(\dfrac{q_0 h}{2} - H_D\right)y$	
	$\qquad - \dfrac{q_0 y^2}{6h}(3h - y)$	

Earth pressure	$M_{DC} = -\dfrac{q_2 \cdot h^2 \cdot \xi^2}{40}\left[\dfrac{\xi}{3U_1}(1+n)\right.$	$H_{DC} = \dfrac{q_2 \cdot h \cdot \xi}{40}\{10 \pm 10$
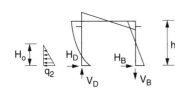	$\qquad \times (5-3\xi) + \dfrac{5\xi}{3} - \dfrac{10}{3}$	$\qquad + \dfrac{\varepsilon^2}{u_1}[5(1+K)$
	$\qquad \left. \mp \left(\dfrac{10}{3} - \dfrac{5n \cdot \xi}{u_2}\right)\right]$	$\qquad - \xi(1+2K)]\}$
	$\xi = \dfrac{H_D}{h}$	$V_{DC} = \pm \dfrac{1}{L}\cdot\left(\dfrac{q_2 H_0^2}{6}\right.$
	$M_{AB} = q_2 h^2 \cdot \xi^2 \cdot \dfrac{n}{40}\cdot\left[\dfrac{1}{3u_1}(5-3\xi)\right.$	$\qquad \left. -M_D - M_C\right)$
	$\qquad \left. \mp \dfrac{5}{u_2}\right]$	

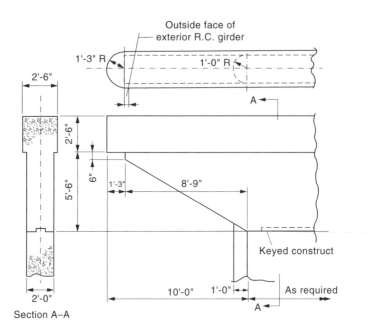

Figure 4.93. Reinforced concrete bridge piers

walls into adjacent units and a 1 m wide 'working-room' gap between units is infilled with concrete to match web and flange thickness of adjoining units. A pair of 1 m × 1 m permanent bearings are installed directly under the infill concrete and all temporary supports are removed.

LUSAS modelling

Three different diaphragm designs were required to cater for standard span units; special 'lay-by' units – with wider decks and with thicker walls; and for units with movement joints. Different LUSAS models were required for each diaphragm type in order to analyse the stresses due to deck loadings, anchorage forces from prestress and bearing reactions. Models of the end 6 m of each span unit type were built using 8-node enhanced strain solid brick elements. Spring supports represented bearings and dead, supported, live, and seismic loadings all had to be considered.

Analysis undertaken

LUSAS was used to analyse 3 stages on construction: Stage 1 prestress in the casting yard; Stage 2 prestress once the units are in final position with infill zones concreted; and Stage 3, to give bearing reactions under normal and seismic loading. A linear static analysis was completed for the various loadcases and, by use of the LUSAS slice section facility, moments and forces at critical sections through the webs and flanges of the diaphragms were easily obtained to allow the diaphragm reinforcement quantities to be calculated.

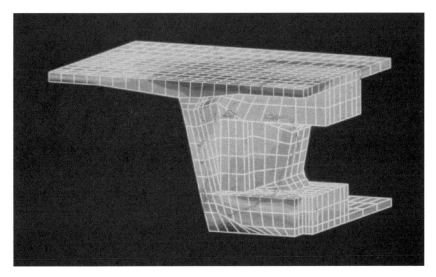

Figure 4.94. Faster diaphragm design on new Tagus crossing

Easy to use

Walid Mahmoud, the senior bridge engineer responsible for the diaphragm design, was very pleased with the capability of LUSAS for solid modelling and its powerful graphical post-processing facilities for viewing the results. "This was the first time I had used LUSAS", he said, "I found it easy to use, and by using the slice section facility, we obtained a better understanding of the behaviour of the structure which helped us to produce a detailed design which could not have been done easily using alternative simplified methods".

Future work
Design work on the viaduct diaphragms is now complete. Further analysis using LUSAS is being carried out to investigate the transverse load effects on the box girders.

SECTION 5
METHODS OF DESIGN

5. Methods of design

5.1 Design of bridge superstructures
5.1.1 Introduction
In this section, design examples are given on steel–concrete composites, reinforced concrete and prestressed concrete using British, American and Canadian codes of practice. Other codes are discussed in the text and their design criteria can be translated into similar examples along the lines suggested therein. Owing to lack of space steel bridges have not been covered completely. Nevertheless, the same principles can be applied to the applications of various loads (live, dead, wind, temperature, etc.) and the final evaluation of stress criteria.

5.1.2 Design examples
5.1.2.1 Example (5.1) Canadian/Ontario practice
A reinforced concrete bridge deck is shown in Fig. 5.1 with T-girders, 225 mm slab and 90 mm surfacing. The bridge has a simple span of 30 m. Use the following data and Code OHBR:

concrete $f'_c = 30\,\text{MPa}\,(\text{MN/m}^2)$

reinforcement $f_s = 400\,\text{MPa}$

$E_c = 0.043 w^{1.5}\sqrt{f_c} = 28\,500\,\text{MPa}$

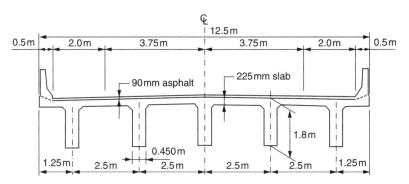

Figure 5.1. Cross-section of a reinforced concrete bridge deck

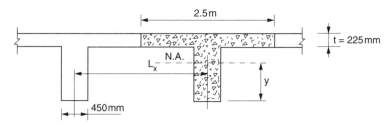

Figure 5.2. T-beam analysis

Based on Clause 3.10.2 (of the Canadian code)

$$\frac{B_e}{B} = 1 - \left(1 - \frac{L}{15B}\right)^3 \ngtr 1.0$$

$$= 1 - \left(1 - \frac{30}{1.5 \times 1.025}\right) = 1.85 > 1.0$$

Take

$$\frac{B_e}{B} = 1.0$$

and therefore the whole slab is taken to be effective.

The flange width = 2.5 m. Thus, from Fig. 5.2:

$$y = \frac{2500 \times 225 \times 1657 + 450 \times 1575 \times 787}{2500 \times 225 + 450 \times 1575}$$

$$= 1185 \, \text{mm}$$

$$I = \frac{2500 \times 225^3}{12} + 2500 \times 225(1575 - 1185)^2$$

$$+ \frac{450 \times 1575^3}{12} + 450 \times 1575(1185 - 787)^2$$

$$= 403 \times 10^9$$

Live load distribution: calculation of structural parameters

$$i = \frac{I}{P_x} = \frac{403 \times 10^9}{2500} = 161 \times 10^6$$

$$j = \frac{t^3}{12(1 - v^2)} = \frac{225^3}{12(1 - 0.15^2)} = 0.971 \times 10^6$$

$$i_0 = \frac{t^3}{6} = \frac{\text{torsional inertia}}{P_x} = \frac{t^3}{6} + \frac{Kab^3}{P_x}$$

$$= \frac{225^3}{6} + \frac{1575 \times 450^3}{2500} \times 0.28 = 17.4 \times 10^6$$

$$j_0 = \frac{t^3}{6} = \frac{225^3}{6} = 1.898 \times 10^6$$

$$D_x = Ei = 161 \times 10^6 E$$

$$D_y = Ej = 0.971 \times 10^6 E$$

$$D_{xy} = Gi_0 = 17.4 \times 10^6 G = 7.56 \times 10^6 E; \quad \left(G = \frac{E}{2(1+v)} = \frac{E}{2 \times 1.15} \right)$$

$$D_{yx} = Gj_0 = 1.898 \times 10^6 G = 0.82 \times 10^6 E$$

$$D_1 = v \text{ (lesser of } D_x \text{ or } D_y) = 0.15 \times 0.971 = 0.145 \times 10^6 E$$

$$D_2 = D_1 = 0.145 \times 10^6 E$$

$$\alpha = \frac{(D_{xy} + D_{yx} + D_1 + D_2)}{2(D_x D_y)^{0.5}}$$

$$= \frac{(7.56 + 0.82 + 0.145 + 0.145)10^6 E}{2(161 \times 0.97)^{0.5} \times 10^6 E} = 0.35$$

$$\theta = \frac{b}{L} \left[\frac{D_x}{D_y} \right]^{0.25} = \frac{12.5}{2 \times 30} \left[\frac{161 \times 10^6 E}{0.97 \times 10^6 E} \right]^{0.25}$$

$$= 0.75$$

Table 5.1. *Live load distribution factors*

		Longitudinal bending		Longitudinal shear
		ULS, SLS II	SLS I	ULS, SLS II
D		2.25	2.5	
C_t		9	9.2	
D_d		2.33	2.7	1.85
$\dfrac{S}{D_d} = \dfrac{2.5}{D_d}$		1.07	0.93	1.35
DLA		0.43	0.37	0.54
DF		1.50	1.30	1.89

$$\mu = \frac{\text{lane width} - 3.3}{0.6} = \frac{3.83 - 3.3}{0.6} = 0.88$$

$$D_d = D\left(1 + \frac{\mu C_t}{100}\right)$$

Calculation of moment and shear dead load
Consider the data given below (and Table 5.2).

$$\text{girder and barrier walls} = 33\,\text{kN/m}$$

$$\text{asphalt} = 4.9\,\text{kN/m}$$

Calculation of dynamic load allowance: first flexural frequency

$$f = \frac{\pi}{2L^2}\sqrt{\frac{EIg}{w}}$$

$$E = 28\,500$$

$$I = 347 \times 10^9$$

$$w = \text{weight of girder} = 30\,\text{kN/m}$$

$$g = 9800$$

$$f = \frac{\pi}{2L^2}\sqrt{\frac{EIg}{w}} = \frac{\pi}{2 \times 30\,000^2}\sqrt{\frac{28\,500 \times 403 \times 10^9 \times 9800}{30}}$$

$$= 3.38\,\text{Hz}$$

$$\text{DLA} = 0.40$$

Table 5.2. Moment and shear dead load data

	Moment		Shear	
	Girder	Asphalt	Girder	Asphalt
0	0	0	4.95	73
1	1336	197	396	58
2	2376	350	297	44
3	3118	459	198	29
4	3564	525	100	15
5	3713	546	0	0

5.1.2.2 Example (5.2)   Canadian practice

A composite concrete–steel beam deck is shown in Fig. 5.3. Use the following data and design for the limit state:

$$\text{weight of concrete} = 24\,\text{kN/m}^3$$

$$\text{weight of steel} = 77\,\text{kN/m}^3$$

$$\text{weight of asphalt} = 23.5\,\text{kN/m}^3$$

$$F_y = 210\,\text{MPa}$$

$$E_s = 200\,000\,\text{MPa}$$

$$\nu = \text{Poisson's ratio} = 0.15$$

$$f_c' = 20\,\text{MPa}$$

$$E_c = 2446^{1.5} \times 0.043\sqrt{20} = 23\,260\,\text{MPa}$$

$$n = \frac{E_s}{E_c} = 8.6$$

$$G_c = \frac{E_c}{2(1+\nu)} = 200\,000\,\text{MPa} = 200\,\text{GN/m}^2$$

Dead load

The bridge satisfies the requirements of Clause 3.6.1.1 of the Canadian code, so simplified methods will be used:

$$\text{DL girder} = 1.517\,\text{kN/m}$$

$$\text{DL slab} = 0.229 \times 1.829 \times 24 = 10.052\,\text{kN/m}$$

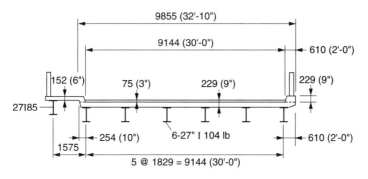

Figure 5.3. Steel–concrete composite deck of span 12 268 mm (40 ft 3 in)

Table 5.3. Dead load factors (no time limit)

	Load factor	
Structural steel	1.1	
Slab, curb, and sidewalk	1.2	
Railing	1.2	
Asphalt	1.2	

W	Unfactored	Factored
Girder	1.517	1.669
Slab	10.052	12.062
Curb and railing	1.36	1.632
Asphalt	2.686	3.223
Total (per girder)	15.615 kN/m	18.586 kN/m

$$\text{DL curb and rail} = [(0.229 \times 0.61 + 0.077 \times 0.254$$
$$+ \tfrac{1}{2} \times 1.575 \times 0.152) \times 24 + 1.46] \times \tfrac{1}{6}$$
$$= 1.36 \,\text{kN/m}$$
$$\text{DL asphalt} = 0.075 \times 9.144 \times 23.5 \times \tfrac{1}{6} = 2.686 \,\text{kN/m}.$$

Data associated with these calculations are given in Table 5.3.

Maximum bending @ ₵ of girder due to DL

$$= \tfrac{1}{8} \times 15.615 \times (12.268)^2$$
$$= 293.8 \,\text{kNm} - \text{unfactored}$$

or

$$= \tfrac{1}{8} \times 18.586 \times (12.268)^2$$
$$= 349.7 \,\text{kNm} - \text{factored}.$$

Maximum shear @ support due to DL

$$= \tfrac{1}{2} \times 15.615 \times 12.268$$
$$= 95.8 \,\text{kN} - \text{unfactored}$$

or

$$= \tfrac{1}{2} \times 18.586 \times 12.268^2$$
$$= 114 \,\text{kN} - \text{factored}.$$

Live load: longitudinal bending moments
Parameters depending upon the cross-section of the support structures.

Internal portion

$$t = \text{deck thickness} = 229 \, \text{mm}$$

$$I_g = \text{girder inertia} = 1610 \times 10^6 \, \text{mm}^4 - \text{in steel}$$

$$i = \frac{229^3}{12} + \frac{8.6 \times 1610 \times 10^6}{1829} = 8571 \times 10^3 \, \text{mm}^4/\text{mm}$$

$$j = \frac{t^3}{12(1 - \nu^2)} = \frac{229^3}{12(1 - 0.15^2)} = 1024 \times 10^3 \, \text{mm}^4/\text{mm}$$

$$i_0 = \frac{229^3}{6} = 2001 \times 10^3 \, \text{mm}^4/\text{mm}$$

$$j_0 = i_0 = 2001 \times 10^3 \, \text{mm}^4/\text{mm}$$

Properties of idealized orthotropic plate:

$$D_x = E \cdot i = 8571 \times 10^3 \cdot E_c$$

$$D_{xy} = G \cdot i_0 = 0.435 E_c \times 2001 \times 10^3$$

$$= 870 \times 10^3 \cdot E_c$$

$$D_y = E \cdot j = 1024 \times 10^3 \cdot E_c$$

$$D_{yx} = G \cdot j_0 = 0.435 E_c \times 2001 \times 10^3$$

$$= 870 \times 10^3 E_c$$

$$D_1 = D_2 = \nu \cdot D_y = 1024 \times 10^3 \times 0.15 \times E_c$$

$$= 154 \times 10^3 E_c$$

$$\therefore \quad \alpha = \frac{D_{xy} + D_{yx} + D_1 + D_2}{2(D_x \cdot D_y)^{0.5}}$$

$$= \frac{(870 \times 10^3 + 154 \times 10^3) \times 2 \times E_c}{2 \times (8571 \times 10^3 \times 1024 \times 10^3)^{0.5} \times E_c}$$

$$= 0.346$$

$$\theta = \frac{b}{L} \cdot \left(\frac{D_x}{D_y}\right)^{0.25}$$

$$= \frac{4928}{12\,268} \times \left(\frac{8571 \times 10^3 E_c}{1024 \times 10^3 E_c}\right)^{0.25}$$

$$= 0.683$$

Here:

$$2b = 9855 \qquad \therefore \quad b = 4928\,\text{mm}$$

$$\mu = \frac{W_e - 3.3}{0.6}$$

$$= \frac{4.572 - 3.3}{0.6} = 2.12 > 1$$

$$\therefore \quad \mu = 1.0$$

Here:

$$W_e = \frac{W_c}{n}$$

$$W_c = 9.144\,\text{m}$$

$$\therefore \quad n = 2$$

$$\therefore \quad W_e = \frac{9.144}{2}$$

Final longitudinal moment distribution factor:
From graphs

$$D = 1.90\,\text{m}$$

$$C_f = 12$$

$$\therefore \quad D_d = D\left(1 + \frac{\mu \cdot C_f}{100}\right) = 2.128\,\text{m}$$

Governing live load fraction for longitudinal moment

$$= \frac{S}{D_d} = \frac{1.829}{2.128}$$

$$= 0.86 \quad \text{of one line of wheels (per girder)}$$

External portion
Since the edge-stiffening effect is negligible and the elastic inertias of external portions are close to those of the internal portions, the α, θ, and μ factors will be about the same as before. From the same graph, D for the external portion is approximately equal to 2.03 m, and $C_f = 12$.

The external portion is not critical.

Longitudinal shear
From Table 3.7.1.4.1 of the code,

$$D_d = 1.7\,\text{m}$$

Since S = spacing of girders = 1.829 m < 2.0 m, so, live load fraction for longitudinal shear is

$$= \frac{1.829}{1.7} \times \left(\frac{1.829}{2.0}\right)^{0.25}$$

$$= 1.052 \quad \text{of one line of wheels (per girder)}$$

Dynamic load allowance
Concrete deck slab:

$$\text{DLA} = 0.4$$

Steel girder:

$$\text{DLA} = 0.3$$

because:

$$\text{span length} = 12.268 \, \text{m} < 22 \, \text{m}$$

Therefore, the governing load cases are the OHBD-Truck with more than one axle for all levels.

Unfactored live load effects (including DLA)
Obtained by interpolation between values from Tables 5.4 and 5.5.

Loading combinations
ULS loading combinations 2 and 3 are deemed to be of no consequence. Only ULS loading combination 1 shall be considered.

Table 5.4. Longitudinal bending moments

OHBR level	Maximum load effects, one lane	Live load fraction of one lane	DLA	Unfactored live load (per girder)
1	851 kN·m	$0.86 \times \frac{1}{2}$	30%	476 kN·m
2	860 kN·m	$0.86 \times \frac{1}{2}$	30%	481 kN·m
3	860 kN·m	$0.86 \times \frac{1}{2}$	30%	481 kN·m

Table 5.5. Longitudinal shear

1	303 kN	$1.052 \times \frac{1}{2}$	30%	207 kN
2	349 kN	$1.052 \times \frac{1}{2}$	30%	239 kN
3	349 kN	$1.052 \times \frac{1}{2}$	30%	239 kN

Case No. 1 – no time limit
Total factored load effects

$$= \text{factored DL} + 1.4 \times (L + \text{DLA})$$

Total factored maximum bending moment

$$= 349.7 + 1.4 \times (476) = 1016\,\text{kN} \cdot \text{m} \qquad \text{OHBR-1}$$
$$= 349.7 + 1.4 \times (481) = 1023\,\text{kN} \cdot \text{m} \qquad \text{OHBR-2 and 3}$$

Total factored maximum shear

$$= 114 + 1.4 \times 207 = 404\,\text{kN} \qquad \text{OHBR-1}$$
$$= 114 + 1.4 \times 239 = 449\,\text{kN} \qquad \text{OHBR-2 and 3.}$$

Case No. 2 – the bridge is to be re-evaluated in 5 years
Total factored load effects

$$= \text{factored DL} + 1.25 \times (L + \text{DLA})$$

provided this 'total' shall not be less than $1.25 \times$ (total unfactored load effects).
   Total factored maximum bending

$$= 349.7 + 1.25 \times 476 = 945\,\text{kN} \cdot \text{m} \qquad \text{OHBR-1}$$
$$= 349.7 + 1.25 \times 481 = 951\,\text{kN} \cdot \text{m} \qquad \text{OHBR-2 and 3}$$

For overall safety

$$1.25 \times (293.8 + 476) = 962 \not< 945$$
$$1.25 \times (293.8 + 481) = 969 \not< 951$$

Final total factored bending moments

$$= 962\,\text{kN} \cdot \text{m} \qquad (612 \text{ for LL}) \qquad \text{OHBR-1}$$
$$= 969\,\text{kN} \cdot \text{m} \qquad (619 \text{ for LL}) \qquad \text{OHBR-2 and 3}$$

Total factored maximum shear

$$= 114 + 1.25 \times 207 = 373\,\text{kN} \qquad \text{OHBR-1}$$
$$= 114 + 1.25 \times 239 = 413\,\text{kN} \qquad \text{OHBR-2 and 3}$$

For overall safety

$$1.25 \times (95.8 + 207) = 379\,\text{kN} \not< 373$$
$$1.25 \times (95.8 + 239) = 419\,\text{kN} \not< 413$$

Final total factored shears

$= 379\,\text{kN}$ (283 for LL)   OHBR-1

$= 419\,\text{kN}$ (323 for LL)   OHBR $-$ 2 and 3.

Factored resistance
Concrete deck slabs – no deterioration
Check the requirements of Clause 14.6.5.2 of the code (see Fig. 5.4).

(a)   span $= 1.829\,\text{m} < 4.5\text{m}$
      overhang – right side

      the combined cross-sectional area (hatched) in Fig. 5.4 is

$$= 229 \times 610 \times 2$$
$$-\tfrac{1}{2} \times 229 \times 51$$
$$-\tfrac{1}{2} \times 229 \times 152$$
$$= 256\,137\,\text{mm}^2$$

$$\text{equivalent overhang} = \frac{256\,137}{229} = 1118\,\text{mm} > 1000\,\text{mm}$$

      Overhang – left side

$$\cong 1575 \times \frac{152}{229} = 1045 > 1000$$

(b) $\dfrac{\text{span}}{\text{thickness}} = \dfrac{1829}{229} = 8 < 20$

(c)   thickness $= 229 > 150$
(d)   and (e) are also satisfied.

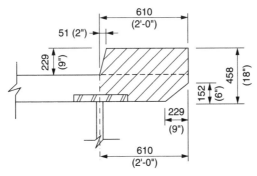

Figure 5.4. Dimensions for concrete deck slab used in factored resistance calculations

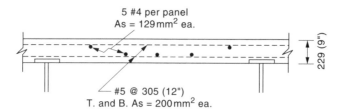

Figure 5.5. A non-composite deck slab

Therefore the unfactored resistance of the non-composite deck slab may be determined from Fig. 5.5.

$$d = 180\,\text{mm} \quad \text{(average of two directions)}$$

$$g = \frac{1}{2}\left(\frac{3 \times 129}{1829 \times 180} + \frac{200}{305 \times 180}\right) \times 100$$

$$= 0.24\%$$

Therefore the *unfactored deck resistance*

$$R_n = 700\,\text{kN}$$

Concrete deck slab – deteriorated
Assume only 150 mm of deck slab is competent

$$\frac{\text{span}}{\text{thickness}} = \frac{1829}{150} = 12.19 < 20$$

$$d = 100\,\text{mm}$$

$$g = \frac{1}{2} \times \left(\frac{3 \times 129}{1829 \times 100} + \frac{200}{305 \times 100}\right) \times 100$$

$$= 0.43\%$$

Then:

$$R_n = 330\,\text{kN}$$

Steel girders – 271104

$$W = 1.517\,\text{kN/m}$$

$$Z_x = 2 \times (255 \times 22 \times 337 + 326 \times 12 \times 163)$$

$$= 5.056 \times 10^6\,\text{mm}^3$$

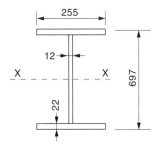

Figure 5.6. Cross-section of an 'I' steel girder

Check compactness (see Fig. 5.6)

    Flange

$$\frac{b}{t} = \frac{255}{2 \times 22} = 5.8 < \frac{170}{\sqrt{210}} = 11.73$$

    Web

$$\frac{h}{w} = \frac{697 - 44}{12} = 54.4 < \frac{1370}{\sqrt{210}} = 94.54$$

Factored bending moment resistance
Since the top flange is cast in the slab, so

$$M_r = \phi Z_x F_y$$

$$= 0.9 \times 5.056 \times 10^6 \times 210 = 955 \times 10^6 \, \text{N} \cdot \text{mm}$$

or

$$M_r = 955 \, \text{kN} \cdot \text{m}$$

Factored shear resistance
For sections without web stiffener

$$k_V = 5.34$$

Therefore

$$\frac{h}{w} = 54.4 < 502 \sqrt{\frac{5.34}{210}} = 80.05$$

$$\therefore \quad F_s = \frac{290\sqrt{F_y k_V}}{(h/w)} = 178.5 \, \text{MPa} > 0.58 F_y = 121.8 \, \text{MPa}$$

Use

$$F_s = 0.58F_y = 121.8 \, \text{MPa}$$

$$V_r = \phi A_w \cdot F_s$$

$$= 0.9 \times 697 \times 12 \times 121.8 = 917\,000 \, \text{N}$$

or

$$V_r = 917 \, \text{kN}$$

Since the total factored shear, 445 kN, is less than V_r, no transverse web stiffener is required.

Check bearing stiffener

$$B_r = 1.25\phi w(N + K)F_y$$

$$= 1.25 \times 0.9 \times 12 \times (230 + 0) \times 210$$

$$= 652 \times 10^3 \, \text{N}$$

or

$$= 652 \, \text{kN} > 445 \, \text{kN}$$

No bearing stiffener is therefore required.

5.1.2.3 Example (5.3) American practice
A two-span continuous steel–concrete composite section has a typical cross-section shown in Fig. 5.7. Each span is 72 ft 3 in effective (22.02 m) and wide flange sections are used for the steel beams. The kerb-to-kerb width is 24 ft (7.315 m). Use the following data in claculations.

Dead load

$$\text{concrete } 5.17 \times 0.15 \times \frac{0.5}{12} = 0.420$$

$$\text{WF* section and cover plates (assumed)} = 0.200$$

$$\text{steel details} = 0.020$$

$$\text{future wear surface } 5.17 \times 0.035 = \underline{0.181}$$

$$\text{parapet and railings} = 0.240/6 = 0.040 = 0.821$$

$$\text{Use } w = 0.86 \, \text{k/ft length} = \underline{0.040}$$

$$\text{DL to be used in centre beam} = 0.86 - 0.2 = 0.66 \, \text{k/ft} = 0.861$$

---

* Wide flange WF is cited in the tables as *W*.

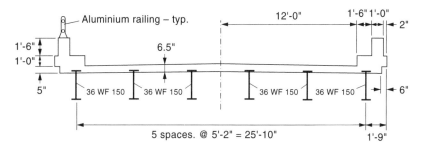

Figure 5.7. A steel–concrete composite bridge deck

Live load

AASHTO: H20-S16-44 or lane whichever is a maximum. Number of lanes is 2, hence no reduction of live loads.

Impact factors

$$I = \frac{50}{125 + 72.25} = 0.254 \quad \text{for all but middle reaction}$$

$$I = \frac{50}{125 + 144.5} = 0.186 \quad \text{for middle reaction}$$

Design of interior beam

Live load H20-S16-44 or lane loading, whichever gives a maximum:

$$\text{live load distribution factor} = \frac{5.17}{2 \times 5.5} = 0.47 \text{ lanes}$$

Two-span continuous portion

Because the splice is a supplementary STL, DL values are calculated on the basis of two simple spans.

Design of interior beam

Dead load moments and reactions are based on Fig. 5.8.

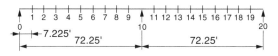

Figure 5.8. Divisions in spans (interior beam design)

Notation:

M_6 = moment of panel pt 6, etc.

$$wL^2 = 0.66 \times \frac{1}{72.25^2}$$

$$= 3450^{K'}$$

(Note that K' denotes ft kips, which is equal to 1.356 kNm, and K denotes kips.)

$$M_{1DL} = 0.0325 \times 3450 = +112^{K'} = M_{19DL}$$

$$M_{2DL} = 0.0550 \times 3450 = +190^{K'} = M_{18DL}$$

$$M_{3DL} = 0.0675 \times 3450 = +233^{K'} = M_{17DL}$$

$$M_{4DL} = 0.0700 \times 3450 = +242^{K'} = M_{16DL}$$

$$M_{5DL} = 0.0625 \times 3450 = +216^{K'} = M_{15DL}$$

$$M_{6DL} = 0.0450 \times 3450 = +155^{K'} = M_{14DL}$$

$$M_{7DL} = 0.0175 \times 3450 = +60^{K'} = M_{13DL}$$

$$M_{8DL} = -0.0200 \times 3450 = -69^{K'} = M_{12DL}$$

$$M_{9DL} = -0.0675 \times 3450 = -233^{K'} = M_{11DL}$$

$$M_{10DL} = -0.125 \times 3450 = -431^{K'}$$

$$R_{0DL} = \frac{1}{2} \times 0.86 \times 72.25 - \frac{535}{72.25}$$

$$= 29.6 - 7.4 = 22.2$$

$$R_{10DL} = 59.2 + 14.8$$

$$= 74.0 \, K$$

Live load moments and reactions are based on Fig. 5.9:

$$\frac{14}{2225} = 1.94 \qquad \frac{30}{7.275} = 4.15$$

$$0.47 \times 1.254 = 0.59 = DF \times \text{impact}$$

$$32 \times 72.25 \times 0.59 = 1364^{K'}$$

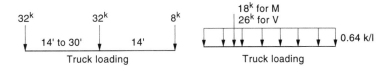

Figure 5.9. Live load moments and reactions

Most positive moments – truck loading:

$$M_{2LL+I} = 1364 \left[0.1504 + 0.1446 + \frac{0.0632}{4} \right] = 370^{K'}$$

$$M_{3LL+I} = 1364 \left[0.1895 + 0.1239 + \frac{0.0666}{4} \right] = 450^{K'}$$

$$M_{4LL+I} = 1364 \left[0.2064 + 0.1241 + \frac{0.1039}{4} \right] = 486^{K'}$$

Using 36 WF 150 for the stringers (and referring to Fig. 5.10):

$$\text{maximum moment due to STL DL} = 0.15 \times \frac{(72.25)^2}{8} = 80.3 \, \text{kip-ft}$$

$$\text{maximum positive moment (i.e. @ 0.4 span)} = 320 + 486 = 806 \, \text{kip-ft}$$

$$\text{maximum negative moment} = -431 - 394 = -825 \, \text{kip-ft}$$

$$\text{maximum negative moment (due to DL)} = (4312 \times 1.18) = 511 \, \text{kip-ft}$$

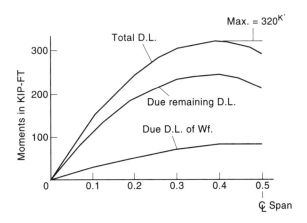

Figure 5.10. Moment curves

(exterior beam)

$$R_{0DL} = \frac{1}{2} \times 0.66 \times 72.25 - \frac{511}{72.25} + \frac{1}{2} \times 0.075 \times 72.25$$

$$= 23.80 - 7.15 + 2.71 = 19.36 \text{ kips}$$

$$R_{10DL} = 47.60 + 14.30 + 5.42 = 67.32 \text{ kips}$$

At point four moment $M = 78$ k-ft (due to dead load of the steel beam).

(interior beam)

$$M_{5LL+I} = 1364 \left[0.2031 + \frac{0.1082}{4} + 0.1184 \right] = 476^{K'}$$

Lane loading:

$$M_{5LL+I} = \left[0.64 \times \frac{313}{72.25^2} \times 0.0938 + 18 \times 0.2031 \times 72.25 \right] 0.59 = 341^{K'}$$

Truck loading governs for the positive moment in the span.
Most negative moments – lane loading:

$$M_{9LL+I} = -0.59[3341 \times 0.0500 + 18 \times 0.0768 \times 72.25] = -157^{K'}$$

$$M_{7LL+I} = -0.59[3341 \times 0.0736 + 18 \times 0.0864 \times 72.25] = -212^{K'}$$

$$M_{10LL+I} = -0.59[3341 \times 0.1250 + 2 \times 18 \times 0.0960 \times 72.25] = -394^{K'}$$

Truck loading:

$$M_{12LL+I} = -1364 \left[0.0960 + 0.0846 + \frac{0.0730}{4} \right] = -262^{K'}$$

$$M_{9LL+I} = -1364 \left[0.0864 + 0.0761 + \frac{0.0657}{4} \right] = -242^{K'}$$

$$M_{8LL+I} = -1364 \left[0.0768 + 0.0677 + \frac{0.0584}{4} \right] = -217^{K'}$$

Lane loading governs at the support; truck loading at other points.
Maximum reaction at exterior supports:

$$R_{0LL+I} = 0.59 \times 60.6 = 35.8^{K'}$$

$$R_{0LL} = 0.47 \times 60.6 = 28.5^{K'}$$

Maximum reaction at interior supports:

$$R_{10LL+I} = 47 \times 1.186 \times 32 \left[1.000 + 0.9465 + \frac{0.9465}{4} \right] = 39.0^{K'}$$

Combined moments and reactions:

maximum positive moment is @ point 4

$$= 320 + 486 = 806\,\text{k-ft}$$

maximum negative moment is @ point 10

$$= 431 - 394 = -825\,\text{k-ft}$$

Selection of the WF section
Since a single span length is $< 80\,\text{ft}$, the splice will be at the interior support. The WF section will be designed for maximum positive moment and the splice will be designed to carry maximum negative moment plus 10% additional or $825 + 83 = 908^{K'}$:

$$Z = \frac{12 \times 806}{20} \quad \leftarrow \text{A36 steel} \quad = 480.0\,\text{in}^3$$

Use 36 WF 150 (36 W 150):

$$Z = 502.9\,\text{in}^3$$

$$Z_{\text{splice}} = 908 \times \frac{12}{20} = 545\,\text{in}^3$$

Design of exterior beam
Live load of H20-S16-44 on lane loading, whichever gives a maximum

$$\text{live load distribution factor} = \frac{5.17}{2 \times 5.5} = 0.47\,\text{lanes}$$

The dead load comprises:

$$\text{concrete } 3.83 \times 0.15 \times \frac{6.5}{12} = 0.311$$

$$\text{WF section and cover plates and details } = 0.200$$

concrete kerb and parapet and aluminium railings $=$

$$1.0 \times 2.69 \times 0.15 + \frac{0.240}{6} = 0.426$$

$$\text{future wear of surface} = 0.035 \times 1.67 = \underline{0.058}$$

$$w = 0.994$$

Dead load moments and reactions comprise DL without STL DL$=0.79$ and these will be the previous values multiplied by the ratio

$$\frac{0.79}{0.66} = 1.19$$

Live load moments and reactions will be the same as the previous values.

Combined moments and reactions are those that do not include moments due to STL DL:

$$M_{2DL+LL+I} = 190 \times 1.19 + 370 = 597^{K'}$$

$$M_{3DL+LL+I} = 233 \times 1.19 + 450 = 728^{K'}$$

$$M_{4DL+LL+I} = 242 \times 1.19 + 486 = 775^{K'}$$

$$M_{5DL+LL+I} = 216 \times 1.19 + 476 = 734^{K'}$$

$$M_{8DL+LL+I} = -69 \times 1.19 - 217 = -300^{K'}$$

$$M_{9DL+LL+I} = -233 \times 1.19 - 242 = -520^{K'}$$

$$M_{10DL+LL+I} = -431 \times 1.19 - 394 = 905^{K'}$$

$$R_0 = 22.2 \times \frac{0.94}{0.86} = 25.0$$

$$R_{10} = 7.4 \times \frac{0.99}{0.86} = 85.5$$

Therefore, maximum positive moment $= 775 + 78$

$$= 853 \, \text{k-ft}$$

Selection of the WF section or W section

The WF section will be designed for maximum positive moment and the splice will be designed and lengthened to carry maximum negative moment plus 10% additional or $905 + 91 = 996^{K'}$:

$$Z = \frac{853 \times 12}{20} \quad \leftarrow \text{A36 steel} \quad = 511.0 \, \text{in}^3$$

Use 36 WF 150:

$$Z = 503 \, \text{in}^3$$

$$Z_{\text{splice}} = \frac{996 \times 12}{20} = 595.0 \, \text{in}^3$$

Live load deflection – interior and exterior beams

Δ for a concentrated load @ $\mathcal{L}$ of a simple span $= \dfrac{f_s l^2}{d \times 6E}$

Δ for a continuous beam would be less than Δ for a simple span so that Δ for simple spans is a conservative estimate.

Maximum combined shear at the internal support
Values here will be for the exterior beam (see Fig. 5.11) as only one splice design
will be made for both interior and exterior beams.
   Shear due to LL (see Fig. 5.12):

$$R_{10} = 0.59 \times 32 \left[1 + 0.9465 + \frac{0.8024}{4} \right] = 40.6^{K'}$$

$$R_{10} = 0.59 \times 32 \left[0 + 0.702 + \frac{0.0952}{4} \right] = 1.8^{K'}$$

Therefore, maximum shear at the interior support $= 40.6 + 33.7 = 74.3^{K'}$

Web shear
This is given by:

$$v = \frac{74.3}{35.84 \times 0.625} = 3.31 \text{ ksi} < 12 \text{ ksi}$$

Note that $1 \text{ ksi} = 1 \text{ kip/in}^2 = 6.895 \text{ MN/m}^2$

Design of the splice
Consider the following data:

$$f_s = 20\,000 \text{ psi}$$

$$\text{web shear} = 12\,000 \text{ psi}$$

$$\text{bearing} = 29\,500 \text{ psi} \quad \text{at } 3\% \text{ splice } \mathbb{P}\text{s}$$

$$\text{shop rivet stress} = 13.5^{K} \text{ in}^2 \text{ shear}$$

$$P - \tfrac{7''}{8} \oslash \text{ rivet} = 0.6013 = 13.5 = 8.12^{K}$$

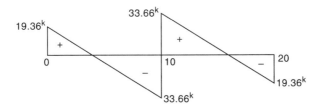

Figure 5.11. SF diagram (DL only)

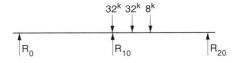

Figure 5.12. Shear calculations

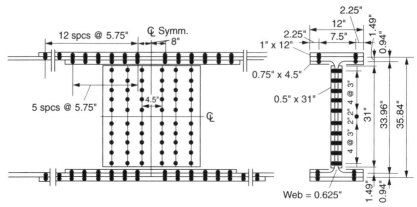

Figure 5.13. Design of the splice

Use A-36 steel of 20 000 for all splice ₽s (see Fig. 5.13):

design moments $= 898^{K'} \times 1.10 = 998^{K'}$

$$I \text{ gross } 36 \text{ WF } 150 = \quad 9012.1 \; (S = 502.9 \text{ in}^3)$$

$$I \text{ web holes} = 0.625(1)(\overline{2}^2 + \overline{5}^2 + \overline{8}^2 + \overline{11}^2 + \overline{14}^2)2$$

$$= -410$$

$$I \text{ ₽holes} = 0.94(1)(17.45)^3 4 = \underline{-1146}$$

$$I \text{ net} = \quad 7456 \text{ m}^4$$

$$S_{\text{net}} = 416 \text{ m}^3$$

$$S_{\text{required}} = \frac{988 \times 12}{20} = 593 \text{ in}^2$$

$$I_{\text{net}} \text{ for } \tfrac{1}{2}'' \text{ web ₽s} = [(0.5)(31)^3/12 - 2(410)0.5]2$$
$$= (1240 - 410)2$$
$$= \quad 1660 \text{ in}^4$$

$$I_{\text{net}} \text{ for } \tfrac{3}{4}'' \text{ Æ ₽s} = 4(3.5)(0.75)(16.60)^2 = \quad 2890$$

$$I_{\text{net}} \text{ for } 1'' \text{ Æ ₽s} = 2(10)(1)(18.42)^2 = \quad \underline{6800}$$

$$\text{net } I \text{ splice ₽s} = 11\,350 \text{ in}^4$$

$$\text{net } S \text{ splice ₽s} = \frac{11\,350}{18.92} = 600 \text{ m}^3 > 593 \text{ m}^3$$

$$\text{maximum capacity of web } \text{Ł}\text{s} = \frac{f_s I}{C} = \frac{20 \times 166.0}{15.5} = \left(\frac{15.5}{18.92}\right) = 1755^{''\text{K}}$$

$$I \text{ web rivets} = 3(2)410 = 2460 \, \text{in}^4$$

$$\text{shear capacity } 36 \, \text{WF} \, 150 = 12 \, \text{K/in}^2 \, 10(35.84)(0.625) = 269^{\text{K}}$$

$$75\% \, V = 202^{\text{K}}$$

$$\text{average of capacity and actual } V = \frac{269 + 88.1}{2} = 173^{\text{K}} \quad (\text{use } 210^{\text{K}})$$

Web rivet stress

$$V = \frac{210^{\text{K}}}{30 \, \text{riv}} = 7.00^{\text{K/riv}}$$

$$M = \frac{1755 \times 14}{2460} = 10.0^{\text{K/riv}}$$

$$R = \sqrt{7^2 + 10^2} = 12.21^{\text{K/riv}}$$

$$\text{bearing on a } 0.625'' \text{ web} = \frac{12.21^{\text{K}}}{0.625 \times 0.75} = 22.4 \, \text{K/in}^2 < 29.5$$

$$\text{shear on a } \tfrac{7}{8}'' \oslash \text{ rivet} = \frac{12.21^{\text{K}}}{2 \times 0.6013} = 10.15 \, \text{K/in}^2 < 13.5$$

$$\text{moment capacity of } 1'' \text{ Ł Ł}\text{s} = \frac{20}{18.92} \times 6800 = 7180 \, \text{kip-ins}$$

$$\text{moment capacity of } \tfrac{3}{4}'' \text{ Ł Ł}\text{s} = \frac{20 \times 2890}{16.98} \left(\frac{16.78}{18.92}\right) = 3035 \, \text{kip-ins}$$

$$\text{force on } \tfrac{3}{4}'' \oslash \text{ Ł Ł}\text{s} = \frac{3055}{33.96} = 90.0 \, \text{kips}$$

$$\text{rivets required} = \frac{90}{8.12} = 11.1 \, (= 12 \text{ say}) \quad \text{or 2 rows of 6 each}$$

$$\text{bearing on } \tfrac{3}{4}'' \text{ Ł} = \frac{90}{12} \times 0.75 \times 0.875 = 11.4 \, \text{kip/in}^2 < 29.5$$

$$\text{force on } 1'' \text{ Ł Ł}\text{s} = \frac{7180}{35.84} = 200 \, \text{kips}$$

$$\text{rivets required} = \frac{200}{8.12} = 24.6 \, (= 26 \text{ say}) \quad \text{or 2 rows of 13}$$

$$\text{force/rivet} = \frac{90}{12} + \frac{200}{26} = 7.5 + 7.7 = 15.2\,\text{kips}$$

$$\text{bearing on } \mathbb{E}\ \mathbb{P} = \frac{15.2}{0.94} \times 0.875 = 18.5\,\text{kip/in}^2 < 29.5\,\text{kip/in}^2$$

calculated moment @ support $= 898$ (refer to Fig. 5.14)

design for $1.1 \times 898 = 988$

calculated moment @ $0.1 = 518 + 30 = 538^{K'}$

design for $1.1 \times 538 = 592^{K'}$

$$\text{capacity 36 WF 150} = 20 \times \frac{502.9}{12} = 838\,\text{kip-ft}$$

$$x = \frac{150}{396} \times 7.25 = 2.75'$$

Therefore, minimum length of cover $\mathbb{P} = 2(2.75 + 1) = 7.50'$

  or

$$= 2d + 3 = 2 \times 3 + 3 = 9.00'$$

Allowable compressive stress @ support $= 20\,000 - 7.2L^2/b^2$

$$\therefore \quad \frac{L}{b} = 12 \times \frac{12}{12} = 12$$

$$20\,000 - 7.2(12)^2 = 18\,960\,\text{psi}$$

At the support

$$f_s = 1.2 \times 18\,960 = 22\,750\,\text{psi}$$

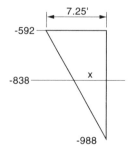

Figure 5.14. Calculated moment at the support

Therefore use 20 ksi.

At the point of cut-off $f_s = 18.96\,\text{ksi}$

$$I\ 36\,\text{WF}\ 150\ (\text{net}) = 9012 - 1146 = 7866\,\text{in}^4$$

$$\text{Therefore,}\ M = \frac{18.96 \times 7866}{12 \times 18.96} = 665$$

Thus, distance from support to the last rivet $= (988 - 665) \times \dfrac{7.25}{396} = 5.92' = 6'.0$

and pitch of rivets $= \dfrac{72 - 3}{12} = 5\frac{3}{4}''$

Therefore, increase length of cover ₽s accordingly.

STL DL deflections will be based on the fact that we have two simple spans of $72'\text{-}3''$ before the splice is made:

$$W = 0.15 \times 72.25 = 10.9\,\text{kips}$$

$$y_{\frac{1}{4}\,\text{pt}} = \frac{0.00928 \times 10.9 \times (72.25)^3 \times 1728}{29\,600 \times 9012 \times 12} = 0.00928 \times 2.2618 = 0.021'$$

$$y_{\frac{1}{2}\,\text{pt}} = 0.01302 \times 2.2618 = 0.029'$$

$$y_{\frac{3}{4}} = 0.021'$$

For DL of 0.79 kip/ft (i.e. remaining DL) deflections are based on continuity:

$$W = 0.79 \times 72.25 = 57^{\text{K}}$$

$$\therefore\quad y = \frac{(72.25)^3 \times 1728}{29\,000 \times 9012} \left[57C - \frac{516}{72.25} C_{\text{F}} \right]$$

$$y_{\frac{1}{4}\,\text{pt}} = 2.49(57 \times 0.00928 - 7.16 \times 0.0391) = 0.6175'' = 0.051'$$

$$y_{\frac{1}{2}\,\text{pt}} = 2.49(57 \times 0.01302 - 7.16 \times 0.0625) = 0.7321'' = 0.061'$$

$$y_{\frac{3}{4}} = 2.49(57 \times 0.0928 - 7.16 \times 0.0547) = 0.3386'' = 0.028'$$

Concrete dead load deflection at 10' points

Consider all steel beams to act as a single unit with total concrete dead load on them to compute deflections. Referring to Figs. 5.15 and 5.16 and the following:

$x = $ point at which deflection is sought

$$y = \text{deflection} = \frac{L^3}{EI} \left[CW - C\frac{M_A}{L} - C_{\text{F}}\frac{M_B}{L} \right]$$

$$I = 4(9012) + 2(10\,470) = 56\,988\,\text{in}^4$$

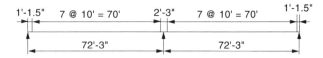

Figure 5.15. Dead load deflections: spacing of points for which deflection is figured

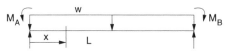

Figure 5.16. Dead load deflection analysis

$$L = 72.25'$$

$$W = wL = (4 \times 0.6 + 2 \times 1.0)72.25 = 317.9^K$$

$$M_A = 0$$

$$M_B = \frac{4.4}{0.8L} \times 535 = 2871^{K'}$$

C and C_F from Table 5.6 are dependent on the point at which deflection is sought:

$$y = \frac{\overline{72.25}^3 \times 1728}{29\,000 \times 57\,000}\left[317.9C - \frac{2871}{72.25} C_F\right] = 0.394[317.9C - 39.7C_F]$$

(in inches).

Table 5.6. Concrete dead load deflections at 10 points

Distance x from right or left support	$\frac{x}{L}$	C	C_F	$317.9C$	$39.7C_F$	Deflection (inches)	Deflection (feet)
1.12	0.016	0.00067	0.0027	0.213	0.107	0.042	0.0035
11.12	0.154	0.00613	0.0251	1.950	0.996	0.376	0.0313
21.12	0.292	0.01040	0.0448	3.31	1.778	0.605	0.0504
31.12	0.430	0.01272	0.0584	4.05	2.32	0.682	0.0569
41.12	0.570	0.01272	0.0641	4.05	2.55	0.591	0.0493
51.12	0.110	0.01040	0.0587	3.31	2.33	0.386	0.0322
61.12	0.847	0.00613	0.0399	1.950	1.583	0.145	0.0121
71.12	0.986	0.00067	0.0046	0.213	0.183	0.012	0.0010
72.25	1	0	0	0	0	0	0

Camber diagram for interior beam and exterior beam at quarter points
Consider the camber diagram given by Fig. 5.17 and the data provided by Table 5.7:

$$a = \text{PG elev } 5 - \frac{\text{PG elev } 9 + \text{PG elev } 1}{2}$$

$$= 923.025 - \frac{923.220 + 922.498}{2} = 0.166' = 2'' \uparrow$$

$$\text{VC}_2 = \text{PG elev } 2 - \left[922.498 + \frac{7}{8}(923.220 - 922.498)\right] - \frac{1}{4}(0.166)$$

$$= 923.202 - (922.498 + 0.632) - 0.042$$

$$= 0.030' \uparrow$$

$$\text{VC}_3 = \text{PG elev } 3 - \left[922.498 + \frac{3}{4}(923.220 - 922.498)\right] - \frac{1}{2}(0.166)$$

$$= 923.164 - (922.498 + 0.542) - 0.083$$

$$= 0.041' \uparrow$$

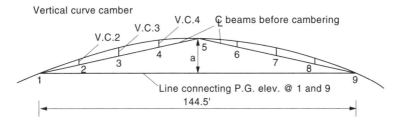

Figure 5.17. Analysis for camber

Table 5.7. Profile grade elevations on vertical curve at $\frac{1}{4}$ points

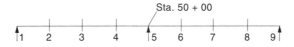

Point	Station on ℄	Tangent gradient	Vertical curve correction	Profile grade elevation
1	49 + 27.75	930.482	−7.262	923.220
2	49 + 45.81	931.024	−7.822	923.202
3	49 + 63.87	931.566	−8.402	923.164
4	49 + 81.94	932.108	−9.003	923.105
5	50 + 00	932.65	−9.625	923.025
6	50 + 18.05	931.928	−9.003	922.925
7	50 + 36.13	931.205	−8.402	922.803
8	50 + 54.19	930.483	−7.822	922.661
9	50 + 72.25	929.760	−7.262	922.498

$$VC_4 = 923.105 - \left[922.498 + \frac{5}{8}(923.220 - 922.498)\right] - \frac{3}{4}(0.166)$$

$$= 923.105 - (922.498 + 0.451) - 0.125$$

$$= 0.031' \uparrow$$

$$VC_5 = 0$$

$$VC_6 = 922.925 - \left[922.498 + \frac{3}{8}(923.220 - 922.498)\right] - \frac{3}{4}(0.166)$$

$$= 922.925 - (922.498 + 0.271) - 0.125$$

$$= 0.031' \uparrow$$

$$VC_7 = 922.803 - \left[922.498 + \frac{1}{4}(923.220 - 922.498)\right] - \frac{1}{2}(0.166)$$

$$= 922.803 - (922.498 + 0.180) - 0.803$$

$$= 0.042' \uparrow$$

$$VC_8 = 922.661 - \left[922.498 + \frac{1}{8}(923.220 - 922.498)\right] - \frac{1}{4}(0.166)$$

$$= 922.661 - (922.498 + 0.090) - 0.042$$

$$= 0.031' \uparrow$$

Dead load deflections were given in Fig. 5.15 for the $\frac{1}{4}$ points. Combine these with the VC camber to obtain the final camber figures:

$$y_{DL} \ @ \ \tfrac{1}{4}\mathrm{pt} = 0.021 + 0.051 = 0.072'$$

$$y_{DL} \ @ \ \tfrac{1}{2}\mathrm{pt} = 0.029 + 0.106 = 0.090'$$

$$y_{DL} \ @ \ \tfrac{3}{4}\mathrm{pt} = 0.021 + 0.028 = 0.049'$$

$$\text{Camber} \ @ \ \tfrac{1}{4}\mathrm{pt} = 0.072 + 0.030 = 0.102 = 1\tfrac{1}{4}''$$

$$\text{Camber} \ @ \ \tfrac{1}{2}\mathrm{pt} = 0.090 + 0.041 = 0.131 = 1\tfrac{9}{16}''$$

$$\text{Camber} \ @ \ \tfrac{3}{4}\mathrm{pt} = 0.049 + 0.031 = 0.080 = \tfrac{15}{16}''$$

Make interior and exterior beam camber the same (see Fig. 5.18).

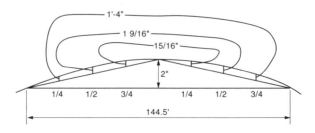

Figure 5.18. Camber diagram

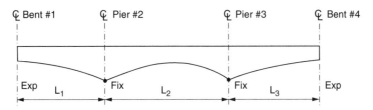

Figure 5.19. Reinforced concrete bridge – expansion plate and shoe

5.1.2.4 Example (5.4) American practice

A reinforced concrete girder has fixed bearings (see Fig. 5.19) at piers 2 and 3 and expansion bearings are placed at bents 1 and 4. Set the expansion plate for the bridge deck for the following temperatures:

$$0 \quad 20 \quad 30 \quad 40 \quad 60 \quad 80 \quad 100 \quad 120°F$$

The coefficient of linear expansion is 0.000006. Thus:

for southbound $L_1 = 39'$ $L_2 = 53'\text{-}9''$ $L_3 = 39'$

for northbound $L_1 = 36'$ $L_2 = 49'\text{-}9''$ $L_3 = 36'$

Southbound

$$\text{expansion length} = 39' + \frac{53'\text{-}9''}{2} = 65.875'$$

$$\frac{\text{expansion}}{20°F} = 0.000006 \times 65.875 \times 12 \times 20 = 0.095''$$

Table 5.8. At bent No. 1 (bent No. 4 opposite)

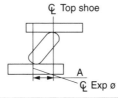

	$0°$	$20°$	$40°$	$60°$	$80°$	$100°$	$120°$	*Remarks*
₵ top shoe to ₵ exp ₵	0.785 $\frac{13''}{16}$	0.690 $\frac{11''}{16}$	0.595 $\frac{5''}{8}$	0.500 $\frac{1''}{2}$	0.405 $\frac{3''}{8}$	0.310 $\frac{5''}{16}$	0.215 $\frac{3''}{16}$	Starting with $\frac{1''}{2}$ Deflection at 60°F

A

Northbound

$$\text{expansion length} = 36' + \frac{49'\text{-}7''}{2} = 60.875'$$

$$\frac{\text{expansion}}{20°\text{F}} = 0.000006 \times 60.875 \times 12 \times 20 = 0.088''$$

Table 5.9. At bent No. 1 (bent No. 4 opposite)

	0°	20°	40°	60°	80°	100°	120°	Remarks
℄ top shoe to ℄ exp ℄	0.764 $\frac{3''}{4}$	0.676 $\frac{11''}{16}$	0.588 $\frac{9''}{16}$	0.500 $\frac{1''}{2}$	0.412 $\frac{7''}{16}$	0.324 $\frac{5''}{16}$	0.236 $\frac{1''}{4}$	Starting with $\frac{1''}{2}$ deflection at 60°F

$\longleftarrow \qquad\qquad\qquad A \qquad\qquad\qquad \longrightarrow$

5.1.2.5 Example (5.5) American practice

If in example (5.4) only pier 3 has a fixed bearing and elsewhere at 1, 2 and 3 are expansion joints (see Fig. 5.20), carry out calculations for the expansion plate setting for the southbound bridge.

At (D):

$$\text{expansion length} = 39'\text{-}0''$$

$$\frac{\text{expansion}}{20°\text{F}} = 0.000006 \times 39 \times 12 \times 20 = 0.056''$$

Table 5.10. Span III expansion

0°	20°	40°	60°	80°	100°	120°	Remarks
0.668 $= \frac{11''}{16}$	0.612 $= \frac{5''}{8}$	0.556 $= \frac{9''}{16}$	0.5 $= \frac{1''}{2}$	0.444 $= \frac{7''}{16}$	0.388 $= \frac{3''}{8}$	0.332 $= \frac{5''}{16}$	Starting with $\frac{1''}{2}$ deflection

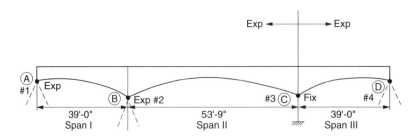

Figure 5.20. Expansion plate setting

At (B):

expansion length $= 53.75'$

$$\frac{\text{expansion}}{20°F} = 0.000006 \times 53.75 \times 12 \times 20 = 0.077''$$

Table 5.11. Span II expansion

0°	20°	40°	60°	80°	100°	120°	Remarks
0.231 $= \frac{1}{4}''$	0.154 $= \frac{1}{8}''$	0.077 $= \frac{1}{16}''$	0	0.077 $= \frac{1}{16}''$	0.154 $= \frac{1}{8}''$	0.231 $= \frac{1}{4}''$	Starting with 0 deflection

At (A):

expansion length $= 92.75'$

$$\frac{\text{expansion}}{20°F} = 0.000006 \times 92.75 \times 12 \times 20 = 0.134''$$

Table 5.12. Span I expansion

0°	20°	40°	60°	80°	100°	120°	Remarks
0.902 $= \frac{7}{8}''$	0.768 $= \frac{3}{4}''$	0.634 $= \frac{5}{8}''$	0.5 $= \frac{1}{2}''$	0.366 $= \frac{3}{8}''$	0.232 $= \frac{1}{4}''$	0.028 $= \frac{1}{8}''$	Starting with $\frac{1}{2}''$ deflection

5.1.2.6   Example (5.6)   American practice

A vertical curve camber is needed for a two-span continuous beam of $65'$-$6''$ span, each as shown in Fig. 5.21. Various elevations are marked. Note that 1 ft $= 0.3048$ m:

EL PT A $= 899.082$

EL PT C $= 899.221$

EL PT E $= 899.186$

EL PT B $= 906.09 - 90.150(0.01848) - (509.85)^2 0.0000202 = 899.173'$

EL PT D $= 906.09 - 155.65(0.01848) - (444.35)^2 0.0000202 = 899.226'$

EL PT B$' = (899.082 + 899.221) \div 2 = 899.152'$

EL PT D$' = (899.221 + 899.186) \div 2 = 899.203'$

EL PT F $= (899.082 + 899.186) \div 2 = 899.134'$

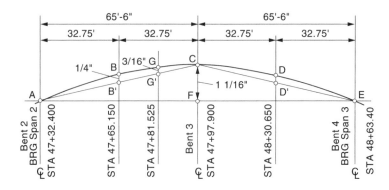

Figure 5.21. A vertical curve camber

$$\left.\begin{array}{l} \text{B-B}' = 0.173 - 0.152 = 0.021' \\ \text{D-D}' = 0.226 - 0.703 = 0.023' \end{array}\right\} \text{ say } 0.022' = \frac{1}{4}''$$

$$\text{C-F} = 899.221 - 899.134 = 0.087' = 1\frac{1}{16}''$$

$$\text{EL PT G} = 906.09 - (0.01848)106.525 - (498.475)^2 0.0000202 = 899.202'$$

$$\text{EL PT G}' = 899.186'$$

$$\text{G-G}' = 899.202 - 899.186 = 0.016' = \frac{3}{16}''$$

Dead load deflection (using SHDI STD 5-15)

Find the total deflection at $\frac{1}{4}$ points and concrete deflection at 10 ft points using Figs 5.22 and 5.23 and Table 5.13.

Solve the deflection using total DL acting on seven stringers as a unit:

$$W(\text{conc.}) = 5(0.553) + 2(0.775) = 2.77 + 1.55 = 4.32 \,\text{K}$$

$$w(\text{STL not including STL DL}) = 0.763 \times 7 = 5.35 \,\text{kip/ft}$$

$$y = \frac{L^3}{EI}\left[C_W - C_F \frac{M_F}{L}\right]$$

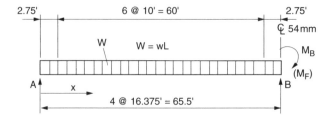

Figure 5.22. Dead load deflection

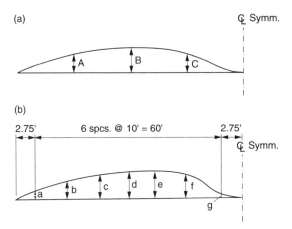

Figure 5.23. (a) Total deflection. (b) Cone deflection

$$I = 7 \times 9012.1 = 63\,084.7\,\text{in}^4$$

$$E = 29 \times 10^3\,\text{K/in}^2$$

$$M_B \text{ for } w = 1\,\text{kip/ft} = 1 \times 0.125 \times 65.5^2 = 536\,\text{kip-ft}$$

$$\frac{M_B}{L} = \frac{536}{65.5} = 8.20^K$$

$$\frac{L^3}{EI} = \frac{65.5^3 \times 1728}{29 \times 10^3 \times 63\,485} = 0.2655\,\text{kip-in}$$

Table 5.13. Deflection computation (units in udl)

X	$\frac{X}{L}$	C	① C_W	C_F	② $C_F \dfrac{M_F}{L}$	① − ②	y (unit)	y (conc.)	y (Total)
Total deflection @ $\frac{1}{4}$ points									
16.375	0.25	0.00928	0.608	0.0391	0.320	0.288	0.0765		0.409″
32.750	0.50	0.01302	0.853	0.0625	0.512	0.341	0.0905		0.484″
49.125	0.75	0.00928	0.608	0.0547	0.448	0.160	0.0425		0.228″
Concrete deflection @ 10 points									
2.75	0.042	0.00174	0.114	0.0070	0.082	0.032	0.0085	0.037″	
12.75	0.195	0.0075	0.496	0.0313	0.256	0.240	0.0637	0.272″	
22.75	0.347	0.01158	0.758	0.0509	0.416	0.342	0.0908	0.392″	
32.75	0.500	0.01302	0.853	0.0625	0.512	0.341	0.0905	0.391″	
42.75	0.653	0.01158	0.758	0.0625	0.512	0.246	0.0654	0.282″	
52.75	0.805	0.00757	0.496	0.0472	0.387	0.109	0.0290	0.124″	
62.75	0.958	0.00174	0.114	0.0131	0.107	0.007	0.0019	0.008″	

5.1.2.7 Example (5.7) American practice

A concrete T-beam deck for a bridge of simple span of 38'-0" (11.58 m) is shown in Fig. 5.24. Design the bridge deck and sketch reinforcement details using the following data:

DL interior beams

Parapet and railing $= [(1.5)(1.0)(0.15) + 0.10]1/2.5$	$= 0.094$
Slab $= (8)(0.54)(0.15)$	$= 0.648$
BM $= (2.29)(2)(0.15)$	$= 0.686$
FWS $= (0.035)(8)$	$= 0.280$
	1.708

DL exterior beams

Parapet and railing	$= 0.094$
Slab $= (6.17)(0.54)(0.15)(7.08/8)$	$= 0.442$
Kerb $= (0.93)(3.17)(0.15)8.58/8$	$= 0.423$
BM	$= 0.686$
FWS $= (3.0)(0.035)(5.5/8)$	$= 0.073$
	1.718

LL distribution on interior beam

$$\frac{5}{6} \times 2 = \frac{8}{12} = 0.67$$

LL distribution on exterior beam

$$\frac{5}{8} \times \frac{1}{2} = 0.312$$

Therefore design interior beam and adopt the same for exterior and interior and exterior beams will be detailed the same.

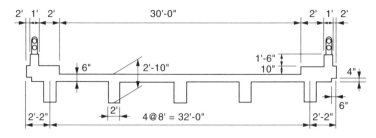

Figure 5.24. Reinforced concrete bridge deck

Interior beam

$$M_{DL} = \frac{1.708 \times (38)^2}{8} = 308'^K$$

$$M_{LL+I} = 0.67 \times 414.3 \times 1.3 = 355.5$$

$$\Sigma M = 663.5'^K$$

$$V_{DL} = 1.708 \times \frac{38}{2} = 32.5^K$$

$$V_{LL+I} = 0.67 \times 54.3 \times 1.3 = 46.6$$

$$\Sigma V = 79.1^K$$

$$R_B = \frac{32(19+5)}{38} = 20.2^K \quad \text{(see Fig. 5.25)}$$

$$V\mathcal{L}_{LL+I} = 20.2 \times 0.67 \times 1.3 = 17.3^K$$

Exterior beam

$$M_{DL} = \frac{1.718 \times (38)^2}{8} = 310'^K$$

$$M_{LL+I} = 0.312 \times 414.3 \times 1.3 = 168'^K$$

$$\Sigma M = 478'^K$$

$$V_{DL} = 1.718 \times \frac{38}{2} = 32.6$$

$$V_{LL+I} = 0.312 \times 54.3 \times 1.3 = 22.0$$

$$\Sigma V = 54.6'^K$$

$$V\mathcal{L}_{LL+I} = 20.2 \times 0.312 \times 1.3 = 8.2^K$$

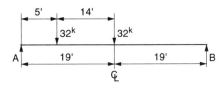

Figure 5.25. Wheels on span

Concrete characteristics

$$f_s = 20\,000\,\text{psi}$$

$$f_c = 12\,00\,\text{psi}$$

$$n = 10$$

$$v = 90\,\text{psi without web reinforcement}$$

$$v = 60\,\text{psi to be taken by concrete with stirrups}$$

$$v = 225\,\text{psi with stirrups}$$

$$u = 300\,\text{psi}$$

$$E_s = 30\,000\,000\,\text{psi}$$

Interior beam design (34″ depth)
Investigate the T-beam shown in Fig. B.26 using two rows of 6#10 and 6#11:

$$A_S = 7.62 + 9.36 = 16.98\,\text{in}^2$$

$$(24 \times Kd)\frac{Kd}{2} + 72 \times 6.25(Kd - 3.125) = 10 \times 16.98(29.15 - Kd)$$

$$12\overline{Kd^2} + 450Kd - 1410 = 4950 - 169.8Kd$$

$$12\overline{Kd^2} + 619.8Kd = 6360$$

$$\overline{Kd^2} + 52Kd = 530$$

$$\overline{Kd^2} + 52.0Kd + \left(\frac{52}{2}\right)^2 = 530 + 676 = 1206$$

$$Kd + 26 = \sqrt{1206} = \pm 34.7$$

$$Kd = 8.7''$$

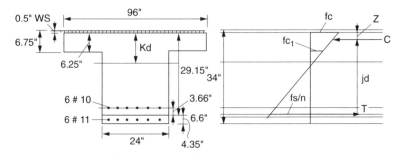

Figure 5.26. Analysis and design of T-beams

$$f_{c_1} = (8.7 - 6.25) \times \frac{f_c}{8.7} = 0.282 f_c$$

$$(96 \times 8.7) \frac{f_c}{2} = 412.5 f_c \times \frac{8.7}{3} \, (\text{ARM from } f_c) = 1196 f_c$$

$$-(72)(8.7 - 6.25)\left[\frac{(0.282)f_c}{2}\right] = -24.9 f_c \times \left(6.25 + \frac{2.45}{3}\right) = -176 f_c$$

$$\underline{387.6 f_c} \qquad\qquad \underline{1020 f_c}$$

$$Z = \frac{1020 f_c}{387.6 f_c} = 2.63$$

$$Jd = 29.15 - 2.63 = 26.52$$

$$T = C = \frac{663.5 \times 12}{26.52} = 300$$

$$f_c = \frac{300}{387.6} = 775 \, \text{psi} < 1200 \quad (\text{acceptable})$$

$$f_{s(\text{average})} = \frac{300}{16.98} = 17.7 \, \text{kip/in}^2 \quad (\text{acceptable})$$

$$f_{s_{\max}} = (17.7)\frac{29.15 - 8.7 + 1.64}{29.15 - 8.7}$$

$$= (17.7)(1.10) = 19.47 \, \text{kip/in}^2 < 20 \, \text{kip/in}^2$$

Adopt 34″ depth for interior and exterior beams. Detail exterior and interior beam the same for future expansion.

Note that $1 \, \text{kip/in}^2 = 6894.76 \, \text{KN/m}^2 = 6.89476 \, \text{MN/m}^2$.

Bond

$$u = \frac{V}{\Sigma_o jd} = \frac{79.100}{(6 \times 4.4)(6 \times 4) \times 26.52} = 59.2 \, \text{psi} < 300 \, \text{psi}$$

Shear

$$v = \frac{79\,100}{24 \times 2652} = 140 \, \text{psi} > 90 \quad \text{Therefore, stirrups required}$$

$$< 225 \quad \text{Therefore, acceptable with stirrups}$$

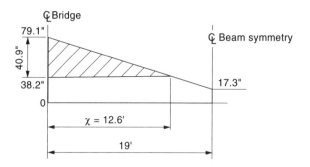

Figure 5.27. Diagram for shear without stirrups

Allow V without stirrups (see Fig. 5.27):

$$v = \frac{60 \times 24 \times 26.52}{1000} = 38.2^K$$

$$\chi = 40.9 \times \frac{19}{61.8} = 12.6'$$

Spacing of 2# 11 45° stirrups (see Figs 5.28 and 5.29):

$$s = \frac{1.414 A_v f_v jd}{V'} = \frac{1.414(2 \times 1.56)20 \times 26.52}{40.9} = 50''$$

Therefore, use $18''$ as standard sheet C10.05.

Vertical stirrup spacing
Refer to Fig. 5.30 and the following data:

$$s = \frac{A_v f_v jd}{V'} \quad \text{use # 4-stirrups: } A_v = 2 \times 0.20 = 0.40\,\text{in}^2$$

At $4.75'$ from ℄ BRG:

$$V' = (12.6 - 4.75) \times \frac{40.9}{12.6} = 25.5^K$$

$$s = \frac{0.40 \times 20 \times 26.52}{25.5} = \frac{212}{25.5} = 8.3''$$

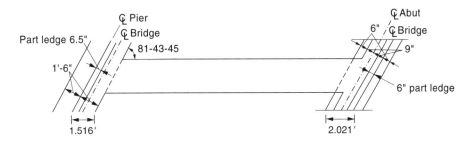

Figure 5.28. Beam plan

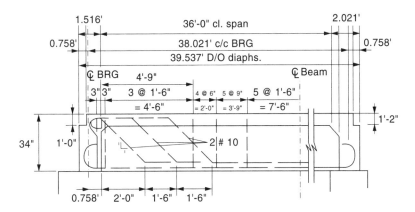

Figure 5.29. Beam elevation and reinforcement

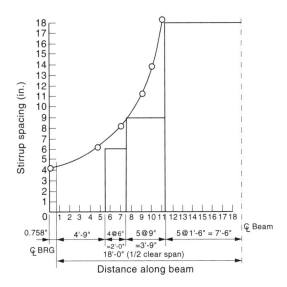

Figure 5.30. Stirrup spacings along the beam span

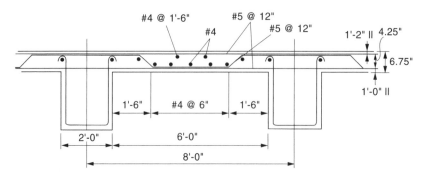

Figure 5.31. Reinforcement for the deck slab

At $7'$ from ℄ BRG: $V' = (14.2 - 7)3.36 = 24.2^K$; $s = \dfrac{196}{24.2} = 8.10''$

At $9'$ from ℄ BRG: $V' = (14.2 - 9)3.36 = 17.5^K$; $s = \dfrac{196}{17.5} = 11.20''$

At $11'$ from ℄ BRG: $V' = 3.2 \times 3.36 = 1075^K$; $s = \dfrac{196}{10.75} = 18.22''$

At $10'$ from ℄ BRG: $V' = 4.2 \times 3.36 = 14.1^K$; $s = \dfrac{196}{14.1} = 13.90''$

At the support: $V' = 47.7$; $s = \dfrac{196}{47.7} = 4.10''$

Final reinforcement for the bridge deck of Example (5.7) is shown in Fig. 5.31.

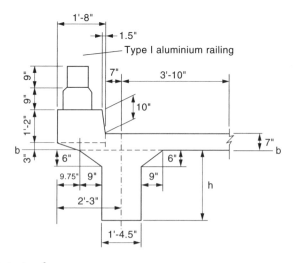

Figure 5.32. Exterior beam

5.1.2.8 Example (5.8)   American practice

The exterior stringer of a concrete deck is shown in Fig. 5.32 and the associated data are given below. Determine the live load distribution factor for the exterior stringer and the dead load distribution factors. Using both dead and live load distribution factors, calculate end reactions for a three-span continuous bridge.

Data

Note that 1 lb/ft = 14.59 N/m.

$$\text{slab: } 4.41 \times 0.583 \times 150 = 386$$

$$\text{haunches: } 0.75 \times 0.50 \times 150 = 56$$

$$\text{kerb: } \tfrac{1}{2} \times 0.25 \times 0.81 \times 150 = 15$$

$$1.17 \times 1.67 \times 150 = 293$$

$$-\tfrac{1}{2} \times 0.83 \times 0.125 \times 150 = -8$$

$$0.85 \times 0.25 \times 150 = 32$$

$$\text{railing concrete and railing} = \underline{34}$$

$$808$$

$$\text{diaphragms} = \underline{12}$$

$$820 \text{ lb/ft}$$

$$\text{future working surface: } 4.42 \times 35 = \underline{155}$$

$$975 \text{ lb/ft}$$

Interior stringer distribution factor	Spans
UDL 1350 lb/ft	36' 49'–49''
LL distance $f = 1.280$ lb/ft	36': 49'-9'': 36'
	Three spans

Live load distribution factor

Simple beam distribution, where P = wheel load (Fig. 5.33):

$$\frac{6.25}{7.67} P + \frac{0.25}{7.67} P = (0.814 + 0.033)P$$

$$= 0.847P$$

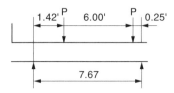

Figure 5.33. Load distribution factor

Railing concrete

$$0.75 \times 1.00 \times 150 = 112$$
$$0.75^2 \times 150 = 84$$
$$\text{railing} = \underline{10}$$
$$206$$

$$\frac{206\,\text{lb/ft}}{6\ \text{stringers}} = 34\,\text{lb/ft}$$

Stress area of slab

$$6.5 \times 73 = 475$$
$$-\tfrac{1}{2} \times 3 \times 9.75 = \underline{-15}$$
$$460$$

I_{bb} of slab

$$\tfrac{1}{3} Ah^2 = \tfrac{1}{3}(460)6.5^2 = 6490\,\text{in}^4$$

$$-\frac{bd^3}{12}\ \text{for a right angle} = \frac{9.75 \times 3^3}{12} = \underline{-20}$$

$$I_{bb} = 6470\,\text{in}^4$$

$$Ad = 460x - 3.75 = 1500$$

$$\text{constant portion of the web} = 975\,\text{lb/ft}$$
$$\underline{309}$$
$$1284\,\text{lb/ft}$$

The data are compared below.

	Interior stringer	Exterior stringer
UDL	1350 lb/ft	1284 lb/ft
LL distance f	1.280 lb/ft	0.847 lb/ft

Therefore, use the same design for the exterior stringer as for the interior stringer.

Exterior stringer reactions

For R_A:

Dead load (DL)

$$\left.\begin{array}{l} \text{uniform DL} = \dfrac{1284}{1350} \times 15.83 = 15.01 \\[2mm] \text{varying DL} \qquad\qquad = \ \ 1.01 \end{array}\right\} 16.11^K$$

$$\text{live load} = \frac{0.847}{1.28} \times 32.45 = 21.50$$

$$\text{impact} = \frac{0.847}{1.28} \times 9.75 = \underline{\ \ 6.45}$$

$$\text{Total} = 44.06^K$$

For R_B:

Dead load

$$\left.\begin{array}{l} \text{uniform DL} = \dfrac{1284}{1350} \times 73.10 = 69.60 \\[2mm] \text{varying DL} \qquad\qquad = 12.58 \end{array}\right\} 82.18^K$$

$$\text{live load} = \frac{0.847}{1.28} \times 44.84 = \ \ 29.65$$

$$\text{impact} = \frac{0.847}{1.28} \times 13.00 = \underline{\ \ 8.60}$$

$$\text{Total} = 120.43^K$$

Northbound spans are 36'-0"–49'9"–36'-0". Consider now the moments about the spans:

$$\text{DL span 1} \quad \text{NB} = \frac{36^2}{39^2} \times \text{SB} = \frac{1296}{1521} \text{SB} = 0.852\text{SB}$$

$$\text{DL span 2} \quad \text{NB} = \frac{49.75^2}{53.75^2} \times \text{SB} = \frac{2475}{2890} \text{SB} = 0.856\text{SB}$$

At the support use NB = 0.8545SB.

$$\text{LL span 1} \quad \text{NB} = \frac{36}{39} \times \text{SB} = 0.923\text{SB}$$

$$\text{LL span 2} \quad \text{NB} = \frac{49.75}{53.75} \times \text{SB} = 0.925\text{SB}$$

At the support use NB = 0.854SB.

For reactions and shears NB = 0.925SB.

Moments northbound at various points along span 1 are detailed below:

Span 1
Point 4

$$DL = 0.852 \times 1\,159\,184 = \quad 990\,000$$

$$LL = 0.923 \times 2\,480\,000 = 2\,290\,000$$

$$I = 0.923 \times \quad 744\,000 = \quad 686\,000$$

$$\text{Total} = 3\,966\,000 \text{ lb-in} = 331 \text{ kip-ft}$$

Point 10 (negative zones)

$$DL = 0.854 \times 5\,358\,766 = -4\,580\,000$$

$$LL = 0.854 \times 3\,536\,000 = -3\,020\,000$$

$$I = 0.854 \times 1\,025\,000 = - \quad 875\,000$$

$$\text{Total} = -8\,475\,000 \text{ lb-in} = -706 \text{ kip-ft}$$

Point 15

$$DL = 0.856 \times \quad 933\,236 = \quad 799\,000$$

$$LL = 0.925 \times 1\,956\,000 = 1\,810\,000$$

$$I = 0.925 \times \quad 548\,000 = \quad 506\,000$$

$$\text{Total} = 3\,115\,000 \text{ lb-in} = 260 \text{ kip-ft}$$

Note that 1 kip-ft = 1.356 kNm.

Where reinforcement (stringers) is required, then:

Point 4

$$\frac{331}{365} \times 10.74 = 0.906 \times 10.74 = 9.74 \text{ sq in} \qquad 8-^{\#}10(A_S = 1/0.16 \text{ sq in})$$

Point 10

$$\frac{706}{827} \times 10.27 = 0.854 \times 10.27 = 8.76 \text{ sq in} \qquad 12-^{\#}8(A_S = 9.48 \text{ sq in})$$

Point 15

$$\frac{260}{286} \times 10.74 = 0.908 \times 10.74 = 9.76 \text{ sq in} \qquad 8-^{\#}10(A_S = 10.16 \text{ sq in})$$

Design of northbound stringers same as SB except use 8–#10 in place of 6–#10 and 2–#11. Also, reduce cut-off lengths proportionally and use the same stirrup spacing.

Reactions at stringers are:

Interior stringer

$$R_A = 0.925 \times \quad 59.04\,\text{kip} = \underline{\quad 54.7\,\text{kip}}$$

$$R_B = 0.925 \times 143.52\,\text{kip} = \underline{132.8\,\text{kip}}$$

Exterior stringer

$$R_A = 0.925 \times \quad 44.06\,\text{kip} = \underline{\quad 40.8\,\text{kip}}$$

$$R_B = 0.925 \times 120.43\,\text{kip} = \underline{111.5\,\text{kip}}$$

Note that 1 kip = 4.448 kN.

5.1.2.9 Example (5.9) American practice

The total span of a continuous bridge is 131′-9″ (40.16 m) and three spans are in the ratio 1 : 1.37 : 1 (39′ : 53′-9″ : 39′) (11.9 m : 16.4 m : 11.9 m). Using the Portland cement continuous bridge (reference details in the text), calculate moments caused by dead and live loads and design a concrete T-girder for this bridge. Use the following data for the figure shown (Fig. 5.34):

$$r_{AB} = 0 \qquad r_{BA} = 1.3 \qquad r_{BC} = 1.3$$

$$r_{CB} = 1.3 \qquad r_{CD} = 1.3 \qquad r_{DC} = 0$$

$$C_{AB} \text{ and } C_{DC} = -0.89$$

$$C_{BA} \text{ and } C_{CD} = -0.416$$

$$C_{BC} \text{ and } C_{CB} = -0.730$$

$$k_{BA} = k_{CD} = 10.5$$

$$k_{BC} = k_{CB} = 15.0$$

$$\begin{matrix} k_{BA} = k_{CD} \\ \text{(corrected)} \end{matrix} = [1 - (0.89)(0.416)]10.5 = (1 - 0.37)10.5 = 6.62$$

$$D_{BA} \text{ and } D_{CD} = \frac{\dfrac{kI_cE}{L}}{\sum \dfrac{kI_cE}{L}} = \frac{6.62}{6.62 + \dfrac{15.0}{1.37}} = \frac{6.62}{17.57} = 0.377$$

$$D_{BC} \text{ and } D_{CB} = 1 - 0.377 = 0.623$$

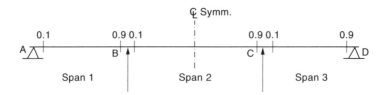

Figure 5.34. A continuous bridge schematic

Moments at supports due to a load in any position on the span
For a load on span 1:

$$M_B = \left(\frac{1 - D_{BA} - U}{1 - U} \right) M_1$$

$$= \left(\frac{1 - 0.377 - 0.207}{1 - 0.207} \right) M_1$$

$$= \frac{0.416}{0.793} M_1 = 0.525 M_1$$

$$U = C_{BC} C_{CB} D_{BC} D_{CB}$$

$$= (-0.730)^2 (0.623)^2 = 0.207$$

$$M_C = \frac{V}{1 - U} (M_1)$$

$$= \left(\frac{-0.171}{1 - 0.207} \right) M_1 = -0.216 M_1$$

$$V = C_{BC} D_{BC} D_{CD}$$

$$= (-0.730)(0.623)(0.377) = -0.171$$

Dead load moments
For loads in span 1 (unit load; see Fig. 5.35) it follows:

$$M_{AB}^F = (0.592) w L_1^2$$

$$M_{BA}^F = 0.140 w L_1^2$$

$$M_1 = M_{BA}^F - C_{AB} M_{AB}^F$$

$$= 0.140 w L_1^2 - (0.89) 0.0592 w L_1^2 = 0.193 w L_1^2 = -294 w$$

$$\underline{M_B = -0.525 \times 294 w = -154 w}$$

$$M_C = -0.216 \times 294 w = -63.5 w$$

$$M_C = -M_B \quad \text{for loads in span 3 by symmetry}$$

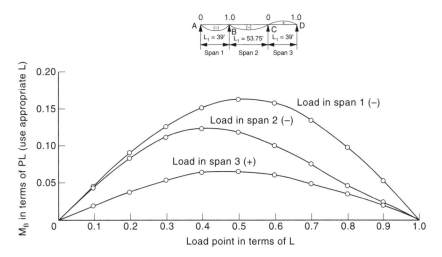

Figure 5.35. Influence line for moment M_B

For loads in span 1 (haunched load):

$$M_{AB}^F = -0.001\,W_{BA}L_1^2$$

$$M_{BA}^F = -0.018\,W_{BA}L_1^2$$

$$M_1 = -0.018\,W_{BA}L_1^2 - 0.89 \times 0.001\,W_{BA}L_1^2$$

$$= -0.019\,W_{BA}L_1^2 = -28.9\,W_{BA}$$

$$\underline{M_B = -0.525 \times 28.9\,W_{BA} = \underline{-15.2\,W_{BA}}}$$

$$M_C = -0.216 \times 28.9\,W_{BA} = -6.24\,W_{BA}$$

For loads in span 2 (haunched load):

$$M_{BC}^F = M_{CB}^F = -(0.0168 + 0.0026)\,W_{BC}L_2^2$$

$$= -(0.0194)\,W_{BC}(53.75)^2 = -56.0\,W_{BC}$$

$$\underline{M_B = (0.476 + 0.216)(-56.0\,W_{BC}) = \underline{-38.8\,W_{BC}} = M_C}$$

For loads in span 2 (unit load):

$$M_{BC}^F = M_{CB}^F = -0.105\,wL_1^2 = -303w$$

$$\underline{M_B = (0.475 + 0.216)(-303w) = \underline{-210w} = M_C}$$

$$W_{BA} = W_{BC}$$

$$\underline{M_C = M_B = -154w + 63.5w - 210w - 15.2\,W_{BA} + 6.24\,W_{BA} - 38.8\,W_{BA}}$$

$$= -300.5w - 47.34\,W_{BA}$$

Maximum live load moment at B
Refer to Fig. 5.36(a)–(f) and the details that follow.

Lane load

$$M_B = (0.1029)(0.64)(39)^2 + 18(0.1608)(39)$$

$$+ (0.0737)(0.64)(53.75)^2 + 18(0.1222)(53.75)$$

$$= 100 + 113 + 137 + 118 = 468 \text{ kip-ft}$$

This value governs.

Military load

$$M_B \atop \text{span 1} = (0.1608 + 0.1553)24 \times 39 = 296 \text{ kip-ft}$$

$$M_B \atop \text{span 2} = (0.122 + 0.121)24 \times 53.75 = 314 \text{ kip-ft}$$

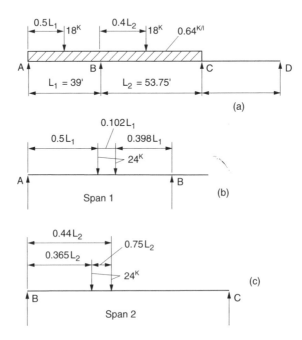

Figure 5.36 (above and facing). Different loads on spans

H20-S16 load

$$M_B = [0.064 \times 8 + (0.161 + 0.069)32]39 = 306 \text{ kip-ft}$$
span 1

$$M_B = [0.06 \times 8 + (0.122 + 0.083)32]53.75 = 378' \text{ kip-ft}$$
span 2

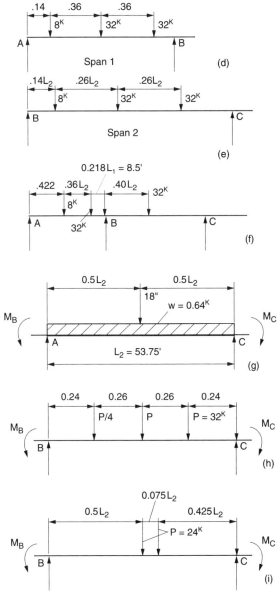

Figure 5.36. (Continued)

$$M_{\mathrm{B}} \qquad = (0.152 \times 8 + 0.103 \times 32)39 + 0.122 \times 32 \times 53.75$$

spans 1 and 2

$$= 386 \, \mathrm{kip\text{-}ft}$$

Maximum live load moment, span 2
Refer to Fig. 5.36(g)-(i) and the details that follow.

Lane load at 0.5

$$M_{\mathrm{B}} = (0.0737)(53.75)^2(0.64) + (0.1178)(18)(53.75)$$

$$= -136 - 114 = -250 \, \mathrm{kip\text{-}ft} = M_{\mathrm{C}}$$

$$M_{0.5} = \left[9 + \left(\frac{53.75}{2}\right) 0.64 \right] \frac{53.75}{2} - 0.64 \left(\frac{53.75}{2}\right) \left(\frac{53.75}{4}\right) - 250$$

$$= 705 - 231 - 250 = 224 \, \mathrm{kip\text{-}ft}$$

H20-S16 load at 0.5

$$M_{\mathrm{B}} = \left(\frac{0.0938}{4} + 0.1178 + 0.0573\right) PL_2 = (0.1986)(32)(53.75)$$

$$= -341 \, \mathrm{kip\text{-}ft}$$

$$M_{\mathrm{C}} = \left(\frac{0.0573}{4} + 0.1178 + 0.0938\right) PL_2 = (0.259)(32)(53.75)$$

$$= -389 \, \mathrm{kip\text{-}ft}$$

$$R_{\mathrm{B}} = \left[\frac{P}{4}(0.76) + P(0.5) + P(0.24)\right] + \frac{341 - 389}{53.75}$$

$$= 29.8 - 0.9 = 28.9^{\mathrm{K}}$$

$$M_{0.5} = (28.9)\frac{53.75}{2} - 340 - 8(0.26 \times 53.75)$$

$$= 778 - 340 - 112 = \underline{326 \, \mathrm{kip\text{-}ft}}$$

This value governs.

Military load at 0.5

$$M_{\mathrm{B}} = (0.1178 + 0.1034)PL_2 = 0.2212 \times 24 \times 53.75 = 285 \, \mathrm{kip\text{-}ft}$$

$$M_{\mathrm{C}} = (0.117 + 0.1212)PL_2 = 0.2390 \times 24 \times 53.75 = 308 \, \mathrm{kip\text{-}ft}$$

$$R_{\mathrm{B}} = 0.425P + 0.50P + \frac{285 - 308}{L_2} = 22.20 - 0.43 = 21.77^{\mathrm{K}}$$

$$M_{0.5} = (21.77)(0.5)(53.75) - 285 = 585 - 285 = 300 \, \mathrm{kip\text{-}ft}$$

For loads in span 3

$$M_B = \left(\frac{W}{1-V}\right) M_3$$

$$W = C_{CB} D_{CB} D_{BA} A$$

By symmetry

$$W = V = -0.171$$

Therefore $\quad M_B = \left(\frac{V}{1-V}\right) M_3 = -0.216 M_3$

(see M_C for span 1 loaded)

Also by symmetry

$$M_C = 0.525 M_3$$

For loads in span 2

$$\underline{M_B} = \frac{D_{BA} M_{BC}^F - W M_{CB}^F}{1-U} = \frac{0.377 M_{BC}^F - (-0.171) M_{CB}^F}{1-0.207}$$

$$= \underline{0.475 M_{BC}^F + 0.216 M_{CB}^F}$$

By symmetry

$$M_C = 0.475 M_{CB}^F + 0.216 M_{BC}^F$$

$$M_1 = M_{BA}^F - C_{AB} M_{AB}^F = M_{BA}^F + (0.89) M_{AB}^F$$

$$M_3 = M_{CD}^F - C_{DC} M_{DC}^F = M_{CD}^F + (0.89) M_{DC}^F = M_{BA}^F + (0.89) M_{AB}^F$$

Influence lines for M_B can be calculated based upon previous equations and the data given in Table 5.14. Calculated M_C values will be opposite by symmetry.

Maximum live load moments, span 1
Refer to Fig. 5.37 and the details that follow.

Lane load at point 0.35

$$M_B \text{ (load in span 3)} = +0.64 \times 0.0423 \times \overline{39}^2 = +1.04 \times 39$$

$$M_B \text{ (unit load in span 1)} = -0.64 \times 0.1029 \times \overline{39}^2 = -2.59 \times 39$$

$$M_B \text{ (18}^K \text{ load in span 1)} = -18 \times 0.1369 \times 39 = -2.41 \times 39$$

$$\sum M_B = -3.96 \times 39$$

Table 5.14. Influence lines in loaded spans for moments

Point	Load in span 1				
	M_{AB}^F	M_{BA}^F	M_1	M_B	M_C*
0.1	$-0.0770PL_1$	$-0.0194PL_1$	$-0.0879PL_1$	$-0.0461PL_1$	$+0.0190$
0.2	$-0.1140PL_1$	$-0.0675PL_1$	$-0.1688PL_1$	$-0.0885PL_1$	$+0.0364$
0.3	$-0.121PL_1$	$-0.130PL_1$	$-0.236PL_1$	$-0.1240PL_1$	$+0.0510$
0.4	$-0.106PL_1$	$-0.191PL_1$	$-0.285PL_1$	$-0.1498PL_1$	$+0.0615$
0.5	$-0.079PL_1$	$-0.236PL_1$	$-0.306PL_1$	$-0.1608PL_1$	$+0.0661$
0.6	$-0.0497PL_1$	$-0.252PL_1$	$-0.296PL_1$	$-0.1553PL_1$	$+0.0640$
0.7	$-0.026PL_1$	$-0.230PL_1$	$-0.253PL_1$	$-0.1329PL_1$	$+0.0546$
0.8	$-0.0103PL_1$	$-0.1745PL_1$	$-0.1887PL_1$	$-0.0965PL_1$	$+0.0396$
0.9	$-0.0021PL_1$	$-0.0947PL_1$	$-0.0966PL_1$	$-0.05071PL_1$	$+0.0289$
			Total area	-0.1029	$+0.0423$

Point	Load in span 2		
	M_{BC}^F	M_{CB}^F	M_B
0.1	$-0.0927PL_2$	$-0.0052PL_2$	$-0.0451PL_2$
0.2	$-0.1650PL_2$	$-0.0240PL_2$	$-0.0835PL_2$
0.3	$-0.206PL_2$	$-0.0605PL_2$	$-0.1107PL_2$
0.4	$-0.2075PL_2$	$-0.1135PL_2$	$-0.1222PL_2$
0.5	$-0.1705PL_2$	$-0.1705PL_2$	$-0.1178PL_2$
0.6	$-0.1135PL_2$	$-0.2075PL_2$	$-0.0986PL_2$
0.7	$-0.0005PL_2$	$-0.206PL_2$	$-0.0728PL_2$
0.8	$-0.0240PL_2$	$-0.1650PL_2$	$-0.1470PL_2$
0.9	$-0.0052PL_2$	$-0.0927PL_2$	$-0.0225PL_2$
		Total area	-0.0737

* Reversing points (such as $0.9 = 0.1$) gives $M_C = M_B$ for a load in span 3.

$$M_{0.35L_1} = \left[\frac{18(0.65 \times 39) + 0.64(39)^2/2 - 3.96 \times 39}{39} \right.$$

$$\left. \times (0.35 \times 39) - (0.64)\frac{(0.35 \times 39)^2}{2} \right.$$

$$= 276 - 59.5 = 216.5 \, \text{kip-ft}$$

Lane load at point 0.40

$$M_B \ (18^K \text{ load in span 1}) = -18 \times 0.1498 \times 39 = -2.72 \times 39$$

$$\sum M_B = (+1.04 - 2.59 - 2.72)39' = -4.27 \times 39$$

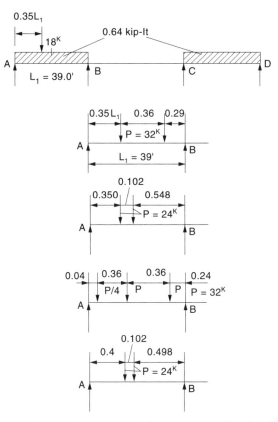

Figure 5.37. Loads on alternative spans with corresponding load positioning

$$M_{0.4L_1} = [18(0.6) + 12.5 - 4.27](0.4 \times 39)$$

$$- (0.64) \frac{(0.4 \times 39)^2}{2}$$

$$= 296 - 78 = 218 \,\text{kip-ft}$$

H20-S16 load at point 0.35

$$M_B = (0.1369 + 0.1293)PL = -0.266PL_1$$

$$M_{0.75} = \left[\frac{P(0.29L_1) + P(0.65L_1) - 0.266PL}{2} \right] 0.35L_1$$

$$= 0.67P \times 0.35 \times 39 = 32^K(9.15) = 293 \,\text{kip-ft}$$

Military load at point 0.35

$$M_B = -(0.1369 + 0.1555)PL = -0.292PL$$

$$M_{0.35} = (0.548P + 0.65P - 0.292P)0.35(39)$$

$$= 0.906 \times 24 \times 0.35 \times 39 = 297\,\text{kip-ft}$$

This value governs for span 1.

H20-S16 load at point 0.4

$$M_B = \left(\frac{0.0184}{4} + 0.1498 + 0.1111\right) PL = -0.2655PL$$

$$M_{0.4} = \left[P(0.24) + P(0.60) + \frac{P}{4}\,(0.96) - 0.266P\right](0.4)(39) - \frac{P}{4}\,(0.36 \times 39)$$

$$= 0.784 \times 32 \times 0.4 \times 39 - 8 \times 0.36 \times 39 = 391 - 112 = 279\,\text{kip-ft}$$

Military load at point 0.4

$$M_B = -(0.1498 + 0.1608)PL = -0.3106PL$$

$$M_{0.4} = (0.498 + 0.60 - 0.3106)24 \times 39 \times 0.40 = 294\,\text{kip-ft}$$

Girder design
For the girder spacing use the value of $7'$-$8''$ (see Fig. 5.38):

approx. $b' = 0.0025\sqrt{b} \times L = 0.0025\sqrt{92} \times 39 \times 12 = 11.2''$

Use the value of $13''$ which will accommodate 3-#11 bars. Slab $= 6\frac{3}{4}''$, which includes $\frac{1}{4}''$ wearing surface. Reinforcing #5 bars @ $5\frac{1}{2}''$ from <u>Indiana std. C10.30.</u>

$$\text{FWS} = 35\,\text{psi}$$

$$f_s = 20\,000$$

$$f_c = 1200$$

$$n = 10$$

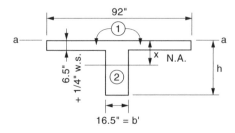

Figure 5.38. Schematic for girder design

Check width:

$$12(6.5) + 12 = 90 < 92$$

Therefore, make $b' = 16\frac{1}{2}''$, which will accommodate 4-#11 bars.

Calculate 'I' for gross T-section where values of h are between $0.04L$ and $0.12L$; $L = 39'\text{-}0''$:

$$h \text{ values} = 18'', 24'', 30'', 36'', 42'', 48'', 54'', 60''$$

From Fig. 5.38:

$$\text{Area} \circled{1} = (6.5)(75.5) = 490 \text{ in}^3$$

$$\text{Area} \circled{2} = 16.5h$$

$$\text{moment area} \circled{1} = 490 \times 3.25 = 1590 \text{ m}^3$$

$$\text{moment area} \circled{2} = 16.5h \times \frac{h}{2} = 8.25h^2$$

$$I_0 \circled{1} = \frac{75.5(6.5)^3}{12} = 1725 \text{ in}^4$$

$$I_0 \circled{2} = \frac{(16.5)h^3}{12} = 1.375h^3 \text{ in}^4$$

Note that $1 \text{ in}^3 = 16\,387 \text{ mm}^3$ and $1 \text{ in}^4 = 416\,231 \text{ mm}^4$.

When $h = 18''$

$$x = \frac{1590 + 2670}{490 + 297} = \frac{4260}{787} = 5.42''$$

$$d_{\circled{1}} = 5.42 - 3.25 = 2.17''$$

$$d_{\circled{2}} = 9 - 5.42 = 3.58''$$

$$I_{18} = 1725 + 490(2.17)^2 + 1.375(16)^3 + 297(3.58)^2 = \underline{15\,845 \text{ in}^4}$$

When $h = 24''$

$$x = \frac{15\,904 + 4750}{490 + 396} = \frac{6340}{886} = 7.15''$$

$$d_{\circled{1}} = 7.15 - 3.25 = 3.90''$$

$$d_{\circled{2}} = 12 - 7.15 = 4.85''$$

$$I_{24} = 1725 + 490(3.9)^2 + 1.375(24)^3 + 396(4.85)^2 = \underline{37\,495 \text{ in}^4}$$

When $h = 30''$

$$x = \frac{1590 + 7920}{490 + 495} = \frac{9010}{985} = 9.15''$$

$d_① = 9.15 - 3.25 = 5.90''$

$d_② = 15 - 9.15 = 5.85''$

$\underline{I_{30}} = 1725 + 490(5.9)^2 + 1.375(30)^3 + 495(5.85)^2 = \underline{72\,875\,in^4}$

When $h = 36''$

$$x = \frac{1590 + 10\,700}{490 + 594} = \frac{12\,290}{1084} = 11.32''$$

$d_① = 11.32 - 3.25 = 8.07''$

$d_② = 19 - 11.32 = 6.68''$

$\underline{I_{36}} = 1725 + 490(8.07)^2 + 1.375(36)^3 + 594(6.68)^2 = \underline{124\,325\,in^4}$

When $h = 42''$

$$x = \frac{1590 + 14\,550}{490 + 693} = \frac{16\,140}{1183} = 13.45''$$

$d_① = 13.65 - 3.25 = 10.40''$

$d_② = 21 - 13.65 = 7.35''$

$\underline{I_{42}} = 1725 + 490(10.4)^2 + 1.375(42)^3 + 693(7.35)^2 = \underline{193\,425\,in^4}$

When $h = 48''$

$$x = \frac{1590 + 19\,000}{490 + 792} = \frac{29\,590}{1292} = 16.02''$$

$d_① = 16.02'' - 3.25 = 12.77''$

$d_② = 24 - 16.02 = 7.98''$

$\underline{I_{48}} = 1725 + 490(12.77)^2 + 1.375(48)^3 + 792(7.98)^2 = \underline{284\,225\,in^4}$

When $h = 54''$

$$x = \frac{1590 + 24\,050}{490 + 890} = \frac{25\,640}{1380} = 18.6''$$

$d_① = 18.6'' - 3.25 = 15.35''$

$d_② = 27 - 18.6 = 8.4''$

$\underline{I_{54}} = 1725 + 490(15.35)^2 + 1.375(54)^3 + 890(8.4)^2 = \underline{396\,225\,in^4}$

When $h = 60''$

$$x = \frac{1590 + 29\,700}{490 + 990} = \frac{31\,290}{1480} = 21.16''$$

$$d_{\textcircled{1}} = 21.16'' - 3.25 = 17.91''$$

$$d_{\textcircled{2}} = 30 - 21.16 = 8.84''$$

$$\underline{I_{60}} = 1725 + 490(17.91)^2 + 1.375(60)^3 + 990(8.64)^2 = \underline{533\,225\,in^4}$$

The values of I are plotted against h in Fig. 5.39.

Using the following:

$\quad h_s = $ depth at support $= 60'' + \frac{1}{4}''$ wearing surface

$\quad I_s = 533\,225\,in^4$

Therefore, I_h for depth at $\text{\textcentoldstyle}$ of span $= \dfrac{533\,225}{(1 + 1.3)^3} = \dfrac{533\,225}{12.18} = 43\,700\,in^4$

Using $h = 25''$, and the following dead load values:

Slab	$(0.56)(6.29)(0.15)$	$= 0.528$
25″ beam @ $\text{\textcentoldstyle}$	$(2.08)(1.37)(0.15)$	$= 0.427$
FWS	$(0.035)(7.67)$	$= 0.268$
Railing	$(0.004/3)$	$= 0.001$
Parapet	$(1.0)(1.50)(0.15)/3$	$= 0.075$
Haunches	$(0.75)(0.5)(0.15)(2)(\frac{1}{2}) = \underline{0.056}$	
	$w = 0.056$ kip-ft	

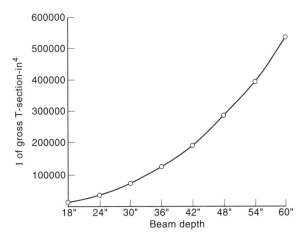

Figure 5.39. Second moment of area (I) versus beam depth (h)

Note that kip/ft $= 14.594$ kN/m. Then:

$$W_{BA} = (2.92)(1.37)(0.15) = 0.60 \, \text{kip/ft}$$

$$M_{BDL} = M_{CDL} = -300.5w - \frac{47.3}{W_{BA}} = -300.5(1.355) - 47.31(0.40)$$

$$= -435 \, \text{kip-ft}$$

Live load distribution factor $= \dfrac{7.67}{2 \times 5} = 0.767$. Thus:

$$I = \frac{50}{53.75 + 125} = 0.28 \quad \text{for span 2}$$

$$I = \frac{50}{39 + 125} = 0.3 \quad \text{for span 1 and } R_A$$

$$I = \frac{50}{46.38 + 125} = 0.292 \quad \text{for } M_B$$

$$I = \frac{50}{92.75 + 125} = 0.23 \quad \text{for } R_B$$

$$M_{BLL+I} = -461 \times 0.767 \times 1.292 = -458 \, \text{kip-ft}$$

$$\sum M_B = 458 + 435 = 893 \, \text{kip-ft}$$

$$d = 5\text{'-}0\tfrac{1}{4}'' - 2\tfrac{1}{4}'' = 58.0''$$

Investigate the section at the support using RCDH:

$$K = 197$$

$$M_R = \frac{0.197}{12} \times 16.5 \times (58.0)^2 = 910 > 893 \, \text{kip-ft}$$

Use $h = 6\text{'-}0\tfrac{1}{4}''$. Then $M = 893$

$$A_s = \frac{893 \times 12}{20 \times 0.875 \times 58} = 10.55 \, \text{in}^2$$

Use 18–#8 bars. Then $A_S = 10.5 \, \text{in}^2$

Check for the assumed section plus moments
Using $h = 25'' + \tfrac{1}{4}''$ wearing surface.

Moment at point 0.4 span I

$$\text{simple beam moment due to } \omega = \frac{1.355}{2}(0.4)(0.6)(39)^2 = \quad 248 \text{ kip-ft}$$

$$\text{simple beam moment due to } W_{BA} = \frac{0.60}{3} \times \frac{39}{2} \times \frac{1}{8} \times 0.4 \times 39 = \quad 7 \text{ kip-ft}$$

$$\text{Total:} \quad 255 \text{ kip-ft}$$

$$\text{portion of } M^F_{B_{DL}} \text{ at } 0.4 = -0.4(435) = -174 \text{ kip-ft}$$

$$\sum M_{DL} = \quad 81 \text{ kip-ft}$$

$$\sum M_{LL+I} = 294 \times 0.767 \times 1.3 = \quad 294 \text{ kip-ft}$$

$$\sum M_{0.4} = \quad 375 \text{ kip-ft}$$

Moment at point 0.35 span I

$$\text{simple beam moment due to } \omega = \frac{1.355}{2}(0.35)(0.65)(39)^2 \quad = \quad 235 \text{ kip-ft}$$

$$\text{simple beam moment due to } W_{BA} = \frac{0.60}{3} \times \frac{39}{2} \times \frac{1}{8} \times 0.35 \times 39 = \quad 7 \text{ kip-ft}$$

$$\text{Total:} \quad 242 \text{ kip-ft}$$

$$\text{portion of } M^F_{B_{DL}} \text{ at } 0.35 = -0.35(435) = - 152 \text{ kip-ft}$$

$$90 \text{ kip-ft}$$

$$\sum M_{LL+I} = 297 \times 0.767 \times 1.3 = \quad 296 \text{ kip-ft}$$

$$\sum M_{0.4} = \quad 386 \text{ kip-ft}$$

This value governs span 1.

Moment at point 0.5 span 2

$$\text{simple beam moment due to } \omega = \frac{1.355 \times 53.75^2}{3} = \quad 490 \text{ kip-ft}$$

simple beam moment due to W_{BA}

$$= \left[\left(\frac{0.60}{3} \times \frac{53.75}{2} \right) \left(\frac{7}{8} + \frac{1}{8} \right) \times \frac{53.75}{2} \right]$$

$$- \left[\frac{0.6}{3} \times \frac{53.75}{2} \times \frac{3}{4} \times \frac{53.75}{2} \right] \qquad = \quad 36 \text{ kip-ft}$$

$$\text{portion of } M^F_B \text{ and } M^F_C \qquad = \quad 526 \text{ kip-ft}$$

$$\sum M_{LL+I} = -297 \times 0.767 \times 1.28 \qquad = -435 \text{ kip-ft}$$

$$91 \text{ kip-ft}$$

$$317 \text{ kip-ft}$$

$$408 \text{ kip-ft}$$

Since the moment at point 0.5 in span 2 is the highest, it is essential to check the section against this moment:

$$h = 25'' + \tfrac{1''}{4} \text{ wearing surface}$$

$$d = 25 - 2.5 = 22.5$$

Using data from the reinforced concrete handbook (and referring to Fig. 5.40):

$$\frac{t}{d} = \frac{6.5}{22.5} = 0.289$$

$$K = 189$$

$$a = 1.47$$

$$M_{\mathrm{R}} = \frac{Kbd^2}{12\,000} = \frac{189 \times 92 \times 22.5^2}{12\,000}$$

$$= 734 > 408 \text{ kip-ft}$$

The section is therefore safe.

$$A_{\mathrm{S}} = \frac{408}{1.47 \times 22.5} = 12.33 \text{ in}^2$$

and the area of

$$8 - \#11 = 8 \times 1.56 = 12.48 \text{ in}^2.$$

Thus, the section should comprise two layers of $4 - \#11$ each.

Summary of the steel

section at the support $\rightarrow 13 - \#8$ bar

$$A_{\mathrm{S}} = 10.5 \text{ in}^2$$

section at $0.5L \rightarrow 8 - \#11$

$$A_{\mathrm{S}} = 12.48 \text{ in}^2$$

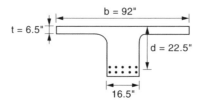

Figure 5.40. Check for assumed direction and moments

5.1.2.10   Example (5.10)   Standard prestressed concrete beams (British practice)

Standard bridge beams for spans of 7 m to 36 m have been prepared by the Prestressed Concrete Development Group of the Concrete Society of the UK. The original work was completed by the Cement and Concrete Association and then enhanced by the British Cement Association (see Figs 5.41–5.44). The standard inverted T-beams when combined with *in situ* concrete provide a rapidly erected alternative to the *in situ* slab. The economic range is a span from 7 to 16 m. For spans above 16 m, a multi-cell construction or a beam-slab construction is recommended. The I- and box-sections are generally more economical for spans of 20 m and above. For spans of more than 29 m, special constructional arrangements and permission will be required.

It is often necessary to use standard beams and the reader will find some standard examples for their usage. Again the British loadings HA and HB are recommended for these beams. Section properties are listed in Tables 5.15 to 5.17. Similar beam examples can be found in other countries.

5.1.2.11   Example (5.11)   British practice

A standard I-beam deck bridge in prestressed concrete having a three-lane carriageway is shown in various detail in Figs 5.45 and 5.46. Twelve standard I-beams at 1.5 m centres are acting in composite with a 180 mm thick structural slab. The beam section for a 22.5 m span bridge is taken as No. I11 (Fig. 5.41).

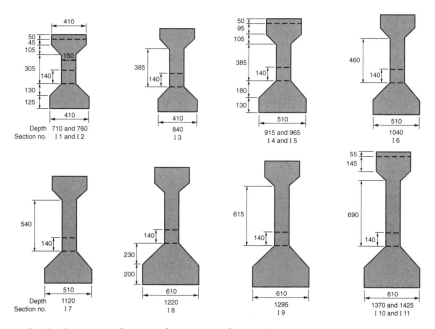

Figure 5.41. I-section beams for spans from 12 to 36 m. Standard sections I1 to I11 (dimensions in millimetres) (courtesy of C&CA, now BCA, and the Concrete Society)

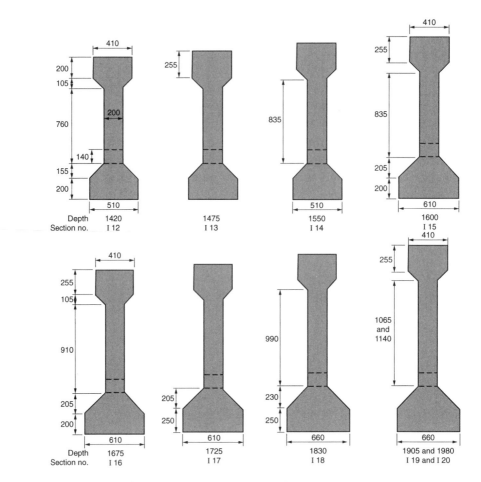

Figure 5.42. Standard sections I12 to I20 (dimensions in millimetres) (Figs 5.42 and 5.43: courtesy of C&CA, now BCA, and the Concrete Society)

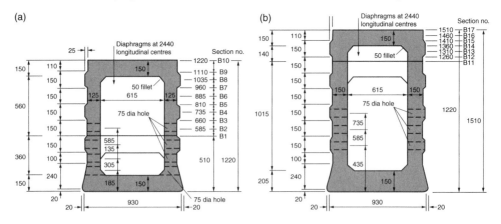

Figure 5.43. Box-section beams for spans from 12 to 36 m. (a) Standard sections B1 to B10. (b) Standard sections B11 to B17 (dimensions in millimetres)

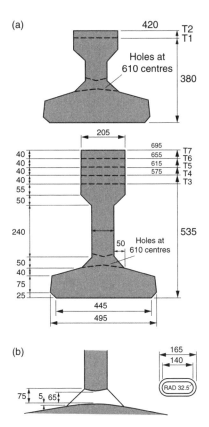

Figure 5.44. Inverted T-beams for spans from 7 to 16 m. (a) The standard inverted T-sections T1 to T7. The top surface of each beam is to be roughened. (b) Transverse and longitudinal aspects of the enlarged hole in the web (dimensions in millimetres) (courtesy of C&CA, now BCA, and the Concrete Society)

Table 5.15. Section properties of inverted T-beams

Section No.	Depth (mm)	Area (mm²)	Height of centroid above bottom fibre (mm)	Section moduli (mm³ × 10⁶)		Self-weight (kN/m)
				Top fibre	Bottom fibre	
T1	380	98 000	140	5.18	8.89	2.31
T2	420	106 200	160	6.76	10.98	2.50
T3	535	114 275	196	9.57	16.55	2.69
T4	575	122 475	220	11.92	19.23	2.89
T5	615	130 675	244	14.30	21.81	3.08
T6	655	138 875	267	16.73	24.36	3.27
T7	695	147 075	289	19.20	26.91	3.47

Table 5.16. Section properties of box-beams

Section No.	Depth (mm)	Area (mm²)	Height of centroid above bottom fibre (mm)	Section moduli (mm³ × 10⁶)		Self-weight (kN/m)
				Top fibre	Bottom fibre	
B1	510	337 550	251	37.80	38.91	7.95
B2	585	356 300	287	47.26	49.12	8.39
B3	660	375 050	323	57.51	60.15	8,84
B4	735	396 925	361	69.92	72.37	9.36
B5	810	418 800	400	82.75	84.99	9.87
B6	885	437 550	435	94.34	97.58	10.31
B7	960	456 300	471	106.59	110.83	10.75
B8	1035	478 175	510	121.68	125.43	11.26
B9	1110	500 050	548	137.10	140.38	11.79
B10	1220	527 550	600	157.00	162.06	12.43
B11	1220	604 625	580	165.09	182.43	14.25
B12	1260	616 625	598	173.47	191.99	14.53
B13	1310	633 501	623	185.98	204.91	14.93
B14	1360	651 001	649	199.30	218.27	15.34
B15	1410	667 877	674	212.20	231.58	15.74
B16	1460	682 876	697	223.44	244.38	16.09
B17	1510	697 876	720	235.01	257.52	16.44

Table 5.17. Section properties of I-beams

Section No.	Depth (mm)	Area (mm²)	Height of centroid above bottom fibre (mm)	Section moduli (mm³ × 10⁶)		Self-weight (kN/m)
				Top fibre	Bottom fibre	
I1	710	176 375	318	24.38	30.01	4.16
I2	760	194 357	357	30.73	34.73	4.58
I3	840	206 375	395	36.54	41.24	4.86
I4	915	254 625	391	44.02	58.95	6.00
I5	965	272 625	427	52.32	65.80	6.42
I6	1040	283 875	461	59.56	74.76	6.69
I7	1120	295 875	497	67.67	84.68	6.97
I8	1220	369 375	492	80.75	119.32	8.70
I9	1295	380 625	523	89.55	132.11	8.97
I10	1370	391 875	554	98.71	145.24	9.23
I11	1425	411 675	595	113.14	157.87	9.70
I12	1420	423 050	668	124.36	140.19	9.97
I13	1475	445 600	707	138.81	150.79	10.50
I14	1550	460 600	744	151.34	164.07	10.85
I15	1600	508 600	725	165.98	200.29	11.98
I16	1675	523 600	760	179.76	216.18	12.34
I17	1725	554 100	767	190.22	237.46	13.06
I18	1830	598 475	793	214.03	279.77	14.10
I19	1905	613 475	827	229.58	299.05	14.46
I20	1980	628 475	862	245.57	318.73	14.81

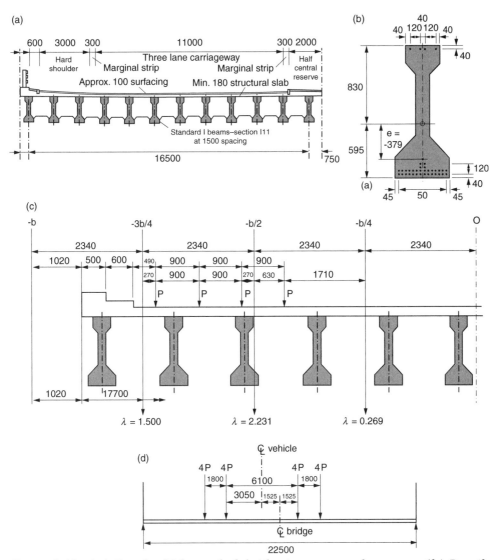

Figure 5.45. (a) Standard I-beam deck bridge in prestressed concrete. (b) Details of the I-beam. (c) Transverse position of HB loading for maximum longitudinal moment. (d) Longitudinal position of HB loading for maximum longitudinal moment (dimensions in millimetres) (courtesy of C&CA, now BCA, and the Concrete Society)

A surface loading of $2.4\,\text{kN/m}^2$ for the deck surface is included. The beam-slab bridge is to be designed for HA loading and checked for HB45 units. Use the following data:

Precast:

$$f_{cu} = 50\,\text{N/mm}^2$$
$$f_{yt} = 40\,\text{N/mm}^2$$

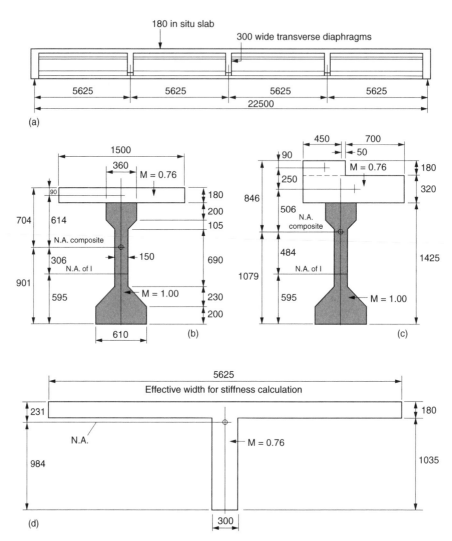

Figure 5.46. (a) General layout of bridge (dimensions in millimetres). (b), (c) Dimensions (mm) of composite longitudinal beams. (d) Dimensions (mm) of a transverse diaphragm and top slab (courtesy of C&CA, now BCA, the Concrete Society and View Point Publications, London)

In situ

$$f_{cu} = 30 \, \text{N/mm}^2$$

$$\frac{G}{E} = 0.435$$

As stated, the precast I11 beam is adopted. See Table 5.17 for its properties.

Composite interior beam

The properties are assessed from Fig. 5.46(b) as follows:

$$\text{depth} = 1605\,\text{mm}$$

$$y_b = 901\,\text{mm}$$

$$Z_b = 233.5 \times 10^6\,\text{mm}^3$$

$$\text{area} = 616\,880\,\text{mm}^2$$

$$Z_{\text{top precast}} = 401.59 \times 10^6\,\text{mm}^3$$

$$Z_{\text{top in situ}} = 298.84 \times 10^6\,\text{mm}^3$$

$$\text{second moment of area} = 210.38 \times 10^9\,\text{mm}^4$$

Composite edge beam

The properties are assessed from Fig. 5.46(c) as follows:

$$\text{depth} = 1925\,\text{mm}$$

$$y_b = 1079\,\text{mm}$$

$$Z_b = 284.38 \times 10^6\,\text{mm}^3$$

$$\text{area} = 771\,920\,\text{mm}^2$$

$$Z_{\text{top precast}} = 866.84 \times 10^6\,\text{mm}^3$$

$$Z_{\text{top in situ}} = 362.70 \times 10^6\,\text{mm}^3$$

$$\text{second moment of area} = 306.85 \times 10^9\,\text{mm}^4$$

In situ transverse diaphragms plus top slab

Figure 5.46(d) yields the following data:

$$\text{depth} = 1215\,\text{mm}$$

$$y_b = 984\,\text{mm}$$

$$Z_b = 91.65 \times 10^6\,\text{mm}^3$$

$$\text{area} = 1\,022\,570\,\text{mm}^2$$

$$Z_t = 390.39 \times 10^6\,\text{mm}^3$$

$$\text{second moment of area} = 90.182 \times 10^9\,\text{mm}^4$$

Load distribution
The grillage method for beams is utilized in this analysis:

$$2a = 22.5\,\text{m}$$

$$2b = \text{No. of interior beam} \times 1.5 + \frac{1.5\,I_{\text{comp}}\ \text{edge beam}}{I_{\text{comp}}\ \text{interior beam}}$$

$$= 18.72\,\text{m}$$

$$i = \frac{I_{\text{comp}}\ (\text{interior})}{\text{spacing: }1.5 \times 10^3} = 140.25 \times 10^6\,\text{mm}^4/\text{mm width}$$

$$j = \frac{I_{\text{diaphragm}}}{\text{diaphragm spacing}} = \frac{90.182 \times 10^9}{5.75 \times 10^3}$$

$$= 15.686 \times 10^6\,\text{mm}^4/\text{mm width}$$

$$\theta = \frac{b}{2a}\sqrt[4]{\frac{i}{j}} = 0.716 \qquad (\alpha\text{-torsional parameter})$$

$$C = K_1 c^3 d$$

$$c \leq d$$

$$i_0 = \frac{\text{torsional inertia}}{\text{unit width}} = 4.88 \times 10^6\,\text{mm}^4/\text{mm}$$

$$j_0 = \frac{\text{torsional inertia}}{\text{unit length}}$$

$$\frac{G}{E} = 0.435$$

$$\alpha = \frac{G(i_0 + j_0)}{2E\sqrt{ij}} = 0.0307$$

Width of the edge beam stringer taken from the deck:

$$1.5 \times \frac{I_{\text{comp}}\ \text{edge}}{I_{\text{comp}}\ \text{interior}} = 2.2\,\text{m}, \quad \text{i.e} = 0.234b$$

Now, the centre of the edge beam $= 0.883b$. Interpolating K_α between b and $\frac{3}{4}b$ for HB units (see Table 5.18), it follows that:

$$K_\alpha = 2.37$$

Table 5.18. Distribution coefficient K_α for HB loading

Reference point b	$+\frac{3}{4}b$	$+\frac{1}{2}b$	$+\frac{1}{4}b$	0	$-\frac{1}{4}b$	$-\frac{1}{2}b$	$-\frac{3}{4}b$	$-b$
K_α	2.51	2.22	1.88	0.788	0.49	0.16	−0.015	−0.36

Longitudinal moment/unit width for HB loading at $P = 112.5\,\text{kN}$ is given by:

$$M_\text{L} = \left[\frac{9.975 \times 4(4P)}{L = 22.5} \times 9.975 - 4P \times 1.8\right]\frac{1}{2b} = 3.395P$$

$$= 3.395 \times 112.5 = 381.95\,\text{kNm/m}$$

$$M_\text{max}\ \text{on edge beam} = 2.19 \times 381.95 \times 2.38 \times \frac{(500 + 600)}{1000}$$

$$= 2137\,\text{kNm}$$

From the third HA loading, using the K_α value above, additional moment on the edge beam $= 2265\,\text{kNm}$.

Dead load

Dead load (DL) due to precast beam $= 9.70\,\text{kN/m}$

$$\text{DL moment} = \frac{9.70 \times (22.5)^2}{8} = 613.83\,\text{kNm}$$

$$\text{additional } in\ situ \text{ concrete moment at } 12\,\text{kN/m} = \frac{12}{9.7} \times 613.83$$

$$= 759.375\,\text{kNm}$$

$$\text{Moment due to surfacing} = 2.4 \times 0.75 \times \frac{(22.5)}{8}$$

$$= 114\,\text{kNm}$$

Design of a section

Cables with 36 No. 15.2 strands are laid out as shown in Fig. 5.47:

area of each strand $= 138.7\,\text{mm}^2$

total area $A_\text{ps} = 36 \times 138.7 = 4993.2\,\text{mm}^2$

tensile $f_\text{yt} = 226.9\,\text{kN}$

$P_\text{initial} = 70\%$ of UTS

$$= 5717\,\text{kN}$$

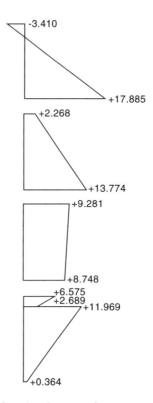

Figure 5.47. Line diagrams for the design of a section

$e = 379\,\text{mm}$ over middle

$e = 247\,\text{mm}$ at ends

Note that four strands from the bottom at third points to the top are deflected.
Assume all other losses (due to creep, shrinkage wobbling effects, friction, anchorage deformation etc.) to be

at transfer, $P_\text{e} = 4900\,\text{kN}$

after losses (service) $P = 3700\,\text{kN}$

$$f = 3700 \times 10^3 \left(\frac{1}{411.68 \times 10^3} \pm \frac{e = 379}{157.87 \times 10^6} \right)$$

$$\text{prestress} \left\{ = \begin{array}{ll} +17.885\,\text{N/mm}^2 & \text{bottom} \\ -3.401\,\text{N/mm}^2 & \text{top} \end{array} \right.$$

Deadweight due to selfweight

$$f_{\text{bottom}} = -\frac{613.83 \times 10^6}{157.86 \times 10^6} = -3.890 \, \text{N/mm}^2$$

$$f_{\text{top}} = \frac{613.83 \times 10^6}{113.14 \times 10^6} = 5.425 \, \text{N/mm}^2$$

Added weight *in situ*

$$-\frac{759.375 \times 10^6}{157.87 \times 10^6} = -4.81 \, \text{N/mm}^2$$

$$+\frac{759.375 \times 10^6}{113.14 \times 10^6} = 6.712 \, \text{N/mm}^2$$

Surfacing and live load comprises the live moment at the edge beam plus the surfacing moment:

$$= 2265 + 119 = 2384 \, \text{kNm}$$

$$f_{\text{bottom}} = -\frac{2384 \times 10^6}{284.38}, \quad \text{i.e.} \quad \frac{M}{Z_{\text{bot}}}$$

$$= -8.380 \, \text{N/mm}^2$$

$$f_{\text{top}} = -\frac{2384 \times 10^6}{886.84 \times 10^4}, \quad \text{i.e.} \quad \frac{M}{Z_{\text{top}}}$$

$$= 2.689 \, \text{N/mm}^2$$

$$f_{\text{top}_{in \, situ}} = -\frac{2384 \times 10^6}{362.7 \times 10^6}, \quad \text{i.e.} \quad \frac{M}{Z_{\text{top}}}$$

$$= 6.575 \, \text{N/mm}^2$$

On the edge beam, the stresses at transfer are:

bottom $< 20 \, \text{N/mm}^2$

top $+ 1.23 > -1.0 \, \text{N/mm}^2$

Similarly calculations for the transverse bending moments are:

$$M_{y_0} = 1.3557P$$

$$\alpha = 1$$

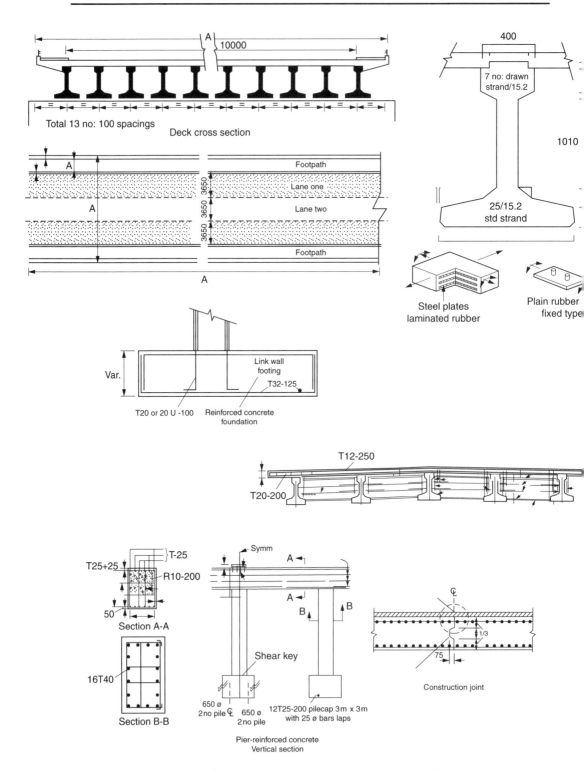

Figure 5.48 (above and facing). Concrete bridge design plans for Example (5.12)

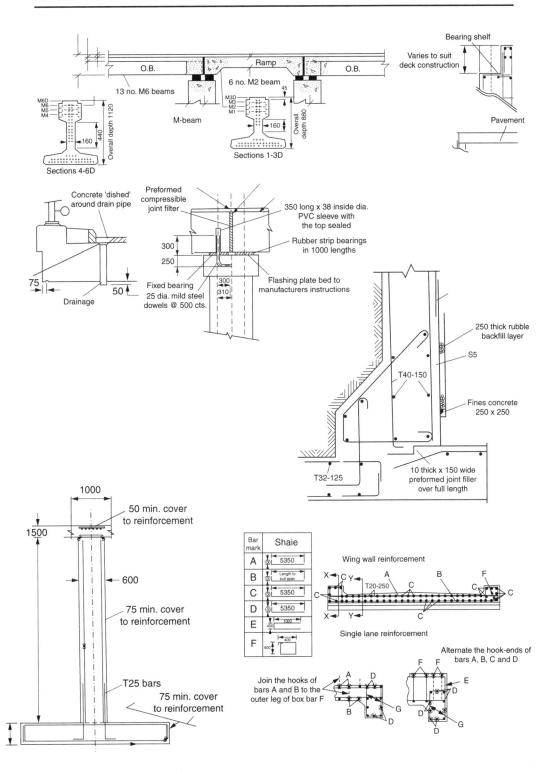

Figure 5.48. (Continued)

$$M_{y_1} = 0.928P$$

$$\alpha = 0.03069$$

$$M_{y_\alpha} = 1.28 \times 1125 = 144\,\text{kNm/m}$$

Therefore, use T25 bars of $A_S = 3930\,\text{mm}^2$.

5.1.2.12 Example (5.12) British practice

A multispan road bridge is to be designed over a whole series of railway tracks. The purpose of the bridge is to enable vehicles to cross the tracks and, via structural ramps, to access platforms to be erected between each track and hence, enter a shuttle train which will transport them. The elevations and plans of these bridges are shown collectively in Fig. 5.48 together with initial layouts in Figs 5.49 and 5.50.

Major data

Geometry and clearances of an overbridge and ramp as detailed in Figs 5.49 and 5.50 are:

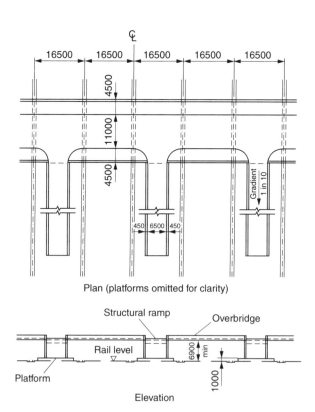

Plan (platforms omitted for clarity)

Elevation

Figure 5.49. Plan and elevation of the proposed scheme

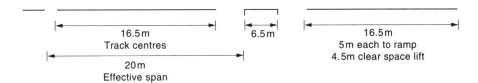

Figure 5.50. Main bridge effective spans

$$\text{track centres} = 16\,500\,\text{mm}$$

$$\text{clear spaces} = 2 \times 450 = 900\,\text{mm}$$

$$\text{total space available} = 16\,500 + 900 = 25\,500\,\text{mm or } 25.5\,\text{m}$$

$$\text{clear space for ramps} = 6500\,\text{mm or } 6.5\,\text{m}$$

$$\text{new ramp in between space} = 16\,500\text{--}6500 = 19\,000 \text{ on each side}$$

$$\text{clear space on each side} = 5000 - 450 = 4500 \text{ or } 4.5\,\text{m}$$

For the purpose of calculations the effective span (simple span) for the open bridge is taken as 20 m. The following gives the preliminary dimensions for the overbridge

clear height = 6900

(inclusive of beams above columns to support bridge beam)

bridge beam = 1010 (M6 type)

bearings (approx.) = 100 thick

deck slab = 160

total = 8270 or 8.27 m

from railway track to the top of the deck level = 8.27 m

from the top of the platform = 8.27 − 1.0 = 7.27 m

pier height = 6900 − 1000 (beam on columns) − 1000 (platforms) = 4900

total height to the top of the foundation = 8.1 m

Figure 5.51 shows a schematic of a two-span continuous overbridge with ramp entering at that level.

Design loads and stresses
Two types of load and five different types of combination are given in BS 5400 and BD 37/88.

    (a)   *Permanent loads* – These are dead loads, superimposed dead loads, loads due to filling materials, differential settlement and loads derived from the nature of the structural material such as shrinkage and creep of the concrete.

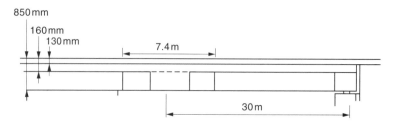

Figure 5.51. Two-span continuous overbridge with ramp entering at that level

(b) *Transient loads* – These are wind loads, temperature loads, exceptional loads, erection loads, the primary and secondary highway loadings and footway and cycle track loadings.
     Primary highway loadings are vertical live loads due to changes in speed or direction. Hence the secondary highway loadings, include centrifugal, braking, skidding and collision loads.

(c) *Load combinations* – There are three principal (1–3) and two secondary (4, 5) combinations of load.
     Combination 1 – Permanent loads plus the appropriate primary live loads for highway and footway or cycle track bridges.
     Combination 2 – Those of combination 1 plus wind loading plus erection loads when appropriate.
     Combination 3 – Combination 1 plus loads from restraint of movements due to temperature range and differential temperature distribution.
     Combination 4 – Applies only to highway, footway or cycle track bridges. The highway bridges need consideration of permanent and secondary live loads with its associated live load. Similarly for cycle tracks and footways.
     Combination 5 – Permanent loads plus loads due to bearings.

Loading and load distributions – evaluation techniques
BS 5400 states that up to 30 m loaded length ($\ngtr 30$ m) shall be taken as

$$W \text{ (load per metre of lane (kN))} = 151\left(\tfrac{1}{2}\right)^{0.425}$$

For $L = 20$ m

$$W = 36.4 \, \text{kN/m}$$

Use 30 kN/m as per Table 13 of BS 5400 Part 2, whereas the existing specifications provided give a formula for up to 50 m loaded length, that is

$$W = 336\left(\tfrac{1}{2}\right)^{0.67} \quad \text{for } L = 20 \, \text{m}$$

$$W = 451.4 \, \text{kN/m} \simeq 45.1 \, \text{kN/m} \text{ as per BD 37/88}$$

In addition, nominal knife-edge load (KEL) per notional lane shall be taken as 120 kN representing an axial load positioned perpendicular to the notional lane or positioned in line with the bearings.

The loading curve for HA and HB loading are given in Fig. 5.52. The comparative increase is by a factor of $45.14/30 = 1.5$, which is taken to update the values calculated on the basis of the formula $151(\frac{1}{2})^{0.425}$ given by BS 5400. The loaded length for the accepted scheme is 20 m.

The knife-edge load is given by:

$$KEL = \frac{120}{3.65} = 32.88 \, kN/m$$

where 3.65 m is the notional lane width:

$$HA \ loading = \frac{45.14}{3.65} = 12.37 \, kN/m^2$$

Here no HB loadings are considered. However, if

$$W = 151(\tfrac{1}{2})^{0.425}$$

HB loading is considered. HB loading is defined in Fig. 5.53.

Figure 5.54 gives the procedures for the placement of loads at lanes.

Note that in BS 5400, all load combinations have to be checked at ULS. However the load combinations that are critical is usually clear. It is usually 1 and 3.

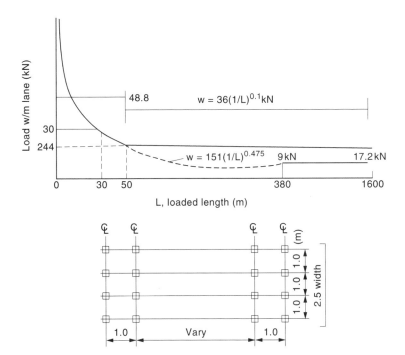

Figure 5.52. Comparative loadings

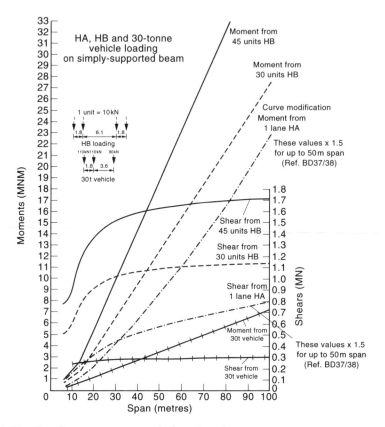

Figure 5.53. Bending moments and shearing forces

Within combination 1 the requirement is to check for HA on its own and HA plus HB. In small bridges the latter check is always critical. Situations where other loads are important would be at the bridge edges: parapet loads and accidental wheel loads, for instance.

5.1.3 Calculations for the deck slab design show how wheel loads are calculated

The concentrated vertical load due to wheel load is computed as

$$W = \frac{PI_0}{e}$$

where

    P = wheel load

    I_0 = impact factor

    e = effective width of dispersion.

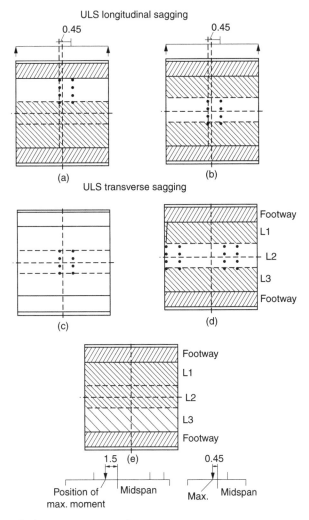

Figure 5.54. Load placement procedure

It is not clear whether the centre or edge of the deck will be critical so both will be considered.

The longitudinal position of this loading needs to be considered. With spans greater than 13 m the worst position is 1.5 m off centres as shown in Fig. 5.54. This gives a maximum moment under the axle which is 1.5 m from the centre-line, marginally greater than with the vehicle on the centre-line. On short-span structures a single bogie of 0.45 m off-centre is a worst case situation.

5.1.3.1 Sample calculations
Here, reference is made to Fig. 5.54(a) and (b).

In both cases the loaded length if 20 m so the nominal HA intensity is 38.7.

The lane factor for the first lane is given by:

$$0.274 \times 3.65 = 1.000 \qquad \text{(Reference 6.2, BS 5400)}$$

hence:

$$\text{load} = 1.000 \times 38.7 = 38.7 \, \text{kN/m}$$

Notice that with narrow lanes, the HB vehicle will not fit in one lane. However, since the remaining width of the adjacent lane exceeds 2.5 m, we still apply HA loading to it, albeit without the knife-edge load and while using the lane-width factor for a 2.5 m wide lane (Reference 6.4.2, BS 5400). This gives a lane factor of:

$$0.274 \times 2.5 = 0.685$$

Hence the load is:

$$0.685 \times 38.7 = 26.51 \, \text{kN/m}$$

The knife-edge load is applied in the remaining lane and is multiplied by the lane factor giving a load of:

$$1.000 \times 120 = 120 \, \text{kN}.$$

Notice that the HB load is applied slightly off-centre as otherwise the knife-edge load would not be applied in any of the lanes.
    The combination 1 load factor for HB and the associated HA is:

$$1.1 \times 1.3 = 1.43$$

Figure 5.54(b) will be unlikely to be significant for the deck as torsional stiffness is not significant. Transverse sagging is ignored. The ultimate shear worst case is at the edge of the deck.
    Note that Fig. 5.54(e) is given in the specification for this problem.

SLS
It is necessary only to check each width at SLS and then only for the 'modified combination 1'. This loading is supposed to represent a 'normal' which occurs relatively frequently.
    The new BD 37/88 HA load does fully represent C and U traffic so there is no longer any reason for the 25 units of HB in the cracking loads cases. The author has been assured that the implementation document for Part 4 of the specification will be modified to make this change shortly. However, this has not been done at the time of writing and it is possible that, when it is, other changes will be made; perhaps a requirement to check the single HA wheels will be adopted. However, it is advised to check this requirement before doing the same on a real contract job. Hence, in order to satisfy oneself, it is better to

check both the normal HA and HB combination and only the modified HA according to BD 37/88. In this case the lane factor is 0.6. If using the same loading as for the ULS lane loading (this is more efficient for computer time) it is necessary to nullify the UDL by a factor which in the case of the third lane is

$$\frac{0.6}{1.000} = 0.6$$

before applying the load factor which is:

$$1.0 \times 1.1 = 1.1$$

5.1.3.2   Additional loads as permanent loads

The surfacing and other 'superdead' loads have to be separated because the load factors are different. The normal loads used here are:

$$\text{road: surfacing} = 0.1 \times 23.6 = 2.3 \, \text{kN/m}^2$$

$$\text{footway: surfacing} = 0.05 \times 23.6 = 1.18 \, \text{kN/m}^2$$

$$\text{other} = 0.12 \times 20 = 2.4 \, \text{kN/m}^2$$

The load factor γ_{f3} is applied in combination. The load factors for permanent loads are the same in all combinations and for the ultimate state they are

$$\text{dead} = 1.1 \times 1.2 = 1.32 - \gamma_{f3} \cdot \gamma_{fL}$$

$$\text{surfacing} = 1.1 \times 1.75 = 1.925$$

$$\text{other super} = 1.1 \times 1.2 = 1.32$$

At servicibility limit states all these factors are 1 except γ_{fL} for the surfacing which is 1.2.

Note that BS 5400 gives two values of γ_{fL} – 1.2 and 1.15. Value 1.15 is only used if the dead weight is not accurately assessed. This definition is quite severe so it is more correct to use 1.2.

5.1.4   Design calculations for the bridge deck: reinforced concrete overbridge deck design

The bridge deck slab is assumed to be 160 mm thick. First check needed is for HB loading.

5.1.4.1   Design of main steel (i.e. transverse to the beam)

In the local analysis both the 30 unit HB and the 45 unit HB wheel will have to be considered.

Contact areas are:

(a)   30 unit HB wheel (based on BD 37/88):

$$\text{nominal load} = 30 \times \frac{10}{4} = 75\,\text{kN}$$

$$\text{Therefore side of square contact area} = \sqrt{\frac{75 \times 10^3}{1.1}} = 261\,\text{mm}$$

compared with 300 mm given in specifications.

Therefore side of the effective square contact area

$$= 261 + \left(\frac{2}{2} \times 100\right) + \left(2 \times \frac{160}{2}\right) = 521\,\text{mm}.$$

(b)   45 unit HB wheel: as above though the side of the effective square contact area is 580 mm. Therefore, for a span of 1000 mm the fixed-ended Pucher's influence surfaces give maximum moments in sagging of:
  (i)   30 unit HB wheel

$$\text{moment} = \frac{3P}{8\pi} = 0.12P$$

  (ii)   45 unit HB wheel

$$\text{moment} = \frac{2.8P}{8\pi} = 0.11P$$

and the maximum moments in sagging, noting that these are based on a span of 1.00 m as the moment at ₵ of the beam is not relevant, are
  (iii)   30 unit HB wheel

$$\text{moment} = \frac{5.1P}{8\pi} = 0.2P$$

  (iv)   45 unit HB wheel

$$\text{moment} = \frac{4.6P}{8\pi} = 0.18P$$

ULS – load combination I
(a)   *Bottom steel*
  (i)   HB moment:

$$(\text{unfactored}) = \text{global} + \text{local}$$

$$= 45(0.58 + 2.5 \times 0.11) = 3.85\,\text{kN/m}$$

(*ii*) HA and footway: the moments are negative so these loads are not applied as they would cut down the moments.

(*iii*) Dead load:

$$\text{local moment} = (1.0)^2 \times 0.16 \times \frac{25}{24} \quad \text{(if adopting fixed ended)}$$

$$= 0.167 \, \text{kNm/m}$$

Note that the global moment is insignificant.

(*iv*) Superimposed dead load: for 100 mm surfacing

$$\text{total moment (unfactored)} = -0.96 \, \text{kN/m}$$

Therefore, total design moment (where $\gamma_{f3} = 1.1$ ULS)

$$= \gamma_{f3} \sum \gamma_{fL} \times \text{moments}$$

$$= 1.1\{38.5 \times 1.3 + 0.167$$

$$\times 1.2 - 0.96 \times 1.2\}$$

$$= 1.1\{50.05 + 200.4 + 1.152\}$$

$$= 56 \, \text{kNm/m}$$

now d represents the cover for the surface protected by permanent formwork. Here, 20 mm bars assumed and thus:

$$d = 160 - 30 - 10$$

$$= 120 \, \text{mm}$$

$$\text{Therefore:} \quad \frac{M}{bd^2} = \frac{56 \times 10^6}{1000 \times 120^2} = 38.9$$

$$\therefore \quad \text{required} \; \frac{A_S}{bd} = \frac{1.10}{10}$$

$$\therefore \quad \text{required} \; A_S = 1300 \, \text{mm}^2/\text{m}$$

Thus either T20-200 steel $= 1570 \, \text{mm}^2$ or T16-150 steel $= 1340$ is acceptable.

(*b*) *Top steel*

(*i*) HB moment:

$$= \text{global} + \text{local} = 45(0.19 + 2.5 \times 0.18)$$

$$= 28.8 \, \text{kNm}$$

Note that these are worst coexistence values.

(*ii*) HA:

$$\frac{45.1}{3.65} = 12.356 \, \text{kNm/m}$$

(*iii*) Footway $= 3.6 \, \text{kNm/m}$
(*iv*) Super dead load (surface) $= 0.2 \, \text{kNm/m}$
(*v*) Super dead load (other) $= 1.6 \, \text{kNm/m}$
(*vi*) Dead load $= 0.6 \, \text{kNm/m}$

Therefore: total design moment

$$= 1.1\{28.8 \times 1.3 + 12.356 \times 1.5 + 3.6 \times 1.5$$
$$+ 0.2 \times 1.2 + 1.6 \times 1.2 + 0.6 \times 1.2\}$$
$$= 1.1\{37.44 + 18.534 + 5.4 + 0.24 + 1.92 + 0.72\}$$
$$= 70.68 \, \text{kNm/m}$$

and

$$d = 160 - 30 - 10 = 120 \, \text{mm}$$

Therefore: $\dfrac{M}{bd^2} = \dfrac{70.68 \times 10^6}{1000 \times 120^2} = 4.91$

$\therefore$ required $\dfrac{A_S}{bd} = 1.48\%$

$\therefore$ required $A_S = 1776 \, \text{mm}^2/\text{m}$

Thus T20-150 steel is chosen $[A_S = 2094 \, \text{mm}^2/\text{m}]$.

The extra area is provision for future wind loading ensuring that the bridge deck reinforcement will be adequate.

ULS – load combination 3

A reference is made to BS 5400, Section 4. Gradients to be considered are given in Fig. 5.55. The positive gradient is clearly the worst case so this only is considered.

Considering the full concrete section the equivalent linear gradient is:

$$\frac{\int \theta x \, da}{(\frac{1}{6}bd^2)} = \pm 3.87°$$

Note that the self equilibrating component and the uniform component have no effect and so are not considered.

The deck slab of the overbridge is continuous and spans are equal so there will be no rotation. Hence:

$$\text{unfactored moment} = \frac{3.87 \times 12 \times 10^{-6} \times 31 \times 10^3 \times 1000 \times 160^2}{6}$$

$$= 6.1 \, \text{kNm/m}^2$$

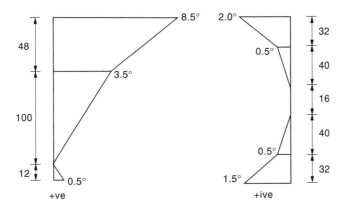

Figure 5.55. Design of main steel: ULS (load combination 3) gradients

Expansion coefficients are taken from BS 5400, Clause 4.3.2.1 as the type of aggregate is not known. Therefore, design combination 3 moment is

$$1.1\{38.5 \times 1.15 + 0.161 \times 1.2 - 0.96 \times 1.20 + 6.1 \times 1.0\}$$

$$= 1.1\{42.35 + 2.004 - 1.152 + 6.1\} = 54.23\,\text{kNm/m}$$

This moment is less than that for the load combination 1 and is therefore not critical.

SLS – cracking

(a) *Bottom steel*
     HB moment:

$$(\text{unfactored}) = 30(0.58 + 2.5 \times 0.12) = 26.4\,\text{kNm/m}$$

Note that the other moments are as for ULS. Therefore:

$$\text{design moment} = 1.0\{26.4 \times 1.10 + 0.167 \times 1.0 - 0.96 \times 1.20\}$$

$$= 28.055\,\text{kNm/m}$$

Now $E_c = 31\,\text{kN/mm}^2$ (live load dominant)

$$\therefore \quad \alpha_e = \frac{E_S}{E_C} = \frac{200}{31} = 6.45$$

$$\therefore \quad \alpha_e \frac{A_S}{bd} = 6.45 \times \frac{1570}{(1000 \times 120)} = 0.0844$$

$$\therefore \quad I_C = 0.050bd^3$$

$$= 86.4 \times 10^6\,\text{mm}^4$$

and

$$\frac{x}{d} = 0.33$$

These values are obtained using the design chart from BS 8110.
Now

$$\omega = \frac{3a_{cr}t_m}{1 + \dfrac{2(a_c - c_{min})}{h - d_c}}$$

$$\therefore \quad t_m = \frac{28.055 \times 10^6 (160 - 0.33 \times 120)}{86.4 \times 10^6 \times 31\,000} = 0.00121$$

and

$$t_m = t_1 - [\cdots][\cdots]$$

$$= t_1 \text{ since } M_q > M_g$$

For a cracked elastic section (Fig. 5.56):

$$a_{cr} = \sqrt{100^2 + (30 + 10)^2} - 10$$

$$= 97.7\,\text{mm}$$

$$\therefore \quad \omega = \frac{3 \times 97.7 \times 0.00121}{1 + \dfrac{2(97.7 - 30)}{(160 - 40)}} \approx 0.17\,\text{mm}$$

The allowable value is 0.25 mm and the above is thus accepted.

(b) *Top steel*
HB moment:

$$(\text{unfactored}) = 30(0.19 + 2.5 \times 0.2) = 20.7\,\text{kNm/m}$$

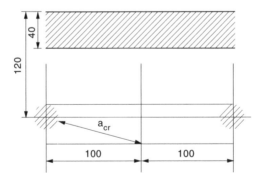

Figure 5.56. Cracked elastic section (SLS cracking analysis)

Note that the other moments are as for ULS. Therefore:

$$\text{design moment} = 1.0\{17.3 \times 1.15 + 12.356 \times 1.15 + 3.6 \times 1.0 + 0.2$$
$$\times 1.2 + 1.6 \times 1.0 + 0.6 \times 1.0\}$$
$$= 40.145 \, \text{kNm/m}$$

Therefore (by comparison with bottom steel)

$$\omega = \frac{40.145}{28.055} \times 0.14 = 0.22 \, \text{mm} < 0.25 \, \text{mm}$$

Crack width is therefore not critical. Thus T20-200 centres are acceptable.

5.1.4.2 Design of secondary steel

In the local analysis there is no global moment in this direction and the slab span is short. This means that the maximum moment comes from only one wheel. This makes the single HA wheel the critical load case (particularly for cracking which will be critical) so only this will be checked.

Side of effective square contact area is:

$$300 + \left(\frac{2}{2} \times 100\right) + \left(2 \times \frac{160}{2}\right) = 560 \, \text{mm}$$

Therefore for a span of 1.0 fixed-ended, Pucher's influence surface give maximum sagging moment

$$= \frac{1.0P}{8\pi} = 0.04P$$

and maximum hogging moment is taken to be

$$= \frac{0.5P}{8\pi} = 0.02P$$

ULS – load combination I

(a)   Bottom steel

$$\text{Design moment} = 1.1 \times 100 \times 1.0 \times 0.06 = 6.6 \, \text{kNm/m}$$

Assume 12 mm bars and

$$d = 160 - 30 - 20 - 6 = 104 \, \text{mm}$$

$$\text{Therefore} \quad \frac{M}{bd^2} = \frac{6.6 \times 10^6}{100 \times 104^2} = 0.61$$

$$\text{required} \quad \frac{A_S}{bd} = 0.15\%$$

$$\text{Therefore} \quad A_S = 156 \, \text{mm}^2/\text{m}$$

Provided for crack width and effects of wind loading in case taken in future. Adopt T12-250 steel ($A_S = 45.2\,\mathrm{mm}^2/\mathrm{m}$).

(b)   Top steel

Design moment $= 1.1 \times 100 \times 1.0 \times 0.02 = 2.2\,\mathrm{kNm/m}$

This is much less than the design moment for the bottom steel. Adopt the minimum steel T12-300 centres.

ULS – load combination 3
The temperature moment is the same in both directions.
Therefore, unfactored moment $= 6.1\,\mathrm{kNm/m}$ and total design moment

$$= 1.1\{100 \times 0.6 \times 1.25 + 6.1 \times 1.0\}$$

$$= 15.0\,\mathrm{kNm/m}$$

$$\therefore\quad \frac{M}{bd^2} = \frac{15 \times 10^6}{1000 \times 104^2} = 1.38$$

$$\therefore\quad \text{required } \frac{A_S}{bd} = 0.36\%$$

$$\therefore\quad \text{required } A_S = 374\,\mathrm{mm}^2/\mathrm{m}$$

The value is less than $452\,\mathrm{mm}^3/\mathrm{m}$ and therefore acceptable.
Here an uncracked section is used and the temperature analysis is very conservative.

SLS cracking analysis

Design moment $= 100 \times 1.2 \times 0.06 = 7.2\,\mathrm{kNm/m}$

and

$$\alpha_e\,\frac{A_S}{bd} = \frac{6.45 \times 452}{1000 \times 104} = 0.028$$

$$\therefore\quad I_C = 0.020bd^3 = 0.020 \times 1000 \times 104^3 = 225 \times 10^6\,\mathrm{mm}^4$$

and

$$\frac{x}{d} = 0.21$$

$$\therefore\quad \varepsilon_1 = \frac{7.2 \times 10^6(160 - 0.21 \times 104)}{22.5 \times 10^6 \times 31\,000}$$

and $t_m = t_1 = 0.014$. Now

$$a_{cr} = \sqrt{125^2 = 56^2} - 6 = 131\,mm$$

$$\therefore \quad w = \frac{3 \times 131 \times 0.0014}{1 + \dfrac{2(131 - 30)}{160 - (0.21 \times 104)}} = 0.23\,mm$$

Values up to 0.25 mm are allowable. Thus the above is accepted.
Therefore T12-250 steel is adopted for this crack width.

SLS – stress limits

Note that in the ULS check, global flange forces were not considered. It is therefore necessary to check the stress limits. The global force in this deck is always compressive. Hence it is clear that the tensile stress limits will not be critical under combined effects. Only the compression limit will be checked. The critical load case is definitely the 45 units of HB.

Local moment under 45 unit HB wheel

$$= 45 \times 2.5 \times 0.06$$

$$= 6.75\,kNm/m \quad \text{(unfactored)}$$

Stress on full concrete section for load combination 1 is:

$$\frac{10 \times 6.75 \times 1.1}{(1000 \times 160^2/6)} = \pm 1.7\,N/mm^2$$

and global stress is:

$$+8.9\,N/mm^2 \quad \text{for the top}$$
$$+8.0\,N/mm^2 \quad \text{for the bottom}$$

Thus total bottom stress $= 8.0 - 1.7 = 6.3\,N/mm^2 > 0$

Therefore section is uncracked and use of the full concrete section is allowed.
Now

$$\text{total top stress} = 8.9 + 1.7 = 10.6\,N/mm^2$$

$$< 0.5 f_{cu} \quad \text{(therefore allowed)}$$

$$(0.5 \times 40 = 20\,N/mm^2)$$

Checking punching shear

A single wheel is critical and therefore the HA wheel is critical (Fig. 5.57).
Critical section has

$$\text{width} = 300 + \left(\frac{2}{2} \times 100\right) + (2 \times 1.5 \times 120) = 760\,mm$$

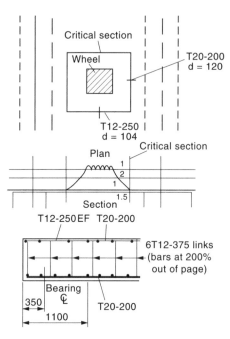

Figure 5.57. Design of secondary steel: critical sections

and

$$\text{length} = 300 + \left(\frac{2}{2} \times 100\right) + (2 \times 1.5 \times 104) = 712\,\text{mm}$$

Unfactored loads are:
- (*i*)   live $= 100\,\text{kN}$
- (*ii*)   dead $= 0.712 \times 0.760 \times 0.16 \times 23.6$
  $$= 2.08\,\text{kN}$$
- (*iii*)   super $= 0.712 \times 0.76 \times 0.1 \times 23 = 1.2\,\text{kN}$

Therefore, the design load $= 1.1(100 \times 1.5 + 2.08 \times 1.2 + 1.2 \times 1.75)$
$$= 170\,\text{kN}$$

and

$$V_{\text{C}} = \sum \xi_{\text{s}} v_{\text{c}} h d$$

For main steel

$$\frac{A_S}{bd} = 1.3\% \qquad \therefore \quad v_{\text{c}} = 0.80\,\text{N/mm}^2$$

and

$$d = 120 \qquad \therefore \quad \xi_{\text{s}} = 1.44$$

For secondary steel

$$\frac{A_S}{bd} = 0.44\% \qquad \therefore \quad v_c = 0.55 \, \text{N/mm}^2$$

and

$$d = 104 \qquad \therefore \quad \xi_s = 1.49$$

$$\therefore \quad V_C = 2 \times 1.44 \times 0.8 \times 7 \times 120 + 2 \times 1.49 \times 0.55 \times 760 \times 104$$

$$= 326 \, \text{kN} > 170 \, \text{kN} \qquad \text{(value acceptable)}$$

5.1.4.3 Design of the precast prestressed M6 beam for the overbridge

Introduction

Figure 5.58 shows a typical M6 beam cross-section provided by the MOT and available from the British Cement Association, Crowthorne, Berkshire. Reference is made to Fig. 5.44 showing the preliminary general arrangement drawing. The total number of 11 M6 beams at 1.0 m centres with effective span 20 m are simply supported. Additional data are detailed below and supplemented by Table 5.19.

Strands

(1)   standard 15.2 mm $A_S = 139 \, \text{mm}^2$

$$f_{pu} \text{ (nominal strength)} = 1670 \, \text{N/mm}^2$$

$$P_u \text{ (characteristic load)} = 232 \, \text{kN}$$

(2)   drawn type 15.2 mm $A_S = 165 \, \text{mm}^2$

$$f_{pu} = 1820 \, \text{N/mm}^2$$

$$P_u = 300 \, \text{kN}$$

initial load $0.8P_u$, $0.7P_u = 0.8P_u$

modulus of elasticity $(E_S) = 195 \pm 10 \, \text{kN/mm}^2$

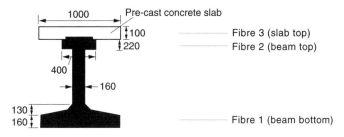

Figure 5.58. Typical M6 beam cross-section

Table 5.19. Beam and composite properties

Property	Beam$_1$	Composite$_2$
Area mm^2	$A_1 = 387 \times 10^3$	$A_2 = 627 \times 10^3$
Centroid mm	$a_{1,1} = 409$	$a_{1,2} = 670$
Second moment mm^4	$I_1 = 47.6 \times 10^9$	$I_2 = 116.8 \times 10^9$
Modulus 1	$z_{1,1} = 116.2 \times 10^6$	$z_{1,2} = 174.3 \times 10^6$
Modulus 2	$z_{2,1} = 75.4 \times 10^6$	$z_{2,2} = 315.7 \times 10^6$
Modulus 3		$z_{3,2} = 233.6 \times 10^6$

Concrete grades

$$\text{beam } f_{cu} = 50 \, \text{N/mm}^2$$

$$f_{ci} = 40 \, \text{N/mm}^2 \quad (\text{max})$$

$$\text{precast slab } f_{cu} = 40 \, \text{N/mm}^2$$

The 11 M6 beams placed at 1 m c/c with 160 mm thick precast RC slab attached to it with fully incorporated dowels have simple spans of 20 m.
    Note that:

$$\text{concrete density} = 23.6 \, \text{kN/m}^2$$

$$\text{surfacing material density} = 3.9 \, \text{kN/m}^2$$

The loading is uniformly distributed per beam.
    Pretensioned beam area cm^2

$$0.387 \times 23.6 = 9.13$$
$$0.160 \times 1.0 \times 23.6 = 3.78$$
$$\overline{}$$
$$12.91 \, \text{kN/m}$$

and for the deck slab total dead surfacing is:

$$1 \times 3.9 = 3.90 \, \text{kN/m}$$

Loading
This considers nominal live loading on footways and future surfacing. Nominal live load (HA + 45 units HB):

$$\text{dead load moment} = \frac{12.91 \times 20^2}{8} = 645.5 \, \text{kNm}$$

$$\text{surfacing} = 3.90 \times \frac{20^2}{8} = 195.5 \, \text{kNm}$$

Moments on beams 3 and 6:

	Beam 3	Beam 6
Additional superdead load (future surfacing)	68.6	9.8
Footway (live)	93.0	13.1
HB (45 units)	1350.2	1285.4
HA (additional) BD 37/88	186.8	391.5
HB (30 units)	900.12	856.9

SLS design moments due to superimposed dead and live loads (load combination I)(LC I)

	γ_{fl}	Beam 3	Beam 6
Surfacing	1.2	207.0	207.0
Additional superdead	1.0	68.3	9.8
Footway (live)	1.0	93.0	13.1
HB (45 units)	1.15	1552.71	1928.05
HA (additional)	1.15	214.32	449.5
		2135.33	2607.65
HB (30 units)	1.15	1035.2	985.5
Other loads		573.8	660.6
		1609.0	1646.1

Allowable stresses

Limiting concrete stresses at transfer and during erection (due to prestress and coexistent deadload and temporary loads during erection; see Fig. 5.59). Limits due to all other load combinations are represented by the lower portion of Fig. 5.59. Allowable stresses apply except for joints in segmental construction. Where residual tension is not offset under service loads, stresses are regarded as class 1.

SLS LC3 moments due to superimposed dead and live loads

	γ_{fl}	Beam 3	Beam 6
Surfacing	1.2	207.0	207.0
Additional superdead	1.0	68.3	9.8
Footway (live)	1.0	93.0	13.1
HB (45 units)	1.0	1350.2	1286.4
HA (additional)	1.0	186.8	391.5
		1905.3	1906.8

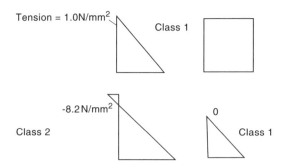

Figure 5.59. Limiting concrete stresses

Stresses at fibre 1 (Fig. 5.58):

	LC1	LC1 mod	LC3
$\dfrac{M_1}{z_{1,1}}$	-4.77	4.77	-4.77
$\dfrac{M_2}{z_{1,2}}$	$\dfrac{-14.97}{-19.74}$	$\dfrac{9.18}{13.95}$	$\dfrac{-10.94}{-15.71}$

Here temperature effects would be added and may become critical.

Temperature difference effects

Simplify the beam section and apply the temperature differences given with a coefficient of thermal expansion taken as $12 \times 10^{-6}/°C$ (Fig. 5.60). Reference is made to Table 3.2.1.3.1 of BS 5400. Take $E_c = 34 \, \text{kN/mm}^2$ based on $f_{cu} = 50 \, \text{N/mm}^2$ so that restrained temperature stress per $°C = 34 \times 10^3 \times 12 \times 10^{-6} = 0.408 \, \text{N/mm}^2$.

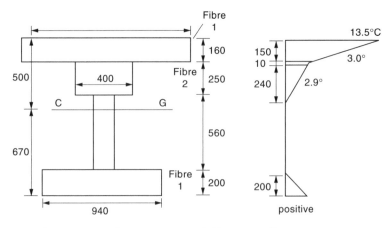

Figure 5.60. Illustration of temperature difference effects

Force F to restrain temperature strain,

$$0.408 \times 1.5\{150(3.0 + 5.25) + 10 \times 2.95\} = 775.4\,\text{kN}$$

$$0.408(0.4 \times 240 \times 1.45 + 0.94 \times 200 \times 1.25) = \underline{152.7\,\text{kN}}$$

$$928.1\,\text{kN}$$

Moment M about centroid of section to restrain curvature due to temperature strain (Fig. 5.61):

$$0.408 \times 1.5\{150(3 \times 0.425 + 5.25 \times 0.45) + 10 \times 2.95 \times 0.345\}$$

$$+ 0.408(0.4 \times 240 \times 1.45 \times 0.260 - 0.94 \times 200 \times 1.25 \times 0.603)$$

$$= 340.15 - 43.05 - 297.1\,\text{kNm}$$

Force F to restrain temperatures strain,

$$-0.408\{1.5 \times 160(3.4 \times 2.35) + 0.4 \times 74(1.2 + 1.1)\}$$

$$-0.408\{0.4 \times 176(0.2 + 0.5) + 0.94 \times 200(2 + 2.2)\}$$

$$-0.408 \times 0.16\{34(1.3 + 0.35) + 200 \times 0.65 + 2.4 \times 0.1\}$$

$$= -5950.8 - 342.3 - 12.3 = -945.54\,\text{kN}$$

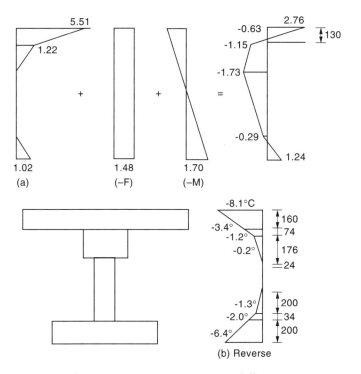

Figure 5.61. *Stresses due to positive temperature difference*

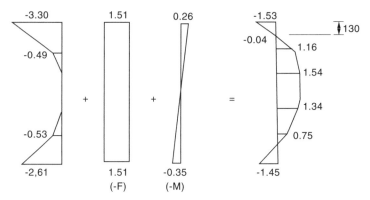

Figure 5.62. Restrain of curvature due to temperature strain

Moment M about centroid of section to restrain curvature due to temperature strain (Fig. 5.62):

$$- 0.408\{240(3.4 \times 0.420 + 2.35 \times 0.447)$$
$$+ 29.6(1.2 \times 0.303 + 1.1 \times 0.315)\}$$
$$- 0.408\{70.4(0.2 \times 0.178 + 0.5 \times 0.207)$$
$$- 188(2 \times 0.57 + 2.2 \times 0.6037)\}$$
$$+ 0.065\{34(1.3 \times 0.453 + 0.35 \times 0.459)$$
$$+ 130 \times 0.369 - 2.4 \times 0.082\}$$
$$= -251.3 + 185.2 + 4.8 = -61.3 \text{ kNm}$$

Note that for the effects of temperature difference at the SLS (LC3), $\gamma_{fl} = 0.8$, so that the stresses shown above are to be multiplied by 0.8 and then combined with the stresses due to the design loads for LC3.

Differential shrinkage effects

Total shrinkage of *in situ* concrete $= 300 \times 10^{-6}$. Suppose two-thirds of this shrinkage takes place (precast concrete section) before the slab is added. The residual shrinkage is assumed to be 100×10^{-6}. The effect of residual creep strains may be considered. Let $E_c = 34 \text{ kN/mm}^2$ for $f_{cu} = 50 \text{ N/mm}^2$.

F = force due to restraining differential shrinkage (Fig. 5.63)

$$= -\varepsilon_{\text{diff}} E_C A_{\text{slab}} \phi = -200 \times 10^{-6} \times 34 \times 1000 \times 160 \times 0.43$$
$$\approx -468 \text{ kN}$$

Eccentricity given by $a_{\text{slab}} = 420 \text{ mm}^2$.

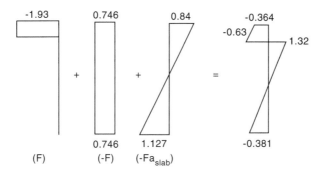

Figure 5.63. Stresses due to differential shrinkage

Maximum stress at fibre 1 (no prestress)

Stress due to design loads for SLS (LC3) plus temperature difference and differential shrinkage effects is given by:

$$f_{1,LC3} = -16.5 - 0.8 \times 1.45 - 0.364 = -18.024 \, \text{N/mm}^2$$

Prestressing force and eccentricity solution

Adopting straight fully bonded tendons (constant force and eccentricity) and allowing for a 20% loss of prestress after transfer, initial prestress at fibre 1 to satisfy class 2 requirements for SLS LC3 is:

$$f_{1P} = \frac{(18.004 - 32)}{0.8} = 18.53 \, \text{N/mm}^2 \quad (\text{say } 20 \, \text{N/mm}^2)$$

Critical selection at transfer occurs at the end of the transmission zone, where the moment due to the self weight of the beam is near to zero and the initial stress conditions are:

$$\frac{P}{A} + \frac{P e}{z_1} = 18.53 \quad ① \qquad \frac{P}{A} - \frac{P e}{z_2} \geq 1 \quad ②$$

Multiplying ① by z_1 ② by z_2 and adding for a maximum prestressing take Eq. ① $= 20$ just to give an excess prestressing force to cater for any future increase of moments

$$P \geq \left(\frac{20 z_1 - 1.0 z_2}{z_1 + z_2}\right) A = \left(\frac{20 \times 116.2 - 75.4}{116.2 + 75.4}\right) 387 = 4542 \, \text{kN}$$

Allowing for a 10% loss of force before and during transfer, initial force

$$P_0 = \frac{4542}{0.9}$$

$$= 5046 \, \text{kN}$$

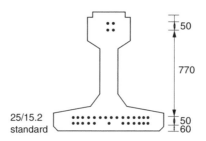

Figure 5.64. Strand layout for prestressing force and eccentricity solution

Using 29/15.2 mm standard strands with an initial force of $0.75P_u$, substituting $P = 4542$ kN in ② for strand layout shown (Fig. 5.64) the moment about fibre 1 is:

$$e \leq \frac{z_2}{A} + \frac{z_2}{P} = 211 \, \text{mm}$$

$$2 \,@\, 930 = 1860$$
$$2 \,@\, 880 = 1760$$
$$14 \,@\, 110 = 1546$$
$$11 \,@\, 60 = 660$$
$$\overline{29} \qquad \overline{5820}$$

$$e = \frac{232 + 5820}{29} = 208 \, \text{mm}$$

Allowing for 1% relaxation loss in steel before transfer and elastic deformation of concrete at transfer, transfer force is given by.

$$P = \frac{0.99P_0}{1 + \dfrac{E_s}{E_c}\left(\dfrac{A_{ps}}{A}\right)\left(1 + \dfrac{Ae^2}{I}\right)}$$

$$= \frac{0.99P_0}{1 + \dfrac{195}{31}\left(\dfrac{29 \times 139}{387 \times 10^3}\right)\left(1 + \dfrac{387 \times 0.208^2}{47.6}\right)}$$

$$= 0.91P_0 = 4592 \, \text{kN}$$

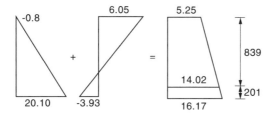

Figure 5.65. Moments for strand layout in Fig. 5.64

Initial stresses due to prestress at end of transmission zone (Fig. 5.65):

(1) $\dfrac{P}{A}\left(1 + \dfrac{Ae}{z_1}\right) = 11.87\left(1 + \dfrac{190}{300}\right) = 20.10\,\text{N/mm}^2$

(2) $\dfrac{P}{A}\left(1 - \dfrac{Ae}{z_2}\right) = 11.87\left(1 - \dfrac{190}{195}\right) = -0.80\,\text{N/mm}^2$

Moment due to self weight of beam at midspan:

$$w = A \times 1 \times 23.6 = 0.387 \times 1 \times 23.6 = 9.13$$

$$M_{\text{swt}} = 9.13 \times \frac{(20)^2}{8} = 456.5$$

Stresses due to self weight of the beam at midspan:

$$f_{1,\text{swt}} = -\frac{456.3}{116.2} = -3.93 \qquad f_{2,\text{swt}} = -\frac{456.5}{75.4} = 6.05\,\text{N/mm}^2$$

$$\left(> \frac{f_{\text{cr}}}{3} \right) = \frac{40}{3} = 13.33\,\text{N/mm}^2$$

Allowing for 2% relaxation loss in the steel after transfer, concrete shrinkage $\varepsilon_{\text{cs}} = 3 \times 10^{-6}$ and concrete specific creep $c_{\text{t}} = 1.1 \times 48 \times 10^{-6}$ per N/mm^2, the loss of force after transfer is due to

steel relaxation $\quad 0.02 \times 5046 = 107$

concrete shrinkage $\quad (\varepsilon_{\text{cs}} E_{\text{s}} A_{\text{ps}})$

$$300 \times 10^{-6} \times 195 \times 29 \times 139 = 236$$

concrete creep $\quad c_{\text{t}} f_{\text{co}} E_{\text{s}} A_{\text{ps}}$

$$1.1 \times 48 \times 10^{-6} \times 14.02 \times 195 \times 29 \times 139 = \underline{582}$$

$$\overline{919\,\text{kN}}$$

Final force after loss of all prestress:

$$P_{\text{e}} = 4592 - 919 = 3673\,\text{kN} \qquad \text{where} \quad \frac{P_{\text{e}}}{P} = 0.8$$

Final stresses due to prestress after loss of all prestress:

$$f_{1,0.8p} = \frac{3673}{4592} \times 20.10 = 16.08 \quad f_{2,0.8p} = \frac{3673}{4592} \times (-0.80) = -0.64 \, \text{N/mm}^2$$

Combined stresses in final condition for worst effects of design loads, differential shrinkage and temperature difference are:

$$f_{1LC1mod} = 16.08 - (14.06 + 0.381) = 1.639 \, \text{N/mm}^2 \quad (\geq 0)$$

$$f_{2LC3} = 16.08 - (18.024) = -1.944 \, \text{N/mm}^2 \quad (\geq -3.2)$$

$$f_{2LC1} = -0.64 + \frac{645.5}{75.4} + \frac{2607.45}{315.7} + 1.32 = 17.50$$

$$f_{3,LC3} = \frac{1907}{233.6} + 0.8 \times 2.76 = 10.37 \, \text{N/mm}^2$$

ULS moment of resistance for solution (a)

Consider only the twenty five strands in the bottom flange (see Fig. 5.66). Centroid of group occurs at

$$\frac{14 \times 110 + 11 \times 60}{14 + 11} = -88 \, \text{mm}$$

from fibre 1 so that effective depth

$$d = 1170 - 88 = 1080 \, \text{mm}$$

Tensile forces in the tendons, assuming that maximum design stress is developed, are given by:

$$F_p = 25 \times 139 \times 0.87 \times 1670 \times 10^{-3} = 5046 \, \text{kN}$$

Compressive force in concrete, in the flange is:

$$F_f = 0.4 \times 40 \times 1000 \times 160 \times 10^{-3} = 2560 \, \text{kN}$$

Compressive force in concrete, in the web, with $160 < x \leq 380$, where $x =$ neutral axis depth, is:

$$F_w = 0.4 \times 50 \times 400(x - 160)10^{-3} = (8x - 1280) \, \text{kN}$$

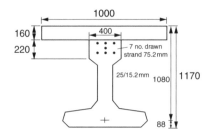

Figure 5.66. Bottom flange with 25 strands for ULS moment calculations

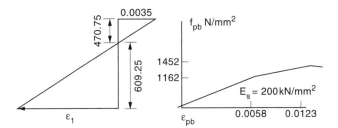

Figure 5.67. Compressive forces in the concrete flange

Equating forces to obtain x,

$$5046 = 2560 + (8x - 1280)$$

$$x = 470.75\,\text{mm}$$

$$8x = 5046 - 2560 + 1280 = 470.75$$

$$F_w = (8 \times 470.75 - 1280) = 2486\,\text{kN}$$

Referring now to Fig. 5.67:

$$\text{prestrain } \varepsilon_{pe} = \frac{f_{pe}}{E_S} = \frac{0.55 \times 1670}{200 \times 10^3} = 0.0046$$

$$\varepsilon_{pb} = \varepsilon_1 + \varepsilon_{pe} = \frac{609.25}{470.75} \times 0.0035 + 0.0046 = 0.00913$$

since

$$\varepsilon_{pb} \nless 0.05 + \frac{f_{pu}}{E_S \gamma_m} = 0.0123$$

The assumptions made about design stress in the tendons is therefore justified.
Taking moments about the centroid of the tendons

$$F_f \quad 2560(1.08 - 0.08) \quad = 2560$$
$$F_w \quad 2486(1.08 - 0.235) = \underline{2101}$$
$$\qquad\qquad\qquad\qquad 4661\,\text{kNm}$$

If all 29 strands with 4 m tops are to be taken into account the neutral axis depth
may be determined by an iterative strain compatibility analysis. Consider
the condition with $x = 352\,\text{mm}$ and determine the strains in the tendons (see
Fig. 5.68):

$$\text{prestrain } \varepsilon_{pe} = \frac{f_{pe}}{E_S} = \frac{0.55 \times 1670}{200 \times 103} - 0.0046$$

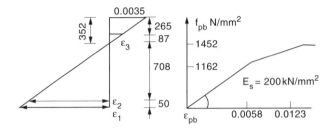

Figure 5.68. Calculating the strain in the tendons

The strain at each level is given by:

$$\varepsilon_{pb1} = \varepsilon_1 + \varepsilon_{pe} = \frac{758}{352} \times 0.0035 + 0.0046 = 0.0121 \, \text{N/mm}^2$$

$$\varepsilon_{pb2} = \varepsilon_2 + \varepsilon_{pe} = \frac{758}{352} \times 0.0035 + 0.0046 = 0.0116 \, \text{N/mm}^2$$

$$\varepsilon_{pb3} = \varepsilon_3 + \varepsilon_{pe} = \frac{-87}{352} \times 0.0035 + 0.0046 = 0.0037 \, \text{N/mm}^2$$

The stress at each level is given by:

$$f_{pb1} = 1162 + 290 \left(\frac{0.0063}{0.0065} \right) = 1443 \, \text{N/mm}^2$$

$$f_{pb2} = 1162 + 290 \left(\frac{0.0058}{0.0065} \right) = 1421 \, \text{N/mm}^2$$

$$f_{pb3} = 0.0037 \times 200 \times 10^3 = -740 \, \text{N/mm}^2$$

The tensile force in the tendons is given by:

$$F_{p1} = 11 \times 139 \times 1443 \times 10^{-3} = 2206$$

$$F_{p2} = 14 \times 139 \times 1421 \times 10^{-3} = 2765$$

$$F_{p3} = 7 \times 165 \times 740 \times 10^{-3} = -854.7$$

$$F_t = 4116.3$$

Compressive force in concrete

$$F_f = 0.4 \times 40 \times 1000 \times 100 \times 10^{-3} = 2560 \atop F_w = 0.4 \times 50 \times 400 \times 192 \times 10^{-3} = 1536 \Bigg\} \quad {F_c \approx 4096 \, \text{kN} \atop F_t \approx F_c}$$

Details of strain, stress, tensile force and compressive force are illustrated in Fig. 5.69.

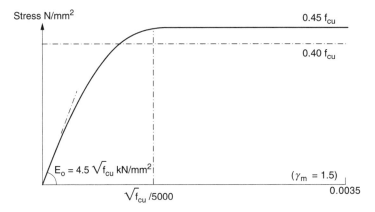

Short term design stress-strain curve for normal weight concrete

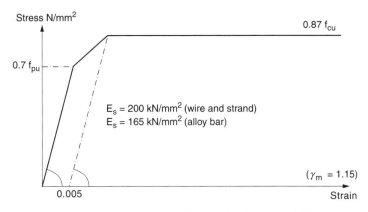

Short term design stress-strain curve for Class 1 and Class 2
relaxation prestressing tendons to B.S. Specifications

Figure 5.69. Stress–strain curves for ULS (prestressed concrete)

Taking moments about the neutral axis

$$F_{p1} \quad 2206 \times 0.758 = 1672$$

$$F_{p2} \quad 2765 \times 0.708 = 1957$$

$$F_f \quad 2560 \times 0.272 = 696.32$$

$$F_w \quad 1536 \times 0.096 = 147$$

$$F_{p3} \quad -854.7 \times 0.087 = -74.36$$

$$\overline{\qquad 4397.6 \text{ kNm}}$$

$$\frac{M_u}{M} = \frac{4397.6}{3770} = 1.17 \ (71.15)$$

The section is therefore acceptable.

Shear in the composite member

The vertical and longitudinal shear capacities of the composite beam are calculated using the tendon layout from solution (a) above. The stirrups arrangements
have to be provided. Section properties are given on Sheet 02/3 and loads on
Sheet (04/1) of the standard. Overall depth $= 1170$ mm. Check shears at point
B 3.7 m from the support and at the face of the diaphragm which is 0.25 m
from support (thickness of the web $= 160$ mm; Tables 5.20 and 5.21).

Note that ULS analysis shows that the section is balanced if, in the upper
zone, 7 drawn strands rather than 4 standard strands are provided. Thus:

$$P_{\text{total}} = \frac{31}{29} \times 3673$$

Shears at point B – 3.7 m from supports (prestress solution A)
Shear of section uncracked in flexure
Stress due to prestress at centroid of composite section:

$$f_{\text{cr}} = \frac{5\,870\,000}{387\,000} - \frac{5\,870\,000 \times 208 \times 261}{47.6 \times 10^9}$$
$$= 15.17 - 6.70 = 8.47 \, \text{N/mm}^2$$

Table 5.20. Loads at point B, 3.7 m from support

Loading	γ_{fL}	Shear	Shear γ_{fL}	Moment	Moment γ_{fL}
HB	1.3	308.3	400.8	920.0	1196
HA	1.3	31.95	41.535	169.74	220.66
Footway	1.5	10.7	16.1	55.0	82.5
Super	1.75	8.0	14.0	41.0	72.3
Dead	1.2	116.6	139.9	557.19	669.4
		Total	612.335		2240.86
		Multiply by $\gamma_{f3} = 1.1$	673.57		2465

Table 5.21. Shears at face of diaphragm ($\gamma_{fL} = 1.3$)

HB	409.4	532.2	modified
HA	36.9	47.97	HA loading
Footway	12.1	18.2	
Super	9.2	16.1	
Dead	180.4	216.5	
	Total	$830.97 \times \gamma_{f3} \to 914 \, \text{kN}$	

Multiply by $\gamma = 0.87$ giving $7.37 \, \text{N/mm}^2$

$$f_t = 0.24\sqrt{50} = 1.70$$

$$V_{CD} = 0.67 \times 160 \times 1170\sqrt{1.7^2 + 1.7 \times 7.37} \times 10^{-3}$$

$$= 492.3 \, \text{kN}$$

Shear of section cracked in flexure
Determine stress at extreme tension of the fibre due to prestress:

$$= 15.4117 + \frac{5\,807\,000 \times 208}{116.2 \times 10^6}$$

$$= 9.49 + 10.30 \approx 20$$

Multiplying by $\gamma = 0.87$ gives $17.4 \, \text{N/mm}^2$.
   Working to properties of composite beams

$$M_{cr} = [0.37\sqrt{f_{cu}} + f_{pl}]\frac{I}{y} = [0.37\sqrt{50} + 17.4]174.5 \times 10^6$$

$$= 3489 \, \text{kNm} > 2384.1$$

Hence

$$V_{cr} = 0.037ba\sqrt{f_{cu}} + \frac{M_t}{M} \cdot V$$

$$= \frac{0.037 \times 160 \times 959\sqrt{50}}{10^3} + \frac{3489}{2384.1} \times 638.4$$

$$= 40.1 + 934.3 = 974.3 \, \text{kN}$$

Shear reinforcement

$$\frac{A_{sv}}{s_v} = (V + 0.4bd_t - V_c)/0.87f_{yv} \cdot d_t$$

$$d_t = \text{depth to lowest tendon} = 1180 \, \text{mm}$$

$$\frac{A_{sv}}{s_v} = \frac{638\,400 + 0.4 \times 160 \times 1100 - 410\,800}{0.87 \times 460 \times 1100}$$

$$\frac{A_{sv}}{s_v} = 0.68$$

giving 10 mm links at 231 centres or 12 mm links at 332 centres.

Longitudinal shear

$$\text{Longitudinal shear force } V_c = V \cdot \frac{Q}{I} = \frac{638.4 \times 10^3 \times 1000 \times 160 \times 420}{116.8 \times 10^9}$$

$$= 367 \, \text{N/mm}$$

Assume surface type 2 ('rough on cast'). Width of top of precast unit $= 300 \, \text{mm}$:

$$V_c = 0.5 \quad \text{and} \quad k_1 = 0.09$$

$$\text{maximum shear} = k_1 \quad \text{for } n_s = 0.09 \times 40 \times 300 = 1080 \, \text{N/mm}$$

$$V_e < V_e h_s + 0.7 A_c f_y$$

$$A_e = \text{area per unit length} = \frac{A_{sv}}{s_v}$$

Hence

$$\frac{A_{sv}}{s_v} = (551 - 0.5 \times 300) \div (0.7 \times 480) = 1.25$$

Thus requirements for longitudinal shear are greater than for vertical shear. Requirement is 12 mm links at 180 centres.

Shears at face of diaphragm
Calculate length of transmission zone, for 15.2 mm standard strand:

$$l_t = \frac{k_t \phi}{\sqrt{f_{ci}}} = \frac{240 \times 15.2}{\sqrt{40}} = 576.8$$

$$\text{face of diaphragm} = 1450 \, \text{mm from end of beam}$$

$$\therefore \quad \text{tendon force} = \frac{450}{576.8} \times 5870 \, \text{kN} = 4579.6 \, \text{kN}$$

Shear of section uncracked in flexure
Stress due to prestress at centroid of composite section

$$= \frac{4\,579\,600}{387\,000} - \frac{4\,579\,600 \times 208 \times 261}{47.6 \times 10^9}$$

$$= 11.84 - 5.23 = 6.61 \, \text{N/mm}^2$$

$$V_{CD} = [10.67 \times 160 \times 1170\sqrt{1.7^2 + 1.7 \times 5.75}] \times 10^{-3} = 445 \, \text{kN}$$

Shear reinforcement

$$\frac{A_{sv}}{s_v} = \frac{4\,579\,000 + 0.4 \times 160 \times 1110 - 445\,000}{0.87 \times 460 \times 1110} = \frac{4\,205\,640}{444\,222}$$

$$= 9.9670$$

Longitudinal shear

$$V_c = \frac{896.5 \times 10^3 (1000 \times 160) \times 420}{116.8 \times 10^9} = 516\,\text{N/mm}$$

Maximum permissible $= 1080\,\text{N/mm}$ as before. Therefore value is acceptable.
Required area of steel interface is given by

$$\frac{A_{sv}}{s_v} = (576 - 0.5 \times 300) \div (0.7 \times 140) = 13.2$$

A_S before requirements for longitudinal shear dominate. Links (required)
T12-117 centres.

Check on maximum vertical shear capacity

maximum shear $= 5.3bd$

$d =$ distance from compression face to tendons in tension zone

$= 1110\,\text{mm}$

$V_{max} = 5.3 \times 160 \times 1160 = 941.3\,\text{kN}$

applied maximum shear $= 914.1\,\text{kN}$

Above value is permitted.

5.1.5 Ramp design

This ramp has six (6 No. M2) beams that are resting on a cross-head (RC beam)
which in turn is supported by two piers. The span chosen is 12.5 m effective for a
length of 80 m (1 in 10). There appears to be a total a number of six spans. Thus a
5 m distance remains where a solid mass of concrete exists (triangular block of
5 m length). The height of this single block will be 0.5 m. The end of the block
has zero height (see Fig. 5.70).

Deck beam design
The maximum longitudinal sagging moments occurring at midpsans are divided
as set out below.

Group I

$$M_1 = \frac{0.65 \times 63.6 \times 12.5^2}{8} = 299.61\,\text{kNm/m}$$

Group II

$$M_2 = 761 - 299.61 = 461.4\,\text{kNm/m} \quad \leftarrow \text{LC1}$$

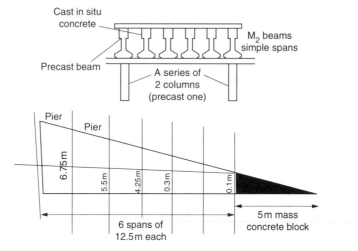

Figure 5.70. Ramp design: positioning of piers in the longitudinal direction

Group III

$$M_3 = 422 \, \text{kNm/m}$$

Group I

$$\text{LC1(mod)} = 372 \, \text{kNm/m}$$

Material properties are the same as for the overbridge beams, i.e.

$$f_{cu} = 50 \, \text{N/mm}^2 \qquad f_{ci} = 40 \, \text{N/mm}^2$$

Service

Compression $0.5 f_{cu} = 25 \, \text{N/mm}^2$ (Tension class $1 = 0$)

Transfer

Compression $0.5 f_{ci} = 20 \, \text{N/mm}^2$ (Tension class $1 = 1 \, \text{N/mm}^2$)

5.1.5.1   Serviceability design of composite concrete section

The dead load (beams and *in situ* concrete) is designed to be supported by the precast beams above (1) and subsequent loading is designed to be supported by the composite slab (2), so that separate moments are required for the moments applied at each of the two stages.

The maximum longitudinal sagging moment occurs at midspan where the moments due to stage 1 loads are:

$$M_1 = 0.65 \times 24 \times \frac{12.5^2}{8} = 305 \, \text{kNm/m}$$

The maximum longitudinal sagging moments due to stage 2 loads are:

$$M_2 = 761 - 305 = 456 \, \text{kNm/m} \ (\text{LC1})$$

$$422 \, \text{kNm/m} \ (\text{LC3}) \quad 372 \, \text{kNm/m} \ (\text{LC1 mod})$$

Allowable stresses in concrete (Clauses 6.3.2 and 7.4.3 of the standard) for precast ($f_{cu} = 50 \, \text{N/mm}^2$, $f_{ci} = 40 \, \text{N/mm}^2$ maximum) are detailed below.

Service

compression $0.5 f_{cu} = 25 \, \text{N/mm}^2$

tension   class $1 = 0$

class $2 = -3.2 \, \text{N/mm}^2$

Transfer

compression $0.5 f_{ci} = 20 \, \text{N/mm}^2$ (maximum)

tension   class $1 = -1 \, \text{N/mm}^2$ (in situ, $f_{cu} = 40 \, \text{N/mm}^2$)

Service

tension $= -4.4 \, \text{N/mm}^2$

compression $f_{cu} = 20 \, \text{N/mm}^2$

The allowable stresses here are illustrated in Fig. 5.71.

Properties of a standard T_4 section (1)

$$A = 122.5 \times 10^3 \, \text{mm}^2$$

$$a = 220 \, \text{mm}$$

$$z_1 = 19.23 \times 10^6 \, \text{mm}^3$$

$$z_2 = 11.92 \times 10^6 \, \text{mm}^3$$

Refer to Fig. 5.72.

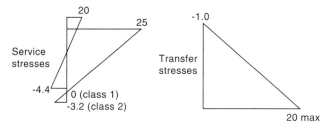

Figure 5.71. Service and transfer stresses in serviceability design

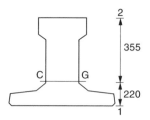

Figure 5.72. Properties of a standard T_4 section

Properties of a composite section

It is common practice to consider a uniform rectangular section for this type of construction, ignoring the modular effects of the two concretes and the fact that *in situ* concrete does not fill the gaps between the bottom flanges of the beams (see Fig. 5.73).

$$A_2 = 508 \times 650 = 330.2 \times 10^3 \, \text{mm}^2$$

$$y_{11} = 0.5 \times 650 = 325 \, \text{mm}$$

$$z_{12} = -z_{32} = \frac{508 \times 650^2}{6} = 35.77 \times 10^6 \, \text{mm}^3$$

$$z_{22} = -\frac{325}{250} \times 35.77 \times 10^6 = 46.57 \times 10^6 \, \text{mm}^3$$

$$z_{42} = \frac{325}{250} \times 35.77 \times 10^6 = 57.68 \times 10^6 \, \text{mm}^3$$

Stresses due to M_1 and M_2

Fibre 1

$$\left(\frac{M_1}{z_1} + \frac{M_2}{z_{12}}\right) = -508 \left(\frac{299.61}{19.23} + \frac{461.4}{35.77}\right) = -14.46 \, \text{N/mm}^2 \quad \text{(LC1)}$$

$$= -14.0 \, \text{N/mm}^2 \quad \text{(LC3)}$$

$$= -13.21 \, \text{N/mm}^2 \quad \text{(LC1 mod)}$$

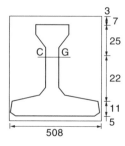

Figure 5.73. Properties of a composite section

Fibre 2

$$\left(\frac{M_1}{z_2} + \frac{M_2}{z_{22}}\right) = 0.508\left(\frac{299.61}{11.92} + \frac{461.4}{46.51}\right) = 18.25\,\text{N/mm}^2 \quad (\text{LC1})$$

$$= 17.61\,\text{N/mm}^2 \quad (\text{LC3})$$

Fibre 3

$$\frac{M_2}{z_{32}} = 0.508\left(\frac{461.4}{35.77}\right) = 6.55\,\text{N/mm}^2 \quad (\text{LC1})$$

$$= 6.05\,\text{N/mm}^2 \quad (\text{LC3})$$

Fibre 4

$$\frac{-M_2}{z_{42}} = -0.508\left(\frac{461.4}{51.68}\right) = -4.54\,\text{N/mm}^2 \quad (\text{LC1})$$

$$= -4.25\,\text{N/mm}^2 \quad (\text{LC3})$$

Allowing for an 18% loss of prestress after transfer ($\alpha = 0.82$) the initial prestress required at fibre 1 for no tension to occur under the modified load combination is

$$f_{1p} \geq \frac{13.34}{0.82} = 16.3\,\text{N/mm}^2$$

For pretensioning with straight fully bonded tendons (constant force and eccentricity), the critical section at transfer occurs at the end of the transmission zone, where the moment due to self weight of the beam is near zero and the stress criteria are as follows:

fibre 1 $\dfrac{P}{A} + \dfrac{Pe}{z_1} \geq 16.3$ (1)

fibre 2 $\dfrac{P}{A} - \dfrac{Pe}{z_2} \geq -1.0$ (2)

Multiplying (1) by z_1, and (2) by z_2 and adding

$$P \geq \left(\frac{16.3z_1 - 1.0z_2}{z_1 + z_2}\right)A = \left(\frac{16.3 \times 19.23 - 11.92}{19.23 + 11.92}\right)122.5 = 1186\,\text{kN}$$

Allowing for 10% loss of force during transfer ($\alpha_1 = 0.9$), the initial force required is $P_0 \geq 1186/0.9 = 1318\,\text{kN}$.

Using 11/12.5 mm standard strands with initial force of 0.75%

$$P_0 = 11 \times 0.75 \times 164 = 1353\,\text{kN}$$

Substituting $P = 0.9 \times 1353 = 1218\,\text{kN}$ in (2)

$$e \leq \left(\frac{z_2}{A} + \frac{1.0z_2}{P}\right) = 107\,\text{mm}$$

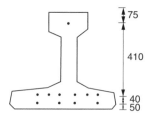

Figure 5.74. Critical section at load transfer

The distance from fibre $1 = 220 - 107 = 113\,\text{mm}$.
   Standard layout from fibre 1 is as follows:

$$
\begin{array}{rcl}
11 \text{ at } 113\,\text{mm} & = & 1243 \\
4 \text{ at } 50\,\text{mm} & = & 200 \\
6 \text{ at } 90\,\text{mm} & = & 540 \\
1 \text{ at } 500\,\text{mm} & = & 500 \\
\hline
11 & = & 1240
\end{array}
$$

The strand layout (Fig. 5.74) has been selected to conform with the standard patterns prepared by bridge beam manufacturers (see the BPCF leaflet).
   With $P = 0.9 \times 1353 = 1218\,\text{kN}$ and $e = 220 - (1240/11) = 107\,\text{mm}$ initial stress at the end of transmission zone at transfer (Fig. 5.75) is:

Fibre 1

$$
\frac{P}{A} + \frac{Pe}{z_1} = 9.94 + 6.78 = 16.7\,\text{N/mm}^2 \quad (\leq 0.5 f_{ci} \text{ where } f_{ci} = 35\,\text{N/mm}^2)
$$

Fibre 2

$$
\frac{P}{A} - \frac{Pe}{z_2} = 9.94 - 10.93 = -1.0\,\text{N/mm}^2 \quad (\geq 1.0)
$$

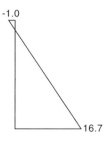

Figure 5.75. Initial stresses at the end of the transmission zone

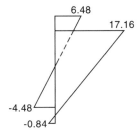

Figure 5.76. Service stresses at midspan under load combination 1

Service stresses at midspan under load combination 1 (Fig. 5.76) are:

Fibre 1

$$0.82\left(\frac{P}{A}+\frac{P_e}{z_1}\right)-14.46=-0.91\,\text{N/mm}^2$$

Fibre 2

$$0.82\left(\frac{P}{A}-\frac{P_e}{z_2}\right)+18.25=17.43\,\text{N/mm}^2 \quad (\leq 25)$$

Fibre 3

$$6.55\,\text{N/mm}^2$$

Fibre 4

$$0.54\,\text{N/mm}^2 \quad (\geq -4.4)$$

The tensile stress at fibre 4 is slightly greater than the limiting value, and this limit may be increased by up to 50% provided that the limiting tensile stress in the prestressed beams is reduced by the same numerical amount.

Service stresses at midspan under load combination 3 (with $\gamma_{fL}=0.8$ for stresses due to temperature difference) are:

Fibre 1

$$0.82\times 16.7-14.0-0.8\times 1.57=-1.56\,\text{N/mm}^2 \quad (\geq 3.2)$$

Fibre 2

$$-0.82\times 1+18.15+0.8\times 0.88=17.50\,\text{N/mm}^2 \quad (\leq 25)$$

Fibre 3

$$6.05 + 0.8 \times 2.54 = 8.02 \, \text{N/mm}^2 \quad (< 20)$$

Fibre 4

$$-4.25 - 0.8 \times 0.32 = -4.51 \, \text{N/mm}^2 \quad (\geq 4.4)$$

5.1.5.2 Moment of resistance at ultimate limit state

Considering the ten strands in the bottom flange, with a centroid at 74 mm above the bottom fibre, $d = 576$ mm. Taking $f_{cu} = 40 \, \text{N/mm}^2$ (*in situ*)

$$\frac{f_{pu}A_{ps}}{f_{cu}bd} = \frac{10 \times 164 \times 10^3}{40 \times 508 \times 576} = 0.14$$

It then follows:

$$\frac{f_{pb}}{0.87f_{pu}} = 1.0$$

$$\frac{x}{d} = 0.304$$

$$M_u = f_{pb}A_{ps}(d - 0.5x) = \frac{f_{pb}}{0.87f_{pu}}(0.87f_{pn}A_{ps})\left(1 - 0.5\frac{x}{d}\right)d$$

$$= 1.0 \times 0.87 \times 10 \times 164 \times 10^3(1 - 0.5 \times 0.304)576 \times 10^6$$

$$= 697 \, \text{kNm}$$

Maximum longitudinal sagging moment under load combination 1 is:

$$= 0.508 \times 1004 = 510 \, \text{kNm}$$

5.1.5.3 Ultimate design of reinforced concrete sections (load combination 1)

Maximum transverse sagging moment $= 143 \, \text{kNm/m}$

Reinforcement will be placed to suit positions of holes through precast beams so that $b = 610$ mm, $d = 650 - 170 = 480$ mm:

$$\frac{M}{f_{cu}bd^2} = \frac{0.6 \times 143 \times 10^6}{40 \times 610 \times 480^2} = 0.0155$$

$$\frac{z}{d} = 0.95 \quad \text{(maximum)}$$

$$A_s = \frac{M}{0.87f_yz} = \frac{0.61 \times 143 \times 10^6}{0.87 \times 460 \times 0.95 \times 480} = 439 \, \text{mm}^2$$

Maximum longitudinal hogging moment $= 129 \, \text{kNm/m}$

With 25 mm cover, $d = 650 - 35 = 615\,\text{mm}$,

$$\frac{z}{d} = 0.95 \quad \text{(maximum)}$$

$$A_s = \frac{129 \times 10^6}{0.87 \times 460 \times 0.95 \times 615} = 552\,\text{mm}^2/\text{m}$$

$$\not< 0.0015 \times 1000 \times 615 = 932\,\text{mm}^2/\text{m}$$

(where T16-200 is $1005\,\text{mm}^2/\text{m}$)

Provide T16-200 steel longitudinally and transversely on top of slab.

5.1.5.4 M2 composite beam
Assumptions
Ultimate moment without fillers [see Fig. 5.77(a)]

linear strain, maximum $\varepsilon_c = 0.0035$

rectangular stress block maximum $\sigma = 0.4f_{cu}$

trial neutral axis $d_n = 310\,\text{mm}$

prestress losses $= 20\%$

Young's modulus $E_s = 210\,\text{kN/mm}^2$

Conditions at midspan
Prestrain 12.7 mm [see Fig. 5.77(b)]

$$\text{strand} = \frac{0.8 \times 115}{93 \times 210} = 0.0047$$

Total strain in strands:

$$\varepsilon_1 = 0.0047 - 0.0035 \times \frac{25}{310} = 0.00442$$

$$\varepsilon_2 = 0.0047 - 0.0035 \times \frac{140}{310} = 0.00627$$

$$\varepsilon_3 = 0.0047 - 0.0035 \times \frac{440}{310} = 0.00966$$

$$\varepsilon_4 = 0.0047 - 0.0035 \times \frac{490}{310} = 0.01023$$

Design curve
Referring to Fig. 5.77(c):

$$\text{yield strain} = \frac{0.8f_y}{E} = 0.068$$

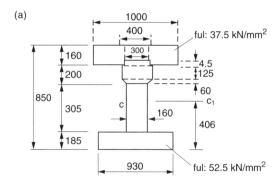

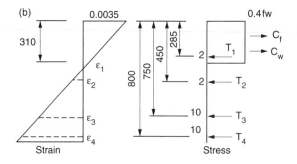

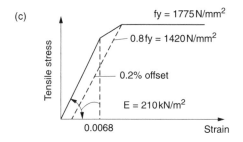

Figure 5.77. M2 beam design criteria

Tensile forces

$$T_1 = 2 \times 86.5 = 173\,\text{kN}$$

$$T_2 = 2 \times 123 = 246\,\text{kN}$$

$$T_3 = 10 \times 165 = 1650\,\text{kN}$$

$$T_4 = 10 \times 165 = \underline{1650\,\text{kN}}$$

$$\sum T = 3719\,\text{kN}$$

Concrete forces

$$C_f = \{(1000 - 300) \times 160 \times 0.4 \times 37.5\} = 1680\,\text{kN}$$

$$C_w = \{(300 \times 130 \times 0.4 \times 37.5)$$

$$+ (45 \times 300 + 125 \times 400 + 10 \times 338)0.04 \times 57.5\}$$

$$= \underline{1999\,\text{kN}}$$

$$\sum C = 3679\,\text{kN}$$

$$\therefore \quad \sum C = \sum T$$

Concrete centroid

$$d_c = \frac{1}{\sum C} [C_f(0.5 \times 160) + C_w 0.4 d_n] = 102\,\text{mm}$$

Ultimate moment of resistance

$$M_u = \{173 \times 0.183 + 245 \times 0.348 + 1650 \times 0.648 + 1650 \times 0.698\}\,\text{kN}$$

$$= 2337\,\text{kNm}.$$

5.1.6 Example (5.13) British practice

A prestressed concrete bridge with a box girder is shown in Fig. 5.78. Design the bridge using British Standard BS 5400 and use relevant data from the standards and literature investigated by the researcher. Take wind loading and HA loading at the appropriate level. The bridge needs to be checked against HB loading. Devise appropriate tendons with tendon profiles. The requisite details for this study are given in Tables 5.21–5.24.

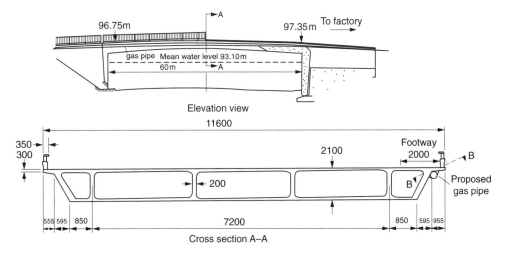

Figure 5.78. Prestressed concrete precast box beam bridge

Table 5.21 (pages 646–647). Carriageway details from BS 5400 related to Example (5.13)

Carriageway		
BS 5400 *Part 2*	*Calculation*	*Output*

	Lanes	
3.2.9.1	Width of carriageway $= 7600$ mm	
3.2.9.3.1	No. of notional lanes $= 2$	
	Therefore width of one lane:	
	$$= \frac{7600}{3} = 3800 \text{ mm}$$	
	Width of central reserve $= 600$ mm	Lane 1: 3500 mm
	Width of one lane $= 3800 - \dfrac{600}{2}$	Lane 2: 3500 mm
	$\qquad = 3500$ mm	

	Wind loading	
5.3	For bridge 60 000 mm span and 7600 mm wide:	
5.3.2.1	Maximum gust $= V_c = v \cdot k_1 \cdot s_1 \cdot s_2$	
Fig. 2 p. 10	Mean hourly wind speed (London) $= 26$ m/s	
5.3.2.1.2	$k_1 = 1.0$	
5.3.2.1.3	$s_1 = 1.0$	
Table 2	$s_2 = 1.4$ (2 m above mean water level)	
	Therefore maximum gust $= 26 \times 1 \times 1 \times 1.4$	Maximum gust
	$\qquad\qquad = 36.4$ m/s	36.4 m/s
	(Without live load)	
	Because V_c with live load > 35 m/s therefore reduction ignored.	
5.3.3.1	To find area A_1 when $L = 60.0$ m	
5.3.3.1.2a	(a) For unloaded: (Table 4) $d = 1.8$ m	
	$\qquad A_1 = 60 \times 1.8$	
	$\qquad\quad = 108 \text{ m}^2$	
	(b) For loaded: $dL = 2.5$ m	
	$\qquad d = 2.5 + 0.1 + 1.6 = 4.2$ m	
	$\qquad A_1 = 60 \times 4.2$	
	$\qquad\quad = 252 \text{ m}^2$	

	Drag coefficient, C_d	
5.3.3.4	(a) For unload: (Table 5b, $d = 1800$ mm)	
	$$b = \frac{11\,600}{2} \text{ mm}$$	
	$\qquad = 5800$ mm	
	$b/d = 5800/1800 = 3.22$	
Figure 5	$C_d = 1.43$	
Note 4	Super elevation 1: 100 $= 0.57°$	
	$C_d = 3 \times 0.57\% = 1.71\%$	

Continued

Table B5.21. Continued

Carriageway

BS 5400 Part 2	Calculation	Output
5.3.3.4 (*Continued*)	Therefore increase for super elevation: $= (1.71\% \times 1.43) + 1.43$ $= 1.45$	
Table 5b	For loaded: $(dL = 2.5\,\text{m})$ $b/dL = 5800/2500$ $\quad = 2.32$ Therefore $C_d = 1.70$ Increase for super elevation $= 1.71\% \times 1.7$ $C_d = 1.77$	Loaded C_d: 1.77
5.3.3	**Dynamic pressure** $q = 0.613 V_c^2 \; \text{N/m}^2$ (*a*) For unloaded: $q = 0.613(36.4)^2/10^3$ $\qquad\qquad\qquad = 0.812\,\text{kN/m}^2$ (*b*) For loaded: $q = 0.613(35)^2/10^3$ $\qquad\qquad\qquad = 0.75\,\text{kN/m}^2$	
	Nominal transverse wind load $P_t = q \cdot A_1 \cdot C_d$ (*a*) Unloaded: $P_t = 0.812 \times 108 \times 1.49$ $\qquad\qquad\qquad = 130.4\,\text{kN}$ (*b*) Loaded: $P_t = 0.751 \times 252 \times 1.768$ $\qquad\qquad\qquad = 334.59\,\text{kN}$	
5.3.4	**Nominal longitudinal wind load** $P_{ls} = 0.25[q \cdot A_1 \cdot C_d]$ (*a*) For unloaded: $\quad P_{ls} = 0.25 \times 0.812 \times 108 \times 1.49$ $\qquad\quad = 32.6\,\text{kN}$ (*b*) For loaded: $\quad P_{ls} = 0.25 \times 0.751 \times 252 \times 1.768$ $\qquad\quad = 83.65\,\text{kN}$	Loaded: 83.65 kN
5.3.5	**Nominal vertical wind load** $P_v = q \cdot A_3 \cdot C_1$, where $A_3 = 11.6 \times 60$ $\qquad\qquad\qquad\qquad\qquad = 692\,\text{m}^2$ $C_1 = + \pm 0.75$ (*a*) For unloaded: $\quad P_v = 0.812 \times 692 \times (\pm 0.75)$ $\qquad\quad = \pm 421.4\,\text{kN}$ (*b*) For loaded: $\quad P_v = 0.751 \times 692 \times (\pm 0.75)$ $\qquad\quad = +389.8\,\text{kN}$	Loaded: ± 389.8 kN

Table 5.22 (pages 648–650). Loading details from BS 5400 related to Example (5.13)

Loading		
BS 5400 Part 2	Calculation	Output

| 6.2 Table 13 | **HA loading** For type HA uniformly distributed load: up to 60 m loaded length = 21.4 kN/m For a unit box beam, i.e. 2.60 m HA = (21.4/2.917) × 2.60 = 19.07 kN/m | HA: 19.07 kN/m |

HB loading

Minimum number of units is 25

One unit = 10 kN per axle (2.5 kN per wheel)

Dimension of HB vehicles = 1.8 m between axles.

For unit box beam, i.e. 2.60 m:

$$HB = \left(\frac{10 \times 25}{3}\right) \times 2.60 = 216.7 \text{ kN}$$

HB: 216.7 kN

KEL (knife edge loading)

The KEL per notional lanes shall be taken as 120 kN.

$$KEL = \frac{120 \times 2.60}{2.917} = 106.9 \text{ kN}$$

KEL: 106.9 kN

Bending moment

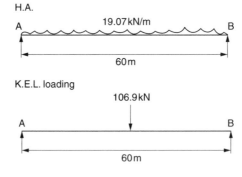

H.A.

A ⎓⎓⎓⎓ 19.07 kN/m ⎓⎓⎓⎓ B

60 m

K.E.L. loading

106.9 kN

A ↓ B

60 m

Continued

Table 5.22. Continued

Loading		
BS 5400 Part 2	*Calculation*	*Output*

Maximum bending moment for HA + KEL:

$$= 8870 + 3260.5$$

$$= 12\,130.4\,\text{kNm}$$

Dimension of HB vehicles:
1.8 m, 6 m, 1.8 m
HB loading:

6.4.3

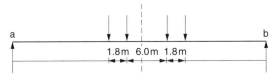

$R_a + R_b = 216.7(4)$
$\qquad = 866.8\,\text{kN}$
Taking moment about a

$216.7[27.2 + 29 + 35 + 36.8] - 60 \cdot R_b = 0$

$\quad R_b = 454.7\,\text{kN}$

$\quad R_a = 412.1\,\text{kN}$

$M = 412.1(32) - 216.7(4.8) - 216.7(3.0)$

$\quad = 11496.9\,\text{kNm}$

Therefore the most severe case is
from HA + KEL loading:

Max BM:
where HA + KEL = 12 130.4 kNm | 12 130.4 kNm

Shear force
(*a*) HA + KEL loading:

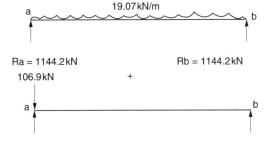

Continued

Table 5.22. Continued

Loading		
BS 5400 Part 2	*Calculation*	*Output*

Therefore maximum shear force at a:

= 1144.2 + 106.9 kN

= 1251 kN

Max SF: 1251 kN

(*b*) HB loading

$R_a + R_b = 866.8$ kN

Taking moment about a:

$216.7[1.8 + 7.8 + 9.6] - 60 \cdot R_b = 0$

Therefore:

$R_a = 797.5$ kN

$R_b = 69.3$ kN

Therefore the most severe case is from

HA + KEL:

= 1251 kN

For HB Max SF: 1251 kN

Table 5.23 (pages 651–654). Section properties from BS 5400 related to Example (5.13)

Section properties

Calculation	*Output*

Depth of section

$$\text{depth} \approx \frac{\text{span}}{(20\ 30)} = \frac{60}{30} = 2.00\,\text{m}$$

Depth of section usually varies from 20 to 30
Try depth = 2.10 m

$$\text{Therefore depth of section} = \frac{\text{span}}{\text{depth}}$$

$$= \frac{60}{2.1} = 28.57 \quad \text{(permitted)}$$ Depth:
2.10 m

Thickness of the top flange

$$\text{thickness} = \frac{\text{depth}}{(6-8)}$$

$$= \frac{2.10}{8} = 0.26\,\text{m}$$

Try thickness: use 300 mm
Therefore thickness of top flange:

$$= \frac{\text{depth}}{\text{thickness}} = \frac{2.10}{0.3} = 7.00 \quad \text{(permitted)}$$ Thickness:
300mm

Thickness of bottom flange
thickness = $(1 - 1.125) \times$ top flange
                          = use 300mm   Thickness:
300mm

Thickness of web

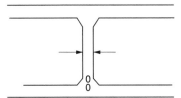

Make 200 mm thick (horizontal dimension) with external
diameter of duct 72 mm and 20 mm cover.

Continued

Table 5.23. Continued

Section properties

Calculation	Output

Minimum depth of 'box'

Depth $= 2100 - 300 - 300$
$\quad\quad = 1500 \text{ mm}$

Min depth:
1500 m

Cross-sectional area

Top flange: $2600 \times 300 = 780 \times 10^3 \text{ mm}^2$

Bottom flange: 2600×300
$\quad\quad\quad\quad = 780 \times 10^3 \text{ mm}^2$

Webs: $2 \times [200 \times 1500]$
$\quad\quad = 600 \times 10^3 \text{ mm}^2$

Therefore total area of cross-section

$\quad = 2[780 \times 10^3] + 600 \times 10^3$
$\quad = 216 \times 10^4 \text{ mm}^2$

Area
$216 \times 10^4 \text{ mm}^2$

Calculation of $\bar{y}$

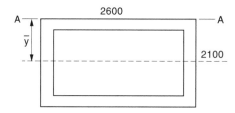

Take moment about A–A:

Outer area $= 2600 \times 2100$
$\quad\quad\quad = 546 \times 10^4 \text{ mm}^2$

Inner area $= 2200 \times 1500$
$\quad\quad\quad = 330 \times 10^4 \text{ mm}^2$

$\bar{y} = (546 \times 10^4)(1050)$
$\quad - (350 \times 10^4)(1050)216 \times 10^4$

$\bar{y} = 1050 \text{ mm}$

y:
1050 mm

Continued

Table 5.23. Continued

Section properties

Calculation	Output
Calculation of $\bar{x}$ $$\bar{x} = \frac{(546 \times 10^4)(1300) - (330 \times 10^4)(1300)}{216 \times 10^4}$$ $\bar{x} = 1300\,\text{mm}$	x: 1300 mm
Calculation of I_{xx} $$I_{xx} = \frac{BD^3}{12} - \frac{bd^3}{12}$$ $$= \frac{2600 \times 2100^3}{12} - \frac{2200 \times 1500^3}{12}$$ $$= 1.39 \times 10^{12}\,\text{mm}^4$$	I_{xx}: 1.39×10^{12} mm
Section modulus $$z = \frac{I_{xx}}{y} = \frac{1.39 \times 10^{12}}{1050}$$ $$= 13.2 \times 10^8\,\text{mm}^3$$	z: 13.2×10^8 mm^3

Calculation of M_d and M_L
Where M_L = service state live moment
$\quad\quad M_d$ = service state dead moment
Assume that:
1. Surfacing taken as a live load at 0.5 kN/m².
2. Services running through the hollow spine, live load 1.0 kN/m² run of beam.
3. A live load across the width of the bridge is taken of 4.0 kN/m².
Therefore:
$\quad$ UDL $= 4 \times 1.7$
$\quad\quad\quad = 0.5 \times 1.7$
Services $= 1.0$
$\quad\quad\quad\overline{}$
$\quad\quad\quad$ 8.65 kN/m

Continued

Table 5.23. Continued

Section properties

Calculation	Output
$M_L = \dfrac{WL^2}{8} = \dfrac{8.65 \times 60^2}{8}$ $= 3892.5\,\text{kNm}$	M_L: 3892.5 kNm
Dead loading (take $V_c = 25\,\text{kN/m}^3$) UDL = cross-sectional $\times V_c$ $= \dfrac{216 \times 10^4 \times 25}{10^6} = 54.0\,\text{kN/m}$ M_d : service state dead moment $= \dfrac{WL^2}{8} = \dfrac{54.0 \times 60^2}{8}$ $= 24\,300\,\text{kNm}$	M_d: 24 300 kN

Table 5.24 (pages 655–658). Tendon force details from BS 5400 related to Example (5.13)

Tendon force	
Calculation	*Output*

Initial estimation of tendon force
and calculation of tendon 'zone' service
state

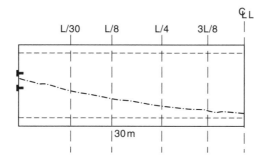

Assuming 2 no. 12/13 cables per web 'e' is
the distance to the edge of 'both ducts'
(at the centre-line)
$d' = (72 + 16 + 20)$ minimum
$d' = 108\,\text{mm}$
Let $d' = 125\,\text{mm}$
$$e = y - d'$$
$$= 1050 - 125 = 925\,\text{mm}$$
i.e. make 900 mm

The equations for the limits of the
cable 'zone ' are given in the
calculation below, together with an
equation for the initial estimate of 'H'
– tendon force. An estimate of 'e'.

The eccentricity of the tendons from
the centroid of the section, must be
in this formula. At this stage H can be
adjusted depending on the number of
cables. When the values of 'e_1' and 'e_2'
are established, the boundaries of the
tendon 'zone' can be settled, and hence
a plot of the actual tendon centroid.

Continued

Table 5.24. Continued

Tendon force		
	Calculation	*Output*

$$H = \frac{(M_L + M_d)}{e + z/A}$$

$$= \frac{(3892.5 + 24\,300) \times 10^6}{[900 + (13.2 \times 10^8/216 \times 10^4)] \times 10^3}$$

$$= \frac{2.82 \times 10^{10}}{1.51 \times 10^6}$$

$$= 18\,675.5\,\text{kN}$$

H:
18 675.5 kN

Now value of 'e_1' and 'e_2' can be calculated at the beam centre-line:

$$e_1 = z/A + M_d/H$$

$$= \frac{13.2 \times 10^8}{216 \times 10^4} + \frac{24\,300 \times 10^6}{18\,675.5 \times 10^3}$$

$$= 1912.3\,\text{mm}$$

e_1:
1912.3 mm

$$e_2 = -z/A + (M_L + M_d)/H$$

$$= \frac{13.2 \times 10^8}{216 \times 10^4} + \frac{(28\,192.5) \times 10^6}{18\,675.5 \times 10^3}$$

$$= 898\,\text{mm}$$

e_2:
898 mm

Since the actual tendon eccentricity, 900 mm, therefore this value lies inside zone.

$898 < 900 < 1912.3\,\text{mm}$ (permitted)

If we choose $e = 0$ (at centroid), will again be in zone. Hence a table for e_1 and e_2 using the general equation for bending to calculate M_L and M_d and the equation for a parabola to calculate e.

General equation:

$$M_{xx} = WL_y/2 - Wy^2/2$$

In which $W_d = 54.0\,\text{kN/m}$, $W(L + d) = 62.25$

$L = 60\,\text{m}$

Continued

Table 5.24. Continued

Tendon force		
	Calculation	Output

Deflection check

4.3.7.1 Deflection of the beam is checked with a limit of span/300 at transfer and

2.2.3.1 at span/250 at serviceability.

At transfer:

$$P = 1.2H$$

$$= 1.2[18\,675.5]$$

$$= 22\,410.6\,\text{kN}$$

Upward deflection due to parabolic cable:

$$\delta = -5/48 \times \frac{P \times e \times L^2}{E_c \times I}$$

$$\delta = -5/48 \times \frac{22\,410.6 \times 10^3 \times 900 \times 60\,000^2}{30 \times 10^3 \times 1.39 \times 10^{12}}$$

$$\delta = -181.4\,\text{mm}$$

Deflection upwards: $-181.4\,\text{mm}$

Downwards deflection:

$$\delta = +5/384 \times \frac{W_d \times L^4}{E_c \times I}$$

$$\delta = +5/384 \times \frac{54 \times 60\,000^4}{30 \times 10^3 \times 1.30 \times 10^{12}}$$

$$\delta = +233.6\,\text{mm}$$

Downward deflection: $+233.6\,\text{mm}$

Therefore net deflection:

$$\delta_n = -181.4 + 233.6$$
$$= 52.3\,\text{mm}$$

Deflection limited to $L/300$

$$L/300 = \frac{60\,000}{300}$$

$$= 200\,\text{mm} > 52.3\,\text{mm} \quad \text{(permitted)}$$

Continued

Table 5.24. Continued

Tendon force

	Calculation	Output
	Deflection check	
4.3.7.1	At serviceability:	
2.2.3.1	$P = 1.0H$	
	$\quad = 1.0[18\,675.5]$	
	$P = 18\,675.5\,\text{kN}$	
	Upward deflection:	
	$\delta = -181.4 \times \dfrac{18\,675.5}{22\,410.6}$	
	$\delta = -151.2\,\text{mm}$	Deflection upward: $-151.2\,\text{mm}$
	Downward deflection:	
	$\delta = +233.6 \times \dfrac{(W_{\text{L}} + W_{\text{d}})}{W_{\text{d}}}$	
	$\delta = +233.6 \, \dfrac{(8.65 + 54.0)}{54}$	
	$\delta = 271\,\text{mm}$	Deflection downward: $+271\,\text{mm}$
	Net deflection:	
	$\delta_{\text{n}} = -151.2 + 271$	
	$\delta_{\text{n}} = 119.8\,\text{mm}$	
	Deflection limited:	
	$L/250 = \dfrac{60\,000}{250}$	
	$L/250 = 240\,\text{mm} > 119.8\,\text{mm} \quad \text{(permitted)}$	

Table 5.25. Tendon load calculations

Segment	L (m)	kL	$\mu\theta$	$kL + \mu\theta$	$e^{-kL-\mu\theta}$	Tendon load P (kN)
AB	1.75	0.014	0	0.014	0.986	$0.986P$
BC	2.5	0.020	0.167	0.087	0.916	$0.986 \times 0 \times P$
						30.901
CD	1.75	0.014	0	0.014	0.986	$= 0.890P$
DE	1.0	0.008	0.10	0.048	0.953	$= 0.848P$

5.1.7 Example (5.14) British practice

The post-tensioned concrete (Fig. 5.79) is continuous over two spans and its curved tendon is to be tensioned from the end at A. If the initial applied load in the tendon at A is 400 kN, calculate the net load in the tendon at the dead end F allowing for friction ($\mu = 0.4$) and wobble effects ($k = 0.008$) only.

Solution

$$P_2 = P_1 e^{-\mu\theta - kL}$$

$$\text{tendon load} = 400\,\text{kN}$$

$$K = 0.008/\text{m}$$

$$\mu = 0.4$$

Half of the tendon is divided into 4 units between A and E. Consider each portion after the losses have been deducted from the preceding portion:

force at A: $P_1 = 400\,\text{kN}$

AB: $kL = 0.008 \times 1.75 = 0.014$

BC: $\left.\begin{array}{l} kL = 0.008 \times 2.5 = 0.02 \\ \mu\theta = 0.4 \times 2.5/15 = 0.067 \end{array}\right\} = 0.087$

CD: $kL = 0.008 \times 1.75 = 0.014$
    $\mu\theta = 0.4 \times 10/100 = 0.04$

Calculations are summarized in Table 5.25.

total loss $A - E = 1 - 0.848 = 0.152$, i.e. 15.2%

tendon load at $F = 400 - (1 - 2 \times 0.152) = 0.696 \times 400 = 278.4\,\text{kN}$

5.1.8 Example (5.15) British practice

Figure 5.80 shows a bending moment diagram envelope for a post-tensioned bridge. Using the following data draw the tendon or cable profile for this bridge, and design the section and bonded steel.

$$M_{i_{max}} = 9769.32\,\text{kNm}$$

$$z = 5 \times 10^8\,\text{mm}^3$$

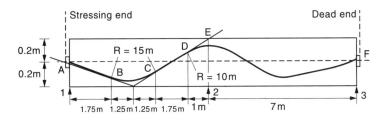

Figure 5.79. Cable profile of a two-span continuous girder

$$A = 1.73 \times 10^6 \, \text{mm}^2$$

$$L_{\text{total}} = 10 \, \text{m}$$

$$I = 4.3 \times 10^{11} \, \text{mm}^4$$

$$f_{\text{cu}} = 60 \, \text{N/mm}^2$$

$$E_{\text{c}} = 38 \, \text{kN/mm}^2$$

$$E_{\text{s}} = 200 \, \text{kN/mm}^2$$

$$d = 1326 \, \text{mm}$$

$$b = 1000$$

strand $\not< 15.2 \, \text{mm}$

maximum jacking force $= 0.8 \times$ force at ULS.

All losses must be checked at the same time, using BS 5400. The girder is 1.73 m × 1.0 m.

The shear envelope for the girder is shown in Fig. 5.80. Check the beam for shear when the final cable profile is established. Design the shear reinforcement if needed.

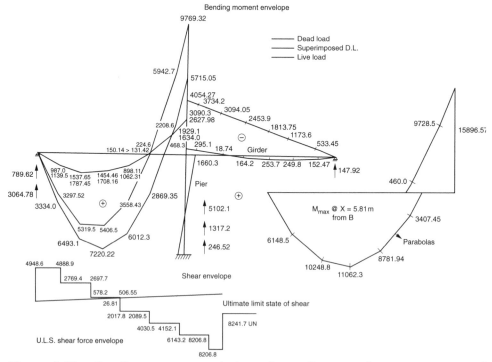

Figure 5.80. Bending moment and shear force diagrams for a post-tensioned bridge

(a)   Prestresssing force

$$M_r = \max M_i - \min M_i = 9769.32 - 0 = 9769.32 \, \text{kNm}$$

$$z_{1,2} = 5.0 \times 10^8 \, \text{mm}^3$$

$$A = 1.73 \times 10^6$$

$$P_{e \, \min} = \frac{M_r \times A}{z_1 - z_2} = \frac{9769.32 \times 10^6 \times 1.73 \times 10^6}{2 \times 5 \times 10^8} = 16\,900.9 \, \text{kN}$$

$$P_{e \, \max} = \frac{(f_{a \, \max}(z_1 + z_2) - M_r)A}{z_1 + z_2}$$

$$= \frac{(2 \times 5.0 \times 10^8 \times 19.8 - 9769.32 \times 10^6) \times 1.73 \times 10^6}{2 \times 5.00 \times 10^8}$$

$$= 17\,353.1 \, \text{kN}$$

$$P_{ef} = 17\,300 \, \text{kN}$$

(b)   Permissible pressure zone

$$e_p \geq \frac{\max M_i + M_d}{P_e} - \frac{z}{A} + \frac{z f_{a \, \min}}{P_e} = -467.64 \tag{5.1}$$

$$e_p \geq \frac{\max M_i + M_d}{P_e} + \frac{z}{A} + \frac{z f_{a \, \max}}{P_e} = -469.86 \tag{5.2}$$

$$e_p \leq \frac{\min M_i + M_d}{P_e} - \frac{z}{A} + \frac{z f_{a \, \max}}{P_e} = -460.09 \tag{5.3}$$

$$e_p \leq \frac{\min M_i + M_d}{P_e} + \frac{z}{A} + \frac{z f_{a \, \min}}{P_e} = -454.3 \tag{5.4}$$

The governing equations are Eqs (5.2) and (5.3). Permissible pressure-zone values for different values of x are detailed in the grid below:

x	0.75	2.25	3.75	5.25	6.75	8.25	9.5
$e_p \geq$	−394.74	−126.06	125.7	232.85	195.4	4.07	−263.23
$e_p \leq$	−171.78	95.71	202.8	277.13	318.72	318.26	−283.23

Permissible lines of pressure are shown in Fig. 5.81.

An attempt can now be made to adjust the tendon profile within permissible pressure zones, and in order to obtain a concordant tendon profile, the tendon must also follow a bending moment diagram such as a live load diagram.

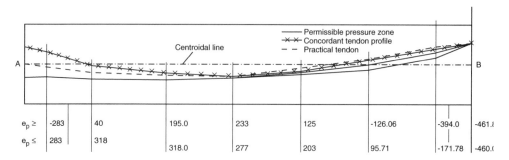

$e_p \geq$	-283	40	195.0	233	125	-126.06	-394.0	-461.8
$e_p \leq$	283	318		277	203	95.71	-171.78	-460.0
			318.0					

Figure 5.81. Tendon profiles

(c) *Maximum eccentricity at B*

$$e_s = \tfrac{1}{2}(469.86 + 460.09) = 461\,\text{mm}$$

Then e_s at any point is:

$$e_s(i) = \frac{M \text{ at } i}{M \text{ at B}} \times 461$$

The idealized concordant tendon profile is shown in Fig. 5.81 and eccentricities for different values of x are detailed in the grid below:

x	0	0.75	2.25	3.75	5.25	6.75	8.25	9.5
$e(s)$	-461	-280.0	-10.0	168.0	255.0	251.0	155.5	0

For the practical tendon profile it is necessary to change the sharp minus in the idealized tendon profile with smooth parabolas. Thus:

$$e_1 = 255\,\text{mm} \qquad e_2 = 469\,\text{mm} \qquad L = 10.0\,\text{m}$$

$$\alpha_1 \times L = 5.25\,\text{m} \quad \Rightarrow \quad \alpha_1 = 0.525$$

$$(1 - \alpha_1) = 0.475$$

$$\alpha_2 \times L = 0.75 \quad \Rightarrow \quad \alpha_2 = 0.075$$

By equating the scope of parabolas 2 and 3 at C

$$h = \frac{\alpha_2}{\alpha_1}(e_1 + e_2) \tag{5.5}$$

$$= \frac{0.075}{0.525}(255.0 + 469.0) = 102.3\,\text{mm}$$

Point C is on the straight line joining points of maximum eccentricity D and B. The slope of parabolas 2 and 3 at C and is

$$Q_C = \frac{2(e_1 + e_2)}{\alpha_1 L} = \frac{2(0.255 + 0.469)}{5.25} = 0.272\,\text{rad} \tag{5.6}$$

(d) *The curvature of each parabola*

$$\mathcal{H}_1 = \frac{1}{R_1} = \frac{2e_1}{L^2(1-\alpha_1)^2} = 0.01994\,\mathrm{m}^{-1} \quad \text{(concave)} \tag{5.7}$$

$$\mathcal{H}_2 = \frac{1}{R_2} = \frac{2(e_1+e_2-h)}{L^2(\alpha_1-\alpha_2)} = 0.0606\,\mathrm{m}^{-1} \quad \text{(concave)} \tag{5.8}$$

$$\mathcal{H}_3 = \frac{1}{R_3} = \frac{2(e_1+e_2)}{\alpha_1 \times \alpha_2 L^2} = 0.3637\,\mathrm{m}^{-1} \quad \text{(convex)} \tag{5.9}$$

Formula for each parabola is displayed in the grid below:

Parabola

1	$y = 0.00997x^2$	$x = 0$	at D
2	$y = 0.0303x^2$	$x = 0$	at D
3	$y = 0.1815x^2$	$x = 0$	at B

The practical tendon profile is shown in Fig. 5.82.

(e) *Friction losses*

$$\frac{P_x}{P_0} = \mathrm{e}^{-x(k+\mu\mathcal{H})} \tag{5.10}$$

$$\left.\begin{array}{l} \mu = 0.2 \\ k = 0.003 \end{array}\right\} \quad \text{represent plastic ducts with lubricants}$$

Now from Table 5.26, friction losses over support B are 15.8% and if we assume that 25% long-term losses require jacking forces, then

$$P_0 = \frac{17\,300}{0.842 \times 0.75} = 27\,395.1\,\mathrm{kN}$$

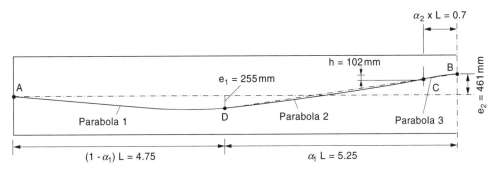

Figure 5.82. Practical tendon profile

Table 5.26. Friction losses

Parabola	1				2			3
x	0	1.75	3.25	4.75	6.25	7.75	9.25	100
$\mathcal{H}$		0.01994			0.0606			0.3637
P_x/P_0	1	0.99	0.98	0.966	0.943	0.92	0.898	0.842
P_i/P_0	0.916	0.93	0.94	0.938	0.935	0.92	0.898	0.842
P_i	25 093.9	25 477.4	25 751.4	25 696.6	25 614.4	25 203.5	24 600.8	23 066.7
P_{EF}	18 820.4	19 108.0	19 313.5	19 272.4	19 210.8	18 902.6	18 450.6	17 300

For a 15.2 mm strand the maximum jacking force is

$$250 \times 0.8 = 200 \, kN$$

(f) Number of strands

$$n = \frac{27 \, 395.1}{200} = 136.97$$

Provided seven cables each contain 20 strands then $A_S = 20 \, 020.0 \, mm^2$ in a 90 mm duct.

(g) Anchorage losses
For a wedge-type anchorage of $\Delta = 2.0 \, mm$, the length of draw in the lane is

$$L_d = \sqrt{\frac{2E_p \, \Delta p \, \Delta}{\alpha}}$$

$$E_p = 200 \, kN/mm^2$$

α = twice scope of the prestress line (Fig. 5.83)

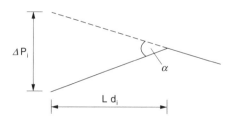

Figure 5.83. Relation of α to the slope of the prestress line

$$\frac{\alpha}{2} = \frac{0.03 \times P_0}{L/2} = \frac{0.03 \times 27\,395.1}{10/2}$$

$$= 164.4 \, \text{N/mm}^2$$

$$L_d = \sqrt{\frac{200\,000 \times 20\,020 \times 2}{1644}} = 6.98 \, \text{m}$$

$$\Delta P_i = \alpha \times L_d = 2 \times 164.4 \times 6979.3 \times 10^{-3}$$

$$= 2249 \, \text{kN} = 0.084 P_0$$

At 6.25 m from support A

$$\Delta P = 2 \times 164.4 \times (6979.3 - 6750)$$

$$= 239.8 \, \text{kN} = 0.0087 P_0$$

Initial prestress P_i values (after friction and anchorage losses) are shown in Table 5.26 together with effective prestress assuming 25% long-term losses.

(h) Long-term losses

$$f_{cu} = 60 \rightarrow E_C = 38 \, \text{kN/mm}^2$$

$$E_s = 200 \, \text{kN/mm}^2$$

$$A = 1.73 \times 10^6 \, \text{mm}^2$$

$$e_s = 461 \, \text{mm}$$

$$I = 4.3 \times 10^{11} \, \text{mm}^4$$

Stress in the concrete at the tendon level after transfer is

$$f_C = \frac{P_T}{A}\left(1 + \frac{e_s^2}{I/A}\right) = \frac{23\,066.7 \times 10^3}{1.73 \times 10^6}\left(1 + \frac{461^2}{2.48 \times 10^5}\right)$$

$$= 24.73 \, \text{N/mm}^2$$

(i) Relaxation of steel
For a 15.2 mm strand prestressed to 0.787 of its breaking load, loss of relaxation can be assumed:

$$\frac{6}{100} \times 195.7 = 11.74$$

Thus, for 140 strands, the load is 1648.7 kN

(j) Elastic shortening

$$\text{strain in concrete} = \frac{24.73}{38 \times 10^3} = 0.00065$$

$$\text{loss in prestress in cable} = \frac{1}{2}\frac{E_S}{E_C} \times f_C$$

$$= \frac{1}{2} \times \frac{200}{38} \times 24.73 = 65.07$$

For seven cables

$$= 65.07 \times 20\,020 = 1302.8\,\text{kN}$$

(k) Shrinkage of concrete

Normal exposure coefficient could be 200×10^{-6}, which leads to shrinkage. Therefore per unit length

$$\text{loss of prestress} = E_S \times 200 \times 10^{-6}$$

$$= 200 \times 200 \times 10^{-6} = 4 \times 10^{-2}\,\text{kN/mm}^2$$

$$\text{loss in the cables} = 4 \times 10^{-2} \times 20\,020 = 800.8\,\text{kN}$$

(l) Creep of concrete

$$\text{creep coefficient } \phi = 10$$

$$\text{total creep strain} = \frac{f_C}{E_C} \times \phi = 0.00065$$

$$\text{loss in stress} = 0.00065 \times 200 = 0.13\,\text{kN/mm}^2$$

$$\text{loss in cables} = 0.13 \times 20\,020 = 2605.7\,\text{kN}$$

(m)   Total loss

$$\frac{\sum P}{P_0} = \frac{6353.06}{27\,395.1} = 23\% \approx \text{assumed } 25\%$$

Effective forces after all losses are shown in Table 5.26.

(n) Stresses in transfer

$$f_{CT} = 50\,\text{N/mm}^2$$

$$f_{a\,\min} = -1.0\,\text{N/mm}^2$$

$$P_i = 23\,066.7 \qquad \text{(immediately after transfer)}$$

Assume mid-tendon only is stressed at transfer. Then:

$$P_i = 23\,066.7 \times \frac{1}{7} = 3295.2\,\text{kN}$$

Considering section B

(1) $\quad f_{a\ min} \geq \dfrac{P_i}{A} - \dfrac{P_i e_p}{z} + \dfrac{M_d}{z}$ (5.11)

(2) $\quad f_{a\ max} \leq \dfrac{P_i}{A} + \dfrac{P_i e_p}{z} - \dfrac{M_d}{z}$ (5.12)

(1) and (2) $= \dfrac{3295.20 \times 10^3}{1.73 \times 10^6} \mp \dfrac{3295.2 \times 461 \times 10^3}{5.0 \times 10^8} \pm \dfrac{468.3 \times 10^6}{5.0 \times 10^8}$

$$(1) = -0.916\,\text{N/mm}^2 > -1\,\text{N/mm}^2$$

$$(2) = 4.04\,\text{N/mm}^2 \ll 50\,\text{N/mm}^2$$

Other tendons will be prestressed as the dead load is developed.

(o) Ultimate limit state of flexure
Refer to Fig. 5.84 and the data below:

$$A_{ps} = 20\,020\,\text{mm}^2 \qquad \text{(bonded)}$$

$$A_C = 1.73 \times 10^6$$

$$I = 4.3 \times 10^{11}\,\text{mm}^4$$

$$P_e = 17\,300\,\text{kN}$$

$$e = 461\,\text{mm}$$

$$d = 1326\,\text{mm}$$

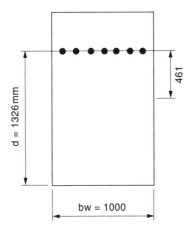

Figure 5.84. Diagram for ULS of flexure calculations

$$E_C = 38\,\text{kN/mm}^2$$

$$E_{ps} = 200\,\text{kN/mm}^2$$

Concrete stress at the tendon level:

$$\frac{17\,300 \times 10^3}{1.73 \times 10^6} + \frac{17\,300 \times 461^2 \times 10^3}{4.3 \times 10^{11}} = 18.55\,\text{N/mm}^2$$

Concrete prestress at the tendon level ε_e:

$$\frac{18.55}{38 \times 10^2} = 0.000488$$

Concrete strain at the tendon level at collapse ε_μ:

$$\frac{1326 - x}{x} \times 0.0035 = \frac{4.641}{x} - 0.0035$$

Change in tendon strain due to ultimate moment:

$$\varepsilon_{pa} = \varepsilon_e + \varepsilon_\mu = \frac{4.641}{x} - 0.003012$$

Tendon prestrain:

$$\frac{17\,300 \times 10^3}{20\,020 \times 200 \times 10^3} = 0.00432$$

So tendon stress at collapse:

$$\varepsilon_{pb} = 0.00432 + \frac{4.641}{x} - 0.003012$$

$$= 0.00131 + \frac{4.641}{x}$$

$$x = \frac{4.641}{\varepsilon_{pb} - 0.00131}$$

From the equilibrium condition:

$$f_{pb}\,\Delta_{ps} = 0.405 f_{cu} \times b \times x$$

$$f_{pb} \times 20\,020.0 = 0.405 \times 60 \times 1000 \times x$$

$$f_{pb} = 1.214 \times x$$

$$f_{pb} = \frac{5.633}{\varepsilon_{pb} - 0.00131}$$

From the stress–strain curve $\rightarrow \varepsilon_{pb} = 0.006$ for $f_{pb} = 1201.1\,\text{N/mm}^2$ and $x = 989.55\,\text{mm}$.

Take moment about centroid of concrete stress block (where $b_2 = 0.45$) as:

$$M_u = f_{pb} \times \Delta_{ps}(d - b_2 x)$$

$$= 1201.1 \times 20\,020.0(1326 - 0.45 \times 989.55) = 21\,177.39\,\text{kNm}$$

$$\max M = 1.75 \times 468.3 + 12 \times 2621.98 + \frac{1.5}{1.2}\,9769.32$$

$$= 15\,896.57 < M_u = 21\,177.4\,\text{kNm}$$

Consider the following data:

$$I = 43 \times 10^{11}\,\text{mm}^3$$

$$\Delta_{ps} = 20\,000\,\text{mm}^2$$

$$A_C = 1.73 \times 10^6\,\text{mm}^2$$

$$b_w = 1000\,\text{mm}$$

$$f_t = 0.24 \times \sqrt{60} = 1.86\,\text{N/mm}^2$$

$$P_C = 17\,300\,\text{kN}$$

$$f_{cp} = \frac{P_e}{A_C} = \frac{17\,300 \times 10^3}{173 \times 10^6} = 10\,\text{N/mm}^2$$

$$d = \frac{h}{2} + e_s = 1326\,\text{mm}$$

$$e_s = 461\,\text{mm}$$

Step 1

$$V_{C0} = 0.67 \times b_w \times h\sqrt{f_t^2 + 0.8 f_{cp} f_t}$$

$$= 4963.8\,\text{kN}$$

Step 2

$$\frac{f_{pe}}{f_{pu}} = \frac{17\,300/140}{250} = 0.50$$

$$\frac{\Delta_{ps}}{b_w d} = \frac{20\,020}{1000 \times 1326} = 1.5\% \rightarrow v_C = 0.84\,\text{N/mm}^2$$

$$f_{pt} = \frac{P_e}{A} + \frac{P_e e_s Y}{I} = \frac{17\,300 \times 10^3}{173 \times 10^6} + \frac{17\,300 \times 461 \times 865 \times 10^3}{4.3 \times 10^{11}}$$

$$= 26.04\,\text{N/mm}^2$$

$M_0 = $ moment necessary to produce compressive stress in
concrete at extreme tension of the fibre

$$M_0 = 0.8 f_{pt} \frac{I}{y} = 0.8 \times 26.04 \frac{4.3 \times 10^{11}}{365} = 10\,357.1 \text{ kN}$$

$$M_0 < M_{max} \qquad \text{(section is cracked in flexure)}$$

$$V_{cr} = \left(1 - \frac{f_{pt}}{f_{pu}}\right) v_c \times b_w \times d + \frac{M_0}{M_{max}} V$$

$$= (1 - 0.5) \times 0.84 \times 1000 \times 1326 + \frac{10\,357.1}{15\,896} \times 8247.7 \times 10^3$$

$$= 5926 \text{ kN}$$

$$\not< 0.1 b_w d \sqrt{f_{cu}} = 1027.11 \text{ kN}$$

Therefore

$$V_C = \text{less of } V_{C0} \text{ and } V_{cr}$$

$$V_{C0} = V_C = 4963.8 \text{ kN}$$

Step 3

$$0.8 \sqrt{f_{cu}} = 6.19 \text{ N/mm}^2 > 5 \text{ N/mm}^2$$

Hence upper limit on $\dfrac{V}{b_w d}$ is 5:

$$\frac{V}{b_w d} = \frac{8241.7 \times 10^3}{1000 \times 1326} = 621 \text{ N/mm}^2 > 5 \text{ N/mm}^2$$

The Code states that in no case should this unit be exceeded. To avoid increasing the cross-section, d (the distance from the extreme compressed fibre to the centroid of the steel area) can be increased by a linear transformation of the cable under support B, but in that case the tendons cease to be concordant and hence hyperstatic reactions have to be found. At this stage, it will be assumed that shear stresses are within units.

Step 5

$$V_C + 0.4 b_w d = 4963.8 + 0.4 \times 1000 \times 1326 \times 10^{-3}$$

$$= 5494.2 \text{ kN} < V = 82\,417 \text{ kN}$$

Therefore

$$\frac{A_{sw}}{sw} = \frac{V - V_C}{0.87 \times 460 \times dt}$$

$dt = $ depth from extreme compression fibre to centroid of tendon or the longitudinal corner bars around which links pass.

Therefore

$$dt = 1680 \, \text{mm}$$

$$\frac{A_{sw}}{sw} = \frac{(8241.4 - 4963.8) \times 10^3}{0.87 \times 460 \times 1630} = 4.87$$

Provided the diameter is 20/125 mm:

$$\frac{A_{sw}}{sw} = 5.01$$

Shear at 0.75 m from support B:

$$V_C = 6214.8 \, \text{kN}$$

$$M_{max} = 9728.5 \, \text{kNm}$$

$$d = 1326 - 102 = 1224 \, \text{mm}$$

$$P_e = 18\,450.6 \, \text{kN}$$

$$f_{cp} = \frac{18\,450.6 \times 10^3}{173 \times 10^6} = 10.66 \, \text{N/mm}^2$$

Step 1

$$V_{C0} = 0.67 \times 1000 \times 1730 \times \sqrt{186^2 + 186 \times 10.66 \times 0.8}$$
$$= 5095 \, \text{kN}$$

Step 2

$$\frac{f_{pe}}{f_{pu}} = 0.53$$

$$\frac{A_{ps}}{b_w d} = \frac{20\,020.0}{1000 \times 1224} = 163\% \rightarrow v_c = 0.88$$

$$f_{pt} = \frac{18\,450.6 \times 10^3}{1.73 \times 10^6} + \frac{18\,450.6 \times 10^3 \times 865 \times 359}{4.3 \times 10^{11}}$$
$$= 24 \, \text{N/mm}^2$$

$$M_0 = 0.8 \times 24 \, \frac{4.3 \times 10^{11}}{865} = 9544.5 \, \text{kNm} < M_{max} = 9728.5 \, \text{kNm}$$

Section cracked in flexure:

$$V_{cr} = (1 - 0.53) \times 0.88 \times 1000 \times 1224 + \frac{9544.5}{9728.5} \times 6214.8$$
$$= 6603.5 \, \text{kN}$$

Therefore

$$V_C = V_{C0} = 5095 \, \text{kN}$$

Step 6

$$\frac{6214.8 \times 10^3}{1000 \times 1224} = 5.07 > 5 \, \text{N/mm}^2$$

The same problem occurs as in the previous case which could also be solved by changing the tendon profile.

Step 7

$$\frac{A_{sw}}{sw} = \frac{(6214.8 - 5095) \times 10^3}{0.87 \times 460 \times 1680} = 1.66$$

Provided the diameter is 16/200 mm:

$$\frac{A_{sw}}{sw} = 2.01$$

At a point 2.25 mm from support B:

$$V = 6143.2 \, \text{kN}$$

$$\max M = 3407.45 \, \text{kN}$$

$$d = 847 \, \text{mm}$$

$$e_{max} = 17.7$$

$$P_e = 18\,902.6 \, \text{kN}$$

$$f_{cp} = \frac{18\,902.6 \times 10^3}{1.73 \times 10^6} = 10.92 \, \text{N/mm}^2$$

Step 1

$$V_{C0} = 0.67 \times 1000 \times 1730\sqrt{1.86 + 0.8 \times 1.86 \times 10.92}$$
$$= 5196.6 \, \text{kN}$$

Step 2

$$\frac{f_{pe}}{f_{pu}} = 0.54$$

$$f_{pt} = 10.92 + \frac{18\,902.6 \times 865 \times 17.7 \times 10^3}{4.3 \times 10^{11}} = 0.67$$
$$= 11.6 \, \text{N/mm}^2$$

$$M_0 = 0.8 \times 11.6 \times \frac{4.3 \times 10^{11}}{865} = 4610.4 \, \text{kNm} > M_{max} = 3407.45$$

The section is uncracked in flexure.

Shear force can be reduced by the formula:

$$V = V_L - P_e \sin y$$

$$V = 6143 - 18\,902.6 \times 0.182$$

$$= 2706.5\,\text{kN}$$

$$V_C = V_{C0} = 5196.6\,\text{kN}$$

$$y = \frac{\text{d}y}{\text{d}x} = 2hx = 2 \times 0.0303 \times 3$$

$$y = 0.182\,\text{rad}$$

Step 3

$$\frac{V}{b_w d} = \frac{2706.5 \times 1000}{1000 \times 847} = 3.99 < 5\,\text{N/mm}^2 \qquad \text{(permitted)}$$

Step 4

$$0.5\,V_C = 2593.3\,\text{kN} < V_L = 2706.5\,\text{kN} < V_C = 0.4b_w d$$

$$= 2937.1\,\text{kN}$$

Therefore minimum links:

$$\frac{A_{sw}}{sw} = \frac{0.4 \times b_w}{0.87f_y} = \frac{0.4 \times 1000}{0.87 \times 460} = 1.0$$

provided the diameter is 16/300 mm:

$$\frac{A_{sw}}{sw} = 1.34$$

The same check should be performed for the remainder of the beam (Fig. 5.85).

At this stage the same links to the end of the beam are provided, which is reasonable in the area adjacent to the support. When $M = 0$ the section is uncracked in flexure, but in area where the section can be uncracked in flexure, the shear force is small.

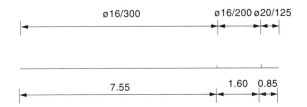

Figure 5.85. Moments about centroid of concrete block

5.2   Substructure and foundation design

5.2.1   Substructure design

This section includes the design of piers, abutments, wing walls, foundations and other appurtenances related to substructure zones. Some known codes related to these structures are explained by examples. The selection of various codes and examples based on them are purely at random.

(A)   Substructures directly supporting deck structures

At the ends of bridges, the deck structures are supported directly on abutments which can be of various types. These are usually of mass, semi-reinforced or reinforced concrete and seldom, if ever of steel. They perform the dual function of supporting the vertical and horizontal forces from the bridge deck, and the horizontal forces from the retained soil behind them. Their stability arises largely from their massive self weight and piles.

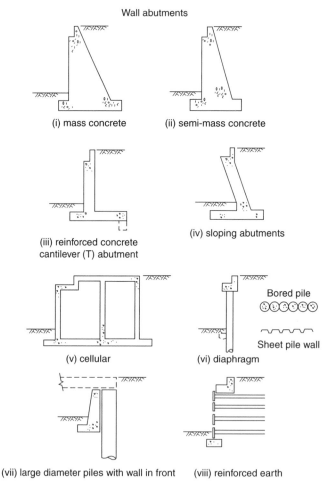

Figure 5.86.   Types of wall abutment

There are three classes of abutment,

(*i*)   Wall abutments
(*ii*) Open abutments
(*iii*) Strutted abutments

(i)   Wall abutments

These are of mass concrete, semi-mass concrete, RC cantilever type, sloping type, cellular type and diaphragm (contiguous bore pile or sheet pile wall. Various types of wall abutment are shown in Fig. 5.86. For light bridges the Americans provide L-shaped bents with straight and raked piles.

(ii)   Open abutments

Open abutments, with the end spans of the deck bearing on seatings at the tops of embankments are often preferable and can look better than retaining wall types of abutment.

Figure 5.87 shows various such cases.

(iii)   Strutted, portal and box sections

Strutted or vertical beam abutments.   This type of abutment is often used for small bridges with spans less than 20 m.

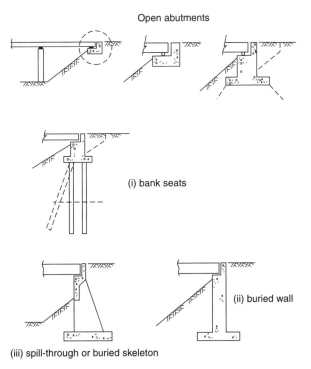

Figure 5.87. Types of open abutment

Portal frames. These have the same advantages as strutted abutments, but are generally more expensive. The foundations should normally have a greater resistance against sliding since horizontal movement of the footings can overstress the top corners of the portal. Sometimes hinges are placed at the bottom of the legs.

Box structures. These are often economic for small spans. Used extensively as culverts or subways.

Flexible corrugated metal structures of circular or derivative cross-sections have been used for many small culverts and underpasses, and a few with spans up to 12 m.

(B) Wing walls

Figure 5.88 shows various types of wing walls. They are self explanatory.

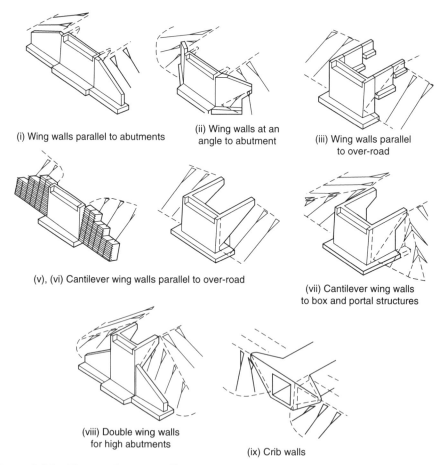

(i) Wing walls parallel to abutments

(ii) Wing walls at an angle to abutment

(iii) Wing walls parallel to over-road

(v), (vi) Cantilever wing walls parallel to over-road

(vii) Cantilever wing walls to box and portal structures

(viii) Double wing walls for high abutments

(ix) Crib walls

Figure 5.88. Types of wing wall structure

(i)   *Wing walls parallel to the abutment*
This is the simplest form to build. They can be independent or monolithic.

(ii) *Wing walls at an angle to abutment*
These are common but difficult to construct when they are between an over-road and under-road on the lines bisecting the angles. They can be cantilevered off the abutment.

(iii) *Wing walls parallel to over-roads*
These provide support for the parapets. However, 'compaction of back-fill problems' exist. Box structures can be stable if they are monolithic with an abutment. If they are on piles, vertical and forward racking piles will provide the best solutions.

5.2.2 Foundation design

Foundations can be simple or more involved. The following types are adopted:

1. Slab type
2. Slab and pile combination
3. Well foundation
4. Caisson foundation – plane or cellular
5. Caisson foundation on piles
6. A mixture of the above.

A number of texts is available for the design of these foundations and for the consideration of space in the text, it was decided not to include individual design cases here. However, the foundations in connection with bridge piers and abutments have been given a suitable treatment in the substructure design portion of this text.

A brief assessment on piles is given under static and dynamic loading conditions in the following sections. An extensive bibliography is given elsewhere on bridge foundations for those who have the desire to carry out an in-depth study.

5.2.3 Empirical formulae for determining safe load on piles

5.2.3.1 Engineering news formula

$$P = \frac{16.70wh}{S + 2.54} \qquad \text{for piles driven with freely falling drop hammer}$$

$$P = \frac{16.70wh}{S + 0.254} \qquad \text{for piles driven with single acting steam hammer}$$

$$P = \frac{16.70(W + ap)}{S + 0.254} \qquad \text{for piles driven with double acting steam hammer}$$

where

P = safe load on pile in kilograms

W = weight of monkey/hammer in kilograms

p = mean effective steam pressure in kilogram per square centimetre

a = effective area of piston in square centimetres

S = average penetration of pile in cm per blow measured as the average of last 5 to 10 blows under a drop hammer or as the average of the last 20 blows under a steam hammer.

5.2.3.2 Simplex formula
For a driven precast pile (in fps units)

$$R_u = \frac{NW_h H_e}{L(1 - S)} \sqrt{\frac{L}{50}}$$

where

R_u = ultimate resistance of pile

N = total number of blows required to produce the ultimate resistance R_u

W_h = weight of hammer

H_e = effective height of fall

L = minimum length of pile

S = final set in tonnes of number of blows for last 1 inch.

5.2.3.3 Gate's formula

$$Q_a = \frac{1}{8.50} \sqrt{KE(1.41 - \log s)}$$

where

Q_a = safe load capacity, tonnes

K = 0.75 for drop hammer; 0.85 for all other hammers (factor of safety = 3)

E = gross hammer energy

s = set per blow for last 15 cm of penetration or for last 20 blows (refusal) in centimetres.

5.2.3.4 Danish formula

$$Q_u = \frac{Wh}{s + (1/2)C_e}$$

$$C_e = \left(\frac{2WhL}{AE}\right)^{1/2}$$

where

$W =$ weight of monkey in kilograms

$h =$ height of fall

$s =$ set per blow for last 15 cm of penetration or for last 20 blows (refusal) in centimetres

$L =$ length of pile

$A =$ area of pile

$E =$ gross hammer energy.

5.2.4 Load carrying capacity – static formulae (Extract from Appendix B of IS: 2911, Part I, Section 2)

5.2.4.1 Piles in granular soils

The ultimate bearing capacity Q_u of piles in granular soils is given by the following formula

$$Q_u = A_p \left(\frac{1}{2} D\gamma N_\gamma + P_D N_q\right) + \sum_{i=1}^{n} KP_{Di} \tan \delta A_{si}$$

where

$A_p =$ cross-sectional area of pile toe in square centimetres

$D =$ stem diameter in centimetres

$\gamma =$ effective unit weight of soil at pile toe in kilogram force per square centimetre

$P_D =$ effective overburden pressure at pile toe in kilogram force per square centimetre

$N_\gamma = N_q =$ bearing capacity factors depending upon the angle of internal friction at toe

$\sum_{i=1}^{n} =$ summation for n layers in which pile is installed

$K =$ coefficient of earth pressure

P_{Di} = effective overburden pressure in kilograms per square centimetre for the ith layer where i varies from 1 to n

δ = angle of wall friction between pile and soil in degrees (may be taken equal to ϕ)

A_{si} = surface area of pile stem in square centimetres in the ith layer where i varies from 1 to n

The following points should be noted:

1. N_γ factor can be taken for general shear failure as per IS: 6403–1971.
2. N_q factor will depend, apart from nature of soil on the type of pile and its method of construction. For bored piles, the values of N_q corresponding to angle of shearing resistance ϕ are given in Fig. 5.89.

    This is based on Berezantseu's curve for D/B of 20 up to $\phi = 35°$ and Vesic's curves beyond $\phi = 35°$.
3. The earth pressure coefficient K depends on the nature of soil strata, type of pile and its method of construction. For bored piles in loose medium sands, K values between 1 and 2 should be used.
4. The angle of wall friction may be taken equal to angle of shear resistance of soil.
5. In working out pile capacities using the static formula, for piles longer than 15 to 20 pile diameter, maximum effective overburden at the pile tip should correspond to pile length equal to 15 to 20 diameter.

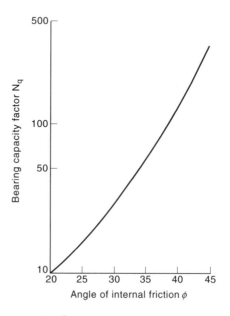

Figure 5.89. Bearing capacity factor curve

5.2.4.2 Piles in cohesive soils

The ultimate bearing capacity of piles Q_u in cohesive soil is given by the following:

$$Q_u = A_p N_e C_p + \alpha \bar{C} A_s$$

where

A_p = cross-sectional area of pile toe in square centimetres

N_e = bearing capacity factor usually taken as 9

C_p = average cohesion at pile tip in kilograms per square centimetre

α = reduction factor

$\bar{C}$ = average cohesion throughout the length of pile in kilograms per square centimetre

A_s = surface area of pile shaft in square centimetres

The following points should be noted:

1. Table 5.27 gives values of α that may be taken depending upon the consistency of the soils.
2. (a) Static formula may be used as a guide only for bearing capacity estimates. Better reliance may be put on load test on piles.
   (b) For working out safe load, a minimum factor of safety 2.5 should be used on the ultimate bearing capacity estimated by static formulae.
3. Values of α may be taken to vary from 0.5 to 0.3 depending upon the consistency of the soil. Higher values of up to one may be used for softer soils, provided the soil is not sensitive.

   When full static penetration data are available for the entire depth, the correlations in Table 5.28 may be used as a guide for the determination of shaft resistance of a pile.

Table 5.27. Vales of α for piles in cohesive soils

Consistency	N value	Value of α	
		Bored pile	Driven cast-in situ
Soft to very soft	less than 4	0.7	1
Medium	4 to 8	0.5	0.7
Stiff	8 to 15	0.4	0.4
Stiff to hard	over 15	0.3	0.3

Table 5.28. Correlations for the shaft resistance of a pile

Type of soil	Local	Side friction f_s
Clays and peats where $q_c < 10$	$\dfrac{q_c}{30}$	$< f_s < \dfrac{q_c}{10}$
Clays	$\dfrac{q_c}{25}$	$< f_s < \dfrac{q_c}{25}$
Silty clays and silty sands	$\dfrac{q_c}{100}$	$< f_s < \dfrac{q_c}{25}$
Sands	$\dfrac{q_c}{100}$	$< f_s < \dfrac{q_c}{100}$
Coarse sands and gravels	$\dfrac{q_c}{25}$	$< f_s < \dfrac{q_c}{25}$

where q_c = static point resistance
$\quad\;\; f_s$ = local side friction

For non-homogeneous soils the ultimate point bearing capacity may be calculated using the following relationships:

$$q_u = \frac{\dfrac{q_{c0} + q_{c1}}{2} + q_{c2}}{2}$$

where

q_u = ultimate point bearing capacity

q_{c0} = average static cone resistance over a depth of $2d$ below the base level of the pile

q_{c1} = minimum static cone resistance over the same $2d$ below the pile tip

q_{c2} = average of the minimum cone resistance values in the diagram over a height of $8d$ above the base level of the pile

d = diameter of the pile base or the equivalent diameter for a non-circular cross-section

The correlation between standard penetration test value N and static point resistance q_c given in Table 5.29 may be used for working the shaft resistance and skin friction of piles.

Table 5.29. The q_c/N correlation for shaft resistance and pile friction

Soil type	q_c/N
Clays	2.0
Silts. sandy silts and slightly cohesive silt sand mixtures	2.0
Clean fine to medium sands and silty sands	3–4
Coarse sands and sands with little gravel	5–6
Sandy gravels and gravel	8–10

5.2.5   Dynamic pile formulae
(Extract from Appendix B of IS: 2911, Part I, Section I)

5.2.5.1   General

These formulae are based on the laws governing the dynamic impact of elastic bodies. They equate the energy of the hammer blow to the work done in overcoming the resistance of the ground to the penetration of the pile. Allowance is made for losses of energy due to the elastic contractions of the pile, cap and subsoil as well as the losses caused by the inertia of the pile. One of the most used of these formulae is the Hiley formula.

5.2.5.2   Hiley formula

The modified Hiley formula is:

$$R = \frac{Whn}{S + (C/2)}$$

where

$R =$ ultimate driving resistance in tonnes. The safe load shall be worked out by dividing it with a factor of safety of 2.5

$W =$ mass of the ram in tonnes

$h =$ height of the free fall of the ram or hammer in centimetres taken at its full value for trigger-operated drop hammers, 80 per cent of the fall of normally proportioned winch-operated drop hammers, and 90 per cent of the stroke for single-acting hammers. When using the McKiernam–Terry type of double-acting hammers, 90 per cent of the maker's rated energy in tonne-centimetre per blow should be substituted for the product (Wh) in the formula. The hammer should be operated at its maximum speed whilst the set is being taken

$n =$ efficiency of the blow, representing the ratio of energy after impact to the striking energy of the ram

$S =$ final set or penetration per blow in centimetres

$C =$ sum of the temporary elastic compressions in centimetres of the pile, dolly, packings and ground calculated or measured as prescribed in the subsection on the value of temporary compression

Where W is greater than P_e and the pile is driven into penetrable ground,

$$n = \frac{W + P_e^2}{W + P}$$

Where W is less than P_e and the pile is driven into penetrable ground,

$$n = \frac{W + P_e^2}{W + P} - \left(\frac{W - P_e}{W + P}\right)^2$$

The values of n in relation to e and to the ratio of P/W are given in Table 5.30. Please note the following:

1. P is the mass of the pile, anvil, helmet and follower, if any, in tonnes.
2. Where the pile finds refusal in rock, $0.5P$ should be substituted for P in the above expressions for n.
3. e is the coefficient of restitution of the materials under impact as classified below:

   (a) For steel ram of double-acting hammer striking on steel anvil and driving concrete pile, $e = 0.5$.
   (b) For cast iron ram of single-acting or drop hammer striking on the head of reinforced concrete pile, $e = 0.4$.
   (c) Single-acting or drop hammer striking a well-conditioned driving cap and helmet with hard wood dolly in driving reinforced concrete piles or directly on the head of timber pile, $e = 0.25$.
   (d) For a deteriorated condition of the head of pile or of dolly, $e = 0$.

5.2.5.3 Deduction for raking
Where single-acting or drop hammers work in leader guides inclined on a batter the percentages given in Table 5.31 should be deducted from the calculated bearing value in the axial direction of the pile.

5.2.5.4 Value of temporary compression
The temporary compression of the pile and ground occurring during driving shall be determined from site measurements whenever possible, especially

Table 5.30. Values of e related to the P/W ratio

Ratio of P/W	$e = 0.5$	$e = 0.4$	$e = 0.32$	$e = 0.25$	$e = 0$
0.5	0.75	0.72	0.70	0.69	0.67
1	0.63	0.58	0.55	0.53	0.50
1.5	0.55	0.50	0.47	0.44	0.40
2	0.50	0.44	0.40	0.37	0.33
2.5	0.45	0.40	0.36	0.33	0.28
3	0.42	0.36	0.33	0.30	0.25
3.5	0.39	0.33	0.30	0.27	0.22
4	0.36	0.31	0.28	0.25	0.20
5	0.31	0.27	0.24	0.21	0.16
6	0.27	0.24	0.21	0.19	0.14
7	0.24	0.21	0.19	0.17	0.12
8	0 22	0.20	0.17	0.15	0.11

Table 5.31. Rake deductions

Rake	Per cent deduction
1 in 12	1.0
1 in 10	1.5
1 in 8	2.0
1 in 6	3.0
1 in 5	4.0
1 in 4	5.5
1 in 3	8.5
1 in 2	14.0

when the set recorder is small. To the measured compression, the value of the dolly and packing (C_1) is added. The value C may be obtained by the calculations given below.

Where measurement cannot be taken, the temporary compression of the pile C_2 and of the ground C_3 may also be obtained by calculations.

For calculation for temporary compression, the value of C is

$$C_1 + C_2 + C_3$$

where

C_1 = temporary compression of dolly and packing

C_2 = temporary compression of pile

C_3 = temporary compression of ground

The values of C_1, C_2 and C_3 may be computed using the following formulae:

$$C_1 = 1.77 \frac{R}{A}$$

where the driving is without dolly or helmet, and the cushion is about 2.5 cm thick. Or

$$C_1 = 9.05 \frac{R}{A}$$

where the driving is with short dolly up to 60 cm long, helmet and cushion up to 7.5 cm thick

$$C_2 = 0.657 \frac{RL}{A}$$

$$C_3 = 3.55 \frac{R}{A}$$

where

> R = ultimate driving resistance calculated in tonnes as in the case of the Hiley formula
>
> L = length of the pile in metres
>
> A = area of the pile in square centimetres

5.2.6 Well foundation

There are different types of well foundation in common use. They are:

1. Circular
2. Twin circular
3. Double-D
4. Double octagonal
5. Single and double rectangular; and
6. Multiple dredge holed

The most common types are:

1. Circular
2. Twin circular
3. Double-D

For bridges with single-line railways and 7.2 m wide roadways, circular types are adequate. Generally, the circular types are limited to an outside diameter of about 9 m. However, recently, in some bridges (Ganga Bridge at Patna and Brahmaputra Bridge at Tezpur) wells of up to 12 m diameters have been used. Where the pier width is much larger, as for double-line railway bridges, double-D wells are popular. Alternatively, twin circular wells or double octagonal wells can be used. A brief description of the common wells follows.

5.2.6.1 Circular well

The main point in favour of the circular well is its simplicity in construction, ease in sinking and its uniform strength in all directions. It has only a single dredge hole. Its weight per square metre of peripheral surface is highest and hence the sinking effort is less, thus facilitating easier sinking. It can be more easily controlled against tilt and tilt correction is also easier in this case. As mentioned earlier, the only disadvantage is the limitation in size which restricts its use to bridges with smaller piers.

5.2.6.2. Twin circular wells

As the name itself suggests, this foundation consists of two independent wells placed close to each other and provided with a common well cap over which the pier can be built.

5.2.6.3 Rectangular wells

These are adopted for bridges with shallow foundations. As mentioned earlier, these are equivalent to block foundations and designed to have the outer dimensions the same as those of the required open foundation block. For larger foundations needing deeper sinking, it can be designed with more dredge holes, whereupon it becomes a well or caisson with multiple dredge holes.

5.2.6.4 Wells with multiple dredge holes

These are used for piers and abutments of very large size and are used for bridges with very long spans such as cantilever, cable-stayed type and suspension bridges, in which the load on each pier is considerable and it is very difficult to design a double-D or other type of well with twin dredge holes. Since these types of long-span bridge are fewer in India, such wells have been rarely used. The wells of such type were used for the towers of the Howrah Bridge, India. The size of the well used for this is 55.3 m × 24.8 m having 21 dredge holes in each. A similar type of well is being adopted for the second Howrah bridge. The largest such wells have been sunk in America, and are of size 60.1 m × 29.6 m having 55 square dredge holes of 5.2 m size and supporting the piers of the San Francisco–Oakland Bridge.

5.2.6.5 Caissons

A caisson is a type of well foundation and is distinct owing to the method of commencing construction. The kerbs for ordinary wells are pitched in the final position either on the dry bed or over an artificially formed island. Caissons are those for which the shell for the kerb and part of the well steining is fabricated or cast outside, floated to the final location and lowered in position there.

5.2.7 Example (5.16) American practice

Estimate the piling length required for the friction type for 14″ diameter (355 mm) steel-encased concrete piles and 12″ diameter (305 mm) timber piles. Use the following data:

$$P_{ult} \text{ (concrete pile)} = 80\,000^{\#} = 40 \text{ ton (6 st.} + 4 \text{ battered)}$$

$$P_{ult} \text{ (timber piles)} = 50\,000^{\#} = 25 \text{ ton (16 st.} + 26 \text{ battered)}$$

Note that $\# = $ lb and $1 \text{ lb/ft}^2 = 992.16 \text{ kN/m}^2$.

1. Piles to be friction type with 20% of pile capacity to be carried by tip in point bearing.
2. Cohesive strength to be $800^{\#}/\text{ft}^2$ (793.73 MN/m²)
3. Safety factor = 1.5. (Effect of group action of piles to be absorbed in this safety factor.)

Steel-encased concrete piles ($14''$ ⌀):

$$P_{ult} = 40\,ton = 80\,000^{\#}$$

$$\therefore\quad P_{FR} = 0.8 \times 1.5 \times 80\,000 = 96\,000^{\#}\ (427\,kN)$$

$$\therefore\quad l = \frac{96\,000}{\pi \times 1.17 \times 800} = 33\,ft\quad(approx.)$$

Timber piles ($12''$ ⌀):

$$P_{ult} = 25\,ton = 50\,000^{\#}\ (222\,kN)$$

$$P_{FR} = 0.8 \times 1.5 \times 50\,000 = 60\,000^{\#}\quad(266\,kN)$$

$$\therefore\quad l = \frac{60\,000}{\pi \times 1 \times 800} = 24\,ft\quad(approx.)$$

Note that 1 ft = 0.3048 m.

Thus, in summary:

$$\text{length of steel-enclosed concrete piles (vertical)} = 34'\quad(10.36\,m)$$
$$\text{length of steel-enclosed concrete piles (battered)} = 35'\quad(10.\text{и}7\,m)$$
$$\text{length of timber piles (vertical)} = 25'\quad(7.62\,m)$$
$$\text{length of timber piles (battered)} = 26'\quad(7.925\,m)$$
$$\text{length of concrete piles} = 34 \times 6 + 35 \times 4 = 344\,\text{linear ft}$$
$$(104.85\,m)$$
$$\text{length of timber piles} = 25 \times 16 + 26 \times 44 = 1544\,\text{linear ft}$$
$$(470.6\,m)$$

5.2.8 Example (5.17) American practice

Figure 5.90 shows a pier on piles. The total number of piles is 28 out of which 18 are battered with a 0.97 batter. Using Case III loading AASHTO type, calculate the pile resistance horizontally and vertically and design the reinforcement.

Pier design

$$N\ (\text{number of piles}) = 10 + 18(0.97) = 27.45$$

$$I_{x-x} = (1.25)^2 10 + (1.25)^2 4(0.97) + (3.75)^2 14(0.97)$$

$$= 15.6 + 6.1 + 191.0 = 212.7$$

$$I_{y-y} = (3.42)^2(4 + 4 \times 0.97) + (6.84)^2(4 + 4 \times 0.97) + (10.25)^2(8 \times 0.97)$$

$$= 92.1 + 368 + 813 = 1273.1$$

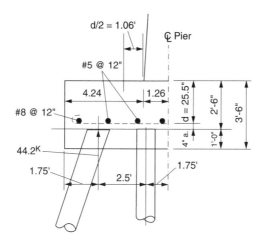

Figure 5.90. Pier on piles

Using Case III loadings at bottom of footing

$$P = [630.8 + (24)(11)(3.5)(0.15)]0.8 = \ \ 615 \text{ kip}$$

$$M_{x-x} = [711 + 3.5(41.23)]0.8 = \ \ 684 \text{ ft-kip}$$

$$M_{y-y} = [1473 + 8(3.5)]0.8 = 1200 \text{ ft-kip}$$

$$\text{pile loads} = \frac{615}{27.45} \pm \frac{648 \times 3.75}{212.7} \pm \frac{1200 \times 10.25}{1273.1}$$

$$= 22.4 \pm 12.1 \pm 9.7 \text{ kip}$$

$$= 44.2 \text{ kip} \quad (\text{max} = 22.1 < 25 \text{ ton})$$

$$= 0.6 \text{ kip} \quad (\text{minimum})$$

Horizontal resistance of piles

$$\text{Horizontal capacity of 1 batter pile} = x = 25 \times \frac{1}{\sqrt{17}} = 6.06 \text{ kip}$$

$$\text{capacity in } PH_{y-y} \text{ direction} = 2 \times 6.06 = 12.12 > 9.8 \text{ (Case II)}$$

$$\text{capacity in } PH_{x-x} \text{ direction} = 7 \times 6.06 = 42.42 > 33.8 \text{ (Case III)}$$

Footing steel
A 44.2 kip pile load acts on a footing width of

$$\left(1.75 + \frac{3.42}{2}\right) = 1.75 + 1.71 = \ \ 3.46 \text{ ft}$$

$$\text{pile load per foot} = \frac{44.2}{3.46} = 12.8 \text{ kip/ft}$$

$$M = (2.49)(12.8) - \frac{(4.24)^2}{2}(3.5)(0.15) = 31.9 - 4.7$$

$$= 27.2\,\text{ft-kip}$$

$$A_S = \frac{27.2 \times 12}{20 \times 0.875 \times 25.5} = 0.73\,\text{in}^2 \quad (4.71\,\text{cm}^2)$$

Therefore, use #8 @ 12″, $A_S = 0.79\,\text{in}^2$, $\Sigma_0 = 3.1\,\text{in}$

$$V @ \frac{25.5''}{2} \text{ from wall} = 12.8 - (3.18)(3.5)(0.15)$$

$$= 12.8 - 1.7 = 11.1$$

$$\Sigma_0 = \frac{11.1}{0.3 \times 0.875 \times 25.5} = 1.66 < 3.1$$

Use $\frac{1}{3}A_S$ for distribution steel $= \frac{1}{3} \times 0.73 = 0.243\,\text{in}^2$ $(1.4956\,\text{cm}^2)$

Thus, use #5 @ 12″, $A_S = 0.31\,\text{in}^2$.

5.2.9 Example (5.18) British practice
The pier column is under biaxial moments M_{tx} of 9760 kNm and M_{ty} of 1495 kNm as shown in Fig. 5.91. The axial load on it is a bridge load reaction of 4008 kN + 115 kN dead weight of the column. The width of the base, B, is 5.5 m and length is 6 m. Using $f_{cu} = 40\,\text{N/mm}^2$ and $f_y = 460\,\text{N/mm}^2$, check the stresses in the foundation cap. The following case loads are considered for the pile group design

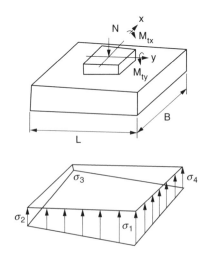

Figure 5.91. Pile cap under actions and pressures

Case I $= 2378.8 \, \text{kN}$

Case II $= 4644.15 \, \text{kN}$

Column $= 600 \times 600$

Design the piles and pile caps for the pier of the bridge, when:

$$z_x = \frac{BL^2}{6} = 33 \, \text{m}^2$$

$$z_y = \frac{LB^2}{6} = 30.25 \, \text{m}^3$$

Bearing pressures

$$\max \sigma_1 = \frac{N}{BL} + \frac{M_x}{z_x} + \frac{M_y}{z_y} = \frac{4172.5}{33} + \frac{976}{33} + \frac{1495}{30.2} = 205.52$$

$$\sigma_2 = \frac{N}{BL} - \frac{M_x}{z_x} + \frac{M_y}{z_y} = \frac{4172.5}{33} - \frac{976}{33} + \frac{1495}{30.2} = 146.38$$

$$\min \sigma_3 = \frac{N}{BL} - \frac{M_x}{z_x} - \frac{M_y}{z_y} = \frac{4172.5}{33} - \frac{976}{33} - \frac{1495}{30.2} = 47.36$$

$$\sigma_4 = \frac{N}{BL} + \frac{M_x}{z_x} - \frac{M_y}{z_y} = \frac{4172.5}{33} + \frac{976}{33} - \frac{1495}{30.2} = 106.51$$

Equations are only valid if positive pressure is applied on the whole of the base area.

Pile foundations
All loads are considered including impact. The pad footings supporting each pier has come out to be $6 \, \text{m} \times 5.5 \, \text{m}$. This is not practical. Here it is decided to use bored piles of $650 \, \text{mm}$ diameter having an ultimate capacity of $2400 \, \text{kN/pile}$. A reference is made to the specifications given:

$$\text{preliminary size} = \frac{(P + W)}{N} \quad \text{or} \quad 2400 = \frac{4123}{N}$$

$$N - \text{the number of piles} = \frac{4123}{2400} = 1.72 \approx 2 \, \text{piles}$$

When moments are included the number of piles could be more than 2. Take four such piles. The pile cap is assumed to rotate about the centroid of the pile group and the pile loads resisting the moment vary uniformly from 0 at the centroid axis to a maximum for the piles furthest away. The axial loading only gives 2 piles. Group B is critical and it transpires to be a worst combination for piers. The piles are symmetrical (Fig. 5.92). Thus:

$$I_{xx} = I_{yy}$$

where

$x = $ pile spacing

$y = $ pile spacing

The maximum additional pile load

$$F_m = \pm \frac{M_x}{I_y} \pm \frac{M_y}{I_x}$$

where the axial load $= 1487\,\text{kN}$.

Case I

$$F_{m_{total}} = 1602 + 459.375 + 317.4$$

$$= 2378.8 < 4 \times 2400 = 9600\,\text{kN}$$

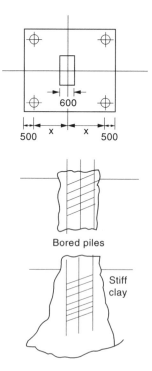

Figure 5.92. Plan of pile foundations

Case II

Axial load on the column $= 4123\,\text{kN}$ and $M_{tx} = 1261.2\,\text{kNm}$, $M_{ty} = 823.44\,\text{kN}$:

$$F_{m_{\text{additional}}} = \frac{1261.8 \times 1}{4} + \frac{823.4 \times 1}{4} = 521.15\,\text{kN}$$

$$F_{m_{\text{total}}} = 4644.15 = 4644.15 < 9600\,\text{kN}$$

Further data are:

$2x = 2000\,\text{mm}$

$x = 1000\,\text{mm}$

$\text{\c{C}}$ of pile $= 1\,\text{m}$

distance to edge of cap $= 500\,\text{mm}$

$2y = 2000\,\text{mm}$

$I_{xx} = I_{yy} = 2(x^2 + y^2) = 4\,\text{m}^4$

$H = $ horizontal loading from the traffic braking at deck level (8.1 m height)

$\quad = 347\,\text{kN}$

Moment $= 347 \times 8.1 = 2810.7\,\text{kNm}$

This moment is considered with Group III loading.

Case III

$$177\,\text{kN} + M_{ty} = (1407)\tfrac{1}{4} + M_{tx} = 497 \times \tfrac{1}{4} + 2810.7 \times \tfrac{1}{4}$$

$$= 3458.1175 < 9600$$

Assuming the braking of the traffic occurs with Case II, then:

total load on pile $F_{m_{\text{total}}} = 4123 + 521.15 + 702.675$

$$= 5346.825\,\text{kN}$$

$$\approx 5347\,\text{kN}$$

$$< 9600\,\text{kN}$$

Therefore, adopt a four-pile group of 650 mm pile diameter each. A margin is left in the event that wind loading is considered.

Pile cap design

The caps are designed either using bending theory or using the truss analogy. When the truss method is used, the truss should be of triangulated form with

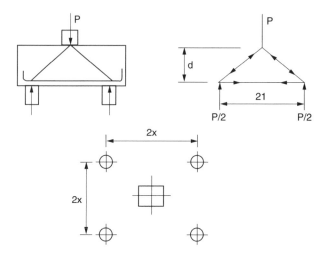

Figure 5.93. Tensile forces in the pile caps and truss

a node at the centre of the loaded area. The lower nodes are to lie at the inter-section of the centre-lines of piles with the tensile reinforcement. Tensile caps on the pile caps are given for the four-pile cap as shown in Fig. 5.93.

The spacing is no more than $3 \times 650 = 1950$ mm. Reinforcement shall be $1.5\oslash$ from the centre of the pile and is considered to form a tension member as those of the truss. Where pile spacing $\leq 3\oslash$, steel can be used on the whole of the critical section. A full anchorage is provided. Thus,

$$T_{AB} = T_{BC} = T_{CD} = T_{DA} = \frac{P_x}{4d}$$

$$\text{axial load} = 4123\,\text{kN}$$

$$\text{column} = 1000 \times 600 = 6 \times 10^5\,\text{mm}^2$$

Shear forces

The shear strength of a pile cap is normally governed by the shear area on a vertical section through a full width of the cap. The critical section is taken at 20% of the pile diameter inside the force of the piles as shown in Fig. 5.93. The whole of the force from the piles with centres lying outside this line should be considered.

Design shear resistance

The shear check may be made in accordance with provisions for the shear resis-tance of solid slabs given in BS 8110 (Clauses 3.5.5 and 3.5.6 of the code). The following limitations apply with regard to pile caps.

1. The distance a_v from the face of the column to the critical shear plane is as defined in Fig. 5.94. The enhanced shear stress is $2dv_c/a_v$

$$v_c = \text{from BS\,8110}$$

$$\text{max shear stress} \ngtr 0.8\sqrt{f_{cu}} \quad \text{or} \quad 5\,\text{N/mm}^2$$

$$\text{overall depth} = 1600\,\text{mm}$$

$$d = \text{effective depth} = 1400\,\text{mm}$$

$$\text{tensile force } T = \frac{4123 \times 1000}{4 \times 1400} = 736.25\,\text{kN}$$

$$A_S = \frac{7326.25 \times 10^3}{0.87 \times 460} = \frac{1880\,\text{mm}^2 \text{ per tie or } 3760\,\text{mm}^2}{\text{across two ties}}$$

Provide 12T25 bars

$$= 4915\,(10\text{ bars}) + 983\,(2\text{ bars}) = 5898\,\text{mm}^2 \text{ across the full width of two ties}$$

$$\text{minimum reinforcement} = 0.13 \times 3000 \times \frac{1400}{100}$$

$$= 5460\,\text{mm}^2$$

$$< 5898\,\text{mm}^2 \text{ (permitted)}$$

The spacing

$$2000 > 3 \times 650 = 1950\,\text{mm (almost equal)}$$

The reinforcement can be spaced equally across the section.
When the spacing is 200 mm

$$a_v = 1500 - 130 - 300 = 1070$$

$$a_v = 1500 - 130 - 500 = 870$$

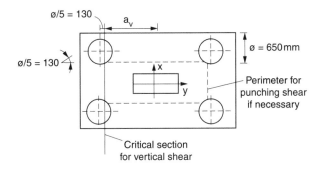

Figure 5.94. Layout of piles for design shear resistance

shear $= 2061.5\,\text{kN}$

$$v = \frac{2061.5 \times 10^3}{3000 \times 1400} = 0.491\,\text{N/mm}^2$$

$$v_c = 0.79 \left(\frac{100 \times 5898}{3000 \times 1400} \right)^{1/3} \left(\frac{40}{25} \right)^{1/3} \bigg/ 1.25$$

$$= 0.79 \times 0.519 \times \frac{1.1696}{1.25} = 0.3842\,\text{N/mm}^2$$

2. The enhanced design shear stress on a 600 mm column edge is:

$$0.3842 \times 2 \times 1400 = 1.24\,\text{N/mm}^2 < 5\,\text{N/mm}^2$$

For 1000 mm column side 870 (minimum value) would be less. The shear stress at critical section is acceptable. No shear reinforcement is required. Check for shear stress on the perimeter of the column:

$$v = \frac{4123 \times 10^3}{600 \times 1000 \times 1400} = 0.005\,\text{N/mm}^2 < 5\,\text{N/mm}^2$$

Note that the pile spacing is no greater than $3\varnothing$.
   No check for punching shear is therefore required.

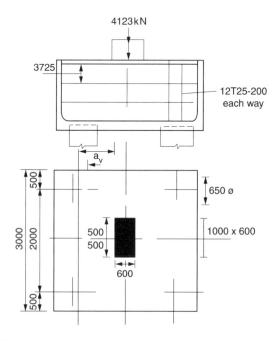

Figure 5.95. Pile cap reinforcement

Arrangement of reinforcement
Anchorage of the main reinforcement

$34 \times \text{diameter} = 34 \times 25 = 850 \text{ mm}$ spacing $200 \not> 750 \text{ mm}$ (permitted)

Thus, 25 mm diameter bars are required on the sides of pile caps.
The reinforcement is shown in Fig. 5.95.

5.2.10 Example (5.19) American practice (bridge piers)
For a two-span bridge (Fig. 5.96) each span is of length 72 ft-6 in (22 m) for which the deck and pier arrangements are shown in Fig. 5.97. Calculations are required for dead loads, wind loads, earth pressure loads, longitudinal forces due to braking vehicles and temperature.
Determine

1. Pile arrangement for the pier column
2. The size and reinforcement for the pier stem and pier cap

Use load cases (AASHTO) I, II and III which are given below:

Case I $D + E + L$
Case II $D + E + W$ (125% unit stresses)
Case III $D + E + L + LF + F + 30\% W + WL$

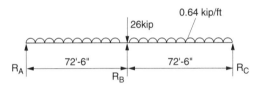

Figure 5.96. Reactions on piers

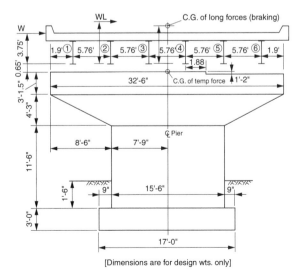

[Dimensions are for design wts. only]

Figure 5.97. Deck and pier arrangement for Example (5.19)

Design reinforcement for the pier stem and the cap
For maximum reaction at interior support (i.e. pier 3), the lane load governs:

$$R_B = 26 + 1.25 \times 0.64 \times 72.5 = \quad 84.8 \, \text{kip}$$

$$R_B \, \text{(interior beams) due to DL} = 1.25 \times 0.82 \times 72.5 = \quad 74.0 \, \text{kip}$$

$$R_B \, \text{(exterior beams) due to DL} = 1.25 \times 1.20 \times 72.5 = 108.2 \, \text{kip}$$

Since the pier rests on timber piles it is not required to check factor of safety against overturning or sliding:

$$\text{weight of cap} = 32.5 \times 3.12 \times 2.0 \times 0.15 = \quad 30.6 \, \text{kip}$$
$$\text{weight of trapeze} = 24.0 \times 4.25 \times 2.0 \times 0.15 = \quad 30.6 \, \text{kip}$$
$$\text{weight of column} = 15.5 \times 2.0 \times 11.5 \times 0.15 = \quad 53.5 \, \text{kip}$$
$$\underline{\text{weight of footing} = 17.0 \times 10.5 \times 3.0 \times 0.15 = \quad 80.5 \, \text{kip}}$$
$$195.2 \, \text{kip}$$

Wind load (on the structure)
Consider the following data and their relationship in Fig. 5.98:

depth of deck $= 6'\text{-}1''$

length of deck $= 72'\text{-}6''$

exposed area $= 445 \, \text{ft}^2$

$$W_{\text{transverse}} = 50 \, \text{lb/ft}^2 = 445 \times 50 = 22.2 \, \text{kip}$$
$$W_{\text{long.}} = 12 \, \text{lb/ft}^2 = 445 \times 12 = \quad 5.35 \, \text{kip}$$

Comp. force longitudinal to pier $= 22.2 \cos 26°\text{-}14' - 5.35 \cos 63°\text{-}46'$
$$= 17.4 \, \text{kip}$$

Comp. force transverse to pier $= 22.2 \sin 26°\text{-}14' + 5.35 \sin 63°\text{-}46'$
$$= 14.6 \, \text{kip}$$

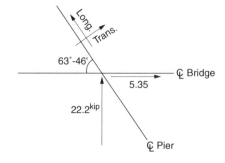

Figure 5.98. Schematic for wind load calculations

Wind load (on live load)

$$W_{\text{transverse}} = 100\,\text{lb/lin ft} = 72.5 \times 100 = 7.25\,\text{kip}$$
$$W_{\text{long.}} = 40\,\text{lb/lin ft} = 72.5 \times 40 = 2.90\,\text{kip}$$
$$\text{Comp. force longitudinal to pier} = 6.45 - 1.30 = 5.15\,\text{kip}$$
$$\text{Comp. force transverse to pier} = 3.20 + 2.60 = 5.80\,\text{kip}$$

The above loads act at 6 ft above the deck.

Earth load
This is given by:

$$147 \times 1.5 \times 0.12 = 26.3\,\text{kip}$$

Longitudinal forces

$$F = 0.05(18 + 0.64 \times 145) = 5.55\,\text{kip/lane}$$
$$= 11.10\,\text{kip}$$
$$F_{\text{transverse}} = 10.0\,\text{kip}$$
$$F_{\text{longitudinal}} = 4.9\,\text{kip}$$

Longitudinal force due to temperature
Since the expansion shoe is so designed that $R = H/2$ there is no thrust due to temperature expansion.

However assuming one expansion shoe becomes ineffective the thrust due to temperature may be taken as 5% of the DL. Thus:

$$R_A \text{ (due to DL interior beams)} = 0.375 \times 0.32 \times 72.5 = 22.3\,\text{kip}$$
$$R_A \text{ (due to DL exterior beams)} = 0.375 \times 1.20 \times 72.5 = 32.6\,\text{kip}$$
$$\therefore \quad \text{total DL on pier } 2 = (22.3 \times 4) + (32.6 \times 2)$$
$$= 154.2\,\text{kip}$$
$$\therefore \quad \text{thrust due to temperature} = 0.05 \times 154.2 = 7.7\,\text{kip}$$
$$\therefore \quad F_{\text{longitudinal}} = 3.4\,\text{kip}$$
$$F_{\text{transverse}} = 6.9\,\text{kip}$$

Piling arrangement
Referring to Fig. 5.99:

$$I_{xx} = 2[6 \times (1.25)^2 + 6 \times (3.75)^2] = 187\,\text{pile-ft}^2$$
$$I_{yy} = 2[4 \times (1.40)^2 + 4(4.2)^2 + 4(7.0)^2] = 548\,\text{pile-ft}^2$$
$$A = 24\,\text{piles}$$

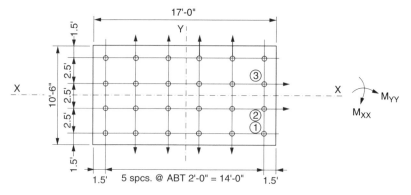

Figure 5.99. Piling arrangement for Example (5.19)

The piling arrangements for the three AASHTO cases are summarized in Table 5.32.

Design of the stem

Considering the loads above top/footing:

$$P_{\text{actual}} = 819.0 - 80.5 - 26.3 = 712.2 \text{ kip}$$

$$P_{\text{design}} = 0.8 \times 712 = 570 \text{ kip} \quad \text{(normalized)}$$

$$\begin{aligned} \underset{\text{(transverse)}}{M_{xx}} &= 6.9 \times 18.87 + 10.0 \times 27.02 + 14.6 \times 23.27 \times 0.3 \\ &+ 5.80 \times 29.02 = 671.2 \text{ kip-ft} \end{aligned}$$

$$\begin{aligned} \underset{\text{(longitudinal)}}{M_{yy}} &= 3.4 \times 18.87 + 4.9 \times 27.02 + 17.4 \times 23.27 \times 0.3 \\ &+ 5.15 \times 29.02 + 665.0 = 1134.0 \text{ kip-ft} \end{aligned}$$

Therefore, design as:

$$\left.\begin{aligned} M_{xx} &= 0.8 \times 671.2 = 540.0 \text{ kip-ft} \\ M_{yy} &= 0.8 \times 1134.0 = 910.0 \text{ kip-ft} \end{aligned}\right\} \quad \text{normalized}$$

Case I

$D + E + L$ (100% unit stresses)

$$\begin{aligned} \text{weight of pier} &= 195.2 \text{ kip} \\ \text{weight of earth} &= 26.3 \text{ kip} \\ \text{weight of DL (stringers)} &= 512.4 \text{ kip} \\ \text{weight of LL (one lane)} &= 84.8 \text{ kip} \end{aligned}$$

$$\therefore \quad P = 818.7 \text{ kip}$$

Table 5.32. Normalized cases for the piling arrangment

	Case I	Case II	Case III
$\dfrac{P}{A}$	$\dfrac{819}{24} = 34.0\,\text{kip}$	$\dfrac{585}{24} = 24.4\,\text{kip}$	$\dfrac{654}{24} = 27.0\,\text{kip}$
$\dfrac{M_{xx}C}{I_{xx}}$	$\dfrac{0 \times 3.75}{187} = 0$	$\dfrac{296 \times 3.75}{187} = 5.9\,\text{kip}$	$\dfrac{580 \times 3.75}{187} = 11.6\,\text{kip}$
$\dfrac{M_{yy}C}{I_{yy}}$	$\dfrac{655 \times 7.0}{548} = 8.5\,\text{kip}$	$\dfrac{352 \times 7.0}{548} = 4.5\,\text{kip}$	$\dfrac{935 \times 7.0}{548} = 12.0\,\text{kip}$
Maximum pile load	$34 + 8.5 = 42.5\,\text{kip}$	$24.4 + 5.9 + 4.5 = 34.8\,\text{kip}$	$27.0 + 11.6 + 12.0 = 50.6\,\text{kip}$
Minimum pile load	$34.0 - 8.5 = 25.5\,\text{kip}$	$24.4 - 5.9 - 4.5 = 14.0\,\text{kip}$	$27.0 - 11.6 - 12.0 = 3.4\,\text{kip}$

Notes to Table

1. As the maximum pile load is 50.6 kip (allowable = 50.0 kip), the piling arrangement shown in Fig. 5.99 is workable.
2. There is no uplift on any pile in any case of loading:

$$\text{maximum horizontal force} = [3.4 + 4.9 + 5.15 + 0.3 \times 17.4]0.8$$
$$= 15.0\,\text{kip}$$
$$\text{vertical load (piles 2 and 3)} = 78\,\text{kip}$$
$$\text{batter} = 1 : 4$$
$$\therefore \quad \text{total horizontal resistance} = \frac{108}{4}$$
$$= 26\,\text{kip} \quad \text{(safe)}$$
$$= 30\,\text{kip} \quad \text{(minimum)}$$

$$M_{xx} = 0$$
$$M_{yy} = 84.8 \times 7.85 = 665.0\,\text{kip-ft}$$

Case II
$D + E + W$ (125% unit stresses)

$$P = 818.7 - 84.8 = 734\,\text{kip}$$
$$M_{xx} = 14.6 \times 25.27 = 370\,\text{kip-ft} \ @ \ \text{top/piles}$$
$$M_{yy} = 17.4 \times 25.27 = 440\,\text{kip-ft} \ @ \ \text{top/piles}$$

Case III

$D + E + L + LF + F + 30\%W + WL$ (125% unit stresses)

$$P = 818.7\,\text{kip}$$

$$M_{xx} = 10.0 \times 29.02 + 14.6 \times 25.27 \times 0.3 + 5.80 \times 31.02$$

$$= 725.0\,\text{kip-ft}$$

$$M_{yy} = 4.9 \times 29.02 + 17.4 \times 25.27 \times 0.3 + 5.15 \times 31.02 + 665$$

$$= 1170.0\,\text{kip-ft}$$

The normalized design loads for Cases I–III are summarized in Table 5.33, while specific design treatment of Case III is given below.

Case III (Group III loading)

$$P = 570\,\text{kip}$$

$$M_{xx} = 540\,\text{kip-ft}$$

$$M_{yy} = 910\,\text{kip-ft}$$

$$e_{yy} = \frac{910}{570} = 1.60\,\text{ft}$$

$$e_{xx} = \frac{540}{570} = 0.95\,\text{ft}$$

As e is less than $0.5t$ in both cases, the design is based on an uncracked section (AASHTO 1.7.8.f) as shown in Fig. 5.100.
  Assume

$$p = 1\% = 0.01$$

$$A_g = 15.5 \times 2.0 = 31.0\,\text{ft}^2 = 31 \times 144 = 4470\,\text{in}^2$$

$$A_S = 44.7\,\text{in}^2.$$

Table 5.33. Normalized design loads

	Case I	Case II	Case III
P	819.0	585.0	654.0
M_{xx}	0	296.0	580.0
M_{yy}	665.0	355.0	935.0

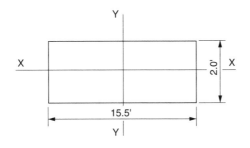

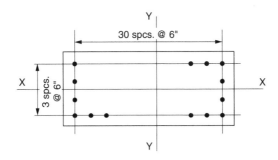

Figure 5.100. Plans for Case III design loads

Perimeter along ℄ steel bars $= 15 + 15 + 1.5 + 1.5 = 33' = 396''$

using bar spacing $= 6''$

no. of bars $= 29 + 29 + 4 + 4 = 66$

$$\frac{A_S}{\text{bar}} = \frac{44.7}{66} = 0.68\,\text{in}^2 \qquad \text{(Therefore use #8)}$$

$$\therefore \quad \text{revised } p = \frac{0.79 \times 66 \times 100}{4470} = 1.17\%$$

The material areas for the section are:

$$\text{steel} = \frac{0.79 \times 66(10.1)}{144} = 3.26$$

$$\text{concrete} = 15.5 \times 2 = 31.00$$

$$A = 34.26$$

For moment I_{xx}:

$$\text{concrete} = \frac{1}{12} \times 15.5 \times 8 = 10.3\,\text{ft}^4$$

$$\text{steel} = \frac{2 \times 2 \times 0.79}{144} \left(\frac{6}{12}\right)^2 (0.25 + 2.25) \times 9 = 0.12\,\text{ft}^4$$

$$+ \frac{2 \times 29 \times 0.79}{144} \times (0.75)^2 \times 9 = 1.60\,\text{ft}^4$$

$$I_{xx} = 10.3 + 0.12 + 1.60 = 12.0\,\text{ft}^4$$

For moment I_{yy}:

$$\text{concrete} = \frac{1}{12} \times 2.0 \times (15.5)^3 = 616\,\text{ft}^4$$

$$\text{steel} = \frac{2 \times 2 \times 0.79}{144} \times (7.50)^2 \times 9 = 11.00\,\text{ft}^4$$

$$+ \frac{2 \times 2 \times 0.79}{144} \times 0.25(1 + 4 + 9 + 16 \cdots 225) \times 9 = 61.3\,\text{ft}^4$$

$$\therefore \quad I_{yy} = 616 + 11 + 61.3 = 688.3\,\text{ft}^4$$

$$\therefore \quad r_{xx} = \sqrt{\frac{12}{34.26}} = 0.59\,\text{ft}$$

$$\therefore \quad r_{yy} = \sqrt{\frac{688.3}{34.3}} = 4.46\,\text{ft}$$

$$\therefore \quad K_{xx} = \frac{t_{xx}^2}{2r_{xx}^2} = \frac{4}{2 \times (0.59)^2} = 5.71\,\text{ft}$$

$$\therefore \quad K_{yy} = \frac{t_{yy}^2}{2r_{yy}^2} = \frac{(15.5)^2}{2(4.46)^2} = 6.00\,\text{ft}$$

$$\frac{K_{xx}e_{xx}}{t_{xx}} = \frac{5.71 \times 0.95}{2.0} = 2.72\,\text{ft}$$

$$\frac{K_{yy}e_{yy}}{t_{yy}} = \frac{6.00 \times 1.60}{15.5} = 0.62\,\text{ft}$$

$$= 3.34\,\text{ft}$$

$$f_c = \frac{P}{A_g} \frac{1 + 3.34}{1 + 9 \times 0.0117} = \frac{570 \times 4.34}{4470 \times 2.05} = 0.27\,\text{kip/in}^2$$

$$= 270\,\text{lb/in}^2$$

As allowable $f_c = 1200$, the design will have to be revised using a lower value of p. Using Table 27 from the ACI Design Handbook:

$$g_x = \frac{1.5}{2.0} = 0.75; \quad g_y = \frac{15}{15.5} = 0.97$$

Using #6 at $18''$, the number of bars $= 11 + 11 = 22$.
   Therefore:

$$p = \frac{22 \times 0.44}{4470} \times 100 = 0.216\% = 0.002$$

$$(n - 1) p = (10 - 1) \times 0.002 = 0.018$$

Using Table 27 (ACI Handbook)

$$K_{xx} = K_{yy} = 6.0 \quad \text{(approximately)}$$

$$\left.\begin{array}{l} \therefore \quad \dfrac{K_{xx} e_{xx}}{t_{xx}} = \dfrac{6 \times 0.95}{2} = 2.85 \, \text{ft} \\[4mm] \therefore \quad \dfrac{K_{yy} e_{yy}}{t_{yy}} = \dfrac{6 \times 1.60}{15.5} = 0.62 \, \text{ft} \end{array}\right\} \quad (\text{total} = 3.47 \, \text{ft})$$

$$\therefore \quad \frac{f_c}{(\text{max})} = \frac{570}{4470} \times \frac{1 + 3.47}{1 + 0.018} = \frac{570 \times 4.47}{4470 \times 1.018} = 0.568$$

$$= 563 \, \text{psi} \quad (< 1200 \, \text{psi} \quad \therefore \quad \text{safe})$$

The final column design is given in Fig. 5.101.

Check on the final design
The column designed by AASHTO 1.7.8.f may be checked by the conservative interaction formula:

$$f_c = \frac{P}{A} \pm \frac{M_{xx} C_{xx}}{I_{xx}} \pm \frac{M_{yy} C_{yy}}{I_{yy}}$$

$$f_c = \frac{NK}{bt}$$

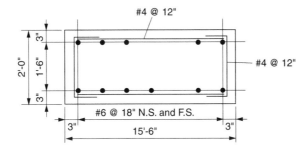

Figure 5.101. Schematic of final column design

$$npg = 10 \times 0.002g = 0.02g$$

$$(npg)_x = 0.02 \times 0.75 = 0.015 \qquad \left(\frac{e}{t}\right)_x = 0.48$$

$$(npg)_y = 0.02 \times 0.97 = 0.02 \qquad \left(\frac{e}{t}\right)_y = 0.10$$

From Tables in the ACI Handbook:

$$K_x = 6.0 \qquad K_y = 1.5 \qquad K = 7.5$$

$$f_c = \frac{7.5 \times 570 \times 1000}{4470} = 958 \, \text{psi} \qquad (<1200 \, \text{psi and therefore safe})$$

$f_{s(\text{max})}$ is obtained when only M_{xx} acts (Fig. 5.102):

$$f_c = \frac{6.0 \times 570}{4470} = 0.764 \, \text{ksi} = 764 \, \text{psi}$$

$$k = 0.35$$

$$\therefore \quad kt = 0.35 \times 24 = 8.4$$

$$f_c = \frac{12.6}{8.4} \times 764$$

$$= 1150 \, \text{psi}$$

$$\therefore \quad f_{s(\text{max})} = 1150 \times 10 = 11\,500 \, \text{psi} \qquad (< 20\,000 \, \text{psi and therefore safe})$$

Design of the cap
Consider the cap at pier 3 (Fig. 5.103):

moment at face due to stringer reactions $= (105.1 \times 0.84) + (116.6 \times 6.60)$

$$= 858.4 \, \text{kip-ft}$$

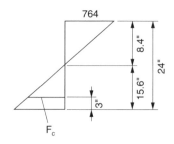

Figure 5.102. Geometry for checking the final design

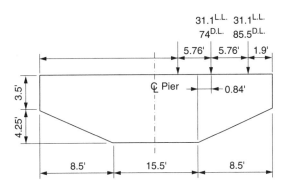

Figure 5.103. Cap design at pier 3

moment at face due to concrete DL $= (3 \times 8.50 \times 2 \times 0.15 \times 4.25)$

$$+ (4.25 \times 4.25 \times 2 \times 0.15 \times 2.83)$$

$$= 48.7 \text{ kip-ft}$$

$$\therefore \quad M_{\text{total}} = 858.4 + 48.7 = 907.1 \text{ kip-ft}$$

$$V \text{ at face} = 105.1 + 116.6 + 13.5 = 235.2 \text{ kips}$$

$$M \text{ at interior stringer} = 116.6 \times 57.6 + 7.66 \times 3 \times 2 \times 0.15 \times 3.83$$

$$+ 3.83 \times 3.83 \times 2 \times 0.15 \times 2.55$$

$$= 707.6 \text{ kip-ft}$$

$$V \text{ at interior stringer} = 116.6 + 6.9 + 4.4 + 105.1 = 233.0 \text{ kips}$$

$$M \text{ at exterior stringer} = 1.90 \times 3.0 \times 2 \times 0.15 \times 0.95$$

$$+ 0.95 \times 0.95 \times 2 \times 0.15 \times 0.63$$

$$= 3.84 \text{ kip-ft}$$

$$V \text{ at exterior stringer} = 116.6 + 1.8 = 118.4 \text{ kips}$$

Using two layers of bars at the top, and assuming centre of gravity of steel is 4 ft-2 in from the face

$$d = (7.25 - 0.38)12 = 82.5''$$

$$M = 907.1 \text{ kip-ft}$$

$$A_{\text{S}} = \frac{M}{ad} = \frac{907}{1.44 \times 82.5} = 7.64 \text{ in}^2$$

Minimum area requirement is then:

$$A_S = 0.005 \times B \times d$$

$$= 0.005 \times 24 \times 82.5 = 9.9\,\text{in}^2$$

Use 4 #10 at the top and bottom (see Fig. 5.104):

$$A_S = 10.16\,\text{in}^2$$

$$\Sigma_0 = 32$$

Bond check

V at pier face $= 235.2\,\text{kip}$

$$u = \frac{235.2}{32 \times 0.87 \times 82.5}$$

$$= 0.102\,\text{ksi}$$

$$= 102\,\text{psi}$$

Stirrup design

Shear taken by concrete is assumed to be 60 psi:

$$V \text{ at face} = 235.2\,\text{kip}$$

$$v \text{ at face} = \frac{235.2 \times 1000}{24 \times 0.87 \times 82.5} = \frac{235\,200}{1722.6} = 137.0\,\text{psi}$$

V at interior stringer $= 233\,\text{kip}$

$$v \text{ at interior stringer} = \frac{233 \times 1000}{24 \times 0.87 \times 77.14} = \frac{233\,000}{1610.68} = 145\,\text{psi}$$

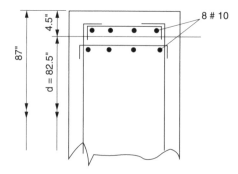

Figure 5.104. Plan for checking the cap design

V at exterior stringer $= 118.4\,\text{kip}$

$$v \text{ at exterior stringer} = \frac{118.4 \times 1000}{24 \times 0.87 \times 48.2} = \frac{118\,400}{1006.42} = 118\,\text{psi}$$

Shear stresses are above 90 psi.

Stirrups will have to be provided. Use #5 stirrups. Thus:

$$\text{spacing of stirrups} = \frac{A_{\text{s}}f_{\text{v}}jd}{V'}$$

$$= \frac{0.62 \times 20 \times 0.87 \times d}{V'}$$

$$V' = \frac{(v-60)(0.87)(24)(d)}{1000}$$

$$\text{spacing} = \frac{516.5}{(v-60)}$$

$$\text{spacing at face} = \frac{516.5}{77} = 6.7''$$

$$\text{spacing at interior stringer} = \frac{516.5}{85} = 6.1''$$

$$\text{spacing at exterior stringer} = \frac{516.5}{58} = 9''$$

The stirrup design is summarized in Fig. 5.105.

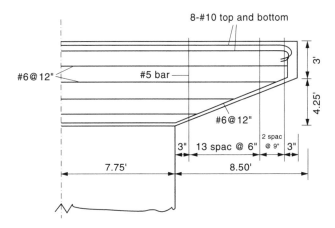

Figure 5.105. Pier design reinforcement (showing main steel and stirrups)

Design of footing

Case III gives a maximum pile load and therefore shall be considered here. Using Fig. 5.106:

$$\text{maximum pile load on pile } 1 = 50.6 \, \text{kip}$$

$$\text{maximum pile load on pile } 2 = 27.0 + 12.0 + \frac{580 \times 1.25}{187}$$

$$= 42.37 \, \text{kip}$$

$$\text{max. (positive) mom. at face of column} = 50.6 \times 2.75 + 42.37 \times 0.25$$

$$= 149.7 \, \text{kip-ft}$$

$$\text{moment (negative)} = [(4.25 \times 3 \times 0.15)$$

$$+ (4.25 \times 1.5 \times 0.12)]2.13$$

$$= 5.70 \, \text{kip-ft}$$

$$\therefore \quad \text{net maximum moment} = 149.7 - 5.70 \times 2.38$$

$$= 133.3 \, \text{kip-ft}$$

It can be assumed that this moment is carried by the breadth of the section:

$$= 1.5 + \frac{2.75}{2} = 2.88$$

$$\frac{\text{moment}}{\text{ft}} = \frac{133.3}{2.88} = 46.4 \, \text{kip-ft}$$

$$\therefore \quad F = \frac{50}{197} = 0.25$$

$$\therefore \quad d = 16'' = 1'\text{-}4''$$

$$\text{depth of footing} = 1' + 1'\text{-}4'' + 4\tfrac{1}{2}'' = 2'\text{-}8\tfrac{1}{2}'' \quad (\text{use } 2'\text{-}9'')$$

$$A_S = \frac{M}{ad} = \frac{46.4}{1.44 \times 16} = 2.61 \, \text{in}^2$$

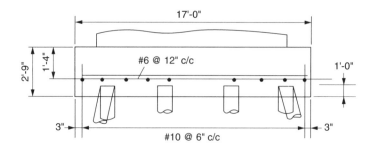

Figure 5.106. Footing design plan

Thus, use #10 @ 6". Now:

V to be used for bond $= 50.6 + 42.9 - 7.7 = 85.8\,\text{kips}$

$$\therefore \quad \frac{V}{ft} = \frac{85.8}{2.88} = 29.6\,\text{kip}$$

$$\therefore \quad \mu = \frac{29.6 \times 1000}{8 \times 0.87 \times 16} = 0.266\,\text{ksi} = 266\,\text{psi} \quad (<300 \text{ and therefore safe}).$$

5.2.11 Example (5.20) British practice (pier design)

A bridge deck shown in Fig. 5.107 is supported by four piers made up of individual columns of rectangular shapes 1000 mm × 600 mm. The minimum column height is 8.1 m. Various load combinations are tabulated in Table 5.34 based on BS 5400 and BD 37/88.

Using the following data, design the pier for the worst loading:

soil pressure $= 200\,\text{kN/m}$

span 20 m each continuous

total number of beams $= 30$

total bearings $= 26$ (each of 800 kN capacity)

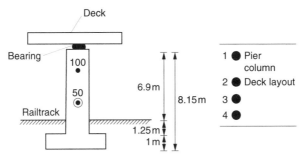

Figure 5.107. A cluster of bridge piers (Example (5.20))

Table 5.34. Load combinations for pier design

Column	ULS combination				SLS combination
	1	2 or 3	4 or 5	Minimum	
1	2182	2182	2177	1814	1649
2	2420	2390	1784	1487	1352
3	3400	3200	1784	1487	1352
4	4008	3722	2177	1814	1649
Total	**12 010 kN**	**1144.4**	**7922**	**6602**	**6602**

SLS = serviceability limit state

ULS = ultimate limit state

Adopt the design for the worst case for all four columns.

The deck has rubber bearings of 800 kN capacity each. Taking the maximum load of 4008 kN as a column load, the number of bearings = 4008/800 = 5; for four columns 4 × 5 = 20 bearings required.

The total number of beams is 13 with approximately 2 bearings per beam tucked together by means of dowels being suitable. Total bearings number 13 × 2 = 26, i.e. one continuous strip bearing replacing two can also be adopted.

Assume column size of 1000 × 600 with a slider on a hinge bearing. A foundation pad of 1.25 m is placed above. All impact forces are acting concurrently. Note that there is 6.9 m clearance to the track level and at 1 m the soil pressure = 200 kN/m².

SLS – Cracking
Combination 1 with 30 units of HB only. Vertical load will remain well within the middle third of the column.

SLS – Stresses
These need not be checked if deformation loads are included at ULS with appropriate γ_{fl}.

ULS
Assume:

l_e = effective height in the plane of buckling

Slenderness ratios are:

$$\frac{l_{ey}}{h_x} = \frac{23 \times 8.1}{0.6} = 31.05$$

$$\frac{l_{ex}}{h_y} = \frac{2.3 \times 8.1}{1.0} = 18.63$$

Therefore the column is slender. Various ULS combinations are detailed below.

Combination 1: DL + LL

Maximum axial load = 4008 kN

Shrinkage shortening will not expose any eccentricity (Fig. 5.108).

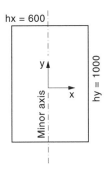

Figure 5.108. Details for the slenderness ratio

Minimum constructional eccentricity $= 20\,\text{mm}$ (assumed)

$$M_{ty} = M_{iy} + \frac{Nh_x}{1750}\left(\frac{l_{ey}}{h_y}\right)^2\left(1 - \frac{0.0035 l_{ex}}{h_y}\right)$$

$$M_{ty} = 4008 \times 0.02 + \frac{4008 \times 0.6}{1750} \times 31.05^2(1 - 0.0035 \times 31.05)$$

$$= 1261.2\,\text{kNm}$$

$$M_{tx} = M_{ix} + \frac{Nh_y}{1750}\left(\frac{l_{ex}}{h_y}\right)\left(1 - \frac{0.0035 l_{ex}}{h_y}\right)$$

$$M_{tx} = 4008 \times 0.02 + \frac{4008 \times 1}{1750} \times 18.63^2(1 - 0.0035 \times 18.63)$$

$$= 832.4\,\text{kNm}$$

The case with minimum axial load need not be considered because $M_t \propto N$ and hence can not be critical.

Combination 2 and 3: DL + LL + wind or temperature
Wind (not allowed in this project) to be resisted at the abutments and temperature difference rotations taken up in the bearings. Effective bridge temperature range controls bearings and expansion joint design.

Combination 4: DL + impact

Maximum axial load $= 2177\,\text{kN}$

$$M_{iy} = (150 \times 2 + 100 \times 4.25) \times \overset{\gamma_{f1}}{1.5} \times \overset{\gamma_{f3}}{1.1} = 1196\,\text{kNm}$$

$$M_{ix} = (50 \times 2 + 100 \times 4.25) \times 1.5 \times 1.1 = 866\,\text{kNm}$$

$$M_{ty} = 1196 + \frac{2177 \times 0.6}{1750} \times (31.05)^2(1 - 0.0035 \times 31.05)$$

$$= 1196 + 641.5 = 1837.5\,\text{kNm}$$

$$M_{tx} = 866 + \frac{2177 \times 1}{1750} \times 18.63^2 \times (1 - 0.035 \times 18.63)$$

$$= 866 + 403.6 = 1269.6\,\text{kNm}$$

Minimum axial load (column 3) = 1487 kN

$$M_{ty} = 1196 + \left(\frac{1487}{2177}\right) \times 641.5 = 1196 + 438.2 = 1634.2\,\text{kNm}$$

$$M_{tx} = 866 + \left(\frac{1487}{2177}\right) \times 403.6 = 866 + 275.1 = 1141.7\,\text{kNm}$$

Combination 5: DL + frictional force

Maximum axial load = 2177 kN

Assuming 5% friction in the bearing and nominal DL and SDL reaction at the bearing:

$$\text{ULS} \qquad \gamma_{f1} \quad \gamma_{f3}$$

$$M_{iy} = (0.05 \times 1649 \times 8.1) \times 1.3 \times 1.1 = 766\,\text{kNm}$$

$$M_{ty} = 766 + 641 = 1407\,\text{kNm}$$

$$M_{tx} = 2177 \times 0.02 + 265 = 447\,\text{kNm}$$

Minimum axial load (column 3) = 1487 kN

$$M_{iy} = (0.05 \times 1352 \times 8.1) \times 1.3 \times 1.1 = 782.6\,\text{kNm}$$

$$M_{ty} = 782.6 + \left(\frac{1487}{2177}\right) \times 641 = 1220.4\,\text{kNm}$$

$$M_{tx} = 1487 \times 0.02 + \left(\frac{1487}{2177}\right) \times 403.6 = 305.44\,\text{kNm}$$

Summary

A summary of all the combinations is provided in Table 5.35.

Table 5.35. Summary of ULS combination results

Comb	N	N/bh	M_{ty}	M_{ty}/bh^2	$100A_S/bh$	M_{tx}	M_{tx}/bh^2	$100A_S/bh$
1	4008	6.7	1261.2	3.53	1.15	823.4	1.45	0
4	2177	3.6	1837.5	5.11	2.3	1296.6	2.13	0.3
4	1487	2.5	1634.2	4.51	2.22	1141.7	1.85	0.4
5	12 177	3.6	1407	3.91	1.75	447	0.72	0
5	1487	2.5	1220.4	3.33	1.40	305.44	0.58	0

Now:

$$f_{cu} = 40 \, \text{N/mm}^2$$

$$f_y = 460 \, \text{N/mm}^2$$

$$\frac{d}{h} = 0.9$$

$$\therefore \quad A_{Sy} = \frac{2.30 \times 600 \times 1000}{100} = 13\,800 \, \text{mm}^2$$

$$A_{Sx} = \frac{0.4 \times 600 \times 1000}{100} = 2400 \, \text{mm}^2$$

$$2T40 = 2513 \, \text{mm}^2 \quad (A_S)$$

$$10T40 = 12\,566 \, \text{mm}^2$$

$$6T40 = 7540 \, \text{mm}^2$$

$$16T40 = 20\,106 \, \text{mm}^2$$

Preliminary assessment suggests these values cater for wind load etc.

Biaxial bending check

$$N = 2177 \, \text{kN}$$

$$M_{ty} = 1837.5 \, \text{kNm}$$

$$M_{tx} = 1269.6 \, \text{kNm}$$

Ignoring bars not at the farthest distance from the nominal axis (Fig. 5.109):

$$A_{Sy} = 12 \, \text{No. 40 bars} = 12\,570 \, \text{mm}^2$$

$$A_{Sx} = 6 \, \text{No. 1251} = 7540 \, \text{mm}^2$$

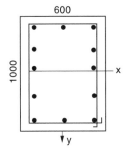

Figure 5.109. Twelve No. 50 mm bars for the biaxial bending check

$$\left(\frac{M_x}{M_{ax}}\right)^{\alpha_n} + \left(\frac{M_y}{M_{ay}}\right)^{\alpha_n} < 1.0$$

$$f_{yc} = \frac{f_y}{\gamma_m + \dfrac{f_y}{2000}}$$

For:

$$\frac{N}{bh} = 3.6 \quad \text{from the chart for} \quad \frac{d}{h} = 0.9$$

$$M_{uy} = 7.1 \times 1000 \times 600^2 \times 10^{-6} = 2556\,\text{kNm}$$

$$M_{ux} = 5.2 \times 600 \times 1000^2 \times 10^{-6} = 3128\,\text{kNm}$$

$$N_{u2} = 0.45 \times 40 \times 1000 \times 600 + \frac{450}{1.15 + \dfrac{425}{2000}} \quad [16\text{T}40\ (A_S = 20\,106)]$$

$$= 17\,502\,\text{kN}$$

$$\frac{N}{N_{u2}} = \frac{2172}{17\,502} = 0.1244$$

Therefore:

$$\alpha = 1 \quad \text{and} \quad \frac{1618}{2556} + \frac{1131}{3128} = 0.633 + 0.362 = 0.995 < 1 \quad \text{(allowed)}$$

Therefore reinforcement against biaxial bending is a requirement. A possible solution is a section of 16 No. 40 mm bars as illustrated in Fig. 5.110.
    This solution will actually be safer if

1. all reinforcements are taken into account in calculating M_{uy} and M_{ux}
2. bars of $f_y = 460\,\text{N/mm}^2$ are used as recently introduced

This solution can also be checked for other combinations of axial load and bending about both axes as indicated in the summary.
    A preliminary check shows that the above is the worst case.

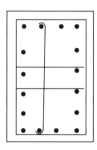

Figure 5.110. Reinforcement solution of 16 No. 40 mm bars

5.2.12 Example (5.21) American practice

Consider an abutment wall 13.26 ft (4.042 m) high with a system of straight and inclined piles supporting the wall and pile cap footing. A 2 ft equivalent surcharge acts along the wall with back fill soil of load 120 lb/ft³ and concrete (density = 150 lb/ft³) (23.56 kN/m³). The following load cases are considered:

Case I Full weight of abutment + back fill + 2′ surcharge due to live load

Case II $DL + LL + E + B$

Case III Case II $+ F + 30\% W$

$F = 2.72 \text{ kip/ft}$ (3.69 kN/m)

Design reinforcement for the wall. Sketch the plan with the pile layout (see Fig. 5.111).

Case I (Construction conditions)
Full weight of abutment plus back fill plus 2 ft LL surcharge:

weight of ① = 3 × 11.00 × 0.15 = 5.00 kip

weight of ② = 1.5 × 13.26 × 0.15 = 2.98 kip

weight of ③ = 0.55 × 13.26 × 0.15 = 1.09 kip

weight of ④ = 0.55 × 13.26 × 0.12 = 0.88 kip

weight of ⑤ = 5.40 × 13.26 × 0.12 = 8.60 kip

weight of ⑥ = 6.50 × 2.0 × 0.12 = 1.56 kip

20.11 kip

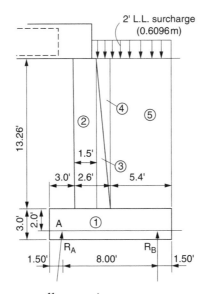

Figure 5.111. Abutment wall on a pier

$$P_{\text{due to surcharge}} = 2 \times 0.035 \times 16.26 = 1.14 \, \text{kip}$$

$$P_{\text{due to fill}} = \frac{0.035 \times 16.26}{2} = 4.62 \, \text{kip}$$

Taking moments about A:

$$8.00 R_B = [(5.00 \times 4.0) + (2.98 \times 2.25) + (1.09 \times 3.37) + (0.88 \times 3.74)$$
$$+ (8.60 \times 6.80) + (1.56 \times 6.25) - (1.14 \times 7.13) - (4.62 \times 4.42)]$$

$$\therefore \quad R_B = \frac{73.83}{8.00} = 9.20 \, \text{kip}$$

$$\therefore \quad V_A = 20.11 - 9.20 = 10.91 \, \text{kip}$$

$$\therefore \quad H_A = \frac{10.91}{3} = 3.64 \, \text{kip}$$

$$\therefore \quad R_A = 00.00 \, \text{kip}$$

Safety factor (SF) against overturning $= 102.36/28.53 = 3.60$ (therefore safe)
   Note that a 150% overstress is permitted for the construction conditions. Thus:

$$\text{all loads on piles} = 1.5 \times 80 = 114 \, \text{kip}$$

$$\text{maximum spacing at batter} = \frac{114}{10.91} = 10.0 \quad \text{(maximum)}$$

$$\text{maximum spacing at vertical} = \frac{120}{9.20} = 10.0 \quad \text{(maximum)}$$

Case II: DL + LL + E + B

$$\text{depth of additional fill} = 2.75 \, \text{ft}$$

$$\text{weight of additional fill} = 2.75 \times 6.50 \times 0.12 = 2.14 \, \text{kip}$$

$$\text{weight of surcharge} = 2.0 \times 6.50 \times 0.12 = 1.56 \, \text{kip}$$

$$\therefore \quad \text{additional restoring moment} = 3.70 \times 6.25 = 23.2 \, \text{kip-ft}$$

$$P_{\text{surcharge}} = 2 \times 0.35 \times 19 = 1.33 \, \text{kip}$$

$$P_{\text{fill}} = \frac{0.035 \times (19)^2}{2} = 6.30 \, \text{kip}$$

$$\text{maximum height of water} = 991.8 - 977.0 = 14.8 \, \text{ft}$$

Thus, based on the schematic given in Fig. 5.112:

uplift due to ① $= 11 \times 3 \times 0.0624 = 2.06\,\text{kip}$

uplift due to ② $= 11.8 \times 1.6 \times 0.0624 = 1.18\,\text{kip}$

uplift due to ③ $= 11.8 \times 1.0 \times 0.0624 = 0.74\,\text{kip}$

moment about A due to ① $= 2.06 \times 4 \quad = \quad 8.24$

moment about A due to ② $= 1.18 \times 2.3 \quad = \quad 2.72$

moment about A due to ③ $= 0.74 \times 3.43 = \quad 2.54$

$$\text{total moment due to uplift} = 13.50\,\text{kip-ft}$$

$$\text{moment due to } P_{\text{surcharge}} = 1.33 \times 8.5 = 11.00$$

$$\text{moment due to } P_{\text{fill}} = 6.30 \times 5.33 = 33.50$$

$$\text{total overturning moment} = 58.00\,\text{kip-ft}$$

$$\text{total restoring moment} = 102.36 + 23.2 + (9.1 \times 2.25) = 146.1$$

$$\therefore \quad \text{static force} = \frac{146.1}{58.00} = 2.50 \qquad \text{(therefore safe)}$$

Case III: Case II + F + 30% W
The 30% W is negligible. Thus:

$F = 2.72\,\text{kip/ft}$

$\therefore \quad$ moment due to $F = 2.72 \times 15.26 = 41.5\,\text{kip-ft}$

total overturning moment $= 41.5 + 58 = 99.50\,\text{kip-ft}$

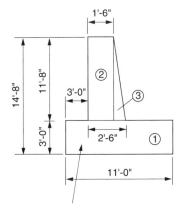

Figure 5.112. Case II moments and uplifts

$$SF = \frac{146.1}{99.50} = 1.47 \qquad \text{(therefore unsafe)}$$

By increasing the bearing pad to $1''$

$$F = 0.75 \times 2.72 = 2.04 \text{ kip-ft}$$

$\therefore$ moment due to $F = 2.04 \times 15.26 = 31.0 \text{ kip-ft}$

overturning moment $= 58 + 31.0 = 89.0 \text{ kip-ft}$

$$SF = \frac{146.1}{89.0} = 1.64 \text{ kip-ft} \qquad \text{(therefore safe)}$$

Therefore retain section but use $1''$ thick bearing pads.

Pile spacing
From Case II:

$$V_B = \frac{146.1 - 13.5 - 58.00}{8} = 9.34 \text{ kip}$$

$\therefore$ $V_A = 20.11 + 2.14 + 1.56 + 9.1 - 9.34 = 23.57 \text{ kip}$

$\therefore$ $H_A = \dfrac{23.57}{3} = 7.85 \text{ kip}$

Assume 100% unit stresses for this case. Therefore all loads on pile $= 80$ kip. Thus:

$$\text{maximum space at batter} = \frac{76}{23.51} = 3.22 \text{ ft}$$

$$\text{maximum space at vertical} = \frac{80}{9.34} = 8.56 \text{ ft}$$

From Case III:

$$V_B = \frac{146.1 - 13.5 - 89.0}{8} = 5.45 \text{ kip}$$

$\therefore$ $V_A = 32.91 - 5.45 = 27.46 \text{ kip}$

$\therefore$ $H_A = \dfrac{27.46}{3} = 9.16 \text{ kip}$

All stresses in this case $= 125\%$. Consequently:

$$\text{all loads on pile} = 1.25 \times 80 = 100 \text{ kip}$$

$\therefore$ $\text{maximum space at batter} = \dfrac{95}{27.46} = 3.42 \text{ kip}$

$$\text{maximum space at vertical} = \frac{100}{5.45} = 10 \text{ ft} \quad \text{(maximum)}$$

Therefore, the pile spacing is governed by Case II.

Therefore use $3'\text{-}3''$ c/c for the batter piles and use $8'\text{-}0''$ c/c for the vertical piles.

Check for bending in the piles
In a $3'\text{-}3''$ dimension there are

$$1 + \frac{3.25}{8} = 1.41 \text{ piles}$$

From Case I:

excess horizontal force $= 5.76 - 3.64 = 2.12 \text{ kip}$

$$\therefore \quad \frac{\text{bending load}}{\text{pile}} = \frac{2.12 \times 3.25}{1.41} = 4.9 \text{ kip} \qquad \text{(therefore safe)}$$

From Case II:

excess horizontal force $= 7.85 - 7.63 = 0.22 \text{ kip}$

$$\therefore \quad \frac{\text{bending load}}{\text{pile}} = \frac{0.22 \times 3.25}{1.41} = 0.50 \text{ kip} \qquad \text{(therefore safe)}$$

From Case III:

excess horizontal force $= 10.35 - 9.16 = 1.19 \text{ kip}$

$$\therefore \quad \frac{\text{bending load}}{\text{pile}} = \frac{1.19 \times 3.25}{1.41} = 2.74 \text{ kip} \qquad \text{(therefore safe)}$$

Design of abutment stem
With reference to Fig. 5.113:

$$\text{DL from superstructure} = 9.1 \text{ kip/ft}$$

$$\text{stem } H_T = 13.26 \text{ ft}$$

$$\text{depth of deck} = 2.75 \text{ ft}$$

$$\therefore \quad A_S = 0.54 \text{ in}^2$$

$$\text{for stem } H_T = 10.00 \text{ ft}$$

$$\therefore \quad A_S = 0.20 \text{ in}^2$$

$$\text{for stem } H_T = 8.00 \text{ ft}$$

$$A_S = 0.04 \text{ in}^2$$

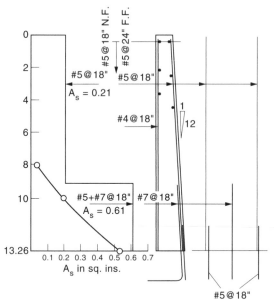

Figure 5.113. Design of abutment stem

Design of toe
From Case II:

$$V_A = 23.57 \, \text{kip}$$

Critical section for shear is at $\dfrac{d}{2} = 10.25 \, \text{inches}$:

$$\therefore \quad V = 23.57 - (3.0 \times 2.15 \times 0.15) = 22.60$$

$$\therefore \quad M = 23.57 \times 1.5 - (3.0 \times 3.0 \times 0.15 \times 1.5) = 35.40 \, \text{kip-ft}$$

$$\text{MR} = 0.173d^2 = 0.173 \times (20.5)^2 = 72.60 \, \text{kip-ft}$$

Therefore no compression steel is required:

$$\therefore \quad A_S = \frac{M}{ad} = \frac{35.40}{1.29 \times 20.5} = 1.34 \, \text{in}^2$$

$$(\therefore \quad m = q = 12 \times 0.055 = 0.65; \qquad \therefore \quad j = 0.80)$$

$$v = \frac{22\,600}{12 \times 0.8 \times 20.5} = 115 \, \text{psi}$$

Therefore increase footing depth to 3'-9".

$$\therefore \quad V_A = 23.57 + 3 \times 0.75 \times 0.15 = 23.91 \, \text{kip}$$

$$\therefore \quad \text{pile spacing at batter} = \frac{76.0}{23.91} = 3.18 \, \text{ft}$$

Therefore revise spacing at batter to $3'$-$0''$ centre to centre. Thus:

$$d = 29.50''$$

$$\frac{d}{2} = 14.75''$$

$$\therefore \quad V = 23.91 - (3.75 \times 1.80 \times 0.15) = 22.9 \, \text{kip}$$

$$\therefore \quad M = 23.91 \times 1.5 - (3.75 \times 3.0 \times 0.15 \times 1.5) = 33.30 \, \text{kip-ft}$$

$$\therefore \quad A_S = \frac{M}{ad} = \frac{33.3}{1.29 \times 29.5} = 0.88 \, \text{in}^2$$

$$A_S = \begin{cases} \#7 \ @ \ 18'' \ \text{(from bent dowels)} = \dfrac{0.40}{0.48} \, \text{in}^2 \\[2mm] \#8 \ @ \ 18'' = 0.53 \, \text{in}^2 \end{cases}$$

$$\therefore \quad A_S = 0.93 \, \text{in}^2$$

$$\therefore \quad \Sigma_0 = 3.9 \, \text{in}^2$$

$$p = \frac{0.93}{12 \times 29.5}$$

$$= 0.026$$

$$\therefore \quad m = q = 12 \times 0.026 = 0.32$$

$$\therefore \quad k = 0.54$$

$$\therefore \quad j = 0.82$$

$$\therefore \quad v = \frac{22\,900}{12 \times 0.82 \times 29.5} = 78 \, \text{psi} \qquad \text{(therefore safe enough)}$$

Check for punching shear:

$$\begin{matrix} \text{maximum pile load} \\ \text{(vertical component)} \end{matrix} = 23.91 \times 3.0 = 71.6 \, \text{kip}$$

$$\text{area for punching} = 12\pi \times 29.5 \times 0.33 = 370 \, \text{in}^2$$

$$\therefore \quad \text{punching stress} = \frac{71\,600}{370} = 194 \, \text{psi}$$

(all punching stress $= 0.15 f'_c = 375 \, \text{psi}$; therefore safe)

Bond check:

$$\mu = \frac{22\,900}{0.82} \times 29.5 \times 3.9 = 243 \, \text{psi} \qquad \text{(safe)}$$

Design of heel
From Case II:

$$V_B = 9.34\,\text{kip}$$

$$\therefore \quad \text{maximum pile load} = 9.34 \times 8 = 74.6\,\text{kip} \qquad \text{(safe)}$$

Critical section for shear is at $\dfrac{d}{2} = 14.75''$, i.e. $4.17'$ from batter face. Thus:

$$V = 9.34 - (17.75 \times 4.17 \times 0.12) - (3.75 \times 4.17 \times 0.15)$$

$$= -2.01\,\text{kip}$$

$$\therefore \quad M = (9.34 \times 3.90) - [(17.75 \times 5.40 \times 0.12) - (3.75 \times 5.40 \times 0.15)]2.7$$

$$= 13.6\,\text{kip-ft}$$

From Case III:

$$V_B = 5.45\,\text{kip}$$

$$\therefore \quad M = (5.45 \times 3.90) - 22.8 = -1.5\,\text{kip-ft}$$

$$\therefore \quad A_S \text{ required at bottom} = \frac{13.6}{1.29 \times 29.5} = 0.36\,\text{in}^2$$

$$\therefore \quad \#8 \text{ @ } 18'' \text{ (carried over from toe will suffice)}$$

$$\therefore \quad A_S \text{ required at top} = \frac{1.5}{1.29 \times 29.5} = 0.04\,\text{in}^2$$

$$\therefore \quad \text{use } \#4 \text{ @ } 18'' \quad \text{(at the top)}$$

$$\Sigma_0 = 2.1\,\text{in}^2$$

$$\therefore \quad u = \frac{2010}{0.87 \times 29.5 \times 2.1} = 37.4\,\text{psi} \qquad \text{(therefore safe)}$$

$$\therefore \quad v = \frac{2010}{12.0 \times 0.87 \times 29.5} = 6.5\,\text{psi} \qquad \text{(therefore safe)}$$

$$\text{punching shear} = \frac{74\,600}{370} = 202\,\text{psi} \qquad \text{(therefore safe)}$$

Final design of abutment
Here, reference is made to Fig. 5.114.

Design of wing walls
Elevation at toe of shoulder slope at abutment is given by:

$$996.02 - 0.21 - 0.50 = 99.31\,\text{ft}$$

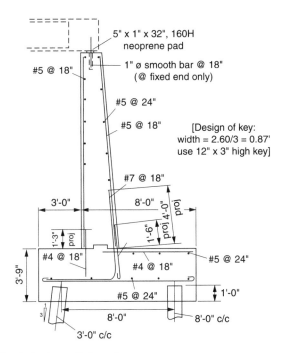

Figure 5.114. Final design of the abutment

Proposed stream bed elevation is 981.00 ft

∴ $H = 14.31$ ft

∴ length of wall $= 1.10H - 1.50 = 15.70 - 1.50 = 14.20$ ft

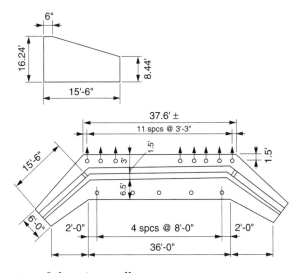

Figure 5.115. Design of the wing walls

Referring to Fig. 5.115:

$\qquad \therefore \quad$ adopt length $= 15'\text{-}6''$

$\qquad \therefore \quad h_2 = 0.63H - 1.20 = 7.80\,\text{ft}$

$\qquad (16.24 - 7.80 = 8.44\,\text{ft})$

5.2.13 Example (5.22)   British practice (cantilever wing wall)

A cantilever wing wall is 3 m high as shown in Fig. 5.116. The surcharge load is 0.33 m. The bridge span is 20 m supported on either side by the wall. The bridge reaction is 680 kN on the wall. The allowable bearing pressure is $200\,\text{kN/m}^2$.

Calculate the required reinforcement and check that all thicknesses shown are adequate. Check also the stability for this wall.

Abutment loads
Consider a 1 m length

$$\text{wall} = 0.5 \times 3.85 \times 23.6 = \quad 45.43\,\text{kN}$$

$$\text{base} = 0.5 \times 2.4 \times 23.6 = \quad 28.32\,\text{kN}$$

$$\text{earth on the toe} = 1 \times 3.85 \times 20 = \quad \underline{77\,\text{kN}}$$

$$\Sigma = 150.75\,\text{kN/m length}$$

$$\text{earth pressure } k_a \gamma h = 0.33 \times 20 \times 3.85 = 25.41$$

$$\text{surcharge} = 0.33 \times 10 = 3.3$$

$$\text{force due to earth pressure} = H_k = (25.45 \times 3.3)4.35 \times \tfrac{1}{2}$$

$$= 62.45\,\text{kN}$$

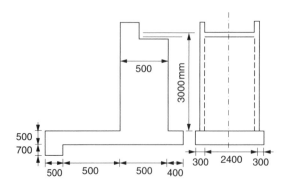

Figure 5.116. General layout of cantilever wing wall

Stability check

Sliding for no heel (at construction). Therefore:

$$\mu(1.0G_k + 1.0Q_u) \geq \gamma_f H_k$$

$$0.45(150.75) = 67.84$$

$$\gamma_f H_k = 99.2$$

$$67.65 \ngeq 99.92 \qquad \text{(therefore, heel needed)}$$

Consider a 700×500 heel:

$$H_{\text{passive}} = k_p \gamma h^2 = 3 \times 200.7^2 = 29.4\,\text{kN}$$

$$\therefore \quad 29.4 + 150.75 = 180.15 > 152 \qquad \text{(permitted)}$$

Overturning

Total moment about O:

$$\text{overturning moment} = \gamma_f H_k \times \tfrac{1}{3}h = 145\,\text{kNm}$$

$$\text{restraining moment} = 45.43 \times 1.15 + 28.32 + 77 \times 1.9$$

$$= 145 < 232.55 \qquad \text{(permitted)}$$

Bearing pressure

$$P = \frac{N}{D} \pm \frac{GM}{D^2}$$

$$M = 62.45 \times \frac{4.35}{3} + 45.43(1.2 - 1.15) + 77(1.2 - 2.4)$$

$$= 0.422\,\text{kNm}$$

$$\text{maximum bearing pressure } P_1 = \frac{150.75}{2.4} + \frac{6 \times 0.422}{2.4^2}$$

$$= 53.25\,\text{kN/m}^2 < 200\,\text{kN/m}^2 \quad \text{(permitted)}$$

Reinforcement

Loads and reactions are illustrated in Fig. 5.117. Thus:

$$\sum M_A = 1.2 \times 12.5 \times 1.25 - 28.32 \times 0.05 - 11.25 \times 68 \times 0.05$$

$$- 117 \times 1.2 + 107 \times 1.2$$

$$\sum M_A = 654\,\text{kNm}$$

$$d_c = 500 - 43 = 457\,\text{mm}$$

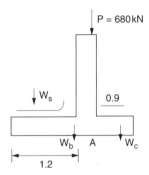

Figure 5.117. Schematic for reinforcement in design calculations

$$\frac{M}{bd^2} = \frac{654 \times 10^6}{3000 \times 457^2} = 1.04$$

$$\frac{100 A_S}{bd} = 0.26$$

$$\therefore \quad A_S = 3569\,\text{mm}^2$$

Therefore, use 18T16-160 steel ($A_S = 3619\,\text{mm}^2$) for the toe.

5.2.14 Example (5.23) British practice
A bridge deck is partially supported by a retaining wall as shown in Fig. 5.118. Below the deck there is an earth fill with the following data:

$$\text{wall} = 9.4\,\text{m}$$

$$N = 10$$

$$\phi = 50°$$

$$\gamma_s = 20\,\text{kN/m}^3$$

$$\gamma_c = 23.6\,\text{kN/m}^3$$

For:

$$\phi' = 30°$$

$$k_n = \frac{1 - \sin\phi'}{1 + \sin\phi} = 0.33$$

$$\therefore \quad k_D = 3.0$$

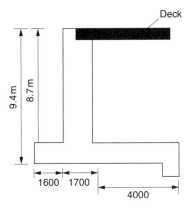

Figure 5.118. Retaining-type wing wall

Load:

$$45.1 + \frac{120}{6.5} = 163.56$$

$$h = 8.1\,\text{m} + 0.6\,\text{m} \qquad \text{(assumed)}$$

$$= 8.7\text{m}$$

Check stability of the structure and design the reinforcement for this wall. The moment on the wall is 16.497 kNm and the wall carries an axial reaction from the deck of 968.57 kN (total).

Stability

$$P + k_A\gamma_s h = 0.33 \times 20 \times 8.7 = 57.42\,\text{kN/m}^2$$

Therefore horizontal force on 1 m length of wall is

$$H_k = 0.5Ph = 0.5 \times 57.42 \times 8.7 = 249.78\,\text{kN}$$

Vertical loads

$$\text{wall} = \tfrac{1}{2} \times 0.7 \times 8.1 \times 23.6 = 124.25\,\text{kN}$$
$$\text{base} = 0.6 \times 7 \times 23.6 = 99.12\,\text{kN}$$
$$\text{earth} = 4.6 \times 8.1 \times 20 = \underline{745.2\,\text{kN}}$$
$$\text{total} = 968.57\,\text{kN}$$

Sliding force

$$\mu(0.9G_k + 0.9V_k) \geq \gamma_f H_x \text{ for no heel beam.}$$

Assuming a value of coefficient of friction $\mu = 0.5$:

frictional resisting force $= 0.5 \times 0.9 \times 968.57 = 435.86\,\text{kN}$

sliding force $= 1.6 \times 249.78 = 399.65\,\text{kN}$

Because the sliding force is greater than the frictional force, passive earth pressure also gives resistance:

$$H_p = \gamma_f \times 0.5 \times k_p \gamma_s a^2$$

$$= 0.9 \times 0.5 \times 3 \times 20 \times 1.2^2 = 38.88\,\text{kN}$$

$$a = \text{depth of heel}$$

$\therefore$ total resisting force $= 399.65 + 38.88 = 438.5\,\text{kN}$

which is greater than the sliding force.

Overturning

Taking moments about point A at the edge of the toe at the ultimate limit state:

$$\text{overturning moment} = \gamma_f H_k \frac{h}{3}$$

$$= 1.6 \times 249.78 \times \frac{8.7}{3}$$

$$= 1154\,\text{kNm} = M_0$$

$$\text{restraining moment} = 0.9(124.25 \times 2.0 + 99.12 \times 3.5 + 745.2 \times 4.7)$$

$$= 4097.86\,\text{kNm}$$

Therefore, the overturning criterion is satisfied.

Bearing pressures

$$P = \frac{N}{D} \pm \frac{6M}{D^2}$$

($M = $ moment about base centre-line)

$$\therefore \quad M = 249.78 \times \frac{8.7}{3} + 124.25(3.5 - 2)$$

$$+ 745.2(3.5 - 4.7) = 16.497\,\text{kNm}$$

Thus, the maximum bearing pressure is:

$$P_1 = \frac{968.57}{7} + \frac{6 \times 16.497}{7^2} = 190.38\,\text{kN/m}^2$$

$$< 200\,\text{kN/m}^2 \qquad \text{(permitted)}$$

Bending reinforcement
(i)   Wall

$$\text{horizontal force} = \gamma_f \times 0.5 k_a \gamma_s h^2$$

$$= 1.6 \times 0.5 \times 0.33 \times 20 \times 8.7^2$$

$$= 399.64\,\text{kN}$$

Considering the effective span, the maximum moment is given by:

$$M = 399.64 \left(0.3 + \frac{8.5}{3} \right) = 1198.92$$

$$d = 600 - 70 = 530$$

$$\frac{M}{bd^2 f_{cu}} = \frac{1198.92 \times 10^6}{1000 \times 530^2 \times 40} = 0.1067$$

lever arm $z = 0.75d$

$$\frac{M}{bd^2} = 0.1067 \times 40 = 4.268$$

$$f_y = 460\,\text{N/mm}^2$$

$$A_S = \frac{1198.2 \times 10^6}{0.75 \times 530 \times 0.87 \times 460} = 7532\,\text{mm}^2/\text{m}$$

$$\frac{100 A_S}{bd} = \frac{7532 \times 100}{1000 \times 530} = 1.27$$

Provide T40 bars at 125 mm centres (T46-150 c/c).

(ii)   Base
The critical partial factors of safety are:

$$\gamma_{f1} = 1.6$$

$$\gamma_{f2} \text{ and } \gamma_{f3} = 1.0$$

$$M = 1.6 \times 724.36 \times 1 \times 186.375 - 1 \times 894.24$$

$$= 451.135\,\text{kNm}$$

$$N = \gamma_{f2}(124.25 + 99.12) + \gamma_{f3} \times 745.2$$

$$= 968.57\,\text{kN}$$

$$\therefore \quad \text{pressure } P_1 = \frac{968.57}{7} + \frac{451.135 \times 6}{7^2} = 193.61\,\text{kN/m}^2$$

$$P_2 = 138.367 - 55.24 = 83.13\,\text{kN/m}^2$$

$$P_3 = 83.12 + 72.6 = 155.72\,\text{kN/m}^2$$

Heel

Taking moments about the stem centre-line for vertical loads and the bearing pressure:

$$M = \left(\gamma_{f0} \times 99.12 \times 27 \times \frac{4.6}{70}\right) + (\gamma_{f3} \times 745.2 \times 2.7)$$

$$- (83.13 \times 4.6 \times 2.7) - \left(155.72 - 83.13 \times \frac{4.6}{2} \times 1.73\right)$$

$$= 866.61 \, \text{kNm}$$

$$A_S = \frac{866.61 \times 10^6}{0.87 \times 460 \times 0.75 \times 530} = 5447.3 \, \text{mm}^2/\text{m}$$

Therefore, use T32-125 steel bars.

Toe

Taking moments about the stem centre-line:

$$M = -\gamma_{f2} \times 99.12 \times 1.2 \times \frac{1.6}{7} = \gamma_{f3} \times 193.61 \times 1.6 \times 1.2$$

$$= -344.55 \, \text{kNm}$$

$$A_S = \frac{344.55 \times 10^6}{0.87 \times 460 \times 0.75 \times 530} = 2166.14 \, \text{mm}^2/\text{m}$$

Provide T20 bars at 125 mm centres, bottom steel ($A_S = 2513 \, \text{mm}^2/\text{m}$).

Bending reinforcement is required in the heel beam to resist the moment due to the passive earth pressure. This reinforcement would probably be in the form of closed links.

Longitudinal distribution steel is also required in the wall and base. The minimum area for this is:

$$A_S = 0.12 \times 1000 \times 600 = 720 \, \text{mm}^2/\text{m}$$

Provide T12 bars at 125 mm centres ($A_S = 905 \, \text{mm}^2/\text{m}$).

Check dead load, KEL and HA

$$\text{slab} \ (0.16 \, \text{m}) = 3.776 \, \text{kN/m}$$

$$\text{surface} \ (0.1 \, \text{m}) = 7.000 \, \text{kN/m}$$

$$\text{parapet} = 0.500 \, \text{kN/m}$$

$$\underline{\text{HA} + \text{KEL} = 63.500 \, \text{kN/m}}$$

$$69.776 \, \text{kN/m} \approx 70 \, \text{kN/m}$$

Restoring moment $= 70 \times 2 \times 4 = 560\,\text{kNm}$

vertical moment $= 968.57 + 560 = 1328\,\text{kNm}$

The reinforcement provided is more than enough.

5.2.15 Example (5.24) Pakistan/Indian practice

Beams of various mass for the north and south abutments that support them are shown in Fig. 5.119. The abutments with various loads are also shown in Fig.

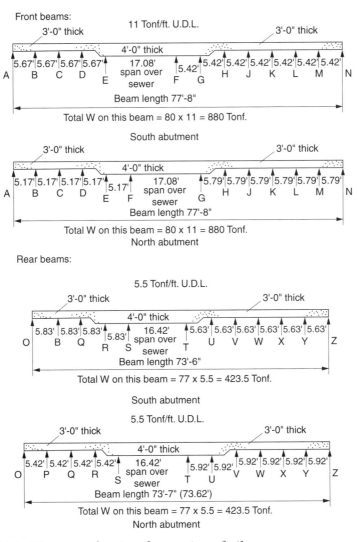

Figure 5.119. Diagrams showing the spacing of piles

5.119. Table 5.36 shows the basic data with important additional dimensions given below:

bridge span clear 27'-6" (8.382 m)

bridge span effective = 42 ft (12.8 m)

Table 5.36. Abutment calculations

Abutment calculations
The abutments and wing walls to be mass, unreinforced concrete with brick facing which will serve as shuttering during abutment construction. From soil report, adopt $\phi = 35°$ and bulk density 110 lbf/ft^3.

Surcharge loadings
(Before placing the deck slab).
(i)   Highway including impact   220 lbf/ft^2
(ii) Road structure
      4" HRA surfacing   60 lbf/ft^2
      10" dense bitmac base   140 lbf/ft^2
      6" hardcore sub-base   60 lbf/ft^2

$\overline{\hspace{6cm}}$

        Total surcharge   480 lbf/ft^2

$$\text{Rankine coefficient, } K_a = \frac{1 - \sin\phi}{1 + \sin\phi} = \frac{1 - \sin 35°}{1 + \sin 35} = 0.27$$

$$\text{Equivalent height} = h_e = \frac{w_s}{w} = \frac{480}{110} = 4.36 \text{ ft}$$

$$\text{Active pressure due to surcharge} = P_S = K_2 \cdot w \cdot h_e$$

$$\therefore \quad P_S = 0.27 \times 4.3 \times 110$$

$$\therefore \quad P_S = 130 \text{ lbf/ft}^2$$

At any depth h the active pressure

$$P = K_2 \cdot w \cdot h + P_S$$

$$= (0.27 \times 110 \times 21.5) + 130$$

$$= 640 + 130 = 770 \text{ lbf/ft}^2$$

Taking moments to find resultant P_R:

$$\frac{(7.16 \times 640 \times 21.5)}{2} + (10.75 \times 130 \times 21.5) = P_R \cdot \bar{y}$$

$$\therefore \quad \bar{y} = \frac{49\,400 + 30\,050}{6890 + 2795} = \frac{79\,450}{9685} = 8.2 \text{ ft}$$

Total pressure = 9685 lbf/ft run acting at 8.2 ft up from base of pile caps.
    Moment about 'T':

$$9685 \times 8.2 = 79\,450 \text{ lbf/ft} = P_a \cdot \bar{y}$$

Depth of prestressed concrete beams 18.4″ (467 mm) to 12.8″ (325 mm) with

$$\text{average depth} = 15.6'' \ (396\,\text{mm})$$

$$\text{hot-rolled asphalt} = 4\tfrac{1}{2}'' \ (114\,\text{mm})$$

Obtain the final pressure diagram based on the model (Fig. 5.120).

Solution
Stability before placing the deck slab and after backfilling:

$$
\begin{aligned}
w_1 &= 13.25 \times 6 & \times 145 &= 11\,528\,\text{lbf} \\
w_2 &= 3.5 \times 7 & \times 145 &= 3\,552\,\text{lbf} \\
w_3 &= 1.5 \times 8 & \times 145 &= 1\,740\,\text{lbf} \\
w_4 &= 3 & \times 9.25 \times 150 &= 4\,163\,\text{lbf} \\
w_5 &= 13.25 \times 1 & \times 100 &= 1\,325\,\text{lbf}
\end{aligned}
$$

$$\left.\begin{aligned}w_1 \\ w_2 \\ w_3 \\ w_4\end{aligned}\right\} \quad 20\,983\,\text{lbf}$$

$$\therefore \quad W = 22\,308\,\text{lbf}$$

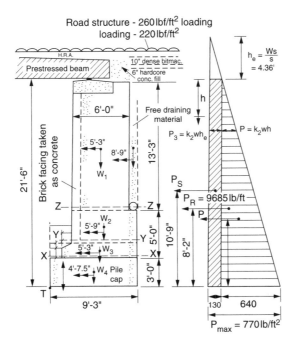

Figure 5.120. Model pressure diagram where pile cap assumed monolithic with the abutment

Moments about toe 'T'

$$11\,528 \times 5.25 = \quad 60\,522\,\text{lbf.ft}$$
$$3\,552 \times 5.75 = \quad 20\,429\,\text{lbf.ft}$$
$$1\,740 \times 5.25 = \quad\; 9\,135\,\text{lbf.ft} \Bigg\} \quad 109\,361\,\text{lbf.ft}$$
$$4\,163 \times 4.63 = \quad 19\,275\,\text{lbf.ft}$$
$$1\,325 \times 8.75 = \quad 11\,594\,\text{lbf.ft}$$

$$\therefore \quad W\bar{x} = 120\,955\,\text{lbf.ft}$$

Hence

$$\bar{x} = \frac{120\,955}{22\,308} = 5.42\,\text{ft}$$

Factor of safety against overturning about 'T':

$$= \frac{W\bar{x}}{P_{\text{a}} \cdot \bar{y}} = \frac{120\,955}{79\,450} = 1.52$$

which will improve with the provision of piles!
   Now:

$$\frac{L}{6} = \frac{9.25}{6} = 1.54\,\text{ft}$$

and

$$'e' = \frac{P_{\text{a}} \cdot \bar{y}}{W} + \frac{L}{2} - \bar{x}$$

$$= \frac{79\,450}{22\,308} + 4.63 - 5.42$$

$$= 3.56 + 4.63 - 5.42 = 2.77\,\text{ft}$$

which is greater than $L/6$ by $15''$.

Data

Clear span of bridge $= 27'6''$ normal to the abutments. Effective span $= 42\,\text{ft}$.
Depth of prestressed beams varies from $18.4''$ to $12.8''$ giving an average depth of
$15.6''$. Hot rolled asphalt has, say, average thickness $4\frac{1}{2}''$.
   Consider 1 ft width of bridge:
   Dead load on one abutment:

(i)	Deck beams $21 \times 1.3 \times 150$	$=$	$3\,705\,\text{lbf}$
(ii)	Surfacing $21 \times 4.5 \times 15$	$=$	$1\,283\,\text{lbf}$
(iii)	Loading including impact $= 21 \times 220 =$		$4\,180\,\text{lbf}$
(iv)	Knife-edge loading	$=$	$2\,700\,\text{lbf}$
	Total load on one abutment	$=$	$11\,868\,\text{lbf}$

Stability after placing deck slab and before placing the back fill

self weight of abutment $= 20\,983\,\text{lbf}\ (W)$

moment about 'T' $= 109\,361\,\text{lbf.ft}\ (W\bar{x})$

$$\therefore \quad \bar{x} = \frac{109\,361}{20\,983} = 5.22\,\text{ft}$$

Distance from toe 'T' to ₵ of bearing of beams $= 3.75\,\text{ft}$

Moment due to deck loading about toe 'T' $= 11\,868 \times 3.75 = 44\,505\,\text{lbf.ft}$

$$\text{FOS} = \frac{\text{righting moment}}{\text{overturning moment}} = \frac{109\,361}{44\,505}$$

$$= 2.45 \text{ which is OK!}$$

Stability after placing both the deck slab and the fill behind the abutment

$W_T = 34\,176\,\text{lbf per ft run}$

To find $\bar{x}_T$ (Fig. 5.121):

$$\bar{x}_T = \frac{(11\,868 \times 3.75) + (22\,308 \times 5.4)}{34\,176}$$

$$= \frac{44\,505 + 120\,955}{34\,176}$$

$$= \frac{165\,460}{34\,176}$$

$$= 4.85\,\text{ft}$$

$$\text{FOS} = \frac{W_T \cdot \bar{x}_T}{P_a \cdot y} = \frac{165\,460}{79\,450} = 2.08 \text{ which is OK}$$

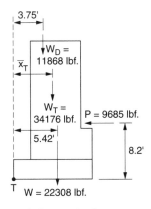

Figure 5.121. Schematic for stability calculations

Now:

$$\frac{L}{6} = 1.54 \, \text{ft}$$

and

$$e = \frac{P_a \cdot \bar{y}}{W_T} + \frac{L}{2} - \bar{x}_T$$

$$= \frac{79\,450}{34\,176} + 4.63 - 4.85$$

$$= 2.32 + 4.63 - 4.85$$

$$\therefore \quad e = 2.1 \, \text{ft. which is greater than } L/6 \text{ by } 6\tfrac{3}{4}''$$

Ground pressure after placing deck slab and backfilling
When

$$e > \frac{L}{6} \qquad P = \left[\frac{4L}{3(L - 2e)}\right] \frac{W_T}{L}$$

$$\therefore \quad P = \frac{34\,176 \times 4 \times 9.25}{2240 \times 9.25 \times 3(9.25 - 4.2)}$$

$$= \frac{5.08 \times 4}{5.05} = \frac{20.32}{5.05} = 4.02 \, \text{tonf/ft}^2 \text{ per ft run}$$

Note that the soil report states that the safe bearing capacity of the soil is 1.41 tf/ft^2.
   This confirms the need for piles:

$$R = \sqrt{15.25^2 + 4.31^2}$$

$$= 15.88 \, \text{tons at } 2'6'' \text{ from front face of the pile cap}$$

$$\cos \alpha = \frac{15.25}{15.88} = 0.96 = 16\tfrac{1}{2}° \quad (16°12')$$

$$\tan \beta = \frac{15.25}{4.31} = 3.54 = 74°12'$$

Therefore say angle of rake on piles $= 16°$ to vertical, i.e. 1 in $3\tfrac{1}{2}$.

Stresses in concrete
Active pressures at selected cross-sections:

$$P_{a_{xx}} = (0.27 \times 110 \times 18.5) + 130 = 550 + 130 = 680 \, \text{lbf}$$

$$\therefore \quad 680 \times \frac{18.5}{2} = 680 \times 9.25 = 6290 \, \text{lbf/ft}$$

$$P_{a_{yy}} = (0.27 \times 110 \times 17) + 130 = 505 + 130$$

$$\therefore \quad 635 \times \frac{17}{2} = 635 \times 8.5 = 5398\,\text{lbf/ft}$$

$$P_{a_{zz}} = (0.27 \times 110 \times 13.5) + 130 = 401 + 130 = 531\,\text{lbf}$$

$$\therefore \quad 551 \times 6.25 = 3584\,\text{lbf/ft}$$

Consider plane x–x about ℄ of the abutment

$$\text{Moment due to } P_a = 6290 \times \frac{18.5}{3} = 6290 \times 6.2 = 38\,998\,\text{lbf.ft}$$

Moment due to eccentrically loaded W_D

$$= 11\,868 \times (5.22 - 3.75)$$

$$= 11\,868 \times 1.47 = 16\,998\,\text{lbf.ft}$$

$$\therefore \quad \text{total moment} = 38\,998$$
$$\underline{16\,998}$$
$$55\,996\,\text{lbf.ft}$$

$$\text{Total moment} = 671\,952\,\text{lbf.in.}$$

$$I \text{ of plane } x\text{–}x = \frac{bd^3}{12} = \frac{12}{12} \times 96^3 = 884\,736\,\text{in}^4$$

Now:

$$f = \frac{My}{I} = \frac{671\,952 \times 48}{884\,736}$$

Therefore stresses in concrete at x–$x = 36\frac{1}{2}\,\text{lbf/in}^2$ which is negligible.

Similarly consider plane y–y about ℄ of the abutment

$$\text{Moment due to } P_a = 5398 \times \frac{17}{3} = 30\,552\,\text{lbf.ft}$$

$$\text{Moment due to loading } W_D = 16\,998\,\text{lbf.ft}$$
$$\underline{}$$
$$47\,550\,\text{lbf.ft}$$

$$\therefore \quad \text{total moment} = 570\,600\,\text{lbf.in}$$

$$f = \frac{My}{I} = \frac{570\,600 \times 42}{592\,702} = 40\frac{1}{2}\,\text{lbf/in}^2 \text{ (which is satisfactory)}$$

$$I = \frac{bd^3}{12} = \frac{12}{12} \times 84^3 = 592\,702\,\text{in}^4$$

Similarly consider plane zz

$$\text{Moment due to } P_a = 3584 \times \frac{13.5}{3}$$

$$= 3584 \times 4.5 = \quad 16\,128 \text{ lbf.ft}$$

$$\text{Moment due to } W_D = \quad 16\,998 \text{ lbf.ft}$$

$$\overline{\phantom{33\,126 \text{ lbf.ft}}}$$

$$33\,126 \text{ lbf.ft}$$

$$\therefore \quad \text{total moment} = 397\,512 \text{ lbf.in}$$

$$I = \frac{12}{12} \times 72^3 = 373\,248 \text{ in}^4$$

$$f = \frac{397\,512 \times 36}{373\,248} = 38\tfrac{1}{2} \text{ lbf.in}^2$$

Notes

As all these stresses are so small unreinforced concrete is suitable.

The foregoing calculations are based on the 'idea' that the abutments and pile caps are monolithic . The method of construction is likely to be such that it is unlikely to be so unless some form of steel is used (e.g. 'L' connectors) to overcome this difficulty.

Calculation for 'Shear Connectors' between abutment and pile caps

Consider moments about point 'S' at junction of abutment with pile cap under, then we get:

$$\text{Moment due to } P_a = 9\,685 \times 4.5 \times 12$$

$$= 524\,000 \text{ lb.in}$$

Moment due to eccentric deck loading

$$= 11\,563 \times (4.7 - 3.8) \times 12 = 138\,756 \text{ lbf.in}$$

$$\therefore \quad \text{total moment} = 662\,756 \text{ lbf.in}$$

Adopting l_a as 84″ then

$$A_{st} = \frac{662\,756}{20\,000 \times 0.857 \times 84} = \frac{33.14}{72}$$

$$= 0.46 \text{ in}^2.$$

Therefore 1 No. 1 diameter MS bar (0.785 in^2) per ft run of abutment will suffice and provide a factor of safety. The minimum bond length required $= 42d$ (i.e. say $3'6''$ for each leg of 'L').

Consider sliding of abutment along surface of pile caps with a skin friction value of $\mu = 0.4$

$$\text{Force causing sliding} = 9685\,\text{lbf}$$

$$\text{Force resisting sliding} = 0.4(34\,176 - 4163)$$

$$= 0.4 \times 30\,013$$

$$= 12\,050\,\text{lbf}$$

Therefore skin friction will resist sliding.

Check for resistance to sliding

Resistance to sliding is given by the frictional resistance of the soil under the base plus the passive resistance (if any) of the soil in front of the wall.

There should be a factor of safety of about 2 against sliding, therefore:

$$\frac{F + P}{R_{\text{H}}} \text{ should} = 2$$

where R_{H} is the force causing sliding which is the horizontal component of resultant R. F is the frictional resistance of the soil which may be taken as $R_{\text{V}} \tan \phi$ for a concrete foundation cast *in situ*. P is the positive resistance of the soil. R_{V} is the vertical component of the resultant R. ($\phi = 35° = $ angle of internal friction of soil.) Then:

$$\text{passive resistance } P_{\text{p}} = \tfrac{1}{2}K_{\text{p}} \times \gamma D^2$$

where

$$K_{\text{p}} = \frac{1 + \sin \phi}{1 - \sin \phi} = \frac{1 + 0.57}{1 - 0.57} = \frac{1.57}{0.43} = 3.65$$

$$\therefore \quad P_{\text{p}} = 3.65 \times \frac{120 \times 36}{2} = 7880\,\text{lbf}$$

and

$$F \doteqdot R_{\text{V}} \tan \phi = 34\,176 \times \tan 35°$$

$$= 34\,176 \times 0.7 = 23\,900\,\text{lbf}$$

$$\therefore \quad F \text{ and } P = 23\,900$$

$$\underline{7\,880}$$

$$\underline{31\,780\,\text{lbf}}$$

$$\therefore \quad \text{FOS (FS) against sliding} = \frac{31\,780}{9685} = 3.28 \quad \text{(which is satisfactory).}$$

The resulting final pressure diagram is given in Fig. 5.122.

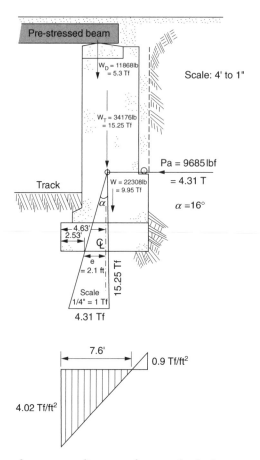

Figure 5.122. Ground pressure diagram from calculations

5.2.16 Example (5.25) British practice

A pile cap shown in Fig. 5.123 is subjected to the following loads and moments:

$$\text{superimposed dead load} = 3249.42\,\text{kN}$$

$$\text{live load} = 8503.5\,\text{kN} \quad (\text{factored total} = 16\,666.2\,\text{kN})$$

$$M_{xx} = 438.8\,\text{kNm}$$

$$M_{yy} = 1088.53\,\text{kNm}$$

Piles No. 8: pile cap size 4.68 m × 5.2 m × 150 mm thick:

$$\text{down load of cap} = 24 \times 4.68 \times 5.2 \times 1.75 \times 1.5 = 1209\,\text{kN}$$

$$\text{modulus of pile group} = \frac{\sum d^2}{d}$$

$$\sum d^2 = \text{group inertia}$$

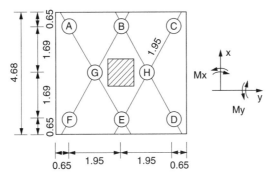

Figure 5.123. Column and pile layout for Example (5.25)

$$y-y = 6 \times 1.69^2 = 17.13\,\text{m}^2$$

$$x-x = 4 \times 1.95^2 + 2 \times 0.975^2 = 17.13\,\text{m}^2$$

$$\frac{\text{direct load}}{\text{pile}} = \frac{(16\,666.2 + 1209.0)}{8} = 2234.4\,\text{kN}$$

Load/pile due to bending
For y–y:

$$\text{force in A, B, C, D, E, F} = \frac{1088.53 \times 1.69}{17.13} = 107.4\,\text{kN}$$

For x–x:

$$\text{force in C, D, F, A} = \frac{438.8 \times 1.95}{17.13} = 49.95\,\text{kN}$$

$$\text{force in G, H} = \frac{438.8 \times 0.975}{17.13} = 24.97\,\text{kN}$$

A summary of loadings is provided in Table 5.37.

Table 5.37. Load/pile bending loads

Pile mark	Direct load	Bending load		Total	Ultimate
		x–x	y–y		
A, C, D, F	2234.4	49.95	107.4	2391.73	<2400
B, E	2234.4	–	107.4	2341.8	<2400
H, G	2234.4	24.97	–	2259.4	<2400

Moments and shear condition

Moment due to cantilever action x–x:

$$\max M_{x-x}^{\mathrm{R}} = 2 \times (2234.4 + 49.95) \times 1.95 + (2234.4 + 24.97) \times 0.975$$

$$= 11\,111.85\,\mathrm{kNm}$$

$$\max M_{x-x}^{\mathrm{L}} = 11\,111.85 - 438.8 = 10\,673.05$$

$$\max M_{y-y}^{\mathrm{R}} = 3 \times (2234.4 + 107.4) \times 1.69 = 11\,872.9\,\mathrm{kNm}$$

Relevant moment diagrams are given in Fig. 5.124.

Bending reinforcement

If 50 mm cover to 12 mm links and 32 mm bars is assumed, then:

For x–x:

$$d = 1500 - 50 - 12 - 16 = 1422$$

and

$$b = \frac{\max M}{f_{\mathrm{cu}}bd^2} = \frac{11\,872.92 \times 10^6}{60 \times 5200 \times 1422^2} = 0.0188 \quad \Rightarrow \quad \frac{z}{d} = 0.978$$

$$z = 1391.6$$

$$A_{\mathrm{S}}\,(\text{required}) = \frac{\max M}{0.87 \times f_y \times z} = \frac{11\,872.92 \times 10^6}{0.87 \times 460 \times 1391.6} = 21\,318.7\,\mathrm{mm}^2$$

Provide 27T32 steel bars:

$$A_{\mathrm{S}} = 21\,708\,\mathrm{mm}^2$$

$$\rho = 0.0029$$

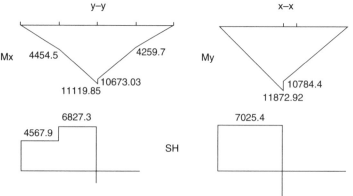

Figure 5.124. Moments and shear diagrams

For y–y:

$$d = 1422 - 32 = 1390$$

$$b = \frac{11\,111.83 \times 10^6}{60 \times 4680 \times 1390^2} = 0.0205 \quad \Rightarrow \quad \frac{z}{d} = 0.976$$

$$z = 1357.6$$

$$A_S \text{ (required)} = \frac{11\,111.83 \times 10^6}{0.87 \times 460 \times 1357.6} = 20\,451.8 \text{ mm}^2$$

Provide 26T32 steel bars:

$$A_S = 20\,904 \text{ mm}^2$$

$$\rho = 0.0032$$

According to BS 8110 the critical shear is located at a distance of $650/5 = 130$ mm from the inner face of the above piles, i.e.

For x–x:

$$1690 - \frac{1000}{2} - \frac{650}{2} + 130 = 995 = 0.699d > 0.6 < 2d$$

This is the full tension anchorage–bond length

$$\left.\begin{array}{l} L = \dfrac{0.87 \times f_y \times \phi}{4f_{bu}} \\[2mm] f_{bu} = 0.28\sqrt{f_{cu}} = 2.17 \\[2mm] L = \dfrac{0.87 \times 460 \times 32}{4 \times 2.17} = 1476.2 \text{ mm} \end{array}\right\} \quad \text{for values} > 0.6d$$

or

$$\left.\begin{array}{l} 12\phi = 384 \\ d = 1422 \end{array}\right\} < 2d$$

For intermediate values interpolation of these two limits gives:

$$1476.2 - \left[\frac{(1476.2 - 1422)(0.699 - 0.6)}{(2 - 0.6)}\right] = 1473 \text{ mm}$$

Bars in both directions will be bent for 90° and extend to the top of the pile cap. Thus:

for x–x:

$$V_{max} = 7025.4 \text{ kN}$$

$$V_c = 1.165 \times 0.425 = 0.495$$

$$\rho = 0.002 = 0.29\%$$

Permissible value for V_c can be increased to

$$\frac{2dV_c}{a_v} = \frac{2 \times 1422.0 \times 0.495}{995} = 1.41 \,\text{N/mm}^2$$

Then shear resistance of concrete is:

$$V_c \times b \times d = 1415 \times 5200 \times 1422 = 7360.52 > 7025.4 \,\text{kN} \qquad \text{(allowed)}$$

and for y–y:

$$\left.\begin{array}{l} V_{max} = 6327.3 \,\text{kN} \\ \rho = 0.032 \end{array}\right\} \quad \Rightarrow \quad v_c = 1.165 \times 0.427 = 0.497$$

$$a_v = 1950 - \frac{1000}{2} - \frac{650}{2} + \frac{650}{5} = 1225 = 0.9d < 2d > 0.6d$$

and

$$\frac{2 \times v_c \times d}{a_v} = \frac{2 \times 0.497 \times 1390}{1225} = 1.13 \quad \text{(therefore same anchorage)}$$

$$V_u = 1.13 \times 4680 \times 1390 = 7337.12 > 6827.3 \,\text{kN} \qquad \text{(allowed)}$$

Suitable bending reinforcement is illustrated in Fig. 5.125.

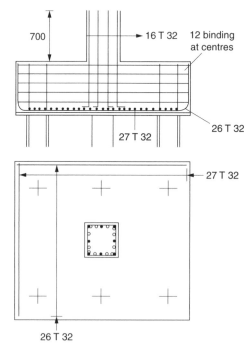

Figure 5.125. Pile cap reinforcement

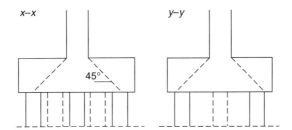

Figure 5.126. Caps on piles – punching shear

Punching shear

From Fig. 5.126 it is seen that load spread of the column embraces all the piles. No calculation for punching shear is required. A check will be made only around column perimeter:

$$V_c = \frac{16\,666.2 \times 10^3}{4 \times 1000 \times 1422} = 2.93\,\text{N/mm}^2 < 5\,\text{N/mm}^2 \qquad \text{(allowed)}$$

Referring to Fig. 5.127, the layout of piles will be done for columns A and C.

Column A (piles)

$$\max N = 11\,949.5 + [(0.8 \times 10 \times 0.6) = (5.07 \times 10 \times 1.3)] \times 24 \times 1.75$$

$$= 12\,102.7\,\text{kN}$$

$$\max M_x = 0.5 \times 5194.46 = 2597.23\,\text{kN}$$

$$\max M_y = 0.5 \times 2663.62 = 1331.81\,\text{kN}$$

$$\frac{\text{direct load}}{\text{pile}} = \frac{12\,102.7 + 1209.0}{8} = 1664.0\,\text{kN}$$

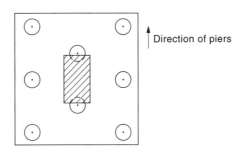

Figure 5.127. General pile arrangement

Load due to bending is

for y–y:

$$\text{force in C, D, F, A} = \frac{1331.89 \times 1.95}{17.13} = \pm 151.61 \,\text{kN}$$

$$\text{force in G, H} = \frac{1331.89 \times 0.975}{17.13} = \pm 75.8 \,\text{kN}$$

for x–x:

$$\text{force in A, B, C, D, E, F} = \frac{2597.23 \times 1.69}{17.13} = 256.23 \,\text{kN}$$

Thus, total force in A

$$= 256.23 + 151.61 + 16\,640 = 2071.8 < 2400 \,\text{kN} \qquad \text{(allowed)}$$

Column C (piles)

$$P_{\max} = 5772.2 + [5.07 \times 1.0^2 \times 24 \times 1.15] = 5912.13$$

Number of piles

$$n = \frac{5912.13}{2400} = 2.46$$

Provide 3 piles as arranged in Fig. 5.128.

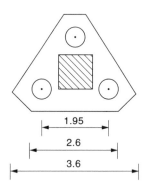

Figure 5.128. Specific pile cap with three piles

SECTION 6
SUSPENSION AND
CABLE-STAYED BRIDGES

6. Suspension and cable-stayed bridges

6.1 Suspension bridges

The construction of suspension bridges with stiffening girders began at the end of 1750. However, it is only recently that suspension bridges have been able to display long-span capabilities. Additional developments include single and double-deck systems, wind and earthquake-resistant designs, cable fabrication and erection technology, fabrication and erection of stiffening girders, towers, saddles, foundation technology (seabed excavation, caisson placement, scour protection, underwater concreting, etc.) and barge impact and hydraulic buffers.

The erection of a suspension bridge involves many challenges with respect to safety and time schedules. Modern computing methods for investigating the different stages of construction are a great help for planning and detailing the erection-work programme. Advanced wind stability calculations and wind tunnel tests also create a safe basis for bridge erection.

Where suspension bridges are subject to wind loading, a lack of analysis during flutter can be crucial to building. A special flutter analysis is therefore needed.

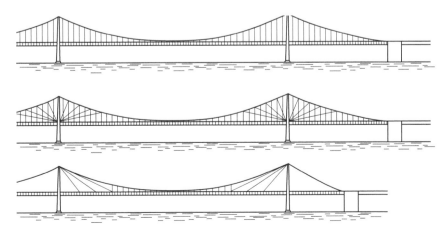

Figure 6.1. Typical cable formation of a suspension bridge

Damping and other systems are needed to minimize deck and tower vibrations and wind and seismic conditions. For suspension bridges simple static problems are introduced. This section contains data on wind and seismic activities. They can be invoked in order to pursue detailed analysis of suspension bridge construction. A comprehensive bibliography on this subject to support the analysis is also provided. A typical suspension bridge is shown in Fig. 6.1. Table 6.1 shows some well-known suspension bridges and their technical parameters. Plate 6.1 shows a suspension bridge of the Great Belt Link designed by the consortium COWI and Hochtief of Denmark and Germany respectively.

Table 6.1. Data on some important suspension bridges

Suspension bridge	Main span (m)	Span 1 (m)	Span 2 (m)	Carriageway (m)	Data for components
1. Tacoma (USA)	854	335	335	18.20 × 10 m high	
2. Verrazo Bridge (Italy)	1298	178	178		
3. Tancarville Bridge (Portugal)	608	176	176		
4. Akashi-Kaikyo (Japan)	1990	890	890		
5. Humber (UK)	1410	530	280		
6. Askoy (Norway)	850			15.50 by 3 m high	2-21 (99 mm) lock-coil strands with 289 galvanized wires in 11 layer
7. Sing Ma (Hong Kong)	355	80	48	28.40	
8. Höga Kustin (Sweden)	1210	310	280	22.0 by 4 m high	Tower: 178 m A-shaped
9. Severn (UK)	987.6	305	305	22.86 by 4.5 m high	
10. Williamsburg (USA)	487.7	18.18	18.18		Suspenders 44.50 mm rope
11. Köln-Rodenkirchen Rhine (Germany)	378	94.5	94.5	913.2 m × 3.3 m high	Tower: 56.873 m H-shaped
12. Stuttgart, Necker (Germany)	114.0			3.6 m	Tower: 21.5 m
13. Elche (Spain)	164.50	87.45	40.23		Tower: 24.0 m
14. Swiss Bay (Czech)	252.0	30.0	30.0		
15. San Francisco Oakland (USA)	704	353	353		
16. Golden Gate	1280	343	343		
17. Beauharnois, Quebec (Canada)	176.695	54.483	54.483	9.14 by 2.591 m	Tower: 22.263 m A-shaped

Plate 6.1. Eastern Bridge, Great Belt Link, Tra, Mare Del Norde (COWI Consult A/S and Hochtief AG Contractor)

6.2   Analytical examples of suspension bridges

Example (6.1)   Suspension bridges (Pakistani practice)
The following data are associated with a single-span suspension bridge shown in
Fig. 6.2:

$L = \text{span} = 63\,\text{m}$

$B = \text{width} = 8\,\text{m}$

$y_C = \text{central dip} = 6\,\text{m}$

$\sigma = f(\text{cable}) = \text{safe working stress}$

$$= 115.832\,\text{MN/m}^2$$

Suspender spacing $= 9\,\text{m}$ and loading $= W = 180\,\text{kN}$ from deck loads.

The method for obtaining horizontal reaction H is based on each vertical at X
and Y having a reaction $= 3 \times 180 = 540\,\text{kN}$:

$H \times 6 = 180(9 + 18 + 27)$

$\qquad = 180 \times 54$

$H = 1620\,\text{kN}$

Construct funicular polygon. The maximum pull in the cable is given by 0a or 0g
(Fig. 6.2):

$T_{\text{max}} = \text{tension in the cable}$

$$= \sqrt{V^2 + H^2}$$

$$= \sqrt{540^2 + (1620)^2}$$

$$= 1707.63\,\text{kN or } 1.70763\,\text{MN}$$

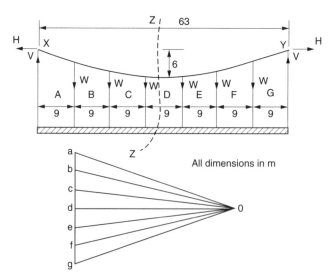

Figure 6.2.   A single-span suspension bridge under imposed deck load

$$\text{permissible stress} = 115.832\,\text{MN/m}^2$$

$$\text{area of the cable} = \frac{1.70763}{115.832} = 0.015\,\text{m}^2$$

Cable diameter

$$A = \frac{\pi d^2}{4} = 0.015\,\text{m}^2$$

$$d = \sqrt{\frac{4 \times 0.015}{\pi}} = 0.1382\,\text{m}$$

$$= 138.2\,\text{mm}$$

Adopt 150 mm cable on either side.

Example (6.2)
Several suspenders are employed in a light suspension such that the behaviour is the same as if the load employed on a simple beam while taking a parabolic profile for bending moment under UDL $= w$ (Fig. 6.3). Develop expressions for the horizontal thrust H and vertical reaction V and maximum tension T_{max}. Prove that it behaves like a beam and hence calculate the length of the cable L for this bridge. Use any numerical data.

$$W = wl \quad \text{and} \quad V = \frac{W}{2} = \frac{wl}{2} \tag{6.1}$$

Load transmitted to

$$\text{AC} = \frac{W}{2} \ \text{acting at}\ \frac{l}{4}\ \text{from C}$$

$$Hy_c = V\frac{l}{2} - \frac{W}{2}\frac{l}{4} \tag{6.2}$$

$$H = \frac{Wl}{8y_c}$$

(Note: $Wl/8$ is a bending moment for a simply supported beam)

$$= \frac{M_c}{y_c} \tag{6.3}$$

$$T_{\text{max}} = \sqrt{V^2 + H^2} = \sqrt{\left(\frac{W}{2}\right)^2 + \left(\frac{Wl}{8y_c}\right)^2}$$

$$= \frac{W}{2}\sqrt{1 + \frac{l^2}{16y_c^2}} \tag{6.4}$$

$$T_{\text{max}} = fA$$

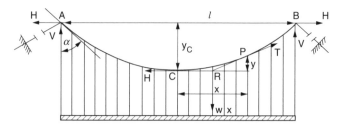

Figure 6.3. Parabolic cable with suspenders

Let (x, y) be the coordinate of P then

$$CQ = x \qquad PQ = y$$

wx is transmitted across hangers to the portion CP. R is the middle point of CQ. Join RP

$$T = \sqrt{(wx)^2 + H^2} \tag{6.5}$$

The shape is a parabola. PQR represents a triangle

$$\frac{PQ}{wx} = \frac{QR}{H} = \frac{RP}{T} \tag{6.6}$$

$$PQ = y \qquad QR = \frac{x}{z}$$

Hence

$$\frac{y}{wx} = \frac{x}{2H} \qquad \text{or} \qquad y = \frac{wx^2}{2H} \quad (H \text{ is constant})$$

$$H = \frac{wx^2}{2y} \tag{6.7}$$

At B:

$$x = \frac{l}{2} \qquad y = y_c \tag{6.8}$$

$$H = \frac{wl^2}{8y_c} = \frac{Wl}{8y_c} \quad \text{(as before)} \tag{6.9}$$

α = inclination at A and B to the vertical

$$\tan \alpha = \frac{H}{V} = \frac{2}{W} \left(\frac{Wl}{8y_c} \right) = \frac{l}{4y_c} \tag{6.10}$$

length of cable $= L$

Take an element δs of length ACB of curve at P

$$\delta s = \sqrt{\delta x^2 + \delta y^2} = \delta x \sqrt{1 + \left(\frac{dy}{dx}\right)^2} \qquad (6.11)$$

$$y = \frac{wx^2}{H^2}$$

$$\delta s = \sqrt{1 + \frac{w^2 x^2}{H^2}}$$

If wx/H is a fraction in a binomial theorem

$$\left(1 + \frac{w^2 x^2}{2H^2}\right)^{1/2} = 1 + \frac{1}{2} \frac{w^2 x^2}{H^2} + \cdots$$

and neglecting higher power terms $\dfrac{w^2 x^2}{H^2}$

$$\delta s = \left(1 + \frac{w^2 x^2}{2H^2}\right) 8x \qquad (6.12)$$

$$\int_0^{L/2} \delta s = \int_0^L l \left[x + \frac{w^2 x^3}{6H^2}\right] dx$$

$$L = l + \frac{w^2 l^3}{24H^2}$$

Since

$$H = \frac{wl^2}{8y_c}$$

$$L = 1 + \frac{8}{3} \frac{y_c^2}{l} \qquad (6.13)$$

Numerical data (Mks or European system)

$$Y_c = \tfrac{1}{10}\text{th span}$$

$$\sigma_c = 1200\,\text{kg/cm}^2$$

density of steel $\rho_s = 7800\,\text{kg/m}^3$

Find the length

$$L = l + \frac{8}{3} \frac{y_c^2}{l^2} = \left(1 + \frac{8}{3} \frac{1}{100}\right) = \frac{308}{300} l$$

$$W = \rho_s V$$

$$= 7800 \times \frac{A}{(100)^2} \times L = \frac{78}{100} \times A \times \frac{308}{300}$$

$$= 0.8008 Al \;(\text{kg})$$

$$H = \frac{Wl}{8y_c} = \frac{W}{8} \frac{l}{\frac{1}{10}l} = \frac{5W}{4} \text{ (kg)}$$

$$T_{max} = \sqrt{V^2 + H^2} = \sqrt{\left(\frac{W}{2}\right)^2 + \left(\frac{5W}{4}\right)^2} = 1.35\,W$$

$$= 1.35 \times 0.8008Al \text{ (kg)}$$

$$1200A = 1.35 \times 0.8008Al$$

$$l = 1103\,\text{m}$$

Example (6.3)   India/Imperial units

Assume a footbridge is 10 ft wide and the span is 120 ft and a central dip $y_c = 12$ ft. Permissible stress $= 7$ tons/in^2. The roadway load is 1 cwt/ft^2. Therefore:

$$L = l + \frac{8}{3}\frac{y_c^2}{l} = l\left(1 + \frac{8}{300}\right) = \frac{120 \times 308}{300} = 123.2\,\text{ft}$$

Total load/cable including its own weight:

$$W = \frac{1}{20} \times 5 \times 120 + \frac{480AL}{2240 \times 144}$$

$$= (30 + 0.1833A) \text{ tons}$$

where

$$A = \text{cross-sectional area (in}^2)$$

$$L = 123.2\,\text{ft}$$

$$H = \frac{Wl}{8y_c} = \frac{5W}{4} \qquad y_c = \tfrac{1}{10}l$$

$$T_{max} = \sqrt{V^2 + H^2} = \sqrt{\left(\frac{W}{2}\right)^2 + \left(\frac{5W}{4}\right)^2}$$

$$= 1.35W$$

$$= 1.35(30 + 0.1833A)$$

Since

$$T_{max} = fA = 7A$$

$$A = 6\,\text{in}^2.$$

Note that 1 ft $= 0.3048$ m; 1 cwt $= 112$ lb/ft$^2 = 111.122$ MN/m^2.

6.2.1 Cable supports at different levels

Determine reactions and the length of the cable (see Fig. 6.4)

$$\text{the horizontal span} = l$$

$$\text{the difference of height} = h$$

Let y_c be the dip of the lowest point C below B. Locate C, the origin at a distance of x_1. The equation of the cable ACB is

$$y = \frac{wx^2}{2H} \qquad (6.14)$$

$w =$ uniform load at the deck

At B $x = x_1, \qquad y = y_c$

At A $x = -(l - x_1) \qquad y = (h + y_c)$

$$H = \frac{wx_1^2}{2H} = \frac{w(l - x_1)^2}{2(h + y_c)} \qquad (6.15)$$

or

$$x_1^2(h + y_c) = y_c(l - x_1^2) \qquad (6.16)$$

Solve for x_1

$$H = \frac{wx_1^2}{2y_c}$$

V_1 at A

$$V_1 l = \frac{Wl}{2} + Hh \qquad (W = wl)$$

$$V_1 = \frac{W}{2} + \frac{Hh}{l}$$

$$V_2 = \frac{W}{2} - \frac{Hh}{l}$$

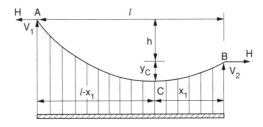

Figure 6.4. Cables at different levels

$$T_{\text{max}} = \text{pull in the cable} = \sqrt{V_1^2 + H^2}$$

$$L = AC + CB$$

$$= \frac{1}{2}\left[2(l - x_1) + \frac{8}{3}\frac{(h + y_c)^2}{2(l - x_1)}\right] + \frac{1}{2}\left[2x_1 + \frac{8}{3}\frac{y_c^2}{2x_1}\right]$$

$$= l + \frac{2}{3}\frac{y_c^2}{x_1} + \frac{2}{3}\frac{(h + y_c^2)}{(l - x_1)} \qquad (6.17)$$

6.2.2 Temperatures in cables

Assuming L is the length of the cable and δL is the change in length due to a rise or fall of temperature then the central dip y_c will also change to $y_c \pm \delta y_c$. Hence an expression can be deduced for this change in the cable. Since

$$L = l + \frac{8}{3}\frac{y_c^2}{l} \qquad (6.18)$$

$$\delta L = \frac{16}{3}\frac{y_c}{l}\delta y_c \qquad \delta y_c = \frac{3}{16}\frac{l}{y_c}\delta L \qquad (6.19)$$

If t is the rise in temperature and L changes to L_1, then

$$L_1 = L(1 \pm \alpha t) \qquad (6.20)$$

where α is the coefficient of expansion and contraction of the cable. The change in length δL is therefore given by

$$\delta L = L_1 - L = L\alpha t \qquad (6.21)$$

$$= \alpha t\left(l + \frac{8}{3}\frac{y_c^2}{l}\right) \qquad (6.22)$$

$$= l\alpha t + \frac{8}{3}\frac{y_c^2}{l}\alpha t \qquad (6.23)$$

Neglecting the second term and $\alpha t = l\alpha t$, the central dip change δy_c becomes

$$\delta y_c = \frac{3}{16}\frac{l}{y_c}(l\alpha t) = \frac{3}{16}\alpha t\frac{l^2}{y_c} \qquad (6.24)$$

Note that if the C length decreases, the central dip decreases.

The maximum intensity of stress induced is

$$T_{\text{max}} = fA = \sqrt{V^2 + H^2} \qquad (6.25)$$

If δL is small V is small; then it can be concluded that $H = fA$ or $f = H/A$ since H varies as l/y_c and f will vary inversely and f changes to f':

$$\frac{f'}{f} = \frac{y_c}{y'_c} \tag{6.26}$$

$$\frac{f'-f}{f} = \frac{y_c - y'_c}{y'_c} = \frac{-(y'_c - y_c)}{y'_c} \tag{6.27}$$

The change in stress is related as

$$\frac{\delta f}{f} = \frac{-\delta y_c}{y'_c} = \frac{-\delta y_c}{y_c} \tag{6.28}$$

6.2.3 Cable anchorage

Assuming the suspension cable has pull T over the guide at the tower neglecting friction (Fig. 6.5), the pull T will be the same on both sides. If the inclinations α and β are different and the central tower height is h, then the vertical load V_T is given by

$$V_T = T \cos \alpha + T \cos \beta \tag{6.29}$$

and

$$H_T = \text{horizontal load} = T \sin \alpha - T \sin \beta \tag{6.30}$$

The bending moment M_T will be

$$M_T = H_T h = T(\sin \alpha - \beta)h \tag{6.31}$$

This bending moment M_T is avoided if cables have separate anchors over the saddle and $T \neq T_1$. Hence

$$T \sin \alpha = T_1 \sin \beta = H \tag{6.32}$$

The vertical load

$$V_T = T \cos \alpha + T_1 \cos \beta \tag{6.33}$$

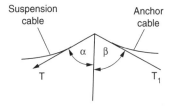

Figure 6.5. Anchor/suspension inclinations

Example (6.4)   European practice
A suspension bridge has a span of 24 m with a cable dip of 2 m. From the vehicle
load, the load established on this portion of the bridge is 2 ton/m. Calculate the sectional area of the cable, A, if the permissible stress in the cable is
1200 kg/cm². Take $\beta = 60°$. Find the dip for temperature 30°C. For this temperature assume $\alpha = 0.000007/°C$:

$$W = \tfrac{1}{2} \times 2 \times 24 = 24 \text{ tons} \qquad V = 12 \text{ tons}$$

$$H = \text{horizontal pull} = \frac{Wl}{8y_c} = 36 \text{ tons}$$

$$T_{max} = \sqrt{V^2 + H^2} = 37.95 \text{ tons} \quad \text{or} \quad 37\,950 \text{ kg}$$

$$\tan \alpha = \tfrac{36}{12} = 3$$

$$T_{max} = fA \quad \text{or} \quad 37\,950 = 1200 \times A$$

$$A = 31.625 \text{ cm}^2$$

Tower area:

$$H = T \sin \alpha = T_1 \sin \beta = 36 \text{ ton}$$

$$T_1 = \frac{2 \times 36}{\sqrt{3}} = 41.58 \text{ ton}$$

$$V_P = \text{vertical pressure or reaction}$$

$$= T \cos \alpha + T_1 \cos \beta = \frac{W}{2} + \frac{1}{2} T_1$$

$$= 32.79 \text{ ton}$$

$$\delta y_c = \frac{3}{16} \alpha_T t \frac{l^2}{y_c} \qquad (\alpha_T = 0.000007; \; t = 30°C; \; y_c = 1.0 \text{ m})$$

$$= \frac{3}{16} \times 7 \times 10^{-6} \times 30 \times \frac{(24)^2}{1.0}$$

$$= 0.02268 \text{ m}$$

$$= 2.268 \text{ cm}$$

The total dip $= 2.0 + 0.02268 = 2.02268 \approx 2.023$ m.

6.2.4   The suspended cable as a catenary

Under its own weight, the suspended cable assumes the shape of a catenary
which can approximate to a parabola provided the central dip is very small. It
is vital to know the behaviour of the cable. Figure 6.6 shows the geometry of

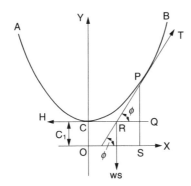

Figure 6.6. Cable as a catenary

such a cable and assumes it has a uniform load w. A position CP is in equilibrium under the following actions:

(a) its own weight ws where s is a portion of length
(b) H at C
(c) T at P

$$\frac{H}{QR} = \frac{ws}{PQ} = \frac{T}{RP}$$

From here

$$ws = H \tan \phi \tag{6.34}$$

$$T = H \sec \phi$$

$$= ws \operatorname{cosec} \phi \tag{6.35}$$

if

$$H = wC_1$$

$$s = C_1 \tan \phi$$

$$= C_1 \frac{dy}{dx} \tag{6.36}$$

where C_1 is the length of the cable whose weight equals H, while SP $= y$, and OS $= x$.

Differentiating

$$\frac{ds}{dx} = C_1 \frac{d^2y}{dx^2} \tag{6.37}$$

Assume $dy/dx = \theta$, then

$$\sqrt{1 + \theta^2} = C_1 \frac{d\theta}{dx} \tag{6.38}$$

$$\frac{C_1 \, d\theta}{\sqrt{1 + \theta^2}} = dx \tag{6.39}$$

Integrating

$$\sinh^{-1}\theta = \frac{x}{C_1} + A \quad \text{(where } A = \text{constant of integrations)}$$

at $x = 0$,

$$\frac{dy}{dx} = 0$$

$$A = 0$$

Hence

$$\theta = \sinh \frac{x}{C_1} = \tan\phi$$

On further integration

$$y = C\cosh\frac{x}{C_1} + B \tag{6.40}$$

at $x = 0$, $y = C_1$, hence $B = 0$. If O is the origin then the catenary equation is given by

$$y = C_1 \cosh\frac{x}{C_1} \tag{6.41}$$

$$s = C_1 \tan\phi = C_1 \sinh\frac{x}{C} \tag{6.42}$$

$$\therefore \quad y^2 - s^2 = C_1^2 \left(\cosh^2\frac{x}{C_1} - \sinh^2\frac{x}{C_1} \right) = C_1^2$$

Hence

$$y = C_1 \sec\phi \tag{6.43}$$

and then

$$T = H\sin\phi = wC_1\sec\phi = wy \tag{6.44}$$

but

$$T = ws\operatorname{cosec}\phi = wy \tag{6.45}$$

$$y = s\operatorname{cosec}\phi = C_1\sec\phi \tag{6.46}$$

For Cartesian coordinates

$$y = C_1 \cosh\frac{x}{C_1} \tag{6.47}$$

$$= C_1 \left\{ 1 + \frac{1}{2!}\left(\frac{x}{C_1}\right)^2 + \frac{1}{4!}\left(\frac{x}{C_1}\right)^4 + \cdots \right\} \tag{6.48}$$

Since x/C_1 is small x^4/C_1^4 would be negligible.
  Hence

$$y = C_1 \left\{ 1 + \frac{x^2}{2C_1^2} \right\} \qquad (6.49)$$

Transferring the origin to C

$$y = \frac{x^2}{2C_1}$$

is a parabola and $H = wC_1$. Therefore

$$y = \frac{wx^2}{2H} \qquad (6.50)$$

expresses a parabolic shape under uniform load w along a horizontal length.

6.2.5 Suspension bridge with three-hinged stiffening girders supporting the deck

Loads are moving on the deck. The dead loads are due to girders, cables, connections, suspension rods and gangways. The live loads are transmitted across the stiffening girders to the cables by suspension rods. The roadway is supported by two such girders (trusses) as shown in Fig. 6.7. The cables are parabolic. All other reactions are indicated with an appropriate dimension. A single rolling load W moves from left to right. An equivalent uniformly distributed load w_e transmitted to the cable is to be evaluated. If the origin is at A, the co-ordinate of P is (x, y) where section X cuts the cable. If y_c is the central dip, the equation of $AC'B$ is given by

$$y = \frac{4y_c}{l^2} x(l - x) \qquad (6.51)$$

For the cable:

$$V = \text{vertical reaction at A and B} = \frac{w_e l}{2} \qquad (6.52)$$

$$H = \text{horizontal force} = \frac{w_e l^2}{8y_c} \qquad (6.53)$$

$$T_{\max} \text{ at A or B} = \sqrt{V^2 + H^2} \qquad (6.54)$$

Therefore, w_e can be evaluated.

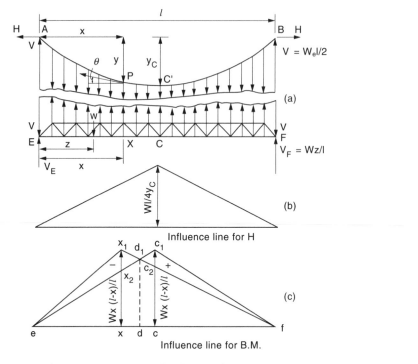

Figure 6.7. *A single-span suspension bridge with a three-hinged-stiffened girder*

Equilibrium of the portion AP:
  Taking moment about P

$$M_P = -Vx + \frac{w_e x^2}{2} + Hy = 0$$

$$Hy = Vx - \frac{w_e x^2}{2} \tag{6.55}$$

For the girder:
  System of forces

  (a) W at a distance z from E
  (b) upward vertical reactions due to W at hinges E and F

$$V_E = \frac{W(l - z)}{l} \qquad V_F = \frac{Wz}{l} \tag{6.56}$$

  (c) w_e causing upward pull per unit length exerted by the hangers
  (d) downward reactions $V = w_e l/2$ at hinges E and F.

Bending moment at a section X

$$M_X = \left\{ -V_E x - W(x-z) + Vx - \frac{w_e x^2}{2} \right\} \quad \text{when } x > z \tag{6.57}$$

$$M_X = \left\{ -V_E x \right\} + \left\{ Vx - \frac{w_e x^2}{2} \right\} \quad \text{when } x < z \tag{6.58}$$

$$M_X = M_{CX} + Hy \tag{6.59}$$
$$= 0$$

Since a hinge is at C

$\quad M_{CX} = $ the usual bending moment at a section for a freely
$\qquad$ supported beam

$$H = -\frac{M_{CX}}{y_c} \tag{6.60}$$

$$= \frac{w_e l^2}{8 y_c}$$

$$w_e = \frac{-8 M_{CX}}{l^2} \tag{6.61}$$

When the load W is at a distance z from E in the portion EC

$$M_{CX} = \frac{-V_F l}{2} = -\frac{Wz}{l}\frac{l}{2} = -\frac{Wz}{2} \tag{6.62}$$

$$H = \frac{Wz}{2 y_c} \tag{6.63}$$

Therefore

$$w_e = \frac{8 y_c}{l^2} \times H = \frac{4 Wz}{l^2} \tag{6.64}$$

Influence line for H
H varies with the load portion z and when $z = l/2$, i.e. the load is near or it reaches the centre of the span

$$H \to \frac{W}{2 y_c}\frac{l}{2} = \frac{Wl}{4 y_c} \tag{6.65}$$

When the load is in CF, i.e. $z > l/2$

$$M_{CX} = -V_F \frac{l}{2} = -\frac{W(l-z)}{2} \tag{6.66}$$

Hence

$$H = -\frac{M_{CX}}{y_c} = \frac{W(l-z)}{2 y_c} \tag{6.67}$$

It is a straight line with maximum value:

$$H = \frac{Wl}{4y_c} \quad \text{[see Fig. 6.7(b)].} \tag{6.68}$$

Influence line for bending moment
The influence line at a given section X can easily be drawn:

$$M_X = M_{CX} + Hy$$

M_X is a triangle with the ordinate $-Wx(l - x)/l$ at X.
   Superimposing the influence line for Hy, which is a triangle, with the ordinate is equal to

$$+\frac{Wl}{4y_c} \times \frac{4y_c}{l^2} \, x(l - x) \tag{6.69}$$

The areas '−' and '+' represent the bending moment influence line in Fig. 6.7(c). The maximum negative occurs at X when the load is on the section itself.
   The maximum positive bending moment occurs when the load is at the centre of the span. The maximum negative bending moment [Eq. (6.70)] and positive bending moment [Eq. (6.71)] are given by:

$$-M_{max} = -xx_1 + xx_2$$

$$= -\frac{Wx(l - x)}{l} + \frac{Wx}{2y_c}\left[\frac{4y_c}{l^2} \, x(l - x)\right]$$

$$= -\frac{Wx(l - x)(l - 2x)}{l^2} \tag{6.70}$$

$$+M_{max} = -cc_2 + cc_1$$

$$= -\frac{Wx}{2} + \frac{Wx(l - x)}{l}$$

$$= +\frac{Wx(l - 2x)}{l} \tag{6.71}$$

The value of x
Differentiate Eq. (6.70) with regard to x and equate it to zero

$$(l - x)(l - 2x) - x(l - 2x) - 2x(l - x) = 0 \tag{6.72}$$

$$x = (0.5 \pm 0.289)l$$

$$x = 0.211l \quad \text{or} \quad 0.789l \tag{6.73}$$

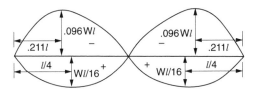

Figure 6.8. Maximum bending moment diagram

Substituting in the same equation (6.70)

$$-M_{max} = -\frac{Wl}{6\sqrt{3}} = -0.096W \tag{6.74}$$

at $x = l/4$

$$+M_{max} = +\frac{Wl}{16} \tag{6.75}$$

Figure 6.8 illustrates the solution for the maximum bending moment.

When a moving load is a uniformly distributed load 'w'

$$-M_{max} = -w \times \text{area of the triangle underneath, } \text{ex}_1\text{d}_1 \quad [\text{Fig. 6.7(c)}]$$

$$+M_{max} = +w \times \text{area of the triangle underneath, } \text{d}_1\text{c}_1\text{f} \quad [\text{Fig. 6.7(c)}]$$

$$\frac{\text{dd}_1}{\text{cc}_1} = \frac{\text{ed}}{\text{ec}} = \frac{z}{l/2} \tag{6.76}$$

$$\text{cc}_1 = \text{xx}_1$$

$$\frac{z}{l/2} = \frac{l-z}{l-z} = \frac{l}{3l/2 - z} \tag{6.77}$$

or

$$z = \frac{l^2}{(3l - 2x)}$$

$$\text{dd}_1 = \frac{2x(l - x)}{(3l - 2x)}$$

$$\Delta\text{ex}_1\text{d}_1 = \Delta\text{ex}_1\text{f} - \Delta\text{ed}_1\text{f}$$

$$= \frac{x(l - x)(l - 2x)}{2(3l - 2x)} \tag{6.78}$$

$$M_{max \text{ at } X} = -w\Delta\text{ex}_1\text{d}_1 = +w\Delta\text{d}_1\text{c}_1\text{f}$$

$$= \pm \frac{wx(l - x)(l - 2x)}{2(3l - 2x)}. \tag{6.79}$$

Put $x = Kl$

$$M_{\text{max}} = \pm wl^2 \, \frac{K(1-K)(1-2K)}{2(3-2K)} \tag{6.80}$$

Differentiating with respect to K and equating it to zero, the final equation becomes

$$8K^3 - 24K^2 + 18K - 3 = 0$$

$$K = 0.234$$

$$x = 0.234l$$

$$M_{\text{max}} = \pm 0.01883 wl^2 \tag{6.81}$$

$$z = \frac{l^2}{(3l-2x)} = \frac{l}{2.532} = 0.359l \tag{6.82}$$

This is shown in Fig. 6.9 along with the bending moment diagram.

Influence lines for shear

$$F_{\text{X}} = V_{\text{F}} + T \sin \theta \quad \text{at any section X} \tag{6.83}$$

Since

$$T \cos \theta = H \tag{6.84}$$

Hence

$$T \sin \theta = H \tan \theta \tag{6.85}$$

$$F_{\text{X}} = f_{\text{X}} + H \tan \theta \tag{6.86}$$

where f_{X} is the shear force at X

$$y = \frac{4y_{\text{c}}}{l^2} \, x(l-x)$$

$$\tan \theta = \frac{dy}{dx} = \frac{4y_{\text{c}}}{l^2} (l-2x)$$

When $x = Kl$, the influence lines for shear force for $x = l/4$ and $x < l/4$ are as drawn in Fig. 6.10.

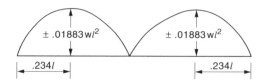

Figure 6.9. Influence lines for maximum moment

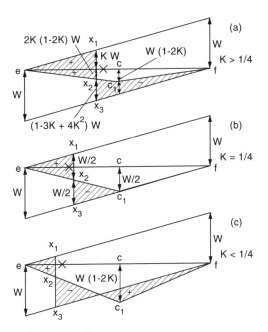

Figure 6.10. Influence lines for shear

The maximum shear force occurs (negative shear force) when the load has just crossed the section. For $x < l/4$, the maximum positive shear force may occur when the load is at the centre of the span. Referring to Fig. 6.10:

$$Xx_1 = KW$$

$$\frac{Xx_2}{cc_1} = \frac{eX}{ec} = \frac{Kl}{l/2} = 2K$$

$$Xx_2 = 2K \times cc_1 = 2K(1 - 2K)W \tag{6.87}$$

$$F_{max}(\text{positive}) = x_1x_2 = Xx_1 - Xx_2 = KW = 2K(1 - 2K)W$$

$$= K(3 - 4K)W \tag{6.88}$$

$$F_{max}(\text{negative}) = -x_2x_3 = -Xx_3 + Xx_2$$

$$= -(1 - 3K + 4K^2)W \tag{6.89}$$

For a maximum shear force

$$3 - 8K = 0$$

$$K = 3/8$$

Hence

$$F_{max} = \frac{3}{8}\left(3 - \frac{4 \times 3}{8}\right)W = \frac{9}{16}W \tag{6.90}$$

Figure 6.11 shows the maximum shear force diagram.

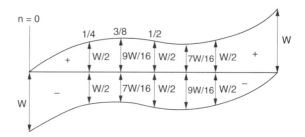

Figure 6.11. Maximum shear force diagram (moving load)

Uniformly distributed load 'w' – shear force

At section $x < l/4$
Maximum positive shear $= w\Delta e x_1 x_2$
ef loaded and Xf unloaded
The maximum negative shear force $= -w \times$ area $x_2 c_1 f x_3$
xf loaded and eX unloaded
If $W = 1$, the unit load influence lines are given for $x = 0$, $x = l/4$ and $x = l/2$ in Fig. 6.12.

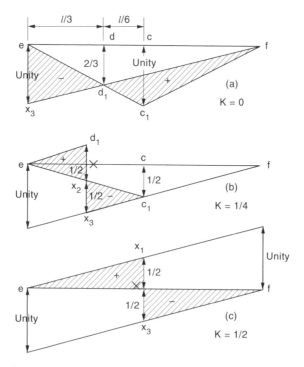

Figure 6.12. Uniform load influence lines

For $x = 0$,

$$cc_1 = W(1 - 2K) = \text{unity} \qquad (6.91)$$
$$K = 0 \qquad W = 1 \qquad cc_1 = ex_3 = \text{unity}$$

To locate point d:

$$\frac{dd_1}{cc_1} = \frac{ed}{ec} \qquad ec = ef$$

$$\frac{ed}{ec} = \frac{fd}{ef} = \frac{ed + df}{ec + ef} = \frac{ef}{\frac{1}{2}ef} = \frac{2}{3} \qquad (6.92)$$

$$ed = \frac{2}{3} \times ec = \frac{2}{3} \times \frac{l}{2} = \frac{l}{3}$$

$$\Delta ed_1 x_3 = \frac{1}{3}\frac{l}{3} \times 1 = \frac{l}{6} = \Delta d_1 c_1 f$$

$$F_{max} = +\frac{wl}{6} \quad \text{at } x = 0 \qquad (6.93)$$

For $x = l/4$

$$x_1 x_2 = x_2 x_3 = \frac{1}{2}$$

$$\Delta ex_1 x_2 = \Delta C_1 x_2 x_3 = \frac{1}{2} \times \frac{1}{2} \times \frac{l}{4} = \frac{l}{16}$$

$$F_{max} = \pm\frac{wl}{6} \qquad (6.94)$$

When $x = l/2$, $H \tan\theta = 0$

$$eXx_1 = Xx_3 = \frac{1}{2} \times \frac{1}{2} \times \frac{l}{2} = \frac{l}{8}$$

$$F_{max} = \pm\frac{wl}{8} \quad \text{at } x = \frac{l}{2} \qquad (6.95)$$

Figure 6.13 shows the maximum shear force diagram for this situation.

Example (6.5)   British practice

Three hinged stiffening girders supported by two cables for which l and y_c are:

$$l = 200$$

$$y_c = 20\,\text{m}$$

There are four point loads of 200 kN each placed along the centre line of the roadway at 25, 30, 35 and 40 m from the left hinge. Find the bending moment and shear force in each girder at 50 m from each end.

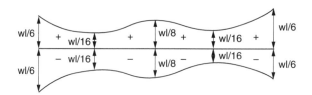

Figure 6.13. Maximum shear force diagram (uniform load)

Calculate maximum torsion T_{max} in the cables.

For the girder:

$$V_F \times 200 = 100(25 + 30 + 35 + 40) = 13\,000$$

$$V_F = 65\,\text{kN}$$

$$V_E = 335\,\text{kN}$$

$$M_{CX} + Hy_c = 0$$

$$H = 325\,\text{kN}$$

At 50 m from E

$$y = \frac{4 \times 20 \times 50 \times 150}{200 \times 200} = 15\,\text{m}$$

$$\tan\theta = \frac{4 \times 20 \times (200 - 100)}{(200)^2} = \frac{1}{5}$$

$$M_{50} = -4875\,\text{kNm}$$

$$F_{50} = V_F + H\tan\theta = +130\,\text{kN}$$

At 150 m from E

$$M_{150} = 1625\,\text{kNm}$$

$$F_{150} = 0$$

For the cable:

$$H = \frac{W_e l}{8y_c} = \frac{W_e \times 200}{8 \times 20} = 32.5$$

$$W_e = 260$$

$$V = \text{the vertical reaction} = \tfrac{1}{2}W_e = 130\,\text{kN}$$

$$T_{max} = \sqrt{V^2 + H^2} = \sqrt{(130)^2 + (325)^2} = 350\,\text{kN}.$$

Example (6.6) European practice
A suspension cable is stiffened by a three-hinged girder. The dead load is
0.75 ton/m. Determine maximum bending moment anywhere in this girder
when a 1 tonne loading rolls from left to right. Determine the maximum tension
in the cells.

Use the following data

$$l = 60\,\text{m} \qquad y_c = 6\,\text{m}$$

For the girder:

$$M_{max}(\text{negative}) \text{ at } 0.211l = 0.211(60) = 12.66\,\text{m}$$

$$= -0.096Wl$$

$$= -0.096 \times 1 \times 60 = 5.76$$

$$M_{max}(\text{positive}) \text{ at } \frac{l}{4} = 20\,\text{m}$$

$$= +\frac{Wl}{16} = \frac{1 \times 60}{16} = 3.75$$

For the cable:

dead load $W_d = 45\,\text{tonne}$

$$H_d = \frac{W_d l}{8 y_c} = \frac{45 \times 60}{8 \times 6} = 56.25$$

The maximum equivalent UDL transmitted to the cable when the live load is at
the centre of the span

$$H_t = \frac{Wl}{4 y_c} = \frac{1 \times 60}{4 \times 6} = 2.5$$

$$\frac{W_e l}{8 y_c} = H_t = 2.5$$

$$\frac{W_e \times 60}{8 \times 6} = 2.5 \qquad W_e = 2\,\text{tonne}$$

$$\text{Total } W = W_d + W_e = 45 + 2 = 47\,\text{tonne}$$

$$H = H_d + H_t = 56.25 + 2.5 = 58.75\,\text{tonne}$$

$$T_{max} = \sqrt{V^2 + H^2} = \sqrt{\left(\frac{47}{2}\right)^2 + (58.75)^2} = 63.28\,\text{tonne}$$

6.2.6 Suspension bridge with a two-hinged stiffening girder

The arrangement is shown in a generalized form for a statically indeterminate structure (Fig. 6.14). Consider a single load W at a distance z from E:

$$W = w_e l \tag{6.96}$$

where $w_e =$ UDL unit length

$$H = \frac{w_e l^2}{8y_c} = \frac{Wl}{8y_c} \tag{6.97}$$

Girder

$$R_E = V_E - V = \left(\frac{W}{z} = \frac{Wz}{l}\right) \tag{6.98}$$

$$R_F = V_F - V = -\left(\frac{W}{z} = \frac{Wz}{l}\right) \tag{6.99}$$

$$R_E = -R_F$$

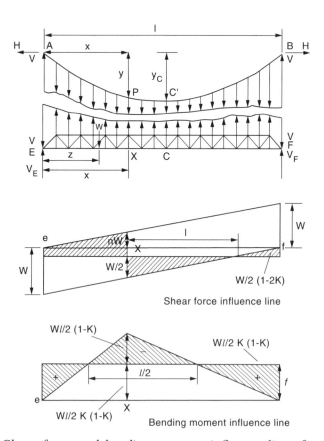

Figure 6.14. Shear force and bending moment influence lines for a two-hinged girder

Similarly to the previous three-hinged analysis:

$$F_X = f_X + H \tan \theta \tag{6.100}$$

$$H \tan \theta = \frac{W}{2}(1 - 2K)$$

$$F_{max} = KW + \frac{W}{2}(1 - 2K) = +\frac{W}{2} \tag{6.101}$$

$$-F_{max} = -\frac{W}{2} \tag{6.102}$$

Bending moment

M_X at section $X = M_{CX} + Hy$

$$= M_{CX} + \frac{Wl}{2}K(1 - K) \tag{6.103}$$

M_{max} (load on the section itself)

$$= WlK(1 - K) + \frac{Wl}{2}K(1 - K)$$

$$= -\frac{Wl}{2}K(1 - K) \tag{6.104}$$

$$M_{max} = +\frac{Wl}{2}K(1 - K)$$

When the load is on either hinge

$$M_{max} \text{ at the central section } = \pm\frac{Wl}{8} \tag{6.105}$$

Uniform load w
Shear force and bending moment

$$F_{max} = -w\frac{1}{2} \times \frac{l}{2} \times \frac{1}{2} = -\frac{wl}{8} \tag{6.106}$$

Note: $w = w_e$ (imposed)

$$F_{max}(\text{positive}) = \frac{wl}{8}$$

$$M_{max} = -\frac{wl^2}{8}K(1 - K)$$

At a section

$$M_{max} = \pm\frac{wl^2}{8}K(1 - K) \tag{6.107}$$

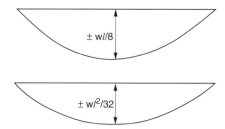

Figure 6.15. Influence lines for maximum bending moment

when ends are loaded and the middle is unloaded.

$$M_{\mathrm{max}} = \pm\frac{wl^2}{32} \tag{6.108}$$

at the centre of the girder.
   The maximum values are shown in Fig. 6.15.

Temperature stresses in the stiffening girder
As before

$$\delta y_{\mathrm{c}} = \frac{3}{16}\alpha t\frac{t^2}{y_{\mathrm{c}}} \tag{6.109}$$

for temperature t.
   Maximum bending stress is related for UDL:

$$\frac{\delta}{l}\times\frac{d}{l} = \frac{5}{24}\frac{f}{E} \tag{6.110}$$

$$f = \frac{24E}{5}\frac{d}{l^2}\times\frac{3}{16}\alpha t\frac{l^2}{y_{\mathrm{c}}}$$

$$= \frac{9}{10}E\alpha t\frac{d}{y_{\mathrm{c}}} \tag{6.111}$$

Data for European practice is as follows:

$$\alpha = 12\times 10^{-6}/{}^{\circ}\mathrm{C}$$
$$E = 2\times 10^6\,\mathrm{kg/cm^2}$$
$$t = 20^{\circ}\mathrm{C}$$
$$y_{\mathrm{c}} = 5\,\mathrm{m}$$
$$\mathrm{span} = 50\,\mathrm{m}\qquad 2\,\mathrm{m\ deep\ girder}$$
$$f = \frac{9}{10}\times 2\times 10^6\times 12\times 10^{-6}\times 20\times\frac{2}{5}$$
$$= 172.762\,\mathrm{kg/cm^2}$$

Example (6.7)   European practice

A three-span suspension bridge is shown in Fig. 6.16. Analyse this bridge for various forces and reactions, using the following data:

$$w = \text{total load including dead weight} = 10\,\text{ton/m}$$

$$\frac{EI_{Girder}}{EA_{Cable}} = 7.61\,\text{m}^2$$

$$\frac{EI_{Girder}}{EA_{Hanger}} = 20\,\text{m}^2$$

$$\frac{EI_{Girder}}{EA_{Tower}} = 0.8\,\text{m}^2$$

$$\text{spans } AB = CD = 60\,\text{m}$$
$$\text{span } BC = 150\,\text{m}$$
$$\text{tower height above deck} = 21.5\,\text{m}$$
$$\text{parabola height} = 20\,\text{m}$$
$$\text{internal parabola equation } y = a + bx + cx^2$$
$$\text{external parabola equation } y = d + bx + cx^2$$
$$E_{Cable} = 2100\,\text{t/cm}^2$$
$$A_{Cable} = 640\,\text{cm}^2$$
$$EA_{Cable} = 1.342 \times 10^6\,\text{tons}$$
$$EI_{Girder} = 7.6EA_{Cable} = 10.2 \times 10^6\,\text{tm}^2$$

A Flexibility Method with influence lines is adopted.

Referring to all parts of Fig. 6.16

$$m_0(AB) = \frac{10 \times 60}{8} = m_0(CD) = 4500\,\text{ton metre} \quad (\text{tm})$$

$$= 4500\,\text{tm}$$

$$m_0(BC) = \frac{10 \times 150^2}{8} = 28\,125\,\text{tm}$$

Two redundancies on X_1 and X_2

$$\delta_{B0} = \delta_{C0} \quad \text{at } B \text{ and } C$$

$$X_B f_{BB} + X_C f_{BC} = -\delta_{B0}$$

$$X_B f_{CB} + X_C f_{BC} = -\delta_{C0}$$

$$X_1 = X_B = -\frac{\delta_{B0}}{f_{BB} + f_{BC}}$$

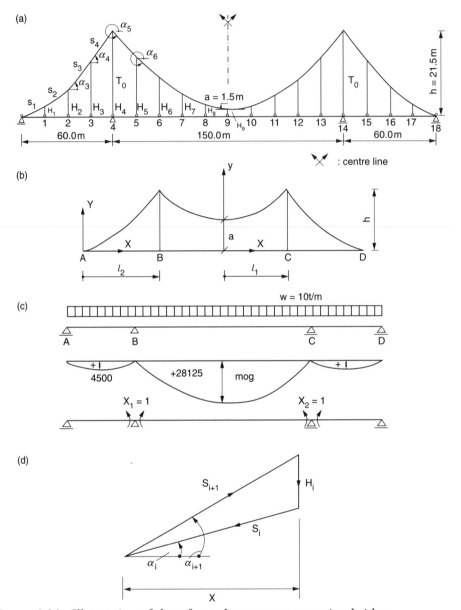

Figure 6.16. Illustration of data for a three-span suspension bridge

Using flexibility tables

$$\delta_{B0} = \frac{1}{3}(1)\left(\frac{36 \times 10^3}{8}\right)60 + \frac{1}{3}(1)\left(\frac{225 \times 10^3}{8}\right)(150)$$

$$= 1\,496\,250$$

$$f_{BB} = \frac{210}{3} = 70 \quad f_{BC} = \frac{150}{6} = 25$$

$$\therefore \quad X_1 = -15\,750\,\text{kNm}$$

$$a = 21.5 - 20 = 1.5\,\text{m}$$

Internal parabola

$$b = 0$$

$$x = l_1$$

$$a = a$$

$$y = h$$

$$= a + c l_1^2$$

$$c = \frac{h - a}{l_1^2}$$

$$y_1 = a + \frac{h - a}{l_1^2} x^2$$

$$= 1.5 + \frac{21.5 - 1.5}{(75)^2} x^2 \qquad \tan \alpha = 0.0071 x$$

$$x = 15\,\text{m} \qquad \tan \alpha = 0.1066$$

x	0	15	30	45	60	75	m
y_1	1.5	2.3	4.7	8.7	14.3	21.5	m

External parabola

$$y = d + bx + cx^2$$

$$x = 0$$

$$y = 0$$

$$d = 0$$

$$c^* = \frac{h - a}{l_1^2}$$

$$x = l_2$$

$$y = h \rightarrow b$$

$$l_2 = \frac{h-a}{l_1^2}l_2^2$$

$$b = \frac{hl_1^2 - (h-a)l_2^2}{l_1^2 l_2}$$

$$y_2 = \frac{hl_1^2 - (h-a)l_2^2}{l_1^2 l_2}$$

Substituting respective values

$$y_2 = 0.146x + 0.00355x^2 \qquad \tan\alpha = 0.146 + 0.0071x$$

$$x = 15\,\text{m} \qquad \tan\alpha = 0.1066$$

x	0	15	30	45	60
y_1	0	2.99	7.58	13.77	21.5

Cables

As shown in Fig. 6.17, the horizontal component of $S_1 \ldots$ etc. is X as a redundant.

The results of equations applied to data in Fig. 6.16 are given in Table 6.2.

Summation of vertical forces in hangers

$$H_4 = (0.992) + (0.992) = 1.984\,\text{tons}$$

$$= 1.99\,\text{tons}$$

$$\sum H_i = 1.99\,\text{tons} \quad (\text{from Table 6.2}).$$

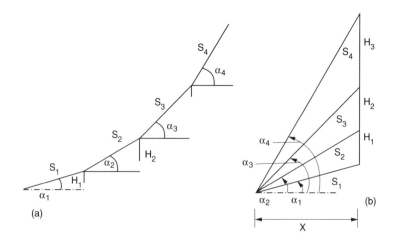

Figure 6.17. Determination of forces due to $X = 1$

Table 6.2. Horizontal components for the girders

Points	y	$y_i - y_{i-1}$	$\tan \alpha$	H_i tons	S_i tons
0	0	0			
1	2.99	2.99	0.2	0.106	1.02
2	7.58	4.59	0.306	0.106	1.046
3	13.77	6.19	0.412	0.106	1.082
4	21.5	7.73	0.514	0.992	1.125
5	14.3	−7.2	0.514	0.106	1.109
6	8.7	−5.2	−0.372	0.106	1.066
7	4.7	−4.2	−0.266	0.106	1.035
8	2.3	−2.4	−0.160	0.106	1.012
9	1.5	−0.8	−0.534	0.106	1.001
10	–				
				$\sum H_i = 1.99$ tons	

Tension in hangers (as UDL)

$$e = \text{eccentricity} = 15\,\text{m} \quad \text{(distance between hangers)}$$

$$T = \frac{H}{e} = \frac{0.106}{15} = 0.00708\,\text{ton/m}$$

$$\text{load ratio} = \frac{T}{w} = \frac{0.00708}{10} = 0.000708$$

$$M = \frac{T}{w} \times X_1 = 11.15\,\text{ton metre (tm)}$$

$$m_{10} = \frac{Tl_1^2}{8} = \frac{0.00708 \times 60^2}{8} = 3.19\,\text{tm}$$

$$m_{20} = \frac{0.00708 \times 150^2}{8} = 19.95\,\text{tm}$$

m_0 due to w and m_1 due to $X_1 = 1$ are illustrated in Fig. 6.18.
The flexibility equations are (*Note:* $D_{10} = \delta_{10}$):

$$X_1 f_{11} + D_{10} = 0 \qquad X_1 = -\frac{D_{10}}{f_{11}}$$

$$f_{iK} = \int m_i m_k \frac{ds}{EI_{\text{Girder}}} + \sum S_i S_k \frac{S}{EA_{\text{Cable}}} + \sum H_i H_k \frac{S}{EA_{\text{Hanger}}}$$

$$+ \sum H_i H_k \frac{S}{EA_{\text{Tower}}}$$

$$EI_{\text{Girder}} D_{10} = \int m_1 m_0 \, ds$$

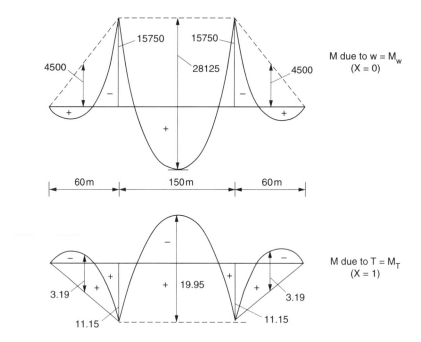

Figure 6.18. Bending moment diagrams for m_0 due to w and m_1 due to X_1

External span flexibilities

$$\frac{1}{3} \times 15\,750 \times 3.19 \times 60 = \quad 1\,002\,000$$

$$-\frac{1}{3} \times 15\,750 \times 11.15 \times 60 = -3\,500\,000$$

$$-\frac{8}{15} \times 4500 \times 3.19 \times 60 = \quad -458\,000$$

$$+\frac{1}{3} \times 4500 \times 11.15 \times 60 = \underline{\quad 100\,200}$$
$$\text{Total} \quad -1\,954\,000$$

Internal span flexibilities

$$+\frac{2}{3} \times 15\,750 \times 19.95 \times 150 = \quad 31\,500\,000$$

$$-15\,750 \times 11.15 \times 150 = -26\,400\,000$$

$$-\frac{8}{15} \times 28\,125 \times 19.95 \times 150 = -44\,900\,000$$

$$+\frac{2}{3} \times 28\,125 \times 11.15 \times 150 = \underline{\quad 3\,150\,000}$$
$$\text{Total} \quad -8\,300\,000$$

$$EI_{Girder}D_{10} = -(1\,954\,000 \times 2 + 8\,300\,000)$$

$$= -12\,208 \times 10^3 \text{ tm}^3$$

$$EI_{Girder}f_{11} = \int m_1^2 \, ds + \sum S_1^2 \frac{EI_{Girder}}{EA_{Cable}} S$$

$$+ \sum H_1^2 \frac{EI_{Girder}}{EA_{Hanger}} + \sum H_1^2 \frac{EI_{Girder}}{EA_{Tower}} S$$

External span

$$\frac{8}{15} \times 19.95 \times 150 = \quad 31\,800$$

$$-\frac{2}{3} \times 19.95^2 \times 11.15 \times 150 = -22\,200$$

$$-\frac{2}{3} \times 19.95^2 \times 11.15 \times 150 = -22\,200$$

$$11.15^2 \times 150 = \quad\underline{18\,700}$$
$$\text{Total} \quad +6\,300$$

$$\int m_1^2 \, ds = +8886$$

$$\frac{EI_{Girder}}{EA_{Cable}} \sum_1^{18} s_i S_i^2 = 2 \times 7.6 \times 159.85$$

$$= 2430$$

Table 6.3. Span flexibilities (see also Fig. 6.19)

Points	S_i	s_i	$s_i S_i^2$	
1	1.02	15.300	15.95	
2	1.046	15.700	17.12	
3	1.082	16.240	19.00	
4	1.125	16.880	21.38	
5	1.109	16.600	20.40	
6	1.066	16.000	18.15	
7	1.035	15.550	16.65	$e/s_i = \cos\alpha_i$
8	1.012	15.200	15.95	$s_i = e = 15\,\text{m}$
9	1.001	15.020	$\underline{15.25}$	
			$\sum 159.85$	

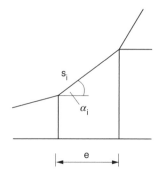

Figure 6.19. Angles for span flexibilities

Hangers

Total $17 - 2 = 15$

y_i is known previously

$$\sum s_i = 110.18\,\text{m}$$

$$\frac{\text{EI}_{\text{Girder}}}{\text{EA}_{\text{Hanger}}} H_i^2 \sum s_i = 20(0.106)^2 \times 110.18$$

$$= 24.8$$

Towers

$$H_4 = H_{14} = -0.992\,\text{ton}$$

Height

$$S_4 = S_{14} = 21.5\,\text{m} = h$$

$$\frac{\text{EI}_{\text{Girder}}}{\text{EA}_{\text{Tower}}} \sum H_i^2 S = 2(-0.902)^2 \times 0.8 \times 2.15$$

$$= 33.8$$

$$\text{EI}_{\text{Girder}} f_{11} = 8886 + 2430 + 24.8 + 33.8$$

$$= 11\,374.6$$

$$X_1 = -\frac{D_{10}}{f_{11}} = 1072\,\text{ton\,m}$$

Moments due to UDL

Due to $T = 10 - 0.00708(1072) = 2.4\,\text{ton/m}$

Due to $w = \dfrac{2.4}{10} = 0.24$

$M_B = M_C = 0.24 \times 15\,750 = 3870\,\text{tm}$

$m_{ab} = m_{cd} = 0.24 \times 4500 = 1080\,\text{tm}$

$m_{bc} = 0.24 \times 28\,125 = 6750\,\text{tm}$

Shear force due to UDL (see Fig. 6.20)

$-\dfrac{M_B}{l_1} = \dfrac{3780}{60} = 63$

$0.5LT = 30 \times 2.4 = 72$

$V = \text{reaction} = R = 72 - 63 = 9\,\text{tons}$

At x when $M = 0$

$$2.4\frac{x^2}{2} = \frac{2 \times 9}{2.4} = 75\,\text{m} \quad m = 0$$

Point of zero shear $= \dfrac{9}{2.4} = 3.75\,\text{m} \quad V = 0 \quad (M_{\max})$

$M_{\max}(\text{positive}) = 2.4 \times 7.5^2 = 16.85\,\text{tm}$

$(\text{LHS})\ \text{shear} = R_{BL} = 72 + 63 = 135\,\text{tons}$

$(\text{RHS})\ \text{shear} = R_{BR} = 2.4 \times 75 = 180\,\text{tons}$

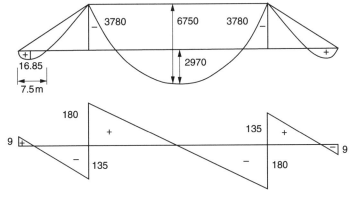

Figure 6.20. Shear forces due to UDL

Forces M and V in each member:

$$\text{vertical tension } V = 1.06 \times 1072 = 113.8 \, \text{tons}$$

$$\text{moment between hangers} = \frac{w(15)^2}{8}$$

Final bending moment and shear force $= 281 \, \text{(tm)}$

Actual deflection
ΔS, i.e. shortening of hanger:

$$\text{EI}_{\text{Girder}} \Delta S = (\text{EI})_{\text{Girder}} D_{10} + X_1 \text{EI}_{\text{Girder}} f_{11}$$

$$M_{\text{st}} = +m_{\text{st}_0} + X_1 m_{\text{st}_1}$$

$$= -15\,750 + X_1(11.15)$$

$$X_1 = 1414 \, \text{ton}$$

$$\text{EI}_{\text{Girder}} \Delta S = -12\,208 \times 10^3 + 1414 \times 11\,374.6$$

$$\Delta S = 38.8 \, \text{cm}.$$

6.3 Cable-stayed bridges

During the last three decades the vast developments within cable-stayed bridge technology have favoured this type of bridge, with engineers moving away from suspension bridge design. Computers carrying out three-dimensional static and dynamic analyses helped considerably in making cable-stayed bridge design easier. For long-span bridges, suspension type remains favoured. Aesthetically, cable-stayed bridges enjoy an advantage over the steel truss clearly visible with suspension bridges. Cable-stayed bridges can be looked upon as essentially a beam/girder bridge supported at several positions by cables in *fan* and *Harper-type* formations. Various shapes of towers or pylons have been suggested for this type of bridge (Fig. 6.21). Tables 6.4–6.9 and Figs. 6.22–6.32 illustrate some typical designs of the well-known cable-stayed bridges in the world. In this respect, the reader is also directed to the bibliography on the subject at the end of the text.

This section gives both design examples and stayed technology in detail. A number of design and analytical techniques is included for cables, cable–tower interaction, cable–deck interaction and cable-stay-bridge components using limit states and the following:

(*a*) flexibility method
(*b*) stiffness method
(*c*) influence lines
(*d*) 2-D and 3-D finite element methods.

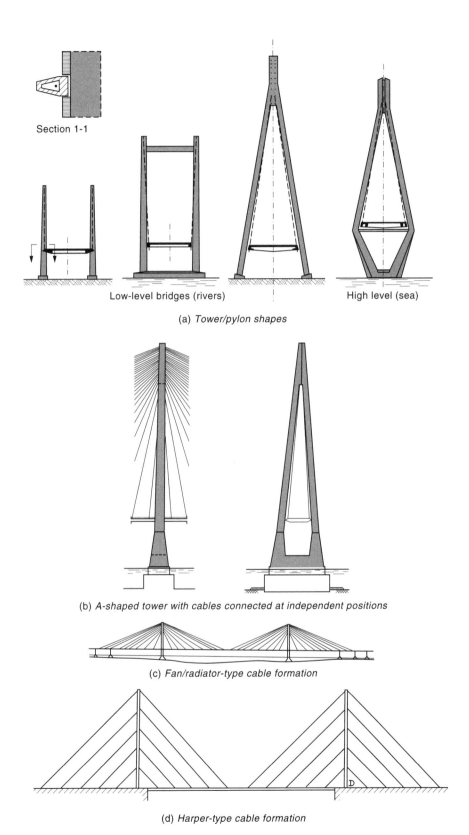

Section 1-1

Low-level bridges (rivers)   High level (sea)

(a) *Tower/pylon shapes*

(b) *A-shaped tower with cables connected at independent positions*

(c) *Fan/radiator-type cable formation*

(d) *Harper-type cable formation*

Figure 6.21. Tower and pylon types for the cable-stayed bridge

Table 6.4 (pages 790–793). Examples of world-wide cable-stayed bridges with details

Bridge	Main span and deck type	Side spans	Pylon (h)
Ikuchi, Japan (multi-stay fan type)	490 m Deck: steel girder width 20.0 m	2NO: 150 m Deck: concrete; girder width 20.0 m	120.2 m 117.8 m
Skytrain, Vancouver, Canada (multi-stay fan type)	340 m Deck: concrete as side spans	2NO: 138 m Deck: concrete width 12.50 m	Dimensions not known A-shaped
James River, USA (multi-stay fan type)	192.024 m Deck: prestressed box girder width 75.1 m	3NO: 45.72 m 3NO: 45.72 m with three column piers each side 2 side spans	Dimensions not known column-shaped
Nanpu, Shanghai, China (multi-stay fan type)	423 m Deck: concrete	2NO: 94.5 m 76.5 m Deck: concrete	A-shaped
Second Severn, UK (Multi-stay fan type)	456 m Deck width 35 m steel truss girder	2NO: 2 side spans 99 m Same as main span	Double-taper vertical H-Type single braced 137.2 m
Straits of Messina, Italy (multi-stay fan type with cross cables)	1300 m Deck width 57.50 m steel girder truss type	2NO: 540 m	294.50 m A-shaped
Cassagne, France (multi-stay fan type)	156.0 m	2NO: 39.0 m each	Single braced column type 29.0 m
Tempul Aqueduct, Spain (single cable-stay type)	60.30 m	2NO: spans 20.10 m	
Helgeland, Norway (multi-stay fan type)	425 m Deck: concrete width 11.95 m	2NO: 117.50 m	Column type 127.3 m
Baytown, Texas, USA	381.0 m Deck: concrete girder 23.83 m	2NO: 146.9 m	Twin type A-shaped, jointed 129.84 m
Bonn, Germany	280 m	2NO: 120.10 m	Column type

(Continued)

Table 6.4. (Continued)

Bridge	Main span and deck type		Side spans	Pylon (h)
China:	Span (m)		Deck width (m)	(m)
Yunyang, Sichuan	75.8	3.8		10.7
Xinwu, Shanghai	54.0	6.6		14.5
Daguhe, Shandong	104.0	10.0		17.5
Ankang, Shaanxi	120.0	12.0		26.0
Sandai, Sichuan	128.0	10.5		30.0
Hongshuihe, Guangxi	96.0	5.6 →	2NO: 85 m	26.6 (railway)
Changxingdao, Liaoning	176.0	8.4		40.6
Jinchuan, Sichuan	70.0	5.5		24.5
Maogang, Shanghai	200.0	11.2		42.5
Jinan Huanghe, Shandong	220.0	29.5 →	2NO: 2, 94.40 m 94.40 m	29.5
Zhangzhen, Zhejiang	72.0	10.7		29.5
Xiqiaoshan, Guangdong	124.6	16.0 →	110.0 m	50.0
Henfeng North Road, Shanghai	76.6	24.1		
Dongying Huanghe, Shandong	288.0	19.5		56.4 (steel)
Yonghe, Tianjin	260.0	14.5 →	2NO: 2, 99.8 m 25.2 m	50.6*
Dong feng, Yunnan	100.0	8.0		23.5
Jiujiang, Guangdong	160.0	16.0		80.0
Haiying, Guangzhou	175.0	35.0		57.4
Shimen, Sichuan	230.0	25.5		113.7
Bengbu, Anhui	224.0	18.8		55.0
Tongzilin, Sichuan	120.0	13.1		51.2
Jianwei, Sichuan	240.0	14.6		56.9
Fendai, Anhui	224.0	18.8		55.0
Xiangjiang, Hunan	220.0	30.1		53.7
Yangpu, Shanghai	602		2NO: 2, 162 m 81 m each side	200 m A-shaped
Knie, Düsseldorf, Germany	319 m deck width steel girder 29.3 m		242.16 m	Column type 94.56 m
Arno, Italy	206 m deck width steel 22.50 m		2NO: 70.5 m	Not known
Great Belt, Denmark	349.90 m deck width steel girder 44.50 m		1NO: 349.90 m	
Brotonne, France	320 m concrete truss girder deck width 19.20 m		2NO: 143.50 m	Column type 70 m

(Continued)

Table 6.4. (Continued)

Bridge	Main span and deck type	Side spans	Pylon (h)
Fieh, Düsseldorf, Germany	780 m Deck: steel girder width 41.7 m (multi-stay fan type)	1NO: 368 m	129.51 m Column on A-shaped
New Burrard, Vancouver, Canada	762 m (multi-stay fan type)	2NO: 335 m	200.56 m A-shaped
CS Riddes, Switzerland	145 m Deck width 29 m (multi-stay fan type)	2NO: 70 m	3NO: columns joined at 14.5 m spaces 33 m
Rio-Parana, Argentina	330 m (multi-stay fan type)	2NO: 110 m	70 m
Pasco-Kennewick, USA	299 m Deck steel girder 2 width 24.54 m	2NO: 123.9 m	H-type shaped horizontally braced at two places 72.94 m
Rio Ebro, Spain	137.12 m steel Deck width 28.90 m (multi-stay fan type)		Column type 59.80 m
Fato, Denmark	290 m (multi-stay fan type) steel deck width 22.40 m	2NO: 120 m	A over V shape A 70.70 m V 24.40 m
Hoechst, Frankfurt, Germany	148.2 m (multi-stay fan type) steel deck width 30.95 m	1NO: 94 m	Twin column 52.47 m
Luna, Spain	440 m (multi-stay fan type) prestressed concrete deck	2NO: 101.71 m	H-type bottom splayed 90 m
Diepoldsau, Switzerland	97.0 m (multi-stay fan type) deck width 14.50 m	2NO: 40.50 m	28.70 m H-type, splayed legs
Rio-Magdalena, Spain	140 m deck width 12.5 m	–	–
Hooghly, Calcutta, India	457.20 m	2NO: 182.68 m	

(Continued)

Table 6.4. (Continued)

Bridge	Main span and deck type	Side spans	Pylon (h)
Arnacis Island, Vancouver, Canada	465 m (multi-stay fan type) deck prestressed girder open web width 29.30 m	2NO: 196.25 m	Tuning fork type H-braced at two locations 102 m tuning fork 59.6 m twisted leg inside
East Huntington, Washington, USA	274.32 m deck width 12.20 m	1NO: 186.32 m	A-type horizontally braced at two positions 89.73 m

* 13.6 m deck; two triangular boxes

Table 6.5. Properties of wire for the Toyosato–Ohhashi Bridge. See also Fig. 6.24

	Properties
Ultimate tensile load	More than 3240 kg
Ultimate tensile stress σ_{ult}	165/185 kg/mm^2
0.7% proof stress	122 kg/mm^2
Strain corresponding to σ_{ult}	More than 4% (gauge length 250 mm)
Dulcility	Wire should not be broken, when it is bounded around a shaft of 15 mm in diameter
Straitness	When individual wire of 10 m in length is laid off, the diameter of rounded wire and the height of its end snaking up should be more than 2 m and less than 45 cm, respectively

Table 6.6. Tensile test of curved strand for the Toyosato–Ohhashi Bridge. See also Fig. 6.24

Specimen	Breaking point	Ultimate tensile load t	Ultimate tensile stress kg/mm^2
PPWS-61(A)	E	209	175
PPWS-61(B)	E	214	179
PPWS-91(A)	E	310	173
PPWS-91(B)	E	314	175

Table 6.7. Stress of strand: Load A (calculated value 809.8 kg/cm²,
average of experimental value 783.8 kg/cm²). See also Fig. 6.25

Strand I	C-1	C-2	C-3	C-4	Average
	738.4	746.6	726.6	720.0	733.0
Stand II	C-5	C-6	C-7	C-8	Average
	861.6	846.6	790.0	840.0	834.6

Table 6.8. Stress of strand: Load B (calculated value 286.0 kg/cm²,
average of experimental value 304.0 kg/cm²). See also Fig. 6.25

Strand I	C-1	C-2	C-3	C-4	Average
	313.4	303.4	315.0	308.4	310.0
Stand II	C-5	C-6	C-7	C-8	Average
	301.6	298.4	291.6	300.0	298.0

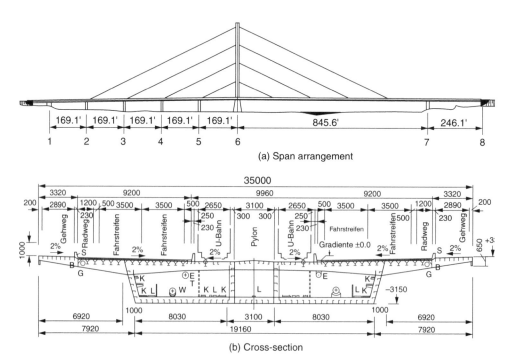

(a) Span arrangement

(b) Cross-section

Figure 6.22. Oberkassel Bridge, Germany

Table 6.9. Bridge statistics for the Second Severn Crossing

Client	UK Department of Transport
Concessionaire	Severn River Crossing plc
Design & Construction Joint Venture	John Laing Construction and GTM-Europe
Government Agent	G. Maunsell & Partners
Design Joint Venture	Halcrow/SEEE
Architect	Percy Thomas Partnership
Finance	Barclays de Zoete Wedd and Bank of America
Overall length of crossing structure	5126 metres
Length of main bridge	948 metres
Length of main span	456 metres
Navigation clearance	37 metres
Length of Gwent approach viaduct	2077 metres
Length of Avon approach viaduct	2102 metres
Height of main span pylon towers	137 metres
Number of approach spans – Gwent side	22
Number of approach spans – Avon side	23
Maximum height of approach piers	34 metres
Number of foundations in caissons	37
Total volume of concrete required	420 000 cu metres
Weight of reinforced steel	45 000 tonnes
Weight of structural steel	7500 tonnes
Total length of pre-stressing steel	6860 km
Number of cable stays in main bridge	420
Total number of concrete deck units	2302
Total number of pre-cast pier units	336
Total area of waterproofing	168 000 sq metres
Total area of surfacing	204 000 sq metres
Men and women employed at peak	1000
Construction period	4/1992 – 4/1996

Cable-stayed bridge technology is a vast subject but the author has carefully summarized it, so that the reader can pick essential analytical and design details without spending too much time in searching for them. The bibliography will help further those who wish to carry out an in-depth study.

6.4 Stay technology
6.4.1 Introduction
Cable steel used for the manufacture of stays requires high quality of anchorages. Prior to the design of suspension and cable-stayed bridges, durability and load-bearing capacity need to be examined. Protective measures demand

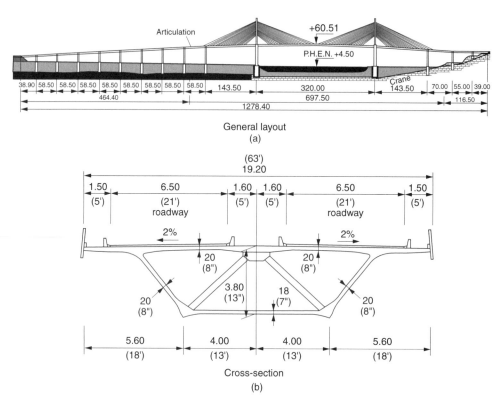

Figure 6.23. Brotonne Bridge, France

that these along with static, fatigue and corrosion resistance require thorough examination and assessment. This section deals with some of these aspects.

6.4.2 Cables and types
The requirements for the stay cables are

(1) high load-bearing capacity
(2) high and stable modulus of elasticity
(3) compact cross-section
(4) high fatigue and corrosion resistance.

The following suspension systems are used

(*a*) parallel bar cables
(*b*) parallel wire cables
(*c*) stranded cables
(*d*) locked-coil cables.

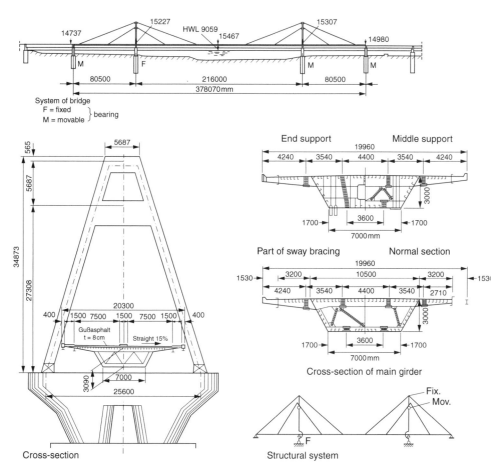

Figure 6.24. Toyosato–Ohhashi Bridge, Osaka, Japan. For structural details see Tables 6.5–6.8

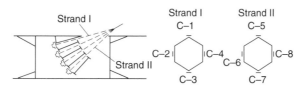

Figure 6.25. Schematic illustrating strand stress for the Toyosato–Ohhashi Bridge. See also Tables 6.7 and 6.8

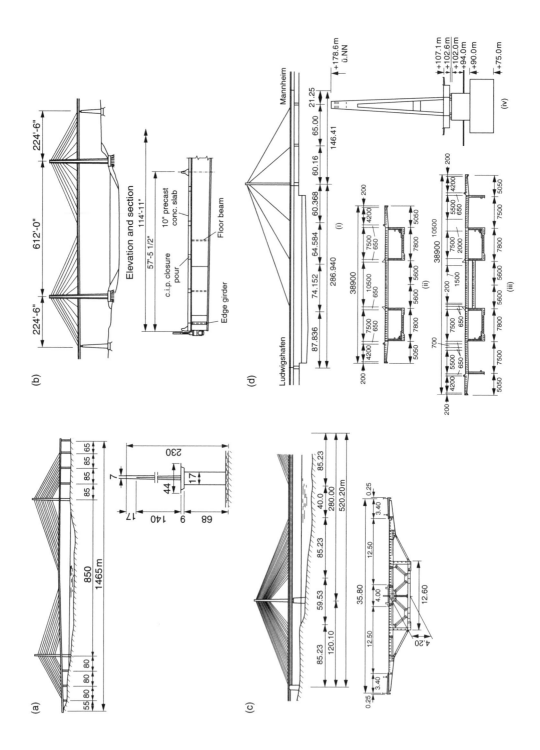

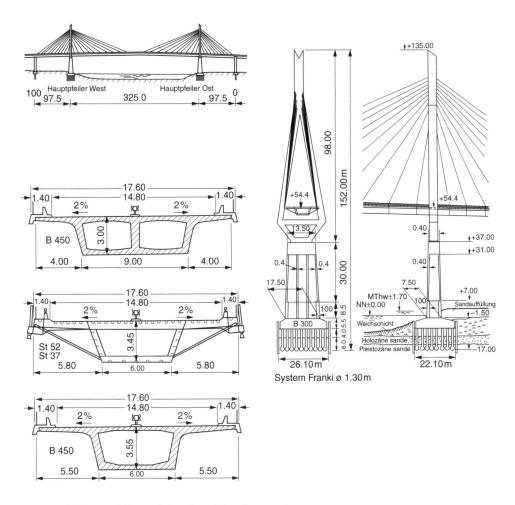

Figure 6.27. Köhlbrand Bridge, Hamburg, Germany

Figure 6.26 (facing). (a) The Upper Bridge, Hamburg, Germany. (b) James River Bridge, USA. (c) Friedrich-Ebert Bridge, Bonn, Germany. (d) Nordbrücke Mannheim–Ludwigshafen Bridge, Germany: (i) elevation; (ii) typical cross-section; (iii) cross-section in the area of the sloping car ramp; and (iv) cross-section at the pylon

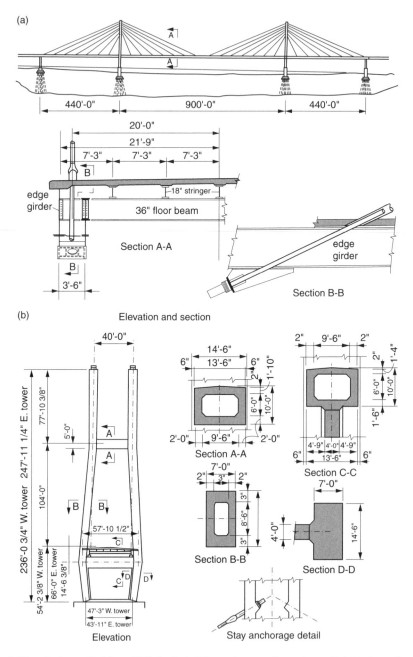

Figure 6.28. Quincy Bridge, USA. (a) Elevation and section. (b) Pylon elevation and sections

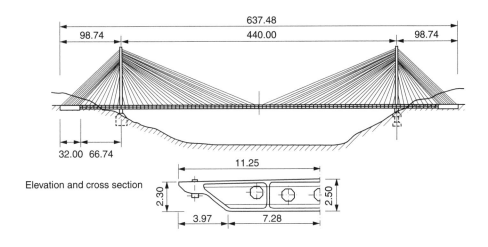

Elevation and cross section

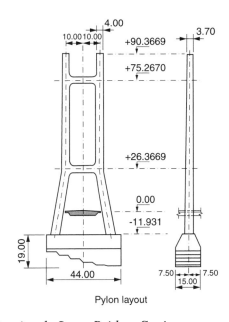

Pylon layout

Figure 6.29. Barrios de Luna Bridge, Spain

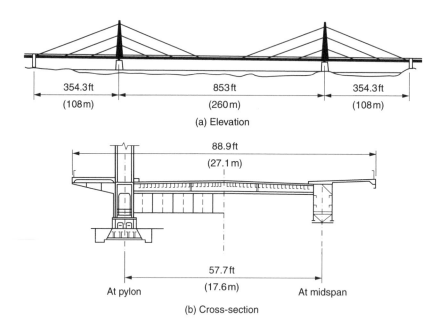

(a) Elevation

354.3 ft
(108 m)

853 ft
(260 m)

354.3 ft
(108 m)

88.9 ft
(27.1 m)

At pylon

57.7 ft
(17.6 m)

At midspan

(b) Cross-section

Figure 6.30. Theodore Heuss-Brücke, Düsseldorf, Germany

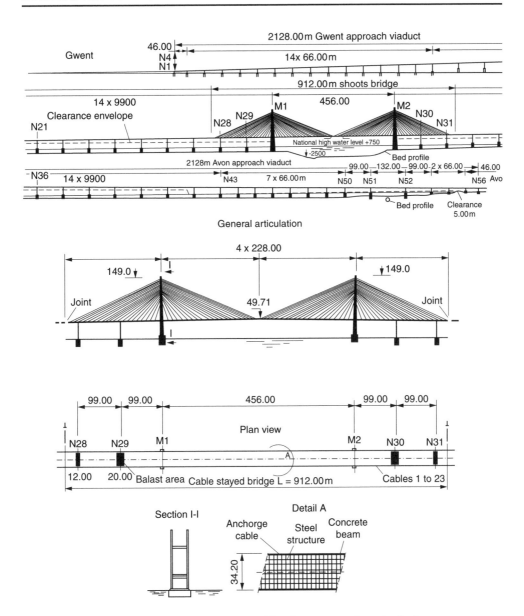

Figure 6.31. Second Severn cable-stayed bridge, general articulation

Plate 6.2. Cable-stayed bridge over the River Lerez, Spain, showing A-shaped pylon with cables of independent positions similar to that shown in Figure 6.21(b) (courtesy CASADO SL)

Figure 6.32. Second Severn Crossing

6.4.3 *Explanations of these systems*

Figures 6.33–6.37 and Tables 6.10–6.14 give structural details and material data for various systems and their anchorages. A parallel wire system (PWS) is a bundle of prestressing wires incorporated in a polyethylene pipe filled with cement grout. They are generally associated with HiAm (high amplitude) anchor sockets as the end fillings. The PWS (wire strand) and PWC (wire cables) are widely used. The wires are available with 7 mm diameter and a strength of 1470/1670 N/mm^2. The biggest cable manufactured so far is 499 $\oslash$ 7 mm wires with $P_{\mathrm{ult}} = 32.1$ MN. The BBRV uses button heads at the ends of the wires or strands sitting on steel plate to set a steel ball. These are HiAm anchorages with stress amplitude of the big cables of $\Delta\sigma = 300$ N/mm^2 normally resisted over 2×10^6 cycles.

VSL has developed wedge anchorages for strands with yielding fatigue amplitude of $\Delta\sigma = 200$ N/mm^2. Tables 6.10–6.14 give various material and anchorage properties for three different systems, namely, BBRV, VSL and Freyssinet. Structural details are given in Tables 6.15–6.20. For corrosion protection, a polyethylene (PE) pipe around the wire or strand bundle is considered the best solution.

At the tower, cables running over a saddle are avoided, instead, they are anchored at each side separately and thus can easily be accessible. Neoprene dampers and rubber sleeves are encased in the concrete. The dampers prevent

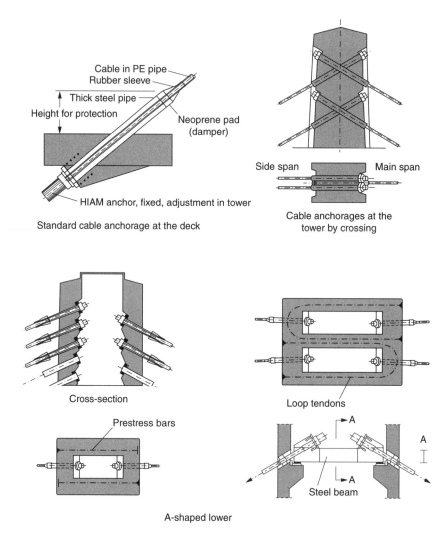

Figure 6.33. BBRV HiAm anchorages (see also Table 6.10)

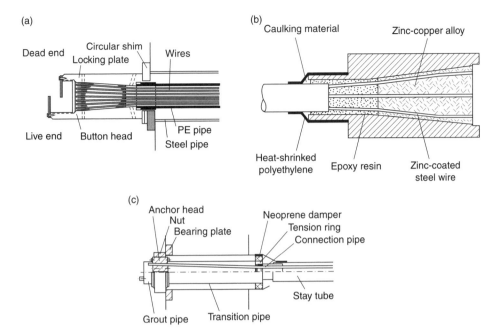

Figure 6.34. (a) BBRV HiAm anchorage. (b) Zinc-alloy filled socket as anchorage, here the 'new PWS' type of Nippon Steel Co. (c) VSL wedge anchorage for strands (see also Table 6.11)

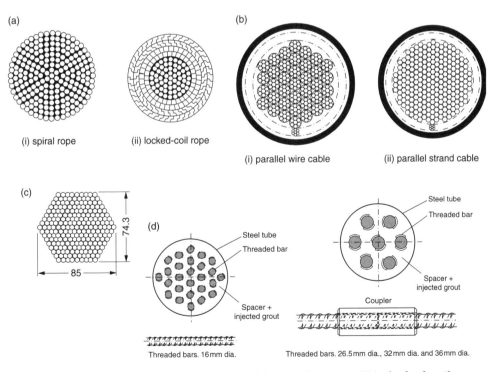

Figure 6.35. (a) Examples of ropes: (i) spiral rope; (ii) locked-coil rope. (b) Examples of cables: (i) parallel wire cable; (ii) parallel strand cable. (c) An example of PWS. (d) Parallel bar cables

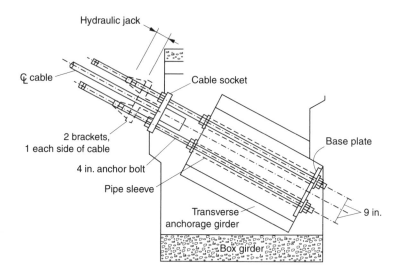

Figure 6.36. Cable anchorage at the girder of the Chaco/Corrientes Bridge

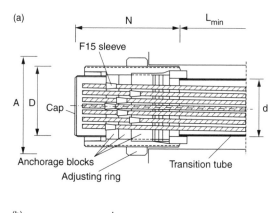

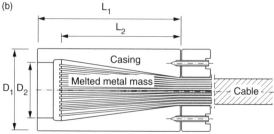

Figure 6.37. (a) Movable Freyssinet anchorage, type HC, for strands.
(b) Anchorage for locked-coil cable (see also Tables 6.12 and 6.13)

Table 6.10. *Loads and dimensions of HiAm anchorages*

Number of wires	61	91	121	163	211	253	313
Ultimate load (at β_z) (kN)	3922	5850.8	7779.7	10480.1	13566.3	16266.6	20124.3
Service load (at $0.45\beta_z$) (kN)	1764.9	2832.9	3500.9	4716	6104.8	7320	9056
D (mm)	200	230	250	290	320	340	380
d (mm)	110	125	140	160	180	180	200
Movable anchorage, L_1 (mm)	350	410	460	520	590	640	710
Fixed anchorage, L_2 (mm)	320	370	400	450	500	540	590

Table 6.11. *Dimensions of movable VSL anchorages*

Number of strands		7	12	19	31	37	61	91
Euronorme 138-79	$\oslash$ 15.7 mm — Ultimate load (at β_z) (kN)	1858.50	3186.0	5044.50	8230.50	9823.50	16195.5	24160.50
	Service load (at $0.45\beta_z$) (kN)	836.30	1433.70	2270.0	3703.70	4420.60	7288.0	10872.20
ASTM A 416-74 Grade 270	$\oslash$ 15.2 mm — Ultimate load (at β_z) (kN)	1822.80	3124.80	4947.60	8072.4	9634.80	15884.40	23696.40
	Service load (at $0.45\beta_z$) (kN)	820.30	1406.20	2226.40	3632.60	4335.70	7148.0	10663.40
$A \oslash$ (mm)		210	240	290	340	370	460	550
$D \oslash$ (mm)		160	190	230	280	300	380	450
$B \square$ (mm)		240	320	400	480	530	660	810
for $\beta_{w28} \geq 45$ N/mm²								
$d \oslash$ (mm)		90	110	125	160	180	200	250
L_{min} (mm)		400	700	1100	1350	1600	2300	2800

Table 6.12. Dimensions of movable Freyssinet anchorages, type HC

Number of strands		27	37	48	61	75	91
Euronorme 138-79	⌀ 15.7 mm	Ultimate load (at β_z) (kN)	7168.5	9823.5	12744.0	16195.5	19912.5	24160.5
		Service load (at 0.45β_z) (kN)	3225.8	4420.6	5734.8	7288.0	8960.5	10872.2
ASTM A416-74 Grade 270	⌀ 15.2 mm	Ultimate load (at β_z) (kN)	7030.8	9634.8	12499.2	15884.4	14530.0	23696.4
		Service load (at 0.45β_z) (kN)	3163.9	4335.7	5624.6	7148.0	8788.5	16663.4
$A \oslash$ (mm)			315	350	410	430	440	475
$D \oslash$ (mm)			232	260	302	320	346	385
$d \oslash$ (mm)			168.3	193.7	219.1	244.5	273	292
N (mm)			370	380	390	420	460	500
L (mm)			1200	1500	1700	2000	2300	2500

Table 6.13. Dimensions of movable Freyssinet anchorages, type H

Number of strands*				37	61	91
Euronorme 138-79	⌀ 15.7 mm	Ultimate load (at β_z) (kN)		9823.5	16 195.5	24 160.5
		Service load (at $0.45\beta_z$) (kN)		4420.6	7288.0	10 872.2
ASTM A416-74 Grade 270	⌀ 15.2 mm	Ultimate load (at β_z) (kN)		9634.8	15 884.4	23 696.4
		Service load (at $0.45\beta_z$) (kN)		4335.7	7148.0	10 663.4
A ⌀ (mm)		Upper position[†]		410	490	565
		Lower position[†]		430	515	600
D ⌀ (mm)		Upper position[†]		275	350	450
		Lower position[†]		305	380	450
B ☐ (mm)				540	685	835
d ⌀ (mm)				160	195	245
L (mm)				650	840	1060
M_{max}				250	350	500

* With standard dimensions.
[†] Position of anchorage with respect to the cable.

oscillations and they are placed at a distance to the anchors. At the top, there is always a thick soft neoprene pad provided to stop flexural movements of the cable. The top is therefore sealed with a rubber sleeve. The simplest solution is to cross the cables and place the sockets outside the tower head. Sometimes the anchors are placed inside the box section of the tower (pylon) head and transfer the horizontal forces from one end to the other in the longitudinal walls of the box section by prestressing them with bars or loops.

The *locked-coil rope* consists of a core of round wires and z-shaped wires. The z-shaped wires as shown in Fig. 6.35(a)(ii) are locked side by side in every layer which makes the cross-section solid and durable.

Table 6.14. Dimensions of anchorages for locked-coil cables [see Fig. B6.37(b)]

Cable diameter (mm)	75	80	85	90	95	100
Ultimate load (at β_z) (kN)	5999	6826	7706	8638	9626	10 665
Service load (at $0.45\beta_z$) (kN)	2700	3072	3468	3887	4332	4799
D_1 (mm)	240	255	270	285	300	320
D_2 (mm)	175	185	200	210	220	240
L_1 (mm)	565	600	645	680	715	760
D_2 (mm)	375	400	425	450	475	500

Table 6.15. Capacity of normal bars

Quality of steel	St 85/105			St 110/125			St 135/150
Nominal diameter (mm)	26.5	32	36	26.5	32	36	16
Nominal cross-section of steel (mm²)	551.5	804.2	1017.9	551.5	804.2	1017.9	201.1
0.2% proof stress, $\sigma_{0.2}$ (N/mm²)	835	835	835	1080	1080	1080	1325
Ultimate strength, β_z (N/mm²)	1030	1030	1030	1230	1230	1230	1470
Ultimate load per bar (kN)	568	828.4	1048.4	678.4	989.2	1252	295.6
Service load per bar (at $0.45\beta_z$) (kN)	225.6	372.7	471.8	305.3	445.1	563.4	133

Table 6.16. Capacity of normal parallel-wire cables, 7 mm diameter

Number of wires	1	61	91	121	163	211	253	313
Nominal cross-section of steel (mm²)	38.5	2348.5	3503.5	4658.5	6275.5	8123.5	9740.5	12050.5
0.2% proof stress, $\sigma_{0.2}$ (N/mm²)	1520	1520	1520	1520	1520	1520	1520	1520
Ultimate strength, β_z (N/mm²)	1670	1670	1670	1670	1670	1670	1670	1670
Ultimate load (kN)	64.3	3922	5850.8	7779.7	10480.1	13556.3	16266.6	20124.3
Service load (at $0.45\beta_z$) (kN)	18.9	1764.9	2632.9	3500.9	4716	6104.8	7320	9056

Table 6.17. Capacity of usual strand cables

	37 strands		61 strands		91 strands	
	Ultimate load (at β_z) (kN)	*Service load (at $0.45\beta_z$) (kN)*	*Ultimate load (at β_z) (kN)*	*Service load (at $0.45\beta_z$) (kN)*	*Ultimate load (at β_z) (kN)*	*Service load (at $0.45\beta_z$) (kN)*
Nominal diameter (mm):						
12.7	6734	3030.3	11 102	4995.9	16 562	7452.9
15.2	9634.8	4335.7	15 884.4	7148	23 696.4	10 663.4
15.7	9823.5	4420.6	16 195.5	7288	24 160.5	10 872.2
17.8	12 772.4	5747.6	21 057.2	9475.7	31 413.2	14 135.9

Table 6.18. Capacity of usual locked-coil cables

Cable diameter +3%, −1% (mm)	75	80	85	90	95	100	105	110
Nominal cross-section of steel (mm²)	3821	4348	4908	5502	6131	6793	7489	8220
Ultimate strength, β_z (N/mm²)	1570	1570	1570	1570	1570	1570	1570	1570
Ultimate load (kN)	5999	6826	7706	8638	9626	10 665	11 758	12 905
Service load (at $0.45\beta_z$) (kN)	2700	3072	3468	3887	4332	4799	5291	5807

Table 6.19. Comparison of cable types

Type of cable	Coupled bars 7 ⌀ 236 steel 835/1030		Uncoupled bars 26 ⌀ 16	Parallel wires 128 ⌀ 7	Strands 27 ⌀ 15	Locked-coil cables
Structure	Bars ⌀ 26.5, 32, 36 mm		Bars ⌀ 16 mm	Wires ⌀ 6, 7 mm	Strands ⌀ 0.5, 0.6, 0.7 in of 7 twisted wires	Wires with different profiles ⌀ 2.9–7 mm
0.2% proof stress, $\sigma_{0.2}$ (N/mm²)	835	1080	1350	1470	1570 ~ 1670	–
Ultimate tensile strength, β_z (N/mm²)	1030	1230	1500	1670	1770 ~ 1870	1000 ~ 1300
Fatigue						
$\Delta\sigma$ (N/mm²)	80		–	350	300 ~ 320	120 ~ 150
σ_{max}/β_z	0.60		–	0.45	0.5 ~ 0.45	~0.45
Modulus of elasticity, E (N/mm²)	210 000		210 000	205 000	190 000 ~ 200 000	160 000 ~ 165 000
Failure load (kN)	7339		7624	7487	7634	7310

Table 6.20. Strand capacities for different standards

Nominal diameter:				
mm	12.7	15.2	15.7	17.8
inch	0.5	0.6	0.6	0.7
Standard	SIA 162	ASTM A 416-74 Grade 270	Euronorme 138-79	SIA 162
Nominal cross-section of steel (mm^2)	100	140	150	195
0.2% proof stress, $\sigma_{0.2}$ (N/mm^2)	(1500) 1640 (1700)	(1500) 1670 (1700)	(1500) 1570 (1700)	(1500) 1590 (1700)
Ultimate strength, β_z (N/mm^2)	(1700) 1820 (1900)	(1700) 1860 (1900)	(1700) 1770 (1900)	(1700) 1770 (1900)
Ultimate load per strand (kN)	182	260.4	265.5	345.2
Service load per strand (at $0.45\beta_z$) (kN)	81.9	117.2	119.5	155.3

For normal loads (live loads Q and dead load G), the ATSI (Tentative Criteria for Structural Applications of Steel Cables in Buildings, 1966) gives the following equation for the ultimate tension load U:

$$U = \gamma_F(G + Q) \tag{6.112}$$

$$\sigma_{adm} = \text{allowable stress} = 0.40 f_{tc} \tag{6.113}$$

$$\gamma_F = 2.5.$$

In this formulation the dynamic effect is ruled out and an emphasis is placed on its total prevention. The Germans, in their bridge code DIN 1073, give for locked-coil cables the value of σ_{adm} as $0.42 f_{ct}$ and for parallel wires σ_{adm} as $0.45 f_{ct}$.

In addition the fatigue stress is limited to the following:

$$\Delta\sigma = 147\,\text{N/mm}^2 - \text{locked cells}$$

$$\Delta\sigma = 197\,\text{N/mm}^2 - \text{parallel wires}$$

The Post-Tensioning Institute (PTI), USA, recommends the following for fatigue $\Delta\sigma$ (N/mm^2):

AASHTO category B case	$\Delta\sigma$ (N/mm^2)
Parallel wires	162 (R)
	148 (NR)
Uncoupled bars	127 (R)
Parallel strands	113 (NR)

where NR = non-redundant and R = redundant.

The FIP does not allow the full use of the development of fatigue-resistant stay cables and hence recommends that the designers should take into account partial safety factor for *actions and resistance* as given below:

wires, strands, bars   *complete cable*

$\gamma_G = 1.0$ $\gamma_G = 1.0$

$\gamma_{stat} = 1.15$ –

$\gamma_{fatigue} = 1.5$ $\gamma_{fatigue} = 1.10$

The FIP recommends that acceptance criteria must be established. After fatigue loading, the specimen shall develop a minimum tensile force of 95% of the ultimate value. DIN 1073 recommends this tensile force shall be 80% of the nominal tensile strength $(0.8 f_{ct})$.

The Bureau of BBR Ltd Zurich (Report 85 1204) Cable-stayed structure, reported by Hans R. Mueller (International Conference on Cable-Stayed Bridges, Bangkok, November 1987) gives the calculations for the acceptance criteria for three cable-stayed bridges, namely Albert Bridge in Belgium, Hooghly Bridge in India and Faroe–Falser Bridge in Denmark. They are reproduced in Figs 6.38–6.42 with details given in the text in Section 6.4.4.

In all aspects, the structural components, cables and anchorages must be proof tested and the final efficiency established. The calculations for other systems must be carried out on similar lines to BBR in order to establish acceptance criteria for a particular cable-stayed bridge.

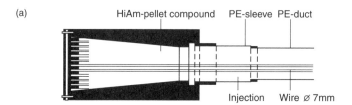

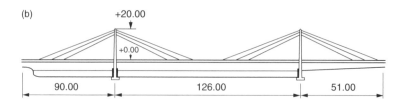

Figure 6.38. (a) HiAm anchor for the bridge stays. (b) Longitudinal section of the bridge over channel 'Albert', Belgium. Main span: 129 m (courtesy FIP Administration Office, London)

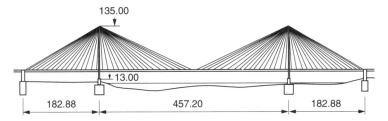

Figure 6.39. Second Hooghly River Bridge, Calcutta (longitudinal section). Main span: 457 m (courtesy CMRS, Dhanbad, Bihar, India)

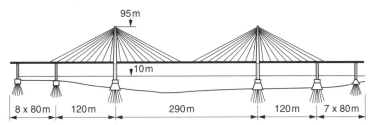

Figure 6.40. Bridge over straits Faroe–Falster, Denmark (longitudinal section). Main span 290 m (courtesy Schweizer Ingenieur und Architekt, Heft 43/1985, Zürich, Switzerland)

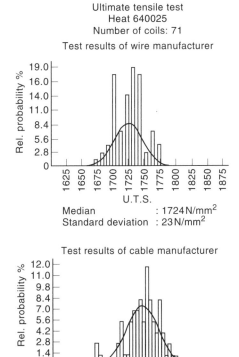

Figure 6.41. Static ultimate tensile test results (courtesy Schweizer Ingenieur und Architekt, Heft 43/1985, Zürich, Switzerland)

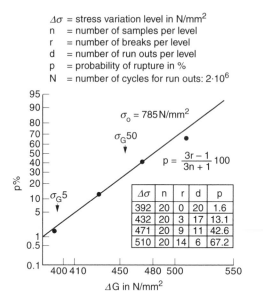

$\Delta\sigma$ = stress variation level in N/mm^2
n = number of samples per level
r = number of breaks per level
d = number of run outs per level
p = probability of rupture in %
N = number of cycles for run outs: $2 \cdot 10^6$

Figure 6.42. Results of fatigue tests: 50% fractile, 480 N/mm^2; 5% fractile, 410 N/mm^2. Wire sample (223 tons) was tested with random blocks. Sample length was 200 mm. Standard deviation: ± 55 N/mm^2 (courtesy Bureau BBR Ltd, Zürich, Switzerland)

6.4.4 Acceptance criteria and acceptance tests on stay cables for bridges

1. Bridge over channel 'Albert', Lixhe, Belgium
Acceptance test according DIN 1073 (see Fig. 6.38).

Bridge over channel 'Albert', Belgium
Longitudinal section, Main span: 129 m

Number of stays:	24
Type of stays:	BBR HiAm, 208 $\oslash$ 7 mm
Wire:	galvanized high tensile wire, 65 tons
Test specimen:	
Length:	5.9 m, 208 wire $\oslash$ 7 mm
Area of bundle:	8004 m^2
Wire material:	galvanized high tensile
Nominal UTS:	1570 N/mm^2
Average UTS:	1650 N/mm^2

(*a*) Fatigue load
upper: 5656 kN   lower: 4478 kN
$\Delta\sigma = 147$ N/mm^2
number of cycles without break: 2×10^6

(b) Static test (after fatigue load)
  Max. load   12 569 kN
                         (according to guaranteed nominal breaking force)
  Result: no break of wires nor other defects

  Efficiency: Nominal: $\dfrac{1570}{1570} = 1$

                         Actual: $\dfrac{1570}{1650} = 0.95$

  Comment: DIN 1073: Requirement for road bridges fulfilled
  Laboratory: Seilprüfstelle
                         Westfällische Berggewerkschaftskasse D-4630
                         Bochum, Germany

(c) Bibliography:
  DIN 1073: Steel road bridges, Design bases
  Beuth, Vertrieb GmbH, Berlin 30, Germany (July 1974)

  FIP Recommendations
  Practical design of reinforced and prestressed concrete structures
  Thomas Telford Ltd, London E14 4JD, UK

  Recommendations for stay cable design and testing (January 1986)
  Post-Tensioning Institute, Phoenix, AZ 85013, USA

  P. Matt, H. R. Müller, U. Morf
  Cables for cable-stayed structures
  FIP Notes 1985/I
  FIP Administrative Office, The Institution of Structural Engineers,
  London SW1X 8BM, UK

2. *Bridge over River Hooghly, Calcutta, India*
Acceptance test (see Fig. 6.39).

Number of stays: 152
Type of stay: BBR HiAm, 102–277 ⊘ 7 mm
Wire: plain high-tensile wire, 1250 tons
Test specimen:
Length: 4.0 m, 67 wire ⊘ 7 mm
Area of bundle: 2578 mm^2
Wire material: plain high tensile
Nominal UTS: 1570 N/mm^2
Average UTS: 1653 N/mm^2
Static test:
Max. load: 4115 kN (break of first wire)

Result: first break of wire at UTS 1596 N/mm^2

Efficiency: Nominal: $\dfrac{1596}{1570} = 1.02$

                           Actual: $\dfrac{1596}{1653} = 0.97$

Comment: The test specimen was a cable with reduced numbers
                           of wires and reduced dimensions of anchors to cope
                           with the available test facilities in India (max. load
                           4500 kN).
Laboratory: CMRS, Dhanbad, Bihar, India

3. Bridge over straits Faroe-Falster, Denmark

Acceptance test and quality checks (see Fig. 6.40).

Number of stays: 36
Type of stays: BBR HiAm, 145–277 ⌀ 7 mm
Wire: plain high-tensile wire, 223 tons
Test specimen:
Length: 5.75 m, 277 ⌀ 7 mm
Area of bundle: 10 659 mm^2
Wire material: plain high-tensile wire
Nominal UTS: 1670 N/mm^2
Average UTS: 1724 N/mm^2
Static test with material taken from manufacturing lot (see Fig. 6.41):
Max. load: 18 070 kN (break of first wire)
Results: actual uts 1695 N/mm^2

Efficiency: Nominal: $\dfrac{1695}{1670} = 1.01$

                           Actual: $\dfrac{1695}{1724} = 0.98$

Elongation at rupture: 3.6%

Calculation of fatigue resistance:
Test results obtained from delivered wires with 200 mm samples (see Fig. 6.42):
mean value: 480 N/mm^2
standard deviation   55 N/mm^2
Calculated value for average length of cables (110 m)
   50% fractile

$$\Delta\sigma_{(110)} = \Delta\sigma_{(0.2)} - 2.5s$$

$$= 480 - 138 = 342 \, \text{N/mm}^2$$

5% fractile

$$\Delta\sigma_{(110)} = \Delta\sigma_{(0.2)} - 3.7s$$
$$= 480 - 204 = 276 \, \text{N/mm}^2$$

Calculated fatigue resistance with partial safety coefficients:

$$\text{mean value } \Delta\sigma_{(110)} = \frac{342}{1.5} = 228 \, \text{N/mm}^2$$

$$5\% \text{ fractile } \Delta\sigma_{(110)} = \frac{276}{1.5} = 184 \, \text{N/mm}^2$$

Bibliography:
Paralleldrahtkabel für die Brücke Faroe-Falster, Dänemark
Schweizer Ingenieur und Architekt, Heft 43/1985, 8021 Zürich, Switzerland
H. R. Müller, *Cable-Stayed Structures*, Report 851204, Bureau BBR Ltd,
CH-8034 Zürich, Switzerland.

6.5 Specifications for suspension and cable-stayed bridges
6.5.1 Loads
Dead, live and wind loads for bridges are fully dealt with in this text. There is a
slight departure on the wind loading and the criteria are given below.

Wind loads
The wind load analysis is divided into:

(*a*) Static wind load;
(*b*) Dynamic wind load including buffeting.

(a) Static wind load
(i) Wind on static load
The intensity of the wind load applied horizontally at the longitudinal axis of the
bridge is computed as

$$W_h = \frac{Z^{0.2} \times V_{10}^2 \times C_h}{25.6} \quad \text{Pa} \tag{6.114}$$

$$\left(W_h = \frac{Z^{0.2} \times V_{30}^2 \times C_h}{600} \quad \text{lbs/ft}^2 \right) \tag{6.115}$$

where

$Z =$ height in m (feet) of the top of the floor system above
ground level, or 10 m (30 feet), whichever is greater

V_{10} $(V_{30}) =$ fastest mile wind speed, in km/hr (mph), at 10 m (30 feet)
above ground, for 100-year mean recurrence interval.

C_h = shape factor for horizontal wind load. C_h, unless wind tunnel data confirms different values, shall be at least

for plate and box girders $C_h = 1.5$
for trusses (applied to one plane only) $C_h = 2.3$.

Example

$$Z = 10\,\text{m}$$

$$V_{10} = 161\ \text{km/hr}$$

The wind load is $W_h = 2.4\,\text{kN/m}^2$.

(ii)   Wind on live load

The load is applied at 1.8 m (6 ft) above the deck and the magnitude of this load WL is

$$WL = \frac{Z^{0.2} \times V_{10}^2 \times C_{hl}}{25.6} \quad \text{Pa} \tag{6.116}$$

$$\left(WL = \frac{Z^{0.2} \times V_{30}^2 \times C_{hl}}{600} \quad \text{lbs/ft}^2 \right) \tag{6.117}$$

where $C_{hl} = 1.0$ and V_{10} (V_{30}) shall not exceed 89 km/hr (55 mph).

(iii)   Wind on substructure

The wind here is the same as above but various shapes have different C_h values and they are:

$C_h = 0.7$ for circular

$C_h = 1.4$ for octagonal

$C_h = 2.0$ for rectangular sections.

(iv)   Vertical wind and overturning forces

The upward force is applied at the windward quarter points. The value of C_h is given above and $C_V = 0.8$ is suitable.

(v)   Across-wind vibrations

For cable-stayed bridges, hangers and towers shall be designed to resist resonant vibrations and the corresponding critical velocity V_{crit} is evaluated as

$$V_{\text{crit}} = 3.6\,\frac{fb}{S} \quad \text{km/hr} \tag{6.118}$$

$$\left(V_{\text{crit}} = 0.68\,\frac{fb}{S} \quad \text{mph} \right) \tag{6.119}$$

where

S = Strouhal number (see Fig. 6.43)

f = frequency in Hertz

b = characteristic width of cross-section in m (ft)

$V_{crit} \not< 0.91 Z^{0.1} V_{10}$ metric

$V_{crit} \not< 0.81 Z^{0.1} V_{30}$ fps

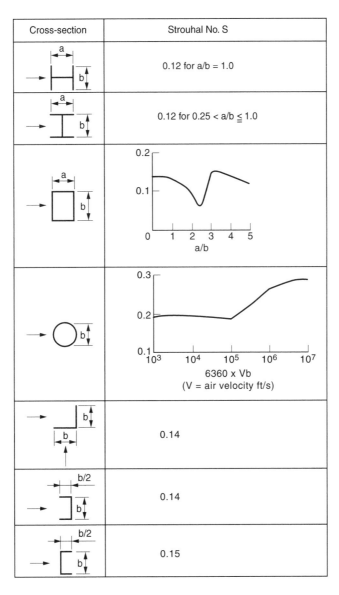

Figure 6.43. Strouhal number (ASCE Special Publication on Cable-stayed Bridges, 1996)

(b) Dynamic wind load

The motion of the cable-stayed bridge derives from the motions and aero-dynamics of cables including vortex shedding, torsional instability, flutter, buffeting and galloping. A number of steps is taken to assess the wind environment. Tests such as model and wind tunnel analyses, behaviour under erection phases and probalistic approaches for the design life, including instability, are performed.

(i) Vortex shedding

The vortex shedding frequency is computed as

$$S = \frac{nB}{V} \tag{6.120}$$

where

$n =$ frequency of vortex shedding, Hz

$B =$ depth of girder plus solid part of barrier, m (ft)

$V =$ wind speed, ms (ft/s).

Motion commences when $n = N$, where N is the modal frequency of the bridge road deck in either vertical bending or torsion. Thus the critical wind speed V_{crit} is

$$V_{crit} = \frac{NB}{S} \quad \text{m/s (ft/s)}$$

$$= 3.6 \frac{NB}{S} \text{ km/hr} \quad \left(= 0.68 \frac{NB}{S} \text{ mph} \right) \tag{6.121}$$

(ii) Torsional instability and flutter

Torsional instability shall be computed by appropriate methods. The Appendix gives some of these methods. Wind tunnel tests may be needed for a specific bridge.

(iii) Buffeting

Appropriate analytical and wind tunnel methods are needed.

(iv) Galloping

Where I-beams, H-beams and box sections are used for hangers they should be checked for galloping.

Examples

(A) The Longs Creek Bridge

The deck motion began at a wind speed of 35 km/hr (9.7 m/s) by vortex shedding:

flexure frequency $f = 0.6$ Hz   for $S = 0.62$.

(B) *The Quincy Bridge, Illinois*

$$\text{Deck width} = 132.5\,\text{m}$$

$$\text{Main span} = 274\,\text{m}$$

$$\text{Girder depth} = 1.98\,\text{m}$$

$$\text{Side spans} = 119\,\text{m}$$

$$\text{Model} = 1 : 30$$

$$\text{wind speed } \frac{V}{fB} = 4 \text{ to } 8$$

Vortex shedding (see Fig. 6.44)

$$\zeta = 0.43, \ 0.6 \text{ and } 0.84\%$$

Thermal forces
A minimum of 10°C temperature differential should be applied. A ±10°C gradient through the deck is recommended. For an open deck ±5°C gradient through the deck is recommended.

Snow and ice on superstructure
The bridge should be designed for such loadings.

Forces due to stream current and floating ice
Forces from stream flow is assessed using

$$P = 515 \times K \times V^2 \tag{6.122}$$

$$(P = K \times V^2)$$

$$P = \text{pressure in Pa (lbs/ft}^2)$$

$$V = \text{water velocity m/s (ft/s)}$$

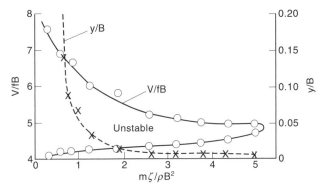

Figure 6.44. Illustrative example of vortex shedding

K = form factor: 1.4 for square ends
0.7 for circular piers
0.5 for angle ends 30° or less.

When currents may become of such magnitude that scour is possible, proper scour protection is required. Ice forces on piers shall be selected with regard to site condition and mode of ice action such as dynamic or static ice pressure, ice jams, or static uplift. Dynamic ice forces may be calculated by:

$$F = C_n \times p \times t \times w \tag{6.123}$$

where

F = ice pressure in N (pounds)

C_n = nose coefficient (1.0 = vertical nose, 0.5 = 30° to 45° nose inclination to vertical)

p = ice strength 0.7 to 2.75 N/mm^2 (100–400 lbs/in^2)

t = ice thickness mm (inch)

w = width of pier in contact with ice mm (inch)

The Appendix is used for analytical assessments.

Forces from ship collision
Piers on navigational waters should be designed for ship impact unless otherwise protected by fendering systems, etc.

A complete analysis of forces due to ship collision is given in *Impact and explosion* by Bangash (Blackwell, 1993, p. 900).

Other loads
(a)   Construction loads
During construction 100% wind on cantilevered members, 50% wind on others.
(b)   Buoyancy and earth pressure
They should be considered where necessary. A reference is made to these topics elsewhere in the text.
(c)   Fatigue loads
A reference is made to various codes.

Earthquakes
In regions where earthquakes should be anticipated, structures shall be designed to resist earthquake motions considering the relationship of the site to active faults, seismic response of soils, and the length of the structure. It may be done by an equivalent static force method, response spectrum method, or multimode spectral procedures. For complex structures a time-history response analysis may be considered.

Multimode spectral procedures should be considered especially if the acceleration coefficient for the bridge site is greater than 0.2. Unlike classical suspension bridges, vibrations of cable-stayed bridges cannot be categorized as solely vertical, lateral or torsional; instead a three-dimensional motion is associated with almost every mode of vibration. For long structures, it is furthermore obvious that the structure is subjected to different motions at each of its foundations.

The suspension and cable-stayed bridges have components with different structural properties and dimensions, they must be simulated into the main theme of the analysis. The methods of analysis must include structural damping. For seismic design, the following methods are recommended:

- (*i*)   seismic coefficient method
- (*ii*) response spectrum analysis
- (*iii*) time-history response analysis.

For detailed analysis, refer to *Prototype building structures: analysis and design* by Bangash (Thomas Telford Ltd, London, 1999, section on Earthquake Analysis).

The P-delta effect

The *P*-delta effect (geometric non-linearity) may be considered by using the nonlinear equations for beam columns. However, it is sufficiently accurate to do the calculation iteratively using the deformed structural shape.

The proper slope of the cable shall also be adjusted in each operation due to the displacement at the cable anchorage points.

Buckling load (ASCE method)

The safety factor (ν) against elastic buckling of a cable-stayed bridge may be calculated for a specific loading to

$$\nu = \frac{\int EIW'' \, \mathrm{d}s + \Sigma(C_n^2 L/EA_{(\mathrm{mod})})}{\int PW'^2 \, \mathrm{d}s} \tag{6.124}$$

where

W = mode shape ordinates

C = cable forces

L = cable length

A = cross-sectional area

E = Young's modulus

I = moment of inertia

P = axial force in member (compression positive)

$(')$ = denote derivative with respect to s

The above formula does not consider the non-linear behaviour of the material properties.

6.5.2 Cables and anchorages (American practice)

The following types of cables are generally used in cable-stayed bridges:

1. Parallel bars
2. Parallel seven-wire strands
3. Parallel or semi-parallel wire cables
4. Locked-coil strands and ropes
5. Helical galvanized bridge strands

The first two types are extensively used in prestressed concrete structures and when applied as cables in stayed girders bridges, a very similar installation technology is used. The cable is installed in a polyethylene tube or steel pipe which is then filled with grout. The grout adds about 30% to the weight of the cable. This adds to the cable sag and decreases its stiffness.

The three latter types have been used for a long time in structures supported primarily by tension members. The guiding principle here has always been ease of inspection and maintenance.

Cable strength (American practice)

Under normal design load (dead plus live plus impact) the static stress in the cable shall not exceed 45% of the guaranteed ultimate tensile strength (GUTS) of the cable.

The design fatigue stress range of the cable is determined by tests. The fatigue strength of the cable is assumed to be the stress range at which 5% of the wires have failed when the cable is subject to an average tensile strength of 45% GUTS. The number of cycles used in the test is normally 2×10^6 for highway bridges and 1×10^7 for railway bridges.

The design fatigue stress range is defined as:

$$\Delta\sigma_{\text{Fat}} = \frac{\Delta\sigma_F}{\gamma_{\text{Fat}}} \tag{6.125}$$

where

$$\Delta\sigma_{\text{Fat}} = \sigma_{\max} - \sigma_{\min} \tag{6.125a}$$

$\Delta\sigma_F$ = fatigue stress range as determined by tests

γ_{Fat} = factor of safety may vary from 1.25 to 1.50

A reference is made to Figs 6.45–6.48 for fatigue curves.

Cable characteristics

The following details are provided for the different types of cables:

(i)   Parallel bars

$$\sigma_{\text{ut}} = \text{ultimate stess} = 1030 \, \text{N/mm}^2 \, \text{GUTS}$$

$$E_c = 200 \, \text{kN/mm}^2$$

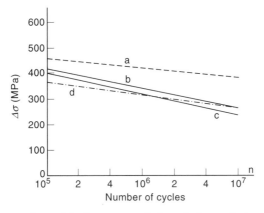

Figure 6.45. Typical Wöhler's curves deduced from fatigue test at Copenhagen University Laboratory: (a) single wire diameter 7 mm (0.276"); (b) cable with 19 wires diameter 7 mm (0.276"); (c) single strand diameter 15 mm (0.591"); (d) cable with 7 strands diameter 15 mm (0.591"); 1 MPa = 0.145 ksi (Reproduced from the Design of cable-stayed bridges, ASCE, 1992)

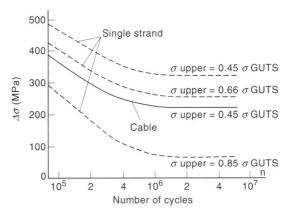

Figure 6.46. Wöhler's curves for a single strand diameter 15 mm (0.591") and a stay cable with Freyssinet anchorages (Reproduced from the Design of cable-stayed bridges, ASCE, 1992)

(*ii*)   Parallel seven-wire strands
          In cables, these generally have a diameter of 15 mm:

$$\sigma_{ut} = 1870 \, \text{N/mm}^2 \, \text{GUTS}$$

$$E_c = 1.8 \text{ to } 1.9 \times 10^5 \, \text{kN/mm}^2$$

(*iii*)   Parallel or semi-parallel wire cables
          Bright wire

$$\sigma_{ut} = 1670 \, \text{N/mm}^2 \, \text{GUTS}$$

$$E_c = 200 \, \text{kN/mm}^2$$

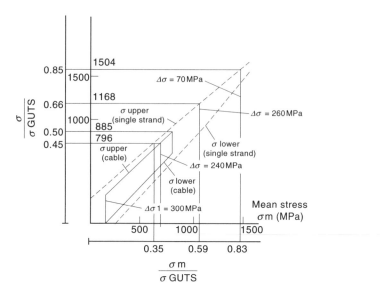

Figure 6.47. Compared Smith's diagrams for a single strand diameter 15 mm (0.591″) and a stay cable. Number of cycles: 2×10^6 (1 MPa = 0.145 ksi) (Reproduced from the Design of cable-stayed bridges, ASCE, 1992)

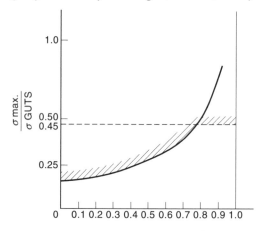

Figure 6.48. Maximum stress in terms of $X = \sigma_{lower}/\sigma_{upper}$ (Reproduced from the Design of cable-stayed bridges, ASCE, 1992)

Galvanized

$$\sigma_{ut} = 1570\,\mathrm{N/mm^2}\ \mathrm{GUTS}$$

$$E_c = 190\,\mathrm{kN/mm^2}$$

Long lay galvanized

$$\sigma_{ut} = 1570\,\mathrm{N/mm^2}\ \mathrm{GUTS}$$

$$E_c = 190\,\mathrm{kN/mm^2}$$

(*iv*) Locked-coil strands and ropes

The locked-coil strand has several layers of round wires while its rope version has several layers of differently shaped wires. They may be galvanized:

$$\sigma_{ut} = 1670 \, \text{N/mm}^2 \, \text{GUTS}$$

$$E_c = 170 \, \text{kN/mm}^2$$

(*v*) Helical galvanized strands

$$\sigma_{ut} = 670 \, \text{N/mm}^2 \, \text{GUTS}$$

$$E_c = 1.6 \text{ to } 1.65 \times 10^5 \, \text{kN/mm}^2$$

Cable non-linearity

If represented by a chord member, the instantaneous stiffness of a stayed cable is

$$EA_{(mod)} = EA \cdot \left(1 + \frac{G^2 \cos^5 \alpha \, EA}{12H^3}\right)^{-1} \tag{6.126}$$

where

$G = $ total weight of cable

$A = $ cross-sectional area

$E = $ Young's modulus

$H = $ horizontal component of cable force

$\alpha = $ angle between cable chord and horizontal

When the cable force changes and its horizontal component varies from H_1 to H_2 under a specific loading, the effective cable stiffness can be calculated as

$$EA_{(mod)} = EA \cdot \left(1 + \frac{G^2 \cos^5 \alpha \, EA(H_1 + H_2)}{24H_1^2 H_2^2}\right)^{-1} \tag{6.127}$$

This variation can be applied in the analysis iteratively.

6.6 Analysis for isolated towers under loads

6.6.1 *A tower under a concentrated load P and a horizontal reaction H at the top*

The tower under loads may deflect and twist and can also deviate from a vertical plane. As a result towers are subject to eccentric loads, and bending and twisting moments.

The vertical reaction is P. Moment $M(z)$ can be written as (see Fig. 6.49)

$$M(z) = Hz - P[\Delta - \delta(x)] \tag{6.128}$$

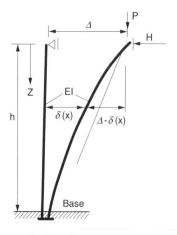

Figure 6.49. Isolated tower under loads

Now

$$EI \frac{d^2\delta(z)}{dz^2} + M(z) = 0 \tag{6.129}$$

or

$$EI \frac{d^2\delta(z)}{dz^2} + + P\delta(z) = P\Delta - Hz \tag{6.130}$$

Take $P/EI = \mu^2$ and substituting in the above equation, the expression is reduced to

$$\frac{d^2\delta(z)}{dz^2} + \mu^2\delta(z) = \mu^2\Delta - \frac{H}{EI} z \tag{6.131}$$

The solution is given by:

$$\delta(x) = A_1 \cos \mu z + A_2 \sin \mu z + \Delta - \frac{Hz}{P} \tag{6.132}$$

$$z = 0 \qquad \delta(z) = \Delta$$

$$z = h \qquad \delta(z) = 0 \qquad \frac{d\delta}{dz} = 0$$

$$\left. \begin{array}{c} A_1 = 0 \qquad A_2 = \dfrac{1}{\sin \mu h} \left(\dfrac{Hh}{P} - \Delta \right) \\[3mm] H = \dfrac{P\mu\Delta \cos \mu h}{\mu h \cos \mu h - \sin \mu h} \end{array} \right\} \tag{6.133}$$

Hence

$$\delta(z) = (\Delta) \frac{\sin \mu h - \sin \mu z - (h - z)\mu \cos \mu h}{\sin \mu h - \mu h \cos \mu h} \tag{6.134}$$

The bending moment $M(z)$ in the tower is given as

$$M(z) = -\Delta P \frac{\sin \mu h}{\sin \mu h - \mu h \cos \mu h} \tag{6.135}$$

$$M_{\text{Base}} = M(h) = -\Delta P \frac{\sin \mu h}{\sin \mu h - \mu h \cos \mu h} \tag{6.136}$$

$$M_{\max} = M_{\text{Base}} \qquad z = \frac{\pi}{2\mu} \tag{6.137}$$

$$M_{\max} = -\Delta P \frac{1}{\sin \mu h - \mu h \cos \mu h} \tag{6.138}$$

6.6.2 A tower under eccentric load P and wind load W

Wind load W is added to the tower in the longitudinal direction of the bridge. The load will have an eccentricity e to the vertical load P. Take I_v as the variable moment of inertia. The tower is divided into 'n' sections. The normal force (see Fig. 6.50)

$$P_i = \sum_{k=0}^{k=i-1} P_k$$

is caused by a concentrated load P. The transverse force V is given as

$$\Delta V_i = P_i \delta_i \tag{6.139}$$

$$\Delta = \delta_0 \tag{6.140}$$

The value of H is determined as in Eq. (6.133). Table 6.21 shows various parameters for tower deformation.

6.6.3 Single tower with a cable under load (Braslislav–Stipanic method)

Let the stay cable have a position ik and a tension T_{i0} and self weight g_0. As a result, the displacement normal to the chord line is δ_0 and the angle between the cable line and end chord is ϕ^* (see Fig. 6.51)

$$\phi^* = \frac{g_0 L}{2 T_{i0}} \tag{6.141}$$

where $L = $ cable actual length.

Then

$$g = g_0 + g_i \qquad T = T_{i0} + T_i \qquad \delta = \delta_0 + \delta_i \tag{6.142}$$

where δ_i, T_i are due to live loads.

The displacement of the tower and the cable is shown in Fig. 6.52.

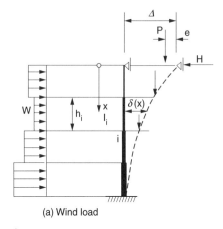

(a) Wind load

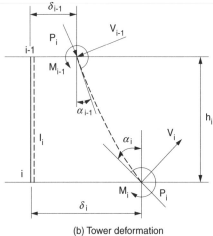

(b) Tower deformation

Figure 6.50. Isolated variable-section tower under wind load. (a) wind load; (b) tower deformation

The equilibrium equations

Take a differential element of the cable as shown in Fig. 6.53. The equilibrium is written as

$$\frac{dV}{dy} + T\frac{d^2\delta}{dy^2} + g' = 0 \tag{6.143}$$

$$\frac{dM}{dy} - V = 0 \tag{6.144}$$

Hence

$$EI\frac{d^4\delta_i}{dy^4} - T\frac{d^2\delta_i}{dy^2} = g' + T + \frac{d^2\delta_0}{dy^2} \tag{6.145}$$

Table 6.21. Parameters for tower deformation

	δ_{i-1}	δ'_{i-1}	M_{i-1}	V_{i-1}	P	Δt
δ_i	1	h_i	$-\dfrac{1}{EI_{Vi}\mu_i^2}(1-\cos\mu_i h_i)$	$-\dfrac{1}{EI_{Vi}\mu_i^2}(\mu_i h_i - \sin\mu_i h_i)$	$\dfrac{1}{EI_{Vi}\mu_i^4}\left(\cos\mu_i h_i - 1 + \dfrac{h_i^4}{2}\right)$	$-\dfrac{\mu_i}{\alpha_i\mu_i^2}(1-\cos\mu_i h_i)$
δ'_i	—	1	$-\dfrac{1}{EI_{Vi}\mu_i}\sin\mu_i h_i$	$-\dfrac{1}{EI_{Vi}\mu_i^2}(1-\cos\mu_i h_i)$	$\dfrac{1}{EI_{Vi}\mu_i^2}(\mu_i h_i - \sin\mu_i h_i)$	$-\dfrac{\mu_i}{\alpha_i\mu_i}\sin\mu_i h_i$
M_i	—	—	$\cos\mu_i h_i$	$\dfrac{1}{\mu_i}\sin\mu_i h_i$	$-\dfrac{1}{\mu_i^2}(1-\cos\mu_i h_i)$	$-\dfrac{EI_{Vi}\mu_i}{\alpha_i}(1-\cos\mu_i h_i)$
V_i	—	—	$-\mu_i\sin\mu_i h_i$	$\cos\mu_i h_i$	$-\dfrac{1}{\mu_i}\sin\mu_i h_i$	$-\dfrac{EI_{Vi}\mu_i}{\alpha+i}(\mu_i\sin\mu_i h_i)$

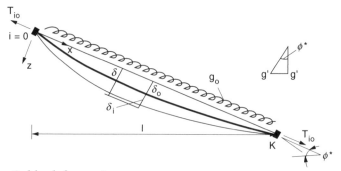

Figure 6.51. Cable deformation

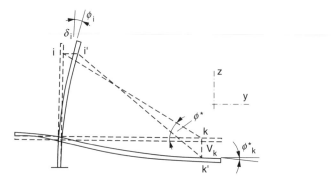

Figure 6.52. Displacements of cable points

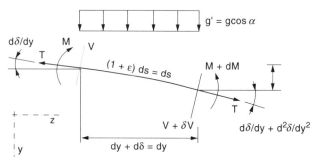

Figure 6.53. Cable differential element

At point i

   $\delta_i =$ displacement horizon

   $\phi_i =$ rotation

At k,

   $\delta_k =$ vertical displacement

   $\phi_k =$ rotation

i', k' are due to the fact that the tower is deformed.

Let

$$k^2 = \frac{T}{EI} \quad \text{and} \quad \bar{g} = \left(\frac{T}{T_0}\frac{g'_0}{g'} - 1\right)g' \tag{6.146}$$

then

$$\frac{\mathrm{d}^4\delta_i}{\mathrm{d}y^4} - k^2\frac{\mathrm{d}^2\delta_i}{\mathrm{d}y^2} = \frac{\bar{g}}{EI} \tag{6.147}$$

$$\delta_i = \rho(C_1 e^{ky} + C_2 y + C_3 + y^2) \tag{6.148}$$

where C_i are integration constants.

Boundary conditions

$$\delta_i(0) = \delta_i^* \qquad \frac{\mathrm{d}\delta_i}{\mathrm{d}y}(0) = \phi_i^* \tag{6.149}$$

$$\delta_i(L) = 0$$

The constants are evaluated as

$$C_1 = \frac{1}{1-kL}C \qquad C_2 = \frac{\phi_1^*}{\rho} + \frac{k}{1-kL}C \tag{6.150}$$

$$C_3 = -\left(\frac{\phi_1^*}{\rho} + \frac{k}{1-kL}C\right)L - L^2$$

where

$$\rho = \frac{\bar{g}}{2EIk^2} = \frac{\bar{g}}{2T} \qquad C = \frac{\delta_i^*}{\rho} + \frac{\phi_1^*L}{\rho} + L^2 \tag{6.151}$$

Bending moments and shear forces

$$M = \frac{T}{kL-1}\left(\delta_1^* + \phi_1^*L + \frac{\bar{g}}{2T}L^2\right)e^{-ky} = -\frac{\bar{g}}{k^2} \tag{6.152}$$

$$V = -\frac{kT}{kL-1}\left(\delta_1^* + \phi_1^*L + \frac{\bar{g}}{2T}L^2\right)e^{-ky} \tag{6.153}$$

The following equation is used prior to the injection of cables:

$$\frac{\mathrm{d}^4 8}{\mathrm{d}y^4} = -k_0\frac{\mathrm{d}^2\delta_0}{\mathrm{d}y^2} = \frac{g'_0}{EI_c} \tag{6.154}$$

where I_c = cable movement of inertia given by:

$$k_0 = \sqrt{\frac{T_{i0}}{EI_c}}$$

The solution of the above equation is given below

$$\delta_0 = \rho_0 (C_{10} e^{-k_0 y} + C_{20} y + C_{30} + y^2)$$

where

$$\rho_0 = \frac{-g_0'}{2T_{i0}} = \frac{-\rho_0'}{2EI_c k_0^2} \qquad\qquad (6.155)$$

Boundary conditions

$$\delta_0(0) = 0$$

$$\frac{d\delta_0}{dy} = \phi_0^*$$

$$\delta_0(L) = 0$$

$$C_{10} = \frac{1}{1 - k_0 L} C_0 \qquad C_{20} = \frac{\rho_0^*}{\rho_0} + \frac{k_0}{1 - k_0 L} C_0$$

$$C_{30} = -\left(\frac{\phi_0^*}{\rho_0} + \frac{k_0}{1 - k_0 L} C_0\right) L - L^2$$

$$C_0 = \frac{\phi_0^* L}{\rho_0} + L^2 \qquad\qquad (6.156)$$

Example (6.8) German practice
The railway bridge over the Sava river in Belgrade is shown in Fig. 6.54. The stay cables are clustered in groups of four. One of the four cables is 116 m long consisting of 240 wires/7 mm$\oslash$ with an area $A = 0.009240\,\text{m}^2$ and $E = 2.05 \times 10^8\,\text{kN/m}^2$. The weight $g = 0.03\,kN/m$ before injecting including polyethylene duct. $T_{i0} = $ dead load $= 2964\,\text{kN}$; $I_f(E_f/E_\phi) = 170.6\,\text{cm}^4$.

Additional data

$$\delta_{AA} = -510\,\text{mm}$$

$$\phi_{AA}^* = 0.3360 \times 10^{-2}\,\text{rad}$$

$$\delta_{BB} = 107\,\text{mm}$$

$$\phi_{BB}^* = 0.2760 \times 10^{-2}\,\text{rad}$$

$$\phi_{i0}^* = 1.436 \times 10^{-2}\,\text{rad}$$

$$k = 1.582L/m \qquad k_{i0} = 21.8L/m.$$

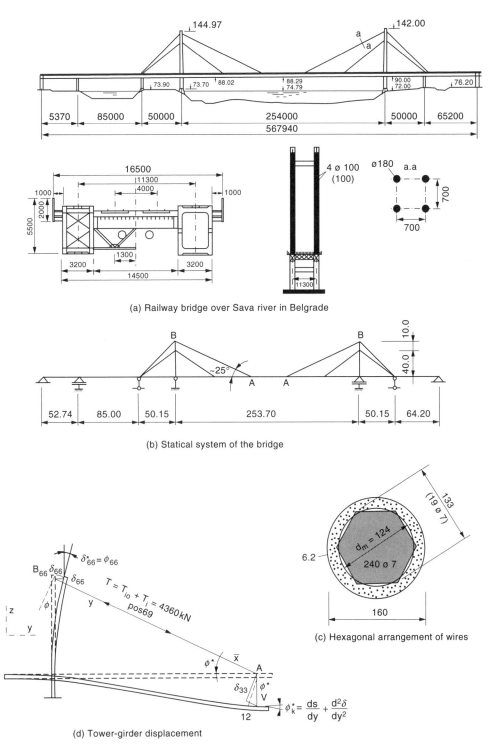

(a) Railway bridge over Sava river in Belgrade

(b) Statical system of the bridge

(c) Hexagonal arrangement of wires

(d) Tower-girder displacement

Figure 6.54. Sava Bridge, Belgrade, Serbia. Use the method presented by B. Stipanic for the analysis of this bridge

Calculate tensile stress σ_t due to total tensile force in the cable and maximum cable stresses in the external wire at cable connection A and B:

$$g_0 = 78.5 \times 0.009240 + 0.30 = 1.025 \, \text{kN/m}$$

$$g_0' = 0.9286 \, \text{kN/m}$$

Assuming no friction exists in a bundle of wires, the cable stiffness before injecting will be a single-wire stiffness

$$EI = 2.05 \times 10^8 (240) \frac{(0.007)^4}{64} = 1.846 \, \text{kNm}^2$$

for dead load

$$T_{i0} = 1364 \, \text{kN}$$

Bundle details are:

$$217 - \oslash 7 + 23 - \oslash 7 \qquad A = 240 \frac{\pi (7)^2}{4} = 9240 \, \text{mm}^2 = 92.4 \, \text{cm}^2$$

$$d_m = \text{average diameter} = 124 \, \text{mm}$$

$$A_f = \text{area of the injected fill in the cable}$$

$$= \frac{\{160 - 2(6.2)\}^2 - (124)^2}{4} = 1602.44 \, \text{mm}^2$$

$$= 16.025 \, \text{cm}^2$$

$$\eta = \text{coefficient of fullness of the bundle of wires}$$

$$= \frac{A}{\frac{1}{4} d_m^2} = \frac{9240}{\frac{1}{4}(124)^2} = 2.404$$

$$I_b = \text{second moment of area of the compacted bundle}$$

$$= \eta^2 \frac{d_m^2}{4} = (2.404)^2 (3844) = 22\,215.3 \, \text{mm}^4$$

$$= 222.1531 \, \text{cm}^4$$

$$I_i = \text{idealized cable second moment area}$$

$$= I_b + I_f \frac{E_f}{E_\phi} = 222.1531 + 170.6 = 392.753 \, \text{cm}^4$$

$$E_\phi I_\phi = 1741 \, \text{kN/m}^2$$

$$T_{C\max}(\text{cable}) = 1600 \, \text{kN (live)}$$

$$\text{Total } T = 2964 + 1600$$

$$= 4560 \, \text{kN}$$

$\phi_{AA}^*, \delta_{AA}, \phi_{BB}^*, \delta_{BB}$ are displacements in tower and cable due to live load. From data the δ and ϕ values are given as

$$\delta_{BB} = 107\,\text{mm}$$

$$\phi_{BB}^* = 0.2760 \times 10^{-2}\,\text{rad}$$

$$\delta_{AA} = -510\,\text{mm}$$

$$\phi_{AA}^* = -0.3360 \times 10^{-2}\,\text{rad}$$

Using the Isopar-3 program (Bangash)

Table 6.22 gives the bridge results for Example (6.8) using the Isopar-3 computer program for the displacements. The stresses are computed correspondingly.

The stresses are computed at the connections A and B due to bending at the ends A and B of the cable (* results from ISOPAR-3):

$$\sigma_A = \frac{11.06}{0.8494} \times 10^{-5} \frac{(18)(0.007)}{2} \times 10^{-3} = 82.2\,\text{N/mm}^2\ (78.6\,\text{N/mm}^2)^*$$

$$\sigma_B = \frac{15.84}{0.8494} \times 10^{-5} \frac{(18)(0.007)}{2} \times 10^{-3} = 117.45\,\text{N/mm}^2\ (118.3\,\text{N/mm}^2)^*$$

The total tensile force in the cable

$$2964\,\text{kN} + 1600\,\text{kN} = 4560\,\text{kN}$$

gives:

$$\sigma_t = \text{tensile stress} = \frac{4560}{0.009968} \times 10^{-3} = 457.5\,\text{N/mm}^2$$

At the A and B connections:

$$\sigma_{\text{total}}(\text{at B}) = 457.5 + 117.45 = 574.95\,\text{N/mm}^2\ (564.85\,\text{N/mm}^2)^*$$

$$\sigma_{\text{total}}(\text{at A}) = 457.5 + 82.2 = 539.70\,\text{N/mm}^2\ (533.80\,\text{N/mm}^2)^*$$

In the output the absolute values (due to bending) of stresses are increased by about 20%.

Tower bending analysis of Example (6.8)

The total height of the tower includes the height from the deck (50 m) plus the remaining height of 10 m above the pier. The total height therefore assumed for the analysis is 60 m. Two cases are examined.

(a) Two legs of the tower acting in unison (free top and pinned at the base) with an equivalent tower shape assumed as a cantilever. Moments are computed.

(b) The two legs acting independently, connected horizontally only at the tower level with a brace. The results include moments, shears and deflections. Here the top is free and the base of each column is fixed.

Table 6.22. Displacements due to dead, live and total loads

Section	$B(x/L) \times 10\,kN/m$	Section	$A(x/L) \times 10\,kN/m$	$V_A(x/L) \times 10\,kN$	$V_B(x/L) \times 10\,kN$	$^*\delta_0/m^L$	$^\dagger\delta_1/m^L$	$^\ddagger\delta/m^L$	Support
0.000	13.50	0.978	0.022	0.32	21.70	0.000	-0.00	0.00	A
0.002	9.27	0.980	0.062	0.50	15.00	0.299		0.226	$\rightarrow$
0.004	6.35	0.982	0.20	0.67	10.50	0.540	-0.110	0.43	B
0.006	4.30	0.984	0.40	0.96	7.25	0.699	-0.130	0.568	
0.008	2.90	0.986	0.65	1.38	5.20	0.799	-0.131	0.668	
0.010	1.97	0.988	1.04	1.98	3.50	0.831	-0.112	0.719	
0.012	1.30	0.990	1.60	2.86	2.40	0.799	-0.078	0.721	
0.014	0.95	0.992	2.40	4.12	1.67	0.699	-0.030	0.639	
0.016	0.50	0.994	3.50	5.93	1.20	0.540	$+0.044$	0.584	
0.018	0.30	0.996	5.20	8.56	0.80	0.299	$+0.180$	0.479	
0.020	0.15	0.998	7.60	12.86	0.20	0	0.232	0.232	
0.022	0.03	1.000	11.06	15.84	0.022				

* Due to dead load before injection.
† Due to live load after injection.
‡ Total load.

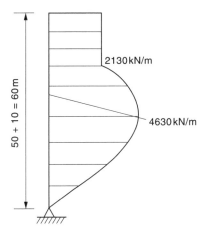

Figure 6.55. Tower moments

(a)   Bottom is pinned

Based on the single-tower approach presented under direct and lateral loads due to added wind in the above analysis, the bending moment diagram (of the tower) is computed as shown in Fig. 6.55. The bottom is assumed pinned.

(b)   Bottom is fixed

A combined tower has been analysed. The spacing of individual cables in any direction is 700 mm and the overall space between them is 11 300 mm. The bending moments, deflections and shear forces when the top is not fixed and acts as a cantilever are given in Fig. 6.56.

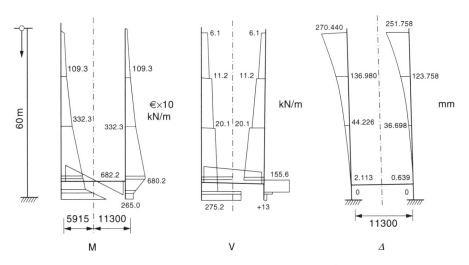

Figure 6.56. Moment, shear and deflection diagrams for a tower

Example (6.9)   Tower analysis using a flexibility method. European practice
An A-shaped tower 17.50 m high with a base of 2.50 m having two braces is shown
in Fig. 6.57. The tower has a constant thickness of 0.80 m and its two sides slope at
an angle of 85.936°. 'Harp-Type' cables are connected to this tower. Each leg has
EI constant. The tower is braced at two locations 4.69 m apart, the lowest being
4.69 m from the base. Determine various reactions and moments in the braces
when the wind load from cable reactions on-site is 128 kg/m². Partial coefficients
should be ignored.

Various geometrical lengths are computed and are shown in Fig. 6.57(c). The
stress resultants are X_1 to X_9 (as redundants) as given in Fig. 6.57(d). Various
flexibility diagrams corresponding to $X_1 \cdots X_9$ are drawn in Figs 6.58(a)–(j).
Wind-determinate moments are given in Fig. 6.58(k) together with the reactions
P acting horizontally at nodes *N* where braces are located.

Wind load $W = 128 \, \text{kg/m}^2$

$$W = \frac{128}{1000} \times 0.8 \sin \alpha \times 10$$

or

$$W = 1.28 \times 0.8 = 1.024 \, \text{kN/m}$$

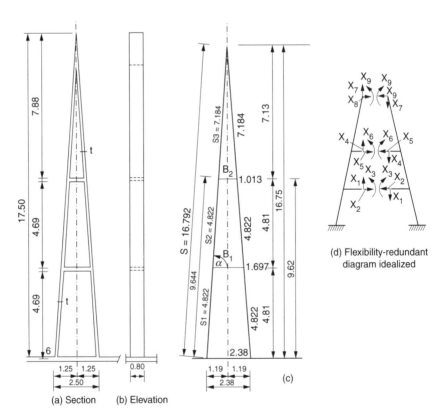

(d) Flexibility-redundant
diagram idealized

Figure 6.57. A-shaped tower analysis using a flexibility method

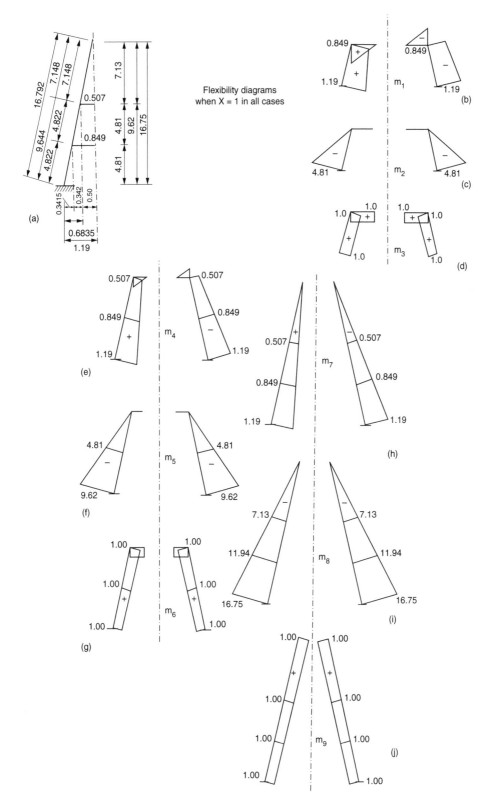

Flexibility diagrams
when X = 1 in all cases

Figure 6.58 (above and overleaf). Tower flexibility diagrams (a) to (k)

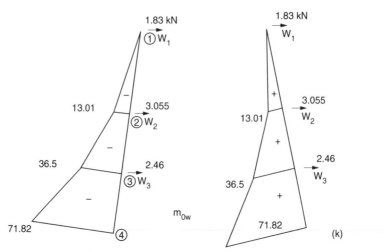

Figure 6.58. Continued

Trignometric relations

$$\tan \alpha = \frac{16.75}{1.19} = 14.07563$$

$$\alpha = 085.936$$

$$\cot \alpha = 0.071045$$

$$\sin \alpha = 0.9975$$

$$\cos \alpha = 0.0709$$

Half-point load on each line

$$W_1 = 1.024 \times \tfrac{1}{2} \times 7.13 = 3.65 \,\text{kN}$$

$$W_2 = 3.65 + 1.024 \times 4.81 \times \tfrac{1}{2} = 6.11 \,\text{kN}$$

$$W_3 = 4.93 \,\text{kN}$$

$$\sum W = (3.65 + 6.11 + 4.93) + 1.024 \times 4.81 \times \tfrac{1}{2} = 17.15 \,\text{kN}$$

Check

$$\sum W = 16.75 \times 1.024 = 17.15 \,\text{kN} \qquad \text{Q.E.D.}$$

Determinate moment due to wind $= m_{0w}$ *[Fig. 6.58(k)]*

$$m_{10}^{W} = \pm \tfrac{1}{2} \times 3.65 \times 7.13 = \pm 13.01 \,\text{kN/m}$$

$$m_{20}^{W} = 0$$

$$m_{30}^{W} = \pm \tfrac{1}{2}(3.65 \times 11.94 + 6.11 \times 4.81) = \pm 36.50 \,\text{kN/m}$$

$$m_{40}^{W} = \pm \frac{1}{2}(3.65 \times 16.75 + 6.11 \times 9.62 + 4.93 \times 4.81)$$

$$= 71.82 \, \text{kN/m}$$

Flexibility coefficients 'f'   [Fig. 6.58(a)–(j) and using flexibility chart]

$$EIf_{11} = \int \frac{m_1^2 \, ds}{EI} = 2[\frac{1}{3}(0.849)^3 + \frac{1}{6}(4.822)\{2(0.849)^2 + 2(0.849) + 2(1.09)^2\}]$$

$$= +10.520$$

$$EIf_{14} = \int m_1 m_4 \, ds = 2[\frac{1}{3}(4.822)\{(0.849)^2 + (1.19)^2 + (0.849)(1.19)\}]$$

$$= +10.113$$

$$= f_{41} = f_{17}$$

$$f_{22} = 2[\frac{1}{3}(4.822)(4.81)^2] = +74.375$$

$$f_{23} = -2[\frac{1}{2}(4.822)(1.00)(4.81)] = -23.194 = f_{32} = f_{26} = f_{29}$$

$$f_{25} = 2[\frac{1}{6}(4.822)(4.81)(4.81 + 2(9.62))] = +185.937 = f_{52}$$

$$f_{28} = 2[\frac{1}{6}(4.822)(4.81)\{(11.94) + (2)(16.75)\}] = +351.309 = f_{82}$$

$$f_{33} = 2[(4.822)(1.00)(1.00) + (0.849)(1.0)] = +11.341$$

$$f_{35} = -2[\frac{1}{2}(4.822)(1.00)(4.81 + 9.62)] = -69.582 = f_{53}$$

$$f_{36} = 2[(4.822)(1.00)(1.00)] = +9.644 = f_{63} = f_{39}$$

$$f_{38} = -2[\frac{1}{2}(4.822)(1.00)(11.94 + 16.75)] = -138.343 = f_{83}$$

$$f_{44} = 2[\frac{1}{3}(0.507)^2 + \frac{1}{3}(9.644)\{(0.507)^2 + (1.19)^2 + (0.507)(1.19)\}]$$

$$= +14.716$$

$$f_{47} = 2[\frac{1}{3}(9.644)\{(0.507) + (1.19)^2 + (0.507)(1.19)\}] = 14.630 = f_{74}$$

$$f_{55} = 2[\frac{1}{3}(9.644)(9.62)^2] = +94.999$$

$$f_{56} = -2[\frac{1}{2}(9.644)(1.00)(9.62)] = -92.775 = f_{65} = f_{59}$$

$$f_{58} = 2[\frac{1}{6}(9.644)(9.62)\{7.13 + (2)(16.75)\}] = +1256.487 = f_{85}$$

$$f_{66} = 2[(9.644)(1.00)^2 + (0.507)(1.00)^2] = +20.301$$

$$f_{68} = -2[\frac{1}{2}(1.00)(9.644)\{(7.13) + (16.75)\}] = -230.299 = f_{86}$$

$$f_{69} = 2[(9.644)(1.00)^2] = +19.288 = f_{96}$$

$$f_{77} = 2[\frac{1}{3}(16.792)(1.19)^2] = +15.853$$

$$f_{88} = 2[\tfrac{1}{3}(16.792)(16.75)^2] = +3140.804$$

$$f_{89} = -2[\tfrac{1}{2}(16.792)(1.00)(16.75)] = -281.266 = f_{98}$$

$$f_{99} = 2[(16.792)(1.002)] = +33.584$$

$$f_{17} = f_{41} = f_{14}$$

$$f_{92} = f_{29} = f_{23}$$

$$f_{93} = f_{39} = f_{36}$$

$$f_{95} = f_{59} = f_{56}$$

$$D_{10} = -2[\tfrac{1}{6}(4.822)\{(2)(0.849)(36.50) + (0.849)(71.82)$$
$$+ (1.19)(36.50) + (2)(1.19)(71.82)\}]$$
$$= -542.07$$

$$D_{40} = -542.07 - 2[\tfrac{1}{6}(4.822)\{(2)(0.507)(13.01)$$
$$+ (0.507)(36.50) + (0.849)(13.01)$$
$$+ (2)(0.85)(36.50)\}]$$
$$- 2[\tfrac{1}{6}(4.822)\{(1.318) + (1.849) + (1.104) + (6.193)\}]$$
$$- \tfrac{1}{3}(4.822)(10.465)$$
$$= -741.68$$

$$D_{70} = -71.027 - 2[\tfrac{1}{3}(71.48)(0.507)(1.301)]$$
$$= -74.168$$

$$X_1 = \frac{-D_{10}}{f_{11}} \qquad X_2 = \frac{-D_{20}}{f_{22}} \quad \text{etc.}$$

The above coefficients are assembled in a matrix form

$$\begin{bmatrix} f_{11} & f_{12} & f_{13} & f_{14} & f_{15} & f_{16} & f_{17} & f_{18} & f_{19} \\ \vdots & & & & & & & & \vdots \\ \vdots & & & & & & & & \vdots \\ & & & & & & & & \\ \vdots & & & & & & & & \vdots \\ f_{91} & f_{92} & f_{93} & f_{94} & f_{95} & f_{96} & f_{97} & f_{98} & f_{99} \end{bmatrix} \begin{Bmatrix} X_1 \\ \vdots \\ \vdots \\ \\ \vdots \\ X_9 \end{Bmatrix}$$

$$= -\left\{\begin{matrix} D_{10} \\ \vdots \\ \vdots \\ \vdots \\ D_{90} \end{matrix}\right\} = \left\{\begin{matrix} 542.207 \\ 0 \\ 0 \\ 0 \\ 710.27 \\ 0 \\ 0 \\ 741.68 \\ 0 \\ 0 \end{matrix}\right\}$$

$$[f_{ij}]\{X_i\} = -\{D_{i0}\}$$

$$\{X_i\} = -\{D_{10}\}[f_{ij}]^{-1}$$

The matrix $[f_{ij}]$ is given below:

$[f_{ij}] =$

$$\begin{bmatrix} 10.520 & 0 & 0 & 10.113 & 0 & 0 & 10.113 & 0 & 0 \\ 0 & 74.735 & -23.194 & 0 & 185.937 & -23.194 & 0 & 351.309 & -23.194 \\ 0 & -23.194 & 11.341 & 0 & -69.582 & 9.644 & 0 & -138.343 & 9.644 \\ 10.113 & 0 & 0 & 14.716 & 0 & 0 & 14.629 & 0 & 0 \\ 0 & 185.938 & -69.582 & 0 & 594.999 & -92.775 & 0 & 1256.487 & -92.775 \\ 0 & -23.194 & 9.644 & 0 & -92.775 & 20.301 & 0 & -230.299 & 19.288 \\ 10.113 & 0 & 0 & 14.629 & 0 & 0 & 15.853 & 0 & 0 \\ 0 & 351.309 & -138.343 & 0 & 1256.487 & -230.299 & 0 & 314.804 & -281.266 \\ 0 & -23.194 & 9.644 & 0 & -92.775 & 19.288 & 0 & 281.266 & 33.584 \end{bmatrix}$$

The inversion of $[f_{ij}]$ when multiplied with $\{D_{i0}\}$ gives the values of the matrix $\{X_i\}$:

$$X_1 = 14.7\,\text{kN}$$

$$X_2 = 0$$

$$X_3 = 0$$

$$X_4 = 11.8\,\text{kN}$$

$$X_5 = 0$$

$$X_6 = 0$$

$$X_7 = 26.6 \, \text{kN}$$

$$X_8 = 0$$

$$X_9 = 0$$

The moment will be

$$M = m_0 + m_1 X_1 + \ldots m_9 X_9; \qquad \text{combined}$$

$$= m_0 + m_1 X_1 + m_4 X_4 + m_7 X_7 \qquad \text{(all others are zero)}.$$

Final moment diagrams can now be drawn.

6.6.4 Single-tower vibration using stiffness method

A tower of height 'h' is fixed at the base and free at the top as shown in Fig. 6.59.

A generalized relation for an element is first developed and then boundary conditions are applied to the kind of fixity imposed on it.

Displacement function:

$$v = y = a_1 + a_2 x + a_3 x^2 + a_4 x^4$$

$$\theta = -\frac{\mathrm{d}v}{\mathrm{d}x}$$

$$= a_2 + 2a_3 x + 4a_4 x^3$$

The matrix for v and θ displacement can be written (see Appendix) as

$$[C] = \begin{bmatrix} 1 & 0 & 0 & 0 \\ 0 & -1 & 0 & 0 \\ 1 & h & h^2 & h^3 \\ 0 & -1 & -2h & -3h^2 \end{bmatrix} \tag{6.157}$$

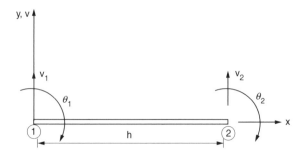

Figure 6.59. Tower as a finite single element

$$[C]^{-1} = \begin{bmatrix} 1 & 0 & 0 & 0 \\ 0 & -1 & 0 & 0 \\ -3/h^2 & 2/h & 3/h^2 & 1/h \\ 2/h^3 & -1/h^2 & -2/h^3 & -1/h^2 \end{bmatrix} \tag{6.158}$$

Mass matrix evaluation

$$M(x,y) = \begin{bmatrix} 1 & x & x^2 & x^3 \end{bmatrix} \tag{6.159}$$

$$[\bar{m}] = \rho \int_{\text{vol}} [M_{(x,y)}]^{\text{T}} [M_{(x,y)}] \, d\,\text{vol} \tag{6.160}$$

$$= \rho A_{\text{T}} \begin{bmatrix} h & h^2/2 & h^3/3 & h^4/4 \\ h^2/2 & h^3/3 & h^4/4 & h^5/5 \\ h^3/3 & h^4/4 & h^5/5 & h'6 \\ h^4/4 & h^5/5 & h^6/6 & h^7/7 \end{bmatrix} \tag{6.161}$$

The dynamic equation is written as

$$|[K] = \omega^2 [M]| = 0 \tag{6.162}$$

$$\left| EI_{\text{T}} \begin{bmatrix} 12/h^3 & 6/h^2 \\ 6/h^2 & 4/h \end{bmatrix} - \omega^2 \frac{\rho A_{\text{T}} h}{420} \begin{bmatrix} 156 & 22h \\ 22h & 4h^2 \end{bmatrix} \right| = 0 \tag{6.163}$$

here

$$[K_{11}]^{-1} = \frac{1}{EI_{\text{T}}} \begin{bmatrix} h^3/3 & -h^2/2 \\ -h^2/2 & h \end{bmatrix}$$

$$\left(\lambda \begin{bmatrix} 1 & 0 \\ 0 & 1 \end{bmatrix} - \frac{\rho A_{\text{T}} h}{420 EI_{\text{T}}} \begin{bmatrix} h^3/3 & -h^2/2 \\ -h^2/2 & h \end{bmatrix} \begin{bmatrix} 156 & 22h \\ 22l & 4h^2 \end{bmatrix} \right) \begin{Bmatrix} v_2 \\ \theta_2 \end{Bmatrix} = \begin{Bmatrix} 0 \\ 0 \end{Bmatrix} \tag{6.164}$$

$$\begin{vmatrix} \dfrac{41\rho A l^4}{420 EI_{\text{T}}} - \lambda & \dfrac{16\rho A_{\text{T}} h^5}{1260 EI_{\text{T}}} \\ -\dfrac{56\rho A h^3}{420 EI_{\text{T}}} & -\dfrac{\rho A h^4}{60 EI_{\text{T}}} - \lambda \end{vmatrix} = 0 \tag{6.165}$$

$$\lambda = 0.0801 \rho A_{\text{T}} h^4 / (EI),$$

Also

$$\lambda = \frac{1}{\omega^2}$$

$$\omega = \frac{3.53}{h^2} \sqrt{\frac{EI_T}{\rho A_T}}$$

with eigenvalue mode

$$[v_2 \theta_2] = [-0.73 \quad 1]$$

In *global coordinates*, a similar procedure is adopted, and the following mass matrix can be obtained

$$
= \frac{\rho A_T h}{420}
\begin{array}{cccccc}
u_1^{\circ} & v_1^{\circ} & \theta_1 & u_2^{\circ} & v_2^{\circ} & \theta_2 \\
\end{array}
\begin{bmatrix}
156s^2 & & & & & \\
-156cs & 156c^2 & & & & \\
22hs & -22hc & 4h^2 & & & \\
54s^2 & -54cs & 13hs & 156s^2 & & \\
-54cs & 54c^2 & -13hc & -156cs & 156c^2 & \\
-13hs & 13hc & -3h^2 & -22hs & 22hc & 4h^2 \\
\end{bmatrix}
\begin{array}{c}
u_1^{\circ} \\
v_1^{\circ} \\
\theta_1 \\
u_2^{\circ} \\
v_2^{\circ} \\
\theta_2 \\
\end{array}
\qquad (6.166)
$$

$$c = \cos\theta$$
$$s = \sin\theta$$

where:

ρ = tower material density

A_T = tower area.

Where the tower has a variable cross-section, an equivalent single value for A_T is calculated. The error is marginal. The mass matrix $[M]$ is then given as (local coordinates):

$$
[M] = \frac{\rho A_T h}{420}
\begin{array}{cccc}
v_1 & \theta_1 & v_2 & \theta_2 \\
\end{array}
\begin{bmatrix}
156 & & & \\
-22h & 4h^2 & & \text{sym} \\
54 & -13h & 156 & \\
13h & -3h^2 & 22h & 4h^2 \\
\end{bmatrix}
\begin{array}{c}
v_1 \\
\theta_1 \\
v_2 \\
\theta_2 \\
\end{array}
\qquad (6.167)
$$

Stiffness matrix [K]

As discussed earlier, the matrix $[K]$ for the tower is written as

$$[k_{1-2}] = [K] = EI_T \begin{array}{cccc} v_1 & \theta_1 & v_2 & \theta_2 \\ \left[\begin{array}{cccc} 12/h^3 & & & \\ -6/h^2 & 4/h & & \text{sym} \\ -12/h^3 & 6/h^2 & 12/h^3 & \\ -6/h^2 & 2/h^2 & 6/h^2 & 4/h \end{array}\right] & \begin{array}{c} v_1 \\ \theta_1 \\ v_2 \\ \theta_2 \end{array} \end{array} \tag{6.168}$$

The corresponding mass matrix is given as

$$[m_{1-2}] = [M] = \frac{\rho A_T h}{6} \begin{array}{cccc} v_1 & \theta_1 & v_2 & \theta_2 \\ \left[\begin{array}{cccc} 156 & & & \\ -22h & 4h^2 & & \\ 54 & -13h & 156 & \\ 13h & -3h^2 & 22h & 4h^2 \end{array}\right] & \begin{array}{c} v_1 \\ \theta_1 \\ v_2 \\ \theta_2 \end{array} \end{array} \tag{6.169}$$

Boundary conditions

The tower is fixed at node ①. The displacement of node ① is suppressed. The coefficient corresponding to the free displacements are considered for $[K_{11}]$ and $[M_{11}]$

$$[K_{11}] = EI_T \begin{array}{cc} v_2 & \theta_2 \\ \left[\begin{array}{cc} 12/h^3 & \\ 6/h^2 & 4/h \end{array}\right] & \begin{array}{c} v_2 \\ \theta_2 \end{array} \end{array} \tag{6.170}$$

$$[M_{11}] = \rho A_T h \begin{array}{cc} v_2 & \theta_2 \\ \left[\begin{array}{cc} 156 & \\ 22h & 4h^2 \end{array}\right] & \begin{array}{c} v_2 \\ \theta_2 \end{array} \end{array} \tag{6.171}$$

Example (6.10)   Single-tower vibrations

Determine the frequency of the isolated tower of a cable-stayed bridge fixed at the base and free at the top. As shown in Fig. 6.60 the height of the tower is 111 m. Using the following data, calculate the natural frequency of the tower prior to attachment of cables:

$$A_T = 0.079\,\text{m}^2 \qquad\qquad I_T = 4.909 \times 10^{-1}\,\text{m}^4$$

$$E = 2 \times 10^5\,\text{MN/m}^2 \qquad \rho = 7860\,\text{kg/m}^3$$

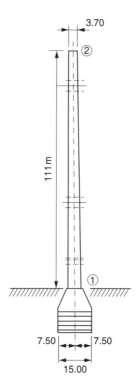

Figure 6.60. Tower fixed at base

Due to stay connections and other fixings at the tower top, there is an added mass of 100 kg with a corresponding mass moment of inertia of 2 kg m²; redetermine the natural frequency.

When the cables are added at spacings of 10.1 m, determine natural frequency in torsion. Take the radius of gyration as $r = 3.5$ m.

Case I. Without added mass

$$\omega = \frac{3.53}{(111)^2} \sqrt{\frac{2 \times 10^{11} \times 4.909 \times 10^{-1}}{7860 \times 0.079}} = 0.36 \, \text{rad/s}$$

$$f = \text{natural frequency} = \frac{\omega}{2\pi} = 0.0573 \, \text{Hz}$$

Case II. With added mass

$$\left| 2 \times 10^{11} \times 0.4909 \begin{bmatrix} 12/(111)^3 & 4/(111)^2 \\ 6/(111)^2 & (4/111)^2 \end{bmatrix} \right.$$

$$\left. - \omega^2 \frac{7860 \times 0.079 \times 111}{420} \begin{bmatrix} 156 & 2442 \\ 2442 & 4928 \end{bmatrix} + \begin{bmatrix} 100 & 0 \\ 0 & 2 \end{bmatrix} \right| = 0$$

Here

$$[K_{11}]^{-1} = \frac{1}{1.3091 \times 10^{11}} \begin{bmatrix} 4/111 & -6/(111)^2 \\ -6/(111)^2 & (12/111)^3 \end{bmatrix}$$

$$= \frac{1}{1.3091 \times 10^{11}} \begin{bmatrix} 0.036036 & -0.000487 \\ -0.000487 & 0.0000088 \end{bmatrix}$$

Therefore the term is simplified as

$$[K_{11}]^{-1} = \frac{7860 \times 0.079 \times 111}{420 \times 2 \times 10^{11} \times 0.4909} \begin{bmatrix} 156 & 2442 \\ 2442 & 4928 \end{bmatrix}$$

$$= 1.6715 \times 10^{-9} \begin{bmatrix} 156 & 2442 \\ 2442 & 4928 \end{bmatrix}$$

Hence

$$\left| \lambda \begin{bmatrix} 1 & 0 \\ 0 & 1 \end{bmatrix} = \frac{1}{1.3091 \times 10^{11}} \begin{bmatrix} 0.036036 & -0.000487 \\ -0.000487 & 0.0000088 \end{bmatrix} \right.$$

$$\left. \times 1.6715 \times 10^{-9} \begin{bmatrix} 156 & 2442 \\ 2442 & 4928 \end{bmatrix} + \begin{bmatrix} 100 & 0 \\ 0 & 2 \end{bmatrix} \right| = 0$$

or

$$\left| \lambda \begin{bmatrix} 1 & 0 \\ 0 & 1 \end{bmatrix} = 1.2768314 \times 10^{-20} \begin{bmatrix} 0.036036 & -0.000487 \\ -0.000487 & 0.0000088 \end{bmatrix} \right.$$

$$\left. \times \begin{bmatrix} 256 & 2442 \\ 2442 & 4930 \end{bmatrix} \right| = 0$$

Solving the quadratic equation gives the value of λ:

$$\lambda = 0.0769 \qquad \omega_1 = \sqrt{\frac{1}{\lambda}}$$

$$\omega_1 = \sqrt{\frac{1}{0.0769}} \qquad f = \frac{\omega}{2\pi} = \frac{3.61 \times 7}{44} = 0.574 \,\text{Hz}$$

$$= 3.61$$

Frequency in torsion f_T
Without added mass

$$f_T = \frac{10.1 \times 0.0573}{2 \times 3.5} = 0.083 \,\text{Hz}$$

With added mass

$$f_T = \frac{10.1 \times 0.0574}{2 \times 3.5} = 0.083 \, \text{Hz}.$$

6.7 Cables and cable assemblies with towers

As explained in the previous sections, cables and towers have different configurations. It is important to classify towers first before considering assemblies with cables in any detail. The towers are:

(*a*) single column or pylon
(*b*) pair of separate columns or double pylon/tower
(*c*) a frame
(*d*) a portal frame.

Where the horizontal cable connecting two towers is not provided, the tower fixed at the bottom moves horizontally at the top, the horizontal movement δH_1 is given by Fig. 6.61:

$$\delta H_1 = \frac{2h^2 + 6hh_1 + 3h_1^2}{3b} \frac{f_{bT0}}{E_{T0}} \tag{6.172}$$

where:

$f_{bT0} = $ bending stress in the lower part of the tower

$E_{bT0} = $ Young's modulus of the tower

$b = $ width of the tower of height h with a pier height h_1.

Where the cables are fixed only, as shown in Fig. 6.62, the horizontal displacement δH_2 is given by

$$\delta H_2 = \frac{h}{\sin \phi_2 \cos \phi_2} \frac{f_{tC}}{E_c} \tag{6.173}$$

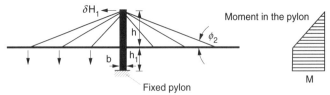

Figure 6.61. Fixed tower

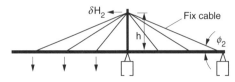

Figure 6.62. Tower with fixed cables

where:

f_{tC} = tensile stress in a fixed cable

E_c = Young's modulus of a cable

As a result, the forces acting on towers can be demonstrated.

Example (6.11)   Column towers fixed to piers
Assuming the load is on one side of the tower and the horizontal displacements $\delta H_1 = \delta H_2$, calculate the width b of the tower, using the following data:

$$\phi_1 = \phi_2 = 20°$$

$$h = 51.8\,\text{m} \qquad \frac{E_c f_{bT0}}{E_{T0} f_{tC}} = 0.4$$

$$h_1 = \frac{h}{2} = 25.9\,\text{m}$$

The span between towers is 333 m

$$\delta H_1 = \delta H_2$$

$$\frac{2h^2 + 6hh_1 + 3h_1^2}{3b} = \frac{h}{\sin\phi\cos\phi_2}(0.4)$$

$$\frac{2h^2 + 6h\dfrac{h}{2} + 3\dfrac{h^2}{4}}{3b} = \frac{h}{\sin 20 \cos 20}$$

$$b = \frac{2h^2 + 3h^2 + 0.75h^2}{3h}(0.4)(0.3420201)(0.9396926)$$

$$= \frac{5.75}{3} \times 51.8(0.1285575)$$

$$= 12.764\,\text{m}$$

Allowable range $0.2h$ to $0.24h$

For the minimum height: $0.2 \times 333 = 66.6\,\text{m} > 51.8\,\text{m}$ Q.E.D.

If the height is 66.6 m then

$$b = \frac{66.6}{51.8} \times 12.764 = 16.41\,\text{m}.$$

The A-shaped frame can achieve sufficient stiffness in a fixed tower. If the loads are symmetrical (Fig. 6.63), the vertical force is $2W$ since reactions at the end of the stay are W. Where the load is not uniform, it gives vertical and horizontal forces at the top of the tower while a horizontal force at the stiffness girder. This horizontal force is $2Wl_c/h$. The moment at the fixed end is $M^F = 2Wl_c$.

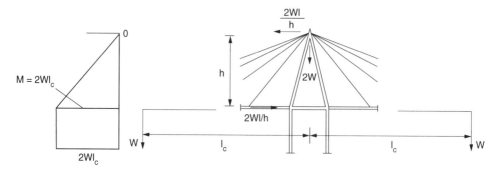

Figure 6.63. Cable systems with a tower under loads

6.7.1 Cable material properties

The cable stiffness is a paramount parameter in the system and was given in detail by Leonhardt and Zellner (see Figs 6.64–6.65):

$$A_s E_{\text{eff}} = \frac{A_s E_0}{1 + \dfrac{\gamma^2 l_c^2 E_0}{12\sigma^3}} \tag{6.174}$$

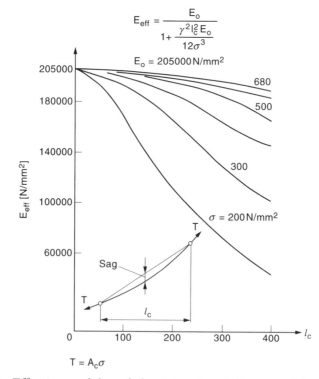

Figure 6.64. Effective modulus of elasticity gives influence of the sag of the cable on its stiffness (courtesy IABSE surveys S-13/80, F. Leonhardt and W. Zellner, May 1980)

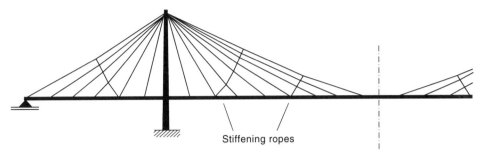

Figure 6.65. Stiffening ropes to reduce the sag effect on the stiffness of the cables (courtesy IABSE S-13/80, F. Leonhardt and W. Zellner, May 1980)

where

A_s = area of cable steel

E_0 = Young's modulus of straight vertical cable = E_c

γ = weight of the cable

l_c = horizontal length or span of cable

σ = tensile stress of the cable = f_{tc}

E_{eff} = effective modulus due to sagging of the cable.

Leonhardt and Zellner have drawn the graph for E_{eff} for various l_c and σ values in Fig. 6.64.

Occasionally stiffening ropes are introduced to reduce the sagging effect on the cable stiffness as shown in Fig. 6.65.

6.7.2 Stress changes and vertical anchoring forces

Leonhardt and Zellner have developed graphs for the ratio l_1/l (where l_1-side span and l is the main span). The idea is to obtain the best ratio so that stress changes due to stay cables that hold the tower head, and those due to live loads may not increase. The l_1/l ratio has an influence also on the extent of vertical anchoring forces at the tower support such as pylons or piers. Figure 6.66 shows l_1/l graphs with and without stiffening ropes.

Regarding stiffening girders and the towers, the following properties will be a useful guide for the initial design:

(1) Three-span fan-type radiating cables with hinge connections
     Girder – area = $1.0\,\text{m}^2$, $I = 2.4\,\text{m}^4$
     Tower – area = $0.4\,\text{m}^2$, $I = 0.25\,\text{m}^4$
(2) Five-span with arrangements as in (1)
     Girder – area = $1.0\,\text{m}^2$, $I = 2.4\,\text{m}^4$
     Tower – area = $0.4\,\text{m}^2$, $I = 2.4\,\text{m}^4$

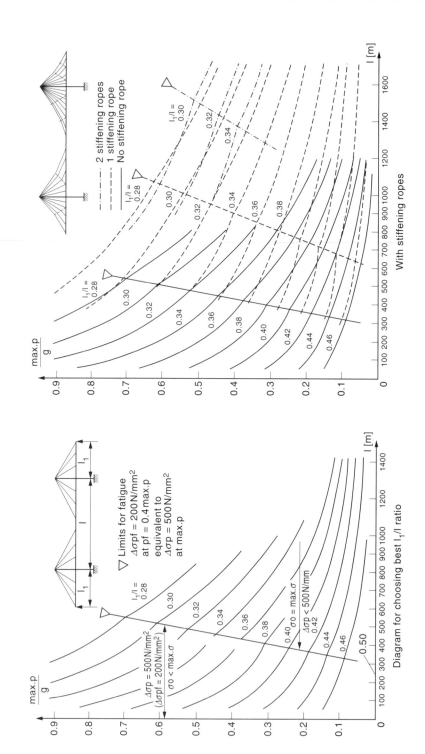

(3) As (2) with fixed connections
     Girder – area $= 1.0\,m^2$, $I = 2.4\,m^4$
     Tower – area $= 0.4\,m^2$, $I = 2.4\,m^4$
(4) Girder – same as in (2) or (3)
     Tower – area $= 0.6\,m^2$, $I = 2.50\,m^4$
(5) Same as (2) but with horizontal fixed cable between the tops of the towers
     Girders – no change
     Tower – area $= 0.4\,m^2$, $I = 0.25\,m^4$
(6) Same as above but with four triangular towers
     Girders – no change
     Tower – area $= 0.7\,m^2$, $I = 0.45\,m^4$.

6.7.3 Buckling phenomenon of the tower

Buckling phenomenon has been described in detail in the text and a finite element version is given in the Appendix. Two approximate methods are suggested also. Generally the towers can be made stiff compared to the girder by a suitable method of a beam on elastic foundations. The reason is based on the variations in cable stiffness that compensate variations in axial force.

(a) Buckling load

$$P_{cr} = \sqrt{4EI\beta} \qquad\qquad (6.175)$$

where

$$\beta = \text{the elastic constant} = E_{T0}A_{T0}/\delta x \times h$$

Data:
$$\delta x = \text{cable spacing} = 10.7\text{m}$$

$$E_{T0}A_{T0} = 1\,333\,546\,\text{kN}$$

$$E = 2 \times 10^8\,\text{kN/m}^2$$

Figure 6.66 (facing). Side span/main span with and without stiffening ropes. Assumptions: $E_0 = 210\,000\,N/mm^2$, $\min E_{eff} = 180\,000\,N/mm^2$, $\max \sigma = 750\,N/mm^2$, $\Delta\sigma p = \sigma_0 - \sigma_u = 500\,N/mm^2$ for $\max p$, $\Delta\sigma pf = 200\,N/mm^2$ for fatigue with $0.4\,\max p$. Formulas for other assumptions:

$$\sigma_u = \frac{1 - 4\eta^2 - 4\eta^2\varepsilon}{1 - 4\eta^2 + \varepsilon} \cdot \sigma_0 \qquad\qquad \eta = \frac{l_1}{l}$$

$$l = \frac{1}{\eta} \sqrt{\frac{E_0 - \min E_{eff}}{E_0 \cdot \min E_{eff}} \cdot \frac{12}{\gamma^2}} \sqrt{\sigma_u^3} \qquad \varepsilon = \frac{p}{g}$$

$$\sigma_0 - \sigma_u = \frac{\max p}{p_{\text{fatigue}}} \cdot \text{allow }\Delta\sigma$$

(courtesy IABSE S-13/80, F. Leonhardt and W. Zellner, May 1980)

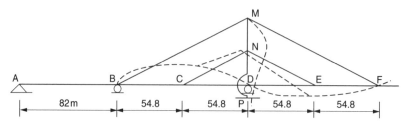

Figure 6.67. Deflection calculated from finite element analysis.

$$h = 57.8\,\text{m}$$

$$\beta = 1\,333\,546/57.8 \times 10.7 = 2156.24\,\text{kN/m}^2$$

$$I = 16.73\,\text{m}^4$$

$$P_{cr} = 2\sqrt{2 \times 10^8 \times 16.73 \times 2156.24}$$

$$= 5\,372\,068\,\text{kN or } 5.3721\,\text{GN}.$$

(b) *Deflection calculated from finite element analysis*
Put 1 kN at E acting upward and 1 kN at C acting downward (Fig. 6.67). The deflection at joint C is computed. The total net deflection is 0.000084 m for both ends:

$$\beta = \frac{1}{\delta x \delta_c} = \frac{1}{54.8 \times 0.0000084} = 2172.4\,\text{kN/m}^2$$

$$\text{I-beam/girder} = 23.24\,\text{m}^2$$

$$P_{cr} = 2\sqrt{2 \times 10^8 \times 23.24 \times 2172.4}$$

$$= 6\,355\,254.6\,\text{kN} = 6.3553\,\text{MN}$$

Difference: Around 18% between the tower and the girder. The difference is around 12% for a complete instability analysis. The approximate method, if adopted, means that effects of around 20% shall be included.

6.8 Combined analysis for cable–girder–tower assemblies
6.8.1 Combined analysis for axial forces in cables and girders
Figure 6.68 shows a typical cable–girder–tower combination. Let l_{cs} and l_{ss} be the cable and stay span, respectively. The tower has a height h. The cable has an angle ϕ_1 to the girder and the stay has a span l_{ss} with an angle ϕ_2. The tension in the cable is T and the load on the girder is q_z/unit length uniformly placed, which equals $(\omega_{DD} + \omega_{LL})$. The equilibrium condition is obtained as

$$T \sin \phi_1 = q_z\,dx$$

$$T \cos \phi_1 = \delta H$$

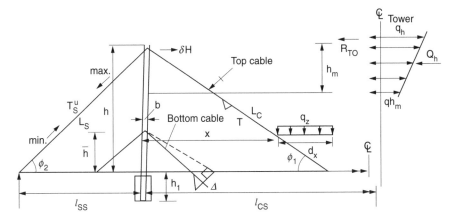

Figure 6.68. External load versus tension in the cable

where δH is the incremental horizontal component of T. The value of δH is given as

$$\delta H = \frac{q_z \, dx}{\sin \phi_1} \cos \phi_1 = \frac{q_z x \, dx}{h} \tag{6.176}$$

and H is the sum of all horizontal components of T for all the cables

$$= \frac{q_z}{h} \int x \, dx$$

The maximum axial force in the girder N_G is then

$$N_{G_{max}} = \frac{q_z}{h} \int_0^{l_{cs}/2} x \, dx = \frac{q_z}{h} \left[\frac{x^2}{2} \right]_0^{l_{cs}/2} = \frac{q_z l_{cs}^2}{8h}$$

$$= \frac{(\omega_{DD} + \omega_{LL}) l_{cs}^2}{8h} \tag{6.177}$$

In the above equations h_1 is not considered.

Tension in the uppermost cable in a side span under dead load
Tension in the side span and half of the main span is given by:

$$T_{SD}^u = \left(\frac{\omega_{DD}}{h} \int_0^{l_{cs}/2} x \, dx - \frac{\omega_{DD}}{h} \int_0^{l_{ss}} x \, dx \right) \operatorname{cosec} \phi_2$$

$$= \left[\frac{\omega_{DD} l_{cs}^2}{8h} - \frac{\omega_{DD} l_{ss}^2}{2h} \right] \cos \phi_2 \tag{6.178}$$

Where the cables are fixed as before

$$\delta H = \frac{h}{\sin \phi_2 \cos \phi_2} \frac{f_{tc}}{E_c} \tag{6.179}$$

where

f_{tc} = tensile stress in a fixed cable

E_c = Young's modulus of a cable.

The displacement is sometimes given in a simplified manner by

$$\delta H = \frac{l_{ss}^2 + h^2}{l_{ss}} \frac{f_{tc}}{E_c} \tag{6.180}$$

At the tower: bending moments

At the tower, there is a statically indeterminate force $\bar{R}_{T0}$ at the girder level in the horizontal direction. The value of $\bar{R}_{T0}$ will then be

$$\bar{R}_{T0} = \frac{1}{2}\left[\frac{qh + qh_m}{h_m}\right]\left(\frac{h + h_1}{8}\right)[8 - 6\beta + \beta^3] + \frac{l_{ss}^2 + h^2}{l_{ss}(h + h_1)^3} f_{tc}I_{T0} \tag{6.181}$$

where

$$\frac{1}{2}\left[\frac{qh + qh_m}{h_m}\right] = Q_h = \frac{\omega_{LL}l_{cs}^2}{8\bar{h}h_m} \tag{6.182}$$

$$\beta = \frac{h_m}{(h + h_1)} \tag{6.182a}$$

I_{T0} = second moment area of tower.

Bending moment in the girder is given by:

$$BM_{(max)} = \frac{1}{2}\frac{(\bar{R})^2}{Q_h} \tag{B.183}$$

Deflection under live load

Let q_z be the load over distance 'x', and Δ be the vertical displacement at the cable girder connecting point (given by $q_z = \omega_{LL_x}$). Then:

$$\Delta = \frac{f_{ct}}{E_c}\left\{\frac{x}{(l_{cs}/2)}\phi_1\frac{L_cL_s}{h + h_1} + \eta\frac{L_c^2}{h + h_1}\right]$$

$$\eta = \frac{(\omega_{LL}/\omega_{DD})}{1 + 1.3(\omega_{LL}/\omega_{DD})} = 0.216 \text{ for maximum ratios.} \tag{6.184}$$

Similarly live load ω_{LL} can be investigated by putting a live load on the main span and on the side span. The uppermost cable has maximum and minimum tension forces. They are given as

N_L = axial force due to live load

$$= \frac{\omega_{LL}l_{cs}^2}{8h} \tag{6.185}$$

$$T^{\mathrm{u}}_{\mathrm{SL(max)}} = N_{\mathrm{L}} \cot \phi \tag{6.186}$$

$$T^{\mathrm{u}}_{\mathrm{SL(min)}} = \frac{\omega_{\mathrm{LL}} l^2_{\mathrm{ss}}}{2h} \cot \phi_2 \tag{6.187}$$

Then, N_{min} = axial force in the tower = $q_z + 2l_{\mathrm{cs}}$. (6.188)

The combined effect due to dead and live loads is given by:

$$T^{\mathrm{U}}_{\mathrm{SD}} + T^{\mathrm{U}}_{\mathrm{SL}} \tag{6.189}$$

For other cables with different lengths and angles of inclination, these effects are computed and are finally combined in the same way. Generally the pier takes an *uplift force*. Such an uplift force is computed by

$$\bar{R} = R_{\mathrm{uplift}} = (T^{\mathrm{U}}_{\mathrm{SD}} + T^{\mathrm{U}}_{\mathrm{SL}}) \sin \phi_2 \tag{6.190}$$

The horizontal displacement δH at the top of the tower is given as before by

$$\delta H = \frac{2h^2 + 6hh_1 + 3h_1^2}{3b} \frac{f_{\mathrm{bT0}}}{E_{\mathrm{T0}}} \tag{6.191}$$

where

f_{bT0} = bending stress in the tower

E_{T0} = Young's modulus of the tower

and where 'η' depends on the $l_{\mathrm{cs}}/l_{\mathrm{ss}}$ ratio and $\omega_{\mathrm{LL}}/\omega_{\mathrm{DD}}$:

$\dfrac{l_{\mathrm{cs}}}{l_{\mathrm{ss}}}$	min. value	1.0	$\dfrac{\omega_{\mathrm{LL}}}{\omega_{\mathrm{DD}}}$	min. value	0.10
	max. value	2.5		max. value	0.30

Based on the maximum value, assuming $l_{\mathrm{cs}} \neq l_{\mathrm{ss}}$, $\eta_{\mathrm{max}} = 0.216$. Hence

$$\Delta = \frac{f_{\mathrm{ct}}}{E_{\mathrm{c}}} \left[\frac{2x}{l_{\mathrm{cs}}} \phi_1 \frac{L_{\mathrm{c}} L_{\mathrm{s}}}{(h + h_1)} + 0.216 \frac{L_{\mathrm{c}}^2}{(h + h_1)} \right] \tag{6.192}$$

$$\text{Spring constant '}K\text{' for } \bar{R}_{\mathrm{T0}} = \frac{\omega_{\mathrm{LL}}}{\Delta}. \tag{6.193}$$

Bending moment in a girder based on Timoshenko's Theory of Elasticity (Fig. 6.69) is:

$$M_{\mathrm{c}} = \frac{\omega_{\mathrm{LL}} \pi}{16\beta^2} + \frac{\omega_{\mathrm{LL}}}{4\beta} \tag{6.194}$$

where

$$\beta = \sqrt{\frac{K}{eE_{\mathrm{G}} I_{\mathrm{G}}}}.$$

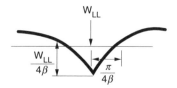

Figure 6.69. Girder bending moment

Example (6.12)   Cable tension tower top force (American practice)
Develop an expression for cable tension in the cable and the back-stay (see the
force diagram, Fig. 6.70) and the stiffness of the cable. Using the following
data, calculate the reactions in a girder for the stays ④, ⑩, ⑮, and ㊵, for
which the strands are defined:

Data
Girder

$$L = \text{girder length} = 945\,\text{ft}\ (288\,\text{m})$$

$$L_c = \text{length of the cable} = 445\,\text{ft}\ (135.64\,\text{m})$$

$$l_c = \text{spacing of the cable at the girder level} = 20\,\text{ft}\ (6.096\,\text{m})$$

$$A_g = \text{girder area} = 102\,\text{ft}^2\ (94\,758\,\text{cm}^2)$$

$$I_g = \text{girder second moment of area} = 48.5\,\text{ft}^4\ (41.86 \times 10^6\,\text{m})$$

$$E_g = \text{girder Young's modulus} = 4.71 \times 10^6\,\text{psi}\ (32.72 \times 10^6\,\text{N/mm}^2)$$

Tower or pylon

$$h = 205\,\text{ft} = \text{tower height}\ (93.0\,\text{m})$$

$$A_T = 120\,\text{ft}^2 = \text{tower area}\ (11\,480\,\text{cm}^2)$$

$$E_T = 4.5 \times 10^6\,\text{psi} = \text{tower Young's modulus}\ (31.0 \times 10^6\,\text{kN/m}^2)$$

$$E_{\text{eff}} = \frac{E}{1 + \dfrac{\gamma^2 l_c E}{12\sigma^3}}$$

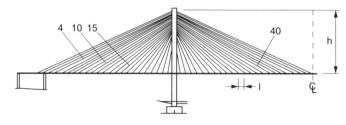

Figure 6.70. A typical cable-stayed assembly

f_{pu} = ultimate tensile stress 15.2 mm seven-wire strand

$\quad\quad$ = 240 ksi (837 MN/m^2)

σ_{perm} = tensile strength = f_{tc};$\quad\quad$ σ_{perm} = 0.45f_{pu}

Use any space frame analysis package for the computation of forces and reactions.

Figure 6.71 shows a bunch of cables where

$$T_i = \frac{R_i}{\sin \phi_i} \tag{6.195}$$

where

$\quad R_i$ = any support reaction

$\quad T_i$ = cable force

$\quad \phi_i$ = angle of the cable to the connection or support where the reaction R_i exists.

The force F_H acting horizontally is given by (see Fig. 6.72):

$$F_H = \sum \frac{R_i''}{\tan \phi_i''} - \sum \frac{R_i'}{\tan \phi_i'} \tag{6.196}$$

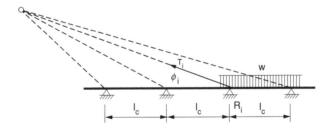

Figure 6.71. Cable tension T_i

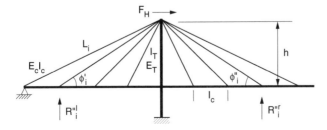

Figure 6.72. Tower and back-stay force

For a typical cable pinned to the tower and the support with various parameters and material properties indicated

$$T_i = \frac{F_H h^3 \cos \phi_i}{3 L_i \left(\dfrac{E_c I_c}{E_p A_i} \right)} \tag{6.197}$$

This expression includes the bending of the tower as well.

If the bending stiffness of the tower is neglected, then T_i has a value

$$T_i = \frac{F_H}{\cos \phi_i} \tag{6.198}$$

R_i at each cable node is equal to wl. Where the load w is continuous, the reactions R can be determined by analysing the deck girder as continuous; w itself can be due to w_{LL} and w_{DL} (imposed and dead load combined).

The stiffness k

Under a unit load, the node displaces by Δ_i vertically, then by pure tegnometry

$$\Delta_i = \frac{L_i}{A_i} E_c \sin^2 \phi_i \tag{6.199}$$

where

$$L_i = h / \sin \phi_i$$

$$L_i = \text{cable length.} \tag{6.200}$$

The value Δ_i becomes

$$\Delta_i = \frac{h \sigma_{per}}{R_i E_c \sin^2 \phi_i} \tag{6.201}$$

$$R_i = (w_{DL} + w_{LL}) l$$

The stiffness of the cable k is given by (see Fig. 6.73):

$$k = \frac{1}{\Delta_i l} - \frac{(w_{DL} + w_{LL}) E_c \sin^2 \phi_i}{h \sigma_{per}} \tag{6.202}$$

where

ϕ_i is as defined earlier

$l = $ space between two cable connections.

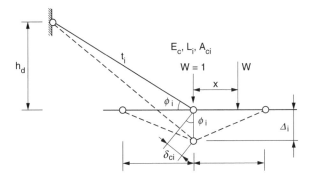

Figure 6.73. Cable stiffness [Example (6.12)]

Where the load W is occurring at a distance x, the value of T_i in the cable by the methods shown by Westergaard in this text is:

$$T_i = \frac{W}{2}\, c\, \frac{l}{\sin \phi_i}\, e^{-c}(\cos cx + \sin cx) \tag{6.203}$$

where

$$c = \sqrt[4]{\frac{k_i}{4 E_c I}} \tag{6.204}$$

The bending moment at point i is thus

$$M_i = \frac{W}{4c}\, e^{-c}\,(\cos cx - \sin cx) \tag{6.205}$$

Space frame analysis

Based on HS 20 loading, space frame analysis has been applied to Example (6.12). The results are given in Table 6.23.

Table 6.23. Space frame analysis results

Cable stay No.	(area)	R_{DL} (kN) kips	T_{DL} (kN) kips	R_{DL+LL} (kN) kips	T_{DL+LL} (kN) kips
4	($A_c = 6.5\,in^2$)	371 (1650.21)	571 (3874.21)	550 (2446)	1080 (4804)
10	($A_c = 3.9\,in^2$)	371 (1650.21)	740 (3291.50)	550 (2446)	850 (3781)
15	($A_c = 3.5\,in^2$)	371 (1650.21)	650 (2891.2)	550 (2446)	754 (3354)
40	($A_c = 4.34\,in^2$)	371 (1650.21)	760 (3380)	550 (2446)	890 (3959)
Back stay					
	A_c (24 in^2)		2810 (12 499 kN)		4110 (18 281.3)

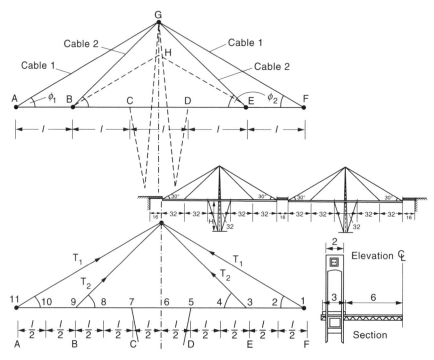

Figure 6.74. Cable stay arrangement for the method of Ray

6.8.2 Cable-stayed bridge analysis using the flexibility method and influence lines. K.C. Ray method*

The cable arrangement is shown in Figs 6.74–6.79. *AF* is supported by rigid supports at *C* and *D*. *A, B, E* and *F* are connected by cables 1 and 2 to the tower peak *G*. Cables 1 and 2 are inclined to the deck at angles ϕ_1 and ϕ_2, respectively. The position of *C* and *D* is at a distance *l*. It is decided to have distances *AB, BC, CD, DF* and *EF* equal to *l*. The structure will be symmetrical if these positions are equally spaced. Node points *A* and *F* can be connected to a similar structure for additional spans. For the purpose of influence lines, the deck is divided into 10 and 11 nodes. A frame-type tower is provided and *C* and *D* have rockers. It is assumed that cable tensions are the same on both sides, i.e. $T_1 = T_3$, $T_2 = T_4$. It is also assumed that for the purposes of analysis, the deck *AF* is uniform. Where the deck is not uniform, the method described, under the influence lines of a deck with variable sections, can be adopted. The idea is to describe and analyse in detail the bridge, where the variable sections can easily be added. The supports *C* and *D* will not have an uplift since it is assumed that engineers have made such a provision. Their influence lines are to be drawn for spacings $l/2$. This means 11 loading positions are situated at $l/2$ apart. Bending

---

* Ray, K. C. Standard Influence Line Coefficient for Bi-cables Cable-stayed Balanced Cantilever Structure. *Institution of Engineers, India. Journal C1*, vol. 53, July 1973, pp. 291–310.

moments for each position with T values as redundants have to be evaluated. It is necessary to obtain flexibility coefficients. When a unit load is applied, say, at 2, reactions of T at 1, 3 and 11 will occur. The vertical reactions are $T_1 \cos \phi_1$ and $T_2 \cos \phi_2$. At 5 it will be $lT_2 \sin \phi_2 + 2lT_1 \sin \phi_1$ which will be the same at 7. At 11 the vertical reaction is upward and is $T_1 \sin \phi_1$, which will be the same at node 1. At 9 the same upward reaction as at 3 of $T_2 \sin \phi$ occurs. Similarly other points or nodes are considered.

Energy values are calculated using:

$$U = \int_0^{l/2} \frac{(xT_1 \sin \phi_1)^2}{2EI} \, dx$$

Zone 1–2
At a distance x [Fig. 6.75(a)]

$$mx = -\frac{\frac{1}{2} T_1 \sin \phi_1}{l/2} x = -xT_1 \sin \phi_1 \tag{6.206}$$

$$\frac{\partial U}{\partial T_2} = 0$$

Assuming EI is constant, using flexibility tables gives:

$$\frac{l^3}{3EI} \left(\frac{1}{8}\right) T_1 \sin^2 \phi \qquad \frac{\partial U}{\partial T_2} = 0$$

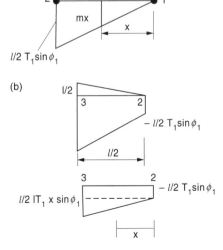

Figure 6.75. Zone flexibility diagrams

Zone 3–2

Referring to Fig. 6.75(b)

$$\text{combined flexibility} = \frac{l^3}{3EI}\left(-\frac{5}{16}\sin\phi_1 + \frac{7}{8}T_1\sin^2\phi_1\right) \tag{6.207}$$

Similarly other values can be obtained for other sections (see Fig. 6.76).

Zone 3–5

$$\frac{\partial U}{\partial T_1} = \frac{l^3}{3EI}\left(-4.75\sin\phi_1 + 7T_1\sin\phi_1 + 2.5T_2\sin\phi_1\sin\phi_2\right) \tag{6.208}$$

$$\frac{\partial U}{\partial T_2} = \frac{l^3}{3EI}\left(-1.75\sin\phi_2 + 2.5T_1\sin\phi_1\sin\phi_2 + T_2\sin^2\phi_2\right) \tag{6.208a}$$

Zone 5–7

$$\frac{\partial U}{\partial T_1} = \frac{l^3}{3EI}\left(-4.5\sin\phi_1 + 12T_1\sin^2\phi_1 + 6T_2\sin\phi_1\sin\phi_2\right) \tag{6.209}$$

$$\frac{\partial U}{\partial T_2} = \frac{l^3}{3EI}\left(-2.25\sin\phi_2 + 3T_2\sin^2\phi_2 + 6T_1\sin\phi_1\sin\phi_2\right)$$

$$\tag{6.209a}$$

Zone 7–9

$$\frac{\partial U}{\partial T_2} = \frac{l^3}{3EI}\left(-2.5T_1\sin\phi_1\sin\phi_2 + T_2\sin^2\phi_2\right) \tag{6.210}$$

$$\frac{\partial U}{\partial T_1} = \frac{l^3}{3EI}\left(7T_1\sin^2\phi_1 + 2.5T_2\sin\phi_1\sin\phi_2\right) \tag{6.210a}$$

Also

$$\frac{\partial U}{\partial T_1} = \frac{l^3}{3EI}T_1\sin^2\phi_1 \qquad \frac{\partial U}{\partial T_2} = 0 \tag{6.210b}$$

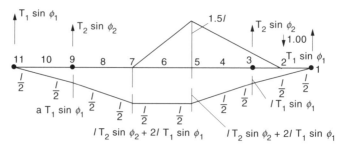

Figure 6.76. Reactions at bridge nodes

For the cable part

$$\frac{\partial U}{\partial T_1} = \frac{2T_1 L_1}{A_1^c E_c} \tag{6.210c}$$

$$\frac{\partial U}{\partial T_2} = \frac{2T_2 L_2}{A_2^c E_c} \tag{6.210d}$$

where

A_1^c, A_2^c are areas of the cables

L_1, L_2 are the cable lengths of cables 1 and 2

E_c is the Young's modulus of the cable.

It follows that:

$$\sum \frac{\partial U}{T_1} = 0 \qquad \sum \frac{\partial U}{\partial T_2} = 0 \tag{6.211}$$

The above equations are collected in terms of T, and the following matrix relations are then established:

$$\left[\frac{I}{l^2 A_1^c} \frac{E_g}{E_c} + 28 \sin^2 \phi_1 \right] T_1 + [11 \sin \phi_1 \sin \phi_2] T_2$$

$$= [9.5625 \sin^2 \phi_1] \tag{6.212}$$

$$[11 \sin \phi_1 \sin \phi_2] T_1 + \left[\frac{I}{l^2 A_2^c} \frac{E_g}{E_c} - 5 \sin^2 \phi_2 \right] T_2$$

$$= 4 \sin^2 \phi_2 \tag{6.213}$$

For a unit load at 2, the values of T and T_2 can be computed:

$$\left[\begin{array}{cc} \dfrac{I}{l^2 A_1^c} \dfrac{E_g}{E_c} + 28 \sin^2 \phi_1 & 11 \sin \phi_1 \sin \phi_2 \\[2ex] 11 \sin \phi_1 \sin \phi_2 & \dfrac{I}{l^2 A_2^c} \dfrac{E_g}{E_c} - 5 \sin^2 \phi_2] \end{array} \right] \left\{ \begin{array}{c} T_1 \\ T_2 \end{array} \right\}$$

$$= \left\{ \begin{array}{c} 9.5625 \sin^2 \phi_1 \\ 4 \sin^2 \phi_2 \end{array} \right\} \tag{6.214}$$

where

E_g = Young's modulus of the span girder

I = second moment of area of the girder.

Hence

$$
T_1 = \frac{-3.81 \sin \phi_1 \sin^2 \phi_2 - 9.5625 \sin \phi_1 \left(\dfrac{I}{l^2 A_2^c} \dfrac{E_g}{E_c} \right)}{\bar{D}}
\tag{6.215}
$$

$$
T_2 = \frac{-6.82 \sin^2 \phi_1 \sin \phi_2 - 4 \sin \phi_2 \left(\dfrac{I}{l^2 A_1^c} \dfrac{E_g}{E_c} \right)}{\bar{D}}
\tag{6.216}
$$

where

$$
\bar{D} = 121 \sin^2 \phi_1 \sin^2 \phi_2 - \left(28 \sin^2 \phi_1 + \frac{I}{l^2 A_1^c} \frac{E_g}{E_c} \right)
$$
$$
\times \left(5 \sin^2 \phi_2 + \frac{I}{l^2 A_2^c} \frac{E_g}{E_c} \right)
\tag{6.217}
$$

Unit load at 1

$$
T_1 = \left[-9.5 \sin \phi_1 \sin^2 \phi_2 - 14 \sin \phi \frac{I}{l^2 A_2^c} \frac{E_g}{E_c} \right] \Big/ \bar{D}
\tag{6.218}
$$

$$
T_2 = -5.5 \sin \phi_2 \frac{F}{l^2 A_1^c} \frac{E_g}{E_c}
\tag{6.219}
$$

Unit load at 2

$$
T_1 = \left[-3.81 \sin \phi_1 \sin^2 \phi_2 - 9.5625 \sin \phi_1 \frac{I}{l^2 A_2^c} \frac{E_g}{E_c} \right] \Big/ \bar{D}
\tag{6.220}
$$

$$
T_2 = \left[-6.82 \sin^2 \phi_1 \sin \phi_2 - 4 \sin \phi_2 \frac{I}{l^2 A_1^c} \frac{E_g}{E_c} \right] \Big/ \bar{D}
\tag{6.221}
$$

Unit load at 3

$$
T_1 = \left[5.5 \sin \phi_1 \frac{I}{l^2 A_2^c} \frac{E_g}{E_c} \right] \Big/ \bar{D}
\tag{6.222}
$$

$$
T_2 = \left[-9.5 \sin^2 \phi_1 \sin \phi_2 - 2.5 \sin \phi_2 \frac{I}{l^2 A_1^c} \frac{E_g}{E_c} \right] \Big/ \bar{D}
\tag{6.223}
$$

Unit load at 4

$$
T_1 = \left[0.75 \sin \phi_1 \sin^2 \phi_2 - 2.1875 \sin \phi_1 \frac{I}{l^2 A_2^c} \frac{E_g}{E_c} \right] \Big/ \bar{D}
\tag{6.224}
$$

$$
T_2 = \left[-5.75 \sin^2 \phi_1 \sin \phi_2 - 1.0625 \sin \phi_2 \frac{I}{l^2 A_1^c} \frac{E_g}{E_c} \right] \Big/ \bar{D}
\tag{6.225}
$$

Unit load at 6

$$T_1 = \left[-0.375\sin\phi_1\sin^2\phi_2 + 0.75\sin\phi_1\,\frac{I}{l^2A_2^c}\,\frac{E_g}{E_c}\right]\Big/\bar{D} \tag{6.226}$$

$$T_2 = \left[2.25\sin\phi_2\sin^2\phi_1 - 0.375\sin\phi_2\,\frac{I}{l^2A_1^c}\,\frac{E_g}{E_c}\right]\Big/\bar{D} \tag{6.227}$$

Reactions at supports 5 and 7 (Fig. 6.77)

$$R_5 = V_5 = -T_1\sin\phi_1 - T_2\sin\phi_2 + \frac{3l\times1.0}{l} \tag{6.228}$$

$$R_7 = V_7 = -T_1\sin\phi_1 - T_2\sin\phi_2 + \left(1 - \frac{3l\times1.0}{l}\right) \tag{6.229}$$

Reactions at the towers

$$R = V = 2T_1\sin\phi_1 + 2T_2\sin\phi_2 \tag{6.230}$$

Moment and shears at point 5 are:

$$M_5 = 2lT_1\sin\phi_1 + \phi_1 T_2\sin\phi_2 - 2l \tag{6.231}$$

$$V_5 = -T\sin\phi_1 - T_2\sin\phi_2 + 1.0 \tag{6.232}$$

$$V = 0 \quad \text{between 5 and 6} \tag{6.233}$$

$$V_{\text{left}} = -2 \tag{6.234}$$

Influence line ordinates due to Ray are shown in Tables 6.24–6.35.

Tables presented provide for influence line ordinates for tensions in cables, reactions on supports 5 and 7; bending moments for sections 2–6 and shears for sections 1–6. Ordinates at points 1 to 11 have been worked out and tabulated.

Tables 6.24–6.29 give values for cable having a single point of suspension from the tower (Fig. 6.78) for different values of $\bar{C}_1$ and $\bar{C}_2$ ranging from 0.001 to 0.200.

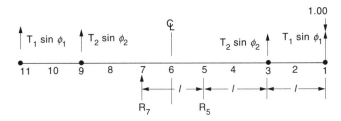

Figure 6.77. Reactions at bridge supports 5 and 7

Table 6.24. Influence line ordinates ($\bar{C}_1 = \bar{C}_2 = 0.001$, single point suspension)

Load at	Cable tension		Reactions			Moments at					Shears at					
	T_1	T_2	R_5	R_7	Tower	2	3	4	5	6	1	2	3	4	5	6
1	0.990	0.028	2.486	−2.514	1.029	−0.253	−0.505	−0.748	−0.991	0.009	0.505R −0.495L	0.505	0.505R 0.795R	0.486	0.486R	−2.00
2	0.410	0.515	1.938	−2.062	1.124	0.103	−0.295	−0.514	−0.733	0.017	−0.205	−0.205L	0.486L 0.795R	0.438	−2.000L 0.438R	−1.50
3	0014	0.715	1.497	−1.503	1.006	0.004	0.007	−0.235	−0.490	0.010	−0.007	−0.007	0.438L 0.993R −0.007 0.497L −0.503 0.035R	0.497	−1.500L 0.497R	−1.00
4	−0.071	0.425	1.241	−0.759	0.518	−0.018	−0.035	0.095	−0.276	−0.026	0.035	0.035	−0.259L	−0.259L	0.741R	−0.50
5	0.00	0.00	1.000	0.000	0.000	0.000	0.000	0.000	0.000	0.000	0.000	0.000	0.000	0.000	−0.500L 1.000R −1.000L 0.000	0.00
6	0.033	−0.171	0.595	0.595	−0.190	0.008	0.016	−0.032	−0.079	0.171	−0.016	−0.016	−0.016R	0.095	0.095R	0.50R
7	0.000	0.000	0.000	1.000	0.000	0.000	0.000	0.000	0.000	0.000	0.000	0.000	0.000	0.000	−0.500L 0.000	−0.50L 0.00
8	−0.071	0.425	−0.759	1.241	0.518	−0.018	−0.035	0.095	0.224	−0.026	0.035	0.035	−0.035R	−0.259	−0.259R	0.50
9	0.014	0.715	−1.503	1.497	1.006	0.004	0.007	0.266	0.510	0.010	−0.007	−0.007	−0.259L −0.007R	−0.503	0.500L −0.503R	1.00
10	0.410	0.515	−2.062	1.938	1.124	0.103	0.205	0.486	0.767	0.017	−0.205	−0.205	−0.503L −0.205R	−0.562	1.000L −0.562R	1.50
11	0.990	0.028	−2.514	2.486	1.029	0.243	0.495	0.752	1.009	0.009	−0.495	−0.495	−0.562L −0.495R	−0.514	1.500L −0.514R −2.000L	2.00

Table 6.25. *Influence line ordinates* ($\bar{C}_1 = \bar{C}_2 = 0.005$, *single point suspension*)

Load at	Cable tension		Reactions			Moments at					Shears at					
	T_1	T_2	R_5	R_7	Tower	2	3	4	5	6	1	2	3	4	5	6
1	0.931	0.113	2.456	−2.544	1.089	−0.267	−0.534	−0.762	−0.940	0.010	0.534R / −0.466L	0.534	0.534R	0.456	0.456R	−2.00
2	0.416	0.487	1.956	−2.044	1.088	0.104	−0.292	−0.520	−0.748	0.002	−0.208	0.792R / −0.208L	0.456L / 0.792R	0.456	−2.000L / 0.456R	−1.50
3	0.059	0.625	1.537	−1.463	0.926	0.014	0.029	−0.240	−0.508	−0.008	−0.029	−0.029	0.456L / 0.971R / 0.537L / −0.463 / 0.019R	0.537	−1.500L / 0.537R	−1.00
4	−0.039	0.365	1.266	−0.734	0.468	−0.009	−0.019	0.098	−0.285	−0.035	0.019	0.019	−0.234L / 0.019R	0.766 / −0.234	−1.000L / 0.766R	−0.50
5	0.000	0.000	1.000	0.000	0.000	0.000	0.000	0.000	0.000	0.000	0.000	0.000	0.000	0.000	−1.000L / 0.000	0.00
6	0.023	−0.145	0.589	0.589	−0.198	0.006	0.012	0.033	−0.078	0.172	−0.011	−0.011	−0.011R / 0.089L	0.089	0.089R	0.50R / −0.50L
7	0.000	0.000	0.000	1.000	0.000	0.000	0.000	0.000	0.000	0.000	0.000	0.000	0.000	0.000	0.000	0.00
8	−0.039	0.365	−0.734	1.266	0.468	−0.009	−0.019	0.098	0.215	−0.035	0.019	0.019	−0.234L / 0.019R	−0.234	−0.500L / 0.000 / −0.234R	0.50
9	0.059	0.625	−1.463	1.537	0.926	0.014	0.029	0.260	0.492	−0.008	−0.029	−0.029	−0.463L / −0.208R	−0.463	0.500L / −0.463R	1.00
10	0.416	0.487	−2.044	1.956	1.088	0.104	0.208	0.480	0.752	0.002	−0.208	−0.208	−0.544L / −0.466R	−0.544	1.000L / −0.544R	1.50
11	0.931	0.113	−2.544	2.456	1.088	0.233	0.466	0.738	1.060	0.010	−0.466	−0.466	−0.544L	−0.544	1.500L / −0.544R / 2.000L	2.00

Table 6.26. Influence line ordinates ($\bar{C}_1 = \bar{C}_2 = 0.010$, single point suspension)

Load at	Cable tension		Reactions			Moments at					Shears at					
	T_1	T_2	R_5	R_7	Tower	2	3	4	5	6	1	2	3	4	5	6
1	0.875	0.185	2.435	-2.565	1.130	-0.282	-0.563	-0.781	-0.998	0.002	0.563R -0.437L	0.563	0.563R	0.435	0.435R	-2.00
2	0.421	-0.465	1.970	-2.030	1.060	0.105	-0.290	-0.525	-0.760	-0.010	-0.210	0.790R -0.210L	0.435L 0.790R	0.470	-2.000L 0.470R	-1.50
3	0.095	0.552	1.569	-1.431	0.862	0.024	0.047	-0.237	-0.522	-0.022	-0.047	-0.047	0.470L 0.953R -0.047 0.569L -0.431 0.006R	0.569	-1.500L 0.569R	-1.00
4	-0.012	0.315	1.286	-0.714	0.428	-0.003	-0.006	0.101	-0.292	-0.042	0.036	0.006	-0.214L	0.786R -0.214L	-1.000L	-0.50
5	0.000	0.000	1.000	0.000	0.000	0.000	0.000	0.000	0.000	0.000	0.000	0.000	0.000	0.000	1.000R 0.000 -1.000L 0.000	0.00
6	0.012	-0.124	0.578	0.578	-0.156	0.003	0.006	-0.033	-0.072	0.178	-0.006	-0.006	-0.006R	0.078	0.078R	0.50R
7	0.000	0.000	0.000	1.000	0.000	0.000	0.000	0.000	0.000	0.000	0.000	0.000	0.078L 0.000 0.006R	0.000	-0.50L 0.000 -0.214R	-0.50L 0.00
8	-0.012	0.315	-0.714	1.286	0.428	-0.003	-0.006	0.101	0.208	-0.042	0.006	0.006	-0.214L -0.047R	-0.214	0.500L -0.431R	0.50
9	0.095	0.552	-1.431	1.569	0.862	0.024	0.047	0.263	0.478	-0.022	-0.047	-0.047	-0.431L -0.210R	-0.431	1.000L -0.530R	1.00
10	0.421	0.465	-2.030	1.970	1.060	0.105	0.210	0.475	0.740	-0.010	-0.210	-0.210	-0.530L -0.437R	-0.530	1.500L -0.565R	1.50
11	0.875	0.185	-2.565	2.435	1.130	0.218	0.437	0.719	1.002	0.002	-0.437	-0.437	0.565L	-0.565	2.000L	2.00

Table 6.27. *Influence line ordinates* ($\bar{C}_1 = \bar{C}_2 = 0.050$, *single point suspension*)

Load at	Cable tension T_1	T_2	Reactions R_5	R_7	Tower	Moments at 2	3	4	5	6	Shears at 1	2	3	4	5	6
1	0.717	0.358	2.394	-2.606	1.212	-0.321	-0.462	-0.839	-1.036	-0.036	0.642R -0.358L	0.642	0.642R	0.394	0.394R	-2.00
2	0.412	0.388	2.024	-1.976	0.952	0.103	-0.294	-0.556	-0.818	-0.068	-0.206	0.794R -0.206L	0.394L 0.794R	0.524	-2.000L 0.524R	-1.50
3	0.186	0.344	1.669	-1.331	0.662	0.046	0.093	-0.242	-0.576	-0.086	-0.093	-0.093	0.524L 0.907R	0.669	-1.500L 0.669R	-1.00
4	0.054	0.177	1.350	-0.650	0.300	0.014	0.029	0.103	-0.323	-0.073	-0.027	-0.027	-0.093 0.669L -0.331 -0.027R	0.850	-1.000L	-0.50
5	0.000	0.000	1.000	0.000	0.000	0.000	0.000	0.000	0.000	0.000	0.000	0.000	0.000	-0.150L	0.850R	0.00
6	-0.016	-0.068	0.555	0.555	-0.110	-0.004	-0.008	-0.036	-0.063	0.187	0.008	0.008	0.008R	0.055	-0.500L 1.00R -1.00L 0.00	0.50R
7	0.000	0.000	0.000	1.000	0.000	0.000	0.000	0.000	0.000	0.000	0.000	0.000	0.000	0.000	0.055R	-0.50L 0.00
8	0.054	0.177	-0.650	1.350	0.300	0.014	0.027	0.103	0.177	-0.073	-0.027	-0.027	-0.027R	-0.150	-0.500L 0.000	0.50
9	0.186	0.344	-1.331	1.669	0.662	0.046	0.093	0.258	0.424	-0.086	-0.093	-0.093	-0.331L -0.093R	-0.331	0.500L -0.331R	1.00
10	0.412	0.388	-1.976	2.024	0.952	0.103	0.206	0.444	0.682	-0.068	-0.206	-0.206	-0.476L -0.358R	-0.476	1.000L -0.476R	1.50
11	0.717	0.358	-2.606	2.394	1.212	0.179	0.358	0.661	0.964	-0.036	-0.358	-0.358	-0.606L	-0.606	1.500L -0.606R 2.000L	2.00

Table 6.28. *Influence line ordinates ($\bar{C}_1 = \bar{C}_2 = 0.100$, single point suspension)*

Load at	Cable tension		Reactions			Moments at					Shears at					
	T_1	T_2	R_5	R_7	Tower	2	3	4	5	6	1	2	3	4	5	6
1	0.647	0.380	2.413	−2.587	1.174	0.338	0.676	−0883	−1.089	0.089	0.676R / −0.324L	0.676	0.676R / 0.413L	0.413	0.413R / −2.000L	−2.00
2	0.400	0.348	2.060	−1.944	0.880	0.100	0.300	0.580	0.860	−0.110	−0.200	0.800R / −0.200L	0.800R / 0.560L	0.560	0.560R / −1.500L	−1.50
3	0.200	0.270	1.713	−1.287	0.574	0.050	0.100	−0.256	−0.613	−0.113	−0.100	−0.100	0.900R / −0.100 · 0.713L / −0.287	0.713	0.713R / −1.000L	−1.00
4	0.068	0.132	1.366	−0.634	0.268	0.017	0.034	0.096	−0.342	−0.092	−0.034	−0.034	−0.034R / −0.124L	0.876R / −0.124L	0.876R / −0.490L	−0.50
5	0.000	0.000	1.000	0.000	0.000	0.000	0.000	0.000	0.000	0.000	0.000	0.000	0.000	0.000	−0.500L / 1.000R / 0.000 / −0.000L	0.00
6	−0.022	0.050	0.546	0.546	0.092	−0.005	0.011	−0.033	−0.057	0.193	0.011	0.011	0.011R / 0.046L	0.046	0.046R	0.50R
7	0.000	0.000	0.000	1.000	0.000	0.000	0.000	0.000	0.000	0.000	0.000	0.000	0.000 / −0.034R	0.000	0.000 / −0.124R	−0.50L / 0.00
8	0.068	0.132	−0.634	1.366	0.268	0.017	0.034	0.096	0.158	0.092	0.034	0.034	−0.124L / −0.100R	−0.124	0.500L / −0.287R	0.50
9	0.200	0.270	−1.287	1.713	0.574	0.050	0.100	0.244	0.387	−0.113	0.100	0.100	−0.287L / −0.200R	−0.287	1.000L / −0.440R	1.00
10	0.400	0.348	−1944	2.060	0.880	0.100	0.200	0.420	0.640	−0.110	−0.200	−0.200	−0.440L / −0.324R	−0440	1.500L / −0.587R	1.50
11	0.647	0.380	−2.587	2.413	1.174	0.162	0.324	0.617	0.911	−0.089	−0.324	0.324	−0.587L	−0.587	2.000L	2.00

Table 6.29. *Influence line ordinates* ($\bar{C}_1 = \bar{C}_2 = 0.200$, *single point suspension*)

Load at	Cable tension		Reactions			Moments at					Shears at					
	T_1	T_2	R_5	R_7	Tower	2	3	4	5	6	1	2	3	4	5	6
1	0.537	0.358	2.483	−2.517	1.034	−0.366	−0.732	−0.973	−1.215	−0.215	0.732R −0.268L	0.732 0.822R	0.732R 0.483L 0.822R	0.483	0.483R −2.000L 0.614R	−2.00
2	0.357	0.302	2.114	−1.886	0.772	0.089	−0.322	−0.629	−0.936	−0.186	−0.178	−0.178L	0.614L 0.904R	0.614	−1.500L 0.754R	−1.50
3	0.191	0.215	1.754	−1.246	0.492	0.048	0.096	−0.281	−0.658	−0.158	−0.096	−0.096	−0.096 0.754L −0.246 −0.035R	0.754	−1.000L	−1.00
4	0.071	0.099	1.396	−0.604	0.208	0.017	0.035	0.086	−0.361	−0.111	−0.035	−0.035	−0.104L	−0.104L	0.896R	−0.50
5	0.000	0.000	1.000	0.000	0.000	0.000	0.000	0.000	0.000	0.000	0.000	0.000	0.000	0.000	−0.500L 1.000R 0.000 −1.000L 0.000	0.00
6	−0.024	−0.037	0.538	0.538	−0.076	−0.006	−0.012	−0.031	−0.050	0.200	0.012	0.012	0.012R	0.038	0.038R	0.50R
7	0.000	0.000	0.000	1.000	0.000	0.000	0.000	0.000	0.000	0.000	0.000	0.000	0.038L 0.000	0.000	0.500L 0.000	−0.50L 0.00
8	0.071	0.099	−0.604	1.396	0.208	0.017	0.035	0.086	0.139	−0.111	−0.035	−0.035	−0.104L −0.096R	−0.104	0.500L −0.246R	0.50
9	0.191	0.215	−1.246	1.754	0.492	0.048	0.096	0.219	0.342	−0.158	−0.096	−0.096	−0.246L −0.178R	−0.246	1.000L −0.386R	1.00
10	0.357	0.302	−1.886	2.114	0.772	0.089	0.178	0.371	0.564	−0.186	−0.178	−0.178	−0.386L −0.268R	−0.386	1.500L −0.517R	1.50
11	0.537	0.358	−2.517	2.483	1.034	0.134	0.268	0.527	0.785	−0.215	−0.268	−0.268	−0.517L	−0.517	2.000L	2.00

Table 6.30. *Influence line ordinates* ($\bar{C}_1 = \bar{C}_2 = 0.001$, *parallel cable suspension*)

Load at	Cable tension		Reactions			Moments at					Shears at					
	T_1	T_2	R_5	R_7	Tower	2	3	4	5	6	1	2	3	4	5	6
1	0.990	0.037	2.486	−2.514	1.028	−0.253	−0.505	−0.749	−0.991	0.009	0.505R −0.495L	0.505 0.797R	0.505R 0.486L 0.797R	0.486	0.486R −2.000L 0.454R	−2.00
2	0.406	0.685	1.954	−2.046	1.092	0.102	0.297	0.524	0.751	0.001	−0.203	−0.203L	0.454L 0.989R	0.454	−1.500L	−1.50
3	0.021	0.935	1.521	−1.479	0.958	0.005	0.011	−0.25	−0.510	−0.010	−0.011	−0.011	−0.011 0.521L −0.479 0.030R	0.521	0.521R −1.000L 0.750R	−1.00
4	−0.061	0.560	1.250	0.750	0.500	0.015	0.030	0.095	0.380	0.030	0.030	0.030	−0.250L	0.750R	−0.500L 1.000R	−0.50
5	0.000	0.000	1.000	0.000	0.000	0.000	0.000	0.000	0.000	0.000	0.000	0.000	0.000	0.000	0.000 −1.000L 0.000	0.00
6	0.036	−0.232	0.598	0.598	−0.196	0.009	0.018	−0.031	−0.080	0.170	−0.018	−0.018	−0.018R	0.098	0.098R	0.50R
7	0.000	0.000	0.000	1.000	0.000	0.000	0.000	0.000	0.00	0.000	0.000	0.000	0.098L 0.000 0.030R	0.000	−0.050L 0.000 −0.250R	−0.50L 0.00
8	−0.061	0.560	−0.750	1.250	0.500	−0.015	−0.03	0.095	0.22	−0.030	0.030	0.030	−0.250L −0.011R	−0.250L	0.500L −0.479R	0.50
9	0.021	0.935	−1.479	1.521	0.958	0.005	0.011	0.250	0.490	−0.010	−0.011	−0.011	−0.479L	−0.479	1.000L	1.00
10	0.406	0.685	−2.046	1.954	1.092	0.102	0.203	0.476	0.749	−0.001	−0.203	−0.203	−0.546L −0.495R	−0.203R −0.546	1.500L −0.514R	−0.546R 1.50
11	0.990	0.037	−2.514	2.486	1.028	0.247	0.495	0.751	1.009	0.009	−0.495	−0.495	−0.546L −0.495R	−0.514	1.500L −0.514R	2.00

Table 6.31. *Influence line ordinates ($\bar{C}_1 = \bar{C}_2 = 0.005$, parallel cable suspension)*

Load at	Cable tension		Reactions			Moments at					Shears at					
	T_1	T_2	R_5	R_7	Tower	2	3	4	5	6	1	2	3	4	5	6
1	0.940	0.141	2.459	−2.541	1.082	−0.265	−0.530	−0.759	−0.989	0.011	0.530R / −0.470L	0.530	0.530R / 0.787R	0.459	0.459R	−2.00
2	0.426	0.616	1.979	−1.021	1.042	0.106	−0.287	−0.527	−0.766	−0.016	−0.213	0.787R / −0.213L	0.479L / 0.957R	0.479	−2.000L / 0.479R	−1.50
3	0.086	0.782	1.566	−1.434	0.868	0.021	0.043	−0.240	−0.523	−0.023	0.043	−0.043	−0.043 / 0.566L / −0.434 / 0.009R	0.566	−1.500L	−1.00
4	−0.019	0.435	1.291	0.709	0.418	−0.005	−0.009	0.095	0.300	−0.050	0.009	0.009	−0.209L	−0.209	0.566R / 0.791R	−0.50
5	0.000	0.000	1.000	0.000	0.000	0.000	0.000	0.000	0.000	0.000	0.000	0.000	0.000	0.000	−1.000L / 0.791R	0.00
6	0.018	−0.194	0.588	0.588	−0.176	0.005	0.009	−0.034	−0.079	0.171	−0.009	−0.009	−0.009R	0.088	−0.500L / 1.000R	0.50R
7	0.000	0.000	0.000	1.000	0.000	0.000	0.000	0.000	0.000	0.000	0.000	0.000	0.088L / 0.000 / 0.009R	0.000	0.000 / 1.002L / 0.000	−0.50L / 0.00
8	−0.019	0.435	−0.709	1.291	0.418	−0.005	−0.009	0.095	0.200	−0.050	0.009	0.009	−0.209L / −0.043R	−0.209	0.088R	0.50
9	0.086	0.782	−1.434	1.566	0.868	0.021	0.043	0.260	0.477	−0.023	−0.043	−0.043	−0.434L / −0.213R	−0.434	0.500L / 0.000 / −0.209R / −0.043R	1.00
10	0.426	0.616	−1.021	1.979	1.042	0.106	0.213	0.473	0.734	−0.016	−0.213	−0.213	−0.521L / −0.470R	−0.521	1.000L / −0.521R	1.50
11	0.940	0.141	−2.541	2.459	1.082	0.235	0.470	0.741	1.011	0.011	−0.470	−0.470	−0.541L	−0.541	1.500L / −0.541R / 2.00L0	2.00

Table 6.32. Influence line ordinates ($\bar{C}_1 = \bar{C}_2 = 0.010$, parallel cable suspension)

Load at	Cable tension		Reactions			Moments at					Shears at					
	T_1	T_2	R_5	R_7	Tower	2	3	4	5	6	1	2	3	4	5	6
1	0.905	0.222	2.436	−2.564	1.128	−0.274	−0.547	−0.765	−0.983	0.017	0.547R −0.453L	0.547	0.547R	0.436	0.436R	−2.00
2	0.455	0.557	1.994	−2.006	1.012	0.114	−0.272	−0.519	−0.766	0.016	−0.228	0.772R	0.436L 0.772R	0.494	−2.000L 0.494R	−1.50
3	0.133	0.656	1.605	−1.395	0.790	0.034	0.067	−0.245	−0.538	−0.038	−0.067	−0.228	−0.494L 0.933R −0.067 0.603L −0.397 −0.006R	0.603	−1.500L 0.603R	−1.00
4	0.011	0.373	1.308	−0.692	0.384	0.003	0.006	0.102	−0.302	−0.057	−0.006	−0.006	−0.194L	0.806	−1.000L 0.806	−0.50
5	0.000	0.000	1.000	0.000	0.000	0.000	0.000	0.000	0.000	0.000	0.000	0.000	0.000	−0.194	−0.500 1.000R 0.000 −1.000L 0.000 0.075	0.00
6	0.005	−0.156	0.575	0.575	−0.150	0.002	0.003	−0.034	−0.072	0.172	0.003	−0.003	−0.003R	0.075	−0.50 0.000 −0.194R	−0.50R −0.50L 0.00
7	0.000	0.000	0.000	1.000	0.000	0.000	0.000	0.000	0.000	0.000	0.000	0.000	0.075L 0.000 −0.006R	0.000	0.000	0.00
8	0.011	0.373	−0.692	1.308	0.384	0.003	0.006	0.102	0.198	−0.052	−0.036	−0.006	−0.194L −0.067R	−0.194	0.500L −0.397R	0.50
9	0.133	0.656	−1.395	1.605	0.790	−0.034	0.067	0.265	0.462	−0.038	−0.057	−0.067	−0.397L −0.228R	−0.397	1.000L −0.506R	1.00
10	0.455	0.557	−2.006	1.994	1.012	0.114	0.228	0.481	0.734	−0.016	−0.228	−0.228	−0.506L −0.453	−0.506	1.500L −0.564R	1.50
11	0.905	0.222	−2.564	2.436	1.128	0.226	0.453	0.735	1.017	0.017	−0.453	−0.453	−0.564L	−0.564	2.000L	2.00

Table 6.33. Influence line ordinates ($\bar{C}_1 = \bar{C}_2 = 0.050$, parallel cable suspension)

Load at	Cable tension		Reactions			Moments at					Shears at					
	T_1	T_2	R_5	R_7	Tower	2	3	4	5	6	1	2	3	4	5	6
1	0.825	0.404	2.386	−2.614	1.228	−0.294	−0.588	−0.781	−0.974	0.026	±0.588R / −0.412L	0.588	0.588R	0.386	0.386R	−2.00
2	0.504	0.437	2.030	1.970	0.940	0.126	−0.248	−0.513	−0.778	−0.028	−0.252	−0.252L / 0.748R	0.386L / 0.748R	0.530	−2.000L / 0.530R	1.50
3	0.243	0.385	1.687	−1.313	0.626	0.060	0.121	−0.223	−0.566	−0.066	−0.121	−0.121	0.530L / 0.879R / −0.121 / 0.687L / −0.313 / −0.041R	0.687	−1.500L / 0.687R	−1.00
4	0.082	0.198	1.360	−0.640	0.280	0.020	0.041	0.110	−0.319	−0.069	−0.041	−0.041	−0.540L	−0.540L / 0.460R	−1.000L	−0.50
5	0.000	0.000	1.000	0.000	0.000	0.000	0.000	0.000	0.000	0.000	0.000	0.000	0.000	0.000	−0.50L / 1.000R / 0.000 / −1.000L / 0.000	0.00
6	−0.024	−0.080	0.552	0.552	−0.104	−0.006	−0.012	−0.038	−0.064	0.186	0.012	0.012	0.012R	0.052	0.052R	0.50 / −0.50
7	0.000	0.000	0.000	1.000	0.000	0.000	0.000	0.000	0.000	0.000	0.000	0.000	0.000	0.000	0.000	0.00
8	0.082	0.198	−0.640	1.360	0.280	0.020	0.041	0.110	0.181	−0.069	−0.041	−0.041	−0.041R	−0.540	−0.540R	0.50
9	0.243	0.385	−1.313	1.687	0.626	0.060	0.121	0.277	0.434	−0.066	−0.121	−0.121	−0.313L / −0.252R	−0.313	0.500L / −0.313R	1.00
10	0.504	0.437	−1.970	2.030	0.940	0.126	0.252	0.487	0.721	−0.028	−0.252	−0.252	−0.470L / −0.412R	−0.470	1.000L / −0.470R	1.50
11	0.825	0.404	−2.614	2.386	1.228	0.206	0.412	0.719	1.026	0.026	−0.412	−0.412	−0.614L	−0.614	1.500L / −0.614R	−2.00 / 2.000L

Table 6.34. Influence line ordinates ($\bar{C}_1 = \bar{C}_2 = 0.100$, parallel cable suspension)

Load at	Cable tension		Reactions			Moments at					Shears at					
	T_1	T_2	R_5	R_7	Tower	2	3	4	5	6	1	2	3	4	5	6
1	0.805	0.443	2.377	−2.623	1.246	−0.299	−0.598	−0.789	−0.975	0.025	0.598R −0.402L	0.598	0.598R 0.377L 0.743R	0.377	0.377R −2.000L	−2.00
2	0.515	0.407	2.040	−1.960	0.920	0.128	−0.243	−0.513	−0.783	−0.033	−0.257	0.743R −0.257L	0.540L 0.743R	0.540	−1.500L 0.706R	−1.50
3	0.270	0.318	1.706	−1.294	0.588	0.067	0.135	0.229	0.571	0.071	0.135	0.135	0.135R 0.706L −0.294 −0.050R	0.865 0.540L 0.706	−1.000L 0.706R	−1.00
4	0.100	0.154	1.373	−0.627	0.254	0.025	0.050	0.113	−0.323	−0.073	−0.050	−0.050	−0.127L −0.050R	−0.127 0.873R	0.873R −0.500L 1.000R	−0.50
5	0.000	0.000	1.000	0.000	0.000	0.000	0.000	0.000	0.000	0.000	0.000	0.000	0.000	0.000	0.000 1.000R 0.000 −1.000L 0.000	0.00
6	−0.032	−0.060	0.546	0.546	−0.092	−0.008	−0.016	−0.039	0.062	0.188	0.016	0.016	0.016R 0.046L	0.046	0.046R −0.050R −0.127R	0.50R
7	0.000	0.000	0.000	1.000	0.000	0.000	0.000	0.000	0.000	0.000	0.000	0.000	0.000	0.000	0.000	−0.50L 0.00
8	0.100	0.154	−0.627	1.373	0.254	0.025	0.050	0.113	0.177	−0.073	−0.050	−0.050	−0.127L −0.135R	−0.127	0.500L −0.294R	0.50
9	0.270	0.318	−1.294	1.706	0.588	0.067	0.135	0.281	0.429	−0.071	−0.135	−0.135	0.294L −0.257R	−0.294	1.000L −0.460R	1.00
10	0.515	0.407	−1.960	2.040	0.920	0.128	0.259	0.487	0.717	−0.033	−0.257	−0.257	−0.460L −0.402R	−0.460	1.500L −0.632R	1.50
11	0.805	0.443	−2.623	2.377	1.246	0.201	0.402	0.713	1.025	0.025	−0.402	−0.402	−0.623L	−0.623	2.000L	2.00 2.00

Table 6.35. Influence line ordinates ($\bar{C}_1 = \bar{C}_2 = 0.200$, parallel cable suspension)

Load at	Cable tension		Reactions			Moments at					Shears at					
	T_1	T_2	R_5	R_7	Tower	2	3	4	5	6	1	2	3	4	5	6
1	0.787	0.472	2.371	−2.629	1.258	−0.304	−0.607	−0.793	−0.978	0.022	0.607R −0.393L	0.607 −0.739R	0.607R	0.371	0.371R −2.000L	−2.00
2	0.523	0.388	2.045	−1.955	0.910	0.130	−0.239	−0.512	−0.784	−0.034	−0.261	−0.261L	0.371 0.739	0.545	0.545R −1.500L	−1.50
3	0.286	0.276	1.719	−1.281	0.562	0.071	0.143	−0.227	−0.376	−0.076	−0.143	−0.143	0.545 0.857R	0.719	0.719R −1.500L	−1.00
4	0.109	0.127	1.383	−0.617	0.234	0.027	0.054	0.112	−0.329	−0.079	−0.054	−0.054	0.719 −0.281L −0.054R	0.883R −0.117L	−1.000L 0.883R	−0.50
5	0.000	0.000	1.000	0.000	0.000	0.000	0.000	0.000	0.000	0.000	0.000	0.000	0.000	0.000	0.000R 1.000 −1.000 0.000L	0.00
6	−0.037	−0.048	0.543	0.543	−0.086	−0.009	−0.019	−0.048	−0.062	0.188	0.019	0.019	0.019R	0.043	0.043R	0.50R −0.50L
7	0.000	0.000	0.000	1.000	0.000	0.000	0.000	0.000	0.000	0.000	0.000	0.000	0.043L 0.000	0.000	−0.50L 0.000	−0.50L 0.000
8	0.109	0.127	−0.617	1.383	0.234	0.027	0.054	0.112	0.171	−0.079	−0.054	−0.054	−0.054R −0.117L −0.143R	−0.117	0.500L −0.281R	0.50
9	0.286	0.276	−1.281	1.719	0.562	0.071	0.143	0.283	0.424	−0.076	−0.143	−0.143	−0.281L −0.261R	−0.281	1.000L −0.455R	1.00
10	0.523	0.388	−1.955	2.045	0.910	0.130	0.261	0.488	0.716	−0.034	−0.261	−0.261	−0.455L −0.393R	−0.455	1.500L −0.629R	1.50
11	0.787	0.472	−2.629	2.371	1.258	0.196	0.393	0.707	1.022	0.022	−0.393	−0.393	−0.629L	−0.629	2.000L	2.00

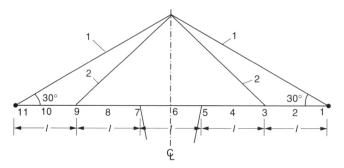

Figure 6.78. Tension of cables having a single point of suspension from the tower

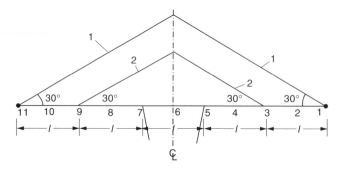

Figure 6.79. Tension of cables having parallel cables as suspenders

Tables 6.30–6.35 are for cables having parallel cables as suspenders (Fig. 6.79). Values of $\bar{C}_1$ and $\bar{C}_2$ have the same range:

Tension T_1 and $T_2 = $ Load $\times$ ordinate

Reaction $=$ Load $\times$ ordinate (positive : upward)

Shear $=$ Load $\times$ ordinate (positive : downward)

Moment $=$ Load $\times$ ordinate $\times l$ (positive : tension bottom)

$$\bar{C}_1 = \frac{I_g}{l^2 A_1} \times \frac{E_g}{E_c}$$

$$\bar{C}_2 = \frac{I_g}{l^2 A_2} \times \frac{E_g}{E_c}$$

Example (6.13)   Indian practice (Check also with BS 5400)
A typical cable-stayed bridge shown in Fig. 6.74 is 360 m long with a carriageway of 12 m and two footways of 3 m each. It is proposed to have two box girders supporting the deck consisting of orthotropic steel-played structures covered with a bitumastic asphalt. Use the following data.

Wire cables

$$f = 9500 \, \text{kg/cm}^2 \qquad \text{(high tensile steel)}$$

Welded steel box

$$f = 3200 \, \text{kg/cm}^2 \qquad \text{(high tensile steel)}$$

RC towers

$$f = 350 \, \text{kg/cm}^2$$

Saddle plates

$$f = 17\,300 \, \text{kg/cm}^2 \qquad \text{(cast steel)}$$

Loads

dead loads (deck) $= 1500 \, \text{kg/m}$

girder weight $= 1500 \, \text{kg/m}$

live loads $= 300 \, \text{kg/m}^2$ to be placed on span to give worst effects.

Cable angles of inclination

$\phi_1 = \phi_2 = 30°$ (at both ends)

Design a box section using these results
Check the girder and the cable sizes using BS 5400 and the following additional data:

Live load (UDL + knife edge) $= 54 \, \text{kN/m}$

Dead load $= 191.21 \, \text{kN/m}$ (based on sections)

Cables:

Parallel-wire cables
Galvanized long-lay type

$$\text{GUTS} = 1570 \, \text{N/mm}^2$$

Allowable stress $= 0.7 \times 1570 = 1090 \, \text{N/mm}^2$

Girder:

High tensile steel for:

$$\text{welded box girder} = 315\,\text{N/mm}^2$$

$$\text{reinforced concrete towers} = 40\,\text{N/mm}^2$$

$$\text{steel saddle plates} = 1696\,\text{N/mm}^2.$$

Referring now to Fig. 6.80:

$$\sin\phi_1 = \sin 30° = 0.5$$

$$\cos\phi_1 = 0.866029$$

$$\sin\beta = 0.693376$$

$$\cos\beta = 0.720577$$

$$L_1 = \frac{2.5l}{\cos\phi_1} = 2.8867394l \approx 2.8674l$$

$$L_2 = \frac{1.5l}{\cos\beta} = \frac{1.5l}{0.720577} = 2.0817l$$

$$F_1 = \text{factor} = \frac{2L_1}{K_1 A_1^c E_c} = \frac{2L_1}{\dfrac{l^3}{3E_g I}A_1^c E_c} = \frac{6IL_1 E_g}{l^3 A_1^c E_c}$$

$$= \frac{6I(2.8674l)E_g}{l^3 A_1^c E_c} = \frac{17.2044 E_g I}{A_1^c l^2 E_c}$$

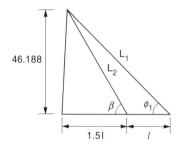

Figure 6.80. Design of a box section in Example (6.13)

where

$$\bar{C}_1 = \frac{E_g I}{A_1^c l^2 E_c}$$

$$F_2 = \text{factor} = \frac{6L_2 I E_g}{l^3 A_2^c E_c} = \frac{6 \times 2.0817 l I E_g}{l^3 A_2^c E_c}$$

where

$$\bar{C}_2 = \frac{E_g I}{l^2 A_2^c E_c} \qquad \text{(Therefore } \bar{C}_1 \text{ and } \bar{C}_2 \text{ are the same).}$$

Note that

$$\phi_2 = \beta_2$$

Now

$$\bar{D} = 121 \sin^2 \phi_1 \sin^2 \phi_2 - \left(28 \sin^2 \phi_1 + \frac{I}{l^2 A_1^c} \frac{E_g}{E_c}\right)\left(5 \sin^2 \phi_2 + \frac{I}{l^2 A_2^c} \frac{E_g}{E_c}\right)$$

$$= -2.26 - (41.55\bar{C}_1 + 87.35\bar{C}_2 + 216\bar{C}_1\bar{C}_2)$$

$$\bar{C}_1 = \bar{C}_2 = 0.05 \quad \text{(Table 6.27).}$$

(a) Based on the Indian code

$$\text{Dead load/girder} = 1500 \times 9 = 13\,500 \,\text{kg/m}$$

$$\text{self-weight} = 1500 \,\text{kg/m}$$

$$\text{Total} = 15\,000 \,\text{kg/m} \quad (147.09 \,\text{kN/m}).$$

For first approximation

$$\bar{C}_1 = \bar{C}_2 = 0.05 \quad \text{(Table 6.27)}$$

$$T_1 = \left[2 \times \frac{0.717 - 0}{2} \times 16 + 2 \times \frac{0.717 + 0.412}{2} \times 16 \right.$$

$$+ 2 \times \frac{0.412 + 0.186}{2} \times 16 + 2 \times \frac{0.186 + 0.054}{2} \times 16$$

$$\left. + 2 \times \frac{0.054 + 0}{2} \times 16 - \frac{0.0156}{2} \times 32\right]^2 \times 15\,000 \,\text{kg}$$

$$= 653\,376 \,\text{kg} \quad (6407.66 \,\text{kN})$$

$$R_5 = R_7(V_5 = V_7) = \left[\frac{2.394 + 0}{2} \times 16 + \frac{2.394 + 2.024}{2} \times 16 \right.$$

$$+ \frac{2.024 + 1.669}{2} \times 16 + \frac{1.169 + 1.350}{2} \times 16$$

$$+ \frac{1.350 + 1.00}{2} \times 16 + \frac{1.00 + 0.555}{2} \times 16$$

$$+ \frac{0.555 + 0}{2} \times 16 - \frac{0 + 0.650}{2} \times 16$$

$$- \frac{0.650 + 1.331}{2} \times 16 - \frac{1.331 + 1.976}{2} \times 16$$

$$\left. - \frac{1.976 + 2.606}{2} \times 16 - \frac{2.606 + 0}{2} \times 16 \right] \times 15\,000\,\text{kg}$$

$$= 582\,960\,\text{kg} \quad (5717\,\text{kN})$$

$$R = V(\text{tower}) = \left[2 \times 16 \times \frac{1.212 + 0}{2} + 2 \times 16 \frac{1.212 + 0.952}{2} \right.$$

$$+ 2 \times 16 \times \frac{0.952 + 0.662}{2} + 2 \times 16 \frac{0.662 + 0.30}{2}$$

$$\left. + 2 \times 16 \times \frac{0.30 + 0}{2} - 2 \times 16 \times \frac{0.110 + 0}{2} \right] \times 15\,000\,\text{kg}$$

$$= 1\,474\,080\,\text{kg} \quad (14\,456\,\text{kN})$$

Check on loads

$$\text{Reactions at supports} = 2 \times 582\,960 = 1\,165\,920\,\text{kg}$$

$$\text{Tower reactions} = 1\,474\,080\,\text{kg}$$

$$\text{Total} = 2\,640\,000\,\text{kg} \quad (25\,890.5\,\text{kN})$$

$$\text{Total load on the bridge} = (5 \times 32 + 16) \times 15\,000$$

$$= 2\,640\,000\,\text{kg}$$

$$= (25\,890.5\,\text{kg}) \quad \text{Q.E.D.}$$

Moments and shear of section 5
Average ordinate method gives:

$$\text{Bending moment} = \frac{16}{2}[-\{(1.036+0)+(1.036+0.818)+(0.818+0.576)$$

$$+(0.576+0.323)+(0.323+0)+2\times0.063\}$$

$$+\{(0+0.177)+(0.177+0.424)+(0.424+0.682)$$

$$+(0.682+0.964)+(0.964+0)\}]\times32\times15\,000\,\text{kgm}$$

$$= -4\,369\,920\,\text{kgm} \quad (-42\,856\,\text{kNm})$$

Similarly:

$$\text{Shear}\begin{cases} V_{\text{right}} = +342\,960\,\text{kg}\ (3363.4\,\text{kN}) \\ V_{\text{left}} = -240\,000\,\text{kg} \quad (-2353.7\,\text{kN}). \end{cases}$$

Live load
Per unit length of the girder $= 300 \times 9 = 2700\,\text{kg/m}$ (26.48 kN/m).

Usage of influence line diagram
Referring to Figs 6.78 and 6.79:

$$T_{1_{\text{max}}} = 118\,281\,\text{kg}\ (1160\,\text{kN})$$

$$T_{2_{\text{max}}} = 109\,468\,\text{kg}\ (1173.6\,\text{kN})$$

$R = V =$ reactions:

$$\text{positive } R_{5_{\text{max}}} = +388\,454\,\text{kg}\ (+3809.6\,\text{kN})$$

$$\text{negative } R_{5_{\text{max}}} = -283\,500\,\text{kg}\ (-27\,803\,\text{kN})$$

$$R_{\text{Tower}_{\text{max}}} = +270\,000\,\text{kg}\ (-2648\,\text{kN}).$$

Moment at section 5

$$\text{Bending moment (positive)}_{\text{max}} = 3\,110\,400\,\text{kg m}\ (60\,210\,\text{kNm})$$

$$\text{Bending moment (negative)}_{\text{max}} = 3\,888\,000\,\text{kg m}\ (75\,263\,\text{kNm})$$

V (shear)

$$\left.\begin{array}{l} V_{\text{max}}(\text{positive}) = +129\,600\,\text{kg} \\ V_{\text{max}}(\text{negative}) = -67\,500\,\text{kg} \end{array}\right\}\ \text{Right}$$

$$\left.\begin{array}{l} V_{\text{max}}(\text{positive}) = +216\,000\,\text{kg}\ (2118\,\text{kN}) \\ V_{\text{max}}(\text{negative}) = -259\,200\,\text{kg}\ (-2542\,\text{kN}) \end{array}\right\}\ \text{Left}$$

These values (maximum) are chosen for the design of bridge structural elements:

$$T_{1_{max}} = 653\,376 + 118\,281 = 771\,657\,\text{kg} \; (7567.6\,\text{kN})$$

$$T_{2_{max}} = 591\,840 + 109\,468 = 701\,308\,\text{kg} \; (6878\,\text{kN})$$

Cable 1 $\quad A_s = \text{area} = \dfrac{771\,657}{95} = 8000\,\text{mm}^2$

Cable 2 $\quad A_s = \dfrac{701\,308}{95} = 7400\,\text{mm}^2$

For the same cable areas, consider the maximum bending moment at section 5:

Bending moment$_{max}$ at section $5 = (-4\,369\,920) + (-3\,888\,000)$

$$= -8\,257\,920\,\text{kg/m} \; (-80\,895\,\text{kNm})$$

$$z = \text{section modulus} = \dfrac{8258 \times 10^4 \times 100}{3200}$$

$$= 25.6 \times 10^4\,\text{cm}^3$$

$$I = 2 \times 2 \times \dfrac{(300)^3}{12} + 2150 \times 5 \times \left(\dfrac{300}{2}\right)^2$$

$$= 43 \times 10^6\,\text{cm}^4$$

$$z = \dfrac{43 \times 10^4}{150}$$

$$= 28.6 \times 10^4\,\text{cm}^3$$

Comparative check for z is acceptable.
  It follows:

$$\bar{C}_1 = \dfrac{I}{l^2 A_1}\dfrac{E}{E_c} = \dfrac{43 \times 10^4}{3200 \times 3200 \times 80}$$

$$= 0.051 \approx 0.05$$

and no recalculation is needed.

Direct force
Direct force subjected to this section is:

$$T_1 \cos \phi_1 + T_2 \cos \phi_2$$

$$F = 771\,653\dfrac{\sqrt{3}}{2} + 701\,308\sqrt{\dfrac{27}{52}} = 1\,198\,000\,\text{kg} \; (11\,749\,\text{kN})$$

$$\text{Direct stress} = \frac{1\,198\,000}{2700} = 440\,\text{kg/cm}^2$$

(b)   Based on BS 5400
The above calculations are repeated and the results summarized below.

$$T_1 = 8328.8\,\text{kN} \qquad T_2 = 7545.2\,\text{kN}$$

$$R_5 = R_7 = 7431.45\,\text{kN}$$

$$R_{\text{Tower}} = 18\,790.59\,\text{kN}$$

Check:

$$\text{Total on structures} = 33\,687.846\,\text{kN}$$

$$\text{Total reaction} = 33\,653.49\,\text{kN}$$

Moments and shears at point 5

$$M_5 = -51\,619.49\,\text{kNm}$$

$$V_{\text{left}} = -4371.9\,\text{kN}$$

$$V_{\text{right}} = +3059.42$$

$$\text{Live load/girder} = 54\,\text{kN/m}$$

$$T_1 = 2365.6\,\text{kN}$$

$$T_2 = 2190\,\text{kN}$$

Reactions R_5 and R_{Tower}

$$R_{5_{\text{max}}} = 7768.5\,\text{kN} \quad \text{(positive)}$$

$$R_{5_{\text{max}}} = -5669.6\,\text{kN} \quad \text{(negative)}$$

$$R_{\text{Tower}_{\text{max}}} = -5399.6\,\text{kN}$$

Shear at nodal point 5

$$\left.\begin{array}{l} V_{\text{max}}(\text{positive}) = 2592\,\text{kN} \\ V_{\text{max}}(\text{negative}) = -1350\,\text{kN} \end{array}\right\} \quad \text{Right}$$

$$\left.\begin{array}{l} V_{\text{max}}(\text{positive}) = 4320\,\text{kN} \\ V_{\text{max}}(\text{negative}) = -5183.6\,\text{kN} \end{array}\right\} \quad \text{Left}$$

Cables

$$T_{1_{max}} = 10\,694.3\,\text{kN} \qquad T_{2_{max}} = 9735.2\,\text{kN}$$

$$\text{Cable area} = \frac{10\,694.3}{1099_2}$$

$$= 9731\,\text{mm}^2$$

$$\text{GUTS} = 1570\,\text{N/mm}^2$$

$$f_{per} = 0.7\,\text{GUTS} = f_t$$

For 15 mm Ø strand

$$\text{cable no.: strands} = \frac{9731}{176.786} = 55\,\text{strands}$$

PPWS (prefabricated parallel wire strand) 127 adopted (Fig. 6.81) to take into consideration other loads such as wind, earthquakes etc.

   Maximum girder moment at point 5 is:

$$-51\,619.49 - 77\,354.3 = -128\,973.79\,\text{kNm}$$

$$Z_e = \frac{M}{f}$$

$$f = 315\,\text{N/mm}^2.$$

	P.P.W.S. 127	
Section of strand	127 wires 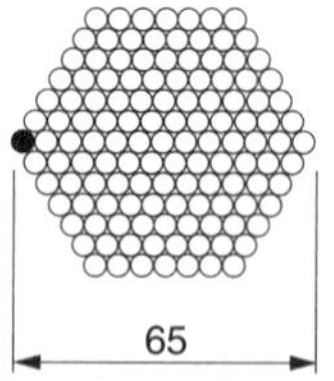 65 Length: 97.6/97.7 m	
Area	24.93 cm²	
Allowable tensile load	391 t	
Weight	19.5 kg/m	
Young's modulus	More than 1900000 kg/cm²	
Accuracy of length	Error of marking length	−0 mm +20 mm

Figure 6.81. Properties of a prefabricated parallel wire strand

Girder

$B = 2000$ with $t_f = 50\,\text{mm}$

$D = 4000$ with $t_w = 20\,\text{mm}$

$I = 82.1334 \times 10^{10}\,\text{mm}^4$ (plate thickness 20 mm throughout)

$z = 26.074 \times 10^8\,\text{mm}^3$

Under BS 5400, the girder section is comparatively heavier (see Fig. 6.82).

Direct force
Calculated as before:

$$T_1 \cos\phi_1 + T_2 \cos\phi_2 = 1627.535\,\text{kN}$$

$$\text{Direct stress} = \frac{\text{force}}{\text{area}}$$

$$\text{Area of the section} = 4000 \times 20 \times 2 + 2000 \times 2 \times 50$$

$$= 360\,000\,\text{mm}^2$$

$$\text{Direct stress} = 45.213\,\text{N/mm}^2.$$

When the cable is attached to the top flange, it will be subject to an eccentric force, producing a moment in the opposite direction, thus reducing the main moment. Similarly the argument is valid for shear.
    Check:

$$\bar{C}_1 = \frac{I}{l^2 A_1}\frac{E_g}{E_c}$$

$$= 0.08677 > 0.051 \quad \text{Q.E.D.}$$

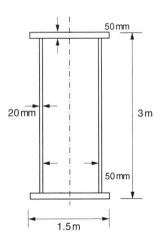

Figure 6.82. Girder section (by BS 5400); checked with Ray's method

Example (6.14)   German practice

The schematic representations of cable-stayed bridges with various boundary conditions are given in Fig. 6.83. Draw influence lines for cable tension T_c and girder moments for the data provided for each case provided by der Stahlbau for several cable-stayed systems.

Cable-stay area is presented as a dimensionless coefficient

$$(E_c A_c L_T^2)/(E_g I_g)$$

where

$\quad E_c$ = modulus of elasticity for the cable stay

$\quad A_c$ = cross-sectional area of the cable stay

$\quad E_g$ = modulus of elasticity for the girder

$\quad I_g$ = moment of inertia for the girder

$\quad L_T$ = overall length of the structure

A detailed graphical analysis is provided in Figs 6.84–6.88, which show resultant influence lines.

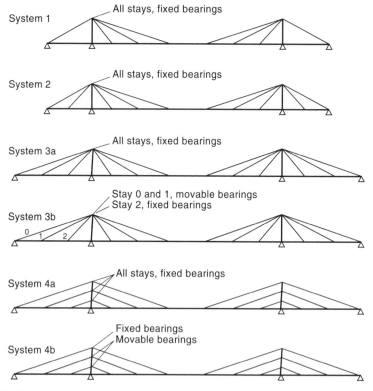

Figure 6.83. Schematic representation of cable-stayed bridges (reproduced courtesy Der Stahlbau). From Design of bridge superstructure by C. O'Conner, John Wiley, 1971

Figure 6.84. Influence lines for (a) the cable-stayed system 1 and (b) cable-stayed system 3a (reproduced courtesy der Stahl-bau). From Design of bridge superstructure by C. O'Conner, John Wiley, 1971

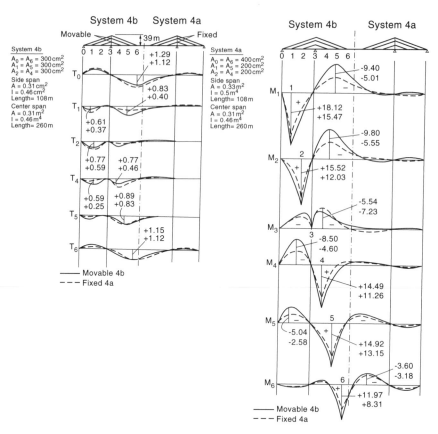

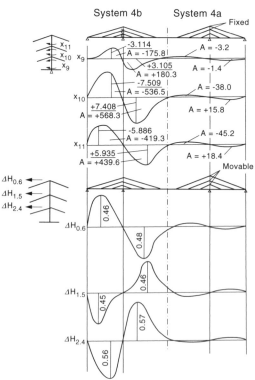

Figure 6.85. Influence lines for cable systems 4a and 4b (reproduced courtesy Der Stahlbau). Design of bridge superstructure by C. O'Conner, John Wiley, 1971

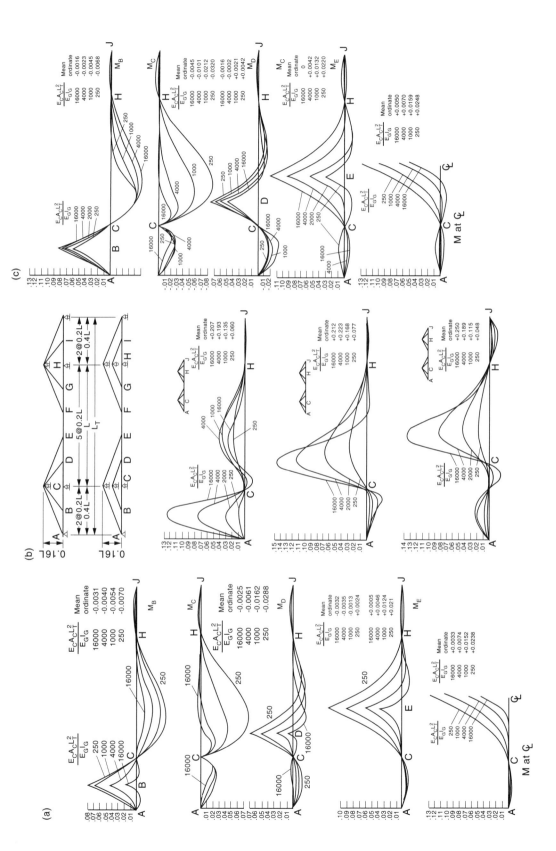

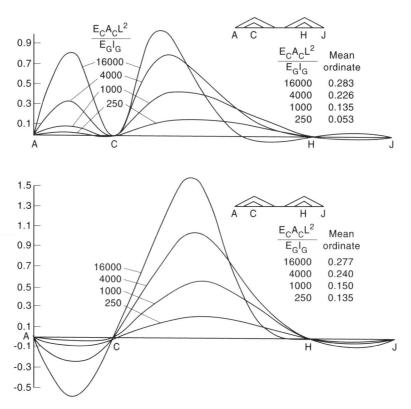

Figure 6.87. Influence lines for cable forces – harp type bridge. Reproduced courtesy Der Stahlbau. Also Design of bridge superstructure, C. O'Connor, John Wiley, 1971

*Figure 6.86 (previous page). Influence lines for deck bending moments. (a) Ordinate × L – radiating type. (b) Moment × L – radiating type. (c) Ordinate × L – harp type (courtesy of B. S. Smith, Proc. Instn Civ. Engrs, 1968, **39**, June, 85–94)*

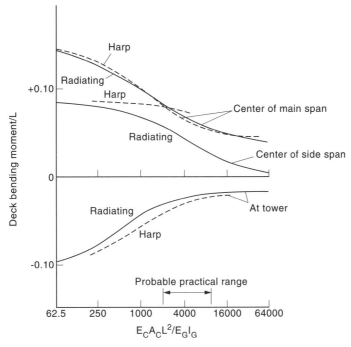

Figure 6.88. A comparative study of different systems. Reproduced courtesy der Stahlbau. Also Design of bridge superstructure, by C. O'Conner, John Wiley, 1971

6.8.3 Cable-stayed analysis using flexibility method – double-cable bridge (British practice). Smith's method

A typical double-cable bridge is shown in Fig. 6.89. An equivalent continuous span is represented in Fig. 6.89.

In this analysis according to Smith (1968), the following actions can easily be simulated:

(a)   tower rotation, tower shortening, bending of towers
(b)   tower-base fixity
(c)   shortening, twist or torsion of girders.

As stated earlier, the combined deformation can easily be established as

$$\begin{bmatrix} f_{11} & f_{12} & f_{13} \\ f_{21} & f_{22} & f_{23} \\ f_{31} & f_{32} & f_{33} \end{bmatrix} \begin{Bmatrix} X_1 \\ X_2 \\ X_3 \end{Bmatrix} = - \begin{Bmatrix} D_{10} \\ D_{20} \\ D_{30} \end{Bmatrix} \tag{6.235}$$

Cable elongation ΔL

$$\Delta_L = \frac{T_1 L}{A^c E_c} \tag{6.236}$$

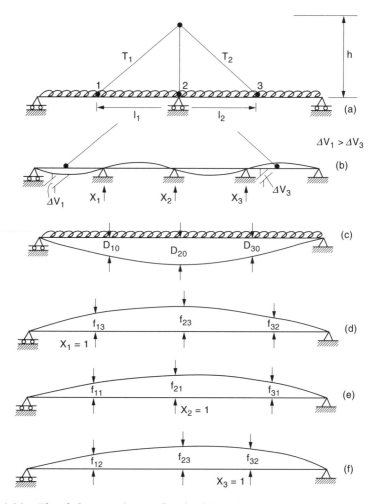

Figure B6.89. Flexibility analysis of a double cable-stayed bridge.

$$\sin \phi_1 = \frac{\Delta_L}{\Delta_V} \qquad (6.237)$$

$$\therefore \quad \Delta_V = \frac{T_1 L}{A^c E_c} \sin \phi_1$$

where

Δ_V = vertical displacement

T_1 = tension in the cable

$A^c E_c$ = area and Young modulus

ϕ_1 = angle of the cable to the horizontal

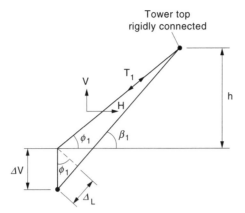

Figure 6.90. Cable elongation

V = vertical component of the force in the cable

  = $T_1 \sin \phi_1$ and is equivalent to reaction X_1

At support or point 1 (Fig. 6.90)

$$\Delta V_1 = \frac{X_1 L}{A^c E_c} \sin^2 \phi_1$$

Similarly at 3

$$\Delta V_3 = \frac{X_3 L}{A^c E_c} \sin^2 \phi_3.$$

Tower shortening
If during the tower shortening, the effects on the girder are Δ_1 at 1 and Δ_3 at 3 due to cables and ΔV_T is for the tower displacement, the matrix $\{D_{i0}\}$ changes to

$$\begin{Bmatrix} D_{10} \\ D_{20} \\ D_{30} \end{Bmatrix} = \begin{Bmatrix} \Delta_1 - \Delta V_1 - \Delta V_T \\ \Delta_2 \\ \Delta_3 - \Delta V_3 - \Delta V_T \end{Bmatrix} \tag{6.238}$$

where

$$\Delta V_T = (X_1 + X_3) \frac{h}{A_T E_T} \tag{6.239}$$

where

  h = tower height

  A_T, E_T = area and young modulus of the tower.

Tower rotation

If the tower rotates by an angle θ (Fig. 6.91) then the matrix $\{D_{i0}\}$ is further modified as

$$\begin{Bmatrix} D_{10} \\ D_{20} \\ D_{30} \end{Bmatrix} = \begin{Bmatrix} \Delta_1 - \Delta V_1 - \Delta V_T - l_1\theta \\ \Delta_2 \\ \Delta_3 - \Delta V_3 - \Delta V_T + l_1\theta \end{Bmatrix} \tag{B6.240}$$

If any item does not occur in the matrix, it should be treated as zero. For equilibrium conditions, all moments are summed and the combined equilibrium of forces would be (Fig. 6.92)

$$X_1 l_1 = X_3 l_2 \qquad l_1 = l_{12} \qquad l_2 = l_{23}$$

The above equations are rewritten as

$$X_1 f_{11} + X_2 f_{12} + X_3 f_{13} + \Delta_{C1} X_1 + \Delta_T (X_1 + X_3) + \theta l_1 = D_{10}$$

$$X_1 f_{21} + X_2 f_{22} + X_3 f_{23} = D_{20}$$

$$\tag{6.241}$$

$$X_1 f_{31} + X_2 f_{32} + X_3 f_{33} + \Delta_{C3} X_3 + \Delta_T (X_1 + X_3) - \theta l_3 = 0$$

$$X_1 l_1 - X_3 l_3 = 0.$$

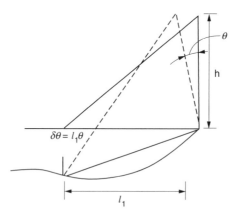

Figure 6.91. Tower deformation

Figure 6.92. Cable reactions

In matrix form the combined flexibility matrix is

$$
\begin{bmatrix}
(f_{11} + \Delta_{C1} + \Delta_T) & f_{12} & (f_{13} + \Delta_T) & l_1 \\
f_{21} & f_{22} & f_{23} & 0 \\
(f_{31} + \Delta_T) & f_{32} & (f_{33} + \Delta_{C3} + \Delta_T) & -l_3 \\
l_1 & 0 & -l_3 & 0
\end{bmatrix}
$$

$$
\times \begin{Bmatrix} X_1 \\ X_2 \\ X_3 \\ \theta \end{Bmatrix} = \begin{Bmatrix} D_{10} \\ D_{20} \\ D_{30} \\ 0 \end{Bmatrix} \qquad l_1 = l_3 \text{ generally} \tag{6.242}
$$

or

$$
[f]\{X\} = -\{D_{i0}\} \tag{6.243}
$$

where

$$
\Delta_{C1}, \Delta_{C3} = \text{cable displacements of 1 and 3}
$$
$$
\Delta_T = \text{tower displacement (net)}
$$

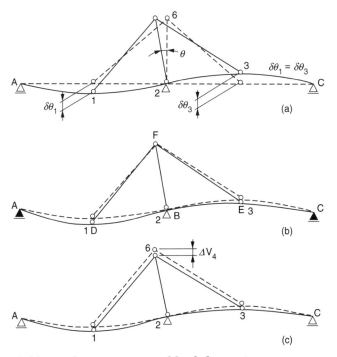

Figure 6.93. Cable–girder–tower assembly deformation

Note that:
   (1) If the tower is fixed, a redundancy should be included in the above relation.
   (2) For multiple-cable bridges the above matrix is enlarged to include additional cables, towers and girder spans.
   (3) The author's symbols have been changed to suit the generalized symbols of this text.

Various deformation quantities of the assembly are shown in Fig. 6.93.

6.8.4 Multiple-cable bridge – fan type
The same actions are involved. Each cable is connected to the girder and tower (Fig. 6.94). The matrix $[f]$ is given below as a result of the flexibility described by Smith (1968).

$$\begin{bmatrix} (f_{11} + \Delta_{C1} + \Delta_T) & (f_{14} + \Delta_T) & f_{12} & (f_{15} + \Delta_T) & (f_{13} + \Delta_T) & l_{12} \\ (f_{41} + \Delta_T) & (f_{44} + \Delta_{C4} + \Delta_T) & f_{42} & (f_{45} + \Delta_T) & (f_{43} + \Delta_T) & l_{24} \\ f_{21} & f_{24} & f_{22} & f_{25} & f_{23} & 0 \\ (f_{51} + \Delta_T) & (f_{54} + \Delta_T) & f_{52} & (f_{55} + \Delta_{C5} + \Delta_T) & (f_{53} + \Delta_T) & -l_{25} \\ (f_{31} + \Delta_T) & (f_{34} + \Delta_T) & f_{32} & (f_{35} + \Delta_T) & (f_{33} + \Delta_{C3} + \Delta_T) & -l_{23} \\ l_{21} & l_{24} & 0 & -l_{25} & -l_{23} & 0 \end{bmatrix}$$

$$\times \begin{Bmatrix} X_1 \\ X_4 \\ X_2 \\ X_5 \\ X_3 \\ 0 \end{Bmatrix} = - \begin{Bmatrix} D_{10} \\ D_{40} \\ D_{20} \\ D_{50} \\ D_{30} \\ 0 \end{Bmatrix}$$

$$[f]\{X\} = -\{D_{10}\}$$

   Some cases are examined (see Fig. 6.95).

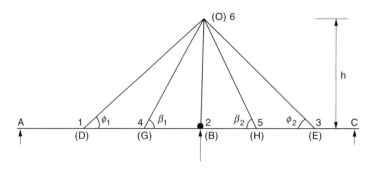

Figure 6.94. A fan-type cable-stayed bridge

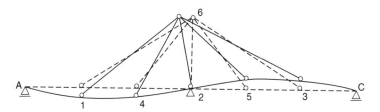

Figure 6.95. Schematic for flexibility method for fan-type cable-stayed bridges

Case (I)
If 1–2 shortens, then the following relation is included

$$\frac{l_{A1}}{l_{A2}} X_1 \cot \phi_1 \frac{l_{12}}{A_g E_g} \tag{6.244}$$

where subscript g relates to the deck or its girder. Here the value of f_{12} for the girder is modified by adding

$$f_{12} = \frac{l_{A1}}{l_{A2}} \frac{l_{12} \cot^2 \phi_1}{A_g E_g}. \tag{6.245}$$

Case (II)
If the girder is free to move at 2, the axial force in the l_{12} zone $= X_1 \cot \phi_1$ and the girder is shortened by

$$X_1 \cot \phi_1 \frac{l_{12}}{A_g E_g} \tag{6.246}$$

In this the increase in the slope of the cable 0–1 allows the point of attachment to drop by

$$X_1 \cot^2 \phi_1 \frac{l_{12}}{A_g E_g} \tag{6.247}$$

Case (III)
If $\beta_1 \neq \beta_2$ the drop at point 4 is given by

$$\Delta_4 = X_4 \cot^2 \beta_1 ((0\text{--}5) - (0\text{--}4)) \quad \text{(cables)} \tag{6.248}$$

and the drop at 5

$$\Delta_5 = X_5 \cot^2 \beta_2 ((0\text{--}4) - (0\text{--}5)) \quad \text{(cables)} \tag{6.249}$$

Case (IV)   *Girder variable section*
Where the girders have variable sections, they can easily be incorporated by using mixed influence and flexibility approaches in order to obtain axial, moment, shear and deflection effects.

6.8.5 Multicable harp-type cable-stayed bridges

A reference is made to Fig. 6.96.

The cable GLH is supported by a saddle on rollers at L and let ϕ_g and ϕ_h be unequal (drop of G and rise of H). Figure 6.96 indicates various deformation and boundary conditions.

Deflection Δ' for total effect

$$\left.\begin{aligned}\Delta'_g &= \left(X_g \frac{\cot^2 \phi_g}{A_g E}\right)\left(\frac{l_h}{\cos^2 \phi_h} - \frac{l_g}{\cos^2 \phi_g}\right) \\[2mm] \Delta'_h &= \left(X_h \frac{\cot^2 \phi_h}{A_h E}\right)\left(\frac{l_g}{\cos^2 \phi_g} - \frac{l_h}{\cos^2 \phi_h}\right)\end{aligned}\right\} \quad \text{If } \phi_g \neq \phi_h \qquad (6.250)$$

$$\left.\begin{aligned}\Delta'_g &= \frac{X_g l_g}{A_g E \sin^2 \phi_g} \\[2mm] \Delta'_h &= \frac{X_h l_h}{A_h E \sin^2 \phi_h}\end{aligned}\right\} \quad \text{If } \phi_g = \phi_h \quad l_g = l_h \qquad (6.251)$$

The isolated action of bending in the tower

Deflection at M caused by bending in the tower is:

$$\Delta'_m = (X_j \cot \phi_j - X_k \cot \phi_k)f_{mm} + (X_g \cot \phi_g - X_h \cot \phi_h)f_{ml} \qquad (6.252)$$

$$f_{mm} = \frac{h_m^2(h_f - h_m)^2}{3EI_T h_f} \qquad (6.253)$$

$$f_{ml} = \frac{h_m(h_f - h_l)[h_f^2 - (h_f - h_l)^2 - h_m^2]}{6EI_{T0} h_f} \qquad (6.254)$$

Similarly deflection at J is given by

$$\begin{aligned}\Delta'_j = X_j &\frac{(h_f - h_m)^2 BJ}{3EI_T h_f}BJ - X_k \frac{(h_f - h_m)^2 BJ}{3EI_T h_f}BK \\[2mm] &+ X_g \frac{(h_f - h_\ell)[h_f^2 - (h_f - h_\ell)^2 - h_m^2]BJ}{6EI_T h_f h_\ell}BG \\[2mm] &- X_h \frac{(h_f - h_\ell)[h_f^2 - (h_f - h_\ell)^2 - h_m^2]BJ}{EI_T h_f h_\ell}BH\end{aligned} \qquad (6.255)$$

where E and T are for the tower.

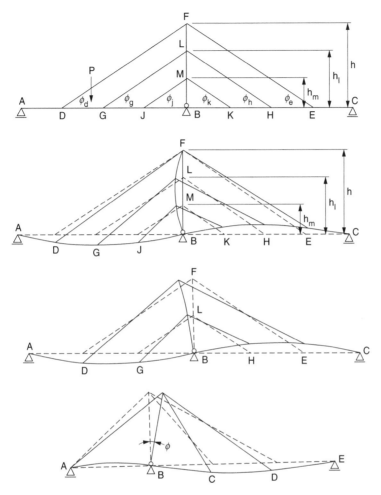

Figure 6.96. (a) Multicable harp system. (b) Bending of tower in a multicable system. (c) Deflection of vertical tower due to applied load system. (d) Single tower with cable attached to rigid support (reproduced courtesy of the Institution of Civil Engineers, London)

The remainder of the procedure is as in the case of the 'fan-type' cable-stayed bridges.

In the case of a multicable Harper-stayed bridge the deflection of D and G due to *axial shortening of the girder* is given by

$$\Delta_d' = (X_g \cot \phi_g + X_d \cot \phi_d) \frac{\cot \phi_g l_{gb}}{A_g E_g} \qquad (6.256)$$

$$\Delta_g = (X_g \cot \phi_g l_{gb} + X_d \cot \phi_d l_{db}) \frac{\cot \phi_g}{A_g E_g}$$

Tower fixed at base

In this solution the flexibility matrix $[f]$ is affected since the tower base is not rotated. The right-hand column and the bottom row representing deflection and stability, respectively, are then omitted.

The horizontal movement of node L, caused by the forces on either side of node L, is given by

$$\Delta'_\ell = (X_g \cot \phi_g - X_h \cot \phi_h) f_{\ell\ell}$$
$$+ (X_d \cot \phi_d - X_e \cot \phi_e) f_{\ell f} \qquad (6.257)$$

where

$$f_{\ell\ell} = \frac{h^2}{3EI_{TO}} \qquad \text{(cantilever of uniform cross-section)}$$

$$f_{\ell f} = \frac{2h_f^3 - 3h_f^2(h_f - h_1) + (h_f - h_1)^3}{6EI_{TO}} \qquad (6.258)$$

Hence when the tower has bending moment, the vertical deflection becomes

$$\Delta'_g = X_g \frac{h_\ell BG}{3EI_{TO}} BG - X_h \frac{h_\ell BH}{3EI_{TO}} BH$$

$$+ X_d \frac{[2h_f^3 - 3h_f^2(h_f - h_\ell) + (h_f - h_\ell)^3]GB}{6EI_{TO}h_f h_\ell} BD$$

$$- X_e \frac{[2h_f^3 - 3h_f^2(h_f - h_\ell) + (h_f - h_\ell)^3]GB}{6EI_{TO}h_f h_\ell} BE \qquad (6.259)$$

Double-plane system (bi-plane system)

The analysis of the double-plane system is similar to that developed by Smith (1968) for the single-plane system. Compatibility equations for deflections are thus formulated whether or not supports are rigid or elastic. The double-plane

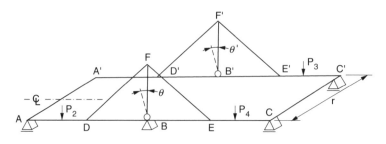

Figure 6.97. Double-plane system

type receives double actions. In addition, it requires that the torque at each support, i.e. the interior support, be released and additional compatibility be formulated for the torsion. Figure 6.97 shows the loaded system with eccentric load P_2. Deflections and rotations of the primary structure are shown in Fig. 6.98.

Assume that cables at nodes D, D' E and E' are completely rigid against deflections and rotations. Then the compatibility equations are written as

$$\delta'_d - (X_d + X'_d)f_{dd} - (X_b + X'_b)f_{db} - (X_e + X'_e)f_{dc} = \Delta_d \tag{6.260}$$

$$\delta'_b - (X_d + X'_d)f_{bd} - (X_b + X'_b)f_{bb} - (X_e + X'_e)f_{bc} = \Delta_b \tag{6.261}$$

$$\delta'_e - (X_d + X'_d)f_{ed} - (X_b + X'_b)f_{eb} - (X_e + X'_e)f_{ee} = \Delta_e \tag{6.262}$$

$$\psi'_d - \frac{(X_d - X'_d)r\psi_{dd}}{2} - \frac{(X_b - X'_b)r\psi_{db}}{2} - \frac{(X_e - X'_e)r\psi_{de}}{2} = \psi_d \tag{6.263}$$

$$\psi'_b - \frac{(X_d - X'_d)r\psi_{bd}}{2} - \frac{(X_b - X'_b)r\psi_{bb}}{2} - \frac{(X_e - X'_e)r\psi_{be}}{2} = \psi_b \tag{6.264}$$

$$\psi'_e - \frac{(X_d - X'_d)r\psi_{ed}}{2} - \frac{(X_b - X'_b)r\psi_{eb}}{2} - \frac{(X_b - X'_b)r\psi_{ee}}{2} = \psi_e \tag{6.265}$$

where

X_d = the vertical component of cable tension at D

f_{dd} = the centre-line deflection at D due to a unit load at D

f_{db} = the centre-line deflection at D due to a unit load at B

δ'_d = the centre-line deflection at D due to the applied loads

l'_c = distance between sets of cables

ψ_{dd} = twist of the girder at D due to a unit torque applied at D

ψ_{db} = twist of the girder at D due to a unit torque applied at B

ψ'_d = twist of the girder at D due to the applied loads

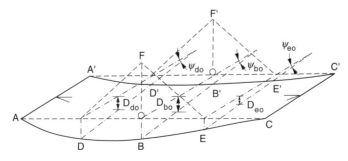

Figure 6.98. Deflections and rotations of the primary structure

Δ_d = predetermined total centre-line deflection at D

ψ_d = predetermined total twist at D.

In *reality the restraint at D and E are not rigid* owing to lower rotation and elastic shortening and cable elongation and hence the above compatibility equations will have to be modified. If the towers rotate as

tower **BF** rotates anticlockwise by θ

tower **B'F'** rotates anticlockwise by θ'

$$\text{the deflection at } D = \frac{(\theta + \theta')l_{bd}}{2} \tag{6.266}$$

$$\text{the uplift at } E = -\frac{(\theta + \theta')l_{be}}{2} \tag{6.267}$$

$$\text{twist at } D = \frac{(\theta - \theta')l_{bd}}{l_c} \tag{6.268}$$

$$\text{twist at } E = -\frac{(\theta - \theta')l_{be}}{l'_c} \tag{6.268a}$$

Deflections at D and E due to cables elongation
At node D

$$\text{deflection} = (X_d + X'_d)\frac{\Delta_{cd}}{2} \tag{6.269}$$

At node E

$$\text{deflection} = (X_e + X'_e)\frac{\Delta_{ce}}{2} \tag{6.270}$$

$\Delta_{cd} = \Delta_{c1}$ and $\Delta_{ce} = \Delta_{c3}$ were defined earlier.

The twist at D and E
At node D

$$\text{twist} = (X_d - X'_d)\frac{\Delta_{cd}}{l'_c} \tag{6.271}$$

At node E

$$\text{twist} = (X_d - X'_d)\frac{\Delta_{ce}}{l'_c}. \tag{6.272}$$

The elastic shortening of the tower and twist
The centre-line deflection at D and E is

$$\tfrac{1}{2}[(X_d + X_e) + (X'_d + X'_e)]\Delta_T \tag{6.273}$$

The twist then at D and E is

$$\frac{1}{l_c}[(X_d + X_e) - (X'_d + X'_e)]\Delta_T \tag{6.273a}$$

where Δ_T is the flexibility coefficient of the tower sometimes denoted as f_T. As shown in Fig. 6.98, the various values D_{i0} and ψ_{i0} are:

$$\Delta_d = \frac{(\theta + \theta')l_{bd}}{2} + \frac{(X_d + X'_d)\Delta_{cd}}{2}$$
$$+ \frac{[(X_d + X_e) + (X'_d + X'_e)]f_T}{2} \tag{6.274}$$

$$D_{b0} = 0 \tag{6.275}$$

$$D_{c0} = \frac{-(\theta + \theta')l_{be}}{2} + \frac{(X_e + X'_e)\Delta_{ce}}{2}$$
$$+ \frac{[(X_d + X_e) + (X'_d + X'_e)]f_T}{2} \tag{6.276}$$

$$\psi'_{d0} = \frac{(\theta - \theta')l_{bd}}{l'_c} + \frac{(X_d - x'_d)\Delta_{cd}}{l'_c}$$
$$+ \frac{[(X_d + X_e) - (X'_d + X'_e)]f_T}{l_c} \tag{6.277}$$

$$\psi'_{b0} = 0 \tag{6.278}$$

$$\psi'_{e0} = \frac{-(\theta - \theta')l_{be}}{l'_c} + \frac{(X_e - X'_e)\Delta_{ce}}{l'_c}$$
$$+ \frac{[(X_d + X_e) - (X'_d - X'_e)]f_T}{l'_c} \tag{6.279}$$

The combined flexibility matrix is given on page 916.

6.8.6 A shaped tower for a double-plane cable-stayed bridge
Here the cables are not separately connected. Instead, they are connected concentrically. Separate tower rotations θ and θ' are now simply θ and the rotational equilibrium is now dependent on the horizontal components of the cable forces in the system (Fig. 6.99).

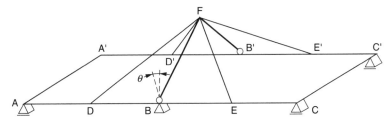

Figure 6.99. A-shaped tower BFB'

$$
\begin{bmatrix}
\left(f_{dd}+\dfrac{c_d}{2}+\dfrac{f_T}{2}\right) & \left(f_{dd}+\dfrac{\Delta_{cd}}{2}+\dfrac{f_T}{2}\right) & (f_{db}) & (f_{db}) & \left(f_{de}+\dfrac{f_T}{2}\right) & \left(f_{de}+\dfrac{f_T}{2}\right) & \left(\dfrac{l_{bd}}{2}\right) & \left(\dfrac{l_{bd}}{2}\right) \\[2ex]
(f_{bd}) & (f_{bd}) & (f_{bb}) & (f_{bb}) & (f_{be}) & (f_{be}) & 0 & 0 \\[2ex]
\left(f_{ed}+\dfrac{f_T}{2}\right) & \left(f_{ed}+\dfrac{f_T}{2}\right) & (f_{eb}) & (f_{eb}) & \left(f_{ee}+\dfrac{\Delta_{ce}}{2}+\dfrac{f_T}{2}\right) & \left(f_{ee}+\dfrac{\Delta_{ce}}{2}+\dfrac{f_T}{2}\right) & -\left(\dfrac{l_{be}}{2}\right) & -\left(\dfrac{l_{be}}{2}\right) \\[2ex]
\left(\dfrac{l_c\psi_{dd}}{2}+\dfrac{\Delta_{cd}}{l_c}+\dfrac{f_T}{l_c}\right) & -\left(\dfrac{l_c\psi_{dd}}{2}+\dfrac{\Delta_{cd}}{l_c}+\dfrac{f_T}{l_c}\right) & \left(\dfrac{l_c'\psi_{db}}{2}\right) & -\left(\dfrac{l_c'\psi_{db}}{2}\right) & \left(\dfrac{l_c'\psi_{dc}}{2}+\dfrac{f_T}{l_c'}\right) & -\left(\dfrac{l_c'\psi_{dc}}{2}+\dfrac{f_T}{l_c'}\right) & -\left(\dfrac{l_{bd}}{l_c'}\right) & -\left(\dfrac{l_{bd}}{l_c'}\right) \\[2ex]
\left(\dfrac{l_c'\psi_{bd}}{2}\right) & -\left(\dfrac{l_c'\psi_{bd}}{2}\right) & \left(\dfrac{l_c'\psi_{bb}}{2}\right) & -\left(\dfrac{l_c'\psi_{bb}}{2}\right) & \left(\dfrac{l_c\psi_{be}}{2}\right) & -\left(\dfrac{l_c'\psi_{be}}{2}\right) & 0 & 0 \\[2ex]
\left(\dfrac{l_c'\psi_{ed}}{2}+\dfrac{f_T}{l_c'}\right) & -\left(\dfrac{l_c'\psi_{ed}}{2}+\dfrac{f_T}{l_c'}\right) & \left(\dfrac{l_c'\psi_{cb}}{2}\right) & -\left(\dfrac{l_c'\psi_{eb}}{2}\right) & \left(\dfrac{r\psi_{ee}}{2}+\dfrac{\Delta_{ce}}{l_c}+\dfrac{f_T}{l_c'}\right) & -\left(\dfrac{l\psi_{ee}}{2}+\dfrac{\Delta_{ce}}{l_c}+\dfrac{f_T}{l_c'}\right) & -\left(\dfrac{l_{bc}}{l_c'}\right) & \left(\dfrac{l_{be}}{l_c'}\right) \\[2ex]
(l_{bd}) & 0 & 0 & 0 & -(l_{be}) & 0 & 0 & 0 \\[2ex]
0 & (l_{bd}) & 0 & 0 & 0 & -(l_{be}) & 0 & 0
\end{bmatrix}
\begin{Bmatrix}
X_d \\ X_d' \\ X_b \\ X_b' \\ X_e \\ X_e' \\ \theta \\ \theta'
\end{Bmatrix}
=
\begin{Bmatrix}
D_{b0}' \\ D_{b0} \\ D_{c0}' \\ \psi_{d0} \\ \psi_{b0} \\ \psi_{e0} \\ 0 \\ 0
\end{Bmatrix}
$$

or $\quad [f_{ij}] \times \{X_{ij}\} = \{D_{ij}\}$

Since the relative rotations of towers are eliminated, the bridge becomes stiffer. The flexibility matrix $\{f\}$ is thus reduced to 7×8 from 8×8 components. The last row and column thus assume the following modification:

$$\begin{bmatrix} & & & & l_{bd} \\ & & & & 0 \\ \nwarrow & & \nearrow & & -l_{bd} \\ & \text{all these as before} & & & 0 \\ \swarrow & & \searrow & & 0 \\ & & & & 0 \\ l_{bd} & l_{bd} & 0 & 0 & -l_{bc} & -l_{bc} & 0 & 0 \end{bmatrix} \begin{Bmatrix} X_d \\ X'_d \\ X_b \\ X'_b \\ X_e \\ X'_e \\ \theta \end{Bmatrix} = \begin{Bmatrix} D'_{d0} \\ D'_{b0} \\ D'_e \\ \psi'_d \\ \psi'_b \\ \psi'_e \\ 0 \end{Bmatrix} \qquad (6.280)$$

6.8.7 H-shaped tower for a double-plane cable-stayed bridge

Figure 6.100 shows an H-type portal frame with stays. In this frame the relative rotation cannot be limited as in the case of the A-shaped towers. A complete analysis is not possible. It is therefore necessary to analyse this kind of tower with all possibilities of boundary conditions included. The most important cases are:

(a) The columns are bending only and the braces such as GG′ in torsion if the supports B and B′ have ball joints.
(b) The columns and the braces are in bending and torsion when supports B and B′ are hinged.
(c) Axial forces and bending are predominant by providing fixity and restraint at B and B′.

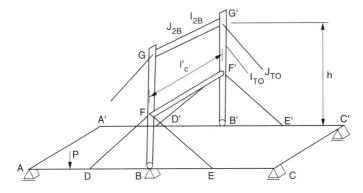

*Figure 6.100. H- or portal-frame towers (courtesy of B. S. Smith, Proc. Instn Civ. Engrs, 1968, **39**, June, 85–94)*

Case (a)

In case (a) $J_{T0} = 0$; $I_{T0} = 0$

The out-of-plane top deflection of the tower D_{G0}^W is given by

$$D_{G0}^W = (X_d \cot \phi_d - X_e \cot \phi)\bar{X} \tag{6.281}$$

where

$$\bar{X} = \left(\frac{h^3}{3EI_{T0}}\right) + \left(\frac{h^2 l_c'}{2GJ_{2B}}\right) \tag{6.282}$$

The left-hand term in the sum given in Eq. (6.282) represents bending in the column while the right-hand term is torsion in the braces.

Downward deflection and upward lift are equal and can be given by:

$$D_{G0}^W \frac{l_{bd}}{h} \tag{6.283}$$

and the girder is twisted at the function D by

$$\psi_{df} = \frac{2(X_d \cot \phi_d - X_e \cot \phi_e)l_{bd}}{h l_c'}[\bar{X}] \tag{6.284}$$

and at E it will be

$$\psi_{ef} = \frac{-2(X_d \cot \phi_d - X_e \cot \phi_e)l_{be}}{h l_c'}[\bar{X}] \tag{6.284a}$$

Here the H-shape warps when compared with the single tower. X_d and X_e are known and the fourth row of the matrix added through modification

$$\pm 2l_{bd} \cot \phi_d \frac{\bar{X}}{h l_c'} \tag{6.285}$$

and modified in the sixth row by

$$\pm 2l_{be} \cot \phi_d \frac{\bar{X}}{h l_c'} \tag{6.286}$$

for nodes E and D, respectively.

Case (b)

In case (b) pinned conditions dictate that in the horizontal plane there is a restraint against rotation. Here I_{T0}, J_{T0} and J_{2B} and I_{2B} exist and $\neq 0$. Using the energy method, torsion at D and E have been computed by Smith (1968) and is given as

$$\psi_{df} = \frac{+\bar{B}l_{bd}}{h l_c'}X'' \qquad \psi_{ef} = \frac{-\bar{B}l_{be}}{h l_c'}X'' \tag{6.287}$$

where

$$\bar{B} = X_{d} \cos \phi_{d} - X_{e} \cot \phi_{e} \tag{6.288}$$

$$X'' = \frac{\bar{X}\bar{Y}}{(\bar{X} + \bar{Y})} \tag{6.289}$$

$$\bar{X} = \frac{h^{3}}{3EI_{T0}} + \frac{h^{2}l_{c}'}{2GJ_{2B}} \qquad \bar{Y} = \frac{(l_{c}')^{2}h}{4GJ_{T0}} + \frac{(l_{c}')^{3}}{24EI_{T0}^{2}} \tag{6.290}$$

The coefficients of X_{d} and X_{e} are given in the 4th and 6th rows of the matrix on p. 174.

Multi-tower continuous girder – double-plane type
The procedure is the same, all interior supports are released and free deflections and torsions are computed. Appropriate compatibility and stability equations can be derived which would expand the matrix. Solution procedures are then followed in the same manner. Where necessary the actions of the tower rotation, stay elongation and tower shortening should be superimposed for the assessment of the overall behaviour of the cable-stayed bridge.

Non-linearity
Where non-linear analysis is justified the following considerations are noted:

(a) Girders and towers – non-linear analysis is justified when heavy compressible loads and bending moments occur simultaneously.
(b) Cables – non-linearity exists in cables when the load increases and the geometry is distorted simultaneously. Material non-linearity is another dimension to be looked at.

The combination of items (a) and (b) produces a very complex situation. Some solutions are discussed later in the text.

6.8.8 Cable-stayed bridges – finite element method

The complete finite element formulation is given in the Appendix. All methods described in this section for the cable-stayed bridges were elastic and material properties were linear. The inherent non-linear behaviour did not exist. The inclusion of non-linear effects requires a detailed finite element analysis, since their influences cannot be ignored both individually and in a combined manner. Conventional stiffness matrices are modified to include large deformations and sagging effects which are interrelated. In addition, geometric non-linearity due to deformation of the bridge components needs to be investigated, e.g. the beam–column effects in the deck and tower. The plane frame and space frame analysis using the finite element method are the obvious choices. In plane frame, the member of the bridge structure under analysis will have, as usual, three degrees of freedom at its ends, namely, axial deformation, lateral deformation and rotation. Owing to these the axial forces, shear forces and moments appear in the structure of the bridge. The Appendix gives the stiffness matrix for a member in three dimensions. In the case of a plane frame, the force deformation relationship is given by

$$\{f\} = [K]\{\delta\} \qquad (6.291)$$

where

$$\{F\} = \begin{Bmatrix} F_i \\ V_i \\ M_i \\ F_j \\ V_j \\ M_j \end{Bmatrix}_{\text{force resultants}} \qquad \{\delta\} = \begin{Bmatrix} u_i \\ w_i \\ \theta_i \\ u_j \\ w_j \\ \theta_j \end{Bmatrix}_{\text{displacements}} \qquad (6.292)$$

$[K] = $ stiffness matrix

$$\begin{bmatrix} \dfrac{EA}{L} & 0 & 0 & \dfrac{-EA}{L} & 0 & 0 \\[2mm] & \dfrac{12EI}{L^3} & \dfrac{6EI}{L^2} & 0 & \dfrac{-12EI}{L^3} & \dfrac{6EI}{L^2} \\[2mm] & & \dfrac{4EI}{L} & 0 & \dfrac{-6EI}{L^2} & \dfrac{2EI}{L} \\[2mm] & & & \dfrac{EA}{L} & 0 & 0 \\[2mm] & & & & \dfrac{12EI}{L^3} & \dfrac{-6EI}{L^2} \\[2mm] & & & & & \dfrac{4EI}{L} \end{bmatrix} \qquad (6.293)$$

The coefficients of the matrix $[K]$ are modified and Fig. 6.101 shows forces and deformations are adjusted to Fig. 6.102 for large deformations. The coefficients of $[K]$ are then

$$L_c = \sqrt{(L + x_j - x_i)^2 + (y_j - y_i)^2} - L \qquad (6.294)$$

$$\alpha_{ij} = \tan^{-1}\left[\frac{y_j - y_i}{x_j - x_i} + L\right]. \qquad (6.295)$$

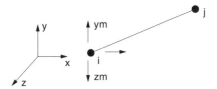

Figure 6.101. A member in three dimensions

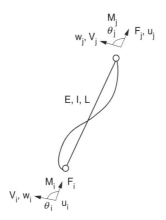

Figure 6.102. Loads, forces and deformations of a member

Non-linearty of cables

The self-weight of the cable introduces non-linearity in the cable forces. The sagging of the cable and the large deformation are interrelated. The interaction analysis is generally needed.

Space frame-type finite element analysis

The stiffness of a member Fig. 6.101 in a space frame has the following properties:

A_x = cross-sectional area

L = original length

I_x, I_z = second moment area with respect to y_m and z_m

where y_m, z_m represent

coordinate i, i.e. (x_i, y_i, z_i) (6.296)

coordinate j, i.e. (x_j, y_j, z_j). (6.297)

The direction cosines of the member are:

$$l_x = \frac{x_j - x_i}{L} \qquad l_y = \frac{y_j - y_i}{L} \quad \text{and} \quad l_z = \frac{z_j - z_i}{L} \qquad (6.298)$$

where

$$L = \sqrt{(x_j - x_i)^2 + (y_i - y_i)^2 + (z_j - z_i)^2}. \tag{6.299}$$

For non-linearity L is changed to L_c. The relation

$$\{f\} = [K]\{\delta\} \tag{6.300}$$

still holds good. The stiffness matrix $[K]$ is given by

$$
\left[
\begin{array}{cccccc|cccccc}
\dfrac{EA_x}{L} & & & & & & \multicolumn{6}{c}{\text{symmetrical}} \\[2mm]
0 & \dfrac{12EI_z}{L^3} & & & & & & & & & & \\[2mm]
0 & 0 & \dfrac{12EI_y}{L^3} & & & & & & & & & \\[2mm]
0 & 0 & 0 & \dfrac{GI_x}{L} & & & & & & & & \\[2mm]
0 & 0 & -\dfrac{6EI_y}{L^3} & 0 & \dfrac{4EI_y}{L} & & & & & & & \\[2mm]
0 & \dfrac{EI_z}{L^2} & 0 & 0 & 0 & \dfrac{4EI_z}{L} & & & & & & \\[2mm]
-\dfrac{EA_x}{L} & 0 & 0 & 0 & 0 & 0 & \dfrac{EA_x}{L} & & & & & \\[2mm]
0 & \dfrac{12EI_z}{L^3} & 0 & 0 & 0 & -\dfrac{6EI_z}{L^2} & 0 & \dfrac{12EI_z}{L^3} & & & & \\[2mm]
0 & 0 & -\dfrac{12EI_z}{L^3} & 0 & \dfrac{6EI_z}{L^2} & 0 & 0 & 0 & \dfrac{12EI_y}{L^3} & & & \\[2mm]
0 & 0 & 0 & -\dfrac{GI_x}{L} & 0 & 0 & 0 & 0 & 0 & \dfrac{GI_x}{L} & & \\[2mm]
0 & 0 & \dfrac{6EI_z}{L^2} & 0 & \dfrac{2EI_y}{L} & 0 & 0 & 0 & \dfrac{6EI_z}{L^2} & 0 & \dfrac{4EI_y}{L} & \\[2mm]
0 & \dfrac{6EI_z}{L^2} & 0 & 0 & 0 & \dfrac{2EI_z}{L} & 0 & -\dfrac{6EI_z}{L^2} & 0 & 0 & 0 & \dfrac{4EI_z}{L}
\end{array}
\right]
$$

The rotational matrix $[\theta]$ is given by

$$
[\theta] =
\begin{bmatrix}
l_x & l_y & l_z \\[3mm]
-\dfrac{l_x l_y}{\sqrt{l_x^2 + l_z^2}} & \sqrt{l_x^2 + l_z^2} & -\dfrac{l_y l_z}{\sqrt{l_x^2 + l_z^2}} \\[4mm]
-\dfrac{l_z}{\sqrt{l_x^2 + l_z^2}} & 0 & \dfrac{l_x}{\sqrt{l_x^2 + l_z^2}}
\end{bmatrix}
\tag{6.301}
$$

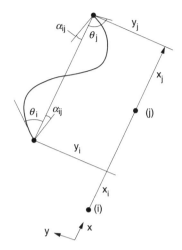

Figure 6.103. Large deformation of a member

The rotational matrix $[\theta]$, valid for all positions, would make the analysis complicated. Leonhardt, as stated earlier, has given an expression for the sag calculation and this is as follows

$$A_s E_{\text{eff}} = \frac{A_s E_0}{1 + \dfrac{\gamma^2 l^2 E_0}{12\gamma^3}}$$

The various elements in the formula have been defined earlier.

Non-linear analysis
Generally the non-linear analysis is of an iterative type. The Newton–Raphson method is recommended in a modified form in which the revised geometry is repeated as shown in Fig. 6.103. The relationship of the deformation in the local and global axis system is given in the Appendix when the member is vertical the matrix $[\theta]$ is given by:

$$[\theta]_{\text{vertical}} = \begin{bmatrix} 0 & l_y & 0 \\ -l_y & 0 & 0 \\ 0 & 0 & 1 \end{bmatrix}. \tag{6.302}$$

6.9 Computer-aided analysis
A number of computer packages is available for plane and space frames and for finite element methods to solve various problems of these types of bridges. The above formulations require computer subroutines. These routines are then linked up with finite element packages in order to obtain the desired results.

6.10 Geometric non-linearity and P–Δ effects

Material non-linearity has been thoroughly dealt with in the text. However, geometric non-linearity of the cables is a complex problem and it now needs to be addressed. The general formulation for the geometric non-linearity and P–Δ effects are given below. They are algebraically added to 2-D or 3-D beam/cable material (Appendix) matrices before resorting to static or dynamic analysis of the cable-stayed bridge. In dynamic analysis, it is vital to carry out Modal Analysis and establish the modes of vibration. The analytical formulation for such an analysis is given in Section 6.10.1. A number of routines has been written for well-known computer packages for the finite element analysis.

Geometric non-linearity

K_T = element tangent stiffness matrix (see Fig. 6.104)

$$= [K_T] = [K_0] + [K_d] + [K_\sigma]$$

where

$$[K_0] = \int [B_0][D][B_0]$$

and

$[K_d]$ = small displacement stiffness matrix

$[k_\sigma]$ = initial stiffness

$\{f\}$ = axial force

} define the geometric nonlinearity.

$$[K_0] = \begin{bmatrix} A/(lI) \\ 0 & 12/l^3 & & \text{Symmetric} \\ 0 & 6/l^2 & 4/l \\ -A/(lI) & 0 & 0 & A/(lI) \\ 0 & -12/l^3 & -6/l^2 & 0 & 12/l^3 \\ 0 & 6/l^2 & 2/l & 0 & -6/l^2 & 4/l \end{bmatrix} EI$$

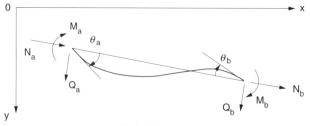

Typical beam element

Figure 6.104. Typical beam element for geometric non-linearity

$$[K_d]^1 = \begin{bmatrix} 0 & & & & & \\ k_{21} & k_{22} & & \text{Symmetric} & & \\ k_{31} & k_{32} & k_{33} & & & \\ 0 & -k_{21} & -k_{31} & 0 & & \\ -k_{21} & -k_{22} & -k_{32} & -k_{21} & k_{22} & \\ k_{62} & k_{62} & k_{63} & -k_{61} & -k_{62} & k_{66} \end{bmatrix}$$

$$k_{21} = \frac{6EA}{5l^2}(\omega_i - \omega_j) - \frac{EA}{10l}(\theta_i + \theta_j)$$

$$k_{31} = \frac{EA}{10l}(\omega_i - \omega_j) - \frac{2EA}{15}\theta_i + \frac{EA}{30}\theta_j$$

$$k_{38} = \frac{EA}{10l}(\omega_i - \omega_j) + \frac{EA}{30}\theta_i - \frac{2EA}{15}\theta_j$$

$$k_{22} = \frac{72EA}{35l^2}(\omega_i - \omega_j)^2 + \frac{18EA}{35l^2}(\omega_i - \omega_j)(\theta_i + \theta_j) + \frac{3EA}{35l}(\theta_i^2 + \theta_j^2)$$

$$k_{32} = \frac{9EA}{35l^2}(\omega_i - \omega_j)^2 + \frac{6EA}{35l}(\omega_i - \omega_j)\theta_i - \frac{EA}{140}(\theta_i^2 - \theta_j^2) + \frac{EA}{70}\theta_i\theta_j$$

$$k_{33} = \frac{3EA}{35l^2}(\omega_i - \omega_j)^2 - \frac{EA}{70}(\omega_i - \omega_j)(\theta_i - \theta_j)\frac{2EAl}{35}\theta_i^2 + \frac{EAl}{210}\theta_i^2 - \frac{EAl}{70}\theta_i\theta_j$$

$$k_{34} = \frac{3EA}{35l^2}(\omega_i - \omega_j)^2 + \frac{6EA}{35l}(\omega_i - \omega_j)\theta_j + \frac{EA}{140}(\theta_i^2 - \theta_j^2) + \frac{EA}{70}\theta_i\theta_j$$

$$k_{35} = \frac{EA}{70}(\omega_i - \omega_j)(\theta_i + \theta_j) - \frac{EAl}{140}(\theta_i^2 + \theta_j^2) + \frac{EAl}{105}\theta_i\theta_j$$

$$k_{36} = \frac{3EA}{35l}(\omega_i - \omega_j)^2 + \frac{EA}{70}(\omega_i - \omega_j)(\theta_i - \theta_j) + \frac{2EAl}{35}\theta_j^2 + \frac{EAl}{210}\theta_i^2 - \frac{EAl}{70}\theta_i\theta_j$$

$$[K_\sigma]_{(1)}^2 = \begin{bmatrix} -1 & & & & & \\ 0 & 0 & & \text{Symmetric} & & \\ 0 & 0 & 0 & & & \\ 1 & 0 & 0 & -1 & & \\ 0 & 0 & 0 & 0 & 0 & \\ 0 & 0 & 0 & 0 & 0 & 0 \end{bmatrix} \frac{(u_i - u_j)}{l^2}EA$$

$$[K_\sigma]^2_{(2)} = \begin{bmatrix} 1 \\ 0 & 0 & & & \text{Symmetric} \\ 0 & 0 & 0 \\ -1 & 0 & 0 & 1 \\ 0 & 0 & 0 & 0 & 0 \\ 0 & 0 & 0 & 0 & 0 & 0 \end{bmatrix} \frac{(u_i - u_j)^2}{2l^3} EA$$

$$[K_\sigma]^2_{(1)} = \begin{bmatrix} k_{11} \\ 0 & 0 & & & \text{Symmetric} \\ 0 & 0 & 0 \\ -k_{11} & 0 & 0 & k_{11} \\ 0 & 0 & 0 & 0 & 0 \\ 0 & 0 & 0 & 0 & 0 & 0 \end{bmatrix}$$

where

$$k_{11} = \frac{3EA}{5l^3}(\omega_i - \omega_j)^2 + \frac{EA}{15l}(\theta_i^2 + \theta_j^2) + \frac{EA}{10l^2}(\omega_i - \omega_j)(\theta_i + \theta_j) - \frac{EA}{30l}\theta_i\theta_j.$$

P–Δ effect
The following matrix $[K_\sigma]^0$ is added to the initial stiffness matrix $[K_0]$ to observe this effect:

$$[K_\sigma]^0 = P \begin{bmatrix} 0 \\ 0 & -6/(5l) & & & & \text{Symmetric} \\ 0 & -1/10 & -2l/15 \\ 0 & 0 & 0 & 0 \\ 0 & 6/5l & 1/10 & 0 & -6/(5l) \\ 0 & -1/10 & l/30 & 0 & 1/10 & -2l/15 \end{bmatrix}$$

P = initial axial force of element.

6.10.1 Modal analysis of cable-stay bridge
Mathematical formulation associated with computerized analysis
The equation for the displaced cable mode position was written by Morris, (Modal Analysis of Cable Network. *J. Struct. Div. ASCE, Jan., 1975, paper STI-11055*):

$$\sum T_{ij} \frac{a_{ij}}{L_{ij}} + x_i = m\ddot{\delta}_j + \sum_\gamma C_{ij}\dot{\delta}_\gamma \qquad (6.303)$$

$$a_{ij} = x_i + \delta_i - x_j - \delta_j$$

$$T_{ij} = T_{ij0} + \left(\frac{EA}{L^3}\right)(B_{ij} + D_{ij}) \tag{6.304}$$

$$B_{ij} = \frac{1}{2}(\delta_i - \delta_j)^2 + (v_i - v_j)^2 + (\omega_i - \omega_j)^2 \tag{6.305}$$

$$D_{ij} = (x_i - x_j)(\delta_i - \delta_j) + (y_i - y_j)(v_i - v_j) + (z_i - z_j)(\omega_i - \omega_j) \tag{6.306}$$

where

$$\frac{a_{ij}}{L_{ij}} = \text{direction cosine of the cable in the } x\text{-direction, say}$$

$$A_{ij} = \text{cross-sectional area of the cable}$$

$$x_i, y_i, z_i = \text{the original coordinates of the node } i$$

$$T_{ij0} = \text{initial tension in cable, } ij$$

$$\delta_i, v_i, \omega_i = \text{components of node displacement vectors}$$

$$C_{ij} = \text{element, i.e. cable, in particular, damping matrix.}$$

If the system is known at the state 'k', then

$$T_{ij} = T_{ijk} + \mathrm{d}T_{ijk} = T_{ijk} + fT_{ij} + sT_{ij} \tag{6.307}$$

$$\delta_i = \delta_{ik} + \mathrm{d}\delta_i$$

$$a_{ij} = a_{ijk} + \mathrm{d}a_{ij}. \tag{6.308}$$

Variables with the 'k' subscript and 'd', prefix are increments. The increment of the tension is divided into fT_{ij} and sT_{ij} first increment and second increment order terms. The incremental equation thus takes the form

$$\sum_i \frac{T_{ijk}(\mathrm{d}\delta_i - \mathrm{d}\delta_j)}{L_{ij}} + \sum_i \frac{fT_{ij}(x_i - x_j)}{L_{ij}} + \sum_i \frac{fT_{ij}(\delta_{ik} - \delta_{jk})}{L_{ij}} \tag{6.309}$$

$$+ \left\{\sum_i \frac{sT_{ij}(x_i - \delta_{ik} - x_j - \delta_{jk})}{L_{ij}} + \sum_i \frac{fT_{ij}(\mathrm{d}\delta_i - \mathrm{d}\delta_j)}{L_{ij}}\right. \tag{6.310}$$

$$\left. + \sum_i \frac{sT_{ij}(\mathrm{d}\delta_i - \mathrm{d}\delta_j)}{L_{ij}}\right\} + \mathrm{d}x_i = m_j\,\mathrm{d}\ddot{\delta}_j + \sum C_{i\gamma}\,\mathrm{d}\dot{\delta}_\gamma. \tag{6.311}$$

Similar equations can be determined in y and z directions. In generalized form, the equation can be written as

$$[M]\{\mathrm{d}\ddot{\delta}\} + [C]\{\mathrm{d}\dot{\delta}\} + K\{\mathrm{d}\delta\} = \{\mathrm{d}F\}. \tag{6.312}$$

The mode shapes are found by solving linear homogeneous equations:

$$[M]\{d\ddot{\delta}\} + [C]\{d\dot{\delta}\} + [K]\{d\dot{\delta}\} + [K]\{d\delta\} = 0. \tag{6.313}$$

Different solutions exist for this equation. Using program ANSYS, a different turn is given to the author's solution. The solution procedure takes into consideration damping while the author did not find it necessary to include the term $[C]$.

Solution procedure techniques are given in the Appendix:

$$\{d\delta\} = \{\phi\}\exp(i\omega t) = [\phi]\{dq\} \tag{6.314}$$

$$\{\phi\} = n \times p \text{ matrix}$$

$$p = \text{mode shapes for the bridge}\,(<n)$$

$$\{dq\} = p \times 1 \text{ matrix}$$

Hence

$$[M][\phi]\{d\ddot{q}\} + [C][\phi]\{d\dot{q}\} + [K][\phi]\{dq\} = \{dF\} \tag{6.315}$$

Premultiplying by $[\phi]^T$, results in

$$[\bar{M}]\{d\ddot{q}\} + [\bar{C}]\{d\dot{q}\} + [\bar{K}]\{dq\} = \{Q\} \tag{6.316}$$

where

$$[\bar{M}] = [\phi]^T[M][\phi]$$

$$[\bar{K}] = [\phi]^T[K][\phi]$$

$$[\bar{C}] = b_1[\bar{M}] + b_2[\bar{K}]$$

$$\{Q\} = [\phi]^T\{df\}$$

b_1, b_2 are constants.

Example (6.15)   British practice

A bicable-stayed bridge with a harp system for the cables is shown in Fig. 6.105. Using the following data and the finite element formulation in the Appendix, carry out linear and non-linear analyses and find forces in the cables and calculate differences between results of two analyses.

Data

$$I_{TB} = 4.33 \times 10^{11} \text{ mm}^4 \left.\right\} \text{ Tower} \qquad I_{TT} = 2.11 \times 10^{11} \text{ mm}^4 \left.\right\} \text{ Tower}$$
$$A_{TB} = 2.69 \times 10^5 \text{ mm}^2 \left.\right\} \text{ base} \qquad A_{TT} = 2.026 \times 10^5 \text{ mm}^2 \left.\right\} \text{ peak}$$

$$I_D = 11.325 \times 10^{11} \text{ mm}^4 \left.\right\} \text{ Deck}$$
$$A_D = 3.20 \times 10^5 \text{ mm}^2 \left.\right\} \text{ girder}$$

15.2 mm ⌀91 strands

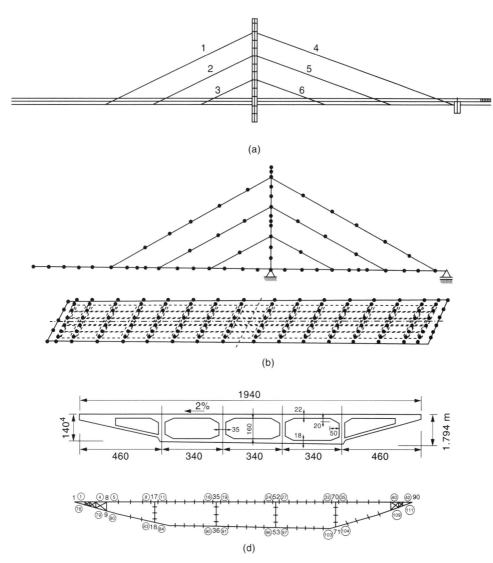

(a)

(b)

1940

2%

140⁴

1.794 m

460   340   340   340   460

(d)

Figure 6.105 (above and overleaf). (a) Cable-stayed bridge for linear and non-linear analysis. (b) Nodes of the cable-stayed bridge. (c) Cross-section of the box girder. (d) Non-linear analysis – finite element mesh. (e) Geometric plot for bending. (f) Elastic analysis results for the deck (HB loading). (g) A comparative study of bending results of the deck

ultimate loading 23 696.4 kN

service loading   10 663.4 kN

Cable areas
$A_C① = 677.46 \, \text{cm}^2$ $E = 200 \, \text{kN/mm}^2$
$A_C② = 270.948 \, \text{cm}^2$ $E_e = 180 \, \text{kN/mm}^2$
$A_C③ = 238.724 \, \text{cm}^2$

Angle of inclination $① = 20.5°$

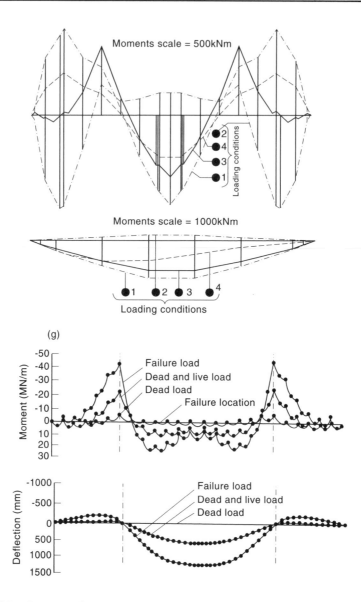

Figure 6.105. Continued

three-span continuous bridge

side spans $= 107.9\,\text{m}$ 2 NO

main span $= 260\,\text{m}$ 1 NO

tower height $= 40\,\text{m}$ 2 NO

carriageway width: box section $= 19.40\,\text{m}$

depth $= 1.794\,\text{m}$

Loading: HA + knife edge:

45 kN/m → uniformly distributed

KEL → 180 kN.

HB loading is used to check the linear analysis only while using a plate-bending (finite element) analysis given in the Appendix. The non-linear analysis is to be carried out on a box constituted of a series of line elements idealizing the true shape shown in Fig. 6.105. The geometric non-linear analysis is to be separately carried out and the results are algebraically added to the material non-linear analysis results. Using the modified Newton–Raphson method, provided the bridge deck-failure conditions. Plot the results for the bending only case.

The following $[K]$ matrices are developed for the linear analysis of the cables:

Stiffness matrix of a fixed cable

$$[K]_{fc} \frac{E_e A}{L} \begin{bmatrix} +1 & 0 & 0 & -1 & 0 & 0 \\ 0 & 0 & 0 & 0 & 0 & 0 \\ 0 & 0 & 0 & 0 & 0 & 0 \\ -1 & 0 & 0 & +1 & 0 & 0 \\ 0 & 0 & 0 & 0 & 0 & 0 \\ 0 & 0 & 0 & 0 & 0 & 0 \end{bmatrix}$$

where

E_e = equivalent modulus = 180 kN/mm^2 while E = 200 kN/mm^2

and for cable 1

$$L = \sqrt{40^2 + 107.9^2} = 115 \, \text{m} \qquad \text{(movable cable)}$$

Similarly for other cables, whether fixed or movable.

Stiffness matrix $[K]_{mc}$ is based on movable cables.

Table 6.36. Summary of analyses

Cable designation	Linear analysis	Non-linear analysis	Difference (Round number)
Cable 1	12 100 kN	13 150 kN	8%
Cable 2	8400 kN	8700 kN	3%
Cable 3	5300 kN	5400 kN	1.7%
Note items below indicate quantities at failure load			
Building moments at interior supports	−25 MNm	27 MNm (45 MNm)	8%
Bending moments in interior spans at centres	6.0 MNm	6.70 MNm (10 MNm)	10%
Bending moments in end spans at centres	3.5 MNm	3.9 MNm (20 MNm)	10.5%

Cable stiffness matrix for movable cable

$$[K]_{mc} = \frac{E_e A}{L_1}$$

$$\times \begin{bmatrix}
0.8774 & 0.3280 & 0 & 0 & -0.6561 & 0 & -0.8774 & 0.3280 & 0 \\
0.3280 & 0.1465 & 0 & 0 & -0.293 & 0 & -0.3280 & 0.1465 & 0 \\
0 & 0 & 0 & 0 & 0 & 0 & 0 & 0 & 0 \\
0 & 0 & 0 & 0 & 0 & 0 & 0 & 0 & 0 \\
-0.6561 & -0.293 & 0 & 0 & 0.586 & 0 & 0.6561 & -0.293 & 0 \\
0 & 0 & 0 & 0 & 0 & 0 & 0 & 0 & 0 \\
-0.8774 & -0.3280 & 0 & 0 & 0.6561 & 0 & 0.8774 & -0.3280 & 0 \\
0.3280 & 0.1465 & 0 & 0 & -0.07325 & 0 & -0.3280 & 0.1465 & 0 \\
0 & 0 & 0 & 0 & 0 & 0 & 0 & 0 & 0
\end{bmatrix}$$

Cables 1 and 4 are movable where $L_1 = 115\,\text{m}$.

Figure 6.105 shows the finite element analysis of cables and towers. The nodes and elements are kept the same for both towers and cables. Line elements in three dimensions are adopted. The deck is treated as an equivalent plate system on top, the depth of which is the thin-walled section with hollow boxes. For movable and fixed stays the stiffness matrices are developed. These were given in Sections 6.8.4 and 6.8.8, respectively. The plate element is given in the Appendix. The interactions of towers and cables are considered and the reactions produced are applied as nodal loads at various connections, especially at towers. Linear static analysis has been carried out, called elastic analysis, under dead and live loads. Prior to material non-linearity, a geometrical nonlinearity is assessed independently on the lines suggested by various matrices summarized in Section 6.10. Material non-linearity is given a chance and was combined with geometrical non-linearity. The results are indicated in Fig. 6.105(g). The longitudinal and transverse moments are plotted for the deck in Fig. 6.105(g). Each section of the hollow box is idealized as shown in Fig. 6.105(d). The nodes visible signify the strips of plates under bending. The box in Fig. 6.105(d) indicates a series of noded line elements forming the box. This case is only restricted to the geometric non-linearity case. For linear cases, the plate between any two verticals is restrained, and a solid isolated plate restrained by verticals, when combined with verticals, the verticals are thin columns supporting such a plate. This method is checked against the finite element analysis of the bridge deck as a thin-walled section. The difference in results is only 10–13%, especially at the functions where the verticals are located. Torsion is ignored. Linear, geometric and non-linear cases are plotted for bending only in Fig. 6.105(e) and (g). Table 6.36 gives a summary of the three analyses.

Example (6.16)   European practice
A ten-span continuous girder fan/radiator-type cable-stayed bridge is to be
analysed using static and dynamic finite element analysis. For the purpose of
analysis, the deck has a joint after three sets of towers, thus permitting the ana-
lyst to carry out the analytical work for three spans only. The number of cables
per tower is 25. The cable stays are connected to A-shaped towers. The connections to the towers or pylons are individual and no provision is thus incorporated
for the cables passing over the saddles on the top of the towers. At the ends,
piers/abutments are provided to the bridge. A single deck of concrete box
10.35 m width (carriageway) is the only one provided. A reference is made to

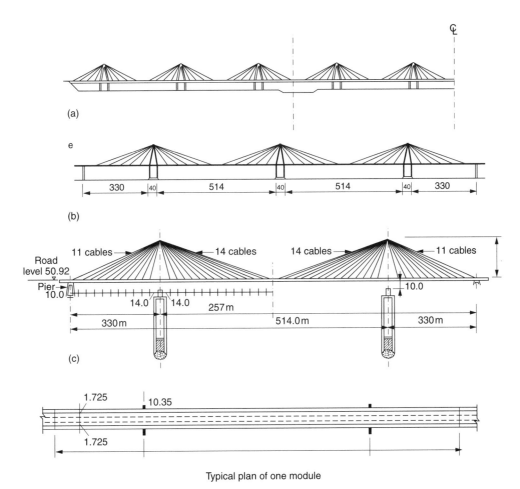

Typical plan of one module

*Figure 6.106 (pages 933-935). (a) Continuous girder fan/radiator-type cable-
stayed bridge. (b) General arrangement of the bridge. (c) Typical elevation of
one module and typical plan of one module. (d) Typical cross-section of deck
with transverse discretization of the stiffening girder flat-shell elements. (e)
Plans of the bridge tower pier, anchor pier and intermediate pier*

Fig. 6.106. The following analysis is required on the basis of data provided in Tables 6.37 to 6.39:

(a) Static finite element analysis (Appendix) in two dimensions is required by adopting two-noded cable elements and 2-D plate-bending elements for the deck. The box is treated as a series of line elements in conjunction with deck-plate bending. Alternatively flat-shell element can be chosen. In all circumstances, the membrane effects cannot be ignored.

(b) Results from the static analysis in terms of loads, moments, and deflections can be treated as *actions*. Using the following codes, carry out the limit state design of a concrete single-box section and of one tower and validate all possible cases needed:
   (1) 'Eurocode 1. Basis of design and actions on structures, Part 3, Traffic loads on bridges' ENV 199-3;
   (2) Eurocode 2 for concrete.

(c) Investigate the seismic behaviour of this bridge on the basis of data given in Table 6.39. The soil–structure interaction criteria given in Table 6.38 shall be adhered to. Where possible 'gap element' should be used for soil–structure interaction between bridge piers and soils. A reference is made to the Appendix.

6.10.2 Description of the analysis

The deck and cable-stayed components have been analysed under static and dynamic load including those from seismic analysis. The two lanes are subject

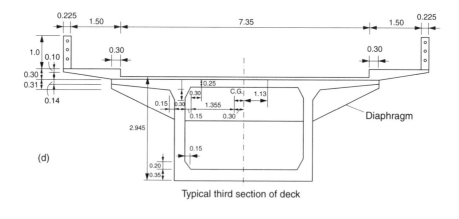

Typical third section of deck

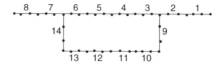

Figure 6.106. Continued

to loads according to the Eurocode provision. The following analyses are performed using the finite element method.

1. *Static finite element and dynamic finite element analyses.* The deck is a plated structure supported by a concrete box. The cables are two-noded elements. Plate-bending elements are used for the deck and the box is made up of the line elements.
2. Analysis has been performed for evaluating cable forces and moments, axial, shear loads and deflections for the deck/box. The results are produced in Tables 6.40–6.42 and Figs 6.108 and 6.109.

The results produced from this analysis are used to carry out detailed design calculations using various relevant Eurocodes associated with the bridge design.

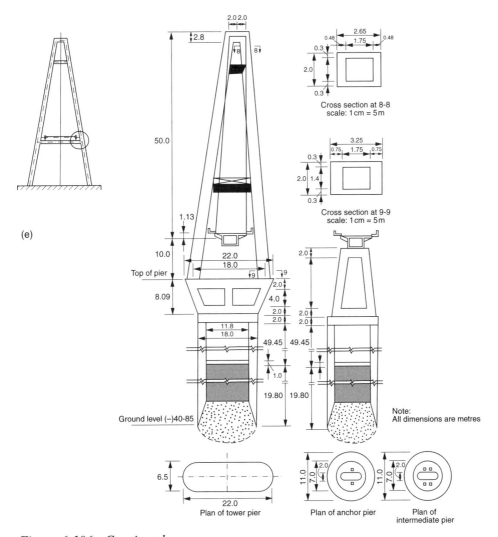

Figure 6.106. Continued

Table 6.37. Data sheet on finite element and limit state parameters

1. *Line elements for cables*:

$\left.\begin{array}{l}\text{two-noded element/stay static analysis}\\\text{three-noded element/stay seismic analysis}\end{array}\right\}$ Reference Appendix for details and Fig. 6.106

   spaces $l_c = 14$ m; $l'_c =$ spaces between cables (along width) $= 10.35$ m
2. *Deck frame 2-D*: Deck analysis for moments, shears, axial loads etc. 320 elements
   Finite element flat-shell analysis: 2-D analysis for deck 330 elements
   Dynamic finite element analysis: 3-D time-domain analysis inclusive of material and geometric non-linearities (see analyses in this section).
3. *Cable and girder material properties*:

$$E_{cable} = 1650\,\text{MN/m}^2 \qquad f_u \ngtr 1850\,\text{MN/m}^2$$

$$f_{py} \ngtr 1680\,\text{MN/m}^2 \qquad \varepsilon_{se} = 0.05$$

$$\sigma_{ce} \leq 0.5 f_{ck} \qquad f_{ck} = 40\,\text{N/mm}^2 \qquad \text{(Grade 40)}$$

For other properties see Table 6.39;

$$\varepsilon_{cu} = \text{strain at rupture} = 0.0035$$
$$\omega_k = \text{allowable crack} = 0.1\,\text{mm}$$
$$f_{ctm} = 3.4\,\text{N/mm}^2 \qquad \text{(Grade 40)}$$
$$\phantom{f_{ctm}} = 2.8\,\text{N/mm}^2 \qquad \text{(Grade 30)}$$

Girder

$$A = 5.277\,\text{m}^2 \qquad I = 6.969\,\text{m}^4 \qquad I_t = 11.2\,\text{m}^4 \qquad E_s = 200\,\text{kN/m}^2$$

$$E_c = 35\,\text{kN/mm}^2 \qquad \nu = 0.15 \qquad \alpha = E_s/E_c = 5.7 \qquad G_c = 0.432 E_c$$

Temperature
(a) $\pm 15°$C whole structure
(b) $+10°$C stay cables
(c) Box section $+5°$C

Prestressed steel

   $51420/570 \rightarrow 12.2\, \oslash$ mm cable

$$\frac{f_{0.2k}}{f_{tk}} = 12.2\, \oslash \qquad f_{0.1k} = 1220\,\text{MN/m}^2$$

$$P_i = \text{axial } P/S \text{ force} = 1.456\,\text{MN}$$

$$f_y = 460\,\text{N/mm}^2 \qquad \text{SWPR 7B} - 12 \qquad A_{PS} = 1664.4\,\text{mm}^2$$

Tower or pylon
A-shaped assumed (Fig. 6.106) cross-sectional area as shown

$$EI_P = 1 \times 10^6\,\text{MN/m}^2 \qquad f_{ck} = 30\,\text{N/mm}^2$$

Alternative
(a) Single bar element
(b) eight-noded elements 22 no/tower constant thickness of 2 m assumed.

Table 6.38. Data sheet on finite element and limit state parameters

---

Loads
Box girder dead load $G = 200\,\text{KN/m}$
Surfacing and others including services $= 59\,\text{KN/m}$

$$\text{Eurocode}\left\{ q_{ik} = \begin{array}{l} \text{live load} = 9\,\text{kN/m}^2 \text{ on lane 1 of 3 m} \\ \text{live load} = 2.5\,\text{kN/m}^2 \text{ on lane 2 of 3 m} \end{array}\right\}$$

$Q_{ik} = 300\,\text{kN}$ on lane 1 and $200\,\text{kN}$ on lane 2

Live loads on girders and cables have been obtained using influence lines prior to the analysis

Pedestrian loads $= 4\,\text{kN/m}^2$ without traffic loads

Pedestrian loads $= 2\,\text{kN/m}^2$ with traffic loads

Soil data: soil–structure interaction

$\gamma_s =$ density of soil $= 19\,\text{kN/m}^3$

$c =$ cohesion $= 0$

$\phi =$ friction $= 12.95$

$P_B =$ normal bearing capacity $= 600\,\text{kN/m}^2$

$P_{SB} =$ seismic bearing capacity $= 900\,\text{kN/m}^2$

coefficient of friction $= 0.6$

Table 6.39 (pages 937–939). Data sheet on dynamic analysis using finite element

---

Seismic analysis
Damping ratio $= 0.02,\ 0.05,\ 0.01,\ 0\%$
Friction coefficient $= 1\%$
Both evaluated from decay of free acceleration

$$\bar{\delta} = \frac{2\pi\eta_c}{\sqrt{1 - \eta_c^2}} = \log_e \frac{X_m}{X_{m+1}}$$

where

$$\bar{\delta} = \text{logarithmic damping ratio}$$

$$X_m \text{ and } X_{m+1} = \text{free oscillations at } m\text{th and } (m+1)\text{th oscillations}$$

$$\eta_c = \text{critical damping ratio}$$

$$\text{shear wave velocity } \bar{V}_S = 150\,\text{m/s and } 300\,\text{m/s}$$

Dynamic complex stiffness of the foundation

$K_x = 8G_a X/(2 - \nu)$

$K_\gamma = 8G_a X^3/3(1 - \nu)$

$C_x = \pi G_a X^2/\bar{V}_S$ – damping coefficient

$C_\gamma = 0.25\pi\sqrt{2(1 - \nu)/(1 - 2\nu)}G_a X^4/\bar{V}_S$

$K_x =$ spring coefficient

Continued

Table 6.39. Continued

K_γ, C_γ = rocking motion

C_x = damping coefficient

$\bar{V}_S$ = shear wave velocity

nodes = 205 (elastic half-space)

Initial time-scale = 5, 10 and 15 seconds.

Radius of foundation = 40 m

Poisson's ratio for soil = 0.4

Deck

I_ϕ = torsional warping moment of inertia

$$= \int_s w_a(d)\, ds$$

$$w_a = \int_0^s r\, ds - \left\{ 2A_e \middle/ \oint \frac{ds}{d} \right\} \int_0^s \left(\frac{ds}{d}\right)$$

where

d = wall thickness

s = peripheral coordinates on the centroidal line of the section

r = tangent radius

A_e = enclosed area of the box section

Distortional moment of inertia (Fig. 6.107)

$$I_{\text{Dis}} = \int_s w_b^2(d)\, ds$$

where

$$s = \frac{BD}{[4(1+K)]}$$

$$s_1 = \left(1 + \frac{2\bar{l}}{B}\right) s_2$$

$$s_3 = K s_2$$

$$K = \frac{(3 + k_1)}{(3 + k_2)}$$

$$k_1 = \frac{B}{D}\left(\frac{h_t}{h_w}\right)\left\{\frac{B + 2C}{B}\right\}^3$$

$$k_2 = \left(\frac{B}{D}\right)\frac{h_b}{h_w}$$

Continued

Table 6.39. Continued

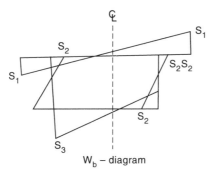

Figure 6.107. Seismic analysis diagram

where h_t, h_b and h_w are thicknesses at the top, bottom and wall of the box, respectively

B = width of the box

D = depth of the box

C = width of the protruding cantilever

Torsional warping shear parameter

$$T_{ws} = 1 - \frac{I_P}{I_C}$$

$$I_P = 4A_e \Big/ \oint \frac{ds}{d} \qquad I_C = \int_A r^2 \, da$$

Distortion second moment of area

$$I_{Dm} = \frac{24I_w}{dx}$$

$$dx = 1 + \frac{2\dfrac{B}{D} + \dfrac{3(I_b + I_t)}{I_w}}{\dfrac{(I_b + I_t)}{I_w} + 6\left(\dfrac{D}{B}\right)\dfrac{I_t I_b}{I_w^2}}$$

where

I_t for top flange ⎫
I_b for bottom flange ⎬ bending moment of inertia
I_w for wall ⎭

Total stress in three dimensions

$$(\text{Axial bending})_{x,y,z} = \left(\frac{I_\phi}{I_{Dis}}\right)_a w_a + \left(\frac{I_\phi}{I_{Dis}}\right)_b w_b + \nu\sigma_t$$

σ_t = tensile stresses

The towers or pylons are treated as cantilevers restrained at the bridge deck level and on the piers. For the general analysis, a typical example using a flexibility method is used for these towers to obtain preliminary quantities. In this analysis, the towers are discretized as a series of eight-noded isoparametric elements of constant thickness. They facilitate for computing accurately stresses and strains and hence the disposition of reinforcement along the towers. The reinforcements are arranged to lie on the eight-noded elements. No provision is made for those reinforcements lying in the body of the element. On the analysis of the box-section, the box is assumed as a series of two-noded elements along the cross-section. Various bending moments, shears and deflections are computed. A reference is made to the Appendix for secondary analysis needed for the bridge deck and cables

A 3-D finite element analysis is devised for the box-section. Program ANSYS is modified and the reinforcements, designed by the limit state approach, are modelled. The reinforcements are smeared in the solid concrete elements. Here it was justifiable to carry out non-linear analysis. The tower–deck–cable interaction was included along the lines suggested in this section, particularly for the seismic analysis. In this analysis, the cables are three-noded elements and the deck is just a box in three dimensions using 3-D solid isoparametric elements with smeared reinforcement.

Bridge loads are discretized as a series of concentrated loads in all cases of the analysis. No wind load analysis on this bridge has been carried out, assuming that seismic and wind loads do not occur simultaneously.

On the subject of the limit state design, the seismic effect is included by a factor $\psi = 0.3$ in frequent and infrequent combinations of loads.

In the static analysis, the membrane effect in the box is combined with bending effects and the results are algebraically added. For detailed analysis, refer to *Prototype building structures: analysis and design* by Bangash (Thomas Telford Ltd, London, 1999, section on Earthquake Analysis).

It is interesting to note that a single cantilever (2-D elastic beam element) and the 3-D flat elements of the towers, produced results differing by 4–6%. One can

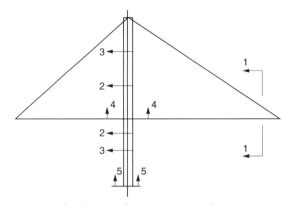

Figure 6.108. Schematic for design forces in a girder

Table 6.40. *Finite element analysis of cables and cable-acting forces*

Cable No.	C_1	C_2	C_3	C_4	C_5	C_6	C_7	C_8	C_9	C_{10}	C_{11}	C_{12}	C_{13}	C_{14}
S*	26	20	20	18	13	15	15	13	16	23	23	23	23	23
D*	52	40	40	36	26	30	30	26	32	46	46	46	46	46
S†	26	20	20	18	13	15	15	13	16	23				
D†	52	40	40	36	26	30	30	26	32	46				
A (mm²) in two planes	7212	5548	5548	4993	3606	4161	4161	3606	4438	6380	6380	6380	6380	6380
T_C (kN)	4302.2	3155.6	3018.4	2675.4	2009	2391.2	2391.2	1979.6	2548	3675	3675	3675	3675	3675
Acting forces N (kN)														
$G_1 + G_T$	4400		3410								2655			4021
G_2	−650		−200								−20			−310
P	−110		−320								−40			−240
Q_{1max}	−80		535								430			405
Q_{1min}	−70		−5								−420			−60
Q_2	33		15								58			100
Q_3	51		10								8			20

* S – single along main span in one cable ⎫
* D – double in two planes ⎪
† S – single side-span stays ⎬ 330 m span
† D – double side-span stays ⎭

Frequent load combinations

$$\bar{s}_1 + 0.57Q_1 \text{ or } Q_3$$

Infrequent load combinations

$$\bar{s}_1 = \left(\sum G + P\right)$$

(a) $\bar{s}_1 + Q_1 + 0.57(Q_2 + Q_3)$
(b) $\bar{s}_1 + Q_3 + 0.57(Q_1 + Q_2)$
(c) $\bar{s}_1 + Q_2 + 0.57(Q_1 + Q_3)$.

Table 6.41. Design forces in the girder derived from finite element analysis

Loading type (action)	Section 1 ↑1 N (kN)*	M (kNm)‡	Section 3 ↑3 (V) N (kN)*	M (kNm)‡	Section 4 ↑4 N (kN)*	M (kNm)‡	Section 5 ↑5 N (kN)*	M (kNm)‡
Finite element analysis (see Fig. B6.108)								
Dead load $= G_1$	−999	24 800	−6532 (−3060)	−28 280	−15 461	−4419	−27 743	−15 658
Tension in cable stay $= T_c$	−4884	−24 041	−6815 (−1990)	27 375	−9783	3603	−5921	14 202
Creep and shrinkage $= G_2$	1440	3040	1050 (−120)	−2380	1450	−240	1000	−2040
Live load (imposed) $= Q_1$	240	7300	1510 (−870)	−6600	−2480	−970	−3100	−4300
Earthquake load $= Q_2$ ($\psi_0 = 0.3$)	1040	540	2900 (−70)	−425	−400	−4400	−398	−1500
Prestress $= P$	−14 250	−1620	−6200 (−320)	−1200	1260	700	900	1560
Temp $= Q_3$	220	1130	200 (−80)	−980	160	−500	160	−1090
$1.35G_1 + 1.0T_c + 1.5Q_1 + (1.5)(0.3)Q_2$	−5405	20 632	−12 063	−20 894	−35 700	−5996	−48 203	−19 003
N_{sd} (kN)	−5405 kN		−12 063 kN		−35 700 kN		−48 203 kN	
M_{sd} (KNm)	20 632 kNm		−20 894 kNm		−5996		−19 003 kNm	

	Section 2 ↑2		
	V (kN)*	N (kN)*	M (kNm)‡
Finite element analysis (see Fig. B6.108)			
Dead load $= G_1$	−2730		
Tension in cable stays $= T_c$	1988		
Live load $= Q_1$	−798		
Earthquake $= Q_2$	−68		
Dead load $+ T_c$		−14 034	−360
Creep and shrinkage		1067	−2189
$0.9 \times$ Prestress		−5480	−465
Total		−18 447	−3011
Frequent combination		$+0.57Q_1$ or Q_3	
Infrequent combinations	(a) $\sum \bar{s} + Q_1 + 0.57(Q_2 + Q_3)$; (b) $\bar{s} + Q_2 + 0.57(Q_1 + Q_3)$; (c) $\bar{s} + 0.57(Q_1 + Q_2)$		

* Axial forces from finite element; $\bar{s} = \sum G + T_c + P$.

* Axial forces from finite element element.
‡ Moments from finite element.

Table 6.42. Design forces in towers

Loading type (action)	Section 4↑___↑4		Section 5↑___↑5	
	N (kN)*	M (kNm)‡	N (kN)*	M (knM)‡
G_1	−16 400		−30 265	−16 520
T_c	−10 300		−6300	−14 900
G_2	−1540		976	−2030
P	−1310		921	1660
Q_1	−2510		−3300	−4300
Q_2	−380		−395	−14 300
Q_3	160		170	−1090

* Axial forces from finite element.
‡ Moments from finite element.
Frequent combination

$$\sum G + T_c + P + 0.57Q_1$$

$$\sum G + T_c + P + 0.57Q_3$$

Infrequent combinations
(a) $\sum G + T_c + P + Q_1 + 0.57(Q_2 + Q_3)$
(b) $\sum G + T_c + P + Q_2 + 0.57(Q_1 + Q_3)$
(c) $\sum G + T_c + P + Q_3 + 0.57(Q_1 + Q_2)$.

easily conclude that even in 3-D analysis, the tower can easily be considered as a cantilever associated with the deck held by cables anchored individually to the tower. The deck can, of course, be safely designed as a 3-D stucture with a single cantilever as a tower.

From plate-bending analysis moments, shears and deflections are computed under dead, and dead plus live loads. The failure load is arrived at by using Ottoson criteria (Appendix) and is imposed on the graph.

The seismic analysis is illustrated in Fig. 6.110. The deck is first statically displaced so as to find initial deformations of the bridge deck and tower. The tower–deck interaction was considered, considering point loads occurring as static loads from the cables. In this case the box-beam was discretized as a series of line elements as shown. The locations of various anchorages were assumed to be able to resist tortional warping moments, distortional moments and distortion warping bimoments. No separate analysis for such effects were included in the global analysis. The results on this subject are shown. The soil–structure foundation was considered in order to assess tower and pier foundations.

Figure 6.109 (overleaf). (a) Vertical displacements along the centre-line. (b) Extreme fibre stresses mid-span (of main span) MN/m². (c) Longitudinal membrane stresses (of main span) MN/m². (d) Comparative displacements

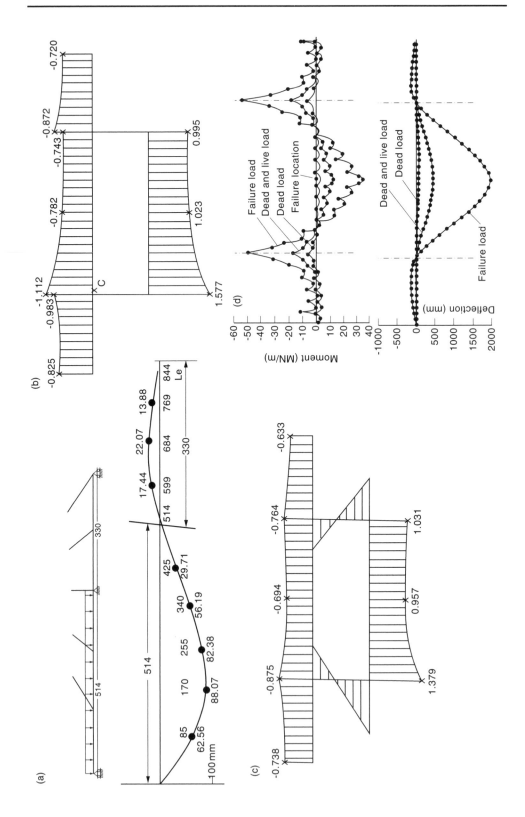

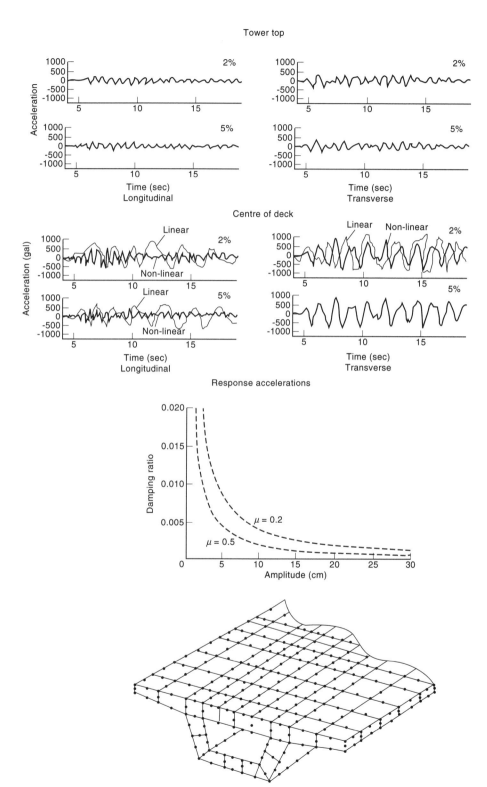

Figure 6.110. Seismic analysis from the finite element method

The earthquake-response characteristics are shown in Fig. 6.110 for a portion of the bridge using 3-D dynamic analysis, presented by the ANSYS program.

Concluding remarks
Cable-stayed bridges have complex dynamic behaviour. It is essential to correctly evaluate their dynamic behaviour and dynamic characteristics for developing a rational seismic design of such a bridge. Due to a lack of space, all results could not be reproduced. The readers are advised to examine the bibliography for specific and relevant parts of the analysis.

6.10.3 Limit state design
This is broken down mathematically into various analyses:

$$z_p(\text{top}) = \frac{6.969}{2.82 - 1.85} = 7.185\,\text{m}^3$$

$$z_p(\text{bottom}) = \frac{6.969}{1.85 - 0.175} = 4.161\text{m}^3$$

$$m_g(\text{positive}) = 20.5\,\text{MN m} \quad (\text{excluding } M_{\text{prest}})$$

Stresses:

$$\sigma_{cg}(\text{top}) = \frac{-20.5}{7.185} = -2.85\,\text{MN/m}^2 \text{ or } \text{N/mm}^2$$

$$\sigma_{cg}(\text{bottom}) = \frac{+20.5}{4.161} = +4.927\,\text{MN/m}^2 \text{ or } \text{N/mm}^2$$

$$\sigma_{cp_i}(\text{top}) = \frac{-23.296}{5.277} - \frac{23.296(-0.022)}{7.185}$$

$$= -4.4163 - 0.07133 = -4.488\,\text{MN/m}^2$$

$$\sigma_{cp_i}(\text{bottom}) = \frac{-23.296}{5.277} = \frac{23.296(-0.022)}{4.161}$$

$$= -4.4163 + (-0.12317)$$

$$\approx 4.5397\,\text{MN/m}^2$$

$(\sigma_{cg} + \sigma_{cp_i})$

$$\text{Top value} = -7.338\,\text{MN/m}^2$$

$$\text{Bottom value} = +0.3873\,\text{MN/m}^2$$

In separate conditions, if this girder is launched the losses shall be no more than 10%.

Serviceability limit state
Based on Eurocode, it is assumed that $\psi_1 = \psi_2 = 0$. From above calculations:

$$M_{max} = 1.05 \times 18.5 + 2.00 + 2.30 + 3.05 = 26.775 \, \text{MN m}$$
$$M_{min} = 1.05(-32.00) = -33.6 \, \text{MN m}.$$

Uncracked condition
The top and bottom stresses are for the M_{max} value:

$$\sigma_{c_{top}} = \frac{-20.966}{5.277} - \frac{26.775 - 20.966 \times 0.022}{6.931} = -7.776 \, \text{MN/m}^2$$
$$\sigma_{c_{bot}} = \frac{-20.966}{5.277} + \frac{26.775 - 20.966 \times 0.022}{4.273} = 2.196 \, \text{MN/m}^2$$
$$\approx \text{the principal diagonal stress}$$

Check:

$$\sigma_c < 0.5 f_{ck} = \tfrac{1}{2}(40) = 20 \, \text{MN/m}^2 \quad \text{(acceptable)}$$

At the top:

$$f_1 = \sigma_c = \sigma_{ck} = 2.6 \, \text{MN/m}^2 \quad \text{(acceptable)}$$

For the M_{min} case $= 33.6 \, \text{MN m}$:

$$\sigma_{c_{top}} = \frac{-20.966}{5.277} - \frac{-33.6 - 20.966 \times 0.022}{6.931} = +0.937 \, \text{MN/m}^2$$

Prestressing steel
Relaxation for launching time of one-half year is around 4%.

$$\text{Effective width} = 0.60 + 4.80 + 0.60$$
$$+ \frac{\text{distance between points of zero moment}}{5}$$

In this case $b_{ef} = 7.35 \, \text{m}$ as shown in Fig. 6.111, and

$$z_c = 3.78 \, \text{m}^3.$$

Sectional properties

Denomination	Concrete	Concrete inclusive of bars and ducts
$A(\text{m}^2)$	4.925	5.277
$y_c(\text{m})$	1.85	1.85
$h^1 - y_c(\text{m})$	1.095	1.095
$I(\text{m}^4)$	6.402	6.969
$z(\text{top})\text{m}^3$	6.77	6.932
$z(\text{bottom})\text{m}^2$	4.054	4.2731

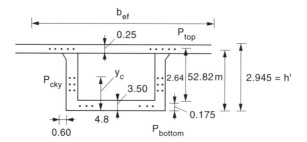

Figure 6.111. Limit state design for prestressing steel

Serviceability

$$\rho = \frac{I}{A(h-y_c)y_c} = \frac{6.402}{4.925(1.095)(1.85)} = 0.62 > 0.5$$

Section is good and acceptable.

Comparison

$\rho(\text{T-section}) \not> 0.45$

$\rho(\text{flat slab}) = 0.33.$

Torsion I_t

$$\text{Torsion } I_t = \frac{4A^2}{\oint(1/t)\,ds} = 11.2\,\text{m}^4$$

$P_i = $ prestressing force for 16 straight tendons.

Each has loading:

$$1.456\,\text{MN} = (10+6) \times 1.456 = 23.296\,\text{MN}$$

Eccentricity of this prestressing force is

$$e = \frac{10 \times 2.82 + 6 \times 0.175}{16} = -0.022\,\text{MN}$$

temperature effects (difference $2.5°\text{C}) = 2.40\,\text{MNm}$.

Losses in straight tendons and stresses

$$(10+6)(1.456) = 23.296\,\text{MN}$$

At the level of straight tendons.

Box section

Dead weight $g_j = 200 \, \text{kN/m}$

Surfacing + edge beam $= g_1 = 60 \, \text{kN/m}$

Heating tubes for inside box $= g_2 = 12 \, \text{kN/m}$

Impact coefficient $= 1.10$

Moderate compressive stress $\sigma_{cc} < \frac{1}{3} f_{ck}$

$w_k =$ cracking $\leq 0.1 \, \text{mm}$ under total load

$\qquad\qquad \leq 0.15 \, \text{mm}$ for deck slab in the bending direction.

Prestressing steel S1420/1570 12.2 mm ⌀

$$f_{0.1k} = 1220 \, \text{MN/m}^2 \qquad \text{Design strength} = \frac{1220}{1.15} = 1061 \, \text{MN/m}^2$$

$$E_{\text{prest}} = 200 \, \text{KN/mm}^2.$$

Initial tendon force for 12 prestressing tendons

$$\sigma_{p_i} = 0.75 f_{ck} = 0.75 \times 1570 = 1177 \, \text{N/mm}^2$$

and

$$0.85 f_{ck} = 0.85 \times 1220 = 1037 \, \text{N/mm}^2$$

$$A_P = \text{area of prestress} = 12 \times 117 \times 10^{-6} = 1404 \times 10^{-6} \, \text{m}^2$$

$$= n \text{ area of wires}$$

$$P_i = \text{initial prestressing force}$$

$$= 0.85 f_{ck} A_P = 1037 \times 1404 \times 10^{-6} = 1.456 \, \text{MN}.$$

Relaxation parameter

$$\frac{\sigma_{p_i}}{f_{yk} = f_{ck}} = \frac{1037}{1570} = 0.66$$

$20°\text{C}, 1000 \, \text{hr} \rightarrow 1037 \, \text{MN/m}^2 \qquad (3\%)$

$$\frac{\Delta\sigma_2}{\Delta\sigma_1} = \left(\frac{t_2}{t_1}\right)^\beta$$

$$= \left(\frac{0.5 \times 10^6}{1000}\right)^{0.2} = 3.47$$

$$\beta = 0.2$$

$$t_2 = 0.5 \times 10^6 h$$

Relaxation of 3%

$$\frac{\Delta\sigma_2}{\Delta\sigma_2} = 3 \times 3.47 = 10.4\%$$

$$\sigma_{C_{bot}} = \frac{-20.966}{5.277} + \frac{-33.6 - 20.966 \times 0.022}{4.273} = -11.793 \, \text{MN/m}^2$$

$$V = 1.9 \, \text{MN}$$

$$v = \tau_C = \frac{VS}{IB_{ef}} = \frac{1.9 \times 3.78}{6.969 \times 0.6} = 1.72$$

$$\text{Web} = \sigma_C \leq 0.5 \, \text{MN/m}^2 \quad \text{(acceptable)}$$

Check for the principal diagonal stress in tension:

$$f_1 = \sigma_{ct} = \frac{0.50}{2} + \frac{1}{2}\sqrt{(0.5)^2 + 4(0.6)^2}$$

$$= 1.99 \, \text{MN/m}^2 < 2.6 \, \text{MN/m}^2 \quad \text{(acceptable)}.$$

Cracked condition
Referring to Fig. 6.112:

$$b_w = 0.6 \, \text{m}$$

$$b_{f_{bottom}} = 4.80 \, \text{m} \qquad h_{bottom} = 0.35$$

$$b_{f_{top}} = 7.5 \, \text{m}$$

$$h_{top} = \text{thickness} = 0.25 \, \text{m}$$

$$P = 20.966 \, \text{MN}$$

$$A_{s_1} = 0.0108 \, \text{m}^2$$

$$A_{s_2} = 0.0214 \, \text{m}^2$$

$$M = 26.775 \, \text{MN/m}$$

$$\sigma_C = \frac{Px}{(b_w(x^2/2) + (b_f - b_w)(2x - h_f)h_f/2)}$$

$$+ 15A_{s_1}(d - x) - 15A_{s_2}(d - x)^{2.945}$$

$$= -4.096 \, \text{MN/m}^2$$

$$\sigma_S = 15 \times 4.096 \times \frac{2.945 - 1.14}{1.14}$$

$$= 90.247 \, \text{MN/m}^2 \quad (A_{s_1} \, \text{level})$$

where $\alpha = 15$.

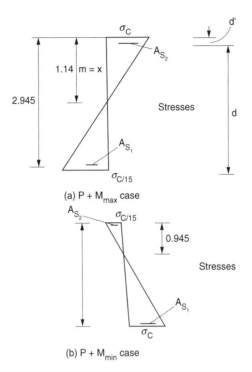

(a) P + M$_{max}$ case

(b) P + M$_{min}$ case

Figure 6.112. Dimensions for the cracked condition

For the A_{S_2} level:

$$\sigma_C = -9.67 \, \text{MN/m}^2$$

$$\sigma_S = 15 \times 9.67 \, \frac{2.945 - 2.00}{2.00} = 68.54 \, \text{MN/m}^2$$

Crack control

(a) $M_{max} = +26.775 \, \text{MNm}$

$$M_{cracking} = 4.273 \left[\frac{1}{7.352} + \frac{0.022}{4.273} \right] \times 20.966 = 12.65$$

$$w_k = \text{crack width} = 0.1 \left(1.5 \frac{3.5 \times 0.05}{0.10} \right) \frac{90.247}{2 \times 10^5}$$

$$\times \left[1 - \left\{ \frac{12.65}{26.775} \right\}^2 \times 10^3 \right]$$

$$= 0.135 \, \text{mm} \quad \text{(acceptable)}.$$

(b) $M_{min} = -33.6 \, \text{MN/m}$

$$M_{\text{cracking}} = -6.931 \left[\frac{1}{7.352} - \frac{0.022}{6.931} \right] \times 20.966 = -19.3\,\text{MNm}$$

$$w_{\text{k}} = 0.1 \left(1.5 + \frac{3.5 \times 0.05}{0.10} \right) \times \frac{68.54}{2 \times 10^5} \left[1 - \left\{ \frac{19.3}{33.6} \right\}^2 \right] \times 10^3$$

$$= 0.068\,\text{mm} \qquad (\text{acceptable}).$$

Ultimate limit state in bending (see Fig. 6.113)
For

$$M_{\text{max}} \qquad \psi_0 \neq 0$$

$$M_{\text{sd}} = 1.35(1.05 \times 18.5 + 2.0 + 3.05 + 2.30)$$

$$= 36.15\,\text{MNm}$$

$$\sigma_{\text{C}} = 0.8\,\frac{f_{\text{ck}}}{\gamma_{\text{C}}} = 0.8 \times \frac{40}{1.5} = 21.3\,\text{MN/m}^2$$

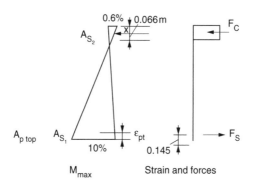

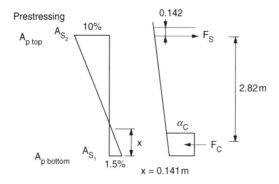

Figure 6.113. Ultimate limit states in bending

ε_{pt} = tensile strain in tendon

$$= \frac{20.966}{16(0.001404) \times 200 \times 10^3}$$

$$= 0.00466$$

$x = 0.166$ (trial value)

$\varepsilon_C = 0.0006$

Area	Strains	Stress MN/m^3
A_{s_1}	$\varepsilon_{s_1} = 0.01$	349
$A_{P_{\text{bottom}}}$	$A_{P_{\text{bottom}}} = 0.01403$	1005
$A_{P_{\text{top}}}$	$A_{P_{\text{top}}} = 0.00464$	550
A_{s_2}	$\varepsilon_{s_2} = -0.00045$	306

For permanent action $\gamma_f = 1.35$.
Ten duct holes in the deck: 0.075 m. It follows:

$$A_\phi = 10\pi \frac{(0.075)^2}{4} = 0.0442 \qquad (y = 2.714\,\text{m})$$

$$F_C = 21.3\{(7.5)(0.8 \times 0.166) - 0.0442\}$$

$$+ 306 \times 0.0214 - 1.35 \times 7.0 \times 5.50 \times 0.001404$$

$$= 21.17\,\text{MNm} + -5.97 = +21.17 + 6.5484 - 7.29729 = 20.42\,\text{MN}$$

$$(y = 0.145\,\text{m})$$

$$F_S = 6 \times 1005 \times 0.001404 + 348 \times 0.0108$$

$$= 20.69\,\text{MN}$$

$$F_S = F_C$$

$$M_{Rd} = 20.69(2.714 - 0.145)$$

$$= 53.153 > 36.15\,\text{MNm} = M_{Sd} \qquad \text{(acceptable)}$$

Shear
Straight tendon $\alpha_P = 0$; stirrups $\alpha = 90°$

$$\tau_{Rd} \text{ for } f_{ck} = 40\,\text{MN/m}^2 = 0.42\,\text{MN/m}^2$$

$$V_{Sd} = \gamma_g V = 1.35 \times 1.9 = 2.565\,\text{MN}$$

$$b_w \text{ (nominal)} = 2 \times 0.5 - 0.5(4 \times 0.075) = 0.85\,\text{m}$$

$$V_{Rd} = 0.3 f_{cd} b_w d = 0.3(26.7)(0.85)(2.945)$$

$$= 20.05 \, \text{MN}$$

$$V_{Sd} < V_{Rd}, \quad \text{i.e.} \quad 2.565 < 20.05 \quad \text{(acceptable)}.$$

Where a check is required for combined torsion shear and bending, calculations should be carried out using

$$\frac{T_{Sd}}{T_{Rd}} + \frac{V_{Sd}}{V_{Rd}} < 1$$

where

$$T_{Sd} = \frac{\phi G I_t}{L \, (\text{span})}$$

$$T_{Rd} = 0.5 f_{cd} A_{ef} h_{ef} \sin(2 \times 45°)$$

If $\theta = 45°$ then:

$$\frac{V_{Sd}}{V_{Rd}} = 0.243$$

$$\frac{T_{Sd}}{T_{Rd}} = 0.25$$

$$\frac{T_{Sd}}{T_{Rd}} + \frac{V_{Sd}}{V_{Rd}} = 0.483 < 1 \quad \text{(acceptable)}.$$

Tower design

$$A_s(7T32) \quad A_s = 5628 \, \text{mm}^2$$

Tensile strain is beyond yield $\varepsilon_s = \varepsilon_y$

$$f_{st} = f_y = \sigma_s$$

Therefore,

$$M_{Rd} = \text{resisting moment} = 19\,223 > M_{Sd}$$

$$= \frac{5996}{2} = 2998 \, \text{KNm} \quad \text{(acceptable)}.$$

Ductility check

These sections must satisfy the following condition.

Girder:

$$\rho_s + \rho_P \frac{f_{0.1k}}{f_{yk}} \le 0.02$$

$$\rho_S = \frac{A_s}{bd} \qquad \rho_P = \frac{A_P}{bd_P}$$

$$f_{0.1k} = 1537\,\text{N/mm}^2$$

$$f_{yk} = 460\,\text{N/mm}^2$$

$$\frac{4.396 \times 10^{-3}}{10.15 \times 1.334} + \left\{ \frac{6.656 \times 10^{-3}}{10.15 \times 1.20} + \frac{6.656 \times 10^{-3}}{10.15 \times 1.00} \right\} \frac{1537}{460}$$

$$= 0.0035 < 0.02 \qquad \text{(acceptable)}.$$

Pylon or tower (see Fig. 6.114):

$$\rho_S = \frac{56.28 \times 10^{-4}}{2.65 \times 1.7}$$

$$= 0.00125$$

$$< 0.02 \qquad \text{(acceptable)}.$$

End piers:
A reference is made to Fig. 6.114 and Table 6.43 for loads and moments
$12\,\text{m} \times 10.35 \times 4.6\,\text{m}$ deep:

$$V = 12 \times 10.35 \times 600\,\text{kN}$$

$$= 74\,520\,\text{kN}$$

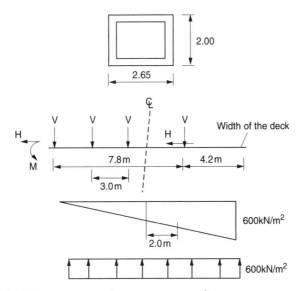

Figure 6.114. Moments at pylons, towers and piers

Table 6.43. Load combination for abutment/pier design*

Load cases	Node 750			Node 751	Node 752	Node 753	
	V 750 (kN)	H 750 (kN)	M 750 (kN)	V 751 (kN)	V 752 (kN)	V 753 (kN)	H 753 (kN)
I G_1+adjustment of stay cable	+650	+7990	+1110	−139	−2370	−1590	−
II Q_1 (live load) full spans	−330	+1090	+1400	+960	−980	0	−240
III Q_1 (live load) part spans	+490	1290	−4450	−2770	+2280	−640	−190
IV Q_1 (live load) part spans (reversed)	−810	−230	+5820	+3760	−3250	+640	−70
V Q_2 earthquake load	+220	+4900	−1800	+1170	−950	+230	−5440

* Reactions from 2D analysis

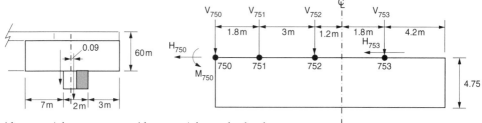

Abutment/pier
12m × 6 m
Carrying 10.35 m
carriageway

Abutment/pier under loads

$$M = \text{maximum bending}$$

$$= \tfrac{1}{2}(600)[12 \times 10.35] \times 2$$

$$= 74\,520\,\text{kN/m}$$

$$R_{H_{max}} = \text{maximum horizontal reactions from soil}$$

$$= \gamma_S x K_{EA} - \tau_C K_{EA}^{1/2} + q'_C K_{EA}$$

$$K_{EA} = \cos^2(\phi - Q_0 - Q) \Big/ \Big[\cos Q_0 \cos^2 Q \cos(Q + Q_0 + \delta)$$

$$\times \left(1 + \left\{ \frac{\sin(\phi + \delta) - \alpha - Q_0}{\cos(Q + Q_0 + \delta)} \cos(Q - \alpha) \right\}^{1/2} \right)^2 \Big]$$

$$\gamma = 19 \, \text{kN/m}^2$$

$$C = 0$$

$$q' \, (\text{external force}) = 0$$

$$\phi = 30° \quad \alpha = 0 \quad Q = 0 \quad \text{and} \quad Q_0 = \tan^{-1} 0.23 = 12.95°$$

$$\therefore \quad K_{EA} = 0.5$$

$$R_{H_{max}} = \tfrac{1}{2} r H^2 K_{EA} L$$

$$= \tfrac{1}{2}(19)(7.5)^2 \times 0.5 \times 10.35 = 2760 \, \text{kN}$$

Weight of the pier/abutment $= 17\,200 \, \text{kN}$

Total horizontal resistance $= 2760 + 0.6 \times 17\,200$

$$= 13\,080 \, \text{kN}.$$

Check for overturning
Moments from Table 6.43 data due to:

$$G_1 = 74\,520 \, \text{kNm}$$

$$G_2 = 17\,200 \times 0.09 - 7790 \times 4.6 + 139 \times 4.2 + 370 \times 1.2$$

$$- 1110 - 1590 \times 1.8 - 650 \times 6$$

$$= -41\,130.7 \, \text{kNm}$$

$$Q_1 = 5820 + 3760 \times 4.2 - 230 \times 4.6 - 810 \times 6 - 3250 \times 1.2$$

$$- 640 \times 1.8 - 70 \times 4.6$$

$$= 10\,320 \, \text{kNm}$$

$$Q_2 = (5440 - 4900) \times 4.6 + 230 \times 1.8 + 950 \times 1.2 + 1800$$

$$- 220 \times 6 - 1170 \times 4.2 = -396$$

$$S_{TB} = 0.9 M_{G_1} + (-1.1 \times M_{G_2}) - 1.5(M_{Q_1}) - (0.45 M_{Q_2}) > 0$$

$$= 67\,068 - 45\,243.77 - 15\,480 - 178.2 = 6166.03 > 0 \quad (\text{acceptable}).$$

Check on horizontal stability

$$H_{G_1} = 2760 + 0.6(17\,200) = 13\,080 \, \text{kN}$$

$$H_{G_2} = 7790 \, \text{kN}$$

$$H_{Q_1} = -230 - 70 = -300$$

$$H_{Q_2} = 5440 - 4900 = 540$$

$$S_{TB} = 0.9H_{G_1} - 1.1H_{G_2} - 1.5H_{Q_1} - 0.45H_{Q_2} > 0$$

$$= 11\,772 - 18\,569 - 450 - 243$$

$$= 2510 > 0$$

Check on vertical stability

$$V_{G_1} = 74\,520\,\text{kN}$$

$$V_{G_2} = -2370 - 1590 - 139 + 650 + 17\,200 = 13\,751\,\text{kN}$$

$$V_{Q_1} = 3760 + 640 - 810 - 3250 = 340\,\text{kN}$$

$$V_{Q_2} = 220 + 1170 - 950 + 230 = 670\,\text{kN}$$

$$S_{TB} = 0.9V_{G_1} + (-1.1V_{G_2}) - 1.5V_{Q_1} - 1.5\psi V_{Q_2}$$

$$= 67\,068 - 15\,126.1 - 510 - 301.5$$

$$= 51\,130.4 > 0 \qquad \text{(acceptable)}.$$

SECTION 7
STRUCTURAL DETAILS OF
SOME IMPORTANT BRIDGES

7. Structural details of some important bridges

7.1 Introduction

This section is devoted to the structural details of the constructed facilities of prototype bridges. The selection is based on a number of basic qualities of the details. These have also been checked by the author using British and European Codes for bridge analysis and design.

7.2 Prototype bridges: details of superstructures

Figures 7.1–7.7 give details of some prototype bridge superstructures.

7.3 Prototype bridges

7.3.1 Poole harbour crossing: bridge design details

Structural design

The steel pylons are simple A-frames with a slender tie between the legs at deck level concealed with the depth of the deck girder. This tie is used to provide the later bearings between the deck and the pylons and to facilitate erection. The 1.2 m diameter high yield steel tubes vary in thickness from 35 mm to 50 mm. (See Figures 7.8–7.10.)

The stays are spiral strands varying from 85 mm to 120 mm in diameter, socketed at both ends and anchored to a lug on the pylon and to a cast steel threaded anchor at deck level.

The top longitudinal stays have screwed tensioning devices incorporated into the socket anchorage at the pylon head, with a special threaded anchor at the abutments similar to the deck anchors.

The deck is not directly supported vertically at the pylons, but is suspended on the stays throughout in order to avoid concentrated high bending moments at the pylon positions. Lateral restraint is provided to the deck with sliding PTFE bearings at each abutment and on the tie between the legs of each pylon. The deck is fixed longitudinally only to the central pylon, being free to expand and contract towards the expansion joints at each end.

The deck edge detail is a continuous inclined flat surface running over the entire length of the bridge including the Triangular Bridge and the Holes Bay Road overbridges, to provide a consistent appearance throughout.

Foundations
All foundations are piled, using tubular steel piles driven into the soft deposits. The main bridge foundations are 1.5 m diameter raking piles, varying in length from about 15 to 30 metres.

Triangular Bridge
The Triangular Bridge is a reinforced concrete deck structure supported on three points, with a ribbed soffit to mirror that of the main bridge.

7.3.2 Bridge over River Lérez Ponteverdra, Spain (European practice)
The bridge crosses the estuary of 125 m width. It has a single span of 125 m and is stayed to a single pylon. Two different stay configurations have been adopted: the first, in the front part hanging over the river, consists of stays contained in two parallel planes; while the other, the rear part, displays stays that diverge towards the counterweights, opening up in two fans. The deck is 18.80 m wide and 2.0 m deep, with a box thickness of 300 mm (average) and is stayed at its centre-line by two planes of cables. The deck has internal diaphragms positioned at 3 m spacings to provide an adequate torsional stiffness. The girder is reinforced with three prestressing cables, comprising 17 dia. 0.6 wires positioned from the upper slab, with connectors at 12 m spacings. They run along the deck, starting from the anchorage blocks located in the box lower slab. The box is supported by pair of stays at 0.70 m spacings anchored in the section at 6 m spacings. The box is solidly joined to the abutment and the deck bears on reinforced elastomer bearings 600 mm × 700 mm × 130 mm. Throughout the concrete used was of 45 MN/m². (See Figures 7.11–7.15.)

The pylon is of a single element set in the space at the centre of the two carriageways. *The author has re-analysed this bridge using the loads recommended in this text by the Eurocodes. The bridge, designed originally using Spanish loading criteria, is found safe for the loads recommended by the Eurocodes.*

Details
Customer: Conselleria De Politica Territorial, Obras Publicas e Vivenda de la Xunta de Galicia, Direccion Xeral de Obras Publicas.
Design: Carlos Fernandez Casado SL, Madrid, Spain.
General contractor: Ferrovial SA y Castro Matelo SA.

7.3.3 Prototype bridges: details of substructures
Figures 7.16–7.21 give details of some prototype bridge substructures.

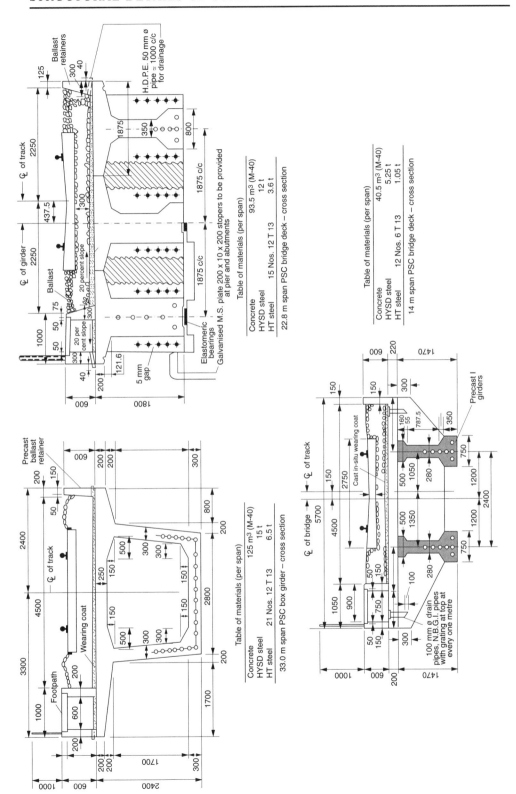

Figure 7.1. Prestressed concrete bridge decks: spans: 14.0 m, 22.8 m and 33.0 m

General notes

Design specifications: AASHTO Standard Specifications for Highway Bridges, 1973, using Load Factor Design (LFD) except for bridge deck, bearings and footings.

Dead Load: Dead load includes 22 psi for future wearing surface on the roadway slab.

Live Load HS20-44

Concrete: Concrete for the bridge deck shall be in accordance with the recommendations contained in Table 7 of the final report "Durability of Concrete Decks, by the Portland Cement Association dated 1970. All other concrete shall be Class A(AE) with a 28 day compressive strength of f'c:4000 psi except abutments and column footings which shall be f'c: 3000 psi. The air entraining agent shall meet with the approval of the engineer. All exposed edges shall be chamfered 3/4" except as noted. Concrete in the superstructure shall be placed in accordance with the Superstructure Placing Sequence shown.

Reinforcing Steel: Reinforcing steel shall conform to ASTM A-615, A-616 or A-617. Reinforcing steel without a required ASTM Bend Test shall not be used for bent bars. Transverse deck bars and footing bars may be Grade 40, 50 or 60 with design being based upon an allowable tensile stress of 20,000 psi. All other bars shall be grade 60 for which L.F.D. criteria apply. Spiral reinforcing steel shall conform to ASTM A-82. Spacing shown are from center to center of bars. Covering shall be 2" clear except as noted.

Piles: Point bearing steel H-piles shall be driven to sustain a load of at least 70 tons per pile at bents and 55 tons per pile at the abutments.

Drainage: No provisions for drainage have been made in these plans. If required, see Appendix A for suggested details.

Summary of quantities

Item	Units	Superstructure	Substructure	Total
		To meet conditions of site and specifications		
Excavation for structures	C.Y.	—	880	880
55 ton steel H-piles (Abut.)	L.F.	—	1040	1040
70 ton steel H-piles (Bent)	L.F.	—		
Concrete	C.Y.	1068.5	265.0	1333.5
Reinforcing steel	Lbs.	268960	38860	307820
Fabricated structural metal	Lbs.	3040*	—	3040*

*Bearing devices

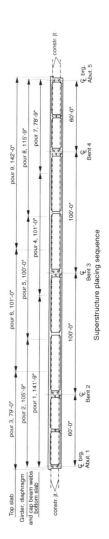

Rustication detail

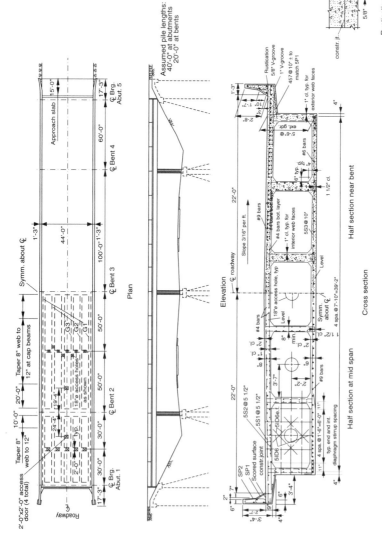

Figure 7.2. Four-span reinforced concrete box girder bridge: spans 60–100–100–60 = 320 ft – general plan and cross-section (American practice) (courtesy of US Department of Transportation, FHA, Washington DC)

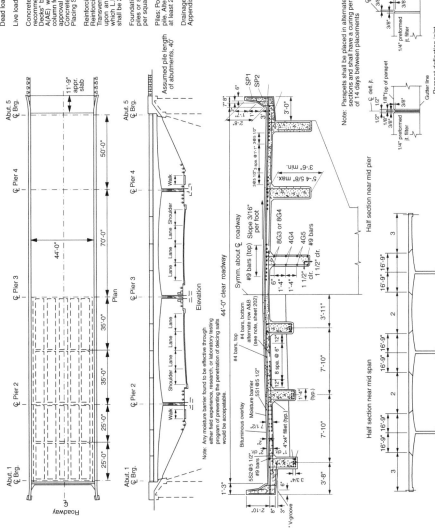

Figure 7.3. *Four-span reinforced concrete T-beam bridge: spans 50–70–70–50 = 240 ft – general plan, sectional elevation and cross-section (American practice) (courtesy of US Department of Transportation, FHA, Washington DC)*

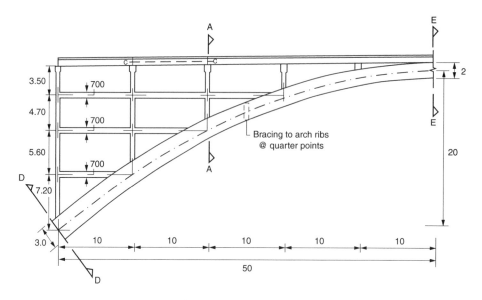

Elevation of 1/2 span of bridge

Scale 1:200

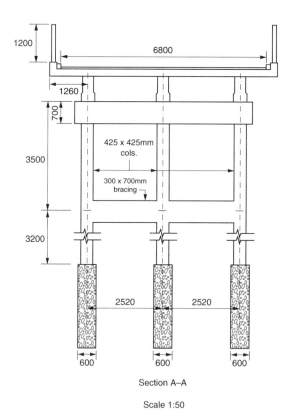

Section A–A

Scale 1:50

Figure 7.4. Concrete open spandrel arch bridge: elevation and section (British practice)

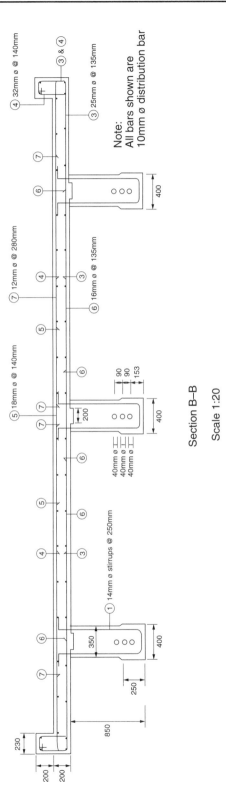

Figure 7.5. *Concrete open spandrel bridge: deck details (British practice)*

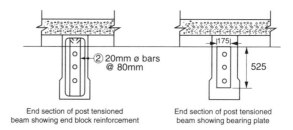

End section of post tensioned
beam showing end block reinforcement

End section of post tensioned
beam showing bearing plate

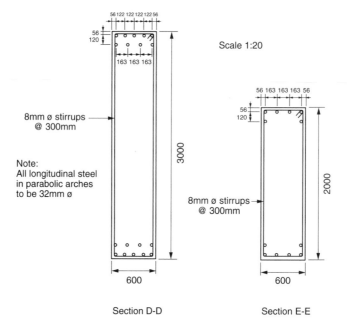

Note:
All longitudinal steel
in parabolic arches
to be 32mm ø

Scale 1:20

Section D-D   Section E-E

*Figure 7.6. Concrete open spandrel arch bridge: sections at crown and abutment
(British practice)*

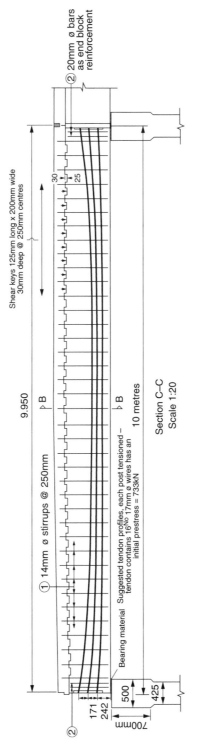

Figure 7.7. Prestressed concrete girder with tendon profiles

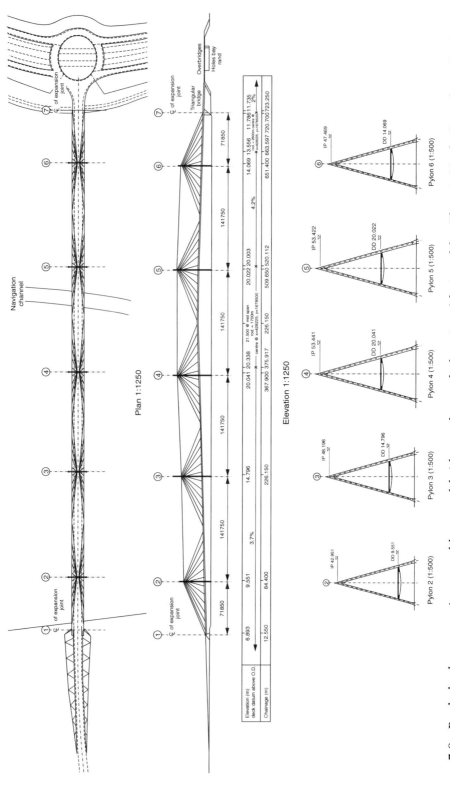

Plan 1:1250

Navigation channel

Elevation 1:1250

Elevation (m) deck datum above O.D.	6.893	9.551	14.796	20.041 20.338	20.022 20.003	14.069 13.556 11.786 11.735
		3.7%		3.7%	4.2%	2%
Chainage (m)	12.550	84.400	226.150	367.900 375.917	509.650 520.112	651.400 663.597 720.700 723.250

71850 · 141750 · 141750 · 141750 · 141750 · 71850

Pylon 2 (1:500) IP 42.951 DD 9.551

Pylon 3 (1:500) IP 48.196 DD 14.796

Pylon 4 (1:500) IP 53.441 DD 20.041

Pylon 5 (1:500) IP 53.422 DD 20.022

Pylon 6 (1:500) IP 47.469 DD 14.069

Figure 7.8. Poole harbour crossing: a cable-stayed bridge – plan and elevation (designed by Flint & Neal, Consulting Engineers, London)

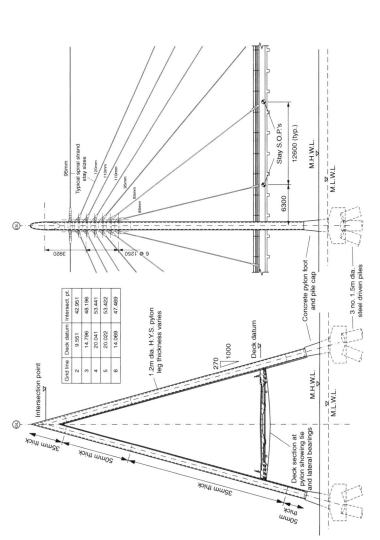

Figure 7.9. Poole harbour crossing: elevations — pylons with cable stays and connections (Flint & Neal, Consulting Engineers, London)

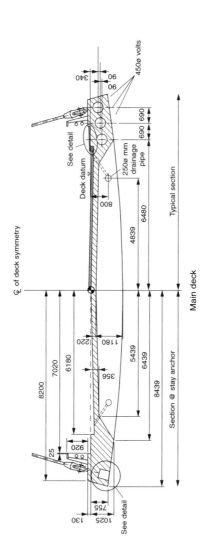

Figure 7.10. Poole Harbour crossing: bridge deck cross-section (Flint & Neal, Consulting Engineers, London)

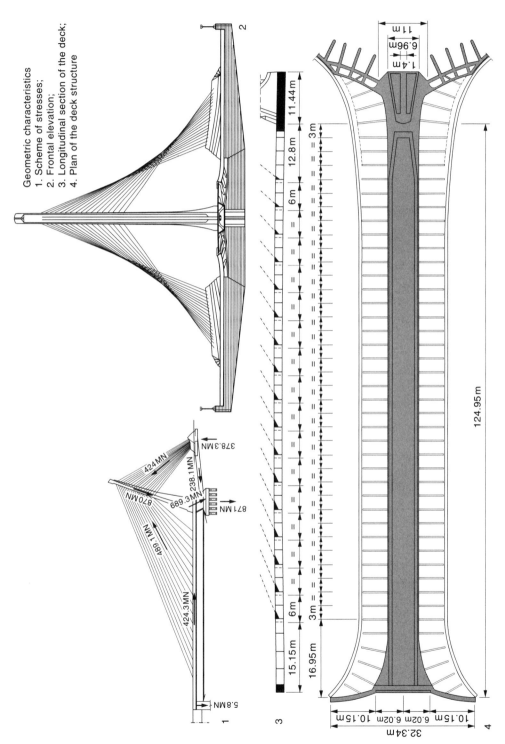

Geometric characteristics
1. Scheme of stresses;
2. Frontal elevation;
3. Longitudinal section of the deck;
4. Plan of the deck structure

Figure 7.11. Geometric characteristics: sections, elevations, plan

974

BANGASH

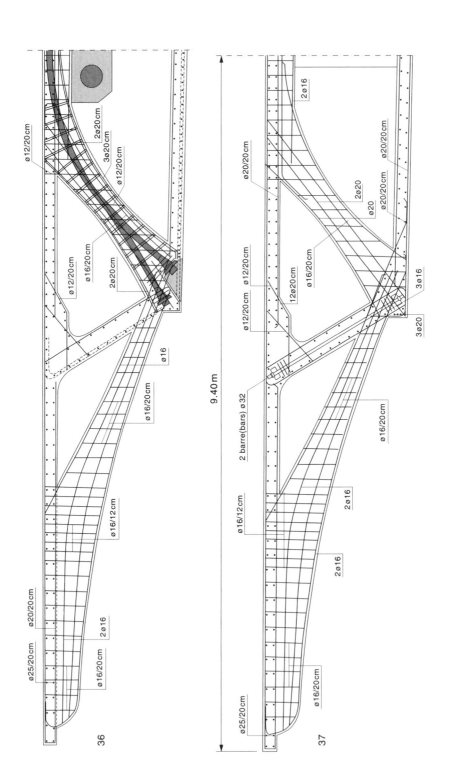

Figure 7.12. Deck reinforcement

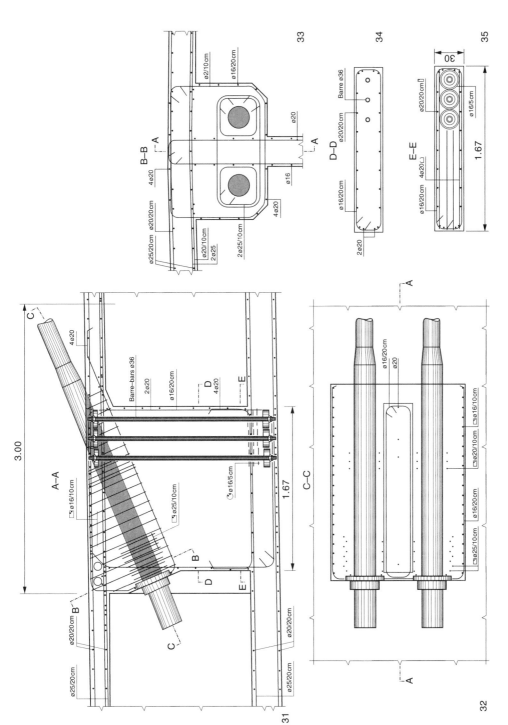

Figure 7.13. Deck section and plan at a cable anchorage

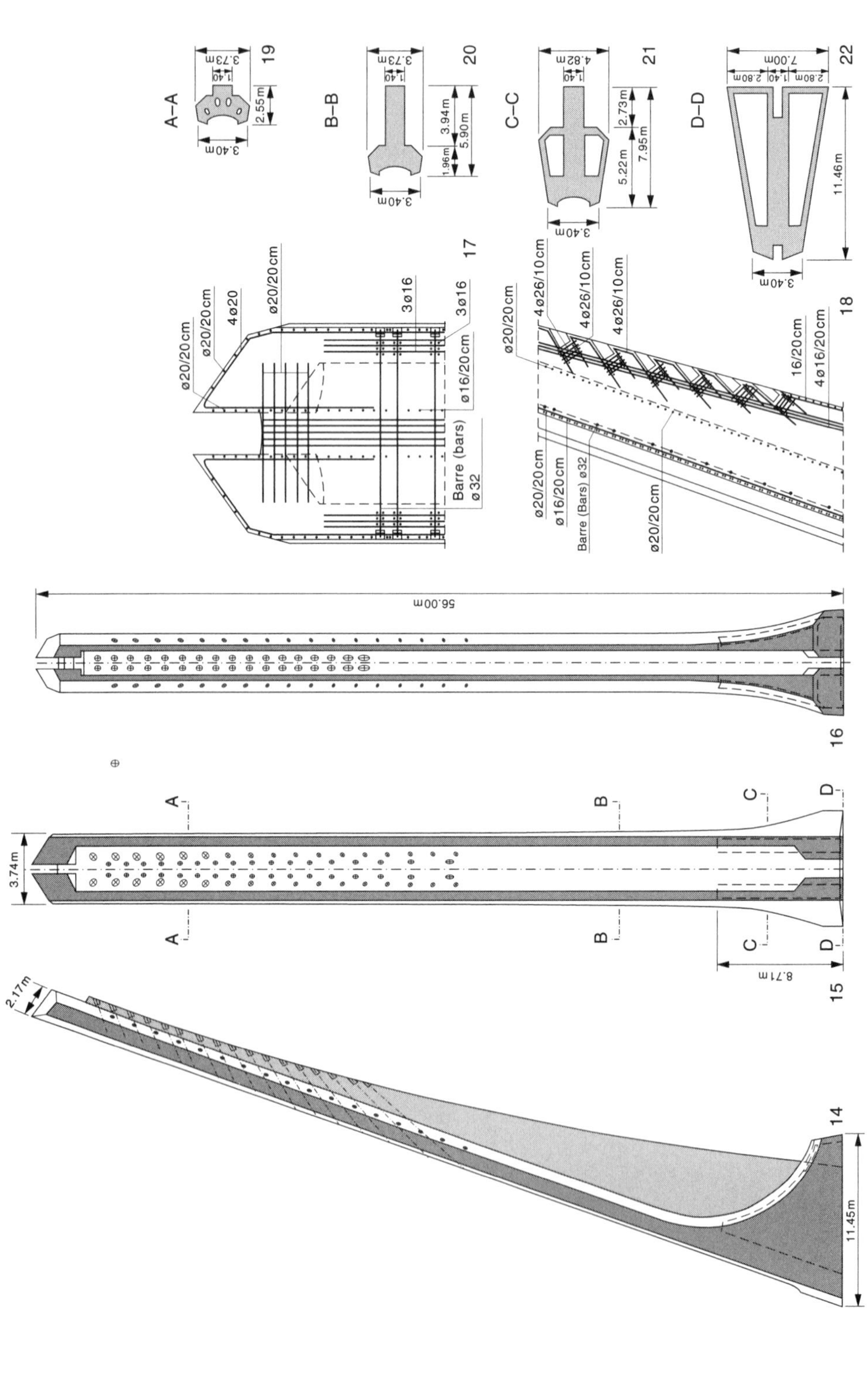

Figure 7.14. *Cable carrier pylon: structural details*

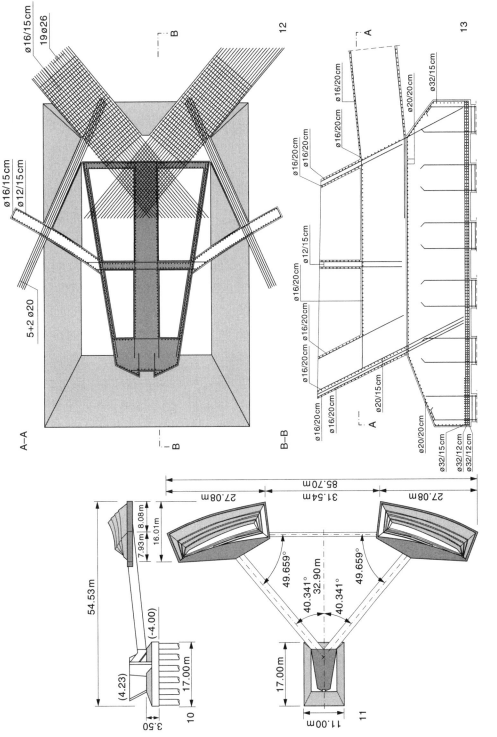

Figure 7.15. Elevation and plan of pylon counterweight, plans and sections of foundations

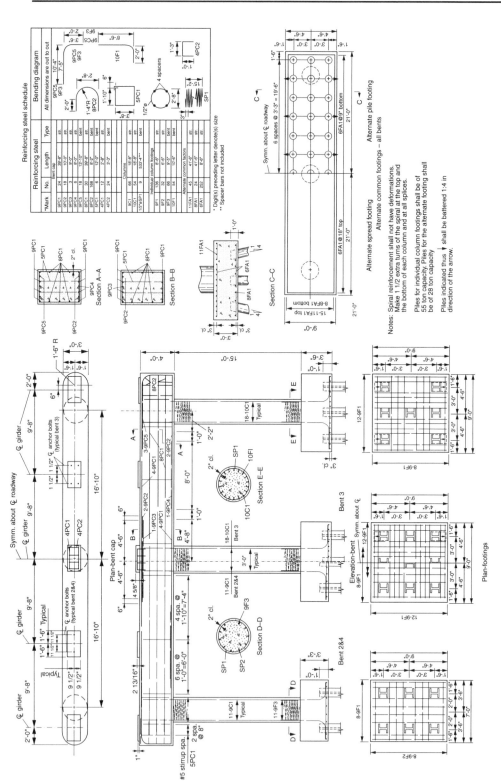

Figure 7.16. Bent and footing details of four-span welded girder bridge (American practice) (courtesy of US Department of Transportation, FHA, Washington DC)

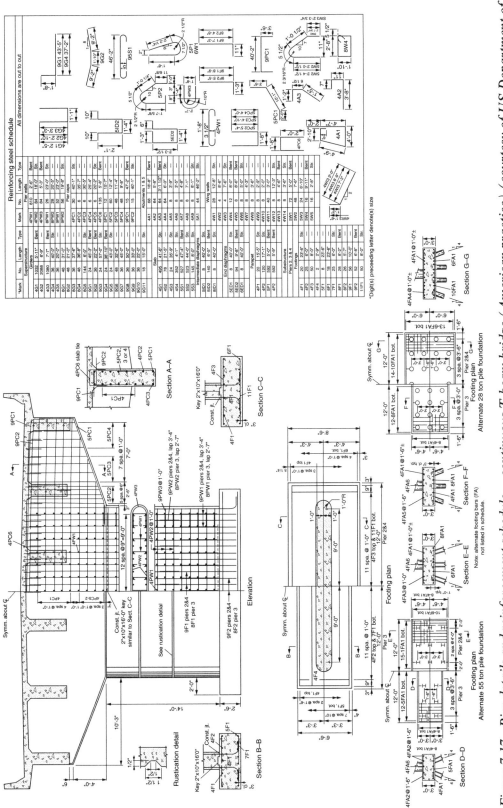

Figure 7.17. Pier details and reinforcement schedule – continuous T-beam bridge (American practice) (courtesy of US Department of Transportation, FHA, Washington DC)

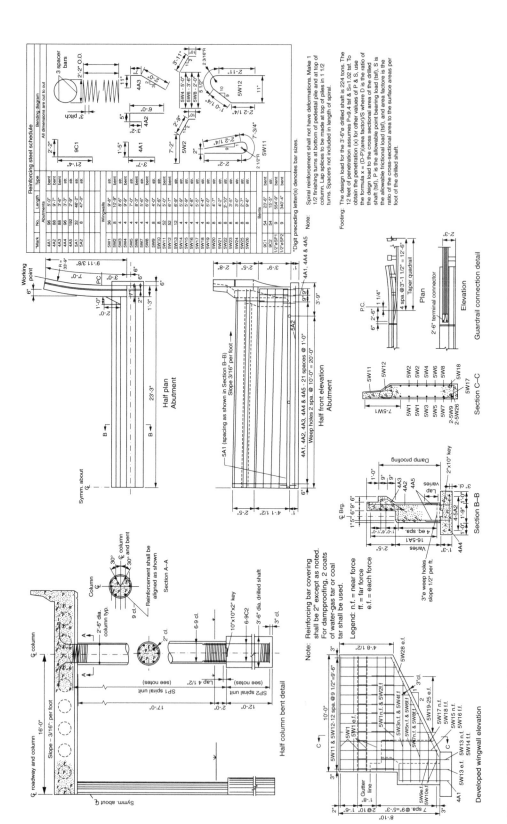

Figure 7.18. Bent, reinforcement and abutment details – continuous four-span voided slab bridge (American practice) (courtesy of US Department of Transportation, FHA, Washington DC)

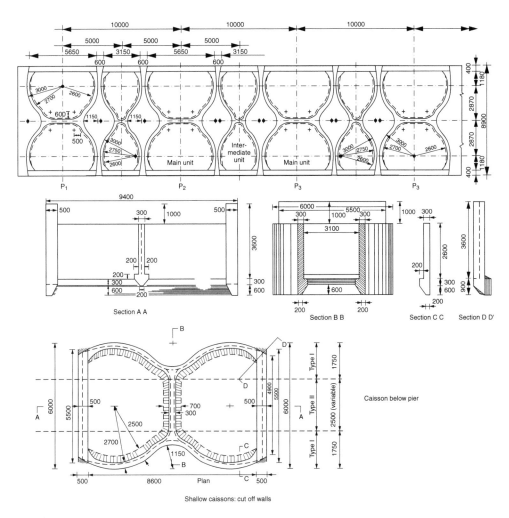

Figure 7.19. Details of shallow caisson (Indian practice) (courtesy of State of Mahrastra, India)

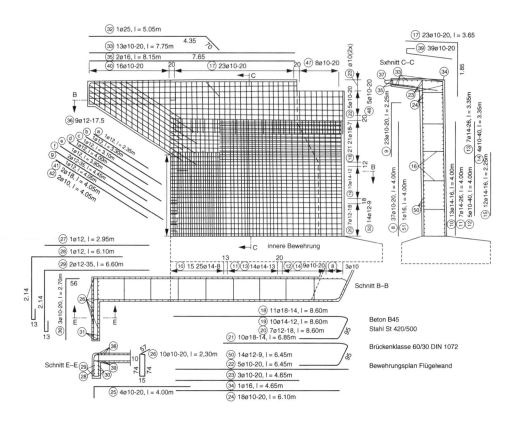

Figure 7.20. Pier details in reinforced concrete (European practice) (courtesy of Stahlbeton und Spannbeton, Karl Heinz Holst, Ernst & Sohn)

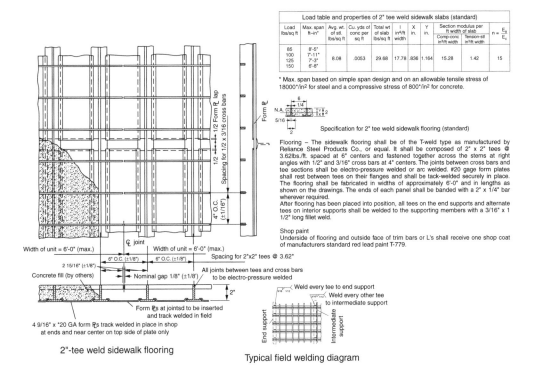

Load table and properties of 2" tee weld sidewalk slabs (standard)											
Load lbs/sq ft	Max. span ft–in*	Avg. wt. of stl. lbs/sq ft	Cu. yds of conc per sq ft	Total wt of slab lbs/sq ft	I in⁴/ft width	X in.	Y in.	Section modulus per ft width of slab		n = $\frac{E_s}{E_c}$
								Comp-conc in³/ft width	Tension-stl in³/ft width	
85	8'-5"									
100	7'-11"									
125	7'-3"	8.08	.0053	29.68	17.78	.836	1.164	15.28	1.42	15
150	6'-8"									

* Max. span based on simple span design and on an allowable tensile stress of 18000*/in² for steel and a compressive stress of 800*/in² for concrete.

Specification for 2" tee weld sidewalk flooring (standard)

Flooring – The sidewalk flooring shall be of the T-weld type as manufactured by Reliance Steel Products Co., or equal. It shall be composed of 2" x 2" tees @ 3.62lbs./ft. spaced at 6" centers and fastened together across the stems at right angles with 1/2" and 3/16" cross bars at 4" centers. The joints between cross bars and tee sections shall be electro-pressure welded or arc welded. #20 gage form plates shall rest between tees on their flanges and shall be tack-welded securely in place. The flooring shall be fabricated in widths of approximately 6'-0" and in lengths as shown on the drawings. The ends of each panel shall be banded with a 2" x 1/4" bar wherever required.
After flooring has been placed into position, all tees on the end supports and alternate tees on interior supports shall be welded to the supporting members with a 3/16" x 1 1/2" long fillet weld.

Shop paint
Underside of flooring and outside face of trim bars or L's shall receive one shop coat of manufacturers standard red lead paint T-779.

2"-tee weld sidewalk flooring

Typical field welding diagram

Figure 7.21. Tee weld sidewalk flooring (American practice) (courtesy of Reliance Steel Products Co., McKeesport, PA, USA)

SECTION 8
BIBLIOGRAPHY

8. Bibliography

Bridges — arts and aesthetics

1 PACHOLIK, L., *Aesthetics of Bridge Structures*, Grafic Publishing House, Prague, 1946 (in Czechoslovakian).
2 DÉMARET, J., *Aesthetic and Construction of the Structure*, Dunode, Paris, 1948 (in French).
3 Ministry of Transport, *The Appearance of Bridges*, HMSO, London, 1969.
4 The Institution of Civil Engineers, The aesthetic aspect of civil engineering design, A record of six lectures delivered at the institution, 1955.
5 MOCK, E. B., *The Architecture of Bridges*, Museum of Modern Art, New York, 1948.
6 MAYS, R. R., Beautiful bridges, *Civ. Eng., ASCE*, August 1989, pp. 72–74.
7 BACKOW, A. F. and KRUCKEMEYER, K. E. (ed.), *Bridge Design — Aesthetics and Developing Technologies*, Massachusetts Department of Public Works, 1986.
8 SHCHUSEV, P. V., *Bridges and Their Architecture*, State Edition on Construction and Architecture, Moscow, 1952 (in Russian).
9 WADDELL, J. A. L., *Bridge Engineering*, Vol. II, Wiley, New York, 1916, pp. 1150–1181.
10 BILLINGTON, D. P., *The Tower and the Bridge*, Basic Books, New York, 1983.
11 STEINMAN, D. B., *A Practical Treatise on Suspension Bridges*, 2nd edn, Wiley, New York, 1953.
12 PODOLNY, W. Jr. and SCALZI, J. B., *Construction and Design of Cable-Stayed Bridges*, 2nd edn, Wiley, New York, 1986.
13 TROITSKY, M. S., *Cable-Stayed Bridges, An Approach to Modern Bridge Design*, 2nd edn, Van Nostrand Reinhold, New York, 1988, pp. 36–41.
14 GIMSING, N. J., *Cable Supported Bridges, Concept and Design*, Wiley, New York, 1983.
15 CLARK, E., *The Britannia and Conway Tubular Bridges*, Vol. I, Day and Son, and John Weale, London, 1850.
16 LEGGE, C., *A Glance at the Victoria Bridge, and the Men Who Built It*, John Lovell, Montreal, 1860.
17 GIES, J., *Bridges and Men*, Doubleday, Garden City, NY, 1963, pp. 156–177.
18 GIES, J., *Bridges and Men*, Doubleday, Garden City, NY, 1963, pp. 216–219.
19 STEINMAN, D. B. and WATSON, S. R., *Bridges and Their Builders*, G. P. Putnam's Sons, New York, 1941, pp. 282–287.
20 STEINMAN, D. B. and WATSON, S. R., *Bridges and Their Builders*, G. P. Putnam's Sons, New York, 1941.
21 BLOCK, A., *The Story of Bridges*, Whittlesey House, London, 1936, p. 104.
22 GIES, J., *Bridges and Men*, Doubleday, Garden City, NY, 1963, pp. 93–99.
23 GIES, J., *Bridges and Men*, Doubleday, Garden City, NY, 1963, pp. 183–187.
24 TRACHTENBERG, A., *Brooklyn Bridge*, Oxford University Press, New York, 1965.

25 STEINMAN, D. B. and WATSON, S. R., *Bridges and Their Builders*, G. P. Putnam's Sons, New York, 1941, pp. 340–345.
26 STRAUSS, J. B., *The Golden Gate Bridge*, Golden Gate Bridge and Highway District, 1938.
27 STEINMAN, D. B., *Miracle Bridge at Mackinac*, Wm. B. Eerdmans, Grand Rapids, MI, 1957.
28 MEHRTENS, G. C., *Lectures on Engineering Sciences, Steel Bridges*, Verlag von Wilhelm Engelmann, Leipzig, 1908, pp. 1–51.
29 TYRRELL, H. G., *History of Bridge Engineering*, published by the Author, Chicago, 1911.
30 BRANGWYN, F. and SPARROW, W. S., *A Book of Bridges*, John Lane the Bodley Head, London, 1914.
31 WADDELL, J. A. L., *Bridge Engineering*, Vol. I, Wiley, New York, 1916, pp. 1–35.
32 WATSON, W. J. and WATSON, S. R., *Bridge in History and Legend*, J. H. Hansen, Cleveland, 1927.
33 BLOCK, A., *The Story of Bridges*, Whittlesey House, London, 1936.
34 STRAUB, H., *A History of Civil Engineering*, Leonard Hill, London, 1952.
35 STEINMAN, D. B. and WATSON, S. R., *Bridges and Their Builders*, Dover Publications, New York, 1957.
36 PANNELL, J. P. M., *An Illustrated History of Civil Engineering*, Thomas and Hudson, London, 1964, pp. 209–258.
37 NARUSE, Y. and KIJIMA, T. (Ed.), *Bridges of the World*, 2nd ed., Morikita Publishing, Tokyo, Japan, 1967.
38 BECKETT, D., *Bridges*, The Hamlyn Publishing Group Limited, London, 1969.
39 MERIN, O. B. (Ed.), *Bridges of the World*, C. J. Bücher Verlag, Luzern and Frankfurt/M., 1971 (in German).
40 SEALEY, A., *Bridges and Aqueducts*, Hugh Evelyn Limited, London, 1976.
41 WITTFOHT, H., *Building Bridges*, Beton-Verlag GmbH, Düsseldorf, 1984.
42 FAUSTUS VERANTIUS, *Machinae Novae Fausti*, Verantii, Venice, 1617.
43 PANNELL, J. P. M., *An Illustrated History of Civil Engineering*, Thomas and Hudson, London, 1964, p. 312.
44 BLOCK, A., *The Story of Bridges*, Whittlesey House, London, 1936.
45 STEINMAN, D. B., *Famous Bridges of the Word*, Random House, New York, 1953, p. 13.
46 TUDOR, D., *Les Ponts du Bas-Danube*, Editura Academiei, Republicii Romania, 1974, p. 48.
47 BLOCK, A., *The Story of Bridges*, Whittlesey House, London, 1936, pp. 40–41.
48 GIES, J., *Bridges and Men*, Doubleday, Garden City, NY, 1963, pp. 13–14.
49 GIES, J., *Bridges and Men*, Doubleday, Garden City, NY, 1963, pp. 37–49.
50 GIES, J., *Bridges and Men*, Doubleday, Garden City, NY, 1963, pp. 27–32.
51 STEINMAN, D. R. and WATSON, S. R., *Bridges and Their Builders*, G. P. Putnam's Sons, New York, 1941, pp. 85–86.
52 STEINMAN, D. B. and WATSON, S. R., *Bridges and Their Builders*, G. P. Putnam's Sons, New York, 1941, pp. 86–89.
53 STEINMAN, D. B. and WATSON, S. R., *Bridges and Their Builders*, G. P. Putnam's Sons, New York, 1941, pp. 81–85.
54 GIES, J., *Bridges and Men*, Doubleday, Garden City, NY, 1963, pp. 90–92.
55 TALESE, G., *The Bridge*, Harper & Row, New York, 1964.
56 ANON., New Civil Engineer reviews the history of the word's longest span suspension bridge, *New Civ. Eng. Suppl.*, May 1981, pp. 4–22.
57 SANSON, R., Saint-Nazaire-Saint Brevin Bridge over the Loire Estuary (France), *Acier-Stahl-Steel*, No. 5, 1976, pp. 116–167.
58 ANON., *The Bridge Spanning Lake Maracaibo in Venezuela*, Bauverlag GmbH, Wiesbaden-Berlin, 1963.
59 TAYLOR, P., *Hybrid design for the world's longest span cable-stayed bridge*, 12th/ABSE Congress, Vancouver, B.C., 3–7 September, 1984, Final Report, pp. 319–324.

60 SILVERBERG, R., *Bridges*, Macrae Smith, Philadelphia, 1966, p. 107.

61 OVERMAN, M., *Roads, Bridges, and Tunnels*, Doubleday, Garden City, NY, 1968, p. 107.

62 STEINMAN, D. B., Messina Strait suspension bridge to span 5000 ft, *Civ. Eng.*, December 1953, pp. 54–57.

63 ANON., Super starts soon, *ENR*, April 6, 1989, p. 18.

64 ROBINSON, R., The French composite: A bridge for Normandy, *Civ. Eng.*, February, 1993, pp. 56–59.

65 ANON., Longest span in the world, *New Civ. Eng.*, 4 August 1988, pp. 18–20.

66 LIN, T. Y., Inter-continental peace bridge, *T. Y. Lin Int. Bull.* **15**(2), December 1986, p. 4.

67 ANON., Gibraltar crossing schemes still alive, *ENR*, October 1, 1984, p. 22.

68 KUESEL, T. R. *Floating bridges for long water crossings*, Structural Engineers Association of Hawaii, 1984 Annual Convention, pp. 1–13.

Codes and recommended practice, texts and design reports

69 *Evaluation of Load Carrying Capacity of Bridges*. Organisation for Economic Cooperation and Development, Paris, 1979.

70 BRITISH STANDARDS INSTITUTION. *Steel, Concrete and Composite Bridges: Specification for Loads*. BSI, London, 1978, BS 5400: Part 2.

71 Departmental Standard BD 23/84: Loads for Highway and Foot/Cycle Track Bridges. Department of Transport, London, 1984.

72 BRITISH STANDARDS INSTITUTION. *Specification for Steel Girder Bridges*. BSI, London, 1958, BS 153.

73 AASHTO, Standard Specifications for Highway Bridges: 12th Edition. The American Association of State Highway and Transportation Officials, Washington, 1977.

74 DEUTSCHE INDUSTRIE NORMEN. *Road and Footbridges: Design Loads*. DIN, Berlin, 1967, DIN 1072.

75 Cahier des prescriptions communes applicables aux marchés de travaux publis relevant des services de l'equipement. Ministere de l'Equipement et du Logement — Ministere des Transports, Paris, 1973.

76 Recommended design loads for bridges. Committee on Loads and Forces on Bridges of the Committee on Bridges of the Structural Division. *Journal of the Structural Division*, Proceedings of the American Society of Civil Engineers, December 1981.

77 DEPARTMENT OF TRANSPORT. Departmental Standard BD 37/88: *Loads for Highway Bridges*. DoT, London, 1988, BD 37/88.

78 DEUTSCHE. INDUSTRIE NORMEN. *Road and Footbridges: Design Loads*. DIN, Berlin, 1983, Draft DIN 1072: August.

79 HAY, J. S., *Estimation of Wind Speed and Air Temperature for the Design of Bridges*. Laboratory Report LR 599, Transport and Road Research Laboratory, U.K., 1974.

80 DEPARTMENT OF TRANSPORT. *Bridge Inspection Guide*. DoT, HMSO, London, 1983.

81 DEPARTMENT OF TRANSPORT. *Queues and Delays at Roadworks (QUADRO2)*. DoT, London, April, 1982 (and subsequent revisions).

82 Report of the Royal Commission into the Failure of Kings Bridge, Government Printer, Melbourne, 1963.

83 DEPARTMENT OF TRANSPORT. *The Assessment of Highway Bridges and Structures*. DoT, London, 1984, BD 21/84.

84 *Assessment of Reinforced and Prestressed Concrete Bridges*. Papers presented at a seminar organised by the Institution of Structural Engineers, September 1988.

85 *Concrete Bridges — Management, Maintenance and Renovation*. Proceedings of one-day conference. Concrete Society, London, February, 1989.

86 Bridge assessment symposium. Leamington Spa. *Construction Marketing*, June, 1989.

87 Diagnosis and assessment of concrete structures. *Bulletin d'Information No. 192*. Committee Euro International du Beton, Lausanne, January, 1989.

88 OECD. *Road Transport Research — Durability of Concrete Road Bridges*, OECD, Paris, 1989.

89 BRITISH STANDARDS INSTITUTION. *Steel, Concrete and Composite Bridges, Part 2, Specifications for Loads*. BSI, London, 1978, BS 5400.

90 *Ontario Highway Bridge Design Code 1979*, Section E. Ministry of Transportation and Communications, Ontario, Canada, 1980.

91 ANGER, G., *Tend Division Influence Lines for Continuous Beams*, Ungar, New York, 1956.

92 APPLIED TECHNOLOGY COUNCIL. *Tentative Provisions for the Development of Seismic Regulations for Buildings*, ATC Report No. 3-06, June, Berkeley, 1978.

93 APPLIED TECHNOLOGY COUNCIL. *Comparisons of United States and New Zealand Seismic Design Practices for Highway Bridges*, ATC-12, CA, 1982.

94 ARBABI, F., *Structural Analysis and Behavior*, McGraw-Hill, New York, 1991.

95 ARMENAKAS, A. E., *Modern Structural Analysis: The Matrix Method Approach*, McGraw-Hill, New York, 1991.

96 ASCE, *Recommended Design Loads for Bridges*, Committee on Loads and Forces on Bridges, Committee on Bridges of the Strut. Div., *J. Struct. Div. ASCE*, Vol. 107, No. ST7, July, 1981, pp. 1161–1213.

97 ASCE–AASHTO, *State-of-the-Art Report on Ultimate Strength Design of I-Beam Bridge Systems*, Subcommittee of Joint ASCE–AASHTO Task Committee on Metals of the Structural Division, 1975.

98 ATC, *Seismic Design for Highway Bridges*, ATC-6, Applied Technology Council, Berkeley, CA, 1981.

99 BAKHT, B. and L. G. JAEGER, *Bridge Analysis Simplified*, McGraw-Hill, New York, 1985.

100 BARES, R., Complement à la méthode Guyon-Massonet de calcul des ponts à poutres multiples, *Ann. Tran. Publ.*, Belg., 1 (Jan.), pp. 7–69; 2 (April), 1965, pp. 145–71.

101 BASU, S. and M. CHI, *Analytic Study for Fatigue of Highway Bridge Cables*, Report No. FHWA-RD-81-090, FHWA, U.S. Dept. Transp., Washington, DC, 1981.

102 BASU, S. and M. CHI, *Design Manual for Bridge Structural Members under Wind-Induced Excitations*, Report No. FHWA TS-81-206, FHWA, U.S. Dept. Transp., Washington, DC, 1981.

103 BEAL, D. B., Load Capacity of Concrete Bridge Decks, *J. Struct. Div. ASCE*, Vol. 108, No. ST4, April, 1982, pp. 814–831.

104 BRITISH STANDARDS INSTITUTION. *Steel, Concrete and Composite Bridges. Part 2: Specification for Loads*. BSI, London, 1978, BS 5400.

105 BUCKLAND, P. G., *et al.*, Traffic Loading of Long Span Bridges, *Proc. Conf. Bridge Eng.*, Trans. Research Board, *Transp. Research Record 665*, Sept., 1978, pp. 146–154.

106 BUCKLAND, P. G., *et al.*, *Proposed Vehicle Loads for Long Span Bridges*, ASCE Spring Conv., April 1978. Preprint 3148, Pittsburgh, PA.

107 BUCKLAND, P. G., F. P. D. NAVIN, J. V. ZIDEK and J. P. McBRYDE, Proposed Vehicle Loading for Long-Span Bridges, *J. Struct. Div. ASCE*, Vol. 106, No. ST4, April, 1980, pp. 915–932.

108 CANADIAN STANDARDS ASSOCIATION. *Design of Highway Bridges*, National Standards of Canada CAN 3-S6-M78, Rexdale, Canada, 1978.

109 CHAPMAN, H. E., Earthquake Resistant Design of Bridges and the New Zealand Ministry of Works Bridge Design Manual, *Proc. 5th World Conf. on Earthquake Eng.*, Vol. 2, Rome, 1973, pp. 2242–2251.

110 COLLINS, M. P. and D. MITCHELL, *Prestressed Concrete Structures*, Prentice-Hall, Englewood Cliffs, NJ, 1991.

111 CROSS, H. and N. D. MORGAN, *Continuous Frames of Reinforced Concrete*, Wiley, New York, 1932.

112 CSAGOLY, P. F. and R. A. DORTON, *The Development of the Ontario Bridge Code*, Ontario Ministry of Transport and Communications, Canada, 1977.

113 CUSENS, A. R. and R. P. PAMA, Design of Concrete Multibeams Bridge Decks, *Proc. ASCE, J. Struct. Div. ASCE*, Vol. 91, No. ST5, Oct., 1965, pp. 255–278.

114 DHAN, E., C. MASSONNET and J. SEYVERT, Experimental Research on Multiple Beam Bridges, *Annales des Travaux Publics de Belgique*, No. 2, Brussels, 1955.

115 DOWRICK, D. J., *Earthquake Resistance Design*, Wiley, New York, 1987.

116 ELLINGWOOD, B., T. B. GALAMBOS, J. G. MacGREGOR and C. A. CORNELL, *Development of a Probability Based Load Criterion for American National Standard A58*, NBS Special Publ. 577, National Bureau of Standards, U.S. Dept. Commerce, Washington, DC, 1980.

117 ELLINGWOOD, B., J. G. MacGREGOR, T. V. GALAMBOS and C. A. CORNELL, Probability Based Load Criteria: Load Factors and Load Combinations, *J. Struct. Div. ASCE*, Vol. 108, No. ST5, May, 1982, pp. 978–996.

118 ELMS, D. G. and G. R. MARTIN, Factors Involved in the Seismic Design of Bridge Abutments, *Proc. Workshop on Earthquake Resistance of Hwy. Bridges*, Applied Technology Council, Berkeley, CA, 1979.

119 EYRE, D. G. and T. V. GALAMBOS, Shakedown of Grids, *J. Struct. Div. ASCE*, Vol. 99, No. ST10, Oct., 1973, pp. 2049–2060.

120 FERRITTO, J. M. and J. B. FOREST, *Determination of Seismically Induced Soil Liquefaction Potential at Proposed Bridge Sites*, Fed. Hwy. Admin., Office of Research and Development, Washington, DC, 1977.

121 MERRISON COMMITTEE. Inquiry into the Basis of Design and Method of Erection of Steel Box Girder Bridges — Interim Report, Department of the Environment, London, 1973.

122 MODJESKI and MASTERS, *Development of Comprehensive Bridge Specifications and Commentary: LRFD Approach*, 3rd draft, NCHRP, TRB, National Res. Board, Washington, DC, 1992.

123 MOFFATT, K. R. and P. J. DOWLING, *Parametric Study on the Shear Lag Phenomenon in Steel Box Girder Bridges*, CESLIC Report BG 17, Imperial College, London, 1972.

124 Y. K. CHEUNG, *Finite Strip Method in Structural Mechanics*, Pergamon Press, Oxford, 1976.

125 E. C. HAMBLY, *Bridge Deck Behaviour*, Chapman and Hall, London, 1976.

126 AASHTO, *Guide Specifications for Fracture Critical Non-Redundant Steel Bridge Members (also Interim)*. AASHTO, 1978.

127 AASHTO, *Standard Specifications for Welding of Structural Steel Highway Bridges*. AASHTO, 1978.

128 AASHTO, *Commentary on Bridge Welding Code 01.5-88*. AASHTO, 1978.

129 AASHTO, *Guide Specifications for Alternate Load Factor Design Procedures for Steel Beam Bridges Using Braced Compact Sections*. AASHTO, 1991.

130 ADEKOLA, A. O., *Interaction Between Steel Beams and a Concrete Floor Slab*, thesis submitted to the Imperial College of Science and Technology, Univ. of London, in partial fulfilment of the requirements for the degree of Doctor of Philosophy, 1959.

131 ADEKOLA, A. O., Effective Widths of Composite Beams of Steel and Concrete, *Struct. Engineer*, Sept., 1968.

132 AISC, *Simple Span Steel Bridges*, American Inst. Steel Construction, Chicago, 1969.

133 AISC, *Load and Resistance Factor Design*, American Inst. Steel Construction, Chicago, 1986.

134 AISI, Suggested Autostress Procedurse for Load Factor Design of Steel Beam Bridges, *Bull. No. 29*, American Iron and Steel Inst., April, 1987.

135 SANDERS, W. W. and W. H. MUNSE, The Lateral and Longitudinal Distribution of Loading in Steel Railway Bridges, *Civ. Eng. Studies Structural Research Series*, Report 208, Univ. of Illinois, Urbana, 1960.

136 SANDERS, W. W. and H. A. ELLEBY, *Distribution of Wheel Loads on Highway Bridges*, NCHRP Report No. 83, Hwy. Research Board, Washington, DC, 1970.

137 SAWKO, F., Bridge Deck Analysis—Electronic Computer vs. Distribution Methods, *Civ. Eng.*, London, Vol. 60, No. 705, April, 1965, pp. 534–538.

138 SCHLAICH, J., K. SCHAFER and M. JENNEWEIN, Towards a Consistent Design of Structural Concrete, *PCI J.*, Vol. 32, No. 3, May–June, 1987, pp. 74–151.

139 O'CONNOR, C., *Design of Bridge Superstructures*, Wiley, New York, 1971.

140 HEINS, C. P., *Bending and Torsional Design of Structural Members*, D.C. Heath, Lexington, MA, 1975.

141 Imbsen and Associates, *Distribution of Loads in Bridges*, NCHRP Project 12–26, Transport Research Board, National Research Council, Washington, DC, 1991.

142 IWAMOTO, K., On the Continuous Composite Girder, *Bulletin 339*, Hwy. Research Board, Tokyo, 1962.

143 AASHTO, *Guide Specifications for Strength Design of Truss Bridges (Load Factor Design)*, AASHTO, 1985.

144 AASHTO, *Standard Specifications for Movable Highway Bridges*. AASHTO, 1988.

145 ASCE, Tentative Recommendations for Cable-Stayed Bridge Structures, ASCE Task Committee on Cable-Suspended Structures, *J. Struct. Div., ASCE* Vol. 103, No. ST5, May, 1977.

146 ASCE, Bibliography and Data on Cable-Stayed Bridges, ASCE Committee on Long-Span Steel Bridges, *J. Struct. Div., ASCE*, Vol. 103, No. ST10, October, 1988.

147 ASCE, *Guidelines for Design of Cable-Stayed Bridges*, ASCE Committee on Cable-Suspended Bridges, ASCE, New York, 1991.

148 BARNOFF, R. M. and W. G. MOONEY, Effect of Floor Systems on Pony Truss Bridges, *Proc. ASCE, J. Struct. Div.* 86, ST4, April, 1960, pp. 25–47.

149 BARKER, R. M. *et al.*, *Manuals for the Design of Bridge Foundations*, NCHRP 343, TRB, National Research Council, Washington, DC. Dec., 1991.

150 WESTERGAARD, H. M., Computation of stresses in bridge slabs due to wheel loads, *Public Roads*, Vol. 2, no. 1, March 1930, pp. 1–23.

151 PUCHER, A., *Influence Surfaces of Elastic Plates*, Springer Verlag, Wien and New York, 1964 (in English and German).

152 JOHANSEN, K. W., *Yield Line Theory*, Cement and Concrete Association, Wexham Springs, Slough, 1962 (Translation from Danish).

153 HILLERBORG, A., *Strip method of design*, Viewpoint Publications, Wexham Springs, Slough, 1975.

154 KEHLBECK, F. *Einfluss der Sonnenstrahlung bei Brückenbauwerken* (Effect of Solar radiation on bridge structures). Technische Universitat Hannover—thesis, publ. Werner-Verlag, Düsseldorf, 1975.

155 LEONHARDT, F. and LIPPOTH, W. *Conclusions Drawn from Distress of Prestressed Concrete Bridges*. P.C.A. Translation from *Beton-und Stahlbetonbau*, No. 10. Berlin, Oct. 1970, Vol. 65, pp. 231–244.

156 MAISEL, B. I. *Analysis of Box Beam Bridges*. TDH 5025, Cement and Concrete Association, 1975 (unpublished).

157 DIRVY, LAV, LEGER. *Constations a Long Terme Sur Un Ouvage En Beton Precontraint: Le Pont De Champigny-sur-Yonne*. Association Francais des Ponts et Charpentes, October 1974, pp. 17–36.

158 LEONHARDT, F., General Report on Long Span Structures—Bridges, *Proceedings of Seminar on Prestressed Concrete Structures*, Indian National Group of International Association of Bridge and Structural Engineering, Bombay, Jan. 1975, Part II, pp. 1–28.

159 FINSTERWALDER, U., Free-cantilever construction of prestressed concrete bridges and mushroom-shaped bridges, *First International Symposium on Concrete Bridge Design*, ACI Publication SP-23, American Concrete Institute, Detroit, 1969, pp. 467–494.

Conventional bridges in steel and concrete

160 DISCHINGER, F., Hängebrücken für Schwerste Verkehrslasten, *Der Bauingenieur*, March, 1949, p. 65, p. 107.

161 FEIGE, A., Steel Motorway Bridge Construction in Germany, *Acier-Stahl-Steel* (English version), No. 3, March, 1964, pp. 113–126.

162 JENSEN, V. P., Moments in Simple Span Bridge Slabs with Stiffened Edges, *Univ. Illinois Bull. No. 315*, Urbana.

163 JENSEN, V. P., Solutions for Certain Rectangular Slabs Continuous over Flexible Supports, *Univ. Illinois, Bull.* No. 303, Urbana.

164 KENNEDY, D. J. L., North American Limit States Design, *Proc. 1985 Int. Eng. Symp. Struct. Steel*, Chicago, AISC, May, 1985.

165 KERFOOT, R. P. and A. OSTAPENKO, *Grillages under Normal and Axial Loads— Present Status*, Lehigh Univ., Fritz Eng. Lab. Report 323.1, June, 1967.

166 KING, CSAGOLY, P. F., and FISHER, *Field Testing of the Aquasabon River Bridge*, Ontario, personal communication, 1975.

167 KLEINLOGEL, A. and A. HASELBACH, *Multibeam Frames*, Ungar, New York, 1963.

168 KUO, T. C., *Elasto-Plastic Behavior of Composite Slab Highway Bridges*, PhD thesis, Univ. Maryland, College Park, 1973.

169 KUO, T. C. and C. P. HEINS, *Live Load Distribution on Composite Highway Bridges at Ultimate Load*, Civ. Eng. Report No. 53, Univ. Maryland, College Park, 1973.

170 LARRABEE, R. D. and C. A. CORNELL, Combinations of Various Loads Processes, *J. Struct. Div. ASCE*, Vol. 107, No. ST1, Jan., 1981, pp. 223–239.

171 LASH, S. D. and R. NAGARAJA, *The Ultimate Load Capacity of Beam and Slab Bridges*, Dept. Highways Report No. RR159, Ontario, Canada, May, 1970.

172 LIGHTFOOT, E. and F. SAWKO, Analysis of Grid Frameworks and Floor Systems by Electronic Computer, *Struct. Engineer*, Vol. 38, No. 3, March, 1960, pp. 79–87.

173 LITTLE, W. A. and R. J. HANSEN, The Use of Models in Structural Design, *J. Boston Society of Civ. Eng.*, Vol. 50, No. 2, April, 1963.

174 LIVESLEY, R. K., *Matrix Methods of Structural Analysis*, Pergamon Press, London, 1964.

175 MACGREGOR, J. G., Safety and Limit States Design for Reinforced Concrete, *Canadian J. Civ. Eng.*, Vol. 3, No. 4, Dec., 1976, pp. 484–513.

176 MACGREGOR, J. G., Load and Resistance Factors for Concrete Design, *ACI J., Proc.*, Vol. 80, No. 4, July–August, 1983, pp. 279–287.

177 MACGREGOR, J. G., *Reinforced Concrete— Mechanics and Design*, Prentice-Hall, Englewood Cliffs, NJ, 1988.

178 MACIAS-RENDON, M. A. and D. A. VAN HORN, Model Study of Beam-Slab Bridge Superstructures, *J. Struct. Div. ASCE*, Vol. 99, No. ST9, Sept., 1973, pp. 1805–1821.

179 MASSONNET, C., Méthode de calcul des ponts à poutres multiples tenant compte de leur résistance à la torsion, (Analysis Method for Multiple Beam Bridges Taking Account of their Torsional Resistance), *Publ. Int. Assoc. for Bridge and Struct. Eng.*, No. 10, Zurich, Switzerland, 1950, pp. 147–182.

180 MASSONNET, C., Study of Structures by Means of Small Scale Models without Use of Microscopes, *Bull. of Center of Studies, Research and Scientific Tests, Civ. Eng. Structures*, Univ. of Liege, Vol. VI, Belgium, 1953.

181 MASSONNET, C., Extension to the Method of Analysis of Multiple Beam Bridges, *Ann. des Travaux Publics de Belgique*, Vol. 107, Brussels, 1954, pp. 680–748.

182 MASSONNET, C., Complete Solutions Describing the Limit of Reinforced Concrete Slabs, *Concrete Research*, Vol. 19, No. 58, 1967, pp. 13–32.

183 TIMOSHENKO, S. P. and GERE, J. M., *Theory of Elastic Stability*, McGraw-Hill Book Company, New York, 1961.

184 CHATTERJEE, S., *Ultimate load analysis and design of stiffened plates in compression*, PhD thesis, London University, 1978.

185 BRITISH STANDARDS INSTITUTION. *Code of Practice for Design of Steel Bridges*. BSI, London, 1982, BS 5400: Part 3.

186 *J. of Dynamic Systems, Measurement and Control*, Series G., Vol. 99, Dec., pp. 284–292.

187 HEINS, C. P. and C. F. GALAMBOS, Highway Bridge Field Tests in the US, 1948–1970, *Public Roads*, U.S. Dept. Transp., Fed. Hwy. Admin., Feb., 1972, pp. 271–291.

188 HEINS, C. P. and C. T. G. LOONEY, *An Analytical Study of Eight Different Types of Highway Structures*, Civ. Eng. Report No. 12, Univ. Maryland, College Park, Sept., 1966.

189 HEINS, C. P. and C. T. G. LOONEY, *The Solution of Continuous Orthotropic Plates on Flexible Supports as Applied to Bridge Structures*, Civ. Eng. Report No. 10, Univ. of Maryland, College Park, March, 1966.

190 HEINS, C. P. and C. T. G. LOONEY, Bridge Analysis Using Orthotropic Plate Theory, *J. Struct. Div. ASCE*, Vol. 93, No. ST2, Feb., 1968, pp. 565–592.

191 HEINS, C. P. and C. T. G. LOONEY, Bridge Tests Predicted by Finite Difference Plate Theory, *J. Struct. Div. ASCE*, Vol. 95, No. ST2, Feb., 1969, pp. 249–265.

192 HENDERSON, W., British Highway Bridge Loading, *Proc. Institution Civ. Engineers*, Road Paper No. 44, March, 1954, pp. 325–373.

193 HENDRY, A. W. and L. G. JAEGER, *The Analysis of Grid Frameworks and Related Structures*, Chatto and Windus, London; Prentice-Hall, Englewood Cliffs, NJ, 1959, 308 pp.

194 HENDRY, A. W. and L. G. JAEGER, *The Analysis of Grid Frameworks and Related Structures*, Prentice-Hall, Englewood Cliffs, NJ, 1959.

195 SCORDELIS, A. C., *Analysis of Simply Supported Box Girder Bridges*, Univ. of California, Berkeley, CA, 1966.

196 SCOTT, R. F., The Calculation of Horizontal Accelerations from Seismoscope Records, *Bull. Seismological Soc. America*, Vol. 63, No. 5, Oct., 1973.

197 SEED, H. B. and P. B. SCHNABEL, *Accelerations in Rock from Earthquakes in Western United States*, Report EERC 72-2, Earthquake Eng. Research Center, Univ. Calif., Berkeley, CA, 1972.

198 SHORE, S. and R. RABIZADEH, *Static and Dynamic Analysis of Horizontally Curved Box Girder Bridges*, CURT Report No. T0174, Research Project HR-2(111), Univ. of Pennsylvania, Dec., 1974.

199 Structural Engineers Association of California, *Recommended Lateral Force Requirements*, Seismology Committee, SEAC, San Francisco, Dec., 1959.

200 Structural Engineers Association of California, *Recommended Lateral Force Requirements and Commentary*, 1975 Edition, SEAC, San Francisco, 1975.

201 Transportation Research Board, *Effects of Studded Tires*, National Cooperative Hwy. Research Program (NCHRP), Synthesis of Highway Practice 32, Washington, DC, 1975.

202 TSENG, W. S. and J. RENZIEN, Seismic Response of Highway Overcrossings, *Proc. Fifth World Conf. Earthquake Eng.*, Vol. 1, Rome, 1973, pp. 942–951.

203 TURKSTRA, C. J. and H. D. MADSEN, Load Combinations in Codified Structural Design, *J. Struct. Div. ASCE*, Vol. 106, No. ST12, Dec., 1980, pp. 2527–2543.

204 University of Illinois, Highway Slab Bridges with Curbs: Laboratory Tests and Proposed Design Method, *Bull. No. 346*, Urbana, 1940.

205 VELETSOS, A. S. and T. HUANG, Analysis of Dynamic Response of Highway Bridges, *J. Eng. Mechanics Div.*, Vol. 96, No. EM5, Oct., 1970, pp. 590–620.

206 WEST, H. H., *Analysis of Structures*, Wiley, New York, 1989.

207 WESTERGAARD, H. M., Computation of Stresses in Bridge Slabs due to Wheel Loads, *Public Roads*, March, 1930.

208 MASSONNET, C. and M. A. SAVE, *Plastic Analysis and Design*, Volume 1, *Beams and Frames*, Blaisdell, New York, 1965.

209 MCDERMOTT, R. J., Longitudinal Forces on Bridge Bearings, *FHWA Report No. FHWA-NY-78-SR58*, National Tech. Information Service, Springfield, VA, 1978.

210 MURAKAMI, E., *et al.*, *Actual Traffic Loadings on Highway Bridges and Stress Levels in Bridge Members*, Int. Assoc. for Bridge and Struct. Eng., Paper V1a, Ninth Congress, Amsterdam, May, 1972.

211 NASSER, K. W., Design Procedure for Lateral Load Distribution in Multi-Beam Bridges, *J. Prestressed Concrete Inst.*, Vol. 10, No. 4, Aug., 1965, 54–68.

212 NAVIN, F. P. D., *et al.*, *Design Traffic Loads for the Lions Gate Bridge*, Transport Research Board, Washington, DC, 1976.

213 NATRELLA, M. G., *Experimental Statistics*, National Bureau of Standards Handbook 91, Washington, DC, 1966.

214 NELSON, H. M., A. BEVERIDGE and P. D. ARTHUR, Tests on a Model Composite Bridge Girder, *Publications, IABSE*, Vol. 23, Zürich, Switzerland, 1963.

215 NEWMARK, N. M., A Distribution Procedure for the Analysis of Slabs Continuous over Flexible Beams, *Eng. Experiment Station Bull. No. 304*, Univ. Illinois, Urbana, 1938.

216 NEWMARK, N. M., A Distribution Procedure for the Analysis of Slabs Continuous over Flexible Beams, *Univ. of Ill. Bull. No. 304*, Urbana, 1939.

217 NEWMARK, N. M., Numeric Procedures for Computing Deflections, Moments, and Buckling Loads, *Trans. ASCE*, Vol. 108, paper 1161, 1943.

218 NEWMARK, N. M., Numerical Procedures for Computing Deflections, Moments, and Buckling Loads, *Trans. ASCE*, Vol. 108, paper 2202, 1943.

219 NEWMARK, N. M., Design of I-Beam Bridges, *Proc. ASCE*, March, 1943, pp. 305–331.

220 NEWMARK, N. M., C. P. SIESS and W. M. PACKHAM, Studies of Slab and Beam Highway Bridges, Part II, Tests of Simple-Span Skew I-Beam Bridges, *Eng. Experiment Station Bull.* No. 375, Univ. of Illinois, Urbana, 1948.

221 NEWMARK, N. M., C. P. SIESS and W. M. PACKHAM, Studies of Slab and Beam Bridges, Part I, Tests of Simple-Span Right I-Beam Bridges, *Eng. Experiment Station Bull. No. 363*, Univ. of Illinois, Urbana, 1946.

222 NEWMARK, N. M. and C. P. SIESS, Research on Highway Bridge Floors, *Univ. of Illinois Bull. No. 52*, Urbana, 1954.

223 O'CONNER, C., *Design of Bridge Superstructures*, Wiley, New York, 1971.

224 Ontario Ministry of Transportation and Communications, *Ontario Highway Bridge Design Code (OHBDC)*, Toronto, Canada, 1979.

225 POOL, R. B., A. S. ARYA, A. R. ROBINSON and N. KHACHATURIAN, Analysis of Multibeam Bridges with Beam Elements of Slab and Box Section, *Univ. Illinois, Eng. Experiment Station Bull., No. 483*, 1965, 93 pp.

226 REDDY, V. M. and A. W. HENDRY, Ultimate Load Behavior of Composite Steel–Concrete Bridge Deck Structures, *Indian Concrete J.*, Bombay, India, May, 1969.

227 RICHARDS, R. and D. G. ELMS, *Seismic Response of Retaining Walls and Bridge Abutments*, Report No. 77-10, Univ. Canterbury, Christchurch, New Zealand, June, 1977.

228 ROGERS, P., *Fixed End Moments*, Ungar, New York, 1953.

229 REESE, R. T., *Load Distribution in Highway Bridge Floors: A Summary and Examination of Existing Methods of Analysis and Design and Corresponding Test Results*, MS thesis, Brigham Young Univ., Provo, UT, 1966.

230 AISC, *Specifications of Structural Steel Buildings — Allowable Stress Design and Plastic Design*, American Inst. of Steel Construction, Chicago, 1989.

231 ALBRECHT, P. and A. H. NAEEMI, *Performance of Weathering Steel in Bridges*, NCHRP Report 272, National Cooperative Highway Research Program, Transportation Research Board, Washington, DC, July, 1984.

232 ALBRECHT, P. and M. SIDANI, *Fatigue Strength of 8-Year Weathered Stiffeners in Air and Salt Water*, NCHRP Project 10-22, National Cooperative Highway Research Program, Transportation Research Board, Washington, DC, Oct., 1987.

233 ALBRECHT, P., COBURN, S. K., WATTAR, F. M., TINKLENBERG, G. L. and W. P. GALLAGHER, *Guidelines for the Use of Weathering Steel in Bridges*, NCHRP Report 314, National Cooperative Highway Research Program, Transportation Research Board, Washington, DC, June, 1989.

234 ALLEN, D. N. DE G. and R. T. SEVERN, Composite Action Between Beams and Slabs under Transverse Load, *Struct. Engineer*, Vol. 39, London, May, 1961, pp. 149–154.

Cables and other materials

235 All-concrete cable-stayed railway bridge. *Concrete International, Design & Construction*, Dec. 1979, Vol. 1, No. 12.

236 LEONHARDT, F., ZELLNER, W. and SAUL, R., Zwei Schrägkabelbrücken für Eisenbahn- und Strassenverkehr über den Rio Paraná (Argentinien). *Der Stahlbau* 48, 1979, Heft 8.

237 HAJDIN, N. and JEVTOVIC LJ., Eisenbahnschrägseilbrücke über die Save in Belgrad. *Der Stahlbau* 47, 1978, Heft 4.

238 ANDRÄ, W. and ZELLNER, W., Zugglieder aus Paralleldrahtbündeln und ihre Verankerung bei hoher Dauerschwellbelastung. *Die Bautechnik* 46, 1969, Hefte 8 und 9.

239 DENGEL, D., Einige grundlegende Gesichtspunkte für die Planung und Auswertung von Dauerschwingversuchen. *Materialprüfung* 13, 1971, Heft 5.

240 MAENNIG, W. W., Untersuchungen zur Planung und Auswertung von Dauerschwing-versuchen an Stahl in den Bereichen der Zeit- und der Dauerfestigkeit. Fortschr.-Ber. *VDI-Z*, Reihe 5, Nr. 5, Düsseldorf: VDI-Verlag, August 1967.

241 WEIBULL, W., A statistical representation of fatigue failures in solids. *Transactions of the Royal Inst. of Technology Stockholm*, Nr. 27, 1949.

242 GASSNER, E., Zur Aussagefähigkeit von Ein- und Mehrstufen-Schwingversuchen. *Materialprüfung* 2, 1960, Heft 4.

243 GUMBEL, E. J., Statistische Theorie der Ermüdungserscheinungen bei Metallen. Mitt.-Bl. *Math. Statistik* 8, 1956, Nr. 2.

244 DUGGAN, T. V. and BYRNE, J., *Fatigue as a design criterion*. The Macmillan Press Ltd., London, 1977.

245 HIRT, M. A., Neue Erkenntnisse auf dem Gebiet der Ermüdung und deren Berücksichtigung bei der Bemessung von Eisenbahnbrücken. *Der Bauingenieur* 52, 1977, S.255–262.

246 SIA Norm 161, *Stahlbauten*, Edition 1979.

247 DEUTSCHE INDUSTRIE NORM. *Stählerne Strassenbrücken*, DIN, Berlin, July 1974, DIN 1073.

248 PALMGREN, A., Die Lebensdauer von Kugellagern. *VDI-Z* 68, 1924, Nr. 14, S.339–341.

249 MINER, M. A., Cumulative damage in fatigue. *Proc. Amer. Soc. Mech. Engrs. Metals* 67, 1945, S.A. 159–164.

250 BORGES, J. F., Safety Concepts for Non-Repeated and Repeated Loadings. Introductory Report, *IABSE Symposium on Resistance and Ultimate Deformability of Structures Acted on by Well Defined Repeated Loads*. Lisbon 1973.

251 GABRIEL, K., Anwendungen von statistischen Methoden und Wahrscheinlichkeits-betrachtungen auf das Verhalten von Bündeln und Seilen als Zugglieder aus vielen und langen Drähten. Vorberichte 2. *Internationales Symposium Stuttgart über weitgespannte Flächentragwerke*, 1979.

252 BARON, F. and S. Y. LIEN, Analytical Studies of a Cable Stayed Girder Bridge, *J. Computers and Structures*, Vol. 3, Pergamon Press, New York, 1973.

253 BASU, S. and M. CHI, *Analytical Study for Fatigue of Highway Bridge Cables*, FHWA Report RD-81/090, Washington, July, 1981.

254 BERT, C. W. and R. A. STEIN, Stress analysis of Wire Rope in Tension and Torsion, *Wire and Wire Products*, 37(5), 621−4 (May); 37(6), 769−70, 772, 816 (June), 1962.

Suspension and cable-stayed bridges

255 F. RŒNEN and J. M. CREMER. Les ponts construits ces dernières années en Belgique. *Annales de l'ITBTP*, February, 1989, p. 15−77.

256 M. VIRLOGEUX, G. LACOSTE, R. CHARVIN, J. F. HÉLAS, J. MAZOU and M. FLÉCHAIRE. Projet et construction du pont de Seyssel. *Travaux*. October 1989, p. 2−21.

257 M. VIRLOGEUX, TH. KRETZ, J. M. LACOMBE, CH. LAVIGNE, H. PORCHEREL and D. BAZILLIER. Chalon sur Saône Northern Bridge Project, a middle span cable-stayed bridge. La Technique Francaise du Béton Précontraint. FIP 11th Congress, Hambourg 1990, French contributions, p. 345−361.

258 J. STRASKY, M. KORENEK and V. MENCL. The cable-stayed bridge across the Elbe river at Podebrady, Czechoslovakia. *Industria Italiana del Cemento*. December 1990, p. 937−963.

259 F. MARTINEZ Y CABRERA. The Sunshine Skyway Bridge in Tampa Bay, Florida. *Industria Italiana del Cemento*, March 1991, p. 149−169.

260 M. CIAMPOLLI. The Ben Ahin Bridge crossing the river Meuse in Belgium. *Industria Italiana del Cemento*, April 1991, p. 232−247.

261 M. VIRLOGEUX. Design and Construction of the Normandie Bridge. *Proceedings of the International Symposium on Cable-Stayed Bridges*, Fukuoka, 1991, p. 23−40.

262 TAYLOR, P. R., Cable Stayed Bridges and Their Potential in Canada, *The Engineering Journal* (Canada), Vol. 52/11, Nov., 1969, pp. 15−21.

263 THUL, H., Cable-Stayed Bridges in Germany, *Proceedings of the Conference on Structural Steelwork*, held at the Institution of Civil Engineers, Sept. 26−28, 1966, The British Constructional Steelwork Association Ltd., London, pp. 69−81.

264 GRATTESAT, G. *Ponts de France*. Presses de l'Ecole Nationale a Ponts et Chaussées, Paris, 1982.

265 LEONHARDT, F. and ZELLNER, W. Cable-stayed bridges: report of latest developments. *Canadian Structural Engineering Conference, 1970*. Canadian Steel Industries Construction Council, Toronto, Ontario.

266 LEONHARDT, F. and ZELLNER, W. Vergleiche zwischen Hängebrücken und Schrägkabelbrücken für Spannweiten über 600 m. *IABS Memoires*, vol. 32, Zürich, 1972, p. 127.

267 LEONHARDT, F. *Latest developments of cable-stayed bridges for long spans*. Bygningsstatiske Meddelelser, Copenhagen, 1974.

268 LEONHARDT, F. *Bridges*. Deutsche Verlags-Anstalt, Stuttgart, 1982.

269 FAUSTUS VERANTIUS. *Machinae novae Fausti*. Venice, 1617.

270 WENK, H. The Strömsund Bridge. *Demag News*, No. 136, Du burg, 1954.

271 MORANDI, R. The bridge spanning Lake Maracaibo. *J. Prestr. Concr. Inst.*, June 1961.

272 MATHIVAT, J. The Brotonne Bridge. *8th Int. Conf. Prestressed Concrete, La technique francaise du béton précontraint*, FIP-AFB, London, 1978.

273 LEONHARDT, F., ZELLNER, W. and SVENSSON, H. Die Spannbeton-Schrägkabelbrücke über den Columbia River zwischen Pasco und Kennewick im Staat Washington, USA. *Beton- u. Stahlbetonbau*, 1980, pp. 29−36, 64−70, 90−94.

274 VOLKE, E. and RADEMACHER, C.-H. Nordbrücke Mannheim−Ludwigshafen (Kurt-Schumacher-Brücke). *Der Stahlbau* 1973, Heft 4, p. 97, Heft 5, p. 138, Heft 6, p. 161.

275 MODEMANN, J. and THÖNNISSEN, K. Die neue Rheinbrücke Düsseldorf−Flehe/Neuss−Vedesheim. *Der Bauingenieur* 1979, Heft 1, pp. 1−12.

276 TESÁR, A. Konstruktion und Ausführung der neuen Straßenbrücke über die Donau in Bratislava Bauplanung—*Bautechnik*, 10/1973, p. 477.

277 DE MIRANDA, F. Il ponte strallato sull'Arno a Firenze in localita l'Indiano, *Costruzioni Metalliche* N. 6-1976.

278 EPPLE, G., RÖSSING, E., SCHABER, E. and WINTERGERST, L. Die neue Rheinbrücke über die Bundesautobahn bei Speyer, *Der Stahlbau*, 1977, Hefte 10, 11, 12.

279 WENK, H. Die Strömsundbrücke (The Strömsund Bridge), *Der Stahlbau*, Vol. 23, No. 4, 1954, pp. 73–76.

280 DISCHINGER, F. Hängebrücken für schwerste Verkehrslasten, *Der Bauingenieur*, Vol. 24, Nos. 3, 4, 1949, pp. 65–75 and 107–113.

281 NAVIER, C. L. Rapport à Monsieur Becquey et Mémoire sur les Ponts Suspendus, *Imprimérie Royale*, Paris, 1823.

282 BEYER, E. and TUSSING, F. Nordbrücke Düsseldorf, *Stahlbau*, Vol. 24, Nos. 2, 3, 4, 1955, pp. 25–33, 63–67 and 79–88.

283 BILLINGTON, D. P. and NAZMY, A. History and Aesthetics in Cable-Stayed Bridges, *ASCE J. Structural Engineering*, 1991.

284 TROITSKY, M. S. *Cable-Stayed Bridges*, Van Nostrand Reinhold, New York, 1988.

285 BILLINGTON, D. P. *The Tower and the Bridge*, Princeton University Press, Princeton, 1985 (originally published by Basic Books Inc., 1983).

286 ANON. *Steel Bridge*, Hitachi Zosen Corporation, 6–14, Edobori 1-chome, Nishi-ku, Osaka 550, Japan, 1983.

287 ANON. *Expressway Bridges*, Japan Highway Public Corporation, Japan, 1986.

288 ANON. *Yodogawa Shinbashi*, Osaka Municipal Office, Japan.

289 GARCIA, A. M. and ROBISON, R. Sunshine Skyway Nears Completion, *Civil Engineering, ASCE*, November 1986, pp. 32–35.

290 ANON. *Drawings for the Sunshine Skyway Bridge*, State of Florida Department of Transportation, 1982.

291 ANON. Hybrid Girder in Cable-Stay Debut, *Engineering News Record*, November 15, 1984, pp. 31–36.

292 ANON. *Ajigawa Bridge*, Hanshin Expressway Public Corporation, 68, 4-Chome, Kita-kyutaro-Machi, Higashi-Ku, Osaka, Japan, 1988.

293 TADA, H. *Recent Trend of Cable-Stayed Bridge Construction Technology*, Bridge Division of Structure and Bridge Department, Public Works Research Institute, Ministry of Construction, Japan, March, 1986.

294 TAYLOR, P. R. and TORREJON, J. E. Annacis Bridge, *Concrete International*, Vol. 9, No. 7, July 1987, pp. 13–22.

295 ANON. Dame Point Bridge Reaches for a Record, *Engineering News Record*, January 7, 1988, pp. 32–36.

296 ANON. *The Tenth CRSI Design Awards 1990*, Concrete Reinforcing Steel Institute, Schaumburg, IL, 1990.

297 PODOLNY, W. and SCALZI, J. B. *Construction and Design of Cable-Stayed Bridges*, John Wiley and Sons, New York, 1986.

298 ANON. *Honshu–Shikoku Bridges*, Honshu–Shikoku Bridge Authority, Second Operation Bureau, Tokyo, Japan, September, 1988.

299 YOSHIDA, I., MURAKAMI, K., TATSUMI, M. and YASUDA, M. *Design and Construction of Hitsuishijima–Iwakurojima Bridges*, Collection of Papers on the Honshu–Shikoku Bridge Project, Honshu–Shikoku Bridge Authority, March 1987, pp. 211–226.

300 ANON. *Yokohama Bay Bridge*, Metropolitan Expressway Public Corporation, Kanagawa Construction Bureau, Japan, November 1984.

301 NORMILE, D. Japan Spans the Inland, *Civil Engineering*, April 1988, pp. 60–63.

302 LEONHARDT, F. *Bridges*, Deutsche Verlags-Anstalt Stuttgart, Germany, 1982.

303 HOSTETLER, M. The Bridge Between Safety and Error, *Michigan Today*, University of Michigan, Vol. 22, No. 3, June 1990, pp. 1–3.

304 ANON. *Annual Report on Roads*, Japan Road Association, Tokyo, Japan, 1984.

305 N. J. GIMSING. *Cable Supported Bridges*, John Wiley & Sons, New York, 1983.

306 MAN CHUNG TANG. Design of Cable-Stayed Girder Bridges, *ASCE, Journal of Structural Division*, p. 1789, August, 1972.

307 GILSANZ, R. E. and J. M. BIGGS. Cable-Stayed Bridges: Degrees of Anchoring, *ASCE, Journal of the Structural Division*, p. 200, January, 1983.

308 TULADHAR, R. *Analysis of Cable-Stayed Bridges Under Seismic Loading*. Thesis No. ST-85-29, 1985, Asian Institute of Technology, Bangkok.

309 HOSHIYA, M. and NAKANE, K. Theoretical assessment of human response against bridge vibration. *Trans. JSCE*, vol. 8, 1976, pp. 16–17.

310 HURTY, W. C. and RUBINSTEIN, M. F. *Dynamics of structures*. Prentice-Hall, Englewood Cliffs, NJ, 1975.

311 KAJIKAWA, Y. and KOBORI, T. Probabilistic approaches to the ergonomical serviceability of pedestrian bridges. *Trans. JSCE*, vol. 9, 1977, pp. 86–87.

312 KAJIKAWA, Y. and KOBORI, T. Probability-based design of pedestrian bridges in consideration of the ergonomical serviceability. *Trans. JSCE*, vol. 11, 1979, pp. 35–36.

313 KAMMERER, J. B. Sur la dynamique d'un pont et du véhicule qui le parcourt. *Annales de l'ITBTP*, No. 368, Jan. 1979.

314 KLÖPPEL, K. Teilmodellversuche zur Beurteilung des aerodynamischen Verhaltens von Brücken. *Der Stahlbau*, 32, 1963, pp. 75–79 and 113–121.

315 KOBORI, T. and KAJIKAWA, Y. Ergonomic evaluation methods for bridge vibrations. *Trans. JSCE*, vol. 6, 1974, pp. 40–41.

316 KOBORI, T. and KAJIKAWA, Y. Study on human response to bridge vibrations. *Trans. JSCE*, vol. 7, 1975, pp. 229–232.

317 KOBORI, T. and KAJIKAWA, Y. Human response to bridge vibration under a single moving vehicle. *Trans. JSCE*, vol. 8, 1976, pp. 31–32.

318 LEONHARDT, F. Zur Entwicklung aerodynamisch stabiler Hängebrücken. *Bautechnik*, 10, 1968, pp. 325–336 and 11, 1968, pp. 372–380.

319 MATSUMOTO, Y., SATO, S., NISHIOKA, T. and SHIOJIRI, H. A study on dynamic design of pedestrian over-bridges. *Trans. JSCE*, vol. 4, 1972, pp. 50–51.

320 MULLENHOFF, A. Der Entwurf von Brücken mit Rücksicht auf den Winddruck. *Bautechnik*, 26, 1949, 57–59/188–189/282–284/348–351/380–381 and 27, 1950, pp. 164–166/308–310.

321 MURRAY, T. M. Design to prevent floor vibrations. *Engineering Journal of the American Institute of Steel Construction*, 1975, pp. 82–87.

322 NAVIER, M. *Mémoire sur les ponts suspendus, Carilian-Goeury, Libraire des Corps Royaux des Ponts et Chaussées et des Mines*, 2nd edn, 1830, pp. 34–36.

323 NISHIWAKI, T. Numerical evaluations of psychological effects and its applications. *Transactions JSCE*, vol. 9, 1977, pp. 3–7.

324 PODOLNY, W. and SCALZI, J. B. *Construction and design of cable-stayed bridges*. John Wiley & Sons, 1976.

325 ROSEMEIER, G. Zur aerodynamischen Stabilität von H-Querschnitten. *Bauingenieur*, 48, 1973, pp. 401–409.

326 SCANLAN, R. H. and SABZAVARI, A. Suspension bridge flutter revisited. *ASCE Structural Engineering Conference*, Seattle, Washington, 1967, paper 468.

327 SIMIU, E., CHANGERY, M. J. and FILLIBEN, J. J. Extreme wind speeds at 129 airport stations. *Proc. ASCE*, ST 4, 1980, pp. 809–817.

328 SIMIU, E. and FILLIBEN, J. J. Weibull distributions and extreme wind speeds. *Proc. ASCE*, ST 12, 1980, pp. 2365–2374.

329 SIMIU, E., FILLIBEN, J. J. and SHAVER, J. R. Short-term records and extreme wind speeds. *Proc. ASCE*, ST 11, 1982, pp. 2571–2577.

330 STEINMAN, D. B. Aerodynamic theory of bridge oscillations. *Proc. ASCE*, 75, 1949, pp. 1147–1184.

331 STEINMAN, D. B. Aerodynamic theory of bridge oscillations. *Trans. ASCE*, 115, 1950, pp. 1180–1260.

332 SZABO, I. *Einführung in die technische Mechanik*. Springer Verlag, 6th edn, 1963.

333 THOMSON, W. T. *Theory of vibration*. Prentice Hall, 1972.

334 THOMSON, W. T. Vibration periods at Tacoma Narrows. *Engineering News-Record*, 27 Mar. 1941.

335 TIMOSHENKO, S. *Théorie des vibrations à l'usage des ingénieurs*. Librairie Polytechnique Ch. Béranger, 1954.

336 TIMOSHENKO, S. and YOUNG, D. H. *Dynamique supérieure*. Librairie polytechnique Ch. Béranger, 1950.

337 TROITSKY, M. S. *Cable-stayed bridges*. Crosby Lockwood Staples, London, 1977.

338 VDI-Richtlinien 2057, 1963/1975/1979/1981.

339 Vornormen-DIN 4150, 1975.

340 WIANECKI, J. *Etude aérodynamique du pont des Meules*. Communication and general reports for 22 and 23 April 1974, Association Francaise des Ponts et Charpentes.

341 WISS, J. F. and PARMELEE, R. A. Human perception of transient vibrations. *Proc. ASCE*, ST 4, 1974, pp. 773–787.

342 WYATT, H. A. and SCRUTON, C. A brief survey of the aerodynamic structural problems of bridges, *Bridge Aerodynamics*, Ch. 1, Thomas Telford, London, 1981.

343 SELBERG, A. Oscillation and aerodynamic stability of suspension bridges, *Acta Polytechnica Scandinavica*, ci 13, 1961.

344 KLÖPPEL, K. and THIELE, F. Wind tunnel tests on the design of bridges to prevent wind excited oscillations (in German), *Der Stahlbau* 36: 11, 12, 1967.

345 KLÖPPEL, K. and SCHWIERIN, G. Results of model tests on the influence of non-horizontal winds on the aerodynamic stability of box-girder bridges (in German), *Der Stahlbau* 44: 7, 1975.

346 IRWIN, P. A. and STONE, G. K. Aerodynamic improvements for plate-girder bridges, *Proc. ASCE Structures Congress, Structural Design, Analysis and Testing*, 1989.

347 RICHMOND, B. *Cable-stayed bridge developments related to wind effects on vehicles*, A.I.T. Press, Bangkok, 1987.

348 UK Department of Transport, Interim rules for the aerodynamic stability of bridges, *Bridge Aerodynamics* (preface), Thomas Telford, London, 1981.

349 B. W. SMITH and T.A. WYATT, Development of the draft rules for aerodynamic stability (*ibid*) (Chapter 2).

350 WYATT, T. A. and TAPPIN, R. G. R. *On the aerodynamic design of cable-stayed bridges of high aspect ratio*, A.I.T. Press, Bangkok, 1987.

351 CULLEN WALLACE, A. A. Wind influence on Kessock bridge, *Engineering Structures*, 7, 1985 (Jan.).

352 HOLMES, V. D. Prediction of the response of a cable-stayed bridge to turbulence, *Proc. 4th Int. Conf. Wind Effects on Buildings and Structures*, Heathrow, 1975.

353 IRWIN, P. A. Wind buffeting of cable-stayed bridges during construction, *Proc. ASCE Structures Congress, Bridges and Transmission Line Structures*, 1987.

354 WALSHE, D. E. J. and WYATT, T. A. Measurement and application of the aerodynamic admittance function for a box-girder bridge, *J. Wind Eng. Ind. Aero.*, 14, 1983.

355 ESDU International. *Characteristics of atmospheric turbulence near the ground*: Part II single point data for strong winds (neutral atmosphere) ESDU Data Item 85020, Rev. E 1990: Part III Variations in space and time. Data Item 86010, 1986. ESDU International, London.

356 DUMANOGLU, A. A. *et al.*, *Modal combination methods in the seismic analysis of the Humber bridge, Steel Structures: advances, design and construction*, Elsevier 1987, (Proc. Conf. Cardiff 1987).

357 YASUDA, M. *et al.*, *Design and Fabrication of Stay Cables for Iwakurojima Bridge*, Honshi Technical Report, No. 39, 1986.

358 HARAGUCHI, T. and TANAKA, Y. *Method for covering cables with sheaths for corrosion protection and/or aesthetics*, US Patent No. 4,569,708, 1986.

359 *Cable-stayed Bridges*, Japan Society of Civil Engineers, 1990 (in Japanese).

360 YOKOYAMA, K. and KUSAKABE, T. Suppression of cable vibration induced by wind in cable stayed bridges, *Bridges and Foundation*, Aug. 1989.

361 NONAKA, K. *et al.*, Erection of Cable-Stayed Steel Bridges, *Bridges and Foundation*, Aug. 1985 (in Japanese).

362 ANDERSON, J. K., HAMILTON, J. A. K., HENDERSON, W., MCNEIL, J. S., SIR GILBERT ROBERTS and SHIRLEY-SMITH, H., Forth Road Bridge, *Proc. Instn Civ. Engrs*, November 1965, Vol. 32, 1965–1966, p. 321.

363 WALSHE, D. E., A Résumé of the Aerodynamic Investigations for the Forth Road and the Severn Bridges, *Proc. Instn Civ. Engrs*, May 1967, Vol. 37, 1966–67, pp. 87–108.

364 DAVENPORT, A. G., ISYUMOV, N., FADER, D. J. and BOWEN, C. F. P., A *Study of Wind Action on a Suspension Bridge During Erection and on Completion: The Narrows Bridge, Halifax, Nova Scotia*, Engineering Science Research Report BLWT-3-69, Univ. of Western Ontario, May 1969.

365 MELBOURNE, W. H., *West Gate Bridge Tunnel Tests, Report to the Lower Yarra Crossing Authority by Monash University*, Dept. of Mech. Eng., Melbourne, Australia, August 1973.

366 REINHOLD, T. A. and STROH, S. L., Wind Tunnel Aeroelastic Model Study of the Baytown Bridge (Steel Alternative), *Proc. Bridges and Transmission Line Structures*, Structures Congress, American Soc. of Civil Engineers, Orlando, FL, August 1987.

367 DAVENPORT, A. G. and KING, J. P. C., The Incorporation of Dynamic Wind Loads into the Design Specifications for Long Span Bridges, *ASCE Fall Convention and Structures Congress*, New Orleans, LA, October 1982.

368 IRWIN, H. P. A. H. and GAMBLE, S. L., The Action of Wind on a Cable-Stayed Bridge During Construction, *Proc. Fifth US National Conference on Wind Engineering*, Lubbock, TX, November 1985.

369 ZAN, S. J., *Wind Tunnel Investigation of the Wind-Induced Response of the Roosevelt Lake Steel Arch Bridge Using an Aeroelastic Model*, National Research Council of Canada, Report NAE LTR-LA-306, October 1987.

370 CERMAK, J. E., Laboratory Simulation of the Atmospheric Boundary Layer, *Journal of the American Institute of Aeronautics and Astronautics*, Vol. 9, No. 9, September 1971, pp. 1746–1754.

371 BIENKIEWICZ, S. E., CERMAK, J. E., PETERKA, J. A. and SCANLAN, R. H., Active Modelling of Large-Scale Turbulence, *Sixth Int. Conf. on Wind Engineering*, Melbourne, Australia, 1983.

372 COOPER, K. R., An Active Turbulence Generator for the Wind Tunnel Simulation of the Large-Scale Turbulence Required for Section-Model Bridge Testing, *Proc. Canada-Japan Workshop on Bridge Aerodynamics*, Ottawa, September 1989.

373 KAWASHIMA, K. and UNJOH, S., *Damping Characteristics of Cable Stayed Bridges for Seismic Design*, Technical Report, Vol. 187, Public Works Research Institute, January 1992.

374 KAWASHIMA, K., UNJOH, S. and AZUTA, Y., Analysis of Damping Characteristics of A Cable Stayed Bridge Based on Strong Motion Records, *Proc. Japan Society of Civil Engineers, Structural Eng./Earthquake Eng.*, Vol. 7, No. 1, April 1990, pp. 181–190.

375 NARITA, N., *Forced Vibration Test for Suigo Bridge*, Technical Note, Vol. 1349, Public Works Research Institute, March 1978.

376 KAWASHIMA, K. and UNJOH, S., Damping Characteristics of Cable Stayed Bridges Associated with Energy Dissipation at Movable Supports, *Proc. Japan Society of Civil Engineers, Structural Eng./Earthquake Eng.*, Vol. 6, No. 1, April 1989, pp. 145–152.

377 KAWASHIMA, K., UNJOH, S. and AZUTA, Y., Damping Characteristics of Cable Stayed Bridges, *Proc. 9th World Conference on Earthquake Engineering*, Tokyo/Kyoto, Japan, August 1988.

378 YAMAHARA, H., Investigation on Vibrational Properties of Foundations and Structures on Elastic Medium, *Proc. Architectural Institute of Japan*, Vol. 115, pp. 6–14, 1965.

379 KAWASHIMA, K. and UNJOH, S., Estimation of Damping Characteristics of Cable Stayed Bridges for Seismic Design, *7th US–Japan Bridge Workshop*, May, 1991, Tsukuba, Japan.

380 Japan Road Association. *Design and Construction of Meiko-nishi Bridge*, March 1986 (in Japanese).

381 KRISHNA, P., ARYA, S. and AGRAWAL, T. P., Effect of Cable Stiffness on Cable-Stayed Bridges, *Journal of Structural Division*, ASCE, Vol. 111(9), September 1985, pp. 2008–2020.

382 LAZAR, B. E., Stiffness Analysis of Cable-Stayed Bridges, *J. Struct. Div.* ASCE, Vol. 98, No. ST7, Proceedings Paper 9036, 1972, pp. 1725–1740.

383 LEONHARDT, F. and ZELLNER, W., Cable-Stayed Bridges, *IABSE Surveys*, S-13-80.

384 BRAULT, J.-L. and MATHIVAT, J., Pont de Brotonne (France). *Revue Travaux*, Feb. 1976.

385 LEONHARDT, F., ANDRÄ, W. and WINTERGERST, L., *Kniebrücke Düsseldorf, Entwurfbearbeitung und Versuche*. Beton Verlag GmbH, Düsseldorf.

386 TROITSKY, M. S., *Cable-stayed bridges*. Crosby Lockwood Staples, London, 1977.

387 DE MIRANDA, F., Il ponte strallato sull'Arno a Firenze in località l'Indiano. *Construzioni Metalliche*, 1978, p. 241.

388 MODEMANN, J. and THONNISSEN, K., Die neue Rheinbrücke Düsseldorf–Flehe/Neuss–Vedesheim, Plannung, Entwurf, Ausschreibung, Vergabe und Überblick über den Ausführungsentwurf. *Der Bauingenieur*, 54, 1979, 1–12, p. 2.

389 LEONHARDT, F., ZELLNER, W. and SAUL, R., Zwei Schrägseilbrücken für Eisenbahn und Strassenverkehr über den Rio Paraná (Argentinien). *Der Stahlbau*, 8/1979, p. 228.

390 GRANT, A. and PROZZI, V., Ponte strallato in cemento armato precompresso sul fiume Columbia negli Stati Uniti. *L'Industria Italiana del Cemento*, 4/1982, p. 230.

392 LEONHARDT, F., *Brücken (Bridges)*, p. 263. Deutsche Verlags-Anstalt, 1982.

393 Podolny, W. and Scalzi, J., *Construction and design of cable-stayed bridges*. John Wiley and Sons, New York, 1976, p. 28.

394 SCHAMBECK, H., *Abgespannte Massivbrücken—erläutert am Beispiel der Donaubrücke Metten*, pp. 114–118. Vorträge Betontag 1981, Deutscher-Verein E.V.

395 CASADO, C. F., JAVIER, M. A. and TROYANO, L., F. Ponte strallato sul fiume Ebro presso Castejon per l'autostrada di Navarra (Spagna). *L'Industria Italiana del Cemento*, 3/1981, p. 154.

396 HESS, H. and VOGEL, G., *Der Stahlbau*, 29, 1960, 8/p. 225, 9/p. 269.

397 FAEMS, L., Ponts à haubans sur le canal Albert à Godsheide. *Acier–Stahl–Steel*, 3/1978, p. 87.

398 FINSTERWALDER, U., *Festschrift 50 Jahre für Dywidag*, Verlag G. Braun, Karlsruhe, 1973, p. 190.

399 PAULIK, L. and SANCHEZ SANCHEZ, A., Proyecto y construccion de los puentes atirantados Coatzacoalcos II y Tampico. *9th Int. Conf. DIP*, Estocolmo, 1982.

400 PAULIK, L., Le pont de Coatzacoalcos, Golfe du Mexique. *Grands travaux rail pont bâtiment*, PCM, 11 Nov. 1982.

401 Association Francaise des Ponts et Charpentes. *12th Congress*, Vancouver, 1984.

402 *The Honshu–Shikoku Bridge Specifications for Galvanized Wire for Parallel Wire Cables*, HBS G3501–1979 (in Japanese).

403 *Recommendations for Stay Cable Design, Testing and Installation*, Post-Tensioning Institute, February 1990.

404 TANAKA, Y., *et al.*, Contributions to Innovative Stay Cables, *Symposium Processing on Innovation in Cable-Stayed Bridges*, Fukuoka, 1991.

405 OTSUKA, A. and YAMASAKI, K., *Cables for Cable-Stayed Bridges, Bridges and Foundation*, Aug. 1985 (in Japanese).

406 WESTERHOFF, D., *et al.*, Dao Khanong Cable-Stayed Bridge, Manufacture and Erection of Large Locked Coil Bridge Ropes, *Proc. of the Int. Conf. on Cable-Stayed Bridges*, Bangkok, 1987.

407 STAFFORD, D. G. and WATSON, S. C., Current World Condition Survey of Cables on Stayed – Girder Bridges, *Oleg Kerensky Memorial Conference*, London, June 1988.

408 SAUL, R. and SVENSSON, H. S., On the Corrosion Protection of Stay Cables, *Stahlbau*, Heft 6/1990.

409 VIRLOGEUX, M., LACOSTE, G. and LE FAUCHEUR, D., La solution à haubans pour la voie 3 à Cergy-Pontoise. *Travaux*. January 1985, 58 – 74.

410 MANTEROLA ARMISEN, J. and FERNANDEZ TROYANO, L., The "Ing. Carlos Fernandez Casado" Bridge on the Campomanes – León motorway in Spain. *Industria Italiana del Cemento*. March 1985, 147 – 176.

411 BACCHETTA, A. and RÜST, M., Rheinbrücke Diepoldsau. Die Schrägkable. *Schweizer Ingenieur und Architekt*, no. 35, 1985, 818 – 821.

412 SANCHEZ SANCHEZ, A., PAULIK, L., JARTOUX, P. and CHAUVIN, A., La construction du pont à haubans de Coatzacoalcos II. *Annales de l'ITBTP*, January 1986, 101 – 161.

413 VIRLOGEUX, M., FOUCRIAT, J. C. and DEROUBAIX, B., Design of the Normandie cable-stayed Bridge, near Honfleur. *Proc. of the Int. Conf. on Cable-stayed Bridges*, Bangkok 1987, 1111 – 1122.

414 PODOLNY, JR., W. and SCALZI, J. B., *Construction and Design of Cable-Stayed Bridges*. John Wiley & Sons, 1976.

Wind on bridges

415 YOSHIMURA, T., UNOUE, A., KAJI, K. and SAVAGE, M. G., *A Study of the Aerodynamic Stability of the Aratsu Bridge, Canada-Japan Workshop on Bridge Aerodynamics*, Ottawa, 25 – 27 Sept. 1989.

416 MASAKI, Y., SANO, S. and SAKAI, F., Analysis and Design of Wind-and-Earthquake-Resistance of an S-Curved Cable-Stayed Bridge, *Proc. Bridges and Transmission Line Structures*, ASCE Structure Congress, Orlando, Florida, 17 – 20 August 1987, pp. 341 – 356.

417 WARDLAW, R. L., Approaches to the Suppression of Wind-Induced Vibrations of Structures, *Proc. Practical Experiences with Flow-Induced Vibration*, pp. 650 – 672, Karlsruhe, Germany, 3 – 6 September 1979.

418 WARDLAW, R. L. and COOPER, K. R., Dynamic Vibration Absorbers for Suppressing Wind-Induced Motion of Structures, *Proc. 3rd Colloq. on Industrial Aerodynamics, Part 2*, Aachen, Germany, June 1978.

419 IRWIN, H. P. A. H., COOPER, K. R. and WARDLAW, R. L., *Application of Vibration Absorbers to Control Wind-Induced Vibration of I-Beam Truss Members of the Commodore Barry Bridge*, National Research Council of Canada, NAE LTR-LA-194, January 1976.

420 HARDY, C. and BOURDON, P., The Influence of Spacer Damper Dynamic Properties in the Control of Bundle Conductor Motion, *IEEE PES Summer Meeting*, Vancouver, Canada, July 1979.

421 WIANECKI, J., Cables Wind Excited Vibrations of Cable Stayed Bridge, *Proc. 5th Int. Conf. on Wind Engineering*, Fort Collins, USA, July 1979, Vol. 2, pp. 1381 – 1393.

422 HIKAMI, Y. and SHIRAISHI, N., Rain-Wind Induced Vibrations of Cables in Cable-Stayed Bridges, *Proc. Seventh Int. Conf. on Wind Engineering*, Aachen, West Germany, 6 – 10 July 1987.

423 OHSHIMA K. and NANJO, M., Aerodynamic Stability of the Cables of a Cable-Stayed Bridge Subject to Rain (A Case History of the Ajigawa Bridge), *Proc. 3rd US–Japan Bridge Workshop*, Tsukuba, Japan, May 1987.

424 MATSUMOTO, M., KNISELY, C. W., SHIRAISHI, J., KITAZAWA, M. and SAITOH, T., Inclined Cable Aerodynamics, *ASCE Structural Design, Analysis and Testing Structures Congress '89*, 1–5 May 1989.

425 SIMPSON, A., On the Flutter of a Smooth Circular Cylinder in a Wake, *AERO Quarterly*, Vol. XXII, p. 25, February 1971.

426 WARDLAW, R. L., COOPER, K. R., KO, R. G. and WATTS, J. A., Wind Tunnel and Analytical Investigations into the Aeroelastic Behaviour of Bundled Conductors, *IEEE Trans. Power Apparatus and Systems*, Vol. PAS-94, March–April 1975, pp. 625–654.

427 IRWIN, H. P. A. H., COOPER, K. R. and WARDLAW, R. L., *A Wind Tunnel Investigation of the Aeroelastic Behaviour of the Laprade Heavy Water Plant*, National Research Council of Canada, NRC-LTR-LA-177, August 1975.

428 BLEICH, F., McCULLOUGH, C. B., ROSECRANS, R. and VINCENT, G. S., *Vibration in Suspension Bridges*, Dept. of Commerce, Bureau of Public Roads, U.S. Government Printing Office, 1951.

429 FARQUHARSON, F. B., SMITH, F. C. and VINCENT, G. S., *Aerodynamic Stability of Suspension Bridges with Special Reference to the Tacoma Narrows Bridge*, Univ. of Washington, Engineering Experiment Station Bulletin No. 116, Parts I to V, 1949–54.

430 LEONHARDT, F., ZELLNER, W. and SAUL, R. Modellversuche für die Schrägkabelbrücken Zarate–Brazo Largo über den Rio Paraná, Argentinien. *Bauingenieur*, 54, 1979, pp. 321–327.

431 MATHIVAT, J. *Construction par encorbellement des ponts en béton précontraint.* Editions Eyrolle, Paris, 1979.

432 SZECHENYI, E. and TOURJANSKI, N. *Stabilité aéroélastique des ponts suspendus à haubans.* Communication and general reports for 6 and 7 June 1978, Association Francaise des Ponts et Charpentes.

433 SZECHENYI, E. and LOISEAU, H. *Mesures aérodynamiques et dynamiques sur le pont de Saint-Nazaire.* Communication and general reports for 6 and 7 June 1978, Association Francaise des Ponts et Charpentes.

434 ROCHE, J. Les méthodes d'etude aerodynamique des ponts à haubans. Communication and general reports for 22 and 23 April 1974, Association Francaise des Ponts et Charpentes. THEODORSEN, T. *General theory of aerodynamic instability and the mechanism of flutter.* National Aeronautics and Space Administration, NASA report 496, 1934–1935.

435 KULICKI, J. M., STRAIN, B. P., MARQUIS, S. W. and DeSTAFANO, R. J., Cable Vibration Problems and Cracked Diaphragm Weld Details on the I-470 Tied-Arch Bridge at Wheeling West Virginia, *Proc. 3rd Annual Bridge Conf.*, Pittsburg, PA, 2–4 June 1986.

436 IRWIN, H. P. A. H., *Wind Tunnel and Analytical Investigation of the Response of Lions' Gate Bridge to Turbulent Wind*, National Research Council of Canada, NAE LTR-LA-210, June 1977.

437 ZAN, S. J., *Analytical Prediction of the Buffeting Response of the ALRT Fraser River Crossing to a Turbulent Wind*, National Research Council of Canada, NAE LTR-LA-280, January 1986.

438 HOLMES, J. D., Prediction of the Response of a Cable-Stayed Bridge to Turbulence, *Proc. Fourth Int. Conf. on Wind Effects on Buildings and Structures*, Cambridge University Press, Heathrow, September 1975.

439 SCANLAN, R. H., *Recent Methods in the Application of Test Results to the Wind Design of Long, Suspended-Span Bridges*, Report No. FHWA-RD-75-115, FHWA, US Dept. of Transportation, Office of R&D, Washington, DC, 1975.

440 ZAN, S. J. and WARDLAW, R. L., Wind Buffeting of Long Span Bridges with Reference to Erection Phase Behaviour, *Proc. Bridges and Transmission Line Structures*, ASCE Structures Congress '87, August 1987.

441 IRWIN, H. P. A. H. and SCHUYLER, G. D., *Experiments on a Full Aeroelastic Model of Lions' Gate Bridge in Smooth and Turbulent Flow*, National Research Council of Canada, NAE LTR-LA-206, October 1977.

442 TANAKA, H. and DAVENPORT, A. G., Response of Taut Strip Models to Turbulent Wind, *J. Engineering Mechanics*, February 1982.

443 ZAN, S. J., *The Effect of Mass, Wind Angle and Erection Technique on the Aeroelastic Behaviour of a Cable-Stayed Bridge Model*, National Research Council of Canada NAE-AN-46, September 1987.

444 XIE, J., TANAKA, H., WARDLAW, R. L. and SAVAGE, M. G., Prediction of the Buffeting Response of Long Span Bridges with Yawed Winds, *Proc. Canada–Japan Workshop on Bridge Aerodynamics*, Ottawa, September 1989.

445 ITO, M., KATAYAMA, T. and NAKAZONE, T., *Some Empirical Facts on Damping of Bridges*, Int. Assoc. for Bridge and Structural Engineering, Reports of the Working Commissions, Vol. 13, Lisbon, 1973.

446 DAVENPORT, A. G. and LAROSE, G., The Structural Damping of Long Span Bridges, An Interpretation of Observations, *Proc. Canada–Japan Workshop on Bridge Aerodynamics*, Ottawa, September 1989.

447 BAMPTON, M. C. C., RAMSDELL, J. V., STROPE, L. A., ATHEY, G. F. and ABBEY, O. B., *Pasco-Kennewick Cable-Stayed Bridge Wind and Motion Data*, US Federal Highways Administration, FHWA-RD-82-067, February 1983.

448 SAITO, T., ITO, M., YAMAGUCHI, H. and EYA, S., Yokohama Bay Bridge—Use of a Dynamic Damper for Aerodynamic Stability of Its Support Tower, *Proc. 4th US–Japan Workshop on Bridge Engineering*, San Diego, USA, 11–12 May 1988.

449 DERRON, M.-H. and DO TRONG, T. *Effets des séismes sur les ouvrages d'art des voies de circulation.* DGC, Ecole Polytechnique Fédérale, Lausanne, 1980.

450 MUELLER, F. P. Baudynamik, *Beton Kalender*, 1978 II.

451 WIEGEL, R. L., *Earthquake engineering.* Prentice-Hall, Englewood Cliffs, NJ, 1970.

452 BACHMANN, H. Annacis Island Bridge, Report 1, IBK, Swiss Federal Institute of Technology, Zürich, 1982.

453 ISLER, W. *Rheinbrücke Diepoldsau, Rapport concernant les effets physiologiques des vibrations dues au trafic.* Institute for Reinforced and Prestressed Concrete, Ecole Polytechnique Fédérale, Lausanne, 1983, internal report.

454 FAVRE, R., KOPRNA, M. and DO TRONG, T. *Effets dynamiques sur les ponts routes.* ISTACO, Ecole Polytechnique Fédérale, Lausanne, 1974, internal report No. 422-4086.

455 BEAUJOINT, M. Similitude et théorie des modèles. *Bulletin RILEM*, No. 7, June 1960.

456 VINCENT, G. S., Golden Gate Bridge Vibration Studies, *J. Struct. Div. ASCE*, Paper 1817, October 1958.

457 WARDLAW, R. L., Some Approaches for Improving the Aerodynamic Stability of Bridge Road Decks, *Proc. Third Int. Conf. on Wind Effects on Buildings and Structures*, Tokyo, September 1971.

458 WALLACE, A. A. C., Wind Influence on Kessock Bridge, *Engineering Structures*, Vol. 7, January 1985.

459 REID LT. COL. WILLIAM, A Short Account of the Failure of a Part of the Brighton Chain Pier in the Gale of the 30th of November 1836, *Prof. Papers of the Corps of Royal Engineers*, Vol. 1 1844, p. 99.

460 FRAZER, R. A. and SCRUTON, C., *A Summarized Account of the Severn Bridge Aerodynamic Investigation*, National Physical Laboratory, UK, NPL Aero Report 222.

461 DAVENPORT, A. G., ISYUMOV, N. and MIYATA, T., The Experimental Determination of the Response of Suspension Bridges to Turbulent Wind, *Proc. Third Int. Conf. on Wind Effects on Buildings and Structures*, Tokyo, September 1971.

462 WARDLAW, R. L. and PONDER, C. A., Wind Tunnel Investigation of the Aerodynamic Stability of Bridges, *Proc. Canadian Structural Engineering Conf—1970*, Univ. of Toronto, Toronto, Canada, February 1970.

463 IRWIN, P. A., Wind Tunnel Tests of Long Span Bridges, *Proc. 12th Congress IABSE*, Vancouver, Canada, September 1984.

464 WARDLAW, R. L., *A Wind Tunnel Study of the Aerodynamics Stability of the Proposed Pasco–Kennewick Intercity Bridge*, National Research Council of Canada, Report NAE LTR-LA-163, July 1974.

465 TEMPLIN, R. J., Aerodynamics Low and Slow, *Canadian Aeronautics and Space Journal*, Vol. 16, No. 8, October 1970.

466 TEUNISSEN, H. W., Characteristics of the Mean Wind and Turbulence in the Planetary Boundary Layer, Inst. for Aerospace Studies, Univ. of Toronto, *UTIAS Review* No. 32, October 1970.

467 PANOFSKY, H. A. and DUTTON, J. A., *Atmospheric Turbulence, Models and Methods for Engineering Applications*. John Wiley & Sons, 1984.

468 BUCKLAND, P. G. and WARDLAW, R. L., Some Aerodynamic Considerations in Bridge Design, *Engineering Journal (Canada)*, Eng. Inst. of Canada, April 1972.

469 WARDLAW, R. L., TANAKA, H. and SAVAGE, M. G., *Wind Tunnel Investigation of the Mississippi River Bridge Steel Alternative, Quincy, Illinois*, National Research Council of Canada, NAE LTR-LA-268, February 1984.

470 SCRUTON, C. and WALSHE, D. E. J., *A Means for Avoiding Wind-Excited Oscillations of Structures with Circular or Nearly Circular Cross-Section*, National Physical Laboratory, NPL Aero 335, 1957.

471 WATSON, S. C. and STAFFORD, D., Cables in Trouble, *Civil Engineering*, Vol. 58, April 1988, pp. 38–41.

472 DOWELL, E. H., CURTISS, C. C., SCANLAN, R. H. and FERNANDO, S., *A Modern Course in Aeroelasticity*, 2nd ed. 1989, Kluwer Academic Publishers, Dordrecht.

473 SCANLAN, R. H., On Flutter and Buffeting Mechanisms in Long-Span Bridges, *US–Austria Seminar*, Boca Raton, Florida, May 1987.

474 BONVALET CH. *Les applications de la similitude physique à l'étude des structures du génie civil*. Editions Eyrolles, Paris, 1971.

475 DEHOUSSE, N. M. and ARNOULD, R. *Les modèles réduits de structures en génie civil*. Dunod, Paris, 1971.

476 RAUD, J. Quelques méthodes d'études sur modèles réduits en résistance des matériaux. *Annales de l'ITBTP*, No. 60, Jan. 1949.

477 ROCHA, M. Dimensionnement expérimental des constructions. *Annales de l'ITBTP*, No. 235, Feb. 1952.

478 BLEICH, F. Dynamic instability of truss-stiffened suspension bridges under wind action. *Trans. ASCE*, 114, 1949, pp. 1177–1232.

479 ROCARD, Y. *L'instabilité en mécanique*. Masson & Cie, Paris, 1954.

480 KLÖPPEL, K. Modellversuche im Windkanal zur Bemessung von Brücken gegen die Gefahr Winderregter Schwingungen. *Der Stahlbau*, 36, 1967, pp. 353–365.

481 KLÖPPEL, K. Ergebnisse von Modellversuchen zur Bestimmung des Einflusses nichthorizontaler Windströmung auf die aerodynamischen Stabilitätgrenzen von Brücken mit Kastenförmigen Querschnitten. *Der Stahlbau*, 44, 1975, pp. 193–203.

482 KAJIKAWA, Y. and KOBORI, T. Probability-based design of pedestrian bridges in consideration of the ergonomical serviceability. *Trans. JSCE*, vol. 11, 1979, pp. 35–36.

483 KAMMERER, J. B. Sur la dynamique d'un pont et du véhicule qui le parcourt. *Annales de l'ITBTP*, No. 368, Jan. 1979.

484 KLÖPPEL, K. Teilmodellversuche zur Beurteilung des aerodynamischen Verhaltens von Brücken. *Der Stahlbau*, 32, 1963, pp. 75–79 and 113–121.

485 KOBORI, T. and KAJIKAWA, Y. Ergonomic evaluation methods for bridge vibrations. *Trans. JSCE*, vol. 6, 1974, pp. 40–41.

486 KOBORI, T. and KAJIKAWA, Y. Study on human response to bridge vibrations. *Trans. JSCE*, vol. 7, 1975, pp. 229–232.

487 KOBORI, T. and KAJIKAWA, Y. Human response to bridge vibration under a single moving vehicle. *Trans. JSCE*, vol. 8, 1976, pp. 31–32.

488 Engineering News-Record. Why the Tacoma Narrows Bridge failed. *Engineering News-Record*, 8 May 1941.

489 FARQUHARSON, F. B., SMITH, F. C. and VINCENT, G. S. *Aerodynamic stability of suspension bridges with special reference to the Tacoma Narrows Bridge*. University of Washington Engineering Experiment Station, Bulletin 116, part I–V, 1941–1954.

Dynamic and seismic analysis and design

490 ABDEL-GHAFFAR, AHMED M. and RUBIN, LAWRENCE I., Multiple-Support Excitations of Suspension Bridges, *J. Eng. Mech., ASCE*, Vol. 108, No. EM2, April 1982, pp. 420–435.

491 BARON, F., ARIKAN, M. and HAMATI, E., The Effects of Seismic Disturbances on the Golden Gate Bridge, Report No. EERL 76-31, Univ. of California, Berkeley, CA, Nov. 1976.

492 ABDEL-GHAFFAR, AHMED, M. and NAZMY, ALY S., Effects of Three-Dimensionality and Nonlinearity on the Dynamic and Seismic Behavior of Cable-Stayed Bridges, *Proceedings of the ASCE Structures Congress '87, Bridge and Transmission Line Structures*, Orlando, Florida, August 17–20, 1987, pp. 389–404.

493 NAZMY, ALY S. and ABDEL-GHAFFAR, AHMED M., Nonlinear Earthquake-Response Analysis of Long-Span Cable-Stayed Bridge: Theory, *Int. J. Earthquake and Struct. Dyn.*, Vol. 19, No. 1, Jan. 1990, pp. 45–62.

494 NAZMY, ALY S. and ABDEL-GHAFFAR, AHMED M., Nonlinear Earthquake-Response Analysis of Long-Span Cable-Stayed Bridges: Applications, *Int. J. Earthquake Eng. and Struct. Dyn.*, Vol. 19, No. 1, Jan. 1990, pp. 63–76.

495 ABDEL-GHAFFAR, AHMED M. and NAZMY, ALY S., Earthquake Resistant Analysis of Cable-Stayed Bridges in Eastern and Central United States, *Proc. of the 3rd US Nat. Conf. on Earthquake Eng.*, Aug. 24–27, 1986, Charleston, South Carolina, pp. 2085–2096 (Vol. III).

496 ABDEL-GHAFFAR, AHMED M. and NAZMY, ALY S., Seismic Design of Cable-Stayed Bridges: Evaluation and Research Needs, *Proceedings ASCE Structures Congress*, San Francisco, CA, May 1–5, 1989.

497 ABDEL-GHAFFAR, AHMED, M. and KHALIFA, MAGDI A., Importance of Cable Vibration in the Dynamics of Cable-Stayed Bridges, *J. Eng. Mechanics, ASCE*.

498 ABDEL-GHAFFAR, AHMED M. and ALI, HOSAM-ELDIN M., Toward Seismic Isolation of Cable-Stayed Bridges, *Proceedings of the 6th US–Japan Bridge Eng. Workshop*, Lake Tahoe, Nevada, May 10–12, 1990; Edition: A. M. Abdel-Ghaffar, Civil Eng. Dept, Univ. of So. Calif., pp. 515–530.

499 KHALIL, M. S. and BUSH, L. H., Vancouver's Skytrain Cable-Stayed Bridge Dynamic Behavior, *Proceedings of Structures Congress '87*, Vol. on Bridges and Transmission Line Structures, ASCE, Orlando, FL, Aug. 17–20, 1987, pp. 357–373.

500 SAKAI, T., NISHIKAWA, K. and KAWASHIMA, K., New Design Considerations for Reducing Seismic Lateral Force of Highway Bridges in Japan, *Proceedings of the 11th IRF World Meeting*, Soul, Korea, April 1989, pp. 1–4.

501 FLEMING, J. F. and EGESELI, E. A., Dynamic Behavior of a Cable-Stayed Bridge, *Int. J. Earthquake Eng. and Struct Dyn.* Vol. 8, 1980, pp. 1–16.

502 UNJOH, S., ABDEL-GHAFFAR, A. M. and MASRI, S. F., A Study on the Effectiveness of Structural Control for Cable-Stayed Bridges, *Proceedings Second Workshop on Bridge Eng. Research in Progress*, Civil Eng. Dept., Univ. of Nevada, Reno, Oct. 29–30, 1990, pp. 51–54.

503 KOVACS, I., LEONHARDT, F. and ANDRÄ, W. Zur Frage der Seilschwingungen und der Seildämpfung. *Bautechnik*, 10, 1982, pp. 325–332.

504 KOBORI, T. and KAJIKAWA, Y. Psychological effects of highway bridge vibrations on pedestrians. *Trans. JSCE*, vol. 6, 1974, pp. 6–7.

505 WHEELER, J. E. Prediction and control of pedestrian induced vibration in footbridges. *Proc. ASCE*, ST 9, 1982, pp. 2045–2065.

506 HARRIS, C. M. and CREDE, C. E. *Shock and Vibration Handbook*. McGraw-Hill, New York, vol. 1/2/3, 1961.

507 HOSHIYA, M. and NAKANE, K. Theoretical assessment of human response against bridge vibration. *Trans. JSCE*, vol. 8, 1976, pp. 16–17.

508 HURTY, W. C. and RUBINSTEIN, M. F. *Dynamics of Structures*. Prentice-Hall, Englewood Cliffs, NJ, 1975.

509 KAJIKAWA, Y. and KOBORI, T. Probabilistic approaches to the ergonomical serviceability of pedestrian bridges. *Trans. JSCE*, vol. 9, 1977, pp. 86–87.

510 HO, M. and Y. NAKAMURA, Aerodynamic Stability of Structures in Wind, *IABSE Surveys S-20/82*, Int. Assoc. for Bridge and Struct. Eng., ETH-Honggerberg, Zurich, May, 1982, pp. 33–56.

511 HINO, M., *Spectral Analysis*. Asakura Book, Co., Tokyo, Japan, 1978, pp. 183–227.

512 HOEL, P. G., *Introduction to Mathematical Statistics*. Wiley, New York, 1965.

513 HONDA, H., Y. KAJIKAWA and T. KOBORI, Spectra of Road Surface Roughness on Bridges, *J. Struct. Div. ASCE*, Vol. 108, No. ST9, Sept., 1982, pp. 1956–1966.

514 HONDROS, G. and J. G. MARSH, Load Distribution in Composite Girder-Slab Systems, *J. Struct. Div. ASCE*, 86(ST11), 1960, 79–109 (Nov.), paper 2645.

515 HUANG, T. and A. S. VELETSOS, Dynamic Response of Three-Span Continuous Highway Bridges, *Tenth Progress Report on Highway Bridge Impact Investigation*, Univ. Illinois, Urbana, Sept., 1960.

516 IMBSEN, R. A., R. V. NUTT, and J. PENZIEN, Evaluation of Analytical Procedures used in Bridge Seismic Design Practice, *Proc. Workshop on Earthquake Resistance of Hwy. Bridges*, Applied Technology Council, Berkeley, CA, Jan., 1979.

517 IVY, R. J., *et al.*, Live Loading for Long Span Highway Bridges, *Trans. ASCE*, Paper No. 3708, June, 1953.

518 IWASAKI, T., J. PENZIEN and R. CLOUGH, *Literature Survey — Seismic Effects on Highway Bridges*, Report EERC 72-11, Earthquake Eng. Research Center, Univ. Calif. Berkeley, CA, Nov., 1972.

519 Japan Society of Civil Engineering, *Earthquake-Resistant Design of Bridges*, Bridge and Struct. Committee, Japan Society Civil Engineering, Tokyo, 1977.

520 FRANGOPOL, D. M. and R. NAKIB, Redundancy in Highway Bridges, *Eng. J., AISC*, Vol. 128, No. 1, 1991.

521 FUNG, G., *et al.*, *Field Investigation of Bridge Damage in the San Fernando Earthquake*, Bridge Dept., Div. of Highways, Calif. Dept. Transp., Sacramento, 1971.

522 GATES, J. H., 1979. Factors Considered in the Development of the California Seismic Design Criteria for Bridges, *Proc. Workshop on Earthquake Resistance of Hwy. Bridges*, Applied Technology Council, Berkeley, CA, Jan., 1979.

523 GATES, J. H., California's Seismic Design Criteria for Bridges, *J. Struct. Div. ASCE*, Vol. 102, No. ST13, Dec., 1976, pp. 2301–2314.

524 GUYON, Y., Analysis of Slab Bridges, *Ann. Ponts Chaussées*, Vol. 119, No. 29, 1949, pp. 555 – 589.

525 GUYON, Y., Calcul des ponts a poutres multiplse solidarisées par des entre-foises, ("Analysis of Wide, Multiple Beam Bridges Stiffened by Cross Beams") *Ann. Ponts Chaussées*, Vol. 166, Nos. 9, 10, Paris, 1946, pp. 553 – 612.

526 HAAIJER, G., Limit States Design — A tool of Reducing the Complexity of Steel Structures, *AISC National Eng. Conf.*, March, 1983.

527 HEALEY, A. J., E. NATHMAN and C. C. SMITH, An Analytical and Experimental Study of Automobile Dynamics with Random Roadway Inputs, *Trans. ASME*, 1977.

528 PARK, R. and R. W. G. BLAKELY, Seismic Design of Bridges, *Bridge Seminar* 1979, Summary Volume 3, Structures Committee, Road Research Unit, National Research Board, New Zealand.

529 PRICE, W. I. J., Transmission of Horizontal Forces and Movements by Bridge Bearings, Joint Sealing and Bearing Systems for Concrete Structures, *ACI Publication* SP-70, Vol. 2, ACI, 1982, pp. 761 – 784.

530 PRIESTLEY, M. J. N. and R. PARK, Strength and Ductility of Concrete Bridge Columns Under Seismic Loading, *ACI Struct. J.*, Jan. – Feb., 1987.

531 ROEDER, C. W. and J. F. STANTON, Elastomeric Bearings: A State of the Art, *J. Struct. Div. ASCE*, Vol. 109, No. ST12, Dec., 1983.

532 ROEDER, C. W. and J. F. STANTON, State of the Art Elastomeric Bridge Bearing Design, *ACI J*, 1991.

533 ROEDER, C. W., J. F. STANTON and A. W. TAYLOR, Performance of Elastomeric Bearings, NCHRP Report 298, TRB, National Research Council, Washington, DC, Oct., 1987.

534 STANTON, J. F. *et al.*, Elastomeric Bearings: A State of the Art, *J. Struct. Div. ASCE*, 1990.

535 STANTON, J. F. *et al.*, Stability of Laminated Elastomeric Bearings, *J. Eng. Mech. ASCE*, 1990.

Selected research on bridges

536 BALDWIN, J. W., HENRY, J. R. and G. M. SWEENEY, *Study of Composite Bridge Stringers, Phase II*, Univ. of Missouri, May, 1965.

537 BARNARD, P. R., Series of Tests on Simply Supported Composite Beams, *J. Am. Concrete Inst.*, Vol. 62, No. 4, April, 1965, pp. 443 – 456.

538 BARNARD, P. R. and R. P. JOHNSON, Ultimate Strength of Composite Beams, *Proc. Instn Civ. Engrs*, Vol. 32, London, Oct., 1965, pp. 161 – 179.

539 ANSOURIAN, P. and J. W. RODERICK, Analysis of Composite Beams, *J. Struct. Div. ASCE*, Vol. 104, No. ST10, Oct., 1978, pp. 1631 – 1645.

540 ASCE, *Commentary on Plastic Design in Steel, Joint Committee*, Welding Research Council and ASCE, 1971, Manual and Reports on Practice No. 41.

541 ASCE, Composite Steel–Concrete Construction, Report of Task Committee on Composite Construction, *J. Struct. Div. ASCE*, Vol. 100, No. ST5, May, 1974, pp. 1085 – 1139.

542 ASCE – AASHTO, Development of Use of Prestressed Steel Flexural Members, Report by Subcommittee of the Joint ASCE – AASHTO Committee on Steel Flexural Members, *J. Struct. Div. ASCE*, Vol. 94, No. ST9, Sept., 1968, pp. 2033 – 2060.

543 ASCE – AASHTO, State-of-the-Art Report on Ultimate Strength of I-Beam Bridge Systems, Subcommittee on Ultimate Strength, Joint ASCE-AASHTO Task Committee on Metals, Struct. Div., *J. Struct. Div. ASCE*, Vol. 101, No. ST5, May, 1975, pp. 1085 – 1096.

544 ASTM, *Specification for Structural Steel (A36-88c)*, American Society for Testing and Materials, Philadelphia, 1988.

545 ASTM, *Specification for High-Strength Low Alloy Steels (A572-88c)*, American Society for Testing and Materials, Philadelphia, 1988.

546 ASTM, *Specification for High-Strength Low-Alloy Structural Steel (A588-88a)*, American Society for Testing and Materials, Philadelphia, 1988.

547 AULTHOUSE, F. D., *Economics of Weathering Steel in Highway Structures*, FHWA Publ. FHWA-TS-89-016, Federal Highway Administration Forum on Weathering Steels for Highway Bridges, Alexandria, Virginia, June, 1989.

548 AWS, *Welding Handbook*, Vol. 1, *Welding Technology*, American Welding Soc., Miami, 1987.

549 AWS, *Structural Welding Code — Steel*, 11th ed., American Welding Soc., Miami, 1988.

550 AASHTO, *Recommendations of Weathering Steel Fatigue Study Group*, AASHTO Technical Committee T-14, Feb. 1990.

551 ANAND, S. C. and A. TALESSTCHI, Prestressed Composite Steel Beam Design, *J. Struct. Div. ASCE*, Vol. 99, No. ST3, March, 1973, pp. 301 – 319.

552 ANSI/AASHTO/AWS, Bridge Welding Code D1.5-88, 1988.

553 ANSOURIAN, P., An Application of the Method of Finite Elements to the Analysis of Composite Floor Systems, *Proc. Institution Civ. Engineers*, Part 2, Vol. 59, Dec., 1975, pp. 699 – 726.

554 ANSOURIAN, P., Plastic Rotation of Composite Beams, *J. Struct. Div. ASCE*, Vol. 108, No. ST3, March, 1982, pp. 643 – 659.

555 BARSOM, J. M., *The Development of AASHTO Fracture-Toughness Requirements for Bridge Steels*, American Iron and Steel Inst., Washington, DC, 1975.

556 BEEDLE, L. S., *Plastic Design of Steel Frames*, Wiley, New York, 1975.

557 BEGUIN, G. H., Composite Bridge Decking by Stage-Deck Jacking, *J. Struct. Div. ASCE*, Vol. 104, No. ST1, Jan., 1978, pp. 171 – 189.

558 Task Committee on Cable-Suspended Structures of the Committee on Metals of the Structural Division, Tentative Recommendations for Cable Stayed-Bridge Structures, *J. Struct. Div. ASCE*, 1977, p. 929.

559 Task Committee on Cable-Suspended Structures of the Committee on Metals of the Structural Division, Commentary on Tentative Recommendations for Cable Stayed-Bridge Structures, *J. Struct. Div. ASCE*, May, 1977, p. 941.

560 BESCHKINE, L., *Determination of the Effective Width of the Compression Flange of T-Beams*, (in French), Publications, Int. Assoc. for Bridge and Structural Engineering, 1937-8, Vol. 5, p. 65.

561 Bethlehem Steel Corporation, *Economics of Simple Span Highway Bridges*, Bethlehem Steel Corp., PA, 1976.

562 BOWDEN, F. P. and L. LEBEN, The Nature of Sliding and Analysis of Friction, *Proc. Royal Soc.*, Series A, Vol. 169, London, 1939, pp. 371 – 390.

563 BURDETTE, E. G. and D. W. GOODPASTURE, *Full Scale Bridge Testing — An Evaluation of Bridge Design Criteria*, Univ. Tennessee, Knoxville, Dec., 1971.

564 CARSKADDAN, P. S., Bending of Deep Girders with A514 Steel Flanges, *J. Struct. Div., ASCE*, Vol. 95, No. ST10, Proc. Paper 6839, Oct., 1969, pp. 2219 – 2242.

565 CARSKADDAN, P. S., G. HAAIJER and M. A. GRUBB, Computing the Effective Plastic Moment, *AISC Eng. J.*, First Quarter, 1982.

566 CHAPMAN, J. C., Composite Construction in Steel and Concrete — The Behavior of Composite Beams, *Struct. Engineer*, Vol. 42, No. 4, April, 1964, pp. 115 – 125.

567 CHAPMAN, J. C. and BALAKRISHNAN, Experiments on Composite Beams, *Struct. Engineer*, Vol. 42, No. 11, Nov., 1964, pp. 369 – 383.

568 CIOLINA, F., Composite Steel–Concrete Bridge Structures, (in French), *Annales de L'Institute Technique du Batiment et des Travaux Publics*, July – Aug., 1971, p. 37.

569 CLIMENHAGA, J. J. and R. P. JOHNSON, Local Buckling in Continuous Composite Beams, *Struct. Engineer*, Vol. 50, No. 9, Sept., 1972, pp. 367 – 374.

570 COLVILLE, J., Tests of Curved Steel–Concrete Composite Beams, *J. Struct. Div. ASCE*, Vol. 99, No. ST7, Proc. Paper 9867, July, 1973, pp. 1555–1570.

571 DAI, P. K. H. and C. P. SIESS, *Analytical Study of Composite Beams with Inelastic Shear Connection*, Univ. Illinois. Struct. Research Ser. 267, June, 1963, 113 pp.

572 DANIELS, J. H., Recent Research on Composite Beams for Bridges and Buildings, *Civ. Eng. Trans.*, The Inst. of Eng., Australia, Vol. CE14, No. 2, Oct., 1972, pp. 228–233.

573 DANIELS, J. H. and J. W. FISHER, *Static Behavior of Composite Beams with Variable Load Position*, Fritz Eng. Lab. Report 324.3, Lehigh Univ., March, 1967, 52 p.

574 DANIELS, J. H. and J. W. FISHER, *Static Behavior of Continuous Composite Beams*, Lehigh Univ., Fritz Eng. Laboratory Report 324.2, March, 1967, 79 p.

575 DANIELS, J. H. and J. W. FISHER, *Fatigue Behavior of Continuous Composite Beams*, Hwy. Research Record No. 253, Hwy, Research Board, 1968, pp. 1–20.

576 DAS, M., MALAIRONGS, K. and R. B. L. SMITH, *Yield-Line Analysis of Reinforced Concrete Slabs Using a Digital Computer*, Pub. SP-33, 1972, American Concrete Institute.

577 DAS, S. C. and J. W. BALDWIN, Shear Connectors in Haunched Composite Beams, *Eng. Experiment Station Bull.*, Univ. Missouri-Columbia, August, 1967.

578 DAVIDSON, J. H. and J. LONGWORTH, *Composite Beams in Negative Bending*, Report No. 20, Dept. Civ. Eng., Univ. Alberta, Edmonton, Canada, May, 1969.

579 EMANUEL, J. H. and J. L. HULSEY, Temperature Distribution in Composite Bridges, *J. Struct. Div. ASCE*, Vol. 104, No. ST1, Jan., 1978, pp. 65–78.

580 FAN, H. M. and C. P. HEINS, *Effective Width of Composite Bridges at Ultimate Load*, Civ. Eng. Report No. 57, Univ. Maryland, College Park, June, 1974.

581 Federal Highway Administration, *Uncoated Weathering Steel in Structures*, FHWA Tech. Advisory (T5140.22), Washington, DC, Oct., 1989.

582 FINN, E. V., The Use of Prestressed Steel in Elevated Roadway, *Struct. Engineer*, Vol. 42, No. 1, Jan., 1964.

583 FISHER, J. W., J. H. DANIELS and R. G. SLUTTER, *Continuous Composite Beams for Bridges*, Prel. Report, Int. Assoc. Bridge and Struct. Eng., Amsterdam, May, 1972, pp. 113–123.

584 FLINT, A. R. and L. S. EDWARDS, Limit State Design of Highway Bridges, *Struct. Engineer*, Vol. 48, No. 3, March, 1970, pp. 93–108.

585 GALAMBOS, T. V., Load Factor Design of Steel Buildings, *AISC Eng. J.*, American Inst. Steel Construction Vol. 9, No. 3 (July), 1972, 108–113.

586 GALAMBOS, T. V., Load and Resistance Factor Design, *AISC Eng. J.*, American Inst. Steel Construction, Vol. 18, No. 3, 1981, pp. 74–82.

587 GALAMBOS, T. V. and M. K. RAVINDRA, Proposed Criteria for Load and Resistance Factor Design, *AISC Eng. J.*, American Inst. Steel Construction Vol. 15, No. 1 (First Quarter), 1978, 8–17.

588 GARCIA, I. and J. H. DANIELS, *Negative Moment Behavior of Composite Beams*, Fritz Eng. Laboratory. Report 359.4, Lehigh Univ., Bethlehem, PA, 1971.

589 GARDNER, N. J. and E. R. JACOBSON, Structural Behavior of Concrete Filled Steel Tubes, *ACI J.* Vol. 64, No. 7, July, 1967, pp. 404–413 (and J. Suppl. No. 2, Title No. 64-38).

590 GOBLE, G. G., *The Influence of Stud Yield Strength on the Strength of Composite Specimens*, Test Report, Case-Western Reserve Univ., 1967.

591 GOBLE, G. G., Shear Strength of Thin Flange Composite Specimens, *AISC Eng. J.*, American Inst. Steel Construction, Vol. 5, No. 2, April, 1968, pp. 62–65.

592 GODFREY, G. G., The Use of Weathering Steels in Composite Highway Bridges, *Int. Symp. on Steel Bridges*, London, Feb., 1988.

593 GRACE, N. F. F., *Effect of Prestressing the Deck in Continuous Bridge of Composite Construction*, thesis presented to the Univ. of Windsor, at Windsor, Ontario, Canada, in partial fulfilment of the requirements for the degree of Master of Science, 1981.

594 GUYON, Y., Composite Steel–Prestressed Concrete Construction, *Annales de l'ITBTP*, No. 298, Oct., 1972, pp. 131–156.

595 HANSELL, W. C. and I. M. VIEST, Load Factor Design for Steel Highway Bridges, *AISC Eng. J.*, American Inst. Steel Construction, Vol. 8, No. 4, Oct., 1971, pp. 113–123.

597 HASSE, G., Effect of Creep on Statically Indeterminate Composite Beams and Frames of Variable Cross Section, (in German), *Verein Deutscher Ingenieure, Berichte*, Part 4, No. 16, Nov., 1968, p. 111.

598 HEINS, C. P., LRF Criteria for Composite Steel I-Beam Bridges, *J. Struct. Div. ASCE*, Vol. 106, No. ST11, Nov., 1980, pp. 2297–2312.

599 HEINS, C. P. and H. M. FAN, Effective Composite Beam Width at Ultimate Load, *J. Struct. Div. ASCE*, Vol. 102, No. ST11, Nov., 1976, pp. 2163–2179.

600 HEINS, C. P. and R. O. HOLLIDAY, *Ultimate Load Response of a Composite Multi-Girder Bridge Model*, Civ. Eng. Report No. 54, Univ. Maryland, College Park, March, 1974.

601 HEINS, C. P. and J. T. C. KUO, Torsional Properties of Composite Girders, *AISC Eng. J.*, American Inst. Steel Construction, Vol. 9, No. 2, April, 1972, pp. 79–85.

602 HEINS, C. P. and J. T. C. KUO, Composite Beams in Torsion, *J. Struct. Div. ASCE*, Vol. 98, No. ST5, Proc. Paper 8921, May, 1972, pp. 1105–1117.

603 HEINS, C. P. and T. C. KUO, *Live Load Distribution on Composite Highway Bridges at Ultimate Load*, Civ. Eng. Report No. 53, Univ. Maryland, College Park, April, 1973.

604 HEINS, C. P. and T. C. KUO, Ultimate Live Load Distribution Factor for Bridges, *J. Struct. Div. ASCE*, Vol. 101, No., ST7, July, 1975, pp. 1481–1496.

605 JOHNSON, R. P., Longitudinal Shear Strength of Composite Beams, *ACI J.* Vol. 67, No. 6, June, 1970, pp. 464–466.

606 JOHNSON, R. P., Design of Composite Beams With Deep Haunches, *Proc. Instn Civ. Engrs, Vol. 51, Jan., 1972, pp. 83–90.*

607 JOHNSON, R. P., Composite Steel-Concrete Construction, Discussion, *ASCE Struct. J.*, May, 1975, p. 1156.

608 JANSS, J., Research on Composite Structures Carried Out by the CRIF at the Univ. of Liege, (in French), *Preliminary Report, Int. Assoc. for Bridge and Structural Engineering, 9th Congress*, Amsterdam, 1972, pp. 125–132.

609 MENZIES, J. B., Structural Behavior of the Moat Street Flyover, Coventry, *Civ. Eng. and Public Works Rev.*, Vol. 63, Sept., 1968, pp. 967–971.

610 MENZIES, J. B., CP 117 and Shear Connectors in Steel–Concrete Composite Beams Made with Normal-Density or Lightweight Concrete, *Struct. Engineer*, Vol. 49, No. 3, March, 1971, pp. 137–154.

611 MODJESKI and MASTERS, *LRFD Bridge Design Code*, NCHRP Project 12-33, Transp. Research Board, National Research Council, Washington, DC, 1991.

612 MORGAN, F., M. MUSKAT and D. W. REED, Studies in Lubrication-X Friction Phenomena and the Stick-Slip Process, *J. Appl. Phys.*, Vol. 12, Oct., 1971, pp. 743–752.

613 O'CONNOR, C., *Design of Bridge Superstructures*, Wiley, New York, 1971.

614 PINKHAM, C. W. and W. C. HANSELL, An Introduction to Load and Resistance Factor Design for Steel Buildings, *AISC Eng. J.*, American Institute of Steel Construction, Vol. 15, No. 1, 1978, (First Quarter), 2–7.

615 PLUM, D. R., Strength of Studs in Composite Construction, *Proc. Instn Civ. Engrs*, Vol. 51, Feb., 1972, pp. 319–335.

616 Prestressing Steel Stringers Reduce Bridge Weight by 25%, *Engineering News-Record*, Vol. 167, No. 16, Oct. 19, 1961, pp. 32–33.

617 PRIESTLEY, M. J. N., *Linear Heat-Flow Analysis of Concrete Bridge Decks*, Research Report 76-3, Dept. Civ. Eng., Univ. Canterbury, New Zealand, Feb., 1976.

618 RAVINDRA, M. K. and T. V. GALAMBOS, Load and Resistance Factor Design for Steel, *J. Struct. Div. ASCE*, Vol. 104, No. ST9, Sept., 1978, 1337–1353.

619 REAGAN, R. S. and N. W. KRAHL, Behavior of Prestressed Composite Beams, *J. Struct. Div. ASCE*, Vol. 93, No. ST6, Proc. Paper 5663, Dec., 1967, pp. 87–108.

620 REDDY, V. M. and A. W. HENDRY, Ultimate Strength of a Composite Beam Allowing for Strain Hardening, *Indian Concrete J.*, Vol. 44, No. 9, Sept., 1970, pp. 388–396.

621 RODERICK, J. W., HAWKINS, N. M. and L. C. LIM, The Behavior of Composite Steel and Lightweight Concrete Beams, *Civ. Eng. Transactions*, The Inst. of Engineers, Australia, Vol. CE9, No. 2, Oct., 1967, pp. 265–275.

622 ROLFE, S. T., Designing to Prevent Brittle Fracture in Bridges, *Proc. Specialty Conf. Safety and Rehabilitation of Metal Structures*, ASCE, 1972, pp. 175–216.

623 KENNEDY, J. B. and D. S. R. GUPTA, Bending of Skew Orthotropic Plate Structures, *J. Struct. Div. ASCE*, Vol. 102, No. ST8, Proc. Paper 12302, Aug., 1976, pp. 1559–1574.

624 KENNEDY, J. B. and N. F. GRACE, Prestressed Decks in Continuous Composite Bridges, *ASCE Struct. J.*, Nov., 1982, pp. 2384–2410.

625 KING, D. C., R. G. SLUTTER and G. C. DRISCOLL, Fatigue Strength of $\frac{1}{2}$-inch Diameter Stud Shear Connectors, *Hwy. Research Record* 103, Hwy. Research Board, 1965, pp. 78–106.

626 KNEE, O. W., The Prestressing of Steel Girders, *Struct. Engineer*, Vol. 44, No. 10, Oct., 1966.

627 KUO, T. C., *Elasto-Plastic Behavior of Composite Slab Girder Highway Bridges*, PhD. Thesis, Univ. Maryland, College Park, 1973.

628 KUO, T. C. and C. P. HEINS, *Live Load Distribution on Composite Highway Bridges at Ultimate Load*, Civ. Eng. Report No. 53, Univ. Maryland, College Park, April, 1973.

629 LAY, M. G. and P. D. SMITH, Role of Strain Hardening in Plastic Design, *J. Struct. Div. ASCE*, Vol. 91, No. ST3, June, 1965, pp. 25–43.

630 LEE, J. A. N., Effective Width of Tee Beams, *Struct. Engineer*, Vol. 40, No. 1, Jan., 1962, pp. 21–27.

631 LEW, H. S., *Effect of Shear Connector Spacing on the Ultimate Strength of Steel-Concrete Composite Beams*, National Bureau of Standards Report No. 10 246, U.S. Dept. Commerce, Washington, DC, Aug., 1970.

632 LI, S. and R. V. BLACKWELL, Design Yield Moment of Continuous Concrete Deck Slabs Under Vehicular Loading, *ACI, Publication* SP-33, 1972.

633 LOWE, P. A. and A. R. FLINT, Prediction of Collapse Loadings for Composite Highway Bridges, *Proc. Instn Civ. Engrs*, April, 1971.

634 MACKEY, S. and F. K. C. WONG, Effective Width of Composite Tee-Beam Flange, *Struct. Engineer*, Vol. 39, No. 9, Sept., 1961, pp. 277–285.

635 VIEST, I. M. (Chairman), Committee Steel-Concrete Construction, Report, Task Committee of the Committee on Metals of the Struct. Div., *J. Struct. Div. ASCE*, Vol. 100, No. ST5, May, 1974, pp. 1085–1139.

636 VINCENT, G. S., Tentative Criteria for Load Factor Design of Steel Highway Bridges, *Bull. No. 15*, American Iron and Steel Inst., March, 1969.

637 WANG, C. K. and C. G. SALMON, *Reinforced Concrete Design*, Harper and Row, New York, 1985.

638 WOOD, W. E. and J. H. DEVLETIAN, *Improved Fracture Toughness and Fatigue Characteristics of Electroslag Weldments*, Report No. FHWA/RD-87/026, Federal Highway Administration, Washington, DC, Aug., 1987.

639 WU, Y. C. and R. G. SLUTTER, *Continuous Composite Beams Under Fatigue Loading*, Fritz Eng. Laboratory Report 359.2, Lehigh Univ., Bethlehem, PA, 1971.

640 WU, Y. C., R. G. SLUTTER and J. W. FISHER, *Analysis of Continuous Composite Beams*, Fritz Eng. Laboratory Report 359.5, Lehigh Univ., Bethlehem, PA, 1971.

641 YAM, L. C. P. and J. C. CHAPMAN, Inelastic Behavior of Simply Supported Composite Beams of Steel and Concrete, *Proc. Instn Civ. Engrs*, Vol. 41, Dec., 1968, pp. 651–683.

642 ZUK, W., Thermal Behavior of Composite Bridges, *Hwy. Research Record* 76, Highway Research Board, 1965, pp. 231–253.

643 ZURASKI, P. D. and J. E. JOHNSON, Research on the Remaining Life in Steel Bridges, *Proc. ASCE Specialty Conf. Probabilistic Mechanics and Struct. Reliability*, Berkeley, CA, Jan., 1985, 11–13.

644 CHERN, C. and A. OSTAPENKO, *Ultimate Strength of Plate Girders Under Shear*, Fritz Eng. Laboratory Report 328.7, Lehigh Univ., Bethlehem, PA, Aug., 1969.

645 CHONG, K. P., Optimization of Unstiffened Hybird Beams, *J. Struct. Div. ASCE*, Vol. 102, No. ST2, Feb., 1976, pp. 401–409.

646 COOPER, P. B., *Bending and Shear Strength of Longitudinally Stiffened Plate Girders*, Fritz Eng. Laboratory Report 304.6, Lehigh Univ., Bethlehem, PA, Sept., 1965.

647 COOPER, P. B., Strength of Longitudinally Stiffened Plate Girders, *J. Struct. Div. ASCE*, Vol. 93, No. ST2, April, 1967, pp. 419–451.

648 CRISFIELD, M. A., *Large-Deflection Elasto-Plastic Buckling Analysis of Plates Using Finite Elements*, TRRL LR593, Transp. and Road Research Lab., Crowthorne, 1973.

649 CSAGOLY, P. F. and L. G. JAEGER, *Multi-Load-Path Structures for Highway Bridges*, Transp. Research Record 711, TRB, National Research Council, Washington, DC, 1979, pp. 34–39.

650 CULVER, C. G., *Instability of Horizontally Curved Members — Design Recommendations for Curved Highway Bridges*, Carnegie-Mellon Univ., Pittsburgh, PA Dept. Transp., June, 1972.

651 BILLINGTON, C. J., *The Theoretical and Experimental Elastic Behavior of Box Girder Bridges*, PhD thesis, University of London, 1974.

652 BILLINGTON, C. J., K. GHAVAMI and P. J. DOWLING, *Parametric Study of Cross-Sectional Distortion due to Eccentric Loading*, CESLIC Report BG16, Imperial College, London, Sept., 1972.

653 BLODGETT, O. W., *Design of Welded Structures*, James F. Lincoln Arc Welding Foundation, Cleveland, OH, 1966.

654 BRESLER, B., T. Y. LIN and J. SCALZI, *Design of Steel Structures*, Wiley, New York, 1968.

655 BRESLER, B., T. Y. LIN and J. B. SCALZI, *Design of Steel Structures*, Wiley, New York, 1969.

656 CALLADINE, C. R., A Plastic Theory of Collapse of Plate Girder Under Combined Shearing Force and Bending Moment, *Struct. Engineer*, London, Vol. 51, No. 4, April, 1973, pp. 147–154.

658 CULVER, C. and J. MOZER, *Horizontally Curved Highway Bridges — Stability of Curved Box Girders*, Report No. B3, Carnegie-Mellon Univ., Pittsburgh, Dec., 1971.

659 CULVER, C. and C. DYM, Elastic Buckling of Stiffened Plates, *J. Struct. Div. ASCE*, Vol. 98, No. ST11, Proc. Paper 9374, Nov., 1972, pp. 2641–2645.

660 DANIELS, J. H., W. KIM and J. L. WILSON, *Recommended Guidelines for Redundancy Design and Rating of Two-Girder Steel Bridges*, NCHRP Report 319, TRB, National Research Council, Washington, DC, 1989.

661 DANIELS, J. H., J. L. WILSON and S. S. CHEN, *Redundancy of Simple Span and Two-Span Welded Steel Two-Girder Bridges*, Final Report, Pennsylvania Dept. Transp. Research Project 84-20, 1987.

662 ASCE–AASHTO, Program Report on Steel Box Girder Bridges, Subcommittee on Box Girders, Joint ASCE–AASHTO Task Committee on Flexural Members, *J. Struct. Div. ASCE*, Vol. 97, No. ST4, April, 1971, pp. 1175–1186.

663 ASCE–AASHTO, Theory and Design of Longitudinally Stiffened Plate Girders, Report of Task Committee, Joint ASCE–AASHTO Committee on Flexural members, *J. Struct. Div. ASCE*, Vol. 104, No. ST4, April, 1978, pp. 697–716.

664 ASCE–AASHTO, State-of-the Art Report on Redundant Bridge Systems, Committee on Flexural Members, *J. Struct. Div. ASCE*, Vol. 111, No. ST12, Dec., 1985, pp. 2517–2531.

665 AZAD, A. K., Economic Design of Homogeneous I-Beams, *J. Struct. Div. ASCE*, Vol. 104, No. ST4, April, 1978, pp. 637–648.

667 AZAD, A. K., Continuous Steel I Girders. Optimum Proportioning, *J. Struct. Div. ASCE*, Vol. 106, No. ST7, July, 1980, pp. 1543–1556.

668 BASLER, K., Strength of Plate Girders in Shear, *J. Struct. Div. ASCE*, Vol. 87, No. ST7, Oct., 1961, pp. 151–180.

669 BASLER, K., Strength of Plate Girders in Shear, *Trans. ASCE*, Vol. 128, Part II, 1961, pp. 693–719.

670 BASLER, K., *et al.*, Web Buckling Tests on Welded Plate Girders, *Welding Research Council Bull.* Ser. No. 64, Sept., 1960.

671 BASLER, K. and B. THURLIMANN, Strength of Plate Girders in Bending, *Trans. ASCE*, Vol. 128, Part II, 1963, pp. 655–682.

672 BENSCOTER, B. V., A Theory of Torsion Bending for Multi-Cell Beams, *J. Appl. Mech.*, Vol. 21, March, 1954.

673 DUBAS, P., Plated Structures with Closed-Section Stiffeners, *Steel Plated Structures, An Int. Symp.*, Crosby Lockwood Staples, London, 1976.

674 ELGAALY, M., Web Design Under Compressive Edge Loads, *Eng. J. AISC*, Vol. 20, No. 4, 4th Quarter, 1983, pp. 153–171.

675 *Engineering News Record*, Cantilevered Box Girder Bridge Collapses During Construction, June 11, 1970.

676 *Engineering News Record*, Australian Box Girder and Pier Collapse, Oct. 22, 1970.

677 *Engineering News Record*, Rib Gaps Blamed for Bridge Failure, Nov. 23, 1972.

678 FISHER, J. W., *et al.*, *Fatigue Strength of Steel Beams with Welded Stiffeners and Attachments*, NCHRP Report 147, TRB, National Research Council, Washington, DC, 1974.

679 FUJII, T., On Improved Theory for Basler's Theory, *Proc. Eighth Congress, Int. Assoc. for Bridge and Struct. Eng.*, New York, Sept., 1968, pp. 477–487.

680 FUJII, T., On Ultimate Strength of Plate Girders, *Japan Shipbuilding and Marine Eng.*, Tokyo, May, 1968.

681 GALAMBOS, T. V., *Guide to Stability Design Criteria for Metal Structures*, 4th ed., Wiley, New York, 1988.

682 GARSON, R., *Highway Bridge Fatigue Life Prediction*, PhD thesis, Case Western Reserve Univ., Cleveland, 1972.

683 GENT, A. R. and V. K. SHEBINI, *Parametric Study Report on Torsional Warping*, CESLIC Report, Imperial College, London, June, 1972.

684 GOLDBERG, J. E. and H. L. LEVE, Theory of Prismatic Folded Plate Structures, *IABSE Publications*, Vol. 16, 1957.

685 GORMAN, M. R., Structural Redundancy, *Proc. Fourth ASCE Specialty Conf. on Probabilistic Mech. and Struct. Reliability*, Berkeley, CA, 1984, pp. 45–49.

686 GRUBB, M. A., Autostress Design Using Compact Welded Beams, *Eng. J. AISC*, Vol. 26, No. 2, 4th Quarter, 1989.

687 GRUBB, M. A. and P. S. CARSKADDAN, *Autostress Design of Highway Bridges, Phase 3: Moment-Rotation Requirements*, Research Lab. Report, US Steel Corp., Monroeville, PA, July, 1981.

689 HAAIJER, G., P. S. CARSKADDAN and M. A. GRUBB, Suggested Autostress Procedures for Load Factor Design of Steel Beam Bridges, *Bull. No. 29*, AISC, April, 1987.

690 HAAIJER, G., C. G. SCHILLING and P. S. CARSKADDAN, *Bridge Design Procedures Based on Performance Requirements*, Transp. Research Record 711, TRB, National Research Council, Washington, DC, 1979, pp. 30–33.

691 SCHILLING, C. G., Unified Autostress Method, *Eng. J., AISC*, Vol. 28, No. 4, 4th Quarter, 1991.

692 SEIM, C. and S. THOMAN, Proposed Specifications for Steel Box Girder Bridges, Discussion, *J. Struct. ASCE*, Dec., 1981, pp. 2457–2458.

693 SHANAFELT, G. O. and W. B. HORN, *Guidelines for Evaluation and Repair of Damaged Steel Bridge Members*, NCHRP Report 271, TRB, National Research Council, Washington, DC, 1984.

694 SKALOUD, M., Ultimate Load and Failure Mechanism of Thin Webs in Shear, *Proc. Colloq. Design of Plate and Box Girders for Ultimate Strength*, Int. Assoc. for Bridge and Struct. Engineering, London, 1971.

695 SSRC Task Group 20, A Specification for the Design of Steel Composite Columns, *AISC Eng. J.*, 4th Quarter, 1988.

696 STEPHENSON, H. K., Highway Bridge Live Load Based on Laws of Chance, *J. Struct. Div. ASCE*, Vol. 83, No. ST4, July, 1957, pp. 1–23.

697 SWEENEY, R. A. P., Importance of Redundancy in Bridge-Fracture Control, *Transp. Research Record* 711, TRB, National Research Council, Washington, DC, 1979, pp. 23–29.

698 TAHA, H. A., *Operations Research*. Macmillan Co., New York, 1876, pp. 208–238.

699 TIMOSHENKO, S. P. and J. M. GERE, *Theory of Elastic Stability*, McGraw-Hill, New York, 1961.

700 TUPULA YAMBA, F., *Buckling Behavior of Steel Box Girder Bridges*, Reports No. 5, 6, and 7, Experimental Investigation, Dept. Civ. Eng., Concordia Univ., Montreal, Canada, June, 1980.

701 United States Steel Group, *Steel/Concrete Composite Box Girder Bridges: A Construction Manual*, AISC Marketing, Pittsburgh, PA, Dec, 1978.

702 VACHAJITPAN, P. and K. C. ROCKEY, Design Method for Optimum Unstiffened Girders, *J. Struct. Div. ASCE*, Vol. 104, No. ST1, 1978, pp. 141–155.

703 WOLCHUK, R., Proposed Specifications for Steel Box Girder Bridges, also known as Report No. FHWA-TS-80-205, *J. Struct. Div. ASCE*, Vol. 106, No. ST12, Dec., 1980, pp. 2463–2474.

704 WOLCHUK, R., Design Rules for Steel Box Girder Bridges, *Proc. Int. Assoc. for Bridge and Structural Engineering*, p. 41/81, Zürich, May, 1981.

705 WOLCHUK, R., Proposed Specifications for Steel Box Girder Bridges, Discussion, *J. Struct. Div. ASCE*, Vol. 108, No. ST8, Aug., 1982, pp. 1933–1936.

706 WOLCHUK, R., Box Girders, Section 19, Steel Plate Deck Bridges, *Str. Eng. Handbook*, McGraw-Hill, New York, 3rd ed, 1900.

707 OSTAPENKO, A. and C. CHERN, *Strength of Longitudinally Stiffened Plate Girders Under Combined Loads*, Fritz Eng. Laboratory Report 378.10, Lehigh Univ., Bethlehem, PA, Dec., 1970.

708 PARR, D. H. and S. P. MAGGARD, Ultimate Design of Hollow Thin-Walled Box Girders, *J. Struct. Div. ASCE*, Vol. 98, No. ST7, July, 1972, pp. 1427–1442.

709 PETZOLD, E. H., *Behavior and Design of Large Steel Box Girder Bridge*, Thesis, Washington Univ., St. Louis, MO, 1974.

710 POLYZOIS, D. and K. H. FRANK, Effect of Overspan and Incomplete Masing of Faning Surfaces on the Slip Resistance of Bolted Connections, *AISC Eng. J.*, 2nd Quarter, 1976.

711 POLYZOIS, D. and K. H. FRANK, Effect of Overspray and Incomplete Masking of Faying Surfaces on the Slip Resistance of Bolted Connections, *AISC Eng. J.*, 2nd Quarter, 1986.

712 PORTER, D. M., K. C. ROCKEY and H. R. EVANS, The Collapse Behavior of Plate Girders Loaded in Shear, *Struct. Engineer*, London, Vol. 53, No. 8, Aug., 1975, pp. 313–325.

713 *Report of the Royal Commission into the Failure of the West Gate Bridge*, C. H. Rixon, Govt. Printer, Melbourne, Australia, 1971.

714 ROCKEY, K. C., H. R. EVANS and D. M. PORTER, The Ultimate Strength Behavior of Long-itudinally Stiffened Reinforced Plate Girders, *Symp. on Nonlinear Techniques and Behavior in Struct. Analysis*, Transport and Road Research Lab., Crowthorne, Dec., 1974.

715 ROCKEY, K. C. and D. M. A. LEGGETT, The Buckling of a Plate Girder Web Under Pure Bending When Reinforced by a Single Longitudinal Stiffener, *Proc. Instn Civ. Engrs*, London, Vol. 21, Jan., 1962, p. 161.

716 ROCKEY, K. C. and M. SKALOUD, The Ultimte Load Behavior of Plate Girders Loaded in Shear, *Struct. Engineer*, London, Vol. 50, No. 11, Jan., 1972, pp. 29–48.

717 RICHMOND, B., *Report on Parametric Study on Web Panels*, Report for the Dept. Environ-ment, Maunsell and Partners, London, July, 1972.

718 ROBERTS, T. M. and C. K. CHONG, Collapse of Plate Girders Under Edge Loading, *J. Struct. Div. ASCE*, Vol. 107, No. ST8, Aug., 1981, pp. 1503–1509.

719 ROCKEY, K. C., H. R. EVANS and D. M. PORTER, Ultimate Load Capacity of Stiffened Webs Subjected to Shear and Bending, *Proc. Int. Conf. on Steel Box Girder Bridges*, Institution of Civil Engineers, London, 1973.

720 BAZANT, Z. P. and M. E. NIMEIRI, Stiffness Method for Curved Box Girders at Initial Stress, *J. Struct. Div. ASCE*, Vol. 100, No. ST10, Oct., 1974, pp. 2071–2090.

721 BELL, L. C. and C. P. HEINS, *The Solution of Curved Bridge Systems Using the Slope-Deflec-tion Fourier Series Method*, Civ. Eng. Dept., Report No. 19, Univ. Maryland, College Park, June, 1968.

722 BELL, L. C. and C. P. HEINS, *Curved Girder Computer Manual*, Civ. Eng. Dept., Report No. 30, Univ. Maryland, College Park, Sept., 1969.

723 BELL, L. C. and C. P. HEINS, Analysis of Curved Girder Bridges, *J. Struct. Div. ASCE*, Vol. 96, No. ST8, Aug., 1970, pp. 1657–1673.

724 KAVANAGH, T. C., Design Concepts for the Rio Bianco River Bridge, Personal Communication, 1970.

725 KLAIBER, F. W., *et al.*, *Methods of Strengthening Existing Highway Bridges*, NCHRP Report 293, TRB, National Research Council, Washington, DC, 1987.

726 KOMATSU, S., Ultimate Strength of Stiffened Plate Girders Subjected to Shear, *Proc. Colloquium on Design of Plate and Box Girders for Ultimate Strength*, Int. Assoc. for Bridge and Struct. Engineers, London, 1971, pp. 49–65.

727 KULAK, G. L., FISHER, J. W. and J. H. A. STRUIK, *Guide to Design Criteria for Bolted and Riveted Joints*, 2nd ed., Wiley, New York, 1987.

728 LITTLE, G. H., Stiffened Steel Compression Panels—Theoretical Failure Analysis, *Struct. Engineer*, London, Vol. 54, No. 12, Dec., 1976, pp. 489–500.

729 LOVEALL, C. L., Advances in Bridge Design and Construction, *Proc. AISC National Eng. Conf.*, Nashville, TN, June, 1986.

730 LYSE, I. and H. J. GODFREY, Investigation of Web Buckling in Steel Beams, *Trans. ASCE*, Vol. 100, 1935, pp. 675–706.

731 MAIR, R. I. and P. T. K. LINN, *Stress Analysis of Rectangular Load-Bearing Diaphragms*, Report Dept. Environment, London, Nov., 1972.

732 MASSONNET, C. and R. MAQUOI, Discussion on a Report by P. Dubas, *Seminar of IABSE*, London, 1971, pp. 381–389.

733 MATTOCK, A. H. and R. S. FOUNTAIN, *Criteria for Design of Steel-Concrete Composite Box Girder Highway Bridges*, US Steel Corp., August, 1967.

734 MATTOCK, R. B., *I-Section Efficiency*, Tech. Reference, Stran-Steel Corp., Houston, TX, April, 1962.

735 KOLBRUNNER, C. F. and K. BASLER, *Torsion in Structures, An Engineering Approach*, Springer-Verlag, New York, 1969.

736 KOMATSU, S. and H. NAKAI, Study on Free Vibration of Curved Girder Bridges, *Trans. Japanese Soc. Civ. Eng.*, No. 136, Dec., 1966, pp. 35–60.

737 KOMATSU, S. and H. NAKAI, Application of the Analogue Computer to the Analysis of Dynamic Response of Curved Girder Bridges, *Trans. Japanese Soc. Civ. Eng.*, No. 2, Part I, 1970, pp. 143–149.

738 KOMATSU, S. and H. NAKAI, Fundamental Study of Forced Vibration of Curved Girder Bridges, *Trans. Japanese Soc. Civ. Eng.*, No. 2, Part I, 1970, pp. 37–42.

739 KOMATSU, S., H. NAKAI and M. NAKANISHI, Statical Analysis of Horizontally Curved Skew Box Girder Bridges, *Trans. Japanese Soc. Civ. Eng.*, No. 3, Part 2, 1971, pp. 134–135.

740 KONISHI, I. and S. KOMATSU, On Fundamental Theory of Thin Walled Curved Girder, *Trans. Japanese Soc. Civ. Eng.*, No. 87, Nov., 1962, pp. 35–48.

741 KONISHI, I. and S. KOMATSU, Three Dimensional Analysis of Simply Supported Curved Girder Bridges, *Trans. Japanese Soc. Civ. Eng.*, No. 90, Feb., 1963, pp. 11–28.

742 BRENNAN, P. and J. A. MANDEL, *Appendix B: Three-Dimensional Analysis of Horizontally Curved Bridges*, CURT Final Report, Syracuse Univ., New York, 1973.

743 BRENNAN, P. J. and J. A. MANDEL, *Users Manual: Program for Three-Dimensional Analysis of Horizontally Curved Bridges*, Research Report, Syracuse Univ., New York, CURT Program, Dec., 1974.

744 BROCKENBROUGH, R. L., Survey of Curved Girder Bridges, *J. Civ. Eng. ASCE*, Vol. 43, No. 2, Feb., 1973, pp. 54–56.

745 CARSKADAN, P. S., *Autostress Design of Highway Bridges; Phase 3, Interior Support Model Test (AISI Project 188)*, Research Report 97-H-045(019-5), Feb., 1980.

746 CHU, K. and S. G. PINJARKAR, Analysis of Horizontally Curved Box Girder Bridges, *J. Struct. Div. ASCE*, Vol. 97, No. ST10, Oct., 1971, pp. 2481–2501.

747 MOZER, J. and C. CULVER, *Horizontally Curved Highway Bridges — Stability of Curved Plate Girders* (Report No. P1), Carnegie-Mellon Univ., CURT Program, Pittsburgh, PA, Sept., 1970.

748 MOZER, J., R. OHLSON and C. CULVER, *Horizontally Curved Highway Bridges — Stability of Curved Plate Girders* (Report No. 2), Carnegie-Mellon Univ., CURT Program, Pittsburgh, PA, Sept., 1971.

749 MURPHY, E. L. and C. P. HEINS, *Dead Load Analysis of Single Span Curved Bridges*, C.E. Report No. 52, Univ. Maryland, College Park, June, 1973.

750 NAKAI, H. and H. KOTOGUCHI, Dynamic Response of Horizontally Curved Girder Bridges Under Random Traffic Flows, *Proc. Japanese Soc. Civ. Eng.*, No. 244, 1975, pp. 117–128.

751 PCI, Recommended Practice for Segmental Construction in Prestressed Concrete, Report PCI Committee on Segmental Construction, *J. Prestressed Concrete Inst.*, Vol. 20, No. 2, March–April, 1975.

752 PCI, Prestressed Concrete Segmental Bridges on FA 412 over the Kishwaukee River, *Bridge Bull. No. 1*, PCI, Chicago, 1976.

753 PODOLNY, W., Evaluation of Transverse Flange Forces Induced by Laterally Inclined Longitudinal Posttensioning in Box Girder Bridges, *J. Prestressed Concrete Inst.*, Vol. 31, No. 1, Jan.–Feb., 1986.

754 PODOLNY, W. and J. M. MULLER, *Construction and Design of Prestressed Concrete Segmental Bridges*, Wiley, New York, 1982.

755 Portland Cement Association, *John F. Kennedy Memorial Causeway, Corpus Christi, Texas*, Bridge Report SR 162.01 E, Skokie, IL, 1974.

756 Portland Cement Association, *Napa River Bridge, California*, Bridge Report SR 194-01 E, Skokie, IL, 1977.

757 POSTEN, R. W., R. L. CARRASQUILLO and J. E. BREEN, Durability of Posttensioned Bridge Decks, *ACI Materials J.*, July–August, 1987.

758 Post-Tensioning Institute, *Post-Tensioning Manual*, 4th ed., Guide Specification for Post-Tensioning Materials, and Recommended Practice for Grouting of Post-Tensioned Prestressed Concrete, PTI, Phoenix, 1985.

759 United States Steel Corporation, Finite Element Modeling Techniques for Analysis of Live Load Distribution in a Stringer Bridge, *US Steel Research Bull.*, Pittsburgh, April, 1982.

760 United States Steel Corporation, Live-Load Lateral Distribution for the Sunshine Skyway Approach Spans, *US Steel Research Bull.*, Pittsburgh, April, 1982.

761 United States Steel Corporation, *V Load—A Computer Program for the Analysis of Horizontally Curved Steel Bridge Girders*, US Steel Engineers and Consultants, Pittsburgh, 1984.

762 VINCENT, G. S., Tentative Criteria for Load Factor Design of Steel Highway Bridges, *Bull. No. 15*, American Iron and Steel Inst., March, New York, 1969.

763 WILLIAMSON, D. M., *Analysis for Cross-Sectional Deformation of Curved Box Girders with Internal Diaphragms*, MS thesis, Carnegie-Mellon Univ., Pittsburgh, PA, 1974.

764 Post-Tensioning Institute, *Design and Construction Specifications for Segmental Concrete Bridges*, NCHRP Report No. 20-7/32, PTI, 1988.

765 PUCHER, A., *Influence Surfaces of Elastic Plates*, 4th rev. ed., Springer-Verlag, New York, 1969.

766 RABBAT, B. G. and K. SOWLAT, Testing of Segmental Concrete Girders with External Tendons, *PCI J.*, Vol. 32, No. 2, March–April, 1987.

767 SCHLAICH, J., SCHAFER, K. and M. JENNEWAIN, Towards a Consistent Design of Reinforced Concrete Structures, *PCI J.*, May–June, Vol. 32, No. 3, 1987.

768 SHUSHKEWICH, K. M., Time-Dependent Analysis of Segmental Bridges, *J. Computers and Structures*, Vol. 23, No. 1, 1986.

769 STONE, W. C., PAES-FILHA, W. and J. E. BREEN, *Behavior of Post-Tensioned Girder Anchorage Zones*, Research Report 208-2, Center for Transportation Research, Univ. of Texas, Austin, April, 1981.

770 STONE, W. C. and J. E. BREEN, *Analysis of Posttensioned Girder Anchorage Zones*, Research Report 208-1, Center for Transportation Research, Univ. Texas, Austin, June, 1981.

771 STONE, W. C. and J. E. BREEN, *Design of Posttensioned Girder Anchorage Zones*, Research Report 208-3F, Center for Transportation Research, Univ. Texas, Austin, June, 1981.

772 TADROS, M. K., GHALI, A. and W. DILGER, Time-Dependent Prestress Loss and Deflection in Prestressed Concrete Members, *PCI J.*, Vol. 20, No. 3, May–June, 1975.

773 TADROS, M. K., GHALI, A. and W. DILGER, Effect of Non-Prestressed Steel on Prestress Loss and Deflection, *PCI J.*, Vol. 22, No. 2, March–April, 1977.

774 VAN ZYL, S. F., *Analysis of Curved Segmentally Erected Prestressed Concrete Box Girder Bridges*, SESM Report No. 78-2, Univ. California, Berkeley, 1978.

775 VAN ZYL, S. F. and A. C. SCORDELIS, Analysis of Curved, Prestressed, Segmental Bridges, *J. Struct. Div. ASCE*, Vol. 105, No. ST11, pp. 2399–2417, 1979.

776 XANTHAKOS, P. P., *Ground Anchors and Anchored Structures*, Wiley, New York, 1991.

777 ZIENKIEWICZ, O. C. and M. WATSON, Some Creep Effects in Stress Analysis with Particular Reference to Concrete Pressure Vessels, *Nuclear Engineering and Design*, No. 4, 1966.

778 SPATES, K. R. and C. P. HEINS, *The Analysis of Single Curved Girders with Various Loadings and Boundary Conditions*, Univ. Maryland, College Park, 1968.

779 TUNG, D. H. H. and R. S. FOUNTAIN, Approximate Torsional Analysis of Curved Box Girders by the M/R Method, *AISC Eng. J.*, Vol. 7, No. 3, July, 1970.

780 United States Steel Corporation, *Analysis of Horizontally Curved Steel Bridge Girders*, US Steel Struct. Report ADUCO 91063, Pittsburgh, PA, 1963.

781 United States Steel Corporation, Horizontally Curved Bridges, *Hwy. Structures Design Handbook*, Vol. I, Pittsburgh, PA, 1967.

782 CHANG, C. K., *Effect of Loaded Length on the Buckling Strength of Slender Arches*, Thesis, Rice Univ., Houston, 1973.

783 CLARK, J. G., *Welded Deck Highway Bridges*, J. F. Lincoln Arc Welding Foundation, Cleveland, 1950.

784 COHN, M. Z. and M. ABDEL-ROHMAN, Analysis Up to Collapse of Elastic-Plastic Arches, *J. Computers and Structures*, Vol. 6, 1976, pp. 511–517.

785 CORONFORTH, R. C. and S. B. CHILDS, Computer Analysis of Two-Hinged Circular Arches, *J. Struct. Div. ASCE*, Vol. 93, No. ST2, Feb., 1967, pp. 319–338.

786 DAPEPPO, B. A. and R. SCHMIDT, Nonlinear Analysis of Buckling and Postbuckling Behavior of Circular Arches, *J. Appl. Mech. and Phys.*, Vol. 20, No. 6, 1969, pp. 847–857.

787 DADEPPO, D. A. and R. SCHMIDT, Sidesway Buckling of Deep Circular Arches Under a Concentrated Load, *J. Appl. Mech. ASME*, Vol. 36, No. 2, June, 1969, pp. 325–327.

788 DADEPPO, D. A. and R. SCHMIDT, Stability of Heavy Circular Arches with Hinged Ends, *J. American Inst. Aeronautics and Astronautics*, Vol. 9, No. 6, June, 1971, pp. 1200–1201.

789 DADEPPO, D. A. and R. SCHMIDT, Stability of Two-Hinged Circular Arches with Independent Loading Parameters, *American Inst. of Aeronautics and Astronautics J.*, Vol. 12, No. 3, March, 1974, pp. 385–386.

790 KOMATSU, S. and T. SHINKE, Practical Formulas for In-Plane Load Carrying Capacity of Arches, *Proc. Japan Soc. Civ. Eng.*, No. 267, 1977, pp. 39–51.

791 KUESEL, T. R., Deck Stiffened Arch Bridges by Robert Maillart, *J. Struc. Div. ASCE*, Vol. 100, No. ST4, April, 1974, pp. 832–833.

792 KURANISHI, S., The Torsional Buckling Strength of Solid Rib Arch Bridge, *Trans. Japan Soc. Civ. Eng.*, No. 75, 1961, pp. 59–67.

793 KURANISHI, S., Analysis of Arch Bridge Under Certain Lateral Forces, *Trans. Japan Soc. Civ. Eng.*, No. 73, 1961, pp. 1–6.

794 KURANISHI, S., Allowable Stress for Two-Hinged Steel Arch, *Proc. Japan Soc. Civ. Eng.*, No. 213, 1973, pp. 71–75.

795 KURANISHI, S. and T. YABUKI, In-Plane Strength of Arch Bridges Subjected to Vertical and Lateral Loads, *Second Int. Colloq. Stab. Steel Struct.*, Prelim. Report, Liège, Belgium, April, 1977, pp. 551–556.

796 KURANISHI, S. and T. YABUKI, Some Numerical Estimations of Ultimate In-Plane Strength of Two-Hinged Steel Arches, *Proc. Japan Soc. Civ. Eng.*, No. 287, 1979, pp. 155–158.

797 KURANISHI, S. and T. YABUKI, *Required Out-of-Plane Rigidities of Steel Arch Bridges with Two Main Ribs Subjected to Vertical and Lateral Loads*, Tech. Report, Tohoku Univ., Sendai, Vol. 46, No. 1, 1981.

798 KURANISHI, S. and T. YABUKI, Ultimate Strength Design Criteria for Two-Hinged Steel Arch Structures, *Proc. Japan Soc. Civ. Eng.*, No. 3005/I-2, 1984.

799 KURANISHI, S. and T. YABUKI, Lateral Load Effect on Arch Bridge Design, *J. Struct. Div. ASCE*, Vol. 110, No. 9, 1984, pp. 2263–2274.

800 GALLI, A. and G. FRANCIOSI, Limit Analysis of Thin Arch Bridges with Stiffening Girders, *G. Genio Civ.*, Vol. 93, No. 11, 1995.

801 GALAMBOS, T. V., *Guide to Stability Design Criteria for Metal Structures*, Wiley, New York, 1988.

802 GARRELTS, J. M., St. Georges Tied Arch Span. *Trans. ASCE*, Vol. 69, No. 108, Paper No. 2188, 1943, pp. 543–554.

803 GIAMMATTEO, M. and G. C. GAVARINI, Limit Analysis of Bridges with Arch-Girder Interaction, *G. Genio Civ.*, Vol. 11a, Nos. 1–2–3, 1972.

804 GODDEN, W. G., The Lateral Buckling of Tied Arches, *Proc. Instn Civ. Engrs*, London, Vol. 3, No. 2, Aug., 1954, pp. 496–514.

805 GODDEN, W. G. and J. C. THOMSON, Experimental Study of Model Tied-Arch Bridge, *Proc. Instn Civ. Engrs*, Vol. 14, Dec., 1959, pp. 383–394.

806 GREENBERG, H. J. and W. PRAGER, On Limit Design of Beams and Frames, *Trans. ASCE*, Vol. 117, Paper No. 2501, 1952, pp. 447–458.

807 HALL, A. S. and R. W. WOODHEAD, *Frame Analysis*, Wiley, New York, 1961, 247 p.

808 HARDESTY, S., *et al.*, Rainbow Arch Bridge Over Niagara Gorge — A Symposium, *Trans. ASCE*, 110, 1945, 2 – 178.

809 HARRISON, H. B., In-Plane Stability of Parabolic Arches, *J. Struct. Div. ASCE*, Vol. 109, No. ST1, Jan., 1982, pp. 195 – 205.

810 HARRISON, H. B., In-Plane Stability of Parabolic Arches, *J. Struct. Div. ASCE*, Vol. 108, No. ST1, Jan., 1982, pp. 195 – 205.

811 HARTWIG, H. J., Die Kaiserleibrücke, *Der Stahlbau*, Vol. 34, No. 4, April, 1965, pp. 97 – 110.

812 HAZELET, C. P. and R. H. WOOD, Six-Line Tied-Arch Bridge Across Ohio River, *Civ. Eng.*, N.Y., Vol. 31, No. 11, Nov., 1961, pp. 43 – 47.

813 HIRSCH, E. G. and E. P. POPOV, Analysis of Arches by Finite Differences, *Proc. ASCE*, Vol. 18, No. 829, Nov., 1955, 18 pp.

814 KLÖPPEL, K. and W. PROTTA, A Contribution to the Buckling Problem of Circular Curved Bars, *Der Stahlbau*, No. 30, 1961, pp. 1 – 15.

815 KOMATSU, S. and T. SAKIMOTO, Ultimate Load Carrying Capacity of Steel Arches, *J. Struct. Div. ASCE*, Vol. 103, No. ST12, Dec., 1977, pp. 2323 – 2336.

816 ORAN, C. and R. S. REAGAN, Buckling of Uniformly Compressed Circular Arches, *J. Eng. Mech. Div. ASCE*, Vol. 95, No. EM4, Aug., 1969, pp. 879 – 895.

817 OSTENFELD, A., *Teknisk Statik*, 3rd ed., Vol. II, Jul. Gjellumps Boghanel, Copenhagen, Denmark, 1925, p. 225.

818 OSTLUND, L., Lateral Stability of Bridge Arches Braced with Transverse Bars, *Trans. Royal Inst. Tech.*, Stockholm, No. 84, 1954.

819 RONCA, P. and M. Z. COHN, Limit Analysis of Reinforced Concrete Arch Bridges, *J. Struct. Div. ASCE*, Vol. 105, No. ST2, Feb., 1979, pp. 313 – 326.

820 RONCA, P., *Limit Analysis of Reinforced Concrete Arch Bridges*, Thesis, Univ. Waterloo, Ontario, Canada, 1977.

821 ROSS, T. J., *Numerical Large Deflection Bending and Buckling Analysis of Arches*, Thesis, Rice Univ., Houston, 1973.

822 SABIR, A. B. and A. C. LOCK, Large Deflection, Geometrically Nonlinear Finite Element Analysis of Circular Arches, *Int. J. Mech. Sci.*, Vol. 15, 1973, pp. 37 – 47.

823 SAKIMOTO, T. and S. KOMATSU, A Possibility of Total Breakdown of Bridge Arches due to Buckling of Lateral Bracing, *Second Int. Colloq. Stab. Steel Struct.*, Final Report, Liège, Belgium, April, 1977, pp. 299 – 301.

824 SAKIMOTO, T. and S. KOMATSU, Ultimate Load Carrying Capacity of Steel Arches with Initial Imperfections, *Second Int. Colloq. Stab. Steel Struct.*, Prelim. report, Liège, Belgium, April, 1977, pp. 545 – 550.

825 SAKIMOTO, T. and S. KOMATSU, Ultimate Strength of Steel Arches under Lateral Loads, *Proc. Japan Soc. Civ. Eng.*, No. 292, 1979, pp. 83 – 94.

826 SAKIMOTO, T. and S. KOMATSU, Ultimate Strength of Arches with Bracing Systems, *J. Struct. Div. ASCE*, Vol. 108, No. ST5, 1982, pp. 1064 – 1076.

827 SAKIMOTO, T. and S. KOMATSU, Ultimate Strength Formula for Steel Arches, *J. Struct. Div. ASCE*, Vol. 109, No. 3, 1983, pp. 613 – 627.

828 SAKIMOTO, T. and S. KOMATSU, Ultimate Strength Formula for Central Arch Girder Bridges, *Proc. Japan Soc. Civ. Eng.*, No. 333, 1983, pp. 183 – 186.

829 SAKIMOTO, T. and Y. YAMAO, Ultimate strength of Deck Type Steel Arch Bridges, *Third Int. Colloq. Stab. Metal Struct.*, Prelim. Report, Paris, Nov., 1983.

830 SAKIMOTO, T., T. YAMAO and S. KOMATSU, Experimental Study on the Ultimate Strength of Steel Arches, *Proc. Japan Soc. Civ. Eng.*, No. 286, 1979, pp. 139 – 149.

831 LIPSON, S. L. and M. I. HAQUE, Optimal Design of Arches Using the Complex Method, *J. Struct. Div. ASCE*, Vol. 106, No. ST12, Dec., 1980, pp. 2509 – 2525.

832 LOUIS, H., P. GUIAUX and E. MAS, Experimental Investigation of End Stiffening of Bow-string or Vierendeel Type Bridge Girder, *Acier – Stahl – Steel*, Vol. 27, No. 3, March, 1962, pp. 119 – 125.

833 LOWE, P. G., Effect of Axial Thrust on Carrying Capacity of Mild Steel Arch Rib, Inst. Eng. Australia, *Civ. Eng. Trans.*, CE3(2), Sept., 1961, pp. 95 – 101.

834 MAILLART, R., Note on Arch Bridges in Switzerland, *Proc. First Int. Congr. for Concrete and Reinforced Concrete*, Liège, Belgium, Sept., 1930.

835 MAILLART, R., Leichte Eisenbeton-Brücken in der Schweiz (Light Reinforced-Concrete Bridges in Switzerland), *Der Bauingenieur*, Berlin, Vol. 10, 1931.

836 MALLETT, R. H. and P. V. MARCAL, Finite Element Analyses of Nonlinear Structures, *J. Struct. Div. ASCE*, Vol. 94, No. ST9, Sept., 1968, pp. 2081 – 2105.

837 MAK, C. K. and D. KAO, Finite Element Analysis of Buckling and Post-Buckling Behavior of Arches with Geometric Imperfections, *J. Computers and Structures*, Vol. 3, 1973, pp. 149 – 161.

838 MALLETT, R. H. and P. V. MARCAL, Finite Element Analyses of Nonlinear Structures, *J. Struct. Div. ASCE*, Vol. 94, No. ST9, Sept., 1968, pp. 2081 – 2105.

839 MCCULLOUGH, C. B. and E. S. THAYER, *Elastic Arch Bridges*, Wiley, New York, 1931.

840 MIKLOGSKY, H. A. and O. J. SOTILLO, Design of Flexible Steel Arches by Interaction Diagrams, *J. Struct. Div. ASCE*, Vol. 83, ST2, March, 1957, 35 pp.

841 MORRIS, C. T., *et al.*, Final Report of the Special ASCE Committee on Concrete and Reinforced Concrete Arches, *Trans. ASCE*, Vol. 100, Paper No. 1922, 1935, pp. 1427 – 1531.

842 MÜLLER-BRESLAU, H., *Die graphische Statik der Baukonstruktionen*, 5th ed., Vol. II, Part 1, Alfred Kroner Verlag, Stuttgart, Germany, 1922, pp. 274 – 294.

843 MÜLLER-BRESLAU, H., *Die graphische Statik der Baukonstruktionen*, 2nd ed., Vol. II, Part 2, Alfred Kroner Verlag, Leipzig, Germany, 1925, pp. 257 – 259.

844 SCHMIDT, R. and D. A. DADEPPO, A Survey of Literature on Large Deflections on Non-shallow Arches, Bibliography of Finite Deflections of Straight and Curved Beams, Rings, and Shallow Arches, *J. Industrial Mathematics*, Industrial Mathematics Soc., Vol. 21, Part 2, 1971, pp. 91 – 114.

845 SCHMIDT, R. and D. A. DADEPPO, Buckling of Clamped Circular Arches Subjected to a Point Load, *J. Applied Mathematics and Physics*, Vol. 23, 1972, pp. 146 – 148.

846 SCOTT, P. A. and G. ROBERTS, The Volte Bridge, *Proc. Instn Civ. Engrs*, London, No. 9, April, 1958, p. 395.

847 SHINKE, T., H. ZUI and T. NAKAGAWA, In-Plane Load Carrying Capacity of Two-Hinged Arches with a Stiffening Girder, *Trans. Japan Soc. Civ. Eng.*, No. 301, 1980, pp. 47 – 59.

848 SHINKE, T., H. ZUI and Y. NAMITA, Analysis of In-Plane Elasto-Plastic Buckling and Load Carrying Capacity of Arches, *Proc. Japan Soc. Civ. Eng.*, No. 244, 1975, pp. 57 – 69.

849 SHUKLA, S. N. and M. OJALVO, Lateral Buckling of Parabolic Arches with Tilting Loads, *J. Struct. Div. ASCE*, Vol. 97, No. ST6, 1971, pp. 1763 – 1773.

850 SORGENTE, V., Experimental Results on a Stiffened Arch Bridge, *G. Genio Civ.*, Vol. 95, Dec., 1957.

851 Spectacular Venezuelan Concrete Arch Bridge, *Eng. News-Record*, 149(11), 28 – 32, Sept. 11, 1952.

852 TOKARZ, F. J., Experimental Study of Lateral Buckling of Arches, *J. Struct. Div. ASCE*, Vol. 97, No. ST2, Feb., 1971, pp. 545 – 559.

853 TOKARZ, F. J. and R. S. SANDHU, Lateral-Torsional Buckling of Parabolic Arches, *J. Struct. Div. ASCE*, Vol. 98, No. ST5, May, 1972, pp. 1161 – 1179.

854 UPSTONE, T. J. and W. N. CARDNO, The Design and Construction of the Superstructure of the Marshal Carmona Bridge at Vila Franca de Xira, Portugal, *Proc. Instn. Civ. Engrs*, Part 3, No. 3, Dec., 1954, pp. 695 – 737.

855 VAN DER WOUDE, F. and B. F. COUSINS, *Deformation of Arches: Linear Elastic Behavior*, Research Report CM-78/3, Univ. of Tasmania, Hobart, Australia, 1978.

856 VAN DER WOUDE, F. and B. F. COUSINS, Deformation of Arches: Elastic Buckling Behavior, *J. Struct. Div. ASCE*, Vol. 105, No. ST12, Dec., 1979, pp. 2677–2694.

857 ASPLUND, S. O., *Structural Mechanics: Classical and Matrix Methods*, Prentice-Hall, Englewood Cliffs, NJ, 1966.

858 AUSTIN, W. J., In-Plane Bending and Buckling of Arches, *J. Struct. Div. ASCE*, Vol. 97, No. ST5, May, 1971, pp. 1575–1592.

859 AUSTIN, W. J. and ROSS, T. J., Elastic Buckling of Arches under Symmetrical Loading, *J. Struct. Div. ASCE*, Vol. 102, No. ST5, May, 1976, pp. 1085–1095.

860 AUSTIN, W. J., T. J. ROSS, A. S. TAWFIK and R. O. VOLZ, Numerical Bending Analysis of Arches, *J. Struct. Div. ASCE*, Vol. 108, No. ST4, April, 1982, pp. 849–868.

861 BALOG, L., Truss-tied Arch Bridge has a Long History, *Civ. Eng.* (New York), 26(12), 69, 70 (Dec.), 1956.

862 BAXTER, J. W., A. F. GEE and H. B. JAMES, Gladesville Bridge, *Proc. Instn Civ. Engrs*, No. 30, March, 1965, pp. 489–530.

863 BILLINGTON, D. O., Deck Stiffened Arch Bridges of Robert Maillart, *J. Struct. Div. ASCE*, Vol. 99, No. ST7, July, 1973, pp. 1527–1539.

864 BOUCHET, A., Le Pont de Fehmarsund, élement de la nouvelle liaison Hambourg–Copenhague, *Technique des Travaux*, Vol. 40, Nos. 1–2, Jan.–Feb., 1964, pp. 56–64.

865 BOX, M. J., A New Method of Constrained Optimization and Comparison with Other Methods, *Computer J.*, Vol. 8, April, 1965, pp. 42–52.

866 CARPENTER, S. T., *Structural Mechanics*, Wiley, New York, 1960, 538 pp.

867 CHANDRANGSU, S. and S. R. SPARKES, A Study of the Bowstring Arch Having Extensible Suspension Rods and Different Ratios of Tie-Beam to Arch-Rib Stiffness, *Proc. Instn Civ. Engrs*, Vol. 3, No. 2, Aug., 1954, pp. 515–563.

868 STEIN, P. and H. WILD, Das Bogentragwerk der Fehmarnsundbrücke, *Der Stahlbau*, Vol. 34, No. 6, June, 1965, pp. 171–186.

869 STEVENS, L. K., Carrying Capacity of Mild Steel Arches, *Proc. Instn Civ. Engrs*, No. 6, March, 1957, pp. 511–693.

870 STÜSSI, F., Lateral Buckling and Vibration of Arches, *Proc. IABSE Publ.*, Vol. 7, 1943, pp. 327–343.

871 TADJBAKHSH, I. and M. FARSHAD, On Conservatively Loaded Funicular Arches and Their Optimal Design, *Proc. IUTAM Symp. Struct. Optimization*, Warsaw, 1973, pp. 215–218.

872 FISHER, J. W., J. R. BELLENOIT and J. H. DANIELS, *High Cycle Fatigue Behavior of Steel Bridge Details—Final Report*, Fritz Eng. Laboratory Report 386-13(82), Lehigh Univ., Bethlehem, PA, Dec., 1982, 136 pp.

873 FISHER, J. W., H. HAUSAMANN and M. D. SULLIVAN, *Detection and Repairs of Fatigue Damage in Welded Highway Bridges*, NCHRP Report 206, 1979.

874 FISHER, J. W., D. R. MERTZ and A. ZHONG, *Steel Bridge Members Under Variable Amplitude Long Life Fatigue Loading*, NCHRP 267, TRB, National Research Council, Washington, DC, Dec., 1983.

875 FISHER, J. W. and A. W. PENSE, *Final Report on I-79 Tied Arch Cracking—Nevill Island Bridge*, Fritz Eng. Laboratory Report 494-1(84), Lehigh Univ., Bethlehem, PA, Dec., 1984.

876 FISHER, J. W. and J. H. A. STRUIK, *Guide to Design Criteria for Bolted and Riveted Joints*, Wiley, New York, 1974.

877 CUDNEY, G. R., Stress Histories of Highway Bridges, *J. Struct. Div. ASCE*, Vol. 94, No. ST12, Dec., 1968, pp. 2725–2737.

878 ACI, Considerations for Design of Concrete Structures Subjected to Fatigue Loading, ACI Committee 215, *ACI J., Proc.*, Vol. 71, No. 3, March, 1974, pp. 97–121.

879 ALBRECHT, P., A. ABTAHI and G. R. IRWIN, *Fatigue Strength of Overloaded Bridge Components*, Report No. FHWA-MD-R-76-7, Dept. Civ. Eng., Univ. Maryland, College Park, Oct., 1975.

880 ALBRECHT, P. and I. M. FRIEDLAND, Fatigue-Limit Effect on Variable-Amplitude Fatigue of Stiffeners, *J. Struct. Div. ASCE*, Vol. 105, No. ST12, Dec., 1979, pp. 2657–2675.

881 DOUGLAS, T. R., *Fatigue of Bridges under Repeated Highway Loadings*, Civ. Eng. Dept. Report 54, Univ. Alabama, April, 1971.

882 DUNCAN, J. M. and C. K. TAN, *Engineering Manual for Estimating Tolerable Movements of Bridges*, NCHRP 343, Transp. Research Board, National Research Council, Washington, DC, 1991.

883 EKBERG, M. and J. H. EMANUEL, *Thermal Movement of Bridges: A Survey*, University of Missouri-Rolla, Oct., 1967.

884 EMERSON, M., *Bridge Temperatures and Movements in the British Isles*, Bridge Section-Road Research Lab., RRL Report LR 228, Ministry of Transport, 1968.

885 EMERSON, M., *Temperature Differences in Bridges: Basis of Design Requirements*, TRRL Lab. Report 765, Dept. of Transport, Berkshire, UK, 1977.

886 EMERSON, M., *Bridge Temperatures for Settling Bearings and Expansion Joints*, TRRL Suppl. Report 479, Dept. of Transport, Berkshire, UK, 1979.

887 BURDETTE, E. G. and D. W. GOODPASTURE, *Full Scale Bridge Testing: An Evaluation of Bridge Design Criteria*, Univ. Tennessee, Knoxville, Dec., 1971.

888 BUSSA, S. L., N. J. SHETH and S. R. SWANTON, Development of a Random Load Life Prediction Model, *Materials Research and Standards ASTM*, Vol. 12, No. 3, March, 1972, pp. 31–43.

889 CADY, P. D. and R. E. WEYERS, Deterioration Rates of Concrete Bridge Decks, *J. Transp. Eng. ASCE*, Vol. 110, No. 1, 1984, pp. 34–44.

890 CICCI, F. and P. F. CSAGOLY, Assessment of the Fatigue Life of a Steel Girder Bridge, *Transp. Research Record* 507, TRB, National Research Council, Washington, DC, 1974.

891 COMEAU, M. P. and G. L. KULAK, *Fatigue Strength of Welded Steel Elements*, Tech. Report 79, Univ. Alberta, Canada, Oct., 1979.

892 CORLEY, W. G., J. M. HANSON and T. HELGASON, Design of Reinforced Concrete for Fatigue, *J. Struct. Div. ASCE*, Vol. 104, No. ST6, June, 1978, pp. 921–932.

893 CORNELL, C. A., Bayesian Statistical Decision Theory and Reliability-Based Design, *Int. Conf. Struct. Safety and Reliab. Eng. Struct.*, Pergamon Press, New York, April, 1969, pp. 47–68.

894 WAESTLUND, G., Stability Problems of Compressed Steel Members and Arch Bridges, *J. Struct. Div. ASCE*, Vol. 86, No. ST6, June, 1960, pp. 47–71.

895 WALKER, A. C., A Nonlinear Finite Element Analysis of Shallow Arches, *Int. J. Solids and Structures*, Vol. 5, 1969, pp. 97–107.

896 WEN, R. K. and J. LANGE, Curved Beam Element of Arch Buckling Analysis, *J. Struct. Div. ASCE*, Vol. 107, No. ST11, Nov., 1981, pp. 2053–2069.

897 WITTFOHT, H., REISSE, H. and H. G. BORCK, Die neue Fuhrparkbrücke in Hagen, *Beton und Stahlbetonbau*, 58(6), 129–37 (June), 1963.

898 YABUKI, T. and S. KURANISHI, Out-of-Plane Behavior of Circular Arches under Side Loadings, *Proc. Japan Soc. Civ. Eng.*, No. 214, 1973, pp. 71–82.

899 YABUKI, T. and S. VINNAKOTA, Stability of Steel Arch Bridges, A State-of-the-Art Report, *Solid Mech. Arch.*, Vol. 9, No. 2, 1984, Noordhoff Int. Publ., Leyden, Netherlands.

900 YABUKI, T., S. VINNAKOTA and S. KURANISHI, Lateral Load Effect on Load Carrying Capacity of Steel Arch Bridge Structures, *J. Struct. Div. ASCE*, Vol. 109, No. ST10, 1983, pp. 2434–2449.

901 ZEZELY, B., Prestressed Concrete Road Bridge in Yugoslavia, *Concrete Construction Eng.*, 57(9), Sept., 1962, pp. 335–344.

902 HOPE, B. B. and J. A. N. LEE, *Tests on Laboratory Bridge-3*, Queen's Univ. – Ontario Joint Hwy. Research Program, Report 23, Oct., 1964, 73 pp.

903 HORNE, M. R., Elastic Lateral Stability of Trusses, *Struct. Engineer*, Vol. 38, No. 5, May, 1960, pp. 147 – 155.

904 JENNINGS, A., Frame Analysis Including Change of Geometry, *Proc. ASCE, J. Struct. Div.*, Vol. 94, ST3, March, 1968, pp. 627 – 644.

905 KAJITA, T. and Y. K. CHEUNG, *Finite Element Analysis of Cable-Stayed Bridges*, Publ. 33-II, Int. Assoc. for Bridge and Struct. Engng, 1973.

906 KANE, T. A., T. F. MAHONEY and J. H. CLARK, West Seattle Swing Bridge, *Trans. Research Record* 1275, TRB, National Research Council, Washington, DC, 1990, pp. 62 – 66.

907 KHALIL, M. S., W. H. DILGER and A. GHALI, Time Dependent Analysis of PC Cable-Stayed Bridges, *J. Struct. Div. ASCE*, Vol. 109, No. ST8, Aug., 1983.

908 LAZAR, B. E., Stiffness Analysis of Cable-Stayed Girder Bridges, *J. Struct. Div. ASCE*, Vol. 98, No. ST7, July, 1972.

909 LAZAR, B. E., M. S. TROITSKY and M. M. DOUGLASS, Load Balancing Analysis of Cable-Stayed Bridges, *J. Struct. Div. ASCE*, Vol. 98, No. ST8, Aug., 1972.

910 LEISSA, A. W., Contact Stresses in Wire Ropes, *Wire and Wire Products*, 34(3), 307 – 14, 372 (March), 1959.

911 LEONHARDT, F., Latest Developments of Cable-Stayed Bridges for Long Spans, *Saetryk af Bygingsstatiske Meddelelser*, Vol. 45, No. 4, 1974, Denmark, Danmarko Teckniske Hojskole.

912 LEONHARDT, F. and W. ZELLNER, Cable-Stayed Bridge — Report on Latest Developments, *Proc. Canadian Struct. Eng. Conf.*, Ontario, 1970.

913 LIN, T. Y., Y. C. YANG, H. K. LU and C. M. REDFIELD, Design of Ruck-A-Chucky Bridge, *Cable-Stayed Bridges, Struct. Eng. Series* No. 4, June, 1978, Bridge Div. FHWA, Washington, DC.

914 LIPSON, C., NOLL, G. C. and L. S. CLOCK, *Stress and Strength of Manufactured Parts*, McGraw-Hill, New York, 1950, 25 pp.

915 LIPSON, S. L. and K. M. AGRAWAL, Weight Optimization of Plane Trusses, *J. Struct. Div. ASCE*, Vol. 100, No. ST5, May, 1974, pp. 865 – 880.

916 LIPSON, S. L. and L. B. GWIN, The Complex Method Applied to Optimal Truss Configuration, *J. Computers and Structures*, Vol. 7, 1977, pp. 461 – 468.

917 LIPSON, S. L. and L. B. GWIN, Discrete Sizing of Trusses for Optimal Geometry, *J. Struct. Div. ASCE*, Vol. 103, No. ST5, May, 1977, pp. 1031 – 1046.

918 MADDOX, S. J., Improving the Fatigue Lives of Fillet Welds by Shot Peening, *Proc. IABSE Colloquium, Lausanne, Fatigue of Steel and Concrete Structures*, 1982, pp. 377 – 384.

919 MAEDA, Y., *et al.*, *Deterioration of Highway Bridges in Japan*, Technology Reports, Osaka University, Vol. 31, No. 1599, Osaka, Japan, March, 1981, pp. 135 – 144.

920 MAHER, D. R. H., The Effects of Differential Temperature on Continuous Prestressed Concrete Bridges, *Civ. Eng. Trans., Instit. Engineers*, Vol. CE12, No. 1, Paper 2793, 1970, pp. 29 – 32, Australia.

921 MAIER, *Einfluss des Spannungzustandes auf das Formänderungsvermögen der metallischen Werkstoffe*, Berlin, 1935.

922 MIKI, C., T. NISHIMURA, J. TAJIMA and A. OKUKAWA, Fatigue Strength of Steel Members Having Longitudinal Single-Bevel-Groove Welds, *Trans. Japan Welding Soc.* Vol. 11, No. 1, April, 1980, pp. 43 – 56.

923 MIKI, C., F. NISHINO, Y. HARABAYASHI and H. OHGA, Fatigue Strength of Longitudinal Welded Joints Containing Blowholes, *Proc. Japan Soc. Civ. Eng.*, No. 325, Sept., 1982, pp. 155 – 165.

924 MIKI, C., F. NISHINO, T. SASAKI and T. MORI, Influence of Root Irregularity of Fatigue Strength of Partially-Penetrated Longitudinal Welds, *Proc. Japan Soc. Civ. Eng.*, No. 337, Sept., 1983, pp. 223–226.

925 MIKI, C., J. TAJIMA, K. ASAHI and H. TAKENOUCHI, Fatigue of Large-Size Longitudinal Butt Welds with Partial Penetration, *Proc. Japan Soc. Civ. Eng.*, No. 322, June, 1982, pp. 143–156.

926 MINDLIN, H., Influence of Details on Fatigue Behavior of Structures, *J. Struct. Div. ASCE*, Vol. 94, No. ST12, Dec., 1968.

927 MINNER, H. H. and T. SEEGER, Improvement of Fatigue Life of Welded Beams by TIG-Dressing, *Proc. IABSE Colloquium-Lausanne*, 1982, pp. 385–392.

928 MOULTON, L. K., H. V. S. GANGARAO and G. T. HALVORSEN, *Tolerable Movement Criteria for Highway Bridges*, Report No. FHWA/RD-85/107, FHWA, Washington, DC, 1985, 118 pp.

929 MUNSE, W. H. *Fatigue of Welded Steel Structures*, Welding Research Council, New York, 1964.

930 MUNSE, W. H. and A. STALLMOYER, *Effect of End Geometry of Cover Plates on Fatigue*, Welding Research Council, New York, 1962.

931 NADAI, A., *Plasticity*, McGraw-Hill, New York, 1931.

932 NADAI, A., Plastic Behavior of Metals in the Strain Hardening Range, *J. Appl. Phys.*, 1937, pp. 205–213.

933 NADAI, A., *Theory of Flow and Fracture of Solids*, McGraw-Hill, New York, 1950.

934 MUELLER, J. A. and B. T. YEN, Girder Web Boundary Stresses and Fatigue, *Welding Research Council Bull. 127*, 1968.

935 MUNSE, W. H., *Fatigue of Welded Steel Structures*, Welding Research Council, New York, 1964.

936 OEHLER, L. T., Vibration Susceptibilities of Various Highway Bridge Types, *J. Struct. Div. ASCE*, Vol. 83, No. ST4, July, 1957.

937 PARIS, P. and F. ERDOGAN, A Critical Analysis of Crack Propagation Laws, *J. Basic Eng. ASME*, Dec., 1970.

938 LIPSON, C., NOLL, G. C. and L. S. CLOCK, *Stress and Strength of Manufactured Parts*, McGraw-Hill, New York, 1950, 259 pp.

939 LU, Z. A., Dynamic Analysis of Cable Hung Ruck-A-Chucky Bridge, *ASCE National Spring Conv.*, Preprint 3180, Pittsburgh, PA, 1978, April 24–28.

940 McCORMAC, J. C., *Structural Analysis*, Intext Educational Publishers, New York, 1975.

941 MODJESKI and MASTERS, *Greater New Orleans Bridge over Mississippi River*, Final Report to Mississippi River Bridge Authority, 1960, 2 vols.

942 NEUBER and H. G. HAHN, Stress Concentration in Scientific Research and Engineering, *Appl. Mech. Rev.* 19(3), 187–256, March, 1966.

943 NORRIS, C. H. and J. B. WILBUR, *Elementary Structural Analysis*, 2nd ed., McGraw-Hill, New York, 1960, 650 pp.

944 O'CONNOR, C., Buckling in Steel Structures—2. The Use of a Characteristic Imperfect Shape in the Design of Determinate Plane Trusses Against Buckling in Their Plane, Univ. Queensland, *Dept. Civ. Eng., Bull.*, 6, July, 1965.

945 *Ontario Highway Bridge Design Code*, Ontario Ministry of Transportation and Communication, 1979.

946 O'CONNOR, C., *Design of Bridge Superstructures*, Wiley, New York, 1971.

947 OKAUCHI, I., A. YABE and K. ANDO, Studies on the Characteristics of a Cable-Stayed Bridge, *Bull. Faculty of Science and Eng.*, Chuo Univ., Vol. 10, 1967.

948 PETERSON, R. E., *Stress Concentration Design Factors, Wiley*, New York, 1953, 155 pp.

949 PODOLNY, W., *Static Analysis of Cable-Stayed Bridges*, PhD thesis, Univ. Pittsburgh, PA, 1971.

950 PODOLNY, W., Cable Connections in Stayed Girder Bridges, *Eng. J. AISC*, Fourth Quarter, Vol. 11, No. 4, 1974.

951 PODOLNY, W., Design Considerations in Cable-Stayed Bridges, *ASCE Specialty Conf. on Metal Bridges*, Nov. 12–13, 1974, St. Louis, MO.

952 PODOLNY, W., Concrete Cable-Stayed Bridges, *Transp. Research Record* 665, *Bridge Eng.*, Vol. 2, TRB Conf., St. Louis, MO, Sept., 1978.

953 PODOLNY, W., The Evolution of Concrete Slab Cable-Stayed Bridges, *Concrete Int. ACI*, 1981, Vol. 3, No. 8, Aug.

954 WILL, K. M., C. P. JOHNSON and H. MATLOCK, *Analytical and Experimental Investigation of the Thermal Response of Highway Bridges*, Research Report 23-2, Texas Dept. Highways and Public Transp., Univ. Texas, Austin, Feb., 1977, 148 pp.

955 WILLENBORG, *et al.*, *A Crack Growth Retardation Model Using an Effective Stress Concept*, AFFDL-TM-FBR-71-1, Wright-Patterson AFB, Ohio, 1971.

956 WIRSHING, P. H. and J. T. P. YAO, Statistical Methods in Structural Fatigue, *J. Struct. Div. ASCE*, Vol. 96, No. ST6, June, 1970, pp. 1201–1219.

957 YAO, J. T. P., Fatigue Reliability and Design, *J. Struct. Div. ASCE*, Vol. 100, No. ST9, Sept., 1974, pp. 1827–1836.

958 YAO, J. T. P., *Reliability Considerations for Fatigue Analysis and Design of Structures*, School Civ. Eng., Purdue Univ., June, 1980.

959 YAMADA, K., *Fatigue Behavior of Structural Components Subjected to Variable Amplitude Loading*, PhD thesis, Univ. Maryland, College Park, 1975.

960 YAMADA, K. and P. ALBRECHT, *A Collection of Live Load Stress Histograms of US Highway Bridges*, C.E. Report, Univ. Maryland, College Park, 1975.

961 YAMADA, K. and P. ALBRECHT, Fatigue Design of Welded Bridge Details for Service Stresses, *Transp. Research Record* 607, TRB, National Research Council, Washington, DC, 1976.

962 CROZIER, W. F., J. R. STOKER, V. C. MARTIN and E. F. NORDLIN, *A Laboratory Evaluation of Full-Size Elastomeric Bridge Bearing Pads*, Research Report, California Dept. Transp., TL-6574-1-74-26, Hwy. Research Report, June, 1979.

963 DABROWSKI, R., *Curved Thin-Walled Girders — Theory and Analysis*, Springer-Verlag, Berlin, 1968.

964 DAHIR, S. H. and D. B. MELLOTT, Bridge Deck Expansion Joints, *Transp. Research Record* 1118, TRB, National Research Council, Washington, DC, 1987, pp. 16–24.

965 FHWA, *Watertight Bridge Deck Joint Seals*, National Experimental and Evaluation Program, Final Report, Project 11, US Dept. Transp., Washington, DC, July, 1977.

966 GENT, A. N., Elastic Stability of Rubber Compression Springs, *ASME J. Mech. Eng. Sci.*, Vol. 6, No. 4, 1964.

967 ISBN, *Acceptance Criteria of Steel Bridge Welds*, Report No. 0-309-04858-3, TRB, National Research Council, Washington, DC, 1990.

968 LIM, K. Y., D. I. MCLEAN and E. H. HENLEY, *Plastic Hinge Details for the Bases of Bridge Columns*, Small-Scale Test Model, Interim Report, Washington Dept. Transp., Olympia, April, 1989.

969 LIM, K. Y., D. I. MCLEAN and E. H. HENLEY, Moment-Reducing Hinge Details for the Bases of Bridge Columns, *Transp. Research Record* 1275, TRB, National Research Council, Washington, DC, 1990, pp. 1–11.

970 MELLOTT, D. B., *Status of Bridge Deck Expansion Dam Systems*, Research Projects 73-15, 73-16, and 74-20, Pennsylvania Dept. Transp., PA, Nov., 1978.

971 OLEINIK, J. O. and C. P. HEINS, *Report No. 58*, Dept. Civ. Eng., Univ. Maryland, College Park, Aug., 1974.

972 YAMADA, K. and P. ALBRECHT, Fatigue Behavior of Two Flange Details, *J. Struct. Div. ASCE*, Vol. 103, No. ST4, April, 1977, pp. 781–791.

973 YAMADA, K. and M. A. HIRT, Fatigue Life Estimation Using Fracture Mechanics, *Proc. IABSE Colloquium, Lausanne, Fatigue of Steel and Concrete Structures*, 1982, pp. 361–368.

974 YAMADA, K. and Y. KIKUCHI, Fatigue Tests of Weathered Welded Joints, *J. Struct. Div. ASCE*, Vol. 110, No. 9, Sept., 1984, pp. 2164–2177.

975 YOKEL, F. Y., *Proposed Design Criteria for Shallow Bridge Foundations*, Report, US Dept. Commerce, National Inst. Standards and Tech., Gaithersburg, MD, 1990.

976 ZHOU, J. and A. S. NOWAK, Nonlinear Analysis of Highway Bridges, *Transp. Research Record* 1118, TRB, National Research Council, Washington, DC, 1987, pp. 25–29.

977 ZUK, W., Thermal and Shrinkage Stresses in Composite Beams, *ACI J.*, Vol. 58, No. 3, Sept., 1961, pp. 327–340.

978 ZUK, W., Simplified Design Check of Thermal Stresses in Composite Highway Bridges, *Hwy. Research Record*, No. 103, 1965, pp. 10–13.

979 ZUK, W., Thermal Behavior of Composite Bridges — Insulated and Uninsulated, *Hwy. Research Record*, No. 76, 1965, pp. 231–253.

980 SHIMOKAWA, H., K. TAKENA, F. HO and C. MIKI, Effects of Stress Ratio on the Fatigue Strength of Cruciform Fillet Welded Joints, *Proc. Japan Soc. Civ. Eng.*, No. 344, April, 1984, pp. 121–128.

981 SMITH, I. F. C., U. BREMEN and M. A. HIRT, Fatigue Thresholds and Improvement of Welded Connections, ICOM 125, Swiss Federal Inst., Lausanne, March, 1984.

982 SUETOH, S., E. G. BURDETTE, D. W. GOODPASTURE and H. DEATHERAGE, Unintended Composite Action in Highway Bridges, *Transp. Research Record* 1275, TRB, National Research Council, Washington, DC, 1990, 89–94.

983 SWANSON, S. R., Random Load Fatigue Testing: A State of the Art Survey, *Materials Research and Standards ASTM*, April, 1968, pp. 10–44.

984 HILLBERRY, B. M., Fatigue Life of 2024-T3 Aluminum Alloy Due to Under Narrow and Random Loading, *ASTM Special Technical Publication* 462, 1970, pp. 167–183.

985 HIRT, M. A. and M. CRISINEL, La résistance à la fatigue des poutres an âme pleine composés-soudées: Effect des plaguettes et groussels soudes a l'aile, ICOM 017, Swiss Federal Inst., Lausanne, 1975.

986 HOURIGAN, E. V. and R. C. HOLT, Design of a Rolled Beam Bridge by New AASHTO Guide Specification for Compact Braced Sections, *AISC Eng. J.*, First Quarter, 1987.

987 HUNT, B. and N. COOKE, Thermal Calculations for Bridge Design, *J. Struct. Div. ASCE*, Vol. 101, No. ST9, Sept., 1975, pp. 1763–1781.

988 IMBSEN, R. A., D. E. VANDERSHAF, R. A. SCHAMBER and R. V. NUTT, *Thermal Effects in Concrete Bridge Superstructures*, NCHRP Report 276, TRB, Washington, DC, Sept., 1985.

989 Institute for Transportation Engineers, *Transportation and Traffic Engineering Handbook*, Prentice-Hall, Englewood Cliffs, NJ, 1976.

990 IUR, *Bending Tests of Structures Consisting of Two Beams Welded at Right Angles*, ORE Report D86, Office of Research and Experiments, Int. Union of Railways, 1971.

991 JAMES, R. W., R. A. ZIMMERMAN and C. R. MCCREARY, Effects of Overloads on Deterioration of Concrete Bridges, *Transp. Research Record* 1118, TRB, National Research Council, Washington, DC, 1987, pp. 65–72.

992 JOHNSON, R. P. and R. J. BUCKBY, *Composite Structures of Steel and Concrete, Volume 2 — Bridges*, 2nd ed., William Collins Sons, London, 1986.

993 KEATING, P. B. and J. W. FISHER, *Evaluation of Fatigue Tests and Design Criteria on Welded Details*, NCHRP 286, TRB, National Research Council, Washington, DC, Sept., 1986.

994 KEATING, P. B. and J. W. FISHER, Fatigue Behavior of Variable Loaded Bridge Details Near the Fatigue Limit, *Transp. Research Record* 1118, TRB, National Research Council, Washington, DC, 1987, pp. 56–64.

995 KEENE, P., Tolerable Movements of Bridge Foundations, *Transp. Research Record* 678, TRB, National Research Council, Washington, DC, 1978.

996 KISSANE, R. J., *Lateral Restraint on Noncomposite Beams*, Research Report 123, Eng. Research and Development Bureau, New York Dept. Transp., Albany, Aug., 1985.

997 KOOB, M. J., P. D. FREY and J. M. HANSON, *Evaluation of Web Cracking at Floor Beam to Stiffener Connections of the Poplar Street Bridge Approaches*, Illinois Dept. Transp., Springfield, Sept., 1985.

998 KORBACHER, G. K., On the Modality of Fatigue-Endurance Distributions, *Experimental Mech.*, Dec., 1971, pp. 540–547.

999 LANIGAN, A. G., *The Temperature Response of Concrete Box Girder Bridges*, PhD dissertation, Univ. Auckland, New Zealand, 1973.

1000 LEE, J. J. and C. CASTIGLIONI, *Displacement Induced Stresses in Multigirder Steel Bridges*, Fritz Eng. Lab. Report 500-1(86), Lehigh Univ., Bethlehem, PA, Feb., 1986.

1001 LITTLE, R. E. and E. H. JEBE, *Statistical Designs of Fatigue Experiments*, Wiley, New York, 1975.

1002 LIU, Y. N. and W. ZUK, Thermoelastic Effects in Prestressed Flexural Members, *PCI J.*, Vol. 8, No. 3, June, 1963, pp. 64–85.

1003 WEIBULL, W., A Statistical Theory of the Strength of Materials, *Proc. Royal Swedish Inst. Eng. Research*, No. 151, 1939, Stockholm.

1004 WEIBULL, W., *Fatigue Testing and Analysis of Results*, Pergamon Press, Oxford, 1961.

1005 WEIBULL, W., Analysis of Fatigue Test Results, *First Seminar on Fatigue and Fatigue Design*, Columbia University, New York, 1966, pp. 68–69.

1006 WHEELER, O. F., *J. Basic Eng. ASME*, March, 1972, pp. 181–186.

1007 SCHILLING, C. G. and K. H. KLIPPSTEIN, *NCHRP Project 12-12: Stress Spectrums*, US Steel Corp., Res. Lab. Report 76.019-001(3), Sept., 1972.

1008 SCHILLING, C. G., K. H. KLIPPSTEIN, J. M. BARSOM and G. T. BLAKE, *Fatigue of Welded Steel Bridge Members Under Variable-Amplitude Loadings*, NCHRP Report 188, TRB, National Research Council, Washington, DC, 1978.

1009 SHANAFELT, G. O. and W. B. HORN, *Guidelines for Evaluation and Repair of Prestressed Concrete Bridge Members*, NCHRP Report 280, TRB, National Research Council, Washington, DC, 1985.

1010 PAROLA, J. F., CHESSON, JR., E., and W. H. MUNSE, Effect of Bearing Pressure on Fatigue Strength of Riveted Connections, *Civ. Eng. Studies*, Structural Research Series No. 286, Univ. of Illinois, Dec., 1964.

1011 PATEL, N. J., *Testing and Evaluation of Irvine Creek Bridge*, SRR-84-11, Research and Development Branch, Ontario Ministry Transp. Communications, Canada, 1984.

1012 PAUW, A., *Time Dependent Deflections of a Box Girder Bridge*, ACI SP27, 1971, pp. 141–158.

1013 PCA, Concrete Bridges under Repetitive Loading, Chicago, 1974.

1014 Pennsylvania Department of Transportation, *Guidelines for Fatigue and Fracture Safety Inspection of Bridges*, Bridge Management Systems Div., Pennsylvania Dept. Transp., 1988.

1015 *Precast Segmental Box Girder Bridge Manual*. Post Tensioning Institute and Prestressed Concrete Institute, 1978, 116 pp.

1016 PRIESTLEY, M. J. N., *Effects of Transverse Temperature Gradients on Bridges*, Report No. 394, Ministry of Works, New Zealand, Sept., 1972.

1017 PRIESTLEY, M. J. N., Thermal Gradients in Bridges—Some Design Considerations, *New England Eng.*, Vol. 27, No. 7, July, 1972, pp. 228–233.

1018 PRIESTLEY, M. J. N., Design Thermal Gradients for Concrete Bridges, *New Zealand Eng.*, Vol. 31, Part 9, Sept., 1976, pp. 213–219.

1019 PRIESTLEY, M. J. N., *Linear Heat Flow and Thermal Stress Analysis of Concrete Bridge Decks*, Research Report No. 76/3, Univ. Canterbury Christchurch, New Zealand, Feb., 1976.

1020 PRIESTLEY, M. J. N. and I. G. BUCKLE, Ambient Thermal Response of Concrete Bridges, *Road Research Unit Bull*. 42, *Bridge Seminar*, Vol. 2, Road Research Unit, New Zealand, 1979.

1021 RAHMAN, F. and K. P. GEORGE, Thermal Stress Analysis in Continuous Skew Bridge, *J. Struct. Div. ASCE*, Vol. 105, No. ST7, July, 1979, pp. 1525–1542.

1022 RAHMAN, F. and K. P. GEORGE, Thermal Stresses in Skew Bridges by Model Tests, *J. Struct. Div. ASCE*, Vol. 106, No. ST1, Jan., 1980, pp. 39–58.

1023 RASCON CHAVEZ, O. A., Stochastic Model to Fatigue, *J. Eng. Mech. Div. ASCE*, Vol. 93, No. EM3, Proc. Paper 5293, June, 1967, pp. 147–156.

1024 RASHID, Y. R., Ultimate Strength Analysis of Prestressed Concrete Pressure Vessels, *Nuclear Eng. and Design*, Vol. 7, 1986, pp. 334–344.

1025 REEMSNYDER, H. S., Procurement and Analysis of Structural Fatigue Data, *J. Struct. Div. ASCE*, Vol. 95, No. ST7, July, 1969.

1026 REYNOLDS, J. C. and J. H. EMANUEL, Thermal Stresses and Movements in Bridges, *J. Struct. Div. ASCE*, Vol. 100, No. ST1, Jan., 1974, pp. 63–78.

1027 ROEDER, C. W. and L. ELTVIK, An Experimental Evaluation of Autostress Design, *Transp. Research Record* 1044, TRB National Research Council, Washington, DC, 1985.

1028 ROLFE, S. T. and J. M. BARSOM, *Fracture and Fatigue Control of Structures*, Prentice-Hall, Englewood Cliffs, NJ, 1977.

1029 SCHILLING, C. G., Impact Factors for Fatigue Design, *J. Struct. Div. ASCE*, Vol. 108, No. ST9, Sept., 1982, pp. 2034–2044.

1030 SCHILLING, C. G., Lateral-Distribution Factors For Fatigue Design, *J. Struct. Div. ASCE*, Vol. 108, No. ST9, Sept., 1982, pp. 2015–2032.

1031 American Concrete Institute, *Reinforced Concrete Design Handbook Working Stress Method SP-3*, 3rd ed., American Concrete Institute, 1980.

1032 Portland Cement Association, *Notes on Load Factor Design for Reinforced Concrete Bridge Structures with Design Applications*, Portland Cement Association, Chicago, IL.

1033 Post-Tensioning Institute, *Post-Tensioning Manual*, Post-Tensioning Institute, Glenview, IL, 1978.

1034 Post-Tensioning Institute, *Post-Tensioning Manual*, Post-Tensioning Institute, Glenview, IL, 1976.

1035 American Association of State Highway and Transportation Officials, *Guide Specifications for Design and Construction of Segmental Concrete Bridges*, 1989.

APPENDIX
NUMERICAL AND FINITE
ELEMENT TECHNIQUES
AND SOLUTIONS:
STATIC, DYNAMIC, SEISMIC,
WIND AND BLAST EFFECTS

Appendix
Numerical and finite element techniques and solutions: static, dynamic, seismic, wind and blast effects

1.1 Element types, stiffness matrices and boundary conditions
IA.1 Element types and shape functions

Eight-node element (linear)

$$Ni(\xi, \eta, \zeta) = \tfrac{1}{8}(1 + \xi\xi_i)(1 + \eta\eta_i)(1 + \zeta\zeta_i) \qquad (I1.1)$$

Twenty-node element (quadratic)

For corner nodes

$$Ni(\xi, \eta, \zeta) = \tfrac{1}{8}(1 + \xi\xi_i)(1 + \eta\eta_i)(1 + \zeta\zeta_i)[\xi\xi_i + \eta\eta_i + \zeta\zeta_i - 2]$$

For midside nodes

(i) where $\xi_i = 0$, $\eta_i = \pm 1$, $\zeta_i = \pm 1$

$$Ni(\xi, \eta, \zeta) = \tfrac{1}{4}(1 - \xi^2)(1 + \eta\eta_i)(1 + \zeta\zeta_i)$$

(ii) where $\xi_i = \pm 1$, $\eta_i = 0$, $\zeta_i = \pm 1$ $\qquad (I1.2)$

$$Ni(\xi, \eta, \zeta) = \tfrac{1}{4}(1 + \xi\xi_i)(1 + \eta^2)(1 + \zeta\zeta_i)$$

(iii) where $\xi_i = \pm 1$, $\eta_i = \pm 1$, $\zeta_i = 0$

$$Ni(\xi, \eta, \zeta) = \tfrac{1}{4}(1 + \xi\xi_i)(1 + \eta\eta_i)(1 - \zeta^2)$$

Thirty-two-node element (cubic)

For corner nodes

$$Ni(\xi, \eta, \zeta) = \tfrac{1}{64}(1 + \xi\xi_i)(1 + \eta\eta_i)(1 + \zeta\zeta_i)[9(\xi^2 + \eta^2 + \zeta^2) - 9]$$

For corner nodes

(i) $\xi_i = 0, \eta_i = \pm 1, \zeta_i = \pm 1$

$Ni = \tfrac{9}{64}(1 - \xi^2)(1 + 3\xi\xi_i)(1 + \eta\eta_i)(1 + \zeta\zeta_i)$

(ii) $\xi_i = \pm 1, \eta = 0, \zeta_i = \pm 1$ (I1.3)

$Ni = \tfrac{9}{64}(1 - \eta^2)(1 + 3\eta\eta_i)(1 + \xi\xi_i)(1 + \zeta\zeta_i)$

(iii) $\xi_i = \pm 1, \eta = \pm 1, \zeta = 0$

$Ni = \tfrac{9}{64}(1 - \zeta^2)(1 + 3\zeta\zeta_i)(1 + \eta\eta_i)(1 + \xi\xi_i)$

where ξ_i, η_i, ζ_i take their nodal values. Extra shape function and their derivatives are given.

Global coordinates of the solid element can be expressed in terms of shape functions and their nodal coordinates. Hence:

$$X = \sum_{i=1}^{n} NiXi$$

$$Y = \sum_{i=1}^{n} NiYi \qquad (I1.4)$$

$$Z = \sum_{i=1}^{n} NiZi$$

where N_i denotes the shape functions of node i and n being the number of element nodes of the element which can be eight, twenty or thirty-two.

Displacement functions, U, V, W can be expressed using the same shape functions in the following form:

$$U = \sum_{i=1}^{n} NiUi$$

$$V = \sum_{i=1}^{n} NiVi \qquad (I1.5)$$

$$W = \sum_{i=1}^{n} NiWi$$

where Ui, Vi and Wi are nodal displacements.

Total strain field can be written as:

$$\{\varepsilon\} = [\varepsilon_X, \ \varepsilon_Y, \ \varepsilon_Z, \ \gamma_{XY}, \ \gamma_{YZ}, \ \gamma_{ZX}]^\mathrm{T}$$

$$= \begin{Bmatrix} \dfrac{\partial U}{\partial X} \\[2mm] \dfrac{\partial V}{\partial Y} \\[2mm] \dfrac{\partial W}{\partial Z} \\[2mm] \dfrac{\partial U}{\partial Y} + \dfrac{\partial W}{\partial X} \\[2mm] \dfrac{\partial V}{\partial Z} + \dfrac{\partial W}{\partial Y} \\[2mm] \dfrac{\partial W}{\partial X} + \dfrac{\partial U}{\partial Z} \end{Bmatrix} = [B]\{U\} \tag{I1.6}$$

where $[B]$ = strain–displacement matrix

$$[B] = [B1, B2, B3 \ldots Bi \ldots Bn] \tag{I1.7}$$

For the ith node $[Bi]$ is given by

$$[Bi] = \begin{bmatrix} \dfrac{\partial Ni}{\partial X} & 0 & 0 \\[2mm] 0 & \dfrac{\partial Ni}{\partial Y} & 0 \\[2mm] 0 & 0 & \dfrac{\partial Ni}{\partial Z} \\[2mm] \dfrac{\partial Ni}{\partial Y} & \dfrac{\partial Ni}{\partial X} & 0 \\[2mm] 0 & \dfrac{\partial Ni}{\partial Z} & \dfrac{\partial Ni}{\partial Y} \\[2mm] \dfrac{\partial Ni}{\partial Z} & 0 & \dfrac{\partial Ni}{\partial X} \end{bmatrix} \tag{I1.7a}$$

The chain rule of partial differentiation can be used to give

$$\frac{\partial Ni}{\partial \xi} = \frac{\partial Ni}{\partial X} \frac{\partial X}{\partial \xi} + \frac{\partial Ni}{\partial Y} \frac{\partial X}{\partial \xi} + \frac{\partial Ni}{\partial Z} \frac{\partial Z}{\partial \xi}$$

Using similar relations for η and ζ the following is formed:

$$
\left\{
\begin{array}{c}
\dfrac{\partial Ni}{\partial \xi} \\[6pt]
\dfrac{\partial Ni}{\partial \eta} \\[6pt]
\dfrac{\partial Ni}{\partial \zeta}
\end{array}
\right\}
= [J]
\left\{
\begin{array}{c}
\dfrac{\partial Ni}{\partial X} \\[6pt]
\dfrac{\partial Ni}{\partial Y} \\[6pt]
\dfrac{\partial Ni}{\partial Z}
\end{array}
\right\}
\tag{I1.8}
$$

where $[J]$ is a 3×3 matrix called the Jacobian matrix and is given by

$$
[J] =
\begin{bmatrix}
\dfrac{\partial X}{\partial \xi} & \dfrac{\partial Y}{\partial \xi} & \dfrac{\partial Z}{\partial \xi} \\[10pt]
\dfrac{\partial X}{\partial \eta} & \dfrac{\partial Y}{\partial \eta} & \dfrac{\partial Z}{\partial \eta} \\[10pt]
\dfrac{\partial X}{\partial \zeta} & \dfrac{\partial Y}{\partial \zeta} & \dfrac{\partial Z}{\partial \zeta}
\end{bmatrix}
\tag{I1.9}
$$

Now Eq. (I1.7a) can be determined using the following equation:

$$
\left\{
\begin{array}{c}
\dfrac{\partial Ni}{\partial X} \\[6pt]
\dfrac{\partial Ni}{\partial Y} \\[6pt]
\dfrac{\partial Ni}{\partial Z}
\end{array}
\right\}
= [J]^{-1}
\left\{
\begin{array}{c}
\dfrac{\partial Ni}{\partial \xi} \\[6pt]
\dfrac{\partial Ni}{\partial \eta} \\[6pt]
\dfrac{\partial Ni}{\partial \zeta}
\end{array}
\right\}
\tag{I1.10}
$$

IA.2 Nodal forces due to surface pressure

In general the structure is loaded by surface pressure acting on finite faces. In finite element analysis these pressures must be converted into consistent nodal forces of

$$
\{p_s\}^e = \int_S [N]^T \{p\}\, ds
\tag{I1.11a}
$$

where $\{p\} = [p_X, p_Y, p_Z]^T$.

Let us assume that the pressurized face is at $\zeta = \pm 1$ of an element of surface ds, and ds is given by

$$
ds = d\xi \times d\eta
\tag{I1.11b}
$$

Equation (I1.11b) can also be written as

$$ds = \left\{ \begin{array}{c} \dfrac{\partial X}{\partial \xi} \\[2mm] \dfrac{\partial Y}{\partial \xi} \\[2mm] \dfrac{\partial Z}{\partial \xi} \end{array} \right\} d\xi \times \left\{ \begin{array}{c} \dfrac{\partial X}{\partial \eta} \\[2mm] \dfrac{\partial Y}{\partial \eta} \\[2mm] \dfrac{\partial Z}{\partial \eta} \end{array} \right\} d\eta$$

$$ds = \det \begin{bmatrix} \hat{i} & \hat{j} & \hat{k} \\[2mm] \dfrac{\partial X}{\partial \xi} & \dfrac{\partial Y}{\partial \xi} & \dfrac{\partial Z}{\partial \xi} \\[2mm] \dfrac{\partial X}{\partial \eta} & \dfrac{\partial Y}{\partial \eta} & \dfrac{\partial Z}{\partial \eta} \end{bmatrix} d\xi \, d\eta$$

$$ds = \left\{ \begin{array}{c} \left(\dfrac{\partial Y}{\partial \xi} \dfrac{\partial Z}{\partial \eta} - \dfrac{\partial Z}{\partial \xi} \dfrac{\partial Y}{\partial \eta} \right) \\[3mm] \left(\dfrac{\partial Z}{\partial \xi} \dfrac{\partial X}{\partial \eta} - \dfrac{\partial X}{\partial \xi} \dfrac{\partial Z}{\partial \eta} \right) \\[3mm] \left(\dfrac{\partial X}{\partial \xi} \dfrac{\partial Y}{\partial \eta} - \dfrac{\partial Y}{\partial \xi} \dfrac{\partial X}{\partial \eta} \right) \end{array} \right\} d\xi \, d\eta \tag{I1.11c}$$

Equation (I1.11c) can be substituted in Eq. (I1.10) to obtain equivalent nodal forces. Similar expressions can be worked out for ds when $\eta = \pm 1$ and $\xi = \pm 1$ are loaded.

IA.3 Stiffness matrix

Let us assume there is a point Q on the element which has local coordinates $X'Y'Z'$ and corresponding displacements $U'V'W'$. Strain in the system is given by:

$$\varepsilon'_X = \frac{\partial U'}{\partial X'}$$

$$\varepsilon'_Y = \frac{\partial V'}{\partial Y'} \tag{I1.12}$$

$$\gamma'_{XY} = \frac{\partial U'}{\partial Y'} + \frac{\partial V'}{\partial X'}$$

or

$$\{\varepsilon'_X\} = [B]\{U'\}$$

Coordinates at any point are given by:

$$X = \sum NiXi$$

$$Y = \sum NiYi \tag{I1.13a}$$

$$Z = \sum NiZi$$

and also displacements

$$U = \sum NiUi$$

$$V = \sum NiVi \tag{I1.13b}$$

$$W = \sum NiWi$$

and thickness,

$$t = \sum Niti$$

Form a vector normal to the membrane

$$\{n\} = \left\{\begin{array}{c} \dfrac{\partial X}{\partial \xi} \\[2mm] \dfrac{\partial Y}{\partial \xi} \\[2mm] \dfrac{\partial z}{\partial \xi} \end{array}\right\} \times \left\{\begin{array}{c} \dfrac{\partial X}{\partial \eta} \\[2mm] \dfrac{\partial Y}{\partial \eta} \\[2mm] \dfrac{\partial Z}{\partial \eta} \end{array}\right\} = \det \begin{bmatrix} i & j & k \\[2mm] \dfrac{\partial X}{\partial \xi} & \dfrac{\partial Y}{\partial \xi} & \dfrac{\partial Z}{\partial \xi} \\[2mm] \dfrac{\partial X}{\partial \eta} & \dfrac{\partial Y}{\partial \eta} & \dfrac{\partial Z}{\partial \eta} \end{bmatrix} \tag{I1.14a}$$

or

$$\{n\} = \left\{\begin{array}{c} n_1 \\[2mm] n_2 \\[2mm] n_3 \end{array}\right\} = \left\{\begin{array}{c} \left(\dfrac{\partial Y}{\partial \xi}\dfrac{\partial Z}{\partial \eta} - \dfrac{\partial Z}{\partial \xi}\dfrac{\partial Y}{\partial \eta}\right) \\[3mm] \left(\dfrac{\partial Z}{\partial \xi}\dfrac{\partial X}{\partial \eta} - \dfrac{\partial X}{\partial \xi}\dfrac{\partial Z}{\partial \eta}\right) \\[3mm] \left(\dfrac{\partial X}{\partial \xi}\dfrac{\partial Y}{\partial \eta} - \dfrac{\partial Y}{\partial \xi}\dfrac{\partial X}{\partial \eta}\right) \end{array}\right\} \tag{I1.14b}$$

Let the thickness of the membrane be t. Since there is no local coordinates in the Z direction, the Jacobian does not have invert. To make this possible, the third row of the Jacobian matrix is substituted by thickness, i.e.

$$
\begin{Bmatrix} \dfrac{\partial Ni}{\partial X} \\[2mm] \dfrac{\partial Ni}{\partial Y} \\[2mm] \dfrac{\partial Ni}{\partial Z} \end{Bmatrix} = \begin{bmatrix} \dfrac{\partial X}{\partial \xi} & \dfrac{\partial Y}{\partial \xi} & \dfrac{\partial Z}{\partial \xi} \\[2mm] \dfrac{\partial X}{\partial \eta} & \dfrac{\partial Y}{\partial \eta} & \dfrac{\partial Z}{\partial \eta} \\[2mm] n_1 t & n_2 t & n_3 t \end{bmatrix} = \begin{Bmatrix} \dfrac{\partial Ni}{\partial \xi} \\[2mm] \dfrac{\partial Ni}{\partial \eta} \\[2mm] 0 \end{Bmatrix} \tag{I1.14c}
$$

Distortion matrix $[d]$ in global coordinates is given by

$$
[d] = \begin{bmatrix} \dfrac{\partial U}{\partial X} & \dfrac{\partial V}{\partial X} & \dfrac{\partial W}{\partial X} \\[2mm] \dfrac{\partial U}{\partial Y} & \dfrac{\partial V}{\partial Y} & \dfrac{\partial W}{\partial Y} \\[2mm] \dfrac{\partial U}{\partial Z} & \dfrac{\partial V}{\partial Z} & \dfrac{\partial W}{\partial Z} \end{bmatrix} = \begin{Bmatrix} \dfrac{\partial Ni}{\partial X} \\[2mm] \dfrac{\partial Ni}{\partial Y} \\[2mm] \dfrac{\partial Ni}{\partial Z} \end{Bmatrix} \begin{bmatrix} Ui & Vi & Wi \end{bmatrix} \tag{I1.14d}
$$

Substitute Eq. (I1.14c) in (I1.14d) to obtain

$$
[d] = [J]^{-1} \begin{Bmatrix} \dfrac{\partial Ni}{\partial \xi} \\[2mm] \dfrac{\partial Ni}{\partial \eta} \\[2mm] 0 \end{Bmatrix} \begin{bmatrix} Ui & Vi & Wi \end{bmatrix} \tag{I1.15a}
$$

Distortion matrix $[d']$ in $X'Y'Z'$ coordinate system:

$$
[d'] = [R]^{T}[d][R] \tag{I1.15b}
$$

Rotation matrix $[R]$ is given by

$$
[R] = \begin{bmatrix} \dfrac{\partial X}{\partial X'} & \dfrac{\partial Y}{\partial X'} & \dfrac{\partial Z}{\partial X'} \\[2mm] \dfrac{\partial X}{\partial Y'} & \dfrac{\partial Y}{\partial Y'} & \dfrac{\partial Z}{\partial Y'} \\[2mm] \dfrac{\partial X}{\partial Z'} & \dfrac{\partial Y}{\partial Z'} & \dfrac{\partial Z}{\partial Z'} \end{bmatrix} = \begin{bmatrix} R_{11} & R_{12} & R_{13} \\ R_{21} & R_{22} & R_{23} \\ R_{31} & R_{32} & R_{33} \end{bmatrix} \tag{I1.15c}
$$

where

$$\{R_1\} = \frac{1}{A_1} = \left\{ \begin{array}{c} \dfrac{\partial X}{\partial \xi} \\[6pt] \dfrac{\partial Y}{\partial \xi} \\[6pt] \dfrac{\partial Z}{\partial \xi} \end{array} \right\} \qquad \{R_3\} = \frac{1}{A_2} = \left\{ \begin{array}{c} \eta_1 \\ \eta_2 \\ \eta_3 \end{array} \right\} \tag{I1.16}$$

and, $\{R_2\} = \{R_3\} \times \{R_1\}$ (cross-product of two vectors).

$$A_1 = \sqrt{\left(\frac{\partial X}{\partial \xi}\right)^2 + \left(\frac{\partial Y}{\partial \xi}\right)^2 + \left(\frac{\partial Z}{\partial \xi}\right)^2} \qquad A_2 = \sqrt{\eta_1^2 + \eta_2^2 + \eta_3^2}$$

Thus,

$$[R] = [\{R_1\}, \{R_2\}, \{R_3\}] \tag{I1.17}$$

After substituting the values of $[R]$ and carrying out multiplication, Eq. (I1.15b) can be written as

$$[d'] = \begin{bmatrix} \dfrac{\partial U'}{\partial X'} & \dfrac{\partial V'}{\partial X'} & \dfrac{\partial W'}{\partial X'} \\[8pt] \dfrac{\partial U'}{\partial Y'} & \dfrac{\partial V'}{\partial Y'} & \dfrac{\partial W'}{\partial Y'} \\[8pt] \dfrac{\partial U'}{\partial Z'} & \dfrac{\partial V'}{\partial Z'} & \dfrac{\partial W'}{\partial Z'} \end{bmatrix} = \begin{bmatrix} S_1 Q_1 & S_1 Q_2 & Q_3 S_1 \\ S_2 Q_1 & S_2 Q_2 & Q_3 S_2 \\ S_3 Q_1 & S_3 Q_2 & Q_3 S_3 \end{bmatrix} \tag{I1.18}$$

where

$$S_1 = R_{11} \frac{\partial Ni}{\partial X} + R_{21} \frac{\partial Ni}{\partial Y} + R_{31} \frac{\partial Ni}{\partial Z}$$

$$S_2 = R_{12} \frac{\partial Ni}{\partial X} + R_{22} \frac{\partial Ni}{\partial Y} + R_{32} \frac{\partial Ni}{\partial Z}$$

$$S_3 = R_{13} \frac{\partial Ni}{\partial X} + R_{23} \frac{\partial Ni}{\partial Y} + R_{33} \frac{\partial Ni}{\partial Z}$$

and

$$Q_1 = R_{11} Ui + R_{21} Vi + R_{31} Wi$$

$$Q_2 = R_{12} Ui + R_{22} Vi + R_{32} Wi$$

$$Q_3 = R_{13} Ui + R_{23} Vi + R_{33} Wi$$

From Eqs (I1.17) and (I1.18) one obtains,

$$\{\varepsilon_X'\} = \left\{ \begin{array}{c} S_1 Q_1 \\ S_2 Q_2 \\ (S_2 Q_1 + Q_2 S_1) \end{array} \right\} = [B]\{U\} \tag{I1.19}$$

$$[B] = [B_1, B_2, B_3 \ldots, B_n] \tag{I1.20a}$$

For the ith node $[Bi]$ is given by

$$[Bi] = \begin{bmatrix} R_{11}S_1 & R_{21}S_1 & R_{31}S_1 \\ R_{12}S_2 & R_{22}S_2 & R_{32}S_2 \\ (R_{11}S_2 + R_{12}S_1) & (R_{21}S_2 + R_{22}S_1) & (R_{31}S_2 + R_{32}S_1) \end{bmatrix} \tag{I1.20b}$$

The stiffness matrix is calculated using $[B]$ of Eq. (I1.20a) as

$$[K]^e = \int\int\int_{\text{vol}} [B]^T [DJ] B \, dV$$

$$= \int_{-1}^{1}\int_{-1}^{1}\int_{-1}^{1} [B]^T [DJ][B] \det J \, d\xi \, d\eta \tag{I1.20c}$$

where

$[DJ]$ = material matrix of membrane element

The stresses are calculated in a local $X'Y'Z'$ coordinate system by

$$\{\sigma_X'\} = [DJ]\{\varepsilon_X'\} \tag{I1.20d}$$

The global stresses can be transformed using the following expression

$$[\sigma_X] = [R][\sigma_X'][R]^T$$

where

$$[\sigma_X'] = \begin{bmatrix} \sigma_X & \tau_{XY} & 0 \\ \tau_{XY} & \sigma_Y & 0 \\ 0 & 0 & 0 \end{bmatrix} \tag{I1.20e}$$

$$[\sigma_X'] = \begin{bmatrix} \sigma_X' & \tau_{XY}' & 0 \\ \tau_{XY}' & \sigma_Y' & 0 \\ 0 & 0 & 0 \end{bmatrix} \tag{I1.20f}$$

IA.4 Line elements
In this section the stiffness matrix of a line element on the basis of a global approach is given briefly. Compatible isoparametric line elements with two, three and four nodes which can be fitted with one side of corresponding solid elements are described. Finally the stiffness matrix of the line element in the body of the solid element using solid element shape functions is described.

IA.5 Stiffness matrix using a global approach
Axial line with length L and nodes I and J is considered. Compatible assumed displacement function for the element is given by

$$U = A_1 + A_2 X' \tag{I1.21}$$

Solving for A_1 and A_2:

$$\begin{Bmatrix} A_1 \\ A_2 \end{Bmatrix} = \begin{bmatrix} 1 & 0 \\ -\dfrac{1}{L} & \dfrac{1}{L} \end{bmatrix} \begin{Bmatrix} U_I \\ U_J \end{Bmatrix} \tag{I1.21a}$$

Thus Eq. (I1.21) becomes

$$\{U\} = \begin{bmatrix} \left(1 - \dfrac{X'}{L}\right) & \dfrac{X'}{L} \end{bmatrix} \begin{Bmatrix} U_I \\ U_J \end{Bmatrix} \tag{I1.21b}$$

Strain within the element is:

$$\{\varepsilon\} = \frac{\partial U}{\partial X'}$$

$$= \begin{bmatrix} -\dfrac{1}{L} & \dfrac{1}{L} \end{bmatrix} \begin{Bmatrix} U_I \\ U_J \end{Bmatrix}$$

$$= [B] \begin{Bmatrix} U_I \\ U_J \end{Bmatrix} \tag{I1.21c}$$

Stress within the element is:

$$\{a\} = E\{\varepsilon\} \tag{I1.21d}$$

where $E = $ Young's modulus of steel.
Stiffness matrix in the local coordinate is:

$$[K]^e = \int_{\text{vol}} [B]^T E [B] \, dV = \int_0^L [B]^T E [B] A \, dX'$$

$$= \frac{EA}{L} \begin{bmatrix} 1 & -1 \\ -1 & 1 \end{bmatrix} \tag{I1.21e}$$

Table API.1. Bond–linkage stiffness matrix

$$[K_B] = \Pi D L \begin{bmatrix} [K_{11}] & [K_{12}] \\ \hline [K_{21}] & [K_{22}] \end{bmatrix}$$

where

$$[K_{11}] = [K_{22}]$$
$$[K_{12}] = [K_{21}] = -[K_{11}]$$

$$[K_{11}] = \begin{bmatrix} (l^2 E_h + p^2 E_v + r^2 E_w) & (lm E_h + pq E_v + rs E_w) & (ln E_h + rt E_v) \\ \hline (lm E_h + pq E_v + rs E_w) & (m^2 E_h + q^2 E_v + s^2 E_w) & (mn E_h + st E_w) \\ \hline (ln E_h + rt E_v) & (mn E_h + st E_w) & (n^2 E_h + t^2 E_v) \end{bmatrix}$$

Element stiffness matrix in the global coordinate system is given by

$$[K] = [T]^{T}[K]^{e}[T] \tag{I1.21f}$$

where transformation matrix $[T]$ is given by

$$[T] = \begin{bmatrix} [l\ m\ n] & [0\ 0\ 0] \\ \hline [0\ 0\ 0] & [l\ m\ n] \end{bmatrix}_{2\times 6} \tag{I1.21g}$$

After carrying out multiplication in Eq. (I1.21) the stiffness matrix $[K]$ is given in Table API.1. The same table gives the direction cosines used in Eq. (I1.21).

IA.6 Stiffness matrix using isoparametric approach
Elements with two, three and four nodes are shown in Fig. (2.3b, c, d). General derivation of shape functions and $[B]$ matrices are given in Table API.2. In the following the element matrix is derived using an isoparametric approach.

Shape functions of these elements are given below:

(a) *Two-node element*

$$N_1 = \frac{(1 - \xi)}{2} \qquad N_2 = \frac{(1 - \xi)}{2} \tag{I1.22a}$$

(b) *Three-node element*

$$N_1 = -\frac{(1 - \xi)\xi}{2} \qquad N_2 = \frac{(1 + \xi)\xi}{2} \qquad N_3 = (1 - \xi^2) \tag{I1.22b}$$

Table API.2. Shape function for a prism element

Shape function

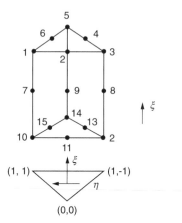

15 Nodes

$$P_1(\xi,\eta,\zeta) = -\tfrac{1}{2}(1+\zeta)(1-\xi^{1/2})(\sqrt{2}\xi^{1/2}-\zeta)$$

$$P_2(\xi,\eta,\zeta) = +\tfrac{1}{2}(1+\sqrt{2})(1+\zeta)(1-\xi^{1/2})(\xi^{1/2}+\eta\xi^{-1/2})$$

$$P_3(\xi,\eta,\zeta) = +\tfrac{1}{4}(1+\zeta)(\xi^{1/2}+\eta\xi^{-1/2})[(2+\sqrt{2})(\xi^{1/2}-1)-(\xi-\eta-\zeta)]$$

$$P_4(\xi,\eta,\zeta) = +\tfrac{1}{2}(1+\zeta)(\xi^{3/2}-\eta^2\xi^{-1/2})$$

$$P_5(\xi,\eta,\zeta) = +\tfrac{1}{4}(1+\zeta)(\xi^{1/2}-\eta\xi^{-1/2})[(2+\sqrt{2})(\xi^{1/2}-1)-(\xi+\eta-\zeta)]$$

$$P_6(\xi,\eta,\zeta) = +\tfrac{1}{2}(1+\sqrt{2})(1+\xi)(\xi^{1/2}-\eta\xi^{-1/2})(1-\xi^{1/2})$$

$$P_7(\xi,\eta,\zeta) = -(1-\zeta^2)(1-\xi^{1/2})$$

$$P_8(\xi,\eta,\zeta) = +\tfrac{1}{2}(1-\zeta^2)(\xi^{1/2}+\eta\xi^{-1/2})$$

$$P_9(\xi,\eta,\zeta) = +\tfrac{1}{2}(1-\zeta^2)(\xi^{1/2}-\eta\xi^{-1/2})$$

$$P_{10}(\xi,\eta,\zeta) = -\tfrac{1}{2}(1-\zeta)(1-\xi^{1/2})(\sqrt{2}\xi^{1/2}+\zeta)$$

$$P_{11}(\xi,\eta,\zeta) = +\tfrac{1}{2}(1+\sqrt{2})(1-\zeta)(\xi^{1/2}+\eta\xi^{-1/2})(1-\xi^{1/2})$$

$$P_{12}(\xi,\eta,\zeta) = +\tfrac{1}{4}(1-\zeta)(\xi^{1/2}+\eta\xi^{-1/2})[(2+\sqrt{2})(\xi^{1/2}-1)-(\xi-\eta+\zeta)]$$

$$P_{13}(\xi,\eta,\zeta) = +\tfrac{1}{2}(1-\zeta)(\xi^{3/2}-\eta^2\xi^{-1/2})$$

$$P_{14}(\xi,\eta,\zeta) = +\tfrac{1}{4}(1-\zeta)(\xi^{1/2}-\eta\xi^{-1/2})[(2+\sqrt{2})(\zeta^{1/2}-1)-(\xi+\eta+\zeta)]$$

$$P_{15}(\xi,\eta,\zeta) = +\tfrac{1}{2}(1+\sqrt{2})(1-\zeta)(1-\xi^{1/2})(\xi^{1/2}+\eta\xi^{-1/2})$$

(c) *Four-node element*

$$N_1 = \tfrac{1}{3}(1-\xi)(2\xi^2-\tfrac{1}{2})$$

$$N_2 = \tfrac{1}{3}(1-\xi)(2\xi^2-\tfrac{1}{2})$$

$$N_3 = \tfrac{4}{3}(\xi^2-1)(\xi-\tfrac{1}{2})$$

$$N_4 = \tfrac{4}{3}(1-\xi^2)(\xi+\tfrac{1}{2}) \hspace{3cm} (I1.22c)$$

Coordinates can be expressed in terms of shape functions and nodal coordinates as

$$X = \sum_{l=1}^{n} NiXi$$

$$Y = \sum_{l=1}^{n} NiYi \tag{I1.22d}$$

$$Z = \sum_{l=1}^{n} NiZi$$

And also displacements

$$U = \sum_{l=1}^{n} NiUi$$

$$V = \sum_{l=1}^{n} NiVi \tag{I1.22e}$$

$$W = \sum_{l=1}^{n} NiWi$$

where n = number of nodes in the element.
Strain in the axial element is given by

$$\{\varepsilon\} = \frac{1}{L^2}\left[\left(\frac{\partial X}{\partial \xi}\right)\left(\frac{\partial U}{\partial \xi}\right) + \left(\frac{\partial Y}{\partial \xi}\right)\left(\frac{\partial V}{\partial \xi}\right) + \left(\frac{\partial Z}{\partial \xi}\right)\left(\frac{\partial W}{\partial \xi}\right)\right] \tag{I1.23}$$

where

$$L = \left[\left(\frac{\partial X}{\partial \xi}\right)^2 + \left(\frac{\partial Y}{\partial \xi}\right)^2 + \left(\frac{\partial Z}{\partial \xi}\right)^2\right]^{1/2} \tag{I1.24a}$$

Equations (I1.22a) and (I1.22e) are used to obtain

$$\frac{\partial X}{\partial \xi} = \sum_{l=1}^{n} \frac{\partial Ni}{\partial \xi} Xi$$

$$\frac{\partial Y}{\partial \xi} = \sum_{l=1}^{n} \frac{\partial Ni}{\partial \xi} Yi$$

$$\frac{\partial Z}{\partial \xi} = \sum_{l=1}^{n} \frac{\partial Ni}{\partial \xi} Zi$$

$$\frac{\partial U}{\partial \xi} = \sum_{l=1}^{n} \frac{\partial Ni}{\partial \xi} \, Ui$$

$$\frac{\partial V}{\partial \xi} = \sum_{l=1}^{n} \frac{\partial Ni}{\partial \xi} \, Vi$$

$$\frac{\partial W}{\partial \xi} = \sum_{l=1}^{n} \frac{\partial Ni}{\partial \xi} \, Wi \tag{I1.24b}$$

Equation (I1.24b) is substituted into Eq. (I1.23) to obtain

$$\{\varepsilon\} = [B]\{U\} \tag{I1.24c}$$

where $[B]$ is given for two-, three- and four-node elements.
Stiffness matrix is given by

$$[K]^e = \int_{\text{vol}} [B]^T E[B] \, dV \tag{I1.24d}$$

$$dV = A(\xi) dr$$

but

$$dr = r \cdot d\xi$$

and

$$A(\xi) = \sum_{l-1}^{n} Ni Ai \tag{I1.24e}$$

where

$$Ai = \text{area of element at the } i\text{th node}$$

Thus the element stiffness matrix becomes

$$[K] = \int_{-1}^{+1} [B]^T E[B] \, A(\xi) r \cdot d\xi \tag{I1.24f}$$

The above matrix is solved again using numerical integration. Stresses at any point in the element are calculated using the following expressions:

$$\{\varepsilon\} = [B]\{U\}^e$$

$$\{\sigma\} = E\{\varepsilon\} \tag{I1.24g}$$

where $\{U\}^e$ = nodal displacements of the element.

IA.7   Line elements in the body of the solid element

Line elements inside the solid element are shown in Fig. 2.4(a, b, c). In this case the line element has to be parallel to one of the local coordinates, e.g. ξ, η, ζ. Let us assume that the steel is lying parallel to the ξ-axis. The displacement at any point is then given by

$$\{U\} = \begin{Bmatrix} U \\ V \\ W \end{Bmatrix} = [N(\xi, \eta_c, \zeta_c)]\{U\}^e \tag{I1.25}$$

Since the steel element can only transmit axial strain, the axial strain contribution to strain energy is given by

$$\varepsilon'_X = \frac{\partial U'}{\partial X'}$$

at point Q on the steel element with local coordinate system $X'Y'Z'$ and U', V', W' being the corresponding displacements.

The distortion matrix can be defined at any point in the element as

$$[d] = \begin{bmatrix} \dfrac{\partial U}{\partial X} & \dfrac{\partial V}{\partial X} & \dfrac{\partial W}{\partial X} \\[2mm] \dfrac{\partial U}{\partial Y} & \dfrac{\partial V}{\partial Y} & \dfrac{\partial W}{\partial Y} \\[2mm] \dfrac{\partial U}{\partial Z} & \dfrac{\partial V}{\partial Z} & \dfrac{\partial W}{\partial Z} \end{bmatrix} = \begin{Bmatrix} \dfrac{\partial Ni}{\partial X} \\[2mm] \dfrac{\partial Ni}{\partial Y} \\[2mm] \dfrac{\partial Ni}{\partial Z} \end{Bmatrix} [Ui \ Vi \ Wi]$$

$$= [J]^{-1} \begin{Bmatrix} \dfrac{\partial Ni}{\partial \xi} \\[2mm] \dfrac{\partial Ni}{\partial \eta} \\[2mm] \dfrac{\partial Ni}{\partial \zeta} \end{Bmatrix} [Ui \ Vi \ Wi] \tag{I1.26}$$

The distortion matrix in the local $X'Y'Z'$ coordinate system is given by

$$[d'] = [R]^T[d][R] \tag{I1.27}$$

where $[R]$ is the rotation matrix of direction cosines at point Q and is given by

$$[R] = \begin{bmatrix} \dfrac{\partial X}{\partial X'} & \dfrac{\partial Y}{\partial X'} & \dfrac{\partial Z}{\partial X'} \\[2ex] \dfrac{\partial X}{\partial Y'} & \dfrac{\partial Y}{\partial Y'} & \dfrac{\partial Z}{\partial Y'} \\[2ex] \dfrac{\partial X}{\partial Z'} & \dfrac{\partial Y}{\partial Z'} & \dfrac{\partial Z}{\partial Z'} \end{bmatrix} = \begin{bmatrix} \dfrac{\partial X/\partial \xi}{a_1} & \dfrac{\partial X/\partial \eta}{b_1} & \dfrac{\partial X/\partial \zeta}{c_1} \\[2ex] \dfrac{\partial Y/\partial \xi}{a_1} & \dfrac{\partial Y/\partial \eta}{b_1} & \dfrac{\partial Y/\partial \zeta}{c_1} \\[2ex] \dfrac{\partial Z/\partial \xi}{a_1} & \dfrac{\partial Z/\partial \eta}{b_1} & \dfrac{\partial Z/\partial \zeta}{c_1} \end{bmatrix} \qquad (I1.28a)$$

at ξ, η_c, ζ_c where:

$$a_1 = \sqrt{\left(\frac{\partial X}{\partial \xi}\right)^2 + \left(\frac{\partial Y}{\partial \xi}\right)^2 + \left(\frac{\partial Z}{\partial \xi}\right)^2}$$

$$b_1 = \sqrt{\left(\frac{\partial X}{\partial \eta}\right)^2 + \left(\frac{\partial Y}{\partial \eta}\right)^2 + \left(\frac{\partial Z}{\partial \eta}\right)^2} \qquad (I1.28b)$$

$$c_1 = \sqrt{\left(\frac{\partial X}{\partial \zeta}\right)^2 + \left(\frac{\partial Y}{\partial \zeta}\right)^2 + \left(\frac{\partial Z}{\partial \zeta}\right)^2}$$

Substitute Eqs (I1.26) and (I1.28a) into Eq. (I1.27) to obtain,

$$\begin{bmatrix} \dfrac{\partial U'}{\partial X'} & \dfrac{\partial V'}{\partial X'} & \dfrac{\partial W'}{\partial X'} \\[2ex] \dfrac{\partial U'}{\partial Y'} & \dfrac{\partial V'}{\partial Y'} & \dfrac{\partial W'}{\partial Y'} \\[2ex] \dfrac{\partial U'}{\partial Z'} & \dfrac{\partial V'}{\partial Z'} & \dfrac{\partial W'}{\partial Z'} \end{bmatrix} = \begin{bmatrix} d'_{11} & d'_{12} & d'_{13} \\[1ex] d'_{21} & d'_{22} & d'_{23} \\[1ex] d'_{31} & d'_{32} & d'_{33} \end{bmatrix} \qquad (I1.29a)$$

So, element strain is given by

$$\{\varepsilon'_X\} = \frac{\partial U'}{\partial X'} = d'_{11}$$

$$= [B]\{U\}^e \qquad (I1.29b)$$

where

$$[B] = [B_1, B_2, \ldots, B_n]$$

$$[Bi] = [R_{11}S_1 \quad R_{21}S_1 \quad R_{31}S_1]$$

where

$$S_1 = \left(R_{11} \frac{\partial Ni}{\partial X} + R_{21} \frac{\partial Ni}{\partial Y} + R_{31} \frac{\partial Ni}{\partial Z} \right)$$

$$R_{11} = \frac{\partial X / \partial \xi}{a_1}$$

$$R_{21} = \frac{\partial Y / \partial \xi}{a_1} \qquad (\text{I}1.29\text{c})$$

$$R_{31} = \frac{\partial Z / \partial \xi}{a_1}$$

Using the $[B]$ matrix of Eq. (I1.29b), the stiffness matrix is given by

$$[K]^e = \int_{\text{vol}} [B]^T D[B] \, dv$$

$$dV = A a_1 \, d\xi \qquad (\text{I}1.29\text{d})$$

$$[K] = \int_{-1}^{+1} [B]^T D[B] A a_1 \, d\xi$$

Stresses within the element are worked out using Eq. (I1.29b)

$$\sigma_X' = E[B]\{U\}^e \qquad (\text{I}1.29\text{e})$$

Transform stresses in global coordinate system by:

$$\begin{bmatrix} \sigma_X' & \tau_{XY} & \tau_{XZ} \\ \tau_{XY} & \sigma_Y & \tau_{YZ} \\ \tau_{ZX} & \tau_{ZX} & \sigma_Z \end{bmatrix} = [R] \begin{bmatrix} \sigma_X' & 0 & 0 \\ 0 & 0 & 0 \\ 0 & 0 & 0 \end{bmatrix} [R]^T$$

Therefore

$$\sigma_X = R_{11} \sigma_X' R_{11} \qquad (\text{I}1.29\text{f})$$

IA.8 Cylindrical co-ordinate system

At the point i, the following parameters (Fig. IA.1) can be defined:

$$r_i = \sqrt{X_i^2 + Y_i^2}$$

$$\sin \theta_i = \frac{Y_i}{r_i} \qquad (\text{I}1.30)$$

$$\sin \theta_i = \frac{X_i}{r_i}$$

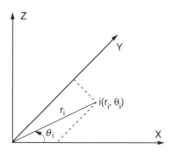

Figure 1A.1. Definition of parameters

Two systems of displacement can be related by the following equations:

$$U_i = U_i' \cos\theta_i - V_i' \sin\theta_i$$

$$V_i = U_i' \sin\theta_i + V_i' \cos\theta_i \tag{I1.31}$$

$$W_i = W_i'$$

The above equations can be written in matrix form as follows:

$$\begin{Bmatrix} U_i \\ V_i \\ W_i \end{Bmatrix} = \begin{bmatrix} \cos\theta_i & -\sin\theta_i & 0 \\ \sin\theta_i & \cos\theta_i & 0 \\ 0 & 0 & 0 \end{bmatrix} \begin{Bmatrix} U_i' \\ V_i' \\ W_i' \end{Bmatrix} \tag{I1.32}$$

or,

$$\{U_i\} = [L]^{\mathrm{T}}\{U_i'\} \tag{I1.33}$$

where U_i', V_i', W_i' refer to cylindrical system and

$$[L] = \begin{bmatrix} \cos\theta_i & \sin\theta_i & 0 \\ \sin\theta_i & \cos\theta_i & 0 \\ 0 & 0 & 1 \end{bmatrix} \tag{I1.34}$$

Strain at ith point is given by

$$\{\varepsilon_i\} = [B_i]^{\mathrm{T}}\{U_i\} \tag{I1.35}$$

From Eqs (I1.33) and (I1.35)

$$\{\varepsilon_i\} = [B_i][L]^{\mathrm{T}}\{U_i'\}$$

$$= [B_i']\{U_i'\} \tag{I1.36}$$

where

$$[B_i'] = [B_i][L]^T$$

$$= \text{strain–displacement matrix of node } i \text{ in a cylindrical system.}$$

Therefore, any node where the stiffness matrix is calculated in a cylindrical co-ordinate system, the strain–displacement matrix, $[B_i]$, should be post-multiplied by a transformation matrix.

After carrying out multiplication in Eq. (I1.36), the final form of $[B_i']$ is given by:

$$[B_i'] = \begin{bmatrix} C\dfrac{\partial N_i}{\partial X} & -S\dfrac{\partial N_i}{\partial X} & 0 \\[2mm] S\dfrac{\partial N_i}{\partial Y} & C\dfrac{\partial Ni}{\partial Y} & 0 \\[2mm] 0 & 0 & \dfrac{\partial N_i}{\partial Z} \\[2mm] \left(C\dfrac{\partial N_i}{\partial Y} + S\dfrac{\partial N_i}{\partial X}\right) & \left(C\dfrac{\partial N_i}{\partial X} - S\dfrac{\partial N_i}{\partial Y}\right) & 0 \\[2mm] S\dfrac{\partial N_i}{\partial Z} & C\dfrac{\partial N_i}{\partial Z} & \dfrac{\partial N_i}{\partial Y} \\[2mm] C\dfrac{\partial N_i}{\partial Z} & -S\dfrac{\partial N_i}{\partial Z} & \dfrac{\partial N_i}{\partial X} \end{bmatrix} \qquad (I1.37)$$

where $C = \cos\theta_i$ and $S = \sin\theta_i$

An alternative to the above approach is the transformation of the stiffness matrix, $[K]$, in the following manner:

Global element stiffness matrix can be written as follows:

$$[K]\{U\} = \{P\} \qquad (I1.38)$$

where $\{U\}$, $\{P\}$ are global displacement and load vectors.

The following cylindrical and global displacement and load vectors can be written as:

$$\{P'\} = [T]\{P\} \qquad \text{or} \qquad \{P\} = [T]^T\{P'\}$$

$$\{U'\} = [T]\{U\} \qquad \text{or} \qquad \{U\} = [T]^T\{U'\} \qquad (I1.39)$$

From Eqs (I1.38) and (I1.39)

$$[K][T]^T\{U'\} = [T]^T\{P'\}$$

Pre-multiplying by $[T]$ in the above expression gives

$$[T][K][T]^{\mathrm{T}}\{U'\} = \{P'\}$$
$$[K']\{U'\} = \{P'\}$$

(I1.40)

where

$$[K'] = [T][K][T]^{\mathrm{T}}$$
$$\{P'\} = [T]\{P\}$$

$$[T] = \begin{bmatrix} [L] & & & & \\ & [L] & & & \\ & & [L] & & \\ & & & \diagdown & \\ & & & & [L] \end{bmatrix} = \begin{array}{c} \text{transformation matrix} \\ \text{of the element} \end{array}$$

IA.9 Inclined supports

Inclined supports are shown in general. Let us suppose that the Ith node has inclined support and θ is the inclination between the global and local axes.

Transformation between local and global displacement at the Ith node is given by:

$$\begin{Bmatrix} U_i' \\ V_i' \\ W_i' \end{Bmatrix} = \begin{bmatrix} \cos\theta & \sin\theta & 0 \\ -\sin\theta & \cos\theta & 0 \\ 0 & 0 & 1 \end{bmatrix} \begin{Bmatrix} U_I \\ V_I \\ W \end{Bmatrix}$$

or

$$\{U_I'\} = [L_I]\{U_I\}$$

(I1.41)

For all nodes the transformation matrix, $[T]$, is given by:

$$[T] = \begin{bmatrix} [I] & & & & & \\ & [I] & & & & \\ & & [I] & & & \\ & & & \diagdown & & \\ & & & & [L_I] & \\ & & & & & \diagdown \\ & & & & & & [I] \end{bmatrix}$$

(I1.42)

Total displacement and load transformation can be written as:

$$\{U'\} = [T]\{U\} \quad \text{or} \quad \{U\} = [T]^T\{U'\}$$
$$\{P'\} = [T]\{P\} \quad \text{or} \quad \{P\} = [T]^T\{P'\} \tag{I1.43}$$

The global load–displacement relationship is given by:

$$[K]\{U\} = \{P\} \tag{I1.44}$$

From Eq. (I1.43) and (I1.44)

$$[K][T]^T\{U'\} = [P]^T\{P'\}$$

Pre-multiply by $[T]$ in the above expression to obtain,

$$[T][K][T]^T\{U'\} = \{P'\} \tag{I1.45}$$
$$[K']\{U'\} = \{P'\}$$

where

$$[K'] = [T][K][T]^T \tag{I1.46}$$

$[K]$ in Eq. (I1.44) can be the element stiffness matrix or global stiffness matrix. Upon expanding Equation (I1.46), one obtains:

$$
\begin{bmatrix}
[K_{11}], [K_{12}, [K_{13}] - - - \mid - [K_{1i}][L]^T - \mid - -[K_{1n}] \\
[K_{21}], [K_{22}, [K_{23}] - - - \mid - [K_{2i}][L]^T - \mid - -[K_{2n}] \\
\mid \qquad\qquad\qquad\qquad \mid \qquad\qquad \mid \\
\mid \; \overline{[L][K_{i1}], [L][K_{i2}],} - - - - \mid \overline{[L][K_{ii}], [L]^T} \; \overline{-[L][K_{in}]} \\
\mid \qquad\qquad\qquad\qquad \mid \qquad\qquad \mid \\
[K_{n1}], [L][K_{n2}], - - - - \mid [K_{n1}], [L]^T \mid - \cdot[K_{nn}]
\end{bmatrix}
\begin{Bmatrix}
\{U_1\} \\
\{U_2\} \\
\mid \\
\{U_i'\} \\
\mid \\
\{U_n\}
\end{Bmatrix}
=
\begin{Bmatrix}
\{P_1\} \\
\{P_2\} \\
\mid \\
\{P_i'\} \\
\mid \\
\{P_n\}
\end{Bmatrix}
\tag{I1.47}
$$

Therefore, for any node which has inclined support the equations of this node should be pre-multiplied by the transformation matrix, $[L]$, and in addition the diagonal term should be post-multiplied by $[L]^T$ as shown in Eq. (I1.47).

An alternative to the above approach is the transformation of the displacement vector at the strain level rather than stiffness level.

Strain at a point is given by:

$$\{\varepsilon\} = [B]\{U\} \tag{I1.48}$$

For the ith node

$$\{\varepsilon\} = [B_i]\{U_i\} \tag{I1.49}$$

From Eqs (I1.41) and (I1.49),

$$\{\varepsilon\} = [B_i][L_I]^{\mathrm{T}}\{U_i'\}$$
$$= [B_i']\{U_i'\}$$
$$(I1.50)$$

where

$$[B_i'] = [B_i][L_I]^{\mathrm{T}} \qquad\qquad\qquad (I1.51)$$
$$= \text{strain–displacement matrix of node '}i\text{'}$$
$$\text{in inclined directions.}$$

Therefore, at any node where inclined restraints are required, the strain–displacement matrix, $[B_i]$, of that node should be post-multiplied by $[L_I]^{\mathrm{T}}$.

Displacements calculated from equilibrium equations at ith nodes are in inclined directions. These should be transformed in the global direction before stresses are calculated. The following transformation is used:

$$\{U_i\} = [L_I]^{\mathrm{T}}\{U_i'\} \qquad\qquad\qquad (I1.52)$$

I.2 Shape functions
2A.1 Shape functions and derviatives of solid isoparametric elements
(a) Eight-node hexahedron

Node 1	Shape functions $Ni(\xi, \eta, \zeta)$	Derivatives		
		$\dfrac{\partial Ni}{\partial \xi}$	$\dfrac{\partial Ni}{\partial \eta}$	$\dfrac{\partial Ni}{\partial \zeta}$
1	$\frac{1}{8}(1-\xi)(1-\eta)(1-\zeta)$	$-\frac{1}{8}(1-\eta)(1-\zeta)$	$-\frac{1}{8}(1-\xi)(1-\zeta)$	$-\frac{1}{8}(1-\eta)(1-\xi)$
2	$\frac{1}{8}(1+\xi)(1-\eta)(1-\zeta)$	$\frac{1}{8}(1-\eta)(1-\zeta)$	$-\frac{1}{8}(1+\xi)(1-\zeta)$	$-\frac{1}{8}(1+\xi)(1-\eta)$
3	$\frac{1}{8}(1+\xi)(1+\eta)(1-\zeta)$	$\frac{1}{8}(1+\eta)(1-\zeta)$	$\frac{1}{8}(1+\xi)(1-\zeta)$	$-\frac{1}{8}(1+\xi)(1+\eta)$
4	$\frac{1}{8}(1-\xi)(1+\eta)(1-\zeta)$	$-\frac{1}{8}(1+\eta)(1-\zeta)$	$\frac{1}{8}(1-\xi)(1-\zeta)$	$-\frac{1}{8}(1-\xi)(1+\eta)$
5	$\frac{1}{8}(1-\xi)(1-\eta)(1+\zeta)$	$-\frac{1}{8}(1-\eta)(1+\zeta)$	$-\frac{1}{8}(1-\xi)(1+\zeta)$	$\frac{1}{8}(1-\eta)(1-\xi)$
6	$\frac{1}{8}(1+\xi)(1-\eta)(1+\zeta)$	$\frac{1}{8}(1-\eta)(1+\zeta)$	$-\frac{1}{8}(1+\xi)(1+\zeta)$	$\frac{1}{8}(1+\xi)(1-\eta)$
7	$\frac{1}{8}(1+\xi)(1+\eta)(1+\zeta)$	$\frac{1}{8}(1+\eta)(1+\zeta)$	$\frac{1}{8}(1+\xi)(1+\zeta)$	$\frac{1}{8}(1+\xi)(1+\eta)$
8	$\frac{1}{8}(1-\xi)(1+\eta)(1+\zeta)$	$-\frac{1}{8}(1+\eta)(1+\zeta)$	$\frac{1}{8}(1-\xi)(1+\zeta)$	$\frac{1}{8}(1-\xi)(1+\zeta)$

(b) Twenty-node hexahedron
Shape functions:

$$N_1 = \frac{1}{8}(1-\xi)(1-\eta)(1-\zeta)(-\xi-\eta-\zeta-2)$$
$$N_2 = \frac{1}{4}(1-\xi^2)(1-\eta)(1-\zeta)$$
$$N_3 = \frac{1}{8}(1+\xi)(1-\eta)(1-\zeta)(\xi-\eta-\zeta-2)$$

$$N_4 = \tfrac{1}{4}(1+\xi)(1-\eta^2)(1-\zeta)$$

$$N_5 = \tfrac{1}{8}(1+\xi)(1+\eta)(1-\zeta)(\xi+\eta-\zeta-2)$$

$$N_6 = \tfrac{1}{4}(1-\xi^2)(1+\eta)(1-\zeta)$$

$$N_7 = \tfrac{1}{8}(1-\xi)(1+\eta)(1-\zeta)(-\xi+\eta-\zeta-2)$$

$$N_8 = \tfrac{1}{4}(1-\xi)(1-\eta^2)(1-\zeta)$$

$$N_9 = \tfrac{1}{4}(1-\xi)(1-\eta)(1-\zeta^2)$$

$$N_{10} = \tfrac{1}{4}(1+\xi)(1-\eta)(1-\zeta^2)$$

$$N_{11} = \tfrac{1}{4}(1+\xi)(1+\eta)(1-\zeta^2)$$

$$N_{12} = \tfrac{1}{4}(1-\xi)(1+\eta)(1-\zeta^2)$$

$$N_{13} = \tfrac{1}{8}(1-\xi)(1+\zeta)(1-\eta)(-\xi-\eta+\zeta-2)$$

$$N_{14} = \tfrac{1}{4}(1-\xi^2)(1-\eta)(1+\zeta)$$

$$N_{15} = \tfrac{1}{8}(1+\xi)(1-\eta)(1+\zeta)(\xi-\eta+\zeta-2)$$

$$N_{16} = \tfrac{1}{4}(1+\xi)(1-\eta^2)(1+\zeta)$$

$$N_{17} = \tfrac{1}{8}(1+\xi)(1+\eta)(1+\zeta)(\xi+\eta+\zeta-2)$$

$$N_{18} = \tfrac{1}{4}(1-\xi^2)(1+\eta)(1+\zeta)$$

$$N_{19} = \tfrac{1}{8}(1-\xi)(1+\eta)(1+\zeta)(-\xi+\eta+\zeta-2)$$

$$N_{20} = \tfrac{1}{4}(1-\xi)(1-\eta^2)(1+\zeta)$$

Derivatives:

$$N_{1,\xi} = \tfrac{1}{8}(1-\eta)(1-\zeta)(2\xi+\eta+\zeta+1)$$

$$N_{1,\eta} = \tfrac{1}{8}(1-\xi)(1-\zeta)(2\eta+\xi+\zeta+1)$$

$$N_{1,\zeta} = \tfrac{1}{8}(1-\xi)(1-\eta)(2\zeta+\eta+\xi+1)$$

$$N_{3,\xi} = \tfrac{1}{8}(1-\eta)(1-\zeta)(2\xi-\eta-\zeta-1)$$

$$N_{3,\eta} = \tfrac{1}{8}(1+\xi)(1-\zeta)(2\eta-\xi+\zeta+1)$$

$$N_{3,\zeta} = \tfrac{1}{8}(1+\xi)(1-\eta)(2\zeta-\xi+\eta+1)$$

$$N_{5,\xi} = \tfrac{1}{8}(1+\eta)(1-\zeta)(2\xi+\eta-\zeta-1)$$

$$N_{5,\eta} = \tfrac{1}{8}(1+\xi)(1-\zeta)(2\eta+\xi-\zeta-1)$$

$$N_{5,\zeta} = \tfrac{1}{8}(1+\xi)(1+\eta)(2\zeta-\xi-\eta+1)$$

$$N_{7,\xi} = \tfrac{1}{8}(1+\eta)(1-\zeta)(2\xi-\eta+\zeta+1)$$

$$N_{7,\eta} = \tfrac{1}{8}(1-\xi)(1-\zeta)(2\eta-\xi-\zeta-1)$$

$$N_{7,\zeta} = \tfrac{1}{8}(1-\xi)(1+\eta)(2\zeta-\eta+\xi+1)$$

$$N_{13,\xi} = \tfrac{1}{8}(1-\eta)(1+\zeta)(2\xi+\eta-\zeta+1)$$

$$N_{13,\eta} = \tfrac{1}{8}(1-\xi)(1+\zeta)(2\eta+\xi-\zeta+1)$$

$$N_{13,\zeta} = \tfrac{1}{8}(1-\xi)(1-\eta)(2\zeta-\eta-\xi-1)$$

$$N_{15,\xi} = \tfrac{1}{8}(1-\eta)(1+\zeta)(2\xi-\eta+\zeta-1)$$

$$N_{15,\eta} = \tfrac{1}{8}(1+\zeta)(1+\xi)(2\eta-\xi-\zeta+1)$$

$$N_{15,\zeta} = \tfrac{1}{8}(1-\eta)(1+\xi)(2\zeta+\xi-\zeta-1)$$

$$N_{17,\xi} = \tfrac{1}{8}(1+\eta)(1+\zeta)(2\xi+\eta+\zeta-1)$$

$$N_{17,\eta} = \tfrac{1}{8}(1+\xi)(1+\zeta)(2\eta+\xi+\zeta-1)$$

$$N_{17,\zeta} = \tfrac{1}{8}(1+\xi)(1+\eta)(2\zeta+\eta+\xi-1)$$

$$N_{19,\xi} = \tfrac{1}{8}(1+\eta)(1+\zeta)(2\xi-\eta-\zeta+1)$$

$$N_{19,\eta} = \tfrac{1}{8}(1-\xi)(1+\zeta)(2\eta-\xi-\zeta-1)$$

$$N_{19,\zeta} = \tfrac{1}{8}(1-\xi)(1+\eta)(2\zeta-\xi+\eta-1)$$

$$N_{2,\xi} = -\xi(1-\eta)(1-\zeta)/2$$

$$N_{2,\eta} = -(1-\xi^2)(1-\zeta)/4$$

$$N_{2,\zeta} = -(1-\xi^2)(1-\eta)/4$$

$$N_{4,\xi} = -(1-\eta^2)(1-\zeta)/4$$

$$N_{4,\eta} = -(1+\xi)(1-\zeta)\eta/2$$

$$N_{4,\zeta} = -(1-\eta^2)(1+\xi)/4$$

$$N_{6,\xi} = -\xi(1+\eta)(1-\zeta)/2$$

$$N_{6,\eta} = -(1-\xi^2)(1-\zeta)/4$$

$$N_{6,\zeta} = -(1-\xi^2)(1+\eta)/4$$

$$N_{8,\xi} = -(1-\eta^2)(1-\zeta)/4$$

$$N_{8,\eta} = -\eta(1-\xi)(1-\zeta)/2$$

$$N_{8,\zeta} = -(1-\eta^2)(1-\xi)/4$$

$$N_{9,\xi} = -(1 - \eta)(1 - \zeta^2)/4$$

$$N_{9,\eta} = -(1 - \xi)(1 - \zeta^2)/4$$

$$N_{9,\zeta} = -\zeta(1 - \xi)(1 - \eta)/2$$

$$N_{10,\xi} = (1 - \eta)(1 - \zeta^2)/4$$

$$N_{10,\eta} = -(1 + \xi)(1 - \zeta^2)/4$$

$$N_{10,\zeta} = -\zeta(1 + \xi)(1 - \eta)/2$$

$$N_{11,\xi} = (1 + \eta)(1 - \zeta^2)/4$$

$$N_{11,\eta} = (1 + \xi)(1 - \zeta^2)/4$$

$$N_{11,\zeta} = -\zeta(1 + \xi)(1 + \eta)/2$$

$$N_{12,\xi} = -(1 + \eta)(1 - \zeta^2)/4$$

$$N_{12,\eta} = (1 - \xi)(1 - \zeta^2)/4$$

$$N_{12,\zeta} = -\zeta(1 - \xi)(1 + \eta)/2$$

$$N_{14,\xi} = -\xi(1 - \eta)(1 + \zeta)/2$$

$$N_{14,\eta} = -(1 - \xi^2)(1 + \zeta)/4$$

$$N_{14,\zeta} = (1 - \xi^2)(1 - \eta)/4$$

$$N_{16,\xi} = (1 - \eta^2)(1 + \zeta)/4$$

$$N_{16,\eta} = -(1 + \xi)(1 + \zeta)\eta/2$$

$$N_{16,\zeta} = (1 + \xi)(1 - \eta^2)/4$$

$$N_{18,\xi} = -(1 + \eta)(1 + \zeta)\xi/2$$

$$N_{18,\eta} = (1 - \xi^2)(1 + \zeta)/4$$

$$N_{18,\zeta} = (1 - \xi^2)(1 + \eta)/4$$

$$N_{20,\xi} = -(1 - \eta^2)(1 + \zeta)/4$$

$$N_{20,\eta} = -(1 - \xi)(1 + \zeta)\eta/2$$

$$N_{20,\zeta} = (1 - \xi)(1 - \eta^2)/4$$

(c)   Thirty-two-node hexahedron

Shape functions:

$$N_1 = \tfrac{1}{64}(1-\xi)(1-\eta)(1-\zeta)[9(\xi^2+\eta^2+\xi^2)-19]$$

$$N_2 = \tfrac{9}{64}(1-\xi^2)(1-3\xi)(1-\eta)(1-\zeta)$$

$$N_3 = \tfrac{9}{64}(1-\xi^2)(1+3\xi)(1-\eta)(1-\zeta)$$

$$N_4 = \tfrac{1}{64}(1+\xi)(1-\eta)(1-\zeta)[9(\xi^2+\eta^2+\xi^2)-19]$$

$$N_5 = \tfrac{9}{64}(1-\eta^2)(1-3\eta)(1+\xi)(1-\zeta)$$

$$N_6 = \tfrac{9}{64}(1-\eta^2)(1+3\eta)(1+\xi)(1-\zeta)$$

$$N_7 = \tfrac{1}{64}(1+\xi)(1+\eta)(1-\zeta)[9(\xi^2+\eta^2+\xi^2)-19]$$

$$N_8 = \tfrac{9}{64}(1-\xi^2)(1+3\xi)(1+\eta)(1-\zeta)$$

$$N_9 = \tfrac{9}{64}(1-\xi^2)(1-3\xi)(1+\eta)(1-\zeta)$$

$$N_{10} = \tfrac{1}{64}(1-\xi)(1+\eta)(1-\zeta)[9(\xi^2+\eta^2+\xi^2)-19]$$

$$N_{11} = \tfrac{9}{64}(1-\eta^2)(1+3\eta)(1-\xi)(1-\zeta)$$

$$N_{12} = \tfrac{9}{64}(1-\eta^2)(1-3\eta)(1-\xi)(1-\zeta)$$

$$N_{13} = \tfrac{9}{64}(1-\zeta^2)(1-3\zeta)(1-\eta)(1-\xi)$$

$$N_{14} = \tfrac{9}{64}(1-\zeta^2)(1-3\zeta)(1-\eta)(1+\xi)$$

$$N_{15} = \tfrac{9}{64}(1-\zeta^2)(1-3\zeta)(1+\eta)(1+\xi)$$

$$N_{16} = \tfrac{9}{64}(1-\zeta^2)(1-3\zeta)(1+\eta)(1-\xi)$$

$$N_{17} = \tfrac{9}{64}(1-\zeta^2)(1+3\zeta)(1-\eta)(1-\xi)$$

$$N_{18} = \tfrac{9}{64}(1-\zeta^2)(1+3\zeta)(1-\eta)(1+\xi)$$

$$N_{19} = \tfrac{9}{64}(1-\zeta^2)(1+3\zeta)(1+\eta)(1+\xi)$$

$$N_{20} = \tfrac{9}{64}(1-\zeta^2)(1+3\zeta)(1+\eta)(1-\xi)$$

$$N_{21} = \tfrac{1}{64}(1-\xi)(1-\eta)(1+\zeta)[9(\xi^2+\eta^2+\zeta^2)-19]$$

$$N_{22} = \tfrac{9}{64}(1-\xi^2)(1-3\xi)(1-\eta)(1+\zeta)$$

$$N_{23} = \tfrac{9}{64}(1-\xi^2)(1+3\xi)(1-\eta)(1+\zeta)$$

$$N_{24} = \tfrac{1}{64}(1+\xi)(1-\eta)(1+\zeta)[9(\xi^2+\eta^2+\zeta^2)-19]$$

$$N_{25} = \tfrac{9}{64}(1-\eta^2)(1-3\eta)(1+\xi)(1+\zeta)$$

$$N_{26} = \tfrac{9}{64}(1-\eta^2)(1+3\eta)(1+\xi)(1+\zeta)$$

$$N_{27} = \tfrac{1}{64}(1+\xi)(1+\eta)(1+\zeta)[9(\xi^2+\eta^2+\zeta^2)-19]$$

$$N_{28} = \tfrac{9}{64}(1-\xi^2)(1+3\xi)(1+\eta)(1+\zeta)$$

$$N_{29} = \tfrac{9}{64}(1-\xi^2)(1-3\xi)(1+\eta)(1+\zeta)$$

$$N_{30} = \tfrac{1}{64}(1-\xi)(1+\eta)(1+\zeta)[9(\xi^2+\eta^2+\zeta^2)-19]$$

$$N_{31} = \tfrac{9}{64}(1-\eta^2)(1+3\eta)(1-\xi)(1+\zeta)$$

$$N_{32} = \tfrac{9}{64}(1-\eta^2)(1-3\eta)(1-\xi)(1+\zeta)$$

Derivatives:

$$N_{1,\xi} = \tfrac{1}{64}(1-\eta)(1-\zeta)[9(2\xi-3\xi^2)-(9\eta^2+9\zeta^2-19)]$$

$$N_{1,\eta} = \tfrac{1}{64}(1-\xi)(1-\zeta)[9(2\eta-3\eta^2)-(9\xi^2+9\zeta^2-19)]$$

$$N_{1,\zeta} = \tfrac{1}{64}(1-\xi)(1-\eta)[9(2\zeta-3\zeta^2)-(9\xi^2+9\eta^2-19)]$$

$$N_{2,\xi} = \tfrac{9}{64}(9\xi^2-3\xi-3)(1-\eta)(1-\zeta)$$

$$N_{2,\eta} = -\tfrac{9}{64}(1-\xi^2)(1-3\xi)(1-\zeta)$$

$$N_{2,\zeta} = -\tfrac{9}{64}(1-\xi^2)(1-3\xi)(1-\eta)$$

$$N_{3,\xi} = \tfrac{9}{64}(3-2\xi-9\xi^2)(1-\eta)(1-\zeta)$$

$$N_{3,\eta} = -\tfrac{9}{64}(1-\xi^2)(1+3\xi)(1-\zeta)$$

$$N_{3,\zeta} = -\tfrac{9}{64}(1-\xi^2)(1+3\xi)(1-\eta)$$

$$N_{4,\xi} = \tfrac{1}{64}(1-\eta)(1-\zeta)[9(3\xi^2+2\xi)+(9\zeta^2+9\eta^2-19)]$$

$$N_{4,\zeta} = \tfrac{1}{64}(1+\xi)(1-\eta)[9(2\zeta-3\zeta^2)-(9\xi^2+9\eta^2-19)]$$

$$N_{4,\eta} = \tfrac{1}{64}(1+\xi)(1-\zeta)[9(2\eta-3\eta^2)-(9\xi^2+9\zeta^2-19)]$$

$$N_{5,\xi} = \tfrac{9}{64}(1-\eta^2)(1-3\eta)(1-\zeta)$$

$$N_{5,\eta} = \tfrac{9}{64}(9\eta^2-2\eta-3)(1+\xi)(1-\zeta)$$

$$N_{5,\zeta} = -\tfrac{9}{64}(1-\eta^2)(1-3\eta)(1+\xi)$$

$$N_{6,\xi} = \tfrac{9}{64}(1-\eta^2)(1+3\eta)(1-\zeta)$$

$$N_{6,\eta} = \tfrac{9}{64}(3-2\eta-9\eta^2)(1+\xi)(1-\xi)$$

$$N_{6,\zeta} = -\tfrac{9}{64}(1-\eta^2)(1+3\eta)(1+\xi)$$

$$N_{7,\xi} = \tfrac{1}{64}(1+\eta)(1-\zeta)[9(2\xi+3\xi^2)+(9\eta^2+9\zeta^2-19)]$$

$$N_{7,\eta} = \tfrac{1}{64}(1+\xi)(1-\zeta)[9(2\eta+3\eta^2)+(9\xi^2+9\zeta^2-19)]$$

$$N_{7,\zeta} = \tfrac{1}{64}(1+\xi)(1+\eta)[9(2\zeta-3\zeta^2)-(9\xi^2+9\eta^2-19)]$$

$$N_{8,\xi} = \tfrac{9}{64}(3-2\xi-9\xi^2)(1+\eta)(1-\zeta)$$

$$N_{8,\eta} = \tfrac{9}{64}(1-\xi^2)(1+3\xi)(1-\zeta)$$

$$N_{8,\zeta} = -\tfrac{9}{64}(1-\xi^2)(1+3\xi)(1+\eta)$$

$$N_{9,\xi} = \tfrac{9}{64}(9\xi^2-2\xi-3)(1+\eta)(1-\zeta)$$

$$N_{9,\eta} = \tfrac{9}{64}(1-\xi^2)(1-3\xi)(1-\zeta)$$

$$N_{9,\zeta} = -\tfrac{9}{64}(1-\xi^2)(1-3\xi)(1+\eta)$$

$$N_{10,\xi} = \tfrac{1}{64}(1+\eta)(1-\zeta)[9(2\xi+3\xi^2)-(9\eta^2+9\zeta^2-19)]$$

$$N_{10,\eta} = \tfrac{1}{64}(1+\xi)(1-\zeta)[9(2\eta+3\eta^2)+(9\xi^2+9\zeta^2-19)]$$

$$N_{10,\zeta} = \tfrac{1}{64}(1-\xi)(1+\eta)[9(2\zeta-3\zeta^2)-(9\xi^2+9\eta^2-19)]$$

$$N_{11,\xi} = -\tfrac{9}{64}(1-\eta^2)(1+3\eta)(1-\eta)$$

$$N_{11,\eta} = \tfrac{9}{64}(3-2\eta-9\eta^2)(1-\xi)(1-\zeta)$$

$$N_{11,\zeta} = -\tfrac{9}{64}(1-\eta^2)(1+3\eta)(1-\xi)$$

$$N_{12,\xi} = -\tfrac{9}{64}(1-\eta^2)(1-3\eta)(1-\zeta)$$

$$N_{12,\eta} = \tfrac{9}{64}(9\eta^2-2\eta-3)(1-\xi)(1-\zeta)$$

$$N_{12,\zeta} = -\tfrac{9}{64}(1-\eta^2)(1-3\eta)(1-\xi)$$

$$N_{13,\xi} = -\tfrac{9}{64}(1-\zeta^2)(1-3\zeta)(1-\eta)$$

$$N_{13,\eta} = -\tfrac{9}{64}(1-\xi)(1-\zeta^2)(1-3\zeta)$$

$$N_{13,\zeta} = \tfrac{9}{64}(9\zeta^2-2\zeta-3)(1-\xi)(1-\eta)$$

$$N_{14,\xi} = \tfrac{9}{64}(1-\eta)(1-\zeta^2)(1-3\zeta)$$

$$N_{14,\eta} = -\tfrac{9}{64}(1+\xi)(1-\zeta^2)(1-3\zeta)$$

$$N_{14,\zeta} = \tfrac{9}{64}(9\zeta^2 - 2\zeta - 3)(1 - \eta)(1 + \xi)$$

$$N_{15,\xi} = \tfrac{9}{64}(1 - \zeta^2)(1 - 3\zeta)(1 + \eta)$$

$$N_{15,\eta} = \tfrac{9}{64}(1 - \zeta^2)(1 - 3\zeta)(1 + \xi)$$

$$N_{15,\zeta} = \tfrac{9}{64}(1 + \xi)(1 + \eta)(9\zeta^2 - 2\zeta - 3)$$

$$N_{16,\xi} = -\tfrac{9}{64}(1 - \zeta^2)(1 - 3\zeta)(1 + \eta)$$

$$N_{16,\eta} = \tfrac{9}{64}(1 - \zeta^2)(1 - 3\zeta)(1 - \xi)$$

$$N_{16,\zeta} = \tfrac{9}{64}(1 + \eta)(1 - \xi)(9\zeta^2 - 2\zeta - 3)$$

$$N_{17,\xi} = -\tfrac{9}{64}(1 - \zeta^2)(1 + 3\zeta)(1 - \eta)$$

$$N_{17,\eta} = -\tfrac{9}{64}(1 - \zeta^2)(1 + 3\zeta)(1 - \xi)$$

$$N_{17,\zeta} = \tfrac{9}{64}(1 - \xi)(1 - \eta)(3 - 2\zeta - 9\zeta^2)$$

$$N_{18,\xi} = \tfrac{9}{64}(1 - \zeta^2)(1 + 3\zeta)(1 - \eta)$$

$$N_{18,\eta} = -\tfrac{9}{64}(1 - \zeta^2)(1 + 3\zeta)(1 + \xi)$$

$$N_{18,\zeta} = \tfrac{9}{64}(1 + \xi)(1 - \eta)(3 - 2\zeta - 9\zeta^2)$$

$$N_{19,\xi} = \tfrac{9}{64}(1 - \zeta^2)(1 + 3\zeta)(1 + \eta)$$

$$N_{19,\eta} = \tfrac{9}{64}(1 - \zeta^2)(1 + 3\zeta)(1 + \xi)$$

$$N_{19,\zeta} = \tfrac{9}{64}(1 + \xi)(1 + \eta)(3 - 2\zeta - 9\zeta^2)$$

$$N_{20,\xi} = -\tfrac{9}{64}(1 - \zeta^2)(1 + 3\zeta)(1 + \eta)$$

$$N_{20,\eta} = \tfrac{9}{64}(1 - \zeta^2)(1 + 3\zeta)(1 - \xi)$$

$$N_{20,\zeta} = \tfrac{9}{64}(1 + \eta)(1 - \xi)(3 - 2\zeta - 9\zeta^2)$$

$$N_{21,\xi} = \tfrac{1}{64}(1 - \eta)(1 + \zeta)[9(2\xi - 3\xi^2) - (9\eta^2 + 9\zeta^2 - 19)]$$

$$N_{21,\eta} = \tfrac{1}{64}(1 - \xi)(1 + \zeta)[9(2\eta - 3\eta^2) - (9\xi^2 + 9\zeta^2 - 19)]$$

$$N_{21,\zeta} = \tfrac{1}{64}(1 - \xi)(1 - \eta)[9(2\zeta + 3\zeta^2) + (9\xi^2 + 9\eta^2 - 19)]$$

$$N_{22,\xi} = \tfrac{9}{64}(9\xi^2 - 2\xi - 3)(1 - \eta)(1 + \zeta)$$

$$N_{22,\eta} = -\tfrac{9}{64}(1 - \xi^2)(1 - 3\xi)(1 + \zeta)$$

$$N_{22,\zeta} = \tfrac{9}{64}(1 - \xi^2)(1 - 3\xi)(1 - \eta)$$

$$N_{23,\xi} = \tfrac{9}{64}(3 - 2\xi - 9\xi^2)(1 - \eta)(1 + \zeta)$$

$$N_{23,\eta} = -\tfrac{9}{64}(1-\xi^2)(1+3\xi)(1+\zeta)$$

$$N_{23,\zeta} = \tfrac{9}{64}(1-\xi^2)(1+3\xi)(1-\eta)$$

$$N_{24,\xi} = \tfrac{1}{64}(1+\zeta)(1-\eta)[9(2\xi+3\xi^2)+(9\zeta^2+9\eta^2-19)]$$

$$N_{24,\eta} = \tfrac{1}{64}(1+\xi)(1+\zeta)[9(2\eta-3\eta^2)-(9\xi^2+3\zeta^2-19)]$$

$$N_{24,\zeta} = \tfrac{1}{64}(1+\xi)(1-\eta)[9(2\zeta+3\zeta^2)+(9\xi^2+9\eta^2-19)]$$

$$N_{25,\xi} = \tfrac{9}{64}(1-\eta^2)(1+3\eta)(1+\zeta)$$

$$N_{25,\eta} = \tfrac{9}{64}(9\eta^2-2\eta-3)(1+\xi)(1+\zeta)$$

$$N_{25,\zeta} = \tfrac{9}{64}(1-\eta^2)(1+3\eta)(1+\xi)$$

$$N_{26,\xi} = \tfrac{9}{64}(1-\eta^2)(1+3\eta)(1+\zeta)$$

$$N_{26,\eta} = \tfrac{9}{64}(3-2\eta-9\eta^2)(1+\xi)(1+\zeta)$$

$$N_{26,\zeta} = \tfrac{9}{64}(1-\eta^2)(1+3\eta)(1+\xi)$$

$$N_{27,\xi} = \tfrac{1}{64}(1+\eta)(1+\zeta)[9(2\xi+3\xi^2)+(9\eta^2+9\zeta^2-19)]$$

$$N_{27,\eta} = \tfrac{1}{64}(1+\xi)(1+\zeta)[9(2\eta+3\eta^2)+(9\xi^2+3\zeta^2-19)]$$

$$N_{27,\zeta} = \tfrac{1}{64}(1+\xi)(1+\eta)[9(2\zeta+3\zeta^2)+(9\xi^2+9\eta^2-19)]$$

$$N_{28,\xi} = \tfrac{9}{64}(1+\eta)(1+\zeta)(3-2\xi-9\xi^2)$$

$$N_{28,\eta} = \tfrac{9}{64}(1-\xi^2)(1+3\xi)(1+\zeta)$$

$$N_{28,\zeta} = \tfrac{9}{64}(1-\xi^2)(1+3\xi)(1+\eta)$$

$$N_{29,\xi} = \tfrac{9}{64}(1+\eta)(1+\zeta)(3\xi^2-2\xi-3)$$

$$N_{29,\eta} = \tfrac{9}{64}(1-\xi^2)(1-3\xi)(1+\zeta)$$

$$N_{29,\zeta} = \tfrac{9}{64}(1-\xi^2)(1-3\xi)(1+\eta)$$

$$N_{30,\xi} = \tfrac{1}{64}(1+\eta)(1+\zeta)[9(2\xi-3\xi^2)-(9\eta^2+9\zeta^2-19)]$$

$$N_{30,\eta} = \tfrac{1}{64}(1-\xi)(1+\zeta)[9(2\eta+3\eta^2)+(9\zeta^2+9\xi^2-19)]$$

$$N_{30,\zeta} = \tfrac{1}{64}(1-\xi)(1+\eta)[9(2\zeta+3\zeta^2)+(9\xi^2+9\eta^2-19)]$$

$$N_{31,\xi} = -\tfrac{9}{64}(1-\eta^2)(1+3\eta)(1+\zeta)$$

$$N_{31,\eta} = \tfrac{9}{64}(3-2\eta-9\eta^2)(1-\xi)(1+\zeta)$$

$$N_{31,\zeta} = \tfrac{9}{64}(1-\eta^2)(1+3\eta)(1-\xi)$$

$$N_{32,\xi} = -\tfrac{9}{64}(1-\eta^2)(1-3\eta)(1+\zeta)$$

$$N_{32,\eta} = \tfrac{9}{64}(9\eta^2-2\eta-3)(1-\xi)(1+\zeta)$$

$$N_{32,\zeta} = \tfrac{9}{64}(1-\eta^2)(1-3\eta)(1-\xi)$$

2A.2 Shape functions and derivatives of the membrane element
(a) Four-node membrane element

Node i	Shape functions $N_i(\xi, \eta)$	Derivatives	
		$\partial N_i/\partial\xi$	$\partial N_i/\partial\eta$
1	$\tfrac{1}{4}(1-\xi)(1-\eta)$	$-\tfrac{1}{4}(1-\eta)$	$-\tfrac{1}{4}(1-\xi)$
2	$\tfrac{1}{4}(1+\xi)(1-\eta)$	$\tfrac{1}{4}(1-\eta)$	$-\tfrac{1}{4}(1+\xi)$
3	$\tfrac{1}{4}(1+\xi)(1+\eta)$	$\tfrac{1}{4}(1+\eta)$	$\tfrac{1}{4}(1+\xi)$
4	$\tfrac{1}{4}(1-\xi)(1+\eta)$	$-\tfrac{1}{4}(1+\eta)$	$\tfrac{1}{4}(1-\xi)$

(b) Eight-node membrane element

Node i	Shape functions $N_i(\xi, \eta)$	Derivatives	
		$\partial N_i/\partial\xi$	$\partial N_i/\partial\eta$
1	$\tfrac{1}{4}(1-\xi)(1-\eta)(-\xi-\eta-1)$	$\tfrac{1}{4}(1-\eta)(2\xi+\eta)$	$\tfrac{1}{4}(1-\xi)(2\eta+\xi)$
2	$\tfrac{1}{2}(1-\xi^2)(1-\eta)$	$-\xi(1-\eta)$	$-\tfrac{1}{2}(1-\xi^2)$
3	$\tfrac{1}{4}(1+\xi)(1-\eta)(\xi-\eta-1)$	$\tfrac{1}{4}(1-\eta)(2\xi-\eta)$	$\tfrac{1}{4}(1+\xi)(2\eta-\xi)$
4	$\tfrac{1}{2}(1-\eta^2)(1+\xi)$	$\tfrac{1}{2}(1-\eta^2)$	$-\eta(1+\xi)$
5	$\tfrac{1}{4}(1+\xi)(1+\eta)(\xi+\eta-1)$	$\tfrac{1}{4}(1+\eta)(2\xi+\eta)$	$\tfrac{1}{4}(1+\xi)(2\eta+\xi)$
6	$\tfrac{1}{2}(1-\xi^2)(1+\eta)$	$-\xi(1+\eta)$	$\tfrac{1}{2}(1-\xi^2)$
7	$\tfrac{1}{4}(1-\xi)(1+\eta)(-\xi+\eta-1)$	$\tfrac{1}{4}(1+\eta)(2\xi-\eta)$	$\tfrac{1}{4}(1-\xi)(2\eta-1)$
8	$\tfrac{1}{2}(1-\eta^2)(1-\xi)$	$-\tfrac{1}{2}(1-\eta^2)$	$-\eta(1-\xi)$

(c) Twelve-node membrane element

Node i	Shape functions $Ni(\xi, \eta)$	Derivatives $\partial Ni/\partial \xi$	$\partial Ni/\partial \eta$
1	$\frac{1}{32}(1-\xi)(1-\eta)[9(\xi^2+\eta^2)-10]$	$\frac{1}{32}(1-\eta)[9(2\xi-3\xi^2)-(9\eta^2-10)]$	$\frac{1}{32}(1-\xi)[9(2\eta-3\eta^2)-(9\xi^2-10)]$
2	$\frac{9}{32}(1-\xi)(1-\xi^2)(1-\eta)$	$\frac{9}{32}(1-\eta)(3\xi^2-2\xi-1)$	$-\frac{9}{32}(1-\xi)(1-\xi^2)$
3	$\frac{9}{32}(1-\eta)(1-\xi^2)(1+\xi)$	$\frac{9}{32}(1-\eta)(1-2\xi-3\xi^2)$	$-\frac{9}{32}(1-\xi^2)(1+\xi)$
4	$\frac{1}{32}(1+\xi)(1-\eta)[9(\xi^2+\eta^2)-10]$	$\frac{1}{32}(1-\eta)[9(2\xi+3\xi^2)+(9\eta^2-10)]$	$\frac{1}{32}(1+\xi)[9(2\eta-3\eta^2)-(9\xi^2-10)]$
5	$\frac{9}{32}(1+\xi)(1-\eta^2)(1-\eta)$	$\frac{9}{32}(1-\eta^2)(1-\eta)$	$\frac{9}{32}(1+\xi)(3\eta^2-2\eta-1)$
6	$\frac{9}{32}(1+\xi)(1-\eta^2)(1+\eta)$	$\frac{9}{32}(1-\eta^2)(1+\eta)$	$\frac{9}{32}(1+\xi)(1-2\eta-3\eta^2)$
7	$\frac{1}{32}(1+\xi)(1+\eta)[9(\xi^2+\eta^2)-10]$	$\frac{1}{32}(1+\eta)[9(2\xi+3\xi^2)+(9\eta^2-10)]$	$\frac{1}{32}(1+\xi)[9(2\eta+3\eta^2)+(9\xi^2-10)]$
8	$\frac{9}{32}(1+\eta)(1-\xi^2)(1+\xi)$	$\frac{9}{32}(1+\eta)(1-2\xi-3\xi^2)$	$\frac{9}{32}(1-\xi^2)(1+\xi)$
9	$\frac{9}{32}(1+\eta)(1-\xi^2)(1-\xi)$	$\frac{9}{32}(1+\eta)(3\xi^2-2\xi-1)$	$\frac{9}{32}(1-\xi^2)(1-\xi)$
10	$\frac{1}{32}(1-\xi)(1+\eta)[9(\xi^2+\eta^2)-10]$	$\frac{1}{32}(1+\eta)[9(2\xi-3\xi^2)-(9\eta^2-10)]$	$\frac{1}{32}(1-\xi)[9(2\eta+3\eta^2)+(9\xi^2-10)]$
11	$\frac{9}{32}(1-\xi)(1-\eta^2)(1+\eta)$	$-\frac{9}{32}(1+\eta)(1-\eta^2)$	$\frac{9}{32}(1-\xi)(1-2\eta-3\eta^2)$
12	$\frac{9}{32}(1-\xi)(1-\eta^2)(1-\eta)$	$-\frac{9}{32}(1-\eta)(1-\eta^2)$	$\frac{9}{32}(1-\xi)(3\eta^2-2\eta-1)$

(d) Anisotropic stress–strain relations

Anisotropic stress–strain relations can be written in the form:

$$\varepsilon_X = \frac{\sigma_X}{E_1} - \frac{\nu_{21}}{E_2}\sigma_Y - \frac{\nu_{31}}{E_3}\sigma_Z$$

$$\varepsilon_Y = \frac{\sigma_Y}{E_2} - \frac{\nu_{12}}{E_1}\sigma_X - \frac{\nu_{32}}{E_3}\sigma_Z$$

$$\varepsilon_Z = \frac{\sigma_Z}{E_3} - \frac{\nu_{13}}{E_1}\sigma_X - \frac{\nu_{23}}{E_2}\sigma_Y$$

$$\gamma_{XY} = \frac{\tau_{XY}}{G_{12}}$$

$$\gamma_{YZ} = \frac{\tau_{YZ}}{G_{23}}$$

$$\gamma_{ZX} = \frac{\tau_{ZX}}{G_{13}}$$

Due to symmetry of compliances, the following relations can be written:

$$E_1\nu_{21} = E_2\nu_{12}$$

$$E_2\nu_{32} = E_3\nu_{23}$$

$$E_3\nu_{13} = E_1\nu_{31}$$

In matrix form,

$$\{\varepsilon\} = [A]\{\sigma\}$$

where,

$$[A] = \begin{bmatrix} \dfrac{1}{E_1} & -\dfrac{\nu_{21}}{E_2} & -\dfrac{\nu_{31}}{E_3} & 0 & 0 & 0 \\[2mm] -\dfrac{\nu_{12}}{E_1} & \dfrac{1}{E_2} & -\dfrac{\nu_{32}}{E_3} & 0 & 0 & 0 \\[2mm] -\dfrac{\nu_{13}}{E_1} & -\dfrac{\nu_{23}}{E_2} & \dfrac{1}{E_3} & 0 & 0 & 0 \\[2mm] 0 & 0 & 0 & \dfrac{1}{G_{12}} & 0 & 0 \\[2mm] 0 & 0 & 0 & 0 & \dfrac{1}{G_{23}} & 0 \\[2mm] 0 & 0 & 0 & 0 & 0 & \dfrac{1}{G_{13}} \end{bmatrix}$$

I.3   Material and cracking matrices: other material models and failure criteria

3A.I   Anisotropic material matrix

$$[D] = \begin{bmatrix} D_{11} & D_{12} & D_{13} & \bigcirc & \bigcirc & \bigcirc \\ D_{21} & D_{22} & D_{23} & \bigcirc & \bigcirc & \bigcirc \\ D_{31} & D_{32} & D_{33} & \bigcirc & \bigcirc & \bigcirc \\ \bigcirc & \bigcirc & \bigcirc & D_{44} & \bigcirc & \bigcirc \\ \bigcirc & \bigcirc & \bigcirc & \bigcirc & D_{55} & \bigcirc \\ \bigcirc & \bigcirc & \bigcirc & \bigcirc & \bigcirc & D_{66} \end{bmatrix}$$

where

$$D_{11} = (1 - \nu_{23}\nu_{32})E_1/\nu_K$$

$$D_{22} = (1 - \nu_{13}\nu_{31})E_2/\nu_K$$

$$D_{33} = (1 - \nu_{12}\nu_{21})E_3/\nu_K$$

$$D_{12} = (\nu_{12} + \nu_{13}\nu_{32})E_2/\nu_K$$

$$D_{21} = (\nu_{21} + \nu_{23}\nu_{31})E_1/\nu_K$$

$$D_{13} = (\nu_{13} + \nu_{12}\nu_{23})E_3/\nu_K$$

$$D_{31} = (\nu_{31} + \nu_{21}\nu_{32})E_1/\nu_K$$

$$D_{23} = (\nu_{23} + \nu_{13}\nu_{21})E_3/\nu_K$$

$$D_{32} = (\nu_{32} + \nu_{31}\nu_{12})E_2/\nu_K$$

$$D_{44} = G_{12}$$

$$D_{55} = G_{23}$$

$$D_{66} = G_{13}$$

$$\nu_K = 1 - \nu_{12}\nu_{21} - \nu_{13}\nu_{31} - \nu_{23}\nu_{32} - \nu_{12}\nu_{23}\nu_{31} - \nu_{21}\nu_{13}\nu_{32}$$

Due to symmetry of compliances, the following relations can be written

$$E_1 \nu_{21} = E_2 \nu_{12}$$

$$E_2 \nu_{32} = E_3 \nu_{23}$$

$$E_2 \nu_{13} = E_1 \nu_{31}$$

The values of $G12$, $G23$ and $G13$ are calculated in terms of modulus of elasticity and Poisson's ratio as follows:

$$G_{12} = \frac{1}{2}\left[\frac{E_1}{2(1+\nu_{12})} + \frac{E_2}{2(1+\nu_{12})}\right]$$

$$= \frac{1}{2}\left[\frac{E_1}{2(1+\nu_{12})} + \frac{E_1}{2\left(\frac{E_1}{E_2}+\nu_{12}\right)}\right]$$

$$G_{23} = \frac{1}{2}\left[\frac{E_2}{2(1+\nu_{23})} + \frac{E_3}{2(1+\nu_{32})}\right]$$

$$= \frac{1}{2}\left[\frac{E_2}{2(1+\nu_{23})} + \frac{E_2}{2\left(\frac{E_2}{E_3}+\nu_{23}\right)}\right]$$

$$G_{13} = \frac{1}{2}\left[\frac{E_3}{2(1+\nu_{31})} + \frac{E_1}{2(1+\nu_{13})}\right]$$

$$= \frac{1}{2}\left[\frac{E_3}{2(1+\nu_{31})} + \frac{E_3}{2\left(\frac{E_3}{E_1}+\nu_{31}\right)}\right]$$

3A.2 General steps of flow and crack calculations

In accordance with Fig. 3A.1, the general steps are:

(1)   The load increment $\{\Delta P_n\}$ is applied where n is the load increment.

(2)   The total is accumulated as $\{P_n\} = \{P_{n-1}\} + \{\Delta P_n\}$, and $\{R\} = \{\Delta P_n\}$, where $\{R\}$ is the residual load vector.

(3)   Incremental displacement is computed as $\{\Delta U_i\} = [K]_e^{-1}\{R\}$, where i is the iteration.

(4)   Total displacements are now accumulated in the following form: $\{U_i\} = \{U_{i-1}\} + \{\Delta U_i\}$.

(5)   Strain increments are calculated from step 4 as $\{\Delta\varepsilon_i\} = [B]\{\Delta U_i\}$. The accumulated strains at this stage would then be written as

$$\{\varepsilon_i\} = \{\varepsilon_{i-1}\} + \{\Delta\varepsilon_i\}$$

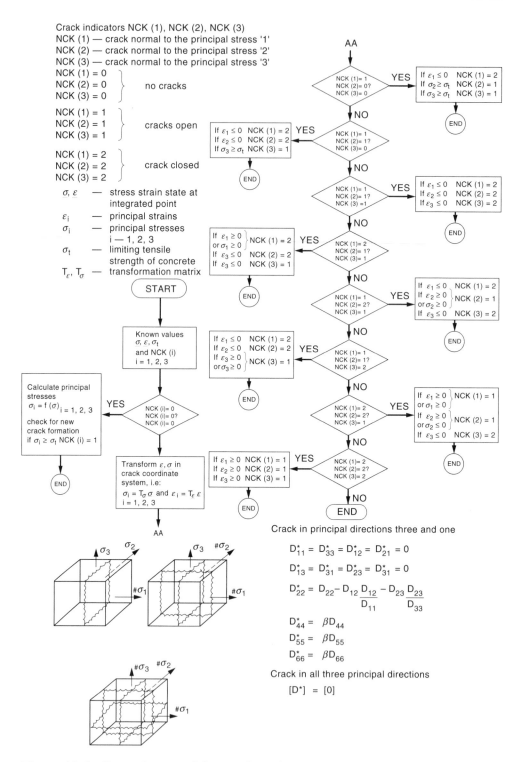

Figure A3.1. General steps of flow and crack calculations

(6)   The stress increments are calculated using the current nonlinear constitutive matrices of various models described earlier: $\{\Delta\sigma_i\} = \{f(\sigma)\}\{\Delta\varepsilon\}$. The accumulated stresses are computed as $\{\sigma_i\} = \{\sigma_{i-1}\} + \{\Delta\sigma_i\}$. In order to differentiate stresses at elastic and plastic conditions, a stress point indicator I_p is introduced.

$$I_p = 0 \quad \text{(elastic point)}$$
$$= 1 \quad \text{(plastic point)}$$
$$= 2 \quad \text{(unloading from plastic state)}$$

(7)   The stress increment is calculated using the elastic material matrix as $\{\Delta\sigma_i'\} = [D']\{\Delta\varepsilon\}$. Total stresses are given as $\{\sigma_i'\}_T = \{\sigma_{i-1}\} - \{\Delta\sigma_i'\}$.

(8)   The stress $\{\sigma_i\}$ is now calculated using step 7: $\{\sigma_i\} = \{f(\sigma_i')\}$, $\{\sigma_{i-1}\} = \{f(\sigma_{i-1})\}$ – any yield criterion required.

(9)   If a plastic point is obtained, step 11 should be considered.

(10)   If $\sigma_i \geq \sigma_y$ – plastic point ($I_p = 1$), transition from elastic to plastic, calculate factor T_{TP}:

$$F_{TP} = \left(\frac{\sigma_y - \bar{\sigma}_{i-1}}{\sigma_i - \sigma_{i-1}}\right)$$

The stress at the yield surface $\{\sigma_i\}_y^* = \{\sigma_{i-1}\} + F_{TP}^*\{\Delta\sigma_i'\}$. Elasto-plastic stress increments are calculated as $\{\Delta\sigma_i\} = [D]_{ep}\{\sigma_i\}^*(1 - F_{TP})\{\Delta\varepsilon\}$. Total stress $\{\sigma_i\}_T = \{\sigma_i\} + \{\Delta\sigma_i\}$.

(11)   Plastic point from steps 9 and 10, check for unloading, i.e. if $\bar{\sigma} \geq \sigma_y$, it is necessary to proceed to step 12. For the unloading case at this point, set $I_p = 2$, total stress $\{\sigma_i\}_T$ is then given by $\{\sigma_i\} = \{\sigma_{i-1}\} + \{\Delta\sigma_i\}$. Set $\{\sigma_y\} = \{\bar{\sigma}_{i-1}\}$, and the procedure is repeated for the additional increments.

(12)   Loading at this point $\{\Delta\sigma_i\} = [D]_{ep}\{\bar{\sigma}_{i-1}\}\{\Delta\varepsilon\}$. Total stress $\{\sigma_i\}_T = \{\bar{\sigma}_{i-1}\} + \{\Delta\varepsilon\}$.

(13)   Sometimes it is necessary to correct stresses from the equivalent stress–strain curve: $\sigma_{corr} = \sigma_{i-1} + S_H \Delta\varepsilon_p$, where $\Delta\varepsilon_p = \sqrt{\frac{2}{3}\Delta\varepsilon_{ij}^P \Delta\varepsilon_{ij}^P} = $ equivalent plastic strain increment. S_H is the strain hardening parameter, such that $\Delta\bar{\varepsilon}_p = \lambda$.

Equivalent stress, calculated from the current stress state, is given by $\{\sigma_i\} = F_{TP}\{(\sigma_i)\}$. The correct stress state, which is on the yield surface, will therefore be given as $\{\sigma_i\} = F_{TP}\{\sigma_i\}$. The total stresses are converted into equivalent nodal loads from $\int_v [B]^T \{\sigma_i\}\, d\,vol$, and the residual load vector is calculated from $\{R\} = \{F_n\} - \int_v [B]^T\{\sigma_i\}\, d\,vol$.

(14)   Check for convergence:

$$(\|R\|/\|F\|) \leq \text{TOL} \qquad (\|\Delta U\|/\|U\|) \leq \text{TOL}$$

where TOL is chosen from 0.01 to 0.001; $\|R\| = \sqrt{R_i^{T''} R_i}$ is the Euclidean norm of the residuals; $\|F\| = \sqrt{P^T P}$ is the Euclidean norm of the externally applied load; and $\|\Delta U\| = \sqrt{\Delta U_i^{T''} U_i}$ is the Euclidean norm.

If convergence is not achieved, step 3 is invoked and all the steps repeated for the next iteration. If convergence is achieved, then proceed with the next load increment.

3A.3 Heat conduction model

Steady state and transient heat-conduction models are developed and problems are solved using finite elements. The equations of heat conduction generally include the effects of surface areas with convection and radiation boundary conditions.

Steady state

The basic thermal equilibrium equation is written as

$$[\bar{K}]\{T\} = \{q\} \tag{11.53}$$

where $[K] =$ the thermal conductivity matrix; $\{Q\} =$ the heat flow vector; and $\{T\} =$ the vector of the nodal point temperatures.

The basic thermal diffusion equation is written as

$$[C]_s\{T\} + [K]\{T\} = \{Q\} \tag{11.54}$$

where $[C]_s$ is the specific heat matrix.

For large and complicated structures a substructuring system on the lines suggested is adopted. In order to distinguish the dynamic transient equations and others from these, the governing equation for the thermal substructure is written as

$$[C]_s\{T\} + [K]_c\{T\} = \{Q\} \tag{11.55}$$

where

$$[K]_c = [K_{\gamma\gamma}] - [K_{\gamma\gamma'}][K_{\gamma'\gamma'}]^{-1}[K_{\gamma'\gamma}]$$

$$[C]_s = [C_{\gamma\gamma}]_s - [K_{\gamma\gamma'}][K_{\gamma'\gamma'}]^{-1}[C_{\gamma'\gamma}]_s - [C_{\gamma'\gamma}]_s[K_{\gamma'\gamma'}]^{-1}[K_{\gamma'\gamma}]$$

$$\qquad + [K_{\gamma\gamma'}][K_{\gamma'\gamma'}]^{-1}[C_{\gamma'\gamma'}]_s[K_{\gamma'\gamma'}]^{-1}[K_{\gamma'\gamma}]$$

$$\{Q\} = \{Q_\gamma\} - [K_{\gamma\gamma'}][K_{\gamma'\gamma'}]^{-1}\{Q_{\gamma'}\}$$

$$\{T\} = \{T_\gamma\}$$

Hence

$$\{T_{\gamma'}\} = [K_{\gamma'\gamma'}]^{-1}\{Q_{\gamma'}\} - [K_{\gamma'\gamma'}]^{-1}[K_{\gamma'\gamma}]\{T_\gamma\} \tag{11.56}$$

In the above equations the convection surfaces are not included.

The temperature at point X, Y, Z is written as

$$T(X,\ Y,\ Z) = \{N\}^{T''}\{T\} \tag{11.57}$$

where $\{N\} =$ the vector of shape functions and $\{T\} =$ the nodal temperature vector.

$\{S\}^T$, the vector of temperature, is related to $\{T\}$ using the definition of $\{S\}^T$ and Eq. (I1.57) to give

$$\{S\}^T = [B]\{T\} \tag{I1.58}$$

where

$$[B] = \begin{bmatrix} \left\{\dfrac{\partial N}{\partial X}\right\}^{T''} \\[2mm] \left\{\dfrac{\partial N}{\partial Y}\right\}^{T''} \\[2mm] \left\{\dfrac{\partial N}{\partial Z}\right\}^{T''} \end{bmatrix} \qquad \{S\}^T = \begin{bmatrix} \left(\dfrac{\partial T}{\partial X}\right) \\[2mm] \left(\dfrac{\partial T}{\partial Y}\right) \\[2mm] \left(\dfrac{\partial T}{\partial Z}\right) \end{bmatrix}_{x,y,z} \tag{I1.59}$$

In thermal terms, the virtual work within one element, i.e. internal work, is written as

$$\Delta U = \int \{\Delta S^T\}^{T''} \{Q\}_{X,Y,Z} \, \mathrm{d\,vol} \tag{I1.60}$$

where

$$\{Q\} = \left\{ \begin{array}{c} Q_X \\ Q_Y \\ Q_Z \end{array} \right\} = \text{the vector of heat flow}$$

Q_X = heat flow in the x direction per unit area

Q_Y = heat flow in the y direction per unit area

Q_Z = heat flow in the z direction per unit area

The heat flows are related to the temperature gradients using the following relation:

$$\{Q\} = [K^c]\{S\}^T \tag{I1.61}$$

where the conductivity matrix $[K^c]$ is given by

$$[K^c] = \begin{bmatrix} K_{XX} & 0 & 0 \\ 0 & K_{YY} & 0 \\ 0 & 0 & K_{ZZ} \end{bmatrix}_c$$

The internal work is written again as

$$\Delta U = \{\partial T\}^{T''} \int_{\mathrm{vol}} [B]^{T''} [D][B] \, \mathrm{d\,vol} \, \{T\} \tag{I1.62}$$

The virtual internal work associated with convection surfaces is given by

$$U = \int_A \partial\Delta T \hat{Q} \, dA$$

where $\hat{} = $ the direction normal to the surface:

$$\partial\Delta T = \partial T(X, Y, Z)|_s \tag{I1.63}$$

The heat flow $\hat{Q}$ over the unit area is given by

$$\hat{Q} = e_f \Delta T \tag{I1.64}$$

where $c_f = $ the film coefficient for heat transfer of the surface and $\partial T(X, Y, Z)|_s$ is the temperature function evaluated at the convection surface.

In finite element form the above equations are then written as

$$U = \{\partial T_e\}^{T''} c_f \int_{area} \{N_s\}^{T''} \, d(area)\{T_e\}$$

$$- \{\partial T_e\}^{T''} c_f T_B \int_{area} \{N_s\} \, d(area) \tag{I1.65}$$

where $\{N_s\}$ are the shape functions evaluated at the convection surface and T_B is the temperature of the coolant.

Similarly, the virtual work associated with specific heat, i.e. thermal damping, is written as

$$\Delta U = \int_V \partial T(X, Y, Z) H \, d\,vol \tag{I1.66}$$

where

$$H = D_c C_p \frac{\partial T(X, Y, Z)}{\partial t}$$

$$= \text{total heat change per unit volume per unit time}$$

$$D_c = \text{density}$$

$$C_p = \text{specific heat}$$

When D_c, C_p and T do not vary over the element, Eq. (I1.66) is written

$$\partial U = \{\partial T\}^{T''} D_c C_p \int_V \{N\}\{N\}^{T''} \, d\,vol \frac{\partial}{\partial t}\{T\} \tag{I1.67}$$

If H_r is the heat generation rate per unit volume, the expression for ∂U is written as

$$\partial U = \{\partial T\}^{T''} H_r \int_V \{N\} \, d\,vol \tag{I1.68}$$

When all the above effects are combined, the following expression is obtained:

$$[[K] + [K^c]]\{T\} + [C]_s \frac{\partial}{\partial t} \{T_e\} = \{Q^c\} + \{Q^h\} + \{Q\} \qquad \text{(I1.69)}$$

where

$[K]$ is the material matrix $= \displaystyle\int_V B^{T''} DB \, \mathrm{d\,vol}$

$[K^c]$ is the conductivity matrix $= c_f \displaystyle\int_A \{N_s\}\{N_s\}^{T''} \mathrm{d}A$

$[C]_s$ is the specific heat matrix $= \rho C_p \displaystyle\int_V \{N\}\{N\}^{T''} \mathrm{d}V$

$\{Q^c\}$ is a total element matrix heat flow matrix per unit area

$$= c_f T_B \int_A \{N_s\} \, \mathrm{d}A$$

$\{Q^h\}$ is a total element matrix heat generated matrix per unit volume

$$= H_r \int_V \{N\} \, \mathrm{d}V$$

t is time

For the nonlinear transient analysis a time integration scheme is adopted on the lines suggested in the dynamic analysis given in Part B.

The usual heat-conduction matrices and thermal load vectors are given below:

$$[K_e] = \begin{bmatrix} K_T + S_1 & -K_T & 0 & 0 & 0 \\ -K_T & 2K_T & -K_T & 0 & 0 \\ 0 & -K_T & 2K_T & -K_T & 0 \\ 0 & 0 & -K_T & 2K_T & -K_T \\ 0 & 0 & 0 & -K_T & K_T + S_2 \end{bmatrix} \qquad \text{(I1.70)}$$

where

$K_T = \dfrac{4(A)K_{XX}^c}{d}$

$S_i = C_{i,f}(A)$

$K_{XX}^c = $ thermal conductivity

$\bar{t} = $ thickness

$f = $ film coefficient

$A = $ area

The thermal damping (specific heat) matrix is

$$[C_e]_s = \begin{bmatrix} 2B_t & B_t & 0 & 0 & 0 \\ B_t & 4B_t & B_t & 0 & 0 \\ 0 & B_t & 4B_t & B_t & 0 \\ 0 & 0 & B_t & 4B_t & B_t \\ 0 & 0 & 0 & B_t & 2B_t \end{bmatrix} \tag{I1.71}$$

3A.4   2-D elastic beam (ANSYS User's Manual, courtesy STRUCOM, London)
Element matrices and load vectors

The element stiffness matrix in element coordinates (Przemieniecki) is:

$$[K_l] =$$

$$\begin{bmatrix} \dfrac{AE}{L} & 0 & 0 & -\dfrac{AE}{L} & 0 & 0 \\[2mm] 0 & \dfrac{12EI}{L^3(1+\phi')} & \dfrac{6EI}{L^2(1+\phi')} & 0 & -\dfrac{12EI}{L^3(1+\phi')} & \dfrac{6EI}{L(1+\phi')} \\[2mm] 0 & \dfrac{6EI}{L^2(1+\phi')} & \dfrac{EI(4+\phi')}{L(1+\phi')} & 0 & -\dfrac{6EI}{L^2(1+\phi')} & \dfrac{EI(2-\phi')}{L(1+\phi')} \\[2mm] -\dfrac{AE}{L} & 0 & 0 & \dfrac{AE}{L} & 0 & 0 \\[2mm] 0 & -\dfrac{12EI}{L^3(1+\phi')} & \dfrac{6EI}{L^2(1+\phi')} & 0 & \dfrac{12EI}{L^3(1+\phi')} & -\dfrac{6EI}{L^2(1+\phi')} \\[2mm] 0 & \dfrac{6EI}{L^2(1+\phi')} & \dfrac{EI(2-\phi')}{L(1+\phi')} & 0 & -\dfrac{6EI}{L^2(1+\phi')} & \dfrac{EI(4+\phi')}{L(1+\phi')} \end{bmatrix}$$

where

A = cross-sectional area

E = Young's modulus

L = element length

I = moment of inertia

$\phi' = \dfrac{12EI}{GA^sL^2}$

G = shear modulus

$A^s = \dfrac{A}{F^s}$ = shear area

F^s = shear deflection constant

The element mass matrix in element coordinates (Yokoyama) is:

$$[M_l] = (\rho A + m)L(1 - \varepsilon^{in})$$

$$\times \begin{bmatrix} 1/3 & 0 & 0 & 1/6 & 0 & 0 \\ 0 & A(r, \phi') & C(r, \phi') & 0 & B(r, \phi') & -D(r, \phi') \\ 0 & C(r, \phi') & E(r, \phi') & 0 & D(r, \phi') & -F(r, \phi') \\ 1/6 & 0 & 0 & 1/3 & 0 & 0 \\ 0 & B(r, \phi') & D(r, \phi') & 0 & A(r, \phi') & -C(r, \phi') \\ 0 & -D(r, \phi') & -F(r, \phi') & 0 & -C(r, \phi') & E(r, \phi') \end{bmatrix}$$

where

$$\rho = \text{density}$$

$$m = \text{added } m$$

$$\varepsilon_{in} = \text{prestrain}$$

$$A(r, \phi') = \frac{13/35 + 7/10\phi' + 1/3\phi'^2 + 6/5(r/L)^2}{(1 + \phi')^2}$$

$$B(r, \phi') = \frac{9/70 + 3/10\phi' + 1/6\phi'^2 - 6/5(r/L)^2}{(1 + \phi')^2}$$

$$C(r, \phi') = \frac{(11/210 + 11/120\phi' + 1/24\phi'^2 + (1/10 - 1/2\phi')(r/L)^2)L}{(1 + \phi')^2}$$

$$D(r, \phi') = \frac{(13/420 + 3/40\phi' + 1/24\phi'^2 - (1/10 - 1/2\phi')(r/L)^2)L}{(1 + \phi')^2}$$

$$E(r, \phi') = \frac{(1/105 + 1/60\phi' + 1/120\phi'^2 + (2/15 + 1/6\phi' + 1/3)(r/L)^2)L^2}{(1 + \phi')^2}$$

$$F(r, \phi') = \frac{(1/140 + 1/60\phi' + 1/120\phi'^2 + (1/30 + 1/6\phi' + 1/6\phi'^2)(r/L)^2)L^2}{(1 + \phi')^2}$$

$$r = \sqrt{\frac{I}{A}} = \text{radius of gyration}$$

The element pressure load vector in element coordinates is:

$$\{F_l^{pr}\} = \lfloor P_1 \quad P_2 \quad P_3 \quad P_4 \quad P_5 \quad P_6 \rfloor^T$$

For uniform lateral pressure,

$$P_1 = P_4 = 0$$

$$P_2 = P_5 = -\frac{PL}{2}$$

$$P_3 = -P_6 = -\frac{PL^2}{12}$$

$P =$ uniform applied pressure (units = force/length)

Stress calculations

The centroidal stress (Fig. 3A.2) at end i is:

$$\sigma_i^{\text{dir}} = \frac{F_{x,i}}{A}$$

where

$\sigma_i^{\text{dir}} =$ centroidal stress

$F_{x,i} =$ axial force

The bending stress is

$$\sigma_i^{\text{bnd}} = \frac{M_i t}{2I}$$

where

$\sigma_i^{\text{bnd}} =$ bending stress at end i

$M_i =$ moment at end i

$t =$ thickness of beam in element z direction

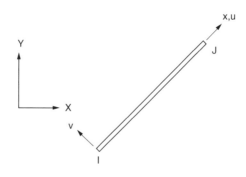

Figure 3A.2. Centroidal stress

3A.5   3-D elastic beam (ANSYS User's Manual, courtesy STRUCOM, London)

Element matrices and load vectors

All element matrices and load vectors are generated in the element coordinate system and must subsequently then be converted to the global coordinate system. The element stiffness matrix is:

$$[K_l] = \frac{AE}{L} \begin{bmatrix} C_1 & 0 & 0 & -C_1 & 0 & 0 \\ 0 & 0 & 0 & 0 & 0 & 0 \\ 0 & 0 & 0 & 0 & 0 & 0 \\ -C_1 & 0 & 0 & C_1 & 0 & 0 \\ 0 & 0 & 0 & 0 & 0 & 0 \\ 0 & 0 & 0 & 0 & 0 & 0 \end{bmatrix}$$

where

A = element cross-sectional area

E = Young's modulus

L = element length

C_1 = value given in Table API.3.

The element mass matrix is the same as the element stress stiffness matrix:

$$[S_l] = \frac{F}{L} \begin{bmatrix} 0 & 0 & 0 & 0 & 0 & 0 \\ 0 & C_2 & 0 & 0 & -C_2 & 0 \\ 0 & 0 & C_2 & 0 & 0 & -C_2 \\ 0 & 0 & 0 & 0 & 0 & 0 \\ 0 & -C_2 & 0 & 0 & C_2 & 0 \\ 0 & 0 & -C_2 & 0 & 0 & C_2 \end{bmatrix}$$

Table API.3. Value of stiffness coefficient (C_1)

Previous iteration resulted in a tensile stress	Previous iteration resulted in a compressive stress
1.0	0.0
1.0	1.0×10^{-6}
0.0	1.0
1.0×10^{-6}	1.0

Table API.4. Value of stress stiffness coefficient (C_2)

Previous iteration resulted in a tensile stress	Previous iteration resulted in a compressive stress
1.0	0.0
1.0	$\dfrac{AE}{F \times 10^6}$
0.0	1.0
$\dfrac{AE}{F \times 10^6}$	1.0

$$F = \begin{cases} \text{for the first iteration:} \quad A E \varepsilon^{\text{in}} \\[1em] \text{for all subsequent iterations: the axial force} \\ \text{in the element as computed in the previous} \\ \text{stress pass of the element (output quantity} \\ \text{FORC)} \end{cases}$$

$C_2 =$ value given in Table (API.4.)

The matrix for the tension-only or compression-only spar (Fig. 3A.3) is given by:

$$[M_l] = \frac{M_t}{2} \begin{bmatrix}
1 \\
0 & 1 \\
0 & 0 & 1 \\
0 & 0 & 0 & 0 \\
0 & 0 & 0 & 0 & 0 \\
0 & 0 & 0 & 0 & 0 & 0 \\
0 & 0 & 0 & 0 & 0 & 0 & 1 \\
0 & 0 & 0 & 0 & 0 & 0 & 0 & 1 \\
0 & 0 & 0 & 0 & 0 & 0 & 0 & 0 & 1 \\
0 & 0 & 0 & 0 & 0 & 0 & 0 & 0 & 0 & 0 \\
0 & 0 & 0 & 0 & 0 & 0 & 0 & 0 & 0 & 0 & 0 \\
0 & 0 & 0 & 0 & 0 & 0 & 0 & 0 & 0 & 0 & 0 & 0
\end{bmatrix}$$

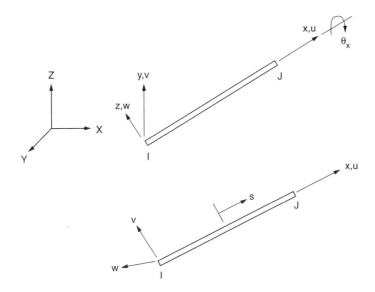

Figure 3A.3. Tension-only or compression-only spar

3A.6 Stiffness and mass matrices (ANSYS User's Manual, courtesy STRUCOM, London)

Orders of degrees of freedom

The order of degrees of freedom (DOFs) is shown in Fig. 3A.4. The stiffness matrix in element coordinates (Przemieniecki) is:

$$[K_l] =$$

$$
\begin{bmatrix}
AE/L \\
0 & a_z \\
0 & 0 & a_y \\
0 & 0 & 0 & GJ/L & & & & & \text{Symmetric} \\
0 & 0 & d_y & 0 & e_y \\
0 & c_z & 0 & 0 & 0 & e_z \\
-AE/L & 0 & 0 & 0 & 0 & 0 & AE/L \\
0 & b_z & 0 & 0 & 0 & d_z & 0 & a_z \\
0 & 0 & b_y & 0 & c_y & 0 & 0 & 0 & a_y \\
0 & 0 & 0 & -GJ/L & 0 & 0 & 0 & 0 & 0 & GJ/L \\
0 & 0 & d_y & 0 & f_y & 0 & 0 & 0 & c_z & 0 & e_y \\
0 & c_z & 0 & 0 & 0 & f_z & 0 & d_y & 0 & 0 & 0 & e_z
\end{bmatrix}
$$

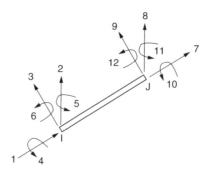

Figure A3.4. Order of degrees of freedom

where

A = cross-sectional area

E = Young's modulus

L = element length

G = shear modulus

$r_y = \sqrt{\dfrac{I_{yy}}{A}}$ = radius of gyration

$r_z = \sqrt{\dfrac{I_{zz}}{A}}$ = radius of gyration

$[M_l] = M_t$

$$
\begin{bmatrix}
1/3 \\
0 & A_z \\
0 & 0 & A_y \\
0 & 0 & 0 & J_x/3A & & & & & & \text{Symmetric} \\
0 & 0 & -C_y & 0 & E_y \\
0 & C_z & 0 & 0 & 0 & E_z \\
1/6 & 0 & 0 & 0 & 0 & 0 & 1/3 \\
0 & B_z & 0 & 0 & 0 & D_z & 0 & A_z \\
0 & 0 & B_y & 0 & -D_y & 0 & 0 & 0 & A_y \\
0 & 0 & 0 & J_x/6A & 0 & 0 & 0 & 0 & 0 & J_x/3A \\
0 & 0 & D_y & 0 & F_y & 0 & 0 & 0 & C_y & 0 & E_y \\
0 & -D_z & 0 & 0 & 0 & F_z & 0 & -C_z & 0 & 0 & 0 & E_z
\end{bmatrix}
$$

where

$$M_t = (\rho A + m)L(1 - \varepsilon^{in})$$

$$\rho = \text{density}$$

$$m = \text{added mass}$$

$$\varepsilon^{in} = \text{prestrain}$$

$$A_z = A(r_z, \phi'_y)$$

$$A_y = A(r_y, \phi'_z)$$

$$B_z = B(r_z, \phi'_y)$$

$$\vdots$$

$$F_z = F(r_z, \phi'_y)$$

$$F_y = F(r, \phi'_z)$$

and where

$$A(r, \phi') = \frac{13/35 + 7/10\phi' + 1/3\phi'^2 = 6/5(r/L)^2}{(1 + \phi')^2}$$

$$B(r, \phi') = \frac{9/70 + 3/10\phi' + 1/6\phi'^2 - 6/5(r/L)^2}{(1 + \phi')^2}$$

$$C(r, \phi') = \frac{(11/210 + 11/120\phi' + 1/24\phi'^2 + (1/10 - 1/2\phi')(r/L)^2)L}{(1 + \phi')^2}$$

$$D(r, \phi') = \frac{(13/420 + 3/40\phi' + 1/24\phi'^2 - (1/10 - 1/2\phi')(r/L)^2)L}{(1 + \phi')^2}$$

$$E(r, \phi') = \frac{(1/105 + 1/60\phi' + 1/120\phi'^2 + (2/15 + 1/6\phi' + 1/3\phi'^2)(r/L)^2)L^2}{(1 + \phi')^2}$$

$$F(r, \phi') = -\frac{(1/140 + 1/60\phi' + 1/120\phi'^2 + (1/30 + 1/6\phi' - 1/6\phi'^2)(r/L)^2)L^2}{(1 + \phi')^2}$$

$$J = \text{torsional moment of inertia} = \left\{ \begin{matrix} J_x & \text{if } I_x = 0 \\ I_x & \text{if } I_x \neq 0 \end{matrix} \right\}$$

$$I_x = \text{input as IXX}$$

$$J_x = \text{polar moment of inertia} = I_y + I_z$$

$$a_z = a(I_z, \phi_y')$$

$$a_y = a(I_y, \phi_z')$$

$$b_z = b(I_z, \phi_y')$$

$$\vdots$$

$$f_z = f(I_z, \phi_y')$$

$$f_y = f(I_y, \phi_z')$$

A_i^s = shear area normal to direction $i = A/F_i^s$

F_i^s = shear coefficient

I_i = moment of inertia normal to direction i

$$a(I, \phi') = \frac{12EI}{L^3(1 + \phi')}$$

$$b(I, \phi') = \frac{-12EI}{L^3(1 + \phi')}$$

$$c(I, \phi') = \frac{6EI}{L^2(1 + \phi')}$$

$$d(I, \phi') = \frac{-6EI}{L^2(1 + \phi')}$$

$$e(I, \phi') = \frac{(4 + \phi')EI}{L(1 + \phi')}$$

$$f(I, \phi') = \frac{(2 - \phi')EI}{L(1 + \phi')}$$

$$\phi_y' = \frac{12EI_z}{GA_z^s L^2}$$

$$\phi_z' = \frac{12EI_y}{GA_y^s L^2}$$

3A.7   Local to global conversion (ANSYS User's Manual, courtesy STRUCOM, London)

The element coordinates are related to the global coordinates by:

$$\{u_l\} = [T_R]\{u\}$$

where

$\{u_l\}$ = vector of displacements in element Cartesian coordinates

$\{u\}$ = vector of displacements in global Cartesian coordinates

$$[T_R] = \begin{bmatrix} T & 0 & 0 & 0 \\ 0 & T & 0 & 0 \\ 0 & 0 & T & 0 \\ 0 & 0 & 0 & T \end{bmatrix}$$

$[T]$ is defined by:

$$[T] = \begin{bmatrix} C_1 C_2 & S_1 C_2 & S_2 \\ (-C_1 S_2 S_3 - S_1 S_3) & (C_1 C_3 - S_1 S_2 S_3) & S_3 C_2 \\ (S_1 S_3 - C_1 S_2 C_3) & (-S_1 S_2 C_3 - C_1 S_3) & C_3 S_2 \end{bmatrix}$$

where

$$S_1 = \begin{cases} \dfrac{Y_2 - Y_1}{L_{xy}} & \text{if } L_{xy} > d \\[2mm] 0.0 & \text{if } L_{xy} < d \end{cases}$$

$$S_2 = \frac{Z_2 - Z_1}{L}$$

$$S_3 = \sin(\theta)$$

$$C_1 = \begin{cases} \dfrac{X_2 - X_1}{L_{xy}} & \text{if } L_{xy} > d \\[2mm] 1.0 & \text{if } L_{xy} < d \end{cases}$$

$$C_2 = \frac{L_{xy}}{L}$$

$$C_3 = \cos(\theta)$$

X_1, etc. $= x$ coordinate of node 1, etc.

L_{xy} = projection of length onto X–Y plane

$d = 0.0001L$

$\theta =$ input

If a third node is given, θ is not used. Rather C_3 and S_3 are defined using:

$\{V_1\}$ = vector from origin to node 1

$\{V_2\}$ = vector from origin to node 2

$\{V_3\}$ = vector from origin to node 3

$\{V_4\}$ = unit vector parallel to global Z axis, unless element is almost parallel to Z axis, in which case it is parallel to the X axis

Then,

$$\{V_5\} = \{V_3\} - \{V_1\} = \text{vector between nodes } I \text{ and } K$$

$$\{V_6\} = \{V_2\} - \{V_1\} = \text{vector along element } X \text{ axis}$$

$$\{V_7\} = \{V_6\} \times \{V_4\}$$

$$\{V_8\} = \{V_6\} \times \{V_5\}$$

$$\{V_9\} = \{V_7\} \times \{V_8\}$$

and

$$C_3 = \frac{\{V_7\} \cdot \{V_8\}}{|\{V_7\}| \cdot |\{V_8\}|}$$

$$S_3 = \frac{\{V_6\} \cdot \{V_9\}}{|\{V_6\}| \cdot |\{V_9\}|}$$

The $\times$ and $\cdot$ refer to vector crosses and dot products, respectively. Thus, the element stiffness matrix in global coordinates becomes:

$$[K_e] = [T_R]^T [K_l][T_R]$$

$$[M_e] = [T_R]^T [M_l][T_R]$$

$$[S_e] = [T_R]^T [S_l][T_R]$$

$$\{F_e\} = [T_R]^T [F_l]$$

3A.8 Buckling analysis

The eigenvalue buckling (bifurcation) analysis is vital where a steel liner is fully or partially anchored to concrete, such as in concrete bridges, tunnels, pressure and containment vessels, cells of offshore platforms, underground shelters, structures for hydroelectricity and irrigation, etc.

Buckling of the liner or its embedded anchors in concrete is possible. The buckling matrix is developed so that at appropriate stages the liner and its anchor system are checked against buckling. The equation below gives the eigenvalue buckling by bifurcation:

$$([K]^e + \lambda_{ei}[K^s])\{\psi\}_i = \{0\} \tag{11.72}$$

where

$[K]^e$ = the elastic stiffness matrix

$[K^s]$ = the stress stiffness matrix

λ_{ei} = the ith eigenvalue
        (used to multiply the loads which generated $[K^s]$)

$\{\psi\}_i$ = the ith eigenvector of displacements

The first step in the solution is to reduce Eq. (I1.72) to its static or dynamic buckling (master) degrees of freedom. The elastic stiffness matrix $[K]^e$ is reduced and the stress stiffness matrix $[K^s]$ is reduced in a manner identical to that by which the mass matrix is reduced. Hence Eq. (I1.72) becomes:

$$([K]_R + \lambda_{ei}[K^s])\{\psi_i\}_R = 0 \tag{I1.73}$$

where $[K]_R$ can be replaced by $[K_t']_R$ when dynamic problems are involved.

When a geometric stiffness matrix is included, the plastic buckling matrix is given as

$$([K^p]_R + \lambda_{ci}[K]_G)\{\psi_i\}_R = 0 \tag{I1.74}$$

where $\lambda_c = 1 + E_{ps}$, and $E_{ps} = $ accuracy parameters.

$\{\psi_i\}_R$ is related to the total initial load vector $\{F_T\}$ of the liner and the studs. Equations (I1.73) and (I1.74) are further condensed by again reducing out those rows and columns of the matrices that have a positive value on the main diagonal of the stress or geometric matrix. The matrices are inverted such that an accuracy is achieved having the lowest eigenvalue. A standard iteration procedure is adopted for the solution of these matrices. The eigenvectors are then normalized such that each has the largest value of 1.0 (Fig. 3A.5):

$$\{\hat{\mathbf{F}}_N\} = [K_{\gamma'\gamma'}]_i\{U_{\gamma'}\}_i = [\Sigma k]\{\Sigma\Delta_i, \Delta_j \ldots\}$$

$$= \{\hat{\vec{\mathbf{F}}}_{i,j}, \ldots\} + \{\pm\mu\hat{\vec{\mathbf{F}}}_n \ldots \pm k\Delta_i \ldots\}$$

$\Delta_{sl} = $ distance of sliding

$$= (\Delta_j - \Delta_i) - \frac{\mu|\hat{\vec{\mathbf{F}}}_N|}{[K_{\gamma'\gamma'}]}$$

$\mu = $ friction

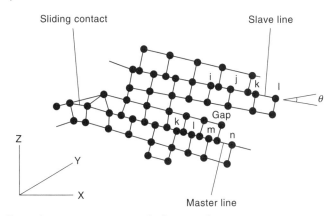

Figure 3A.5. Gap element: master and slave nodes

$$\{\hat{\bar{F}}_{sN}\} \le \mu\{\hat{\bar{F}}_{N}\} \quad \text{no sliding}$$

$$\ge \mu\{\hat{\bar{F}}_{N}\} \quad \text{sliding}$$

$$= 0 \quad \text{contact broken}$$

$$\theta = \cos^{-1}\frac{X}{\gamma} \quad \text{or} \quad \sin^{-1}\frac{Y}{\gamma}$$

3A.9 Bulk and shear moduli model

The material compliance matrix $[D]$ given in a stress–strain equation is written as

$$\{\Delta\sigma\} = [D]\{\Delta\varepsilon\} \tag{I1.75}$$

The rest of the procedure for the finite element analysis is given in detail in this Appendix.

3A.10 Endochronic cracking model

The basic constitutive equations of the endochronic model are given in which deviatoric stress–strain increments are formulated together with stress invariants. The inelastic dilatancy using shear and bulk moduli is included in the derivation of various expressions. Based on the cracking criteria given, the endochronic constitutive relations can be extended for cracking. Based on the material matrix given, the left-hand side of the same equation is modified as

$$\begin{Bmatrix} \Delta\sigma_x + \Delta\sigma_x^p \\ \Delta\sigma_y + \Delta\sigma_y^p \\ \Delta\sigma_z + \Delta\sigma_z^p \\ \Delta\tau_{xy} + \Delta\tau_{xy}^p \\ \Delta\tau_{yz} + \Delta\tau_{yz}^p \\ \Delta\tau_{zx} + \Delta\tau_{zx}^p \end{Bmatrix} = \begin{bmatrix} D_{11} & D_{12} & D_{13} & 0 & 0 & 0 \\ & D_{22} & D_{23} & 0 & 0 & 0 \\ & & D_{33} & 0 & 0 & 0 \\ & & & D_{44} & 0 & 0 \\ \text{sym.} & & & & D_{55} & 0 \\ & & & & & D_{66} \end{bmatrix} \begin{Bmatrix} \Delta\varepsilon_x \\ \Delta\varepsilon_y \\ \Delta\varepsilon_z \\ \Delta\gamma_{xy} \\ \Delta\gamma_{yz} \\ \Delta g_{zx} \end{Bmatrix} \tag{I1.76}$$

where

$$D_{11} = D_{22} = D_{33} = K + 4/3G$$

$$D_{12} = D_{13} = D_{23} = K - 2/3G \tag{I1.77}$$

$$D_{44} = D_{55} = D_{66} = \beta'G$$

($\beta' =$ a factor for concrete aggregate interlocking)

or

$$\{\Delta\sigma\} + \{\Delta\sigma^p\} = [D]\{\Delta\varepsilon\} \tag{I1.78}$$

When concrete cracks, a sudden drop of tensile strength across the crack occurs. This creates a non-equilibrium state in the concrete structure. The residual stress from the non-equilibrium state is redistributed to another part of the structure. The material matrix $[D]$ is modified to include such effects.

Finite element modelling of liner-stud interaction is illustrated in Fig. 3A.6(a).

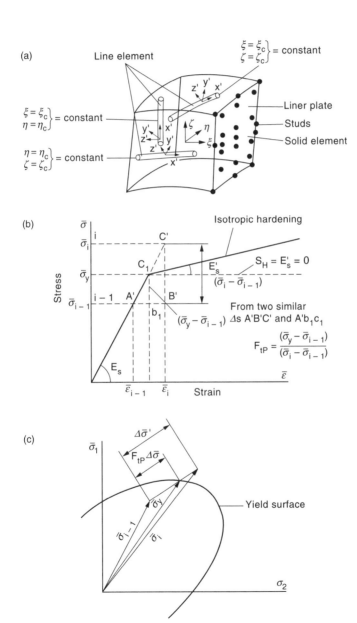

Figure 3A.6. Failure surfaces of steel

Equivalent stress–strain curve for steel is given in Fig. 3A.6(b) where E_s = initial yield modulus; E'_s = post-yield modulus:

S_H = strain hardening

$$S_H = \frac{d\sigma}{d\varepsilon_p} = \frac{E_s E'_s}{E_s + E}$$

$$E_s = K_0$$

The transitional factor, elastic to plastic, from Fig. 3A.6(c) is:

$$\bar{\sigma}_{i-1} + F_{TR}\Delta\bar{\sigma}' = \bar{\sigma}_Y$$

$$F_{tP} = \frac{\bar{\sigma}_Y - \bar{\sigma}_{i-1}}{\Delta\bar{\sigma}'} = \frac{\bar{\sigma}_Y - \bar{\sigma}_i}{\bar{\sigma}_i - \bar{\sigma}_Y}$$

$$\bar{\sigma} = \sigma_{eq}.$$

I.4   Dynamic finite element analysis formulations

In general terms, such formulations are described by the following:

$$\left[\begin{array}{c|c} K & K_R \\ \hline K_R^{T''} & K_{RR} \end{array}\right] \left\{\begin{array}{c} U \\ U_R \end{array}\right\} = \left\{\begin{array}{c} F \\ F_R \end{array}\right\} \tag{I1.79}$$

The subscript R represents reaction forces. The top half of Eq. (I1.79) is used to solve for $\{U\}$:

$$\{U\} = -[K]^{-1}[K_R]\{U_R\} + [K]^{-1}\{F\} \tag{I1.80}$$

The reaction forces $\{F_R\}$ are computed from the bottom half of the equation as

$$\{F_R\} = [K_R]^{T''}\{U\} + \{K_{RR}\}\{U_R\} \tag{I1.81}$$

Equation (I1.80) must be in equilibrium with Eq. (I1.81).

4A.I   The superelement and substructuring

For large structures with complicated features, a substructure (superelement) may be adopted on the lines suggested in Eq. (I1.79). This superelement may then be used as a reduced element from the collection of elements. If subscripts γ and γ' represent the retained and removed degrees of freedom of the equations partitioned into two groups, then the expressions in Eq. (I1.79) can be written as

$$\left[\begin{array}{c|c} K_{\gamma\gamma} & K_{\gamma\gamma'} \\ \hline K_{\gamma'\gamma} & K_{\gamma'\gamma'} \end{array}\right] \left\{\begin{array}{c} U_\gamma \\ U_{\gamma'} \end{array}\right\} = \left\{\begin{array}{c} F_\gamma \\ F_{\gamma'} \end{array}\right\} \tag{I1.82}$$

Equation (I1.82) when expanded assumes the following form:

$$\{F_\gamma\} = [K_{\gamma\gamma}]\{U_\gamma\} + [K_{\gamma\gamma'}]\{U_{\gamma'}\} \tag{I1.83}$$

$$\{F_{\gamma'}\} = [K_{\gamma'\gamma}]\{U_\gamma\} + [K_{\gamma'\gamma}]\{U_{\gamma'}\} \tag{I1.84}$$

When a dynamic analysis is carried out, the subscript γ (retained) represents the dynamic degrees of freedom.

When Eq. (I1.84) is solved, the value of $U_{\gamma'}$ is then written, similarly to Eq. (I1.80),

$$\{U_{\gamma'}\} = [K_{\gamma'\gamma'}]^{-1}\{F_{\gamma'}\} - [K_{\gamma'\gamma'}]^{-1}[K_{\gamma'\gamma}]\{U_\gamma\} \tag{I1.85}$$

Substituting $\{U_{\gamma'}\}$ into Eq. (I1.83) gives:

$$[[K_{\gamma\gamma}] - [K_{\gamma'\gamma}][K_{\gamma\gamma'}]^{-1}[K_{\gamma'\gamma}]]\{U_\gamma\} = [\{F_\gamma\} - [K_{\gamma\gamma'}][K_{\gamma\gamma'}]^{-1}\{F_{\gamma'}\}] \tag{I1.86}$$

or

$$[\bar{K}]\{\bar{U}\} = \{\bar{F}\} \tag{I1.87}$$

where

$$[\bar{K}] = [K_{\gamma\gamma}] - [K_{\gamma\gamma'}][K_{\gamma'\gamma'}]^{-1}[K_{\gamma'\gamma}] \tag{I1.87a}$$

$$\{\bar{F}\} = \{F_\gamma\} - [K_{\gamma\gamma'}][K_{\gamma'\gamma'}]^{-1}\{F_{\gamma'}\} \tag{I1.87b}$$

$$\{\bar{U}\} = \{U_\gamma\} \tag{I1.87c}$$

and $[\bar{K}]$ and $\{\bar{F}\}$ are generally known as the substructure stiffness matrix and load vector, respectively.

In the above equations, the load vector for the substructure is taken as a total load vector. The same derivation may be applied to any number of independent load vectors. For example, one may wish to apply thermal, pressure, gravity and other loading conditions in varying proportions. Expanding the right-hand sides of Eqs (I1.83) and (I1.84) gives:

$$\{F_\gamma\} = \sum_{i=1}^{n} \{F_{\gamma i}\} \tag{I1.88}$$

$$\{F_{\gamma'}\} = \sum_{i-1}^{n} \{F_{\gamma'i}\} \tag{I1.89}$$

where $n =$ the number of independent load vectors.

Substituting into Eq. (I1.87c)

$$\{\bar{F}\} = \sum_{i=1}^{n} \{F_{\gamma\gamma'}\} - [K_{\gamma\gamma'}][K_{\gamma'\gamma'}]^{-1} \sum_{i=1}^{n} \{F_{\gamma'i}\} \tag{I1.90}$$

where the initial load $\{P_t\}$ is specified by

$$\{P_t\} = -[\Delta C_{0 \to t}]\{\dot{U}_t\} - \{\Delta K_{0 \to t}\}\{\delta_t\} \tag{I1.91}$$

To obtain the solution at time $t + \Delta t$, the equation is stated as

$$[M]\{\ddot{U}_{t+\Delta t}\} + [C_0]\{\dot{U}_{t+\Delta t}\} + [K_0]\{U_{t+\Delta t}\}$$
$$= \{R_{t+\Delta t}\} + \{P_t\} + \{\Delta P_{t \to t+\Delta t}\} \tag{I1.92}$$

$\{\Delta P_{t \to t+\Delta t}\}$ represents the influence of the nonlinearity during the time increment t and is determined by iteration and satisfied for $t + \tau$, where $\tau = \theta \Delta t$ ($\theta > 1.37$ for an unconditionally stable method) when applied to a linear problem. $[\Delta C_{0 \to t}]$ and $[\Delta K_{0 \to t}]$ represent the change of $[C]$ and $[K]$, respectively, from $t = 0$ to t.

To obtain the solution at time $t + \Delta t$, Eq. (I1.93) can be written as

$$[M]\{\ddot{U}_{t+\Delta t}\} + [C_0]\{\dot{U}_{t+\Delta t}\} + [K_0]\{U_{t+\Delta t}\}$$
$$= \{R_{t+\Delta t}\} + \{F_t\} + \{\Delta F_{t \to t+\Delta t}\} \tag{I1.93}$$

$\{\Delta P_{t \to t+\Delta t}\}$ represents the influence of the nonlinearity during the time increment t and is determined by iteration:

$$\{\Delta P_{t \to t+\Delta t}\} = -[\Delta C_{0 \to t}]\{\Delta \dot{U}_{t \to t+\Delta t}\} - [\Delta C_{t \to t+\Delta t}](\{\dot{U}\} + \{\Delta \dot{U}_{t \to t+\Delta t}\})$$
$$- [\Delta K_{0 \to t}]\{\Delta U_{t \to t+\Delta t}\}$$
$$- [\Delta K_{t \to t+\Delta t}](\{U_t\} + \{\Delta U_{t \to t+\Delta t}\}) \tag{I1.94}$$

$(\Delta P_{t \to t+\Delta t})$ is calculated using the initial stress approach.

A modified Newton–Raphson or initial stress approach is adopted for solving these nonlinear equations. A step-by-step integration method is given. Using these methods along with acceleration and convergence procedures described in this chapter allows successful solution of finite element-based problems.

4A.2   Reduced linear transient dynamic analysis

This is a reduced form of nonlinear transient dynamic analysis. This analysis is carried out faster than the nonlinear analysis since the matrix in Eq. (I1.93) requires to be inverted once, and the analysis is reduced to a series of matrix multiplications and essential degrees of freedom (dynamic or master of freedoms) to characterize the response of the system. The analysis generally has restrictions such as constant $[M]$, $[C_t]$, $[K_t]$ and time interval for all iterations and nodal forces applied at dynamic or master degrees of freedom.

Quadratic integration

$$\left(\frac{1}{\Delta t^2}[M]_R + \frac{3}{2\Delta t}[\hat{C}_t]_R + [K_t]_R\right)\{U_t\}_R$$

$$= \{F(t)\}_R + [M]_R \frac{1}{\Delta t^2}(2\{U_{t-1}\}_R - \{U_{t-2}\}_R)$$

$$+ \frac{1}{\Delta t}(2\{U_{t-1}\}_R - \tfrac{1}{2}\{U_{t-2}\}_R) \tag{I1.95}$$

The symbol R represents reduced matrices and vectors.

Cubic integration

$$\left(\frac{2}{\Delta t^2}[M]_R + \frac{11}{6\Delta t}[C_t]_R + [K_t]_R\right)\{U_t\}_R$$

$$= \{F(t)\} + [M]_R \frac{1}{\Delta t^2}(5\{U_{t-1}\}_R - 4\{U_{t-2}\}_R + \{U_{t-3}\})$$

$$+ [C_t]_R \frac{1}{\Delta t^2}(3\{U_{t-1}\}_R - \tfrac{3}{2}\{U_{t-2}\}_R + \tfrac{1}{3}\{U_{t-3}\}_R) \tag{I1.96}$$

4A.3 Mode frequency analysis

The equation of motion for an undamped structure with no applied forces is written as

$$[M]\{\ddot{U}_t\} + [K_t']\{U_t\} = \{0\} \tag{I1.97}$$

$[K_t']$ the structure stiffness matrix, may include stress-stiffening effects.

The system of equations is initially condensed down to those involved with the master (dynamic) degrees of freedom.

The number of dynamic degrees of freedom would at least be equal to two times the selected frequencies. The reduced form of Eq. (I1.97) can be written as

$$[M]_R\{\ddot{U}_t\}_R + [K_t']_R\{U\}_R = \{0\} \tag{I1.98}$$

For a linear system, free vibrations of harmonic type are written as

$$\{U_t\}_R = \{\psi_i\}_R \cos\omega_i t \tag{I1.99}$$

where $\{\psi_i\}_R = $ the eigenvector representing the shape of the ith frequency; $\omega_i = $ the ith frequency (radians/unit time); and $t = $ time.

Equation (I1.97) assumes the form

$$(-\omega_i^2[M]_R + [K_t']_R\{\psi_i\}_R = \{0\} \tag{I1.100}$$

which is an eigenvalue problem with n values of ω^2 and n eigenvectors $\{\psi_i\}_R$ which satisfy Eq. (I1.100), where n is the number of dynamic degrees of freedom. Using standard iteration procedures, Eq. (I1.100) will yield a complete set of eigenvalues and eigenvectors.

Each eigenvector, $\{\psi_i\}_R$, is then normalized such that:

$$\{\psi_i\}_R^{T''} [M]_t \{\psi_i\}_R = 1 \tag{I1.101}$$

These n eigenvectors are now expanded to the full set of structure modal displacement degrees of freedom:

$$\{\psi_{\gamma'i}\}_R = [K_{\gamma'\gamma'}]^{-1}[K_{\gamma'\gamma}]\{\psi_i\}_R \tag{I1.102}$$

where $\{\psi_i\}_R =$ the slave degree of freedom vector of mode i; and $[K_{\gamma'\gamma'}]$, $[K_{\gamma'\gamma}] =$ submatrix parts as shown in Eq. (I1.82) onwards.

The above dynamic analysis approach is generally adopted for structures subjected to normal dynamic loads, wind, wave and seismic loads. The above analysis, with modifications, is also applied to missile and aircraft explosions/impact problems.

4A.4 Spectrum analysis

Spectrum analysis is an extension of the mode frequency analysis, with both base and force excitation options. The base excitation option is generally suitable for seismic and wave applications. A direction vector and a response spectrum table will be needed in addition to the data and parameters required for the reduced model analysis. The response spectrum table generally includes displacements, velocities and accelerations. The force excitation is, in general, used for wind and space structures and missile/aircraft impact. It requires a force distribution and an amplitude multiplier table in addition to the data and parameters needed for the reduced modal analysis. A study of the mass distribution is made. Generally the masses are kept close to the reaction points on the finite element mesh rather than the (master) degrees of freedom. It is important to calculate the participation factors in relation to a given excitation direction. The base and forced excitations are given below:

$$\tilde{\gamma}_i = \{\psi_i\}_R^{T''} [M]\{\tilde{b}\} \quad \text{for the base excitation} \tag{I1.103}$$

$$\tilde{\gamma}_i = \{\psi_i\}_R^{T''} \{F_t\} \qquad \text{for the force excitation} \tag{I1.104}$$

where $\{\tilde{b}\} =$ the unit vector of the excitation direction; and $\{F_t\} =$ an input force vector.

The values of $\{\psi\}_R$ are normalized, and the reduced displacement vector is calculated from the eigenvector by using a mode coefficient $\tilde{M}$:

$$\{\tilde{U}\}_i = [\tilde{M}_i]\{\psi\}_i \tag{I1.105}$$

where $\{\tilde{U}_i\} =$ the reduced displacement vector; and $[\tilde{M}_i] =$ the mode coefficient and where (a) for velocity spectra

$$[\tilde{M}_i] = \frac{[V_{si}]\{\tilde{\gamma}_i\}}{\omega_i} \tag{I1.106}$$

(V_{si} = spectral velocity for the ith mode); (b) for force spectra

$$[\tilde{M}_i] = \frac{[\bar{f}_{si}]\{\tilde{\gamma}_i\}}{\omega_i^2} \tag{I1.107}$$

($\bar{f}_{si}$ = spectral force for the ith mode); (c)

$$[\tilde{M}_i] = \frac{[a_{si}]\{\tilde{\gamma}_i\}}{\omega_i^2} \tag{I1.108}$$

(a_{si} = spectral acceleration for the ith mode); (d)

$$[\tilde{M}_i] = \frac{[U_{si}]\{\tilde{\gamma}_i\}}{\omega_i^2} \tag{I1.109}$$

(U_{si} = spectral displacement for the ith mode).
$\{U\}_i$ may be expanded to compute all the displacements, as was done in Eq. (I1.79) onwards.

$$\{U_{\gamma'}\}_i = [K_{\gamma'\gamma'}]^{-1}[K_{\gamma'\gamma}]\{U_i\}_R \tag{I1.110}$$

where $\{U_{\gamma'}\}_i$ = the slave degree of freedom vector of mode i; and $[K_{\gamma'\gamma'}]$, $[K_{\gamma'\gamma}]$ = submatrix parts.

Sometimes an equivalent mass M_i^e is needed for the ith mode since it may not be a function of excitation direction. This M_i^e is computed as

$$[M_i^e] = 1/\{\psi_i\}_R^{T''}\{\psi_i\}_R \tag{I1.111}$$

This is derived from the definition of the diagonal matrix of equivalent masses $[M^e]$

$$[\psi]_R^{T''}[M_e][\psi]_R = [I] \tag{I1.112}$$

where $[I]$ = the identity matrix; and $[\psi]_R$ = a square matrix containing all mode shape vectors.

Where damping is included, the damping ratio D_{Ri} for the data input, including damping C_e, is given for a matrix of coupling coefficient as

$$D_{Ri} = C_e\omega_{i/2} \tag{I1.113}$$

where ω_I is the undamped natural frequency of the ith mode.

In between the modes i and j, a modified damping ratio D'_{Ri} is needed to take into account the concrete structures subjected to wave and seismic effects:

$$D'_{Ri} = D_{Ri} + 2/t_e\omega_i \tag{I1.114}$$

where t_e is the duration.

4A.5 Impact/explosion
Structural response of concrete structures subjected to relatively fast loading rates, such as those from missile and aircraft impact/explosion, bombs and

nuclear detonations, etc., can be influenced by the effect of strain rate on the material properties. These material changes lead to an instantaneous change in strength of materials such as concrete. The finite element is invoked along with the above equations of motion. The normality rules and the proportionality factor $d\lambda$ are used to give an expression for the stress state of the form:

$$d\dot{\sigma}_{ij} = [D]\{d\dot{\varepsilon}_{kl}\} + \tilde{\gamma}_{ij}\{\ddot{\varepsilon}\}^p \tag{I1.115}$$

where, using Von Mises criterion,

$$\tilde{\gamma}_{ij} = \frac{[D^*]\{S_{mn}\}\{S_{kl}\}\{\bar{D}\}}{\alpha^*} \tag{I1.116}$$

$$\alpha^* = \frac{4}{9}\sigma_{eq}^2 \frac{\partial\sigma_{eq}}{\partial\varepsilon^p} + S_{ij}[D]\{S_{kl}\} \tag{I1.117}$$

$$[D^*] = D_{ijmn}$$

$$[\bar{D}] = D_{pqkl}$$

the term $\gamma_{ij}\ddot{\varepsilon}^p$ can be implemented. Where deformation rates do not change too rapidly the term $\gamma_{ij}\ddot{\varepsilon}^p$ is neglected. The rest of the procedure is the same as for general dynamic analysis.

4A.6 Summary of step-by-step integration method
Initialization
(1) Effective stiffness matrix $[K_0^*] = (6/\tau^2)[M] + (3/\tau)[C_0] + [K_0]$ (A)
(2) Triangularize $[K_0^*]$

For each time step:

Calculation of displacement $\{U_{t+\tau}\}$
(1) Constant part of the effective load vector

$$\{R_{t+\tau}^*\} = \{R_t\} + \theta(\{R_{t+\Delta t}\} - \{R_t\}) + \{F_t\} + [M]$$

$$+ \left(\left(\frac{6}{\tau^2}\right)\{U_t\} + \frac{6}{\tau}\{\dot{U}_t\} + 2\{\ddot{U}_t\}\right)$$

$$+ [C_0]\left(\frac{3}{\tau}\{U_t\} + 2\{\dot{U}_t\} + \frac{\tau}{2}\{U_t\}\right) \tag{B}$$

(2) Initialization $i = 0$, $\{\Delta P_{t \to t+\tau}^i\} = 0$
(3) Iteration

  (a) $i \to i+1$

  (b) Effective load vector $\{R_{t+\tau_{tot}}^*\} = \{R^*{}_{t+\tau}\} + \{\Delta P_{t \to t+\tau}^{i-1}\}$ (C)

  (c) Displacement $\{U_{t+\tau}^i\}[K_0^*]\{U_{t+\tau}^i\} = \{R_{t+\tau_{tot}}^{*i}\}$ (D)

  (d) Velocity $\{\dot{U}_{t+\tau}^i\} + (3/\tau)(\{U_{t+\tau}^i\} - \{U_t\}) - 2\{\dot{U}_t\} - (\tau/2)\{\ddot{U}_t\}$

(e) Change of initial load vector caused by the nonlinear behaviour of the material $\{\Delta P^i_{t\to t+\tau}\}$

$$\{\Delta P^i_{t\to t+\tau}\} = -[\Delta C_{0\to t}](\{\dot{U}^i_{t+\tau}\} - \{\dot{U}_t\}) - [\Delta C^i_{t\to t+\tau}]\{\dot{U}^i_{t+\tau}\}$$
$$\times [\Delta K_{0\to t}](\{U^i_{t+\tau}\} - \{U_t\}) - [\Delta K^i_{t\to t+\Delta t}]\{U^i_{t+\tau}\} \quad (E)$$

In fact, $\{\Delta P^i_{t\to t+\tau}\}$ is calculated using the initial-stress method.

(f) Iteration convergence

$$\|\{\Delta P^i_{t\to t+\tau}\} - \{\Delta P^{i-1}_{t\to t+\tau}\}\|/\|\{\Delta P^i_{t\to t+\tau}\}\| < \text{tol} \quad (F)$$

or analogously, on stress.

Note that $\{P\}$ could be any value of $\{F\}$.

Calculation of velocity, acceleration
Calculate new acceleration $\{\ddot{U}_{t+\Delta t}\}$, velocity $\{\dot{U}_{t+\Delta t}\}$, displacement $\{U_{t+\Delta t}\}$ and initial load $\{P_{t+\Delta t}\}$:

$$\{\ddot{U}_{t+\Delta t}\} = (6/\theta\tau^2)(\{U_{t+\tau}\} - \{U_t\}) - (6/\tau\theta)\{\dot{U}_t\} + \left(1 - \frac{3}{\theta}\right)\{\ddot{U}_t\}$$

$$\{\dot{U}_{t+\Delta t}\} = \{\dot{U}_t\} + \frac{\tau}{2\theta}\{\ddot{U}_t\} + \{\ddot{U}_{t+\Delta t}\}$$

$$\{U_{t+\Delta t}\} = \{U_t\} + \frac{\tau}{\theta}\{\dot{U}_t\} + (\tau^2/6\theta^2)(2\{\ddot{U}_t\} + \{\ddot{U}_{t+\Delta t}\})$$

$$\{P_{t+\Delta t}\} = \{P_t\} + \{\Delta P^i_{t\to t+\tau}\} \quad (G)$$

Calculation by quadratic integration
When the velocity varies linearly and the acceleration is constant across the time interval, appropriate substitutions are made into Eq. (I1.93) giving

$$[f_1[M] + f_2[C_t] + [K'_t]]\{U_t\} = \{F(t)\} + \{f_3([C_t], [M], U_t, U_{t2}, \ldots)\} \quad (H)$$

where $f_1, f_2, f_3 = $ functions of time.

This results in an implicit time integration procedure. The only unknown is $\{U_t\}$ at each time point and this is calculated in the same way as in static analysis. Equation (H) is then written as:

$$\left(\frac{2}{\Delta t_0 \Delta t_{01}}[M] + \frac{2\Delta t_0 + \Delta t_1}{\Delta t_0 t_{01}}[C] + [K'_t]\right)\{U_t\}$$

$$= \{F(t)\} + [M]\left(\frac{2}{\Delta t_0 \Delta t_1}\{U_{t-1}\} - \frac{2}{\Delta t_1 \Delta t_{01}}\{U_{t-2}\}\right)$$

$$+ [C_t]\left(\frac{\Delta t_{01}}{\Delta t_0 \Delta t_1}\{U_{t-1}\} - \frac{\Delta t_0}{\Delta t_{01}\Delta t_1}\{U_{t-2}\}\right) \quad (I)$$

where

$$\Delta t_0 = t_0 - t_1$$

$$\Delta t_1 = t_1 - t_2$$

$$\Delta t_2 = t_2 - t_3$$

t_0 = time of current iteration

t_1 = time of previous iteration

t_2 = time before previous iteration

t_3 = time before t_2

$$\Delta t_2 = \Delta t_0 + \Delta t_1 = t_0 - t_2$$

Calculation by cubic integration

Equation (H) becomes cubic and is written as

$$(a_1[M] + a_2[C_t] + [K_t']) \{U_t\}$$
$$= \{F(t)\} + [M](a_3\{U_{t-1}\} - a_4\{U_{t-2}\} + a_5\{U_{t-3}\})$$
$$+ [C](a_6\{U_{t-1}\} - a_7\{U_{t-2}\} + a_8\{U_{t-3}\}) \qquad (J)$$

where a_1 to a_8 are functions of the time increments; these functions are derived by inverting a four by four matrix.

For clear-cut solutions, the size of the time step between adjacent iterations should not be more than a factor of 10 in nonlinear cases and should not be reduced by more than a factor of 2 where plasticity exists.

I.5   Solution procedures: acceleration and convergence criteria
5A.I   Criteria for convergence and acceleration
Convergence criteria

To ensure convergence to the correct solution by finer sub-division of the mesh, the assumed displacement function must satisfy the convergence criteria given below:

(*a*)   displacements must be continuous over element boundaries;
(*b*)   rigid body movements should be possible without straining; and
(*c*)   a state of constant strain should be reproducible.

Euclidean norm is given by $\psi_i / R_i \leq C$. The term ψ_i represents the unbalanced forces and the norm of the residuals. With the aid of the iterative scheme described above, the unbalanced forces due to the initial stresses $\{\sigma_0\}$ become negligibly small. As a measure of their magnitude, the norm of the vector $\|\psi_i\|$

is used. The Euclidean norm and the absolute value of the largest component of the vector are written as

$$\|\psi_i\| = (|\psi_1|^2 + \cdots + |\psi_n|^2)^{1/2} \tag{I1.118}$$

$$\|R_i\| = (|\{R_i\}^T\{R^i\}|)^{1/2}$$

the convergence criterion adopted is

$$\|\psi\| = \max_i |\psi_i| < C = 0.001 \tag{I1.119}$$

Uniform acceleration

Various procedures are available for accelerating the convergence of the modified Newton–Raphson iterations. Figure 5A.1 shows the technique of computing individual acceleration factors when δ_1 and δ_2 are known. Then, assuming a constant slope of the response curve, and from similar triangles, the value of δ_3 is computed:

$$\frac{\delta_1}{\delta_2} = \frac{\delta_2}{\delta_3} \qquad \delta_3 = \delta_2 \frac{\delta_2}{\delta_1} \tag{I1.120}$$

When δ_3 is added to δ_2, then the accelerated displacement δ_2' is expressed as

$$\delta_2' = \delta_2 + \delta_3 = \delta_2 \left(1 + \frac{\delta_2}{\delta_1}\right) = \alpha\delta_2 \tag{I1.121}$$

where the acceleration factor α is

$$\alpha = 1 + \frac{\delta_2}{\delta_1} \tag{I1.122}$$

Generally the range of α is between 1 and 2. The value of $\alpha = 1$ for zero acceleration, and the value of α reaches the maximum value of 2 when the slope of the $\delta - R$ curve approaches zero.

The acceleration factor α is computed individually for every degree of freedom of the system. The displacement vector obtained from the linear stiffness matrix $[k_0]$ is then multiplied by the $[\alpha]$ matrix having the above constants on its diagonals. The remaining components of $[\alpha]$ are zero. The accelerated displacement vector is then expressed as follows:

$$\{\Delta u_i'\} = [a_{i-1}]\{\Delta u_i\} \tag{I1.123}$$

From these accelerated displacements $\{\Delta u_i'\}$, the initial stresses $\{\sigma_0\}$ are found and they are equilibrated with the forces $\{\psi_i\}$. They are then used for the next solution

$$\{\Delta \bar{u}_i\} = [k_0]^{-1}\{\psi_i\} \tag{I1.124}$$

which results in a new set of acceleration factors. Now an estimate for the displacement increment is made in order to find the incremental stresses and total stresses.

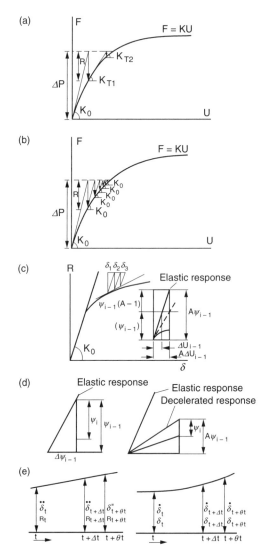

Figure 5A.1. (a) Newton–Raphson method. (b) Initial stress method (Note that ΔP is a specific value of F). (c) Technique of computing acceleration factor. (d) Graphical representation. (e) Linear acceleration and load assumptions of the Wilson θ method (left). Quadratic and cubic variation of velocity and displacement assumptions of the Wilson θ method (right)

The residual forces needed to re-establish equilibrium can now easily be evaluated

$$\{\hat{\psi}_i\} = \int_v [B]^T \{\sigma_{0_T}\} \, dV - \{R_i\} \tag{11.125}$$

where $\{R_i\}$ represents the total external load; dV is the volume.

A new displacement now results from

$$\{\Delta u_{i+1}\} = -[k_0]^{-1}\{\hat{\psi}_i\} \qquad (\text{I1.126})$$

In order to carry out these iterative steps, numerical integration is required. First of all the evaluation of $\{\hat{\psi}_i\}$ from the initial stresses is required, and this requires integration over the elastic–plastic region only. The value of $\{\hat{\psi}_i\}$ is computed by carrying out the integration over the entire domain of the analysis. Since these kinds of accelerated steps unbalance the equilibrium, it therefore has to be re-established by finding the residual forces $\{\hat{\psi}_i\}$. Since the state of stress produced by the accelerated displacements is not in balance with the residual forces of the previous iteration, the new residual forces $\{\hat{\psi}_i\}$ of Eq. (I1.126) must balance $\{\sigma_T\}$ and $\{R_i\}$. Here the acceleration scheme is needed to preserve equilibrium, which will eventually make the equivalent forces over the whole region unnecessary. This is achieved by applying a uniform acceleration, i.e. the same acceleration factor $\bar{A}$ to all displacements, found by averaging the individual factors α_i

$$\bar{A} = \frac{1}{n} \sum_{i=1}^{n} \alpha_i \qquad (\text{I1.127})$$

The force–displacement equation is then written by multiplying both sides with the scalar quantity $\bar{A}$ without disturbing the equilibrium:

$$\bar{A}\{\Delta u_i\} = [k_0]^{-1}\bar{A}\{\psi_i\} \qquad (\text{I1.128})$$

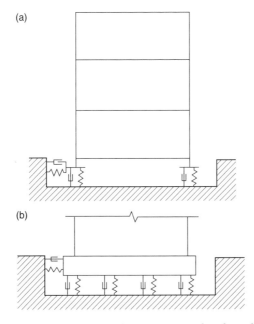

Figure 6A.1. Modelling of springs and dampers under foundations: (a) separate footings with tie; (b) raft foundation

Now to evaluate $\{\psi_{i+1}\}$, the previous values of $\{\psi_i\}$ must be multiplied by $\bar{A}$, and the previously accelerated forces from the initial stresses $\{\sigma_0\}$ must be included such that

$$\{\psi_{i+1}\} = \int_V [B]^{\mathrm{T}}\{\sigma_0\}\,\mathrm{d}V - (A-1)\{\psi_{i-1}\} \tag{I1.129}$$

I.6 Buildings and bridges – soil structure interaction

The Gap Element developed by ANSYS can be used for soil structure interaction. In addition, various springs/dampers are used to model soil with the structure and Figs 6A.1 and 6A.2 give the models for separate footings and for raft foundations. Tables API.5 and API.6 and Fig. 6A.3 show spring formulations for various motions.

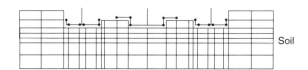

Figure 6A.2. Soil–structure model for a nuclear reactor (the nuclear reactor and heat exchanger models have been simplified; excitation is applied at the base of the model as a time history)

Table API.5. Foundation interaction: spring and damper values for circular bases

Motion	Equivalent spring constant	Equivalent damping coefficient
Horizontal	$k_x = \dfrac{32(1-\nu)GR}{7-8\nu}$	$c_x = 0.576k_x R(\rho/G)^{1/2}$
Rocking	$k_\psi = \dfrac{8GR^3}{3(1-\nu)}$	$c_\psi = \dfrac{0.30}{1+B_\psi}\,k_\psi(\rho/G)^{1/2}$
Vertical	$k_z = \dfrac{4GR}{1-\nu}$	$c_z = 0.85k_z R(\rho/G)^{1/2}$
Torsion	$k_1 = 16GR^3/3$	$c_z = \dfrac{(k_t I_t)^{1/2}}{1+2I_t/\rho R^5}$

ν is Poisson's ratio for the foundation medium, G is the shear modulus for the foundation medium, R is the radius of the circular basemat, ρ is the mass density of the foundation medium, $B_\psi = 3(1-\nu)I_0/8\rho R^5$, I_0 is the total mass amount of inertia of the structure and basemat about the rocking axis at the base and I_t is the polar mass moment of inertia of the structure and basemat

Table API.6. Foundation interaction: spring and damper values for rectangular bases

Motion	Equivalent spring constant	Equivalent damping coefficient
Horizontal	$k_x = 2(1 + \nu)G\beta_x(BL)^{1/2}$	Use the results for a circular base with the following equivalent radius R
Rocking	$k_\psi = \dfrac{G}{1-\nu}\,\beta_\psi BL^2$	$R = (BL/\pi)^{1/2}$ for translation $R = (BL^3/3\pi)^{1/4}$ for rocking
Vertical	$k_z = \dfrac{G}{1-\nu}\,\beta_2(BL)^{1/2}$	
Torsion	$R = [BL(B^2 + L^2)/6\pi]^{1/4}$	

B is the width of the basemat perpendicular to the direction of horizontal excitation, L is the length of the basemat in the direction of horizontal excitation and β_x, β_ψ and β_z are constants that are functions of the dimensional ratio L/B.

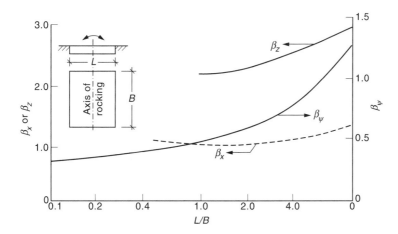

Figure 6A.3. Constants β_x, β_ψ, β_z for rectangular bases (after Whitman and Richart (1967))

I.7   Relevant computer programs for the finite element analysis
I.7(a)   Abstracts from main program ISOPAR based on finite element analysis

SUBROUTINE CRACKD (PROP,NCK,SIG,EPS,PSI,PS2, PS3,DC1,DC2,DC3) IMPLICIT REAL*8(A − H, O − Z)

SET UP MATERIAL MATRICES FOR CRACKED CONCRETE

```
      COMMON /MTMD3D/ D(6,6),STRESS(6),STRAIN(6),IPT,NEL
      DIMENSION DD(6,6),PROP(1),NCK(1),SIG(1),EPS(1),
    @          PS1(1),PS2(1),PS3(1),DC1(1),DC2(1),DC3(1)
      CALL PRINCL (1PT,STRESS,PS1,PS2,PS3,DC1,DC2,DC3)
      CALL RCMOD (PROP,D)
      CALL DMAT (PROP,NCK)
      DO 222 I = 1,6
222   DD(I,J) = 0.0
      JJJ = 1
      LL = 0
      IF (NCK(1).EQ.1) LL = 1
      IF (NCK(2).EQ.1) LL = 2
      IF (NCK(3).EQ.1) LL = 3
      IF (NCK(1).EQ.I.AND.NCK(2).EQ.1) LL = 4
      IF (NCK(2).EQ.I.AND.NCK(3).EQ.1) LL = 5
      IF (NCK(1).EQ.I.AND.NCK(3).EQ.1) LL = 6

      IF (NCK(I).EQ.1.AND.NCK(2).EQ.1.AND.NCK(3).EQ1) LL = 7
      IF (LL.EQ.7) GOTO 99
      IF (JJJ.EQ.0) GOTO 200
      IF (LL.EQ.0) GOTO 999
      GOTO (113,114,115,116.117,118,LL

      ONLY ONE DIRECTON CRACKED

113 CONTINUE

      CRACK IN DIRECTION 1

      DD(1,1) = 0.0
      DD(1,2) = 0.0
      DD(1,3) = 0.0
      DD(2,1) = 0.0
      DD(2,2) = D(2,2) − D(1,2)*D(1,2)/D(1,1)
      DD(2,3) = D(2.3) − D(1,3)*D(1,2)/D(1,1)
      DD(3,1) = 0.0
      DD(3,2) = DD(2,3)
      DD(3,3) = D(3,3) − D(1,3)*D(1,3)/D(1,1)
      DD(4,4) = PROP(12)*D(4,4)
      DD(5,5) = DD(5,5)
```

```
        DD(6,6) = PROP(12)*D(6,6)
        GOTO 121
114 CONTINUE

        CRACK IN DIRECTION 2

        DD(1,1) = D(1,1) − D(2,1)*D(2,1)/D(2,2)
        DD(1,2) = 0.0
        DD(1,3) = D(1,3) − D(1,2)*D(2,3)/D(2,2)
        DD(2,1) = 0.0
        DD 2,2) = 0.0
        DD(2.3) = 0.0
        DD(3.1) = DD(1,3)
        DD(3,2) = 0.0
        DD(3,3) = D(3,3) − D(2,3)*D(2,3)/D(2,2)
        DD(4,4) = PROP(12)*D(4,4)
        DD(5,5) = PROP(12)*D(5,5)
        DD(6,6) = D(6,6)
        GOTO 121
115 CONTINUE

        CRACK IN DIRECTION 3

        DD(1,1) = D(1,1) − D(1,3)*D(1.3)/D(3,3)
        DD(1,2) = D(1,2) − D(1,3)*D(2,3)/D(3,3)
        DD(1,3) = 0.0
        DD(2.1) = DD(1,2)
        DD(2,2) = D(2,2) − D(2,3)*D(2.3)/D(3,3)
        DD(2,3) = 0.0
        DD(3,1) = 0.0
        DD(3,2) = 0.0
        DD(3,3) = 0.0
        DD(4,4) = D(4,4)
        DD(5,5) = D(5,5)*PROP(12)
        DD(6.6) = D(6,6)*PROP(12)
        GOTO 121
116 CONTINUE

CRACKS IN TWO DIRECTIONS
CRACKS IN DIRECTION 1 & 2

DENOM = D(1,1)*D(2,2) − D(1,2)*D(2,1)
        DD(1,1) = 0.0
        DD(1,2) = 0.0
        DD(1,3) = 0.0
        DD(2,1) = 0.0
        DD(2,2) = 0.0
        DD(2,3) = 0.0
        DD(3,1) = 0.0
        DD(3,2) = 0.0
        DD(3,3) = D(3,3)
```

```
   1            −D(3,1)*(D(2,2)*D(1,3) − D(1,2)*D(2,3))/DENOM
   2            −D(3,2)*(D(1,1)*D(2,3) − D(2,1)*D(3,1))/DENOM
     DD(4 4) = PROP(12)*D(4,4)
     DD(5,5) = PROP(12)*D(5,5)
     DD(6,6) = PROP(12)*D(6,6)
     GOTO 121
117 CONTINUE

     CRACKS IN DIRECTIONS 1 & 3
     DENOM = D(2,2)*D(3,3) − D(2,3)*D(3,2)
     DD(1,1) = (1,1)
   1            −D(1,2)*(D(3,3)*D(2,1) − D(3,1)*D(2,3))/DENOM
   2            −D(1,3)*(D(2,2)*D(3,1) − D(2,1)*D(3,2))/DENOM
     DD(1,2) = 0.0
     DD(1,3) = 0.0
     DD(2,1) = 0.0
     DD(2,2) = 0.0
     DD(2,3) = 0.0
     DD(3,1) = 0.0
     DD(3,2) = 0.0
     DD(3,3) = 0.0
     DD(4 4) = PROP(12)*D(4,4)
     DD(5,5) = PROP(12)*D(5,5)
     DD(6,6) = PROP(12)*D(6,6)
     GOTO 121
118 CONTINUE

     CRACKS IN DIRECTION 1 & 3
     DENOM = D(1,1)*D(3,3) − D(3,2)*D(1,3)
     DD(1,1) = 0.0
     DD(1,2) = 0.0
     DD(1,3) = 0.0
     DD(2,1) = 0.0
     DD(2,2) = D(2,2)
   1            −D(2,1)*(D(3,3)*D(1,2) − D(3,2)*D(1,3))/DENOM
   2            −D(2,3)*(D(1,1)*D(3,2) − D(3,1)*D(1,2))/DENOM
     DD(2,3) = 0.0
     DD(3,1) = 0.0
     DD(3,2) = 0.0
     DD(3,3) = 0.0
     DD(4 4) = PROP(12)*D(4,4)
     DD(5,5) = PROP(12)*D(5,5)
     DD(6,6) = PROP(12)*D(6,6)
121 CONTINUE
     GO TO 99

200 CONTINUE
     IF (LL .EQ. 0) GOTO 999
     GOTO (1,2,3,4,5,6),LL
   1 CONTINUE
     DD(2,2) = D(2,2)
     DD(2,3) = D(2.3)
```

```
    DD(3,2) = DD(2,3)
    DD(3,3) = D(3,3)
    DD(4,4) = PROP(12)*D(4,4)
    DD(5,5) = PROP(12)*D(5,5)
    DD(6,6) = PROP(12)*D(6,6)
    GOTO 99
 2  CONTINUE
    DD(1,1) = D(1,1)
    DD(1,3) = D(2.3)
    DD(3,1) = D(1,3)
    DD(3,3) = D(3,3)
    DD(4,4) = PROP(12)*D(4,4)
    DD(5,5) = PROP(12)*D(5,5)
    DD(6,6) = D(6,6)
    GOTO 99
 3  CONTINUE
    DD(1,1) = D(1,1)
    DD(2,2) − D(2.2)
    DD(1,2) = D(1,2)
    DD(3,3) = D(3,3)
    DD(2,1) = DD(1,2)
    DD(4,4) = D(4,4)
    DD(5,5) = PROP(12)*D(5,5)
    DD(6,6) = PROP(12)*D(6,6)
    GOTO 99
 4  CONTINUE
    DD(3,3) = D(3,3)
    DD(4,4) = PROP(12)*D(4,4)
    DD(5,5) = PROP(12)*D(5,5)
    DD(6,6) = PROP(12)*D(6,6)
 5  CONTINUE
    DD(1,1) = D(1,1)
    DD(4,4) = PROP(12)*D(4,4)
    DD(5,5) = PROP(12)*D(5,5)
    DD(6,6) = PROP(12)*D(6,6)
    GOTO 99
 6  CONTINUE
    DD(2,2) = D(2,2)
    DD(4,4) = D(4,4)
    DD(5,5) = D(5,5)
    DD(6,6) = D(6,6)
99  CONTINUE
    CRACKS IN ALL THREE DIRECTIONS
    TRANSFER DD TO D

    DO 101 J = 1,6
    DO 101 K = 1,6
    D(J,K) = DD(J,K)
101 CONTINUE
999 CONTINUE
    RETURN
```

Principal stresses and direction cosines D1, D2, D3 are the direction cosines of principal stresses PS1, PS2, PS3

```
      IF (X5 .GE .X6 .AND. X6 .GE. X7) GOTO 430
      IF (X5 .GE .X7 .AND. X7 .GE. X6) GOTO 431
      IF (X6 .GE .X5 .AND. X5 .GE. X7) GOTO 432
      IF (X6 .GE .X7 .AND. X7 .GE. X5) GOTO 433
      IF (X7 .GE .X5 .AND. X5 .GE. X6) GOTO 434
      IF (X7 .GE .X5 .AND. X6 .GE. X5) GOTO 435
430   X1 = X5
      X2 = X6
      X3 = X7
      GOTO 438
431   X1 = X5
      X2 = X7
      X3 = X6
      GOTO 438
432   X1 = X6
      X2 = X5
      X3 = X7
      GOTO 438
433   X1 = X6
      X2 = X7
      X3 = X5
      GOTO 438
434   X1 = X7
      X2 = X5
      X3 = X6
      GOTO 438
435   X1 = X7
      X2 = X6
      X3 = X5
438   CONTINUE

      PRINCIPAL STRESSES

   PS1(IPT) = X1
   PS2(IPT) = X2
   PS3(IPT) = X3
      DO 440 IS = 1,3
      GOTO (443,445,447),IS
443   AS1 = G1 - X1
      AS2 = G2 - X1
      AS3 = G3 - X1
      GOTO 444
445   AS1 = G1 - X2
      AS2 = G2 - X2
      AS3 = G3 - X2
      GOTO 444
```

```
447 AS1 = G1 − X3
    AS2 = G2 − X3
    AS3 = G3 − X3
444 CONTINUE
    AK = G4
    BK = G5
    CK = G6
    YAP1 = AS2*CK − BK*AK
    YAP2 = AK*AK − AS1*AS2
    IF (YAP1) .EQ. 0.0) YAP1 = 1.0
    IF (YAP2) .EQ. 0.0) YAP2 = 1.0
    BJM1 = (BK*BK − AS2*AS3)/YAP1
    BJM2 = (AS1*BK − AK*CK)/YAP2
    BJ1 = BJM1*BJM1
    BJ2 = BJM2*BJM2
ZIP = DSQRT(BJ1 + BJ2 + 1.0)
```

Orthotropic variable-modulus model for concrete

```
    IMPLICIT REAL*8(A − H, O − Z)
    DIMENSION E(3),G(3,3)D(6,6),PROP(1)
    DO 222 II = 1,6
    DO 222 JJ = 1,6
222 D(II,JJ) = 0.0
    AA = (1.0 − PROP(5))/(1.0 + PROP(5))*(1.0 − 2.0*PROP(5))
    BB = PROP(5)/(1.0 − PROP(5))

    E(1) = PROP(12)*PROP(1)*PROP(6) + PROP(2)*PROP(9)
    E(2) = PROP(12)*PROP(1)*PROP(7) + PROP(2)*PROP(10)
    E(2) = PROP(12)*PROP(1)*PROP(8) + PROP(2)*PROP(11)
    DO 7100 J = 1,3
    DO 7100 K = 1,3
7100 G(J,K) = 0.25*(AA*(E(J) + E(K))) − 2.0*AA*BB*DSQRT(E(J)*E(K))
    D(1,1) = AA*E(1)
    D(1,2) = AA*BB*DSQRT(E(I)*E(2))
    D(1,3) = AA*BB*DSQRT(E(I)*E(3))
    D(2,1) = D(1,2)
    D(2,2) = AA*E(2)
    D(2,3) = BB*DSQRT(E(2)*E(3))
    D(3,1) = D(1,3)
    D(3,2) = D(2,3)
    D(3,3) = AA*E(3)
    D(4,4) = G(1.2)
    D(5,5) = G(1,3)
    D(6,6) = G(2,3)
    RETURN
    END
```

Ottoson Model

```
    IMPLICIT REAL*8(A − H, O − Z)
    COMMON /MTMD3D/ DEP(6,6),STRESS(6),STRAIN(6),IPT,NEL
    DIMENSION PAR(3,5),FS(6,6),FSTPOS(6,6),PROP(1),SIG(1),
```

```
@                    DVJ1DS(6),DVJ2DS(6),DVJ3DS(6),DVTHDS(6)
      OPEN  (UNIT = 5,FILE = 'PARAMETERS',STATUS = 'OLD')
      READ  (5,*,END = 3700)((PAR(1F,JF),JF = 1,5),IF = 1,3)
3700  CLOSE (5)
      PK = PROP(3)/PROP(4)
      IP = 0
      JP = 0
      IF (PK .LE. 0.08)  IP = 1
      IF (PK .EQ. 0.10)  IP = 2
      IF (PK .GE. 0.12)  IP = 3
      IF (PK .LT. 0.10)  JP = I
      IF (PK .GT. 0.10)  JP = 2
      IF (IP .EQ. 0) GOTO 3800
      A = PAR(IP,2)
      B = PAR(IP,3)
      PK1  = PAR(IP,4)
      PK2  = PAR(IP,5)
      GOTO  3900
3800  SUB1 = PK − PAR(JP,1)
      SUB2 = PAR(JP + 1,1) − PAR(JP,1)
      A = SUB1*(PAR(JP + 1,2) − PAR(JP,2))/SUB2 + PAR(JP,2)
      B = SUB1*(PAR(JP + 1,3) − PAR(JP,3))/SUB2 + PAR(JP,3)
      PK1 = SUB1*(PAR(JP + 1,4) − PAR(JP,4))/SUB2 + PAR(JP,4)
      PK2 = SUB1*(PAR(JP + 1,5) − PAR(JP,5))/SUB2 + PAR(JP,5)
3900  VARI1 = SIG(1) + SIG(2) + SIG(3)
      VARJ2 = 1.0/6.0*((SIG(1) − SIG(2))**2 + (SIG(2) − SIG(3))**2 +
@          (SIG(3) − SIG(1))**2) + SIG(4)**2 + SIG(5**2 + SIG(6)**2
      VAR113 = VARI1/3.0
      VI131 = SIG(I) − VARI13
      VI132 = SIG(2) − VARI13
      VI133 = SIG(3) − VARI13
      VARJ3 = VI131*(VI132*VI133 − SIG(5)**2) − SIG(4)*(SIG(4)*VI133
@          −SIG(5)*SIG(5)) + SIG(6)*(SIG(4)*SIG(5) − SIG(6)*VI132)
      VAR3TH = 1 5*30**(0.5)*VARJ3/VARJ2**1.5
      IF (VAR3TH .GE. 00) GOTO 4000
      ALAM = 22.0/21.0 − 1.0/3.0*ACOS(−PK2*VAR3TH)
      TOTLAM = PKI*COS(ALAM)
      DFD3TH = PK1*PK2*VARJ2**0.5*SIN(ALAM)/(3.0*PROP(4)*
@          SIN(ACOS(−PK2*VAR3TH)))
      GOTO 4100
4000  ALAM = 1.0/3.0*ACOS(PK2*VAR3TH)
      TOTLAM = PK1*COS(ALAM)
      DFD3TH = PK1*PK2*VARJ2**0.5*SIN(ALAM)/(3.0*PROP(4)*
@          SIN(ACOS(PK2*VAR3TH)))
4100  DFDI1 = B/PROP(4)
      DFDJ2 = A/PROP(4)**2 + TOTLAM/(PROP(4)*VARJ2**0.5)
      DVI1DS(1) = 1.0
      DVI1DS(2) = 1.0
      DVI1DS(3) = 1.0
      DVI1DS(4) = 0.0
      DVI1DS(5) = 0.0
```

```
        DVI1DS(6) = 0.0
        DVJ2DS(1) = 1.0/3.0*(2.0*SIG(1) − SIG(2) − SIG(3))
        DVJ2DS(2) = 1.0/3.0*(2.0*SIG(2) − SIG(1) − SIG(3))
        DVJ2DS(3) = 1.0/3.0*(2.0*SIG(3) − SIG(1) − SIG(2))
        DVJ2DS(4) = 2.0*SIG(4)
        DVJ2DS(5) = 2.0*SIG(5)
        DVJ2DS(6) = 2.0*SIG(6)
        DVJ3DS(1) = 1.0/3.0*(VI131*(−VI132 − VI131)) + 2.0*VI132*VI131 −
@               2.0*SIG(5)**2 + SIG(4)**2 + SIG(6)**2
        DVJ3DS(2) = 1.0/3.0*(VI132*(−VI131 − VI133)) + 2.0*VI131*VI133 −
@               2.0*SIG(6)**2 + SIG(4)**2 + SIG(5)**2
        DVJ3DS(3) = 1.0/3.0*(VI133*(−VI131 − V1132)) + 2.0*VI131*VI132 −
@               2.0*SIG(4)**2 + SIG(5)**2 + SIG(6)**
        DVJ3DS(4) = −2.0*VI131*SIG(4) + 2.0*SIG(5)*SIG(6)
        DVJ3DS(5) = −2.0.VI131*SIG(5) + 2.0*SIG(4)*SIG(6)
        DVJ3DS(6) = −2.0*VI132*SIG(6) + 2.0*SIG(4)*SIG(5)
        CONVJ2 = 3.0*3.0**0.5/(2.0*VARJ2*1,2)
        VJ3J2 = VARJ3/VARJ2**05
        DVTHDS(1) = CONVJ2*(−0.5*VJ3J2*(2.0*SIG(1) − SIG(2) − SIG(3)) +
@               DVJ3DS(1))
        DVTHDS(2) = CONVJ2*(−0.5*VJ3J2*(2.0*SIG(2) − SIG(1) − SIG(3)) +
@               DVJ3DS(2))
        DVTHDS(3) = CONVJ2*(−0.5*VJ3J2*(2.0*SIG(3) − SIG(1) − SIG(2)) +
@               DVJ3DS(3))
        DVTHDS(4) = CONVJ2*(−3.0*VJ3J2*SIG(4) + DVJ3DS(4))
```

Material matrix for reinforcement

```
        IMPLICIT REAL*8(A − H, O − Z)
        COMMON /MTMD3D/ D(6,6),STRESS(6),STRAIN(6),IPT,NEL
        DIMENSION PROP(1),DS(6,6),SIG(1),EPS(1),NCK(1),PS1(1)PS2(1),
   1            PS3(1),DC1(1),DC2(1),DC3(1)
        DO 111 II = 1,6
        DO 111 JJ = 1,6
 111    DS(II,JJ) = 0.0
        DS(1,1) = PROP(9)/PROP(6)*PROP(2)
        DS(2,2) = PROP(10)/PROP(7)*PROP(2)
        DS(3,3) = PROP(11)/PROP(8)*PROP(2)
        CALL TESTCK (PROP,SIG,EPS,NCK,PS1,PS2,PS3,DC1,DC2,DC3)
        IF (NCK(1) .EQ. 1 .OR. NCK(2) .EQ. 1 .OR. NCK(3) .EQ. 1)
@        GOTO 220
        CALL DMAT(PROP,NCK)
 220    DO 222 III = 1,6
        DO 222 JJJ = 1,6
 222    D(III,JJJ) = D(III,JJJ) + DS(III,JJJ)
        RETURN
        END
```

I.7(b) A computer program for the analysis of concrete elements subject to fire

This program was developed by R. Karuna for his MSc Thesis, City University, London, UK, 1996. Reproduced here by courtesy of R. Karuna.

Note that the author has assisted him in programming and analysis for two years.

Appendix A

```
c    PROGRAM FOR CALCULATING OVERALL STRESS OF
c    PRESTRESSED CONCRETE BEAM DUE TO THE EFFECTS
c    OF TEMPERATURE, PRESTRESS, POINT LOADS AND
c    UNIFORMLY DISTRIBUTED LOAD.
     REAL X(75),Y(75),D(75),TEa,e,H,Yj,B,T,SIGAV,
    +SIGP,SIG,L,F(20),a(20),c,W,PREFOE,SA,NA,
    +SEMO,ARE
     WRITE(*,*)'B=','T=','H=','Yj='
     READ(*,*) B,T,H,Yj
     WRITE(*,*)'L=','c=','W='
     READ(*,*) L,c,W
     WRITE(*,*)'e=','PREFOE=','SA='
     READ(*,*) e,PREFOE,SA
     WRITE(*,*)'NO OF NODES'
     WRITE(*,*)'X=','Y='
     WRITE(*,*) 'M=','F=','a='
     CALL SEMO3(B,T,H,e,SA,NA,ml,ARE,D,AvE,SEMO)
     WRITE(*,*)'SEMO','NA','SA'
     WRITE(*,*) SEMO,NA,SA
     CALL tele(X,Y,B,T,H,Yj,D,SIGAV,L,F,
    +W,a,c,SEMO,NA)
     WRITE(*,*)'SIGAV'
     WRITE(*,*) SIGAV
     CALL telep(B,H,T,e,Yj,O,TEa,SIGP,SA,
    +PREFOE,NA,SEMO)
     WRITE(*,*)'SIGP'
     WRITE(*,*) SIGP
     SIG=SIGAV+SIGP
     WRITE(*,*)'SIG'
     WRITE(*,*) SIG
     END

c    SUBROUTINE FOR CALCULATING AVERAGE STRESS
c    OF CONCRETE BEAM DUE TO TEMPERATURE EFFECT.
     SUBROUTINE tele(X,Y,B,T,H,Yj,D,SIGAV,L,F,
    +W,a,c,SEMO,NA)
     INTEGER I,N
     REAL X(75),Y(75),D(75),Y1(75),F(20),W,
    +TEa(20),E(20),SIGAV3,Yj,SIGAV,L,a(20),c,
```

```
    +SIG12(75),SIGAV1,SIGAV2,SIG3(75),H,MOM,
    +SIGL1,SIGL2,SEMO,NA
    ARE=B*H
    READ(*,*) N
    SUM12=0
    SUM3=0
    DO 10 I=1,N
    READ(*,*) X(I)
    READ(*,*) Y(I)
    IF (X(I).LT.Y(I)) THEN
    D(I)=X(I)
    ELSE
    D(I)=Y(I)
    ENDIF
    Y1(I)=Y(I)-NA
    CALL DIRKF(B,D(I),T,TEa(I))
    WRITE(*,*)' TEa(I)'
    WRITE(*,*) TEa(I)
    CALL faxff(TEa(I),FACT,ecC,E(I))
    WRITE(*,*)'E(I)'
    WRITE(*,*) E(I)
    SIG12(I)=E(I)*7E-06*(TEa(I)-20)
    SIG3(I)=(E(I)*7E-06*(TEa(I)-20)*Y1(I)*ARE*Yj)
    +/(SEMO*N)
    SUM12=SUM12+SIG12(1)
    SUM3=SUM3+SIG3(1)
10  CONTINUE
    SIGAV1= -SUM12/N
    WRITE (*,*)'SIGAV1'
    WRITE (*,*) SIGAV1
    SIGAV2=SUM12/N**2
    WRITE(*,*)'SIGAV2'
    WRITE(*,*) SIGAV2
    SIGAV3=SUM3/N**2
    WRITE(*,*)'SIGAV3'
    WRITE(*,*) SIGAV3
    CALL momt(F,a,L,c,MOM)
    WR1TE(*,*)'MOM'
    WRITE(*,*) MOM
    SIGL1=-(MOM*Yj*10**3)/(SEMO)
    WRITE(*,*)'SIGL1'
    WRITE(*,*) SIGL1
    SIGL2= -(W*c*(L-c)*Yj*10**3)/(2*SEMO)
    WRITE(*,*)'SIGL2'
    WRITE(*,*) SIGL2
    SIGAV=SIGAV 1+SIGAV2+SIGAV3+SIGL1+SIGL2
    WRITE(*,*)'SIGAV'
    WRITE(*,*) SIGAV
    RETURN
    END
```

```
c     SUBROUTENE FOR CALCULATING TEMPERATURE OF A
c     BEAM AT A PARTICULAR DEPTH FOR A GIVEN TIME
c     OF FIRE EXPOSURE.
      SUBROUTINE DIRKF (BX,DX,TX,TEa)
      INTEGER I,J,K
      REAL  B(10),D(75),T(10),TE(10,75,10),TE1,
     +TE2,TE3,TE4,TE5,TE6,
     +TE7,TE8,D1,D2,T1,T2,B1,B2,TE57,TE13,
     +TE86,TE24,TEa1,TEa2,TEa
      OPEN(UNIT=9,FILE='TEMP2',STATUS='OLD')
      REWIND 9
      READ(9,*)(D(J),J= 1,19)
      DO 10 J=1,19
      IF (DX.LT.D(J)) THEN
      JD=J
      GO TO 20
      ENDIF
10    CONTINUE
20    READ(9,*) (T(K),K=1,6)
      DO 30 K= 1,6
      IF (TX.LT.T(K)) THEN
      KT=K
      GO TO 40
      ENDIF
30    CONTINUE
40    READ(9,*) (B(I),I=1,8)
      DO 50 I=1,8
      IF (BX.GT.B(I)) THEN
      IB=1
      GO TO 60
      ENDIF
50    CONTINUE
60    READ(9,*) (((TE(I,J,K),J=1,19),K=1,6),I=1,8)
      TE1=TE(IB-1,JD,KT-1)
      TE2=TE(IB,JD,KT-1)
      TE3=TE(IB-1,JD,KT)
      TE4=TE(IB,JD,KT)
      TE5=TE(IB-1,JD-1,KT)
      TE6=TE(IB,JD-1,KT)
      TE7=TE(IB-1,JD-1,KT-1)
      TE8=TE(IB,JD-1,KT-1)
      D1=D(JD-1)
      D2=D(JD)
      T1=T(KT-1)
      T2=T(KT)
      B1=B(IB-1)
      B2=B(IB)
      TE57=(TX-T2)*(TE5-TE7)/(T2-T1)+TE5
      TE13=(TX-T2)*(TE3-TE1)/(T2-T1)+TE3
      TE86=(TX-T2)*(TE6-TE8)/(T2-T1)+TE6
      TE24=(TX-T2)*(TE4-TE2)/(T2-T1)+TE4
```

```
        TEa1=(DX-D2)*(TE57-TE13)/(D1-D2)+TE13
        TEa2 = (DX-D2)*(TE86-TE24)/(D1-D2)+TE24
        TEa=(BX-B1)*(TEa2-TEa1)/(B2-B1)+TEa1
        CLOSE (9)
        RETURN
        END


c       SUBROUTINE FOR CALCULATING ELASTIC MODULES
c       OF CONCRETE FOR A PARTICULAR TIME OF FIRE
c       EXPOSURE.
        SUBROUTINE faxff(TEa,FACT,ecC,E)
        INTEGER I
        REAL  TE(20),FAC(20),FACT,ec(20),ecC,
       +E,TEa
        OPEN(UNIT=2,FILE='YONG',STATUS-'OLD')
        REWIND 2
        READ  (2,*)  (TE(I),I=1,13)
        READ(2,*)  (FAC(I),I=1,13)
        READ(2,*)  (ec(I),I=1,13)
        DO 10  I=1,13
        IF  (TEa.LT.TE(I))  THEN
        ITE=I
        GO TO 20
        ENDIF
10      CONTINUE
20      TE2=TE(ITE-1)
        TE1=TE(ITE)
        FAC2=FAC(ITE-1)
        FAC1=FAC(ITE)
        ec2=ec(ITE-1)
        ec1=ec(ITE)
        FACT=(TEa-TE2)*(FAC1-FAC2)/(TE1-TE2)+FAC2
        ecC=(TEa-TE2)*(ec1-ec2)/(TE1-TE2)+ec2
        WRITE(*,*)'FACT','ecC'
        WRITE(*,*)  FACT,ecC
        E=(1.5*FACT*43.4)/ecC
        CLOSE (2)
        RETURN
        END


c       SUBROUTINE FOR CALCULATING STRESS OF A CONCRETE
c       BEAM DUE TO PRESTRESS WITH TEMPERATURE EFFECT.
        SUBROUTINE telep(B,H,T,e,Yj,D,TEa,SIGP,SA,
       +PREFOE,NA,SEMO)
        INTEGER I
        REAL  TE(20),COE(20),COEF,FORC,B,H,ARE,Yj,SA,NA,
       +SEMO,T,e,D,TEa,SIGP1,SIGP2,PREFOE,Et,SIGP3,SIGP
        OPEN(UNIT=3,FILE='PRE',STATUS='OLD')
        ARE=B*H
        IF((H/2-e).LT.B/2)THEN
        D=H/2-e
```

```
      ELSE
      D=B/2
      ENDIF
      CALL  DIRKF(B,D,T,TEa)
      WRITE(*,*)'TEa'
      WRITE(*,*)  TEa
      READ  (3,*)  (TE(I),I=1,13)
      READ(3,*)(COE(I),I=1,13)
      DO  10  I=1,13
      IF  (TEa.LT.TE(I))  THEN
      ITE=I
      GO  TO  20
      ENDIF
10    CONTINUE
20    TE2=TE(ITE-1)
      TE1=TE(ITE)
      COE2=COE(ITE-1)
      COE1=COE(ITE)
      COEF=(TEa-TE2)*(COE1-COE2)/(TE1-TE2)+COE2
      WRITE(*,*)  'COEF'
      WRITE(*,*)  COEF
      FORC=COEF*PREFOE
      SIGP1=-FORC/ARE
      WRITE(*,*)'SIGP1'
      WRITE(*,  *)  SIGP1
      SIGP2=(FORC*e*Yj)/SEMO
      WRITE(*,*)'SIGP2'
      WRITE(*,*)SIGP2
      CALL  STLYON(TEa,H,e,B,T,D,RATIO,Et)
      WRITE(*,*)'Et'
      WRITE(*,*)  Et
      SIGP3=-((Et*(TEa-20)*SA)/ARE)*6.5E-06
      WRITE(*,*)'SIGP3'
      WRITE(*,*)  SIGP3
      SIGP=SIGP1+SIGP2+SIGP3
      CLOSE  (3)
      RETURN
      END


c     SUBROUTINE  FOR  CALCULATING  MOMENT  OF
c     A  BEAM  AT  A  PARTICULAR  DISTANCE  FROM
c     THE  SUPPORTS  WITH  NUMBER  OF  POINT  LOADS
      SUBROUTINE  momt(F,a,L,c,MOM)
      INTEGER  I,M
      REAL  F(20),a(20),L,c,SUM1(20),
      +MOM,SUM2(20),SUM11,SUM22
      READ(*,*)  M
      SUM22=0
      SUM11=0
      DO  20  I=1,M
      READ(*,*)  F(I)
```

```
c    SUBROUTINE FOR CALCULATING I-VALUE OF A PRESTRESSED
     CONCRETE BEAM FOR A GIVEN TIME OF FIRE EXPOSURE.
     SUBROUTINE SEMO3(B,T,H,e,SA,NA,m1,ARE,D,AvE,SEMO)
     REAL B,T,H,e,SA,NA,m1,ARE,
    +SEMO,D,AvE
     CALL NAXIS1(B,T,H,e,SA,m1,ARE,AvE,D,NA)
     WRITE(*,*) NA
     SEMO=(B*H**3)/12+B*H*(NA-H/2)**2t+(m1*SA-SA)*(H/2+e-NA)**2
     WRITE(*,*)'SEMO'
     WRITE(*,*) SEMO
     RETURN
     END

c    SUBROUTINE FOR CALCULATING NEUTRAL AXIS DEPTH
c    OF A PRESTRESSED CONCRETE BEAM FOR A GIVEN
c    TIME OF FIRE EXPOSURE.
     SUBROUTINE NAXIS1(B,T,H,e,SA,m1,ARE,AvE,D,NA)
     REAL X(75),Y(75), TEa,B,T,H,AvE,Et,SA,e,NA,m1,ARE,D
     CALL CONYON(X,Y,B,T,AvE)
     WRITE(*,*)' AvE'
     WRITE(*,*) AvE
     CALL STLYON(TEa,H,e,B,T,D,RATIO,Et)
     WRITE(*,*)' Et'
     WRITE(*,*) Et
     m1=Et/AvE
     ARE=B*H
     NA=(ARE*H/2+(m1-1)*SA*(H/2+e))/(ARE+(m1-1)*SA)
     WRITE(*,*)'NA'
     WRITE(*,*) NA
     RETURN
     END

c    SUBROUTINE FOR CALCULATING AVERAGE ELASTIC
c    MODULES OF CONCRETE BEAM FOR A PARTICULAR
c    TIME OF FIRE EXPOSURE.
     SUBROUTINE CONYON(X,Y,B,T,AvE)
     INTEGER I,N
     REAL X(75),Y(75),D(75),TEa(75),E(75),
    +AvE,B,T
     READ(*,*) N
     SUM=0
     DO 10 I=1,N
     READ(*,*) X(I)
     READ(*,*) Y(I)
     IF (X(I).LT.Y(I)) THEN
     D(I)=X(I)
     ELSE
     D(I)=Y(I)
     ENDIF
```

```
      CALL dirkf(B,D(I),T,TEa(I))
      WRITE(*,*)TEa(I)
      CALL faxff(TEa(I),FACT,ecC,E(I))
      WRITE(*,*) E(I)
      SUM=SUM+E(I)
   10 CONTINUE
      AvE=SUMN
      WRITE(*,*)'AvE'
      WRITE(*,*) AvE
      RETURN
      END
```

Appendix B

```
c     PROGRAMME FOR CALCULATING DEFLECTION OF
c     A BEAM AT A DISTANCE FROM THE SUPPORT
c     DUE TO POINT LOADS AND UNIFORMLY
c     DISTRIBUTED LOAD FOR A PARTICULAR TIME
c     OF FIRE EXPOSURE.
      INTEGER I,M
      REAL P(20),a(20),L,c,w,SUM1(20),A,Def,
     +SUM4,SUM,SEMO,SUM2(20),AvE,H1,As,NA,m1,Def2,
     +SUM3(20),B,T,H,Defl,SUM11,SUM22,SUM33,R2
      WRITE(*,*)'B=','T=','H=','H1=','As='
      READ(*,*) B,T,H,H1,As
      WRITE(*,*)'L=','c=','w='
      READ(*,*) L,c,w
      WRITE(*,*)'M='
      WRITE(*,*) 'P=','a='
      READ(*,*) M
      SUM11=0
      SUM22=0
      SUM33=0
      DO 10 I=1,M
      READ(*,*) P(I)
      READ(*,*) a(I)
      SUM1(I)=P(I)*(c-a(I))**3/6
      SUM2(I)=P(I)*(L-a( I))**3/(6*L)
      SUM3(I)=P(I)*(L-a(I))/L
      SUM11=SUM11+SUM1(I)
      SUM22=SUM22+SUM2(I)
      SUM33=SUM33+SUM3(I)
   10 CONTINUE
      SUM=SUM11-SUM22*c+SUM33*(c*L**2-c**3)/6
      SUM4=w*c**4/24+w*c*L**3/24-w*L*c**3/12
      WRITE(*,*)' I','P','a'
      DO 20 I=1,M
      WRITE(*,*) I,P(I),a(I)
   20 CONTINUE
      WRITE(*,*)'SUM11','SUM22','SUM33',
     +'SUM','SUM4'
```

```
        WRITE(*,*)  SUM11,SUM22,SUM33,SUM,SUM4
        WRITE(*,*)  'NO  OF  NODES'
        WRITE(*,*)  'X=','Y='
        CALL  SEMO2(B,T,H,H1,NA,m1,A,As,AvE,SEMO)
        WRITE(*,*)'SEMO','AvE'
        WRITE(*,*)  SEMO,AvE
        WRITE(*,*)  SEMO,AvE,SUM,SUM4
        Def1=((SUM+SUM4)*10**9)/(AvE*SEMO)
        WRITE(*,*)'Def1'
        WRITE  (*,*)  Def1
        CALL  CONYON(X,Y,B,T,A,H,NA,R2)
        WRITE(*,*)  'R2'
        WRITE(*,*)  R2
        WRITE(*,*)'L,c,AvE,SEMO'
        WRITE(*,*)  L,,c,AvE,SEMO
        Def2=(R2*c*(L-c)*10**6)/(2*AvE*SEMO)
        WRITE(*,*)  'Def2'
        WRITE(*,*)  Def2
        Def=Def1+Def2
        WRITE(*,*)  'Def
        WRITE(*,*)  Def'
        END

        SUBROUTINE  DIRKF(BX,DX,TX,TEa)
        INTEGER  I,J,K
        REAL  B(75),D(75),T(75),TE(75,75,75),TE1,
       +TE2,TE3,TE4,TE5,TE6,
       +TE7,TE8,D1,D2,T1,T2,B1,B2,TE57,TE13,
       +TE86,TE24,TEa1,TEa2,TEa
        OPEN(UNIT=9,FILE='TEMP2',STATUS='OLD')
        READ(9,*)(D(J),J=1,19)
        DO  10  J=1,19
        IF  (DX.LT.D(J))  THEN
        JD=J
        GO  TO  20
        ENDIF
10      CONTINUE
20      READ(9,*)  (T(K),K=1,6)
        DO  30  K=1,6
        IF  (TX.LT.T(K))  THEN
        KT=K
        GO  TO  40
        ENDIF
30      CONTINUE
40      READ(9,*)  (B(I),I=1,8)
        DO  50  I=1,8
        IF  (BX.GT.B(I))  THEN
        IB=I
        GO  TO  60
        ENDIF
50      CONTINUE
```

```
60   READ(9,*) (((TE(I,J,K),J=1,19),K=1,6),I=1,8)
     TE1=TE(IB-1,JD,KT-1)
     TE2=TE(IB,JD,KT-1)
     TE3=TE(IB-1,JD,KT)
     TE4=TE(IB,JD,KT)
     TE5=TE(IB-1,JD-1,KT)
     TE6=TE(IB,JD-1,KT)
     TE7=TE(IB-1,JD-1,KT-1)
     TE8=TE(IB,JD-1,KT-1)
     D1=D(JD-1)
     D2=D(JD)
     T1=T(KT-1)
     T2=T(KT)
     B1=B(IB-1)
     B2=B(IB)
     TE57=(TX-T2)*(TE5-TE7)/(T2-T1)+TE5
     TE13=(TX-T2)*(TE3-TE1)/(T2-T1)+TE3
     TE86=(TX-T2)*(TE6-TE8)/(T2-T1)+TE6
     TE24=(TX-T2)*(TE4-TE2)/(T2-T1)+TE4
     TEa1=(DX-D2)*(TE57-TE13)/(D1-D2)+TE13
     TEa2=(DX-D2)*(TE86-TE24)/(D1-D2)+TE24
     TEa=(BX-B1)*(TEa2-TEa1)/(B2-B1)+TEa1
     WRITE (*,*)' TEa'
     WRITE(*,*) TEa
     CLOSE (9)
     RETURN
     END

     SUBROUTINE faxff(TEa,FACT,ecC,E)
     INTEGER I
     REAL  TE(20),FAC(20),ec(20),FACT,ecC,E
     OPEN(UNIT=2,FILE='YONG',STATUS='OLD')
     READ(2,*) (TE(I),I=1,13)
     READ(2,*) (FAC(I),I=1,13)
     READ(2,*) (ec(I),I=1,13)
     DO 10 I=1,13
     IF (TEa.LT.TE(I)) THEN
     ITE=I
     GO TO 20
     ENDIF
10   CONTINUE
20   TE2=TE(ITE-1)
     TE1=TE(ITE)
     FAC2=FAC(ITE-1)
     FAC1=FAC(ITE)
     ec2=ec(ITE-1)
     ec1=ec(ITE)
     WRITE (*,*)'TE1,TE2,FAC1,FAC2,ec1,ec2'
     WRITE (*,*) TE1,TE2,FAC1,FAC2,ec1,ec2
     FACT=(TEa-TE2)*(FAC1-FAC2)/(TE1-TE2)+FAC2
     ecC=(TEa-TE2)*(ec1-ec2)/(TE1-TE2)+ec2
```

```
     WRITE(*,*)' FACT','ecC'
     WRITE(*,*) FACT,ecC
     E=(1.5*FACT*25)/ecC
     WRITE(*,*)' E'
     WRITE(*,*) E
     CLOSE (2)
     RETURN
     END


c    SUBROUTINE FOR CALCULATING NEUTRAL AXIS DEPTH
c    AND I-VALUE OF A CONCRETE BEAM FOR A
c    PARTICULAR TIME OF FIRE EXPOSURE.
     SUBROUTINE semo2(B,T,H,H1,NA,m1,A,As,AvE,SEMO)
     REAL TEa,B,T,H,AvE,Et,As,H1,NA,m1,A,SEMO
     CALL CONYON1(X,Y,B,T,AvE)
     WRITE(*,*) AvE
     CALL STLYON(TEa,H,H1,B,T,Et,D)
     WRITE(*,*) Et
     A=B*H
     m1=Et/AvE
     NA=(m1*As/B)*((1+(2*B*H1)/(m1*As))**0.5-1)
     WRITE(*,*)'NA'
     WRITE(*,*) NA
     SEMO=(B*NA**3)/3+m1*As*(H1-NA)**2
     WRITE(*,*)'SEMO'
     WRITE(*,*) SEMO
     RETURN
     END


     SUBROUTINE CONYON1(X,Y,B,T,AvE)
     INTEGER I,N
     REAL X(75),Y(75),D(75),TEa(75),E(75),
    +AvE,B,T
     READ(*,*) N
     SUM=0
     DO 10 I=1,N
     READ(*,*) X(I)
     READ(*,*) Y(I)
     IF (X(I).LT.Y(I)) THEN
     D(I)=X(I)
     ELSE
     D(I)=Y(I)
     ENDIF
     CALL DIRKF(B,D(I),T,TEa(I))
     WRITE(*,*) TEa(I)
     CALL faxff(TEa(I),FACT,ecC,E(I))
     WRITE(*,*) E(I)
     SUM=SUM+E(I)
10   CONTINUE
     DO 20 I=1,N
     WRITE(*,*)'E','SUM'
```

```
        WRITE(*,*) E(I),SUM
20   CONTINUE
        AvE=SUM/N
        WRITE(*,*)'AvE'
        WRITE(*,*) AvE
        RETURN
        END


        SUBROUTINE STLYON(TEa,H,H1,B,T,Et,D)
        INTEGER I
        REAL  TE(20),RATO(20),Et,TEa,H1,H,D,RATIO
        OPEN(UNIT=2,FILE='YONGST1',STATUS='OLD')
        D=H-H1
        WRITE(*,*)'D'
        WRITE(*,*) D
        CALL  DIRKF(B,D,T,TEa)
        WRITE(*,*)'TEa'
        READ(2,*)(TE(I),I=1,13)
        READ(2,*)(RATO(I),I=1,3)
        DO 10 I=1,13
        IF(TEa.LT.TE(I))THEN
        ITE=I
        GOTO 20
        ENDIF
10   CONTINUE
20   TE2=TE(ITE-1)
        TE1=TE(ITE)
        RATO2=RATO(ITE-1)
        RATO1=RATO(ITE)
        RATIO=(TEa-TE2)*(RATO1-RATO2)/(TE1-TE2)+RATO2
        WRITE(*,*)'RATIO'
        WRITE(*,*) RATIO
        Et=210*10**3*RATIO
        WRITE(*,*)'Et'
        WRITE(*,*) Et
        CLOSE(2)
        RETURN
        END


c    SUBROUTINE FOR CALCULATING MOMENT DUE
c    TO THERMAL STRESS FOR A PARTICULAR TIME
c    OF FIRE EXPOSURE.
        SUBROUTINE CONYON(X,Y,B,T,A,H,NA,R2)
        INTEGER I,N
        REAL  X(75),Y(75),D(75),TEa(75),E(75),
        +B,T,R2,R(75),Y1(75),A,H,NA
        A=B*H
        WRITE(*,*)'NA'
        WRITE(*,*) NA
        READ(*,*) N
        R2=0
```

```
        DO 10 I=1,N
        READ(*,*) X(I)
        READ(*,*)Y(I)
        IF (X(I).LT.Y(I)) THEN
        D(I)=X(I)
        ELSE
        D(I)=Y(I)
        ENDIF
        Y1(I)=Y(I)-NA
        CALL DIRKF(B,D(I),T,TEa(I))
        WRITE(*,*) TEa(I)
        CALL faxff(TEa(I),FACT,ecC,E(I))
        WRITE(*,*) E(I)
        R(I)=E(I)*7E-06*(TEa(I)-20)*Y1(I)*A/N
        R2=R2+R(I)
10      CONTINUE
        DO 20 I=1,N
        WRITE(*,*)'I','R','YI'
        WRITE(*,*) I,R(I),Y1(I)
20      CONTINUE
        WRITE(*,*)'R2'
        WRITE(*,*) R2
        RETURN
        END
```

Appendix C

```
c    PROGRAM FOR CALCULATING DESIGN MOMENT
c    OF A CONCRETE BEAM FOR A PARTICULAR
c    TIME OF FIRE EXPOSURE.
     REAL X(75),Y(75),TEa,B,T,As,D1,Dis,
    +H,Avfcut,fyt,Mu1
     WRITE(*,*)'B=','T=','D1=','H=','As='
     READ(*,*) B,T,D1,H,As
     WRITE(*,*) 'NO OF NODES='
     WRITE(*,*) 'X=','Y='
     CALL consh(X,Y,B,T,Avfcut)
     WRITE(*,*) 'Avfcut'
     WRITE(*,*) Avfcut
     CALL stlsh(TEa,D1,B,T,fyt)
     WRITE(*,*) 'fyt'
     WRITE(*,*) fyt
     Dis=H-D1
     WRITE(*,*)'Dis'
     WRITE(*,*) Dis
     Mul=fyt*As*(Dis-(fyt*As)/(2*Avfcut*B))
     WRITE(*,*)'Mul'
     WRITE(*,*) Mul
     END
```

```
      SUBROUTINE consh(X,Y,B,T,Avfcut)
      INTEGER I,N
      REAL  X(75),Y(75),D(75),TEa(75),fcut(75),
     +Avfcut,B,T
      READ(*,*) N
      SUM=0
      DO 10 I=1,N
      READ(*,*) X(I)
      READ(*,*) Y(I)
      IF (X(I).LT.Y(I)) THEN
      D(I)=X(I)
      ELSE
      D(I)=Y(I)
      ENDIF
      CALL DIRKF(B,D(I),T,TEa(I))
      WRITE(*,*) 'TEa(I)'
      WRITE(*,*) TEa(I)
      CALL faxx(TEa(I),FACT,fcut(I))
      WRITE(*,*) 'fcut(I)'
      WRITE(*,*) fcut(I)
      SUM=SUM+fcut(I)
10    CONTINUE
      Avfcut=SUM/N
      WRITE(*,*)'Avfcut'
      WRITE(*,*) Avfcut
      RETURN
      END

      SUBROUTINE DIRKF(BX,DX,TX,TEa)
      INTEGER I,J,K
      REAL B(75),D(75),T(75),TE(75,75,75),TE1,
     +TE2,TE3,TE4,TE5,TE6,
     +TE7,TE8,D1,D2,T1,T2,B1,B2,TE57,TE13,
     +TE86,TE24,TEa1,TEa2,TEa
      OPEN(UNIT=9,FILE='TEMP2',STATUS='OLD')
      READ(9,*)(D(J),J=1,19)
      DO 10 J=1,19
      IF (DX.LT.D(J)) THEN
      JD=J
      GO TO 20
      ENDIF
10    CONTINUE
20    READ(9,*) (T(K),K=1,6)
      DO 30 K=1,6
      IF (TX.LT.T(K)) THEN
      KT=K
      GO TO 40
      ENDIF
30    CONTINUE
40    READ(9,*) (B(I),I=1,8)
      DO 50 I=1,8
```

```
      IF (BX.GT.B(I)) THEN
      IB=I
      GO TO 60
      ENDIF
50    CONTINUE
60    READ(9,*) (((TE(I,J,K),J=1,19),K=1,6),I=1,8)
      TE1=TE(IB-1,JD,KT-1)
      TE2=TE(IB,JD,KT-1)
      TE3=TE(IB-1,JD,KT)
      TE4=TE(IB,JD,KT)
      TE5=TE(IB-1,JD-1,KT)
      TE6=TE(IB,JD-1,KT)
      TE7=TE(IB-1,JD-1,KT-1)
      TE8=TE(IB,JD-1,KT-1)
      D1=D(JD-1)
      D2=D(JD)
      T1=T(KT-1)
      T2=T(KT)
      B1=B(IB-1)
      B2=B(IB)
      TE57=(TX-T2)*(TE5-TE7)/(T2-T1)+TE5
      TE13=(TX-T2)*(TE3-TE1)/(T2-T1)+TE3
      TE86=(TX-T2)*(TE6-TE8)/(T2-T1)+TE6
      TE24=(TX-T2)*(TE4-TE2)/(T2-T1)+TE4
      TEa1=(DX-D2)*(TE57-TE13)/(D1-D2)+TE13
      TEa2=(DX-D2)*(TE86-TE24)/(D1-D2)+TE24
      TEa=(BX-B1)*(TEa2-TEa1)/(B2-B1)+TEa1
      CLOSE (9)
      RETURN
      END


      SUBROUTINE faxx(TEa,FACT,fcut)
      INTEGER I
      REAL TE(20),FAC(20),FACT,TEa,fcut
      OPEN(UNIT=2,FILE='YONGHZ',STATUS = 'OLD')
      READ (2,*) (TE(I),I=1,13)
      READ(2,*) (FAC(I),I= 1,13)
      DO 10 I=1,13
      IF (TEa.LT.TE(I)) THEN
      ITE=I
      GO TO 20
      ENDIF
10    CONTINUE A:
20    TE2=TE(ITE-1) A:
      TE1=TE(ITE)
      FAC2=FAC(ITE-1)
      FAC1=FAC(ITE)
      WRITE(*,*) 'FAC1,FAC2'
      WRITE (*,*) FAC1,FAC2
      FACT=(TEa-TE2)*(FAC1-FAC2)/(TE1-TE2)+FAC2
      fcut=44 *FACT
```

```
      CLOSE (2)
      RETURN
      END

      SUBROUTINE stlsh(TEa,D1,B,T,fyt)
      INTEGER I
      REAL  TE(20),RATO(20),fyt,TEa,B,D1
      OPEN(UNIT=3,FILE='STRTHHZ',STATUS='OLD')
      D=D1
      CALL  dirkf(B,D,T,TEa)
      WRITE(*,*)'TEa'
      WRITE(*,*)TEa
      READ(3,*)(TE(I),I=1,13)
      READ(3,*)(RATO(I),I=1,13)
      DO 10 I=1,13
      IF(TEa.LT.TE(I))THEN
      ITE=I
      GOTO 20
      ENDIF
10    CONTINUE
      TE2=TE(ITE-1)
      TE1=TE(ITE)
      RATO2=RATO(ITE-1)
      RATO1=RATO(ITE)
      RATIO=(TEa-TE2)*(RATO1-RATO2)/(TE1-TE2)+RATO2
      WRITE(*,*)'RATIO'
      WRITE(*,*) RATIO
      fyt=480*RATIO
      WRITE(*,*)'fyt'
      WRITE(*,*) fyt
      CLOSE (3)
      RETURN
      END
```

Appendix D

Data (TEMP2) sheet for temperature of various width and time of fire exposure of beam at various depths from exposed surface.

Depth from exposed surface (D)
0. 10. 20. 30. 40. 50. 60. 70. 80. 90. 100. 110. 120. 130. 140. 150. 175. 200. 250.

Time of fire exposure (T)
0.0 1.0 1.5 2.0 3.0 4.0

Width of beam (B)
500.0 400.0 300.0 250.0 200.0 150.0 125.0 100

Corresponding temperature (Tea)

20 20 20 20 20 20 20 20 20 20 20 20 20 20 20 20 20 20 20
860 675 530 430 350 290 240 200 160 140 110 90 70 50 40 30 30 30 30
975 750 630 530 450 380 330 280 250 220 190 170 150 140 120 100 100 100 100
1000 850 730 610 530 450 400 350 310 280 260 240 220 200 200 190 190 190 190
1025 870 750 670 600 540 480 440 400 360 330 310 290 270 260 240 240 240 240
1070 900 800 710 650 600 550 500 460 430 400 370 350 340 320 300 300 300 300

20 20 20 20 20 20 20 20 20 20 20 20 20 20 20 20 20 20 20
900 720 570 460 380 320 270 230 190 160 140 120 110 100 100 100 100 100 100
950 800 660 550 460 390 340 290 260 230 200 190 170 160 150 14() 140 140 140
1020 880 750 640 550 480 420 370 340 300 280 260 240 230 220 200 200 200 200
1060 940 800 700 620 550 500 460 430 390 360 340 330 320 310 300 300 300 300
1100 950 830 730 680 610 600 520 490 460 440 420 4()0 390 380 370 370 370 370

20 20 20 20 20 20 20 20 20 20 20 20 20 20 20 20 20 20 20
910 760 620 500 400 350 300 260 230 200 180 170 150 140 120 100 100 100 100
970 840 700 590 490 420 370 340 300 270 260 240 220 200 190 180 180 180 180
1060 910 790 670 580 510 460 430 400 360 350 330 310 300 290 280 280 280 280
1100 960 840 730 650 590 550 520 500 470 460 440 430 420 400 390 390 390 390
1100 1000 870 760 700 650 620 590 560 540 520 510 500 480 460 440 440 440 440

20 20 20 20 20 20 20 20 20 20 20 20 20 20 20 20 20 2()20 20
950 800 660 530 430 370 350 320 300 280 260 250 230 220 200 180 180 180 180
1010 870 730 620 520 470 450 420 400 390 370 360 350 340 330 320 320 320 320
1080 940 820 700 620 560 530 510 500 480 460 460 450 440 430 420 420 420 420
1100 1000 900 790 700 660 640 610 600 590 580 570 560 550 540 530 530 530 530
1100 1030 930 830 750 700 660 640 640 620 610 600 600 590 580 570 570 570 570

20 20 20 20 20 20 20 20 20 20 20 20 20 20 20 20 20 20 20
970 820 690 560 460 420 380 360 340 320 310 305 300 290 280 270 270 270 270
830 900 760 650 560 530 500 480 460 450 440 430 420 410 405 400 400 400 400
1100 970 850 740 660 630 600 580 560 550 540 530 525 520 515 510 510 510 510
1100 1020 920 820 760 730 700 690 680 670 660 650 645 640 630 625 625 625 625
1100 1040 940 840 780 750 730 710 700 700 690 670 665 660 655 650 650 650 650

20 20 20 20 20 20 20 20 20 20 20 20 20 20 20 20 20 20 20
990 860 730 600 510 470 450 440 420 410 400 400 390 380 370 360 360 360 360
1070 940 800 700 630 600 580 570 560 550 540 535 530 525 520 510 510 510 510
1100 1000 890 780 720 680 670 660 650 640 635 630 625 620 615 610 610 610 610
1100 1040 940 860 820 780 760 760 740 730 725 720 715 715 710 710 710 710 710
1100 1050 950 880 840 800 780 780 760 750 740 735 730 725 720 720 720 720 720

Factors from 'Ecro Code'

Data (PRE) for reduction factor in strength of prestressing steel with temperature.

Temperature (TEa)

20 100 200 300 400 500 600 700 800 900 1000 1100 1200

Reduction factor (COE)
1.00 0.99 0.87 0.72 0.46 0.22 0.10 0.08 0.05 0.03 0.00 0.00 0.00

Data (YONGST) for reduction factor in elastic modules of prestressing steel with temperature.
Temperature (TEa)
20 100 200 300 400 500 600 700 800 900 1000 1100 1200

Reduction factor (RATO)
1.00 0.98 0.95 0.88 0.81 0.54 0.41 0.10 0.07 0.03 0.00 0.00 0.00

Data (YONG) for reduction factor of concrete strength and strain with temperature.
Temperature (TEa)
20 100 200 300 400 500 600 700 800 900 1000 1100 1200

Reduction factor (FAC)
1.00 0.97 0.94 0.91 0.85 0.74 0.60 0.43 0.27 0.15 0.06 0.02 0.00

Strain value (ec)
0.0025 0.0035 0.0045 0.0060 0.0075 0.0095 0.0125 0.0140 0.0145 0.0150 0.0150 0.0150 0.0150

Data (STRTH) for reduction factor of steel strength with temperature.
Temperature (TEa)
20 100 200 300 400 500 600 700 800 900 1000 1100 1200

Reduction factor (RATO)
1.00 1.00 1.00 1.00 1.00 0.78 0.47 0.23 0.11 0.06 0.04 0.02 0.00

Data (YONGST1) for reduction factor of steel young modules with temperature.
Temperature (TEa)
20 100 200 300 400 500 600 700 800 900 1000 1100 1200

Reduction factor (RATIO)
1.00 1.00 0.90 0.80 0.70 0.60 0.31 0.13 0.09 0.07 0.04 0.02 0.00

Factors from 'Analysis of prestressed concrete structures exposed to fire' by Hertz.
Data (EstHZ) for reduction factor of elastic modules of steel with temperature.
Temperature
20 100 200 300 400 500 600 700 800 900 1000 1100 1200

Reduction factor
1.000 0.998 0.936 0.829 0.714 0.457 0.243 0.129 0.050 0.025 0.000 0.000 0.000

Data (EvalHZ) for reduction factor of elastic modules of concrete with temperature.
Temperature
20 100 200 300 400 500 600 700 800 900 1000 1100 1200

Reduction factor
1.00 1.00 0.650 0.364 0.186 0.043 0.100 0.000 0.000 0.000 0.00 0.00 0.00

Data (STRTHHZ) for reduction factor of steel strength with temperature.
Temperature
20 100 200 300 400 500 600 700 800 '300 1000 1100 1200

Reduction factor
1.00 0.95 0.875 0.775 0.65 0.475 0.27 0.125 0.05 0.025 0.0 0.0 0.0

Data (YONGHZ) for reduction factor of concrete strength with temperature.
Temperature
20 100 200 300 400 500 600 700 800 900 1000 1100 1200

Reduction factor
1.00 0.975 0.85 0.825 0.66 0.325 0.10 0.08 0.03 0.0 0.0 0.0 0.00

Factors from 'Computer assisted analysis of the fire resistance of steel and composite concrete structures' (C.E.C agreement No. 7210-SA/502)
Data (Evalue) for reduction factor in elastic modules of concrete with temperature.
Temperature
20 100 200 300 400 500 600 700 800 900 1000 1100 1200

Reduction factor
1.00 0.865 0.695 0.520 0.360 0.235 0.130 0.080 0.040 0.020 0.00 0.00 0.00

Appendix E
Sample output for Deflection program.
Script started on Fri May 12 13:07:21 1995□]l;shiplake
(shiplake)1 Script% a.out

```
B=T=H=H1=As=
285mm
1h
580mm
531mm
1631mm**2
L=c=w=
8m
4m
   11000 N/m
```

```
M=
  P=a=
0
IPa
SUM11SUM22SUM33SUMSUM4
   0. 0. 0. 0. 586667.
NO OF NODES
X=Y=
15
47.5
58
   TEa
     314.000
     314.000
   TE1,TE2,FAC1,FAC2,ec1,ec2
     400.000   300.000   0.850000   0.910000   7.50000E-03   6.00000E-03
   FACTecC
     0.901600   6.21000E-03
   E
     5444.44
     5444.44
47.5
58
   TEa
     314.000
     314.000
   TE1,TE2,FAC1,FAC2,ec1,ec2
     400.000   300.000   0.850000   0.910000   7.50000E-03   6.00000E-03
   FACTecC
     0.901600   6.21000E-03
   E
     5444.44
     5444.44
142.5
58
   TEa
     259.000
     259.000
   TE1,TE2,FAC1,FAC2,ec1,ec2
     300.000   200.000   0.910000   0.940000   6.00000E-03   4.50000E-03
   FACTecC
     0.922300   5.38500E-03
   E
     6422.70
     6422.70
47.5
174
   TEa
     314.000
     314.000
```

```
  TE1,TE2,FAC1,FAC2,ec1,ec2
    400.000   300.000   0.850000   0.910000 7.50000E-03   6.00000E-03
  FACTecC
    0.901600   6.21000E-03
  E
    5444.44
    5444.44
47.5
174
  TEa
    314.000
    314.000
  TE1,TE2,FAC1,FAC2,ec1,ec2
    400.000   300.000   0.850000   0.910000   7.50000E-03   6.00000E-03
  FACTecC
    0.901600   6.21000E-03
  E
    5444.44
    5444.44
142.5
174
  TEa
    56.2500
    56.2500
  TE1,TE2,FAC1,FAC2,ec1,ec2
    100.0000   20.0000   0.970000   1.00000   3.50000E-03   2.50000E-03
  FACTecC
    0.986406   2.95312E-03
  E
    12525.8
    12525.8
47.5
290
  TEa
    314.000
    314.000
  TE1,TE2,FAC1,FAC2,ec1,ec2
    400.000   300.000   0.850000   0.910000   7.50000E-03   6.00000E-03
  FACTecC
    0.901600   6.21000E-03
  E
    5444.44
    5444 44
47.5
290
  TEa
    314.000
    314.000
  TE1,TE2,FAC1,FAC2,ec1,ec2
    400.000   300.000   0.850000   0.910000   7.50000E-03   6.00000E-03
```

```
    FACTecC
      0.901600   6.21000E-03
    E
      5444.44
      5444.44
142.5
290
  TEa
    56.2500
    56.2500
  TE1,TE2,FAC1,FAC2,ec1,ec2
    100.0000   20.0000   0.970000   1.00000   3.50000E-03   2.50000E-03
  FACTecC
    0.986406   2.95312E-03
  E
    12525.8
    12525.8
47.5
406
  TEa
    314.000
    314.000
  TE1,TE2,FAC1,FAC2,ec1,ec2
    400.000   300.000   0.850000   0.910000   7.50000E-03   6.00000E-03
  FACTecC
    0.901600   6.21000E-03
  E
    5444.44
    5444.44
47.5
```

Table API.7. Table for variation of steel strength with time
$B = 285\,\text{mm}, \quad H = 580\,\text{mm}, \quad H1 = 531\,\text{mm}, \quad L = 8000\,\text{mm}, \quad As = 1631\,\text{mm}^2$

Times (h)	EC coefficient strength (MPa)	HZ coefficient strength (MPa)
0	420	420
0.5	420	379.3
1	420	322.9
1.5	390	278.3
2	358.4	224
2.5	317.2	192.6
3	263.4	157.1

I.7(c) ULF Wickstrom program on thermal analysis

Reproduced courtesy of U. L. F. Wickstrom and the Lund Institute of
Technology.

```
1745      SUBROUTINE PROG2(IX,IY,NN,NE,NR,N,KTOP,NODFL,MNODFL,X,Y,T,TT,TMAX,
1746     1  ELA,EV4,A,MAX,P,W,EN,F,FLOW,AXIAL,NODCPL,NODINT,DTA)
1747  C-------------------------------------------------------------------------------
1748  C-----
1749  C-----                    * * * T A S E F ***
1750  C-----
1751  C-----TEMPERATURE ANALYSIS OF STUCTURES EXPOSED TO FIRE
1752  C-----
1753  C-----FINITE ELEMENT PROGRAM FOR ANALYSIS OF TRANSIENT NONLINEAR
1754  C-----HEAT TRANSFER PROBLEMS
1755  C-----
1756  C-----PROGRAMMED BY
1757  C-----ULF WICKSTROM
1758  C-----LUND INSTITUTE OF TECHNOLOGY
1759  C-----MARCH 1979
1760  C-----
1761  C-------------------------------------------------------------------------------
1762  C-----THIS IS THE MAIN CONTROL ROUTINE
1763  C-----
1764  C-----DEFINITIONS OF VARIABLES
1765  C-----IX, IY      NUMBER OF X- AND Y- LINES
1766  C-----NN          NUMBER OF NODES IN BASE STRUCTURE
1767  C-----NE          NUMBER OF ELEMENTS IN BASE STRUCTURE
1768  C-----NR          NUMBER OF REGIONS
1769  C-----N           VECTOR OF REGION NUMBERS
1770  C-----KTOP        NODES ADJACENT TO EACH ELEMENT
1771  C-----NODEL       ELEMENTS ADJACENT TO EACH NODE
1772  C-----MNODEL      NUMBER ELEMENTS ADJACENT TO EACH NODE
1773  C-----X, Y        NODE COORDINATES
1774  C-----T           CURRENT NODAL TEMPERATURES
1775  C-----TT          MAXIMUM NODAL TFMPERATURE5
1776  C-----TMAX        TRUE IF MAXIMUM NODAL TEMPERATURE OBTAINED
1777  C-----ELA,EV4     DUMMY GEOMETRICAL CONSTANTS
1778  C-----A           HEAT CONDUCTION MATRIX
1779  C-----P           HEAT CAPACITY VECTOR
1780  C-----W           NODAL VOLUME VECTOR
1781  C-----EN          MODAL ENTHALPY VECTOR
1782  C-----F           INTERNAL NODAL HEAT FLOW VECTOR
1783  C-----FLOW        EXTERNAL NODAL HEAT FLOW VECTOR
1784  C-----AXIAL       TRUE IF AXISYMMETRIC PROBLEM
1785  C-----NODCPL      INDICATES COUPLED NODES
1786  C-----NODINT      INDICATES INTERFACE NODES
1787  C-----DTA         DUMMY VECTOR FOR CRITICAL TIME INCREMENT CALCULATION
1788  C-----
1789  C-----PARAMETER CONSTANT5
1790  C-----
1791  C-----NB          MAXIMUM NUMBER OF NODE GROUPS
```

```
71          SUBROUTINE OUTMA2(IX,IY,NN,NE,X,Y,TIME,KTIME,T,TT,TMAX,FLOW,AXIAL)
72    C-----THIS ROUTNE PRINTS MAXIMUM CALCULATED NODAL TEMPERATURES
73          COMMON/FIRE/TIM(5C),TB(50),TITFIR
74          INTEGER TITFIR(18)
75          LOGICAL TMAX,AXIAL
76          DIMENSION X(NN),Y(NN),T(NN),TT(NN),TMAX(NN),FLOW(NN)
77          PRINT 200,TITFIR,X(NN),Y(NN)
78          IDUM1=1-IY
79          DO 10 I=1,IX
80          IDUM1=IDUM1+IY
81          IDUM2=IDUM1+IY-1
82          IF(IY.LE.7) PRINT 210,(J,TT(J),J=IDUM1,IDUM2)
83          IF(IY.GT.7) PRINT 230,(TT(J),J=IDUM1,IDUM2)
84    10    CONTINUE
85          PRINT 220,TIME,KTIME
86    200   FORMAT(//////1X,75(1HF)/2H,F/*F      MAXIMAL TEMPERATURES'/' F *,
87          1 18A4/' F XMAX=',F8.3,1CX,'YMAX=',F8.3/' F')
88    210   FORMAT(' F',13(I5,F5.0))
89    220   FORMAT(2H F/2H F/' F MAX-TIME',F7.2,10X,'NUMBER OF '
90          1       'TIME INCREMENTS',I5/2H F/2H F/2H F,75(1HF))
91    230   FORMAT(' F',18F7.C)
92          RETURN
93          END
94
95          SUBROUTINE OUT2(IX,IY,NN,NE,X,Y,TIME,KTIME,DELTI,T,TT,TMAX,FLOW,
96          1       TFIRE,NODT,AXIAL)
97    C-----THIS ROUTINE PRINTS NODAL TEMPERATURES AND VOID AIR TEMPERATURES
98          DIMENSION X(NN),Y(NN),T(NN),TT(NN),TMAX(NN),FLOW(NN)
99          LOGICAL TMAX,AXIAL,LDUM,LEN
00          COMMON/ENCON/H(50),TAIR(2)
01          COMMON/ENCLOS/LEN,NENC,NENCNG(2),IGREN(2,4),NNODEN(2),
02          1       INODEN(100),XSYM(7),YSYM(2)
03          COMMON/TOUT/II,TOUT(100),TIMMAX,DTMAX,TIMFAC,KTMAX,KUPDA
04          TIME1=TIME-DELTI
05          DO 5 IJ=1,NN
06          IF(TMAX(IJ)) GOTO 5
07    C-----IF THE NODAL TEMPERATURE DECREASES SET TMAX=.TRUE. AND PRINT
08    C-----MAX TEMPERATURE TT
09          IF(TT(IJ).GT.1.001*T(IJ))
10          1       PRINT 200,IJ,TT(IJ),TIME1,DELTI
11          IF(TT(IJ).GT.1.001*T(IJ)) TMAX(IJ)=.TRUE.
12          TT(IJ)=AMAX1(TT(IJ),T(IJ))
13    5     CONTINUE
14    C-----IF TIME=TOUT PRINT ALL TEMPERATURES
15          IF((TIME-TOUT(II)).LT.-1.E-4) GOTO 70
16          PRINT 100,TIME,KTIME,TFIRE,NODT
17          IF(.NOT.LEN) GOTO 30
18          PRINT 300
19          DO 20 I=1,NENC
```

```
20   20      PRINT 310,I,TAIR(I)
21   30      CONTINUE
22           II1=II+1
23           IDUM1=1-IY
24           LDUM=IY.LT.7
25           DO 10 I=1,IX
26           IDUM1=IDUM1+IY
27           IDUM2=IDUM1+IY-1


201          SUBROUTINE BRBCA(BR,BC,EPSIG,BET,BAR,NUMI,N3,ING1)
202  C-----FORM BOUNDARY RADIATION AND CONVECTION MATRICES
203          DIMENSION BR(NUMI,2),BC(NUMI,2),BAR(NB,NUMI)
204          BR(1,1)=0.
205          BR(1,2)=.33333333*BAR(ING1,2)
206          NUM1=NUMI-1
207          IF(NUM1.EQ.1) GOTO 20
208          DO 10 I=2,NUM1
209          BR(I,1)=.16666667*BAR(ING1,I)
210          BR(I,2)=.3333333*(BAR(ING1,I)+BAR(ING1,I+1))
211  10      CONTINUE
212  20      CONTINUE
213          BR(NUM1,1)=.16666667*BAR(ING1,NUMI)
214          BR(NUM1,2)=.33333333*BAR(ING1,NUMI)
215  C
216          DO 30 I=1,NUMI
217          DO 30 J=1,2
218          BC(I,J)=BET*BR(I,J)
219          BR(I,J)=EPSIG*BR(I,J)
220  30      CONTINUE
221          RETURN
222          END
223
224          SUBROUTINE BRBCB(BR,BC,TR,TC,TRD,TCD,NUMI,DTA,NN,MAX,FLOW,TG,
225         1    T,ING1)
226  C-----THIS ROUTINE CALCULATES EXTERNAL HEAT FLOW BY RADIATION AND
227  C-----CONVECTION AND ADDS THE CORRESPONDING CONTRIBUTIONS TO THE
228  C-----VECTOR DATA FOR CALCULATION OF CRITICAL TIME INCREMENT
229          DIMENSION BR(NUMI,2),BC(NUMI,2),DTA(NN),FLOW(NN),T(NN)
230         1,   TR(NUMI),TC(NUMI),TRD(NUMI),TCD(NUMI)
231          PARAMETER NB=10,NNP=30,NNB2=2*NNB
232          COMMON/BNOD/NUMB(NB),NBOUND(NB,NNB),BAREA(NB,NNB),
233         1    EPSG(NB),BETA(NB),CPG(NB),FA(NB)
234          LOGICAL FA
235  C
236  C-----FIRST NODE
237  C
238          NODE=NBOUND(ING1,1)
239          TR2=TR(1)
240          TC2=TC(1)
241          TR3=TR(2)
242          TC3=TC(2)
```

```
243        TRCD2=TRD(1)
244        TCD2=TCD(1)
245        TRD3=TRD(2)
246        TCD3=TCD(2)
247        BR2=BR(1,2)
248        BC2=BC(1,2)
249        BR3=BR(2,1)
250        BC3=BC(2,1)
251        FLW=BR2*TR2+BC2*TC2
252        FLW=FLW+BR3*TR3
253        FLW=FLW + 5C3*TC3
254        DA=BR2*TRD2+BC2*TCD2
255        DA=DA+BR3*TRD3


           SUBROUTINE PTBNDB (T,TFIRE)
C-----SET PRESCRIBED NODAL BOUNDARY TEMPERATURE
           DIMENSION T(1)
           PARAMETER NB=10,NNB=30,NNB2=2*NNB
           COMMON/PTB/NPTNG,NPTG(NB)
           COMMON/BNOD/NUMB(NP),NBOUND(NB,NNB),BAREA(NB,NNB),TH(NB),
          1      EPSG(NB),BETA(NB),CPG(NB),FA(NB)
           COMMON/UNIT/SIGMA,TABS,TINIT,TAMB,TAMB4
           LOGICAL FA
C-----
           IF(NPTNG.EQ.0) RETURN
C-----EACH PRESCRIBED TEMPERATURE BOUNDARY NODE GROUP
           DO 10 IB=1,NPTNG
           TG=TAMB
           ING1=NPTG(IB)
           IF(FA(ING1)) TG=TFIRE
           NUMI =NUMB(ING1)
           DO 10 I=1,NUMI
           NODE=NBOUND(ING1,I)
           T(NODE) =TG
10         CONTINUE
           RETURN
           END


           SUBROUTINE RADVEC (F,ETA,N,Q)
C-----THIS ROUTINE FORMS THE LOCAL ENCLOSURE SURFACE RADIATION HEAT
C-----EXCHANGE VECTOR Q=E*ETA
           DIMENSION Q(1),ETA(1),E(N,N)
           QTOT=0.
           DO 20 I=1,N
           QT=0.
           DO 10 J=1,N
10         QT=QT+E(I,J)*ETA(J)
           QTOT=QTOT+QT
20         Q(I)=QT
           RETURN
220        FORMAT (/' TOTAL RADIATION HEAT EXCHANGE',E11.3)
```

```
          END

          SUBROUTINE REG2( NN,NE,NR,N,KTOP,X,Y,NODEL,MNODEL)
    C-----THIS SUBROUTINE FORMS VECTOR OF REGION NUMBERS N OF EACH ELEMENT
          DIMENSION X(NN),Y(NN),N(NE),KTOP(4,NE),NODEL(4,NN),MNODEL(NN)
          PARAMETER MNR=10
          COMMON/RGEO/ELFICT(MNR),ET(MNR) ,SRDIAC(4,MNR)
          LOGICAL ELFICT
          EPS=1.E-7
          DO 10 I=1,NE

          N(I)=1
          IF(NR.EQ.1) GOTO 10
          ND1=KTOP(1,I)
          ND2= KTOP(4,I)
          DO 5 J=2,NR
          IF((X(ND1)-SRDIAC(3,J)).GT.-EPS) GOTO 5
          IF((Y(ND1)-SRDIAC(4,J)).GT.-EPS) GOTO 5
          IF((X(ND2)-SRDIAC(1,J)).LT.EPS) GOTO 5
          IF((Y(ND2)-SRDIAC(2,J)).LT.EPS) GOTO 5
          N(I)=J
    5     CONTINUE
    10    CONTINUE
          DO 40 T=1,NN
          II=0
    20    DO 30 IE=1,NE
          N1=N(IE)
          IF(ELFICT(N1)) GOTO 30
          DO 20 J=1,4
          IF(KTOP(J,IF).NF.I) GOTO 20
          II=II+1
          NODEL(II,I)=IE
          IF(II.EQ.4) GOTO 30
    20    CONTINUE
    30    CONTINUE
          MNODEL(I)=II
    40    CONTINUE
          RETURN
          END

589       SUBROUTINE ENCON1
590 C-----THIS ROUTINE FORMS CONVECTION ARRAY H
591       PARAMETER NB=10,NNB=30,NNB2=2*NNB
592       COMMON/BNOD/NUMB(NB),NBOUND(NB,NNB),BAREA(NB,NNB),TH(NB),
593      1    EPSG(NB),BETA(NB),CPG(NB),FA(NB)
594       COMMON/ENCLOS/LEN,NENC,NENCNG(2),IGREN(2,4),NNODEN(2),
595      1    INODEN(100),XSYM(2),YSYM(2)
596       COMMON/ENCON/H(50),TAIR(2)
597       COMMON/DUMMY/HZ(25),DUM2(25)
598       LOGICAL LEN
599       LOGICAL XSYM,YSYM,SYM
```

```
600          INTEGER EN
601          IND=1
602   C-----FORM ZONE CONVECTION ARRAY
603   C-----EACH VOID
604          DO 150 EN=1,NENC
605          SYM=XSYM(EN).OR.YSYM(EN)
606          IN=0
607          NENG=NENCNG(EN)
608   C-----EACH NODE GROUP
609          D0 10 IG=1,NENG
610          I1=IGREN(EN,IG)
611          NUMI=NUMB(I1)
612          BE=BETA(I1)
613   C-----EACH ZONE
614          DO 10 I=2,NUMI
615          IN=IN+1
616   10     HZ(IN)=BE*BAREA(I1,I)
617   C-----FORM NODE CONVECTION ARRAY
618          CALL HTRANS(HZ,H(IND),IN,SYM)
619          N=IN
620          IF(SYM) N=N+1
621          IND=IND+N
622   150    CONTINUE
623          RETURN
624          END
625
2013         SUBROUTINE TIME
2014  C-----READ TIME INTEGRATION CONTROL DATA
2015         COMMON/TOUT/II,TOUT(100),TIMMAX,DTMAX,TIMEAC,KTMAX,KUPDA
2016         PRINT 200
2017  C-----
2018         READ I00,NT,TIMMAX,DTMAX,TIMFAC,KTMAX,KUPDA
2019  C-----
2020         IF(DTMAX.EQ.0) DTMAX=TIMMAX
2021         IF(TIMFAC.EQ.0) TIMFAC=.8
2022         IF(KTMAX.EQ.0) KTMAX=1000
2023         IF(KUPDA.EQ.0) KUPDA=1
2024  C-----
2025         READ 100,(TOUT(I),I=1,NT)
2026  C-----
2027         PRINT 210,TIMMAX,DTMAX,TIMFAC,KTMAX,KUPDA
2028         PRINT 220,(TOUT(I),I=1,NT)
2029  100    FORMAT( )
2030  220    FORMAT(' PRINT OUT TIMES',3X,8G7.2/(19X,8G7.2))
2031  200    FORMAT(//' TIME'/' ****'/)
2032  210    FORMAT(' MAXIMUM TIME=',G8.3/' MAXIMUM TIME INCREMENT=',G8.3/
2033         1    ' CRITICAL TIME INCREMENT FACTOR=',G8.3/
2034         2    ' MAXIMUM NUMBER OF TIME INCREMENTS=',I5/
2035         3    ' NUMBER OF STEPS BETWEEN UPDATING OF CONDUCTION MATRIX=',I5)
2036         RETURN
2037         END
```

```
708          SUBROUTINE ENRAD1(X,Y)
709    C-----FORM RADIATION MATRICES FOR EACH VOID AND STORE THEM IN
710    C-----THE VECTOR E.
711    C-----CALCULATE VIEW-FACTOR MATRIX VIEW AND ZONE AREA VECTOR D
712          DIMENSION X(1),Y(1),A(25,25),B(25,25)
713          PARAMETER NB=10,NNB=30,NNB2=2*NNB
714          COMMON/BNOD/NUMB(NB),NBOUND(NB,NNB),BAREA(NB,NNB),
715         1    EPSG(NB),BETA(NB),CPG(NB),FA(NB)
716          COMMON/ENCLOS/LEN,NENC,NENCNG(2),IGREN(2,4),NNODEN(2),
717         1    INODEN(100),XSYM(2),YSYM(2)
718          COMMON/ENRAD/E(1000)
719          COMMON/UNIT/SIGMA,TABS
720          COMMON/DIM/MAXNG,MAXNOD
721          COMMON/DUMMY/D(25),DUM2(25)
722          DIMENSION VIEW(25,25)
723          EQUIVALENCE (A(1),VIEW(1))
724          DATA IND,IE/0,1/
775          LOGICAL LEN
726          LOGICAL XSYM,YSYM,SYM
727          INTEGER EN
728    C-----EACH VOID
729          DO 150 EN=1,NENC
730          CALL VIEWFC(X,Y,D,EN,VIEW,MAXNOD)
731    C-----FORM THE MATRICES A AND B
732          NENG=NENONG(EN)
733          IN=0
734    C-----EACH NODE GROUP
735          DO 120 IG=1,NENG
736          I1=IGREN(EN,IG)
737          NUMI=NUMB(I1)
738    C-----EACH ZONE
739          DO 120 I=2,NUMI
740          IN=IN+1
741          JN=0
742          DO 120 JG=1,NENG
743          J1=IGREN(EN,JG)
744          NUMJ=NUMB(J1)
745          EPSJ=EPSG(J1)
746          DO 120 J=2,NUMJ
747          JN=JN+1
748          B(IN,JN)=VIEW(IN,JN)*SIGMA
749          A(IN,JN)=-VIEW(IN,JN),(1.-EPSJ)/EPSJ/D(JN)
750          IF B(IN.NE.JN) GOTO 120
751          B(IN,JN)= -SIGMA+B(IN,JN)
752          A(IN,JN)=1./EPSJ/D(JN)+A(IN,JN)
753    120   CONTINUE
754          N=IN
755    C-----INVERT A AND STORE RESULT IN A
756          CALL INVER(A,N,MAXNOD)
757    C-----MULTIPLY A AND B AND STORE RESULT IN A
758          CALL MULT(A,B,N,MAXNOD)
```

```
759          SYM=.FALSE.
760          IF(XSYM(EN).OR.YSYM(EN)) SYM=.TRUE.
761          NZ=N
762          IF(SYM) N=N+1
763   C-----TRANSFORM THE LOCAL RADIATION MATRICE A AND STORE THE RESULT IN
764   C-----VECTOR E
765   C-----B IS EMPLOYED AS A DUMMY MATRIX
766          CALL ETRANS(A,B,E(IE),N,NZ,SYM,MAXNOD)
767          IE=IE+N*N

988          SUBROUTINE FQBNDB(T,FLOW,DTA,NN,MAX,TFIRE)
989   C-----THIS ROUTINE PREPARES CALCULATION OF PRESCRIBED BOUNDARY FLOW
990          DIMENSION T(NN),DTA(NN),FLOW(NN)
991          PARAMETER NB=10,NNB=30,NNB2=2*NNB
992          COMMON/FQB/NFQNG,NFQG(NB),TR(NNB),TC(NNB)
993         1    ,BR(NNB2),BC(NNB2),TRD(NNB),TCD(NNB)
994          COMMON/BNOD/NUMB(NB),NBOUND(NB,NNB),BAREA(NB,NNB),
995         1    EPSG(NB),BETA(NB),CPG(NB),FA(NB)
996          COMMON/UNiT/SIGMA,TABS,TINIT,TAMB,TAMB4
997          LOGICAL FA
998   C-----NULL FLOW VECTOR
999          DO 777 1=1,NN
1000  777    FLOW(I)=0.
1001  C-----RETURN IF NO PRESCRIBED BOUNDARY FLOW
1002         IF(NFQNG.EQ.0) RETURN
1003         TF4=(TFIRE+TABS)**4
1004         IND=1
1055  C-----EACH BOUNDARY FLOW NODE GROUP
1006         DO 30 IB=1,NFQNG
1007         TG4=TAMB4
1008         TG=TAMB
1009         ING1=NFQG(IB)
1010         IF(FA(ING1)) TG=TFIRE
1011         IF(FA(ING1)) TG4=TF4
1012         NUMI=NUMB(ING1)
1013         CP=CPG(ING1)
1014         DO 20 I=1,NUMI
1015         NODE=NBOUND(ING1,I)
1016         TNODE=T(NODE)
1017         TNABS=TNODE+TABS
1018  C-----RADIATION
1019         TRD(I)=4.*TNABS**3
1020         TR(I)=TG4-TNABS**4
1021  C-----CONVECTION
1022         DUM=TG-TNODE
1023         TCD(I)=CP*ABS(DUM)**(CP-1.)
```

Client: A & Z Partners
Quantity: 67
Top dead: $1.750\,\text{kN/m}^2$ (slope)
Bottom dead: $0.250\,\text{kN/m}^2$ (slope)
Spacing: 600 mm
Treatment: PROTIM A
Rise: 1.063 m
Truss weight: 26–30 kg

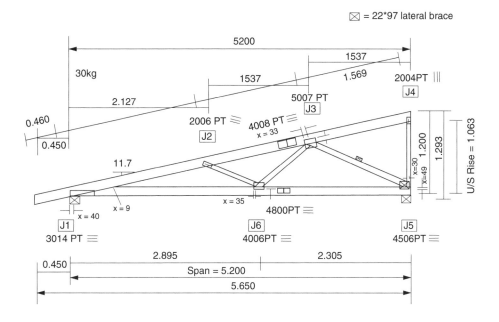

I.7(d)   ISOPAR finite-element program: subroutine

```
      INTEGER*4 MT1,MT2
      IMPLICIT REAL*8(A-H,O-Z)
      COMMON/BBB/ D(6,6),D1(6,6),E(12,3),POIS(12,6),MCODE(12,20),
     1      EK(60,60) ,HG(6,60),LRF(12),IDENT(12),RAW(1),EM(60,60)
      COMMON/LID/ SK(366,165),SM(366,165),SKK(1,1)
      COMMON/BON/ NNODE, NEUB,NETB,NBLOK
      COMMON/REL/ U(366),P(366),PT(366),U1(366),U10(366),U2(366)
     1   ,U20(366),U0(366),P1(366),PS(366),PIU(366),PIT(366)
      COMMON/CCC/ X(128),Y(128),Z(128),NZN(366) ,NFIX(366) ,
     1 AST(12),EST(12),DIA(12),ELINE(6,6),ELINK(6,6)
      COMMON/AAA/ NEL,NNP,NEQ,NHBD,NBC,NTE1,NTE2,NTE3,NTE4,
     1 NNE1,NNE2,NNE3,NNE4,NDF,NRF,NRS,DETJ
      COMMON/GSS/ ZETA(27), ETA(27), ZI(27), W(27), NGP
C ISOPARAMETRIC ELEMENTS REPRESENT V   CONCRETE OF THE VESSEL
CLINE ELEMENTS REPRESENT PRESTRESSING CABLES AND REINFORCEMENTS
C LINKAGE ELEMENTS REPRESENT NON-LINEAR BOND
C+++++
      CALL CTIMEA(MT1)
C...     NBC    NUMBER OF BOUNDARY CONDITIONS
C...     NDF         NUMBER OF DEGREES OF FREEDOM PER NODE
C...     NEL         TOTAL NUMBER OF ELEMENTS
C...     NGP         NUMBER OF GAUSS POINTS FOR INTEGRATION
C...     NNE1        NUMBER OF NODES IN ELEMENT TYPE 1 **20 NODED ISOP**
C...     NNE2                                         2
      CALL TIMING(1)
C+++++
      READ(5, *)NNP,NTE1,NTE2,NTE3,NNE1,NNE2,NNE3,NRF,NBC,NDF,NGP,NRS,
CXXXXX
     1 NNE4 ,NTE4, NTYPE
   10 FORMAT(15I3)
      NEL=NTE1
      WRITE (6,15) NEL,NNP,NTE1,NTE2,NTE3,NNE1,NNE2,NNE3,NRF,NBC,NDF,NGP
     1, NRS
   15 FORMAT(1H1,20X,37HNUMBER OF ELEMENTS                     =,I5//
     1      20X,37HNO OF NODAL POINTS                         =,I5//
     2      20X,37HNO OF TYPE 1 ELEMENT                       =,I5//
     3      20X,37HNO OF TYPE 2 ELEMENT                       =,I5//
     4      20X,37HNO OF TYPE 3 ELEMENT                       =,I5//
     5      20X,37HNO OF NODESIN TYPE1 ELEMENT                =,I5//
     6      20X,37HNO OF NODESIN TYPE2 ELEMENT                =,I5//
     7      20X,37HNO OF NODESIN TYPE3 ELEMENT                =,I5//
     8      20X,36HSECTION REFERENCE FOR TYPE1 ELEMENT=,I5//
     9      20X,37HNO OF BOUNDARY CONDITIONS                  =,I5//
     1      20X,35H NO OF DEGREES OF FREEDOM PER NODE=,I5//
     1      20X,37HNO OF GASS POINTS FOR INTEGRATION          =,I5//
     1      20X,38HSECTION REFERENCE FOR TYPE2 ELEMENT  =,I5////)
      CALL INPUT
C+++++
      CALL BAND
C+++++
      CALL GAUSS
C+++++
      CALL MACRO
C+++++
      CALL TIMING(2)
C+++++
      CALL CTIMEA(MT2)
C+++++
      RT = FLOAT((MT2-MT1)/100.)
      WRITE(6,1000) MT2,MT1,RT
C#####
1000  FORMAT('CPUTIME AT THE END OF EXECUTION =',I10,'CENTISECS'/
     1       'CPU TIME AT THE START OF EXECUTION =',I10,'CENTISECS'/
     2       'CPU TIME TAKEN TO EXECUTE THE PROGRAM   =',F10.2,'SECS'/)
      CALL EXIT
C+++++
      END
C££££££££££££££££££££
      SUBROUTINE INPUT
C...       THIS ROUTINE IS CODED BY THIRU (29/10/80)
      IMPLICIT REAL*8(A-H,O-Z)
C££££££££££££££££££££££
      LOGICAL PCOMP,DYN
      COMMON/CCC/ X(128),Y(128),Z(128),NZN(366) ,NFIX(366) ,
     1 AST(12),EST(12),DIA(12),ELINE(6,6),ELINK(6,6)
      COMMON/SEP/ NDI(366), JRC(3),XJN(12)
      COMMON/BON/ NNODE, NEUB,NETB,NBLOK
      COMMON/AAA/ NEL,NNP,NEQ,NHBD,NBC,NTE1,NTE2,NTE3,NTE4,
     1 NNE1,NNE2,NNE3,NNE4,NDF,NRF,NRS,DETJ
      COMMON/BBB/ D(6,6),D1(6,6),E(12,3),POIS(12,6),MCODE(12,20),
```

```
      1                 EK(60,60)  ,H(6,60),LRF(12),IDENT(12),RAW(1),EM(60,60)
             COMMON/GSS/ ZETA(27), ETA(27), ZI(27), W(27), NGP
             DIMENSION WD(10)
             DATA WD/4HCOOR,4HELEM,4HMATE,4HBOUN,4HFORC,
      1          4HTEMP,4HEND ,4HPRIN,4HNOPR,4HPAGE/
             DATA LIST/10/
C...         DYN            =.FALSE. - STATIC LOADING
200          READ(5,201)CC
C%%%%%
201          FORMAT(A4,75X,A1)
             DO 202 I2=1,LIST
202          IF(PCOMP(CC,WD(I2))) GO TO 203
             GO TO 200
203          GO TO(204,205,206,207,208,209,210,211,212,213),I2
C...         NODAL COORDINATE INPUT
204          WRITE(6,30)
C#####
30           FORMAT(5X,'NODES',10X,'X-COORDINATE',10X,'Y-COORDINATE',
      1          10X,'Z-COORDINATE')
             DO 418 II=1,NNP
             READ(5,*)II,X(II),Y(II),Z(II)
C%%%%%
301          FORMAT(I5,3F10.4)
             WRITE(6,302)II,X(II),Y(II),Z(II)
C#####
418          CONTINUE
302          FORMAT(5X,I4,3(8X,F13.4))
             GO TO  200
C...         CONECTIVITY
205          CONTINUE
             DO 1 I=1,NTE1
1            IDENT(I)=1
             READ(5,*) (LRF(I),I=1,NTE1)
C%%%%%
16           FORMAT(4I2)
66           FORMAT(5X,I5,5X,8I5,18X,I3,14X,I5)
C
             WRITE(6,60)
C#####
60           FORMAT(1H1,5X,'ELEMENT NO.',10X,'CONNECTIVITY ARRAYS(NODE NOS)'
      1          10X,'SECTION REFERENCE',3X,'EL IDENTIFICATION')
             DO 400 I=1,NTE1
             READ(5,*)I,(MCODE(I,J),J=1,NNE1)
C%%%%%
400          CONTINUE
65           FORMAT(21I3)
             DO 19 I=1,NTE1
19           WRITE(6,66) I , (MCODE(I,J),J=1,NNE1)
C#####
             GO TO 200
C..          MATERIAL
206          CONTINUE
             NEQ=NNP*NDF
             WRITE(6,75)
C#####
75           FORMAT(1H1,3X,'SECTION REFERENCE',5X,'ELASTIC MODULUS OF CONCRETE',
      1          1'POISONS RATIO')
             DO 11 I=1,NRF
             READ(5,*) (E(I,J),J=1,3),(POIS(I,M),M=1,3),RAW(I)
C%%%%%
80           FORMAT(3F6.0,4F3.1)
11           WRITE(6,85)I,(E(I,J),J=1,3),(POIS(I,M),M=1,3),RAW(I)
C#####
85           FORMAT(8X,I3,12X,F10.2,2X,F10.2,2X,F10.2,4X,F4.2,2X,F4.2,2X,F4.2
      1          ,2X,F4.2)
C
C            READ YOUNG7S MODULUS FOR PRESTRESSING STEEL
C%%%%%
             GO TO  200
C...         BOUNDARY COND
207          CONTINUE
501          WRITE(6,90)
C#####
90           FORMAT(1H1,5X,'NODES',10X,'CONSTRAINTS')
             NEQ=NNP*NDF
             DO 850 I=1,NEQ
850          NZN(I)=0
             DO 855 I=1,NBC
854          READ(5,*) N,NZN(N*3-2),NZN(N*3-1),NZN(N*3)
C%%%%%
```

```fortran
1500    FORMAT(4I2)
        WRITE(6,1400)N,NZN(N*3-2),NZN(N*3-1),NZN(N*3)
C#####
855     CONTINUE
1400    FORMAT(5X,I5,12X,3I3)
        GO TO 200
C...        LOADING
208     DYN = .FALSE.
        CALL LOAD(DYN)
C+++++
        GO TO 200
209     GO TO 200
210     RETURN
211     GO TO 200
212     GO TO 200
213     GO TO 200
        END
Cffffffffffffffff
Cfffffffffffffffffff
        SUBROUTINE GAUSS
C...        DATA FOR GAUSSIAN 2X2 AND 3X3 INTEGRATION
Cfffffffffffffffff
        IMPLICIT REAL*8(A-H,O-Z)
        COMMON/CAP/ GE1(27),GE2(27),GE3(27),WE(4)
        COMMON/GS/ NG1
        COMMON/GSS/ ZETA(27),ETA(27),ZI(27),W(27),NGP
        IF(NGP.EQ.8) GO TO 25
        NG1=3
        G=0.774596669241483
        GE1(1)=G
        GE2(1)=G
        GE3(1)=G
        GE1(3)=-G
        GE2(3)=-G
        GE3(3)=-G
        GE1(2)=0.0
        GE2(2)=0.0
        GE3(2)=0.0
        WE(3)=0.5555555556
        WE(1)=0.5555555556
        WE(2)=0.88888888889
        GO TO 33
25      NG1=2
        WE(1)=1.0
        WE(2)=1.0
        G=-0.577350269189626
        GE1(1)= G
        GE2(1)= G
        GE3(1)= G
        GE1(2)=-G
        GE2(2)=-G
        GE3(2)=-G
33      CONTINUE
        RETURN
        END
Cffffffffffffffffffff
        SUBROUTINE ASSEMB
Cffffffffffffffffffff
```

```
      IMPLICIT REAL*8(A-H,O-Z)
       COMMON/LID/ SK(366,165),SM(366,165),SKK(1,1)
      COMMON/BBB/ D(6,6),D1(6,6),F(12,3),POIS(12,6),
     1            EK(60,60) ,H(6,60),LRF(12),IDENT(12)
       COMMON/CCC/ X(128),Y(128),Z(128),NZN(366) ,NFI
     1 AST(12),EST(12),DIA(12),ELINE(6,6),ELINK(6,6)
       COMMON/SEP/ NDI(366), JRC(3),XJN(12)
       COMMON/BON/ NNODE, NEUB,NETB,NBLOK
       COMMON/AAA/ NEL,NNP,NEQ,NHBD,NBC,NTE1,NTE2,NTE
     1 NNE1,NNE2,NNE3,NNE4,NDF,NRF,NRS,DETJ
       CALL TIMING(1)
C+++++
      NNODE=NNP
       NEUB=NEQ
      NETB=NEQ
      NBLOK=1
      MATER=0
      NEQN = 0
      DO 105 J=1,NEUB
105   NFIX(J)=NZN(J)
      DO 200 J=1, NETB
      DO 200 IJ=1, NHBD
```

```
        SK(J,IJ) = 0.0
200     CONTINUE
C                               WHEN AN ELEMENT IS PROCESSED THE SIGN OF FIRST NODE
C                               SET TO A NEGATIVE VALUE
        NFST = 1
        DO 270 NBL = 1, NBLOK
        IF(NBLOK .EQ. 1) GO TO 210
        IF(NBL .EQ. NBLOK) GO TO 245
210     CONTINUE
        NLAST = (NBL+1) * NNODE
        DO 240 I=1, NEL
C                                       DETERMINE THE ELEMENT IS PROCESSED
C
        IF( MCODE(I,1) .LT. 0) GO TO 240
        LET = IDENT(I)
215     CONTINUE
        GO TO(117,118,119,120),LET
117     CALL ELSTIF(I)
C+++++
        NER=NNE1
        GO TO 121
118     CONTINUE
119     CALL LINEL(I)
C+++++
        NER = NNE3
        GO TO 121
120     CONTINUE
C                               *****FORM INDICES FOR ROW AND COLUMN OF
C                                    STRUCTURE STIFFNESS MATRIX******
121     CONTINUE
        DO 225 IM = 1, NER
        IND = (IM-1)*NDF
        JND = MCODE(I,IM) - NFST+1
        KND = (JND-1)*NDF
        DO 220 IS = 1, NDF
        KND=KND+1
        NDI(IND+IS)=KND
220     CONTINUE
225     CONTINUE
C                               GIVE MINUS SIGN TO THE FIRST NODE OF THE ELEMEN
C                               BEING PROCESSED
C
        JP = NER * NDF
        DO 235 II = 1, JP
        NR = NDI(II)
        DO 230 JJ = 1, JP
        NCL = NDI(JJ)
        IF(NCL .LT. NR) GO TO 230
        NCL = NCL-NR+1
        GO TO(122, 123, 124, 125) ,LET
122     SK(NR,NCL)=SK(NR,NCL) + EK(II,JJ)
        GO TO 230
123     CONTINUE
        GO TO 230
124     SK(NR,NCL)=SK(NR,NCL) +EK(II,JJ)
        GO TO 230
125     SK(NR,NCL)=SK(NR,NCL) +EK(II,JJ)
230     CONTINUE
235     CONTINUE
240     CONTINUE
        IF(NBLOK .EQ. 1) GO TO 245
        IMIN=NEUB+1
        DO 243 IS = IMIN,NETB
        IDS = IS-NEUB
        IAS=NBL*NEUB+IDS
        IF( IAS .GT. NEQ ) GO TO 245
        NETX(IS) = NZN(IAS)
243     CONTINUE
245     CONTINUE
        IF( MATER .EQ. 0 ) GO TO 251
        WRITE(6,301)
C#####
        WRITE(6,302)NBL
C#####
        DO 250 J = 1,NEUB
        NEQN=NEQN+1
        WRITE(6,303)NEQN,(SK(J,IJ),IJ=1,NHBU)
C#####
250     CONTINUE
C
```

```
C                          THIS BLOCK GOES FOR BOUNDAR MODIFICATION
C
251    CONTINUE
       CALL BCOND
C+++++
270    CONTINUE
       DO 275 I = 1, NEL
       MCODE(I,1) = IABS(MCODE(I,1) )
275    CONTINUE
       WRITE(6,1000)
C#####
1000   FORMAT('TIME TO ASSEMBLE STIFNESS MATRIX = ')
       CALL TIMING(2)
C+++++
       IF (MATER .EQ. 0 ) RETURN
       WRITE(6,304)
C#####
       NEQN=0
       DO 285 NBL =1, NBLOK
       WRITE(6,302) NBL
C#####
       DO 280 J=1, NEUS
       NEQN = NEQN + 1
       WRITE(6,303) NEQN, (SK(J,IJ),IJ=1,NHBD)
C#####
280    CONTINUE
285    CONTINUE
       RETURN
301    FORMAT(1H1,26HSTIFFNESS MATRIX BY BLOCKS)
302    FORMAT(1H0,5HBLOCK, I3, / , 1H0,9HEQUATIONS,/)
303    FORMAT(2X, I3, 10F12.4, (/, 1X, 3X, 10E12.4))
304    FORMAT(1H1,4X,47H BLOCK FORM OF STIFFNESS MATRIX AFTER BOUN.COND)
       END
Cfffffffffffffffffff
       SUBROUTINE ELSTIF(I)
Cffffffffffffffffffff
       IMPLICIT REAL*8(A-H,O-Z)
       COMMON/DLF/S(20,3),CC(3,20),C(3,3)
       COMMON/AAA/ NEL,NNP,NEQ,NHBD,NBC,NTE1,NTE2,NTE3,NTE4,
     1 NNE1,NNE2,NNE3,NNE4,NDF,NRF,NRS,DETJ
       COMMON/CAP/ GE1(27),GE2(27),GE3(27),WE(4)
       COMMON/BBB/ D(6,6),D1(6,6),E(12,3),POIS(12,6),MCODE(12,20),
     1          EK(60,60) ,H(6,60),LRF(12),IDENT(12),RAW(1),EM(60,60)
       COMMON/CCC/ X(128),Y(128),Z(128),NZN(366) ,NFIX(366) ,
     1 AST(12),EST(12),DIA(12),ELINE(6,6),ELINK(6,6)
       COMMON/GSS/ ZETA(27), ETA(27), ZT(27), W(27), NGP
       COMMON /GS/NG1
       JP=NDF*NNE1
       DO 12 IS =1,60
       DO 12 JS =1,60
12     EK(IS,JS) =0.0
       CALL DMAT(I)
C+++++
       IF( NGP .EQ. 14 ) GO TO 23
C
C                    (2X2X2) AND(3X3X3) GAUSS INTEGRATION
C
       DO 39  J1 = 1 , NG1
       DO 39  J2 = 1 , NG1
       DO 39  J3 = 1 , NG1
       CALL ISOP2(I,J1,J2,J3,3,4)
C+++++
       DOS = WE(J1)*WE(J2)*WE(J3)*DETJ
       DO 17 N1=1,6
       DO 17 N2 =1,6
17     D(N1,N2)=DOS*D1(N1,N2)
       DO 38 II=1, JP
       DO 38 JJ=1, JP
       IF(II .GT.  JJ) GO TO 2522
       EIKJ = 0.0
       DO 37 IJ=1,6
       HTDIK = 0.0
       DO 36 JI=1,6
       HTDIK = HTDIK + H(JI,II) * D(JI,IJ)
36     CONTINUE
       EIKJ = EIKJ + HTDIK * H(IJ,JJ)
37     CONTINUE
       EK(II,JJ) = EK(II,JJ) + EIKJ
2522   CONTINUE
38     CONTINUE
```

```
39      CONTINUE
        GO TO 333
23      CONTINUE
        DO21 M=1, NGP
        CALL ISOP2(I,M,M,M,3,1)
C+++++
C
C     MATERIAL PROPERTY MATRIX !D" , !D" IS MULTIPLIED BY
C     WEIGHTING COEFFICIENTS AND DET. OF JACOBIAN DETJ
C
        DOS= W(M)*DETJ
        DO 18 N1=1,6
        DO 18 N2=1,6
18       D(N1,N2)=DOS*D1(N1,N2)
        DO 6  II= 1,24
        DO 5 JJ =1, 24
        IF(II .GT. JJ) GO TO 5
        EIKJ =0.0
        DO 4 IJ =1,6
        HTDIK =0.0
        DO 3 JI = 1, 6
        HTDIK = HTDIK + H( JI, II)*D(JI,IJ)
C
C          H(JI,II)= TRANSPOSE OF  H(II,JI)
C
3       CONTINUE
        EIKJ =EIKJ +HTDIK *H(IJ,JJ)
4       CONTINUE
        EK(II,JJ) = EK(II,JJ) +FIKJ
5       CONTINUE
6       CONTINUE
21      CONTINUE
        GO TO  333
16      WRITE(6,10)
C#####
10      FORMAT(  //8X,32HTHE TERM RATIO  OR  RAT IS  ZERO)
333     CONTINUE
        DO 2523 II=1,JP
        DO 2523 JJ=1,JP
2523    EK(JJ,II)=EK(II,JJ)
        THIRU=1.1
C       WRITE(6,96)THIRU
C#####
96      FORMAT(1X,7HTHIRU==,F5.3)
        RETURN
        END
Cffffffffffffffffffff
        SUBROUTINE DMAT(I)
C...      THIS ROUTINE CALCULATES *D* MATRIX FOR ELEMENT (I)
Cffffffffffffff  fffff
        IMPLICIT REAL*8(A-H,O-Z)
        COMMON/BBB/ D(6,6),D1(6,6),E(12,3),POIS(12,6),MCODE(12,20),
       1          EK(60,60) ,H(6,60),LRF(12),IDENT(12),RAW(1),EM(60,60)
        N= LRF(I)
        IF(N .EQ. LIVER)RETURN
        LIVER=N
C    DUE TO SYMMETRY OF THE COMPLIANCES, THREE RELATION EXIST
        POIS(N,4) = POIS(N,1)* E(N,2)/ E(N,1)
        POIS(N,5) = POIS(N,2)* E(N,3)/ E(N,2)
        POIS(N,6) =POIS(N,3)* E(N,3)/ E(N,1)
        RAT = 1.- POIS(N,1)* POIS(N,4)-POIS(N,3)* POIS(N,6)-POIS(N,2)
       1*POIS(N,5) -POIS(N  ,1) * POIS(N,2)*POIS(N,3) -
       2   POIS(N,4) * POIS(N,5) * POIS(N,6)
13      D1(1,1)= ( 1.-POIS(N,2)  * POIS(N,5))* E(N,1)/ RAT
        D1(1,2)= (POIS(N,1) + POIS(N,3) * POIS(N,5))*E(N,2)/RAT
        D1(1,3)= (POIS(N,3) + POIS(N,1) * POIS(N,2))*E(N,3)/RAT
        D1(2,2)= (1.- POIS(N,3)* POIS(N,6))*E(N,2)/RAT
        D1(2,3)= (POIS(N,2) + POIS(N,3)*POIS(N,4))*E(N,3)/RAT
        D1(2,1)  = D1(1,2)
        D1(3,1) =D1(1,3)
        D1(3,2) = D1(2,3)
        D1(3,3)= (1.-POIS(N,1)*POIS(N,4))* E(N,3)/RAT
        E11 = 0.5 *(E(N,1)/ (1.+POIS(N,1)))
        E22 = 0.5 *(E(N,1)/ (  POIS(N,1) + E(N,1)/E(N,2)))
        D1(4,4)=    0.5 * (E11+ E22)
        E31 = 0.5 * (E(N,2)/(1+ POIS(N,2)))
        E32 = 0.5 * (E(N,2)/(E(N,2)/ E(N,3) + POIS(N,2)))
        D1(5,5)=   0.5 * (E31+ E32)
        E42 = 0.5 *(E(N,3) /(1+ POIS(N,6)))
        E43=0.5*(E(N,3)/(E(N,3)/E(N,1)+POIS(N,6)))
```

```
       D1(6,6)=0.5*(E42+E43)
       SUDM=2.0
       WRITE(6,1)((D1(I1,J),J=1,6),I1=1,6)
C#####
1      FORMAT(6(1X,E10.3)/)
       RETURN
       END
Cffffffffffffffffffff
       SUBROUTINE ISOP2(I,J1,J2,J3,NEJ,NF)
Cffffffffffffffffffff
       IMPLICIT REAL*8(A-H,O-Z)
       COMMON/AAA/ NEL,NNP,NEQ,NHED,NBC,NTE1,NTE2,NTE3,NTE4,
      1 NNE1,NNE2,NNE3,NNE4,NDF,NRF,NRS,DETJ
       COMMON/DLE/S(20,3),CC(3,20),C(3,3)
       COMMON/BBB/ D(6,6),D1(6,6),E(12,3),POIS(12,6),MCODE(12,20),
      1         EK(60,60)  ,H(6,60),LRF(12),IDENT(12),RAW(1),EM(60,60)
       COMMON/MEM/ SP(20),SJ(3,3)
       COMMON/CCC/ X(128),Y(128),Z(128),NZN(366) ,NFIX(366) ,
      1 AST(12),EST(12),DIA(12),ELINE(6,6),ELINK(6,6)
       COMMON/CAP/ GE1(27),GE2(27),GE3(27),WE(4)
C
       JP=NNE1*NDF
       DO 80 J=1,6
       DO 80 K=1,JP
80     H(J,K)=0.0
       S1= 1.0 +  GE1(J1)
       S2= 1.0 -  GE1(J1)
       S3= 1.0 +  GE2(J2)
       S4= 1.0 -  GE2(J2)
       S5= 1.0 +  GE3(J3)
       S6= 1.0 -  GE3(J3)
       A=0.125
       IF(NNE1 .EQ. 20  .OR.NNE1.EQ.32 ) GO TO 34
       IF(NEJ .GT. 2 )GO TO 81
C
       SP(1)  =  A*S2*S4*S6
       SP(2)  =  A*S1*S4*S6
       SP(3)  =  A*S1*S3*S6
       SP(4)  =  A*S2*S3*S6
       SP(5)  =  A*S2*S4*S5
       SP(6)  =  A*S1*S4*S5
       SP(7)  =  A*S1*S3*S5
       SP(8)  =  A*S2*S3*S5
       IF(NEJ .EQ. 1) RETURN
81     CONTINUE
       S(1,1)  =  -A*S4*S6
       S(1,2)  =  -A*S2*S6
       S(1,3)  =  -A*S4*S2
       S(2,1)  =   A*S4*S6
       S(2,2)  =  -A*S1*S6
       S(2,3)  =  -A*S1*S4
       S(3,1)  =   A*S3*S6
       S(3,2)  =   A*S1*S6
       S(3,3)  =  -A*S1*S3
       S(4,1)  =  -A*S3*S6
       S(4,2)  =   A*S2*S6
       S(4,3)  =  -A*S2*S3
       S(5,1)  =  -A*S4*S5
       S(5,2)  =  -A*S2*S5
       S(5,3)  =   A*S2*S4
       S(6,1)  =   A*S4*S5
       S(6,2)  =  -A*S1*S5
       S(6,3)  =   A*S1*S4
       S(7,1)  =   A*S3*S5
       S(7,2)  =   A*S1*S5
       S(7,3)  =   A*S1*S3
       S(8,1)  =  -A*S3*S5
       S(8,2)  =   A*S2*S5
       S(8,3)  =   A*S2*S3
       GO TO 38
34     CONTINUE
       S7= S1*S2
       S8 = S3*S4
       S9 = S5*S6
       S11 = GE1(J1)
       S12 = GE2(J2)
       S13 = GE3(J3)
       IF(NNE3 .EQ. 32 ) GO TO 36
       IF(NEJ .GT. 2 )GO TO 82
C
```

```
C           SHAPE FUNCTIONS FOR 20-NODE ELEMENT
      SP(1)  =    A*  S2*  S4  *S6  *(-S11-S12- S13-2)
      SP(2)  =   2*A*  S7*  S4*S6
      SP(3)  =    A*  S1*  S4*  S6*(S11 -S12-S13 -2)
      SP(4)  =    A*2*S1*S8*  S6
      SP(5)  =    A*S1*S3* S6*  (S11+S12 -S13 -2)
      SP(6)=  2*A*S7*  S3* S6
      SP(7)=    A*  S2*S5*  S6*(-S11+S12-S13-2)
      SP(8)=  2*A*S2*  S8 *S6
      SP(9)=    2*A*S2*S4* S9
      SP(10) =  2*A*S1*  S4*  S9
      SP(11)=  2*A*S1*  S3*  S9
      SP(12)=  2*A*S2*S3*  S9
      SP(13)=A*S2*S4*S5*(-S11-S12+S13-2.)
      SP(14) =   2*A *  S7*  S4*  S5
      SP(15)  =   A*  S1*  S4 *S5*  (S11-S12+  S13-2)
      SP(16) =  2*A*S1*  S8*S5
      SP(17)=A*S1*S3*S5*(S11+S12+S13-2)
      SP(18)  =   2*A*  S7*  S3*S5
      SP(19)=A*S2*S3*S5*(-S11+S12+S13-2)
      SP(20)  =  2*A*  S2*  S8*  S9
C------------------------------------------------------------------------
82    CONTINUE
      IF(NEJ .EQ. 1) RETURN
      S(1,1) = 0.125  * S4  * S6  *(2.0*S11+1.0+S12+S13)
      S(1,2) = 0.125  * S2  * S6*(2.0*S12+1.0+S11+S13)
      S(1,3)=0.125*S2*S4*(2.0*S13+1.0+S12+S11)
      S(2,1) = -0.5*S11*S4*S6
      S(2,2) = -0.25* S7*S6
      S(2,3) = -0.25*S7*S4
      S(3,1)=0.125*S4*S6*(2.0*S11-1.0-S12-S13)
      S(3,2) = 0.125*S1*S6*(2.0*S12+1.0-S11+S13)
      S(3,3) = 0.125*S1*S4*(2*S13 + 1.0- S11+S12)
      S(4,1) = 0.25*S6*S8
      S(4,2) = -0.5*S12*S1*S6
      S(4,3) = - 0.25*S1*S8
      S(5,2) = 0.125*S1*S6*(2*S12 -1.0+S11-S13)
      S(5,3)=0.125*S1*S3*(2.*S13+1.0-S11-S12)
      S(5,1) = 0.125*S3*S6*(2*S11-1.0+S12-S13)
      S(6,1) = -0.5*S3*S6*S11
      S(6,2) = +0.25*S7*S6
      S(6,3) = -0.25 * S7*S3
      S(7,1) = 0.125*S3*S6*(2.*S11+1.0-S12+S13)
      S(7,2)=0.125*S2*S6*(2.0*S12-1.0-S11-S13)
      S(7,3)=0.125*S2*S3*(2.*S13+1.0+S11+S12)
      S(8,1)  = - 0.25*S8*S6
      S(8,2) =-0.50*S12*S2*S6
      S(8,3)  = - 0.25* S2 * S8
      S(9,1)  = - 0.25*S4*S9
      S(9,2)  =  -0.25*S2*S9
      S(9,3) = -0.5*S13*S2*S4
      S(10,1) =   0.25*S4*S9
      S(10,2) =   -0.25*S1*S9
      S(10,3)=-0.5*S13*S1*S4
      S(11,1) =   0.25*S3*S9
      S(11,2) = +0.25*S1*S9
      S(11,3)=-0.5*S1*S3*S13
      S(12,1) = -0.25*S3*S9
      S(12,2) = +0.25*S2*S9
      S(12,3)=-0.5*S13*S2*S3
      S(13,1)=0.125*S4*S5*(2*S11+1.0+S12-S13)
      S(13,2)= 0.125*S2*S5*(2*S12+1.0-S13+S11)
      S(13,3)=0.125*S2*S4*(2.0*S13-1.0-S12-S11)
      S(14,1)= -0.5*S11*S4*S5
      S(14,2) = -0.25*S7*S5
      S(14,3)= 0.25*S7*S4
      S(15,1)=0.125*S4*S5*(2.0*S11-S12+S13-1.0)
      S(15,2)=0.125*S1*S5*(2.0*S12-S13-S11+1.0)
      S(15,3)=0.125*S1*S4*(2.0*S13+S11-S12-1.0)
      S(16,1)  = 0.25*S8*S5
      S(16,2)=-0.5*S12*S1*S5
      S(16,3)  = 0.25*S8*S1
      S(17,1)=0.125*S3*S5*(2.*S11+S13+S12-1.0)
      S(17,2) =0.125*S1*S5*(2.0*S12+S11 +S13-1.0)
      S(17,3) =0.125*S1*S3*(2.0*S13 +S11+S12-1.0)
      S(18,1)=-0.5*S3*S5*S11
      S(18,2)= +0.25*S7*S5
      S(18,3)= 0.25*S7*S3
      S(19,1)=0.125*S3*S5*(2.*S11-S12-S13+1.0)
      S(19,2)=0.125*S2*S5*(2.0*S12-S11+S13-1.0)
```

```
          S(19,3)=0.125*S2*S3*(2.0*  S13-S11+S12-1.0)
          S(20,1)= - 0.25*S8*S5
          S(20,2)= -0.5*S12*S2*S5
          S(20,3) = 0.25*S2*S8
          GO TO 38
36        CONTINUE
38        CONTINUE
          P1=0.0
          P2=0.0
          P3=0.0
          P4=0.0
          P5=0.0
          P6=0.0
          P7=0.0
          P8=0.0
          P9=0.0
          DO 44 J = 1,NNE1
          M1 = MCODE(I,J)
          P1 = P1 +   S(J,2)* Y(M1)`
          P2 = P2 + S(J,3)*Z(M1)
          P3 = P3 + S(J,2)*Z(M1)
          P4 = P4 +S(J,3)*Y(M1)
          P5 = P5 + S(J,1)*Z(M1)
          P6 = P6 + S(J,1)*Y(M1)
          P7 = P7 + S(J,3)*X(M1)
          P8 = P8 + S(J,2)*X(M1)
          P9 = P9 + S(J,1)*X(M1)
44        CONTINUE
          SJ(1,1) = P1*P2-P3*P4
          SJ(1,2)= P3*P7 -P8* P2
          SJ(1,3) = P8*P4 -P1*P7
          SJ(2,1)= P4*P5- P2*P6
          SJ(2,2) =P2*P9 - P5*P7
          SJ(2,3)= P7*P6-P4*P9
          SJ(3,1)= P6*P3 - P5*P1
          SJ(3,2)=P5*P8-P9*P3
          SJ(3,3) = P9*P1 - P6*P8
C
C    DETERMINANT   OF   JACOBIAN
C
          IF(J1.GT.1.AND.J2.GT.1.AND.J3.GT.1)GO TO 200
          DETJ=(P9*(P1*P2-P3*P4)+P8*(P4*P5-P2*P6)
     1      +P7*(P3*P6-P1*P5))
C         DETJ=ABS(DETJ)
C         IF(DETJ .LE. 0.0) WRITE(6,133) I,J1,J2,J3
C#####
133       FORMAT(5X, 44HDETERMINANT OF JACOBIAN IS  ZER(
C         WRITE(6,1111)DETJ
C#####
200       CONTINUE
1111      FORMAT(1X,E16.8)
C
C    JACOBIAN   INVERSION
C
          IF(NEJ .EQ. 2) RETURN
          DO 75 N1=1,3
          DO 75 N2 =1,3
75        C(N2,N1)=SJ(N1,N2)/DETJ
C
          DO 45 K=1,3
          DO 45 J=1,NNE1
          CC(K,J)=0.0
45        CONTINUE
c
```

```
C
      DO 47 K=1,3
      DO 47 J=1,NNE1
      DO 46 N1=1,3
46    CC(K,J) = CC(K,J) + C(K,N1)*S(J,N1)
47    CONTINUE
C
C              STRAIN-DISPLACEMENT MATRIX
C
      DO 54 N1=1,NNE1
      N2 = (N1-1)*NDF
      L1=N2+1
      L2=N2+2
      L3=N2+3
       H(1,L1)=CC(1,N1)
      H(4,L1+1)=CC(1,N1)
      H(6,L1+2)=CC(1,N1)
      H(2,L2)=CC(2,N1)
```

```
       H(4,L2-1)=CC(2,N1)
       H(5,L2+1)=CC(2,N1)
       H(3,L3)=CC(3,N1)
       H(5,L3-1)=CC(3,N1)
       H(6,L3-2)=CC(3,N1)
54     CONTINUE
       IF(NF .EQ. 4) RETURN
C
C      - - - - - - - - - - MODIFY 'H" MATRIX FOR INCLINED BOUNDARY CONDIT
C
       DO 68 J=1,NNE1
       MC=(MCODE(I,J)-1)*NDF
       DO 62 K=1,NDF
       MC=MC+1
       IF(NZN(MC).LT.0)GO TO 64
62     CONTINUE
       GO TO 68
64     NJ=J
       N2=(NJ-1)*NDF
       L1=N2+1
         L2=N2+2
         L3=N2+3
       C1= CC(1,NJ)
       C2 =CC(2,NJ)
       C3=CC(3,NJ)
C
       H(1,L1)=CS*C1
        H(1,L2)=-SN*C1
        H(2,L1)=SN*C2
       H(2,L2)=CS*C2
       H(3,L3)=C3
        H(4,L1)=CS*C2 SN*C1
         H(4,L2)=CS*C1-SN*C2
       H(5,L1)=SN*C3
       H(5,L3)=C2
       H(6,L1)=CS*C3
        H(6,L2)=-SN*C3
       H(6,L3)=C1
68     CONTINUE
C
 118   CONTINUE
       RETURN
       END
CfffffffffffffffffffffC
       SUBROUTINE DECOMP
C...      THIS ROUTINE TRIANGULARIZE STIFFNESS MATRIX STORED
C...      IN BANDED FORM
Cfffffffffffffffffffff
       IMPLICIT REAL*8(A-H,O-Z)
        COMMON/LID/ SK(366,165),SM(366,165),SKK(1,1)
       COMMON/BON/ NNODE, NEUB,NETB,NBLOK
       COMMON/AAA/ NEL,NNP,NEQ,NHBD,NBC,NTE1,NTE2,NTE3,NTE4,
     1 NNE1,NNE2,NNE3,NNE4,NDF,NRF,NRS,DETJ
       CALL TIMING(1)
C+++++
       MATER=0
       NEQN=0
       DO 25 IS=1, NEUB
       DO 24 IJ=2, NHBD
       IF( SK(IS,IJ) .EQ. 0.0) GO TO 24
       II=IS+IJ-1
       CZ = SK(IS,IJ)/SK(IS,1)
       J=0
       DO 23 NI=IJ,NHBD
       J=J+1
       SK(II,J)=SK(II,J)-CZ*SK(IS,NI)
23     CONTINUE
       SK(IS,IJ) = CZ
24     CONTINUE
25     CONTINUE
       IF( MATER .EQ. 0) GO TO 28
       DO 27 IJ = 1,NEUB
       NEQN=NEQN+1
       WRITE(6,300) NEQN, (SK(IJ,J), J=1,NHBD)
C#####
27     CONTINUE
28     CONTINUE
       WRITE(6,1000)
C#####
1000   FORMAT('TIME TO DECOMP =')
```

```
        CALL TIMING(2)
C+++++
        RETURN
300     FORMAT(1H ,I3, 10E12.4, (/, 1H ,3X, 10E12.4))
        END
Cffffffffffffffffff
        SUBROUTINE LOAD(DYN)
C...        THIS ROUTINE IS MODIFIED BY THIRU TO INCLUDE DYNAMIC LOADING
C...        CONVERTS SURFACE PRESSURES TO EQUIVALENT NODAL FORCES
C...        READS IN NODAL FORCES DIRECTLY
C%%%%
C...        CALCULATES LOADS DUE TO TEMPERATURE
Cfffffffffffffffffffff
        IMPLICIT REAL*8(A-H,O-Z)
        INTEGER*4 MTL1,MTL2
        LOGICAL DYN
        COMMON/MEM/ SP(20),SJ(3,3)
        COMMON/CAP/ GE1(27),GE2(27),GE3(27),WE(4)
        COMMON/BBB/ D(6,6),D1(6,6),E(12,3),POIS(12,6),MCODE(12,20),
       1        EK(60,60) ,H(6,60),LRF(12),IDENT(12),RAW(1),EM(60,60)
        DIMENSION TF(60)
        COMMON/CCC/ X(128),Y(128),Z(128),NZN(366) ,NFIX(366) ,
       1 AST(12),EST(12),DIA(12),ELINE(6,6),ELINK(6,6)
        COMMON/AAA/ NEL,NNP,NEG,NHBD,NBC,NTE1,NTE2,NTE3,NTE4,
       1 NNE1,NNE2,NNE3,NNE4,NDF,NRF,NRS,DETJ
        COMMON/SEP/ NDI(366),JRC(3), XJN(12)
        COMMON/GS/ NG1
        COMMON/TOR/ SV(4,3),TE(20),CET(6),CTE
        COMMON/REL/ U(366),P(366),PT(366),U1(366),U10(366),U2(366)
       1 ,U20(366),U0(366),P1(366),PS(366),PIU(366),PIT(366)
C----------------------------------------------------------------------
C----------------------------------------------------------------------
        CALL CTIMEA(MTL1)
C+++++
        DO 8 I=1, NEQ
8       P(I)=0.0
        JP=NNE1*NDF
        READ(5,*)NFACES
C%%%%%
5       FORMAT(I2)
        WRITE(6,100)NFACES
C#####
100     FORMAT(1X,'NFACES=',I5)
        IF( NFACES .EQ. 0)GO TO  37
        DO 35 IS=1, NFACES
        CALL GAUSS
C+++++
C - - - - - - - - - - - - -                - - - - - - - - - - -
C                        DISTRIBUTED  SURFACE  PRESSURE
C-------------------------NS=0<  C  CONSTANT PRESSURE OVER THE SURFACE--
C-------------------------NS=1<      VARIABLE PRESSURE OVER THE SURFACE--
C----------------------------------------------------------------------
10      FORMAT(20F0.0)
9       FORMAT(8F0.0)
        READ(5,*)I,NF,NS
C%%%%%
4       FORMAT(3I3)
        WRITE(6,102)I,NF,NS
C#####
102     FORMAT(1X,'I=',I5,'NF=',I5,'NS=',I5)
        IF(NS .EQ.0)GO TO 16
        IF(NNE1.EQ.00)GO TO 6
        READ(5,*)(TE(J),J=1,NNE1)
C%%%%%
        GO TO 17
6       READ(5,*)(TE(J),J=1,NNE1)
C%%%%%
        GO TO 17
16      READ(5,*)  PRESS
C%%%%%
15      FORMAT(F5.3)
        WRITE(6,101)PRESS
C#####
101     FORMAT(1X,E10.3)
17      CONTINUE
        DO 22 IJ= 1,JP
22      TF(IJ)=0.0
        NM=IABS(NF)
        DO 32 J1=1,NG1
        DO 32 J2=1,NG1
```

```
          IF(NF  .EQ.  1  .OR.  NF  .EQ.  -1)GO TO 21
          IF(NF  .EQ.  2  .OR.  NF  .EQ.  -2)GO TO 23
          IF(NF  .EQ.  3  .OR.  NF  .EQ.  -3)GO TO 24
21        CONTINUE
          IF(NF  .EQ.  1) GE1(1)=1.0
          IF(NF  .EQ.-1) GE1(1)=-1.0
          JL= 1
          JM= J1
          JN= J2
          GO TO 25
23        IF(NF  .EQ.  2) GE2(1)=1.0
          IF(NF  .EQ.-2)GE2(1)=-1.0
          JL=J1
          JM=  1
          JN= J2
          GO TO 25
24        IF(NF.  EQ.  3 ) GE3(1)=1.0
          IF(NF  .EQ.  -3) GE3(1)=-1.0
          JL=J1
          JM= J2
          JN= 1
25        CONTINUE
          CALL ISOP2(I,JL, JM, JN, 2 ,NF)
C+++++
          DOS= WE(J1)*WE(J2)
          IF(NS .EQ. 0) GO TO 41
          PRESS=0.0
          DO 42 J=1,NNE1
42          PRESS=PRESS+SP(J)*TE(J)
41        CONTINUE
C----------------------------------------------------------------
C                          CALCULATE DIRECTION COSINES OF THE SURFACE
          C1=DABS(SJ(NM,1))
          C2=DABS(SJ(NM,2))
          C3=DABS(SJ(NM,3))
C         WRITE(6,103)C1,C2,C3
C#####
103       FORMAT(1X,'C1=',E10.3,'C2=',E10.3,'C3=',E10.3)
          CAZ=DSQRT(C1*C1+C2*C2+C3*C3)
          C1=C1/CAZ
          C2=C2/CAZ
          C3=C3/CAZ
C
C         WRITE(6,101)PRESS
C#####
C         WRITE(6,103)C1,C2,C3
C#####
          XJN(1)=C1*PRESS
          XJN(2)=C2*PRESS
          XJN(3)=C3*PRESS
C         WRITE(6,104)(XJN(IA),IA=1,3)
C#####
104       FORMAT(3(1X,E10.3)/)
          DO 27 JS=1,NNE1
          IF(SP(JS) .EQ. 0.0) GO TO 27
          JJ= (JS-1)* NDF
          DO 26 JK=1, NDF
          JJ= JJ+1
26        TF(JJ)=TF(JJ)+SP(JS)*SJ(NM,JK)*XJN(JK)*DOS
C         WRITE(6,106) JJ,JS,NM,JK
C#####
106       FORMAT(1X,'JJ=',I3,'JS=',I3,'NM=',I3,'JK=',I3)
C         WRITE(6,107) TF(JJ),SP(JS),SJ(NM,JK),XJN(JK),DOS
C#####
107       FORMAT(1X,'TF=',E10.3,'SP=',E10.3,'SJ=',E10.3,'XJN=',E10.3,'DOS=',
     1    1E10.3)
27        CONTINUE
C         WRITE(6,105)(TF(JS),JS=1,NNE1)
C#####
105       FORMAT(10(1X,E10.3)/)
32        CONTINUE
          DO34 IK= 1,NNE1
          M1=(MCODE(I,IK) -1)*NDF
          JJ=(IK-1)*NDF
          DO34 MJ= 1,NDF
          M1=M1+1
          JJ= JJ+1
34        P(M1)= P(M1)+ TF(JJ)
35        CONTINUE
37        CONTINUE
```

```
C----------------------------------------------------------------------
C----------------------------------------------------------------------
      READ(5,*) NCONC
C%%%%%
      IF ( NCONC .EQ.  0 ) GO TO 36
      WRITE(6,218)NCONC
C#####
222   FORMAT(I2)
218   FORMAT(////,20X,25HNO OF CONCENTRATED LOADS=,I5)
219   FORMAT(///,9X, 4HNDF,7X,6HX-LOAD, 9X,6HY-LOAD,9X,6HZ-LOAD)
      WRITE(6,219)
C#####
      DO  224 I = 1,NCONC
      READ(5,*) ND, (XJN(J),J=1,NDF)
C%%%%%
      WRITE(6,221)ND,(XJN(J),J=1,NDF )
C#####
220   FORMAT(I3,3F6.3)
221   FORMAT(9X,I4,5X,3F14.4)
      JK=(ND-1)*NDF
      DO 230 J=1, NDF
      JK= JK+1
230   P(JK)=P(JK) + XJN(J)
224   CONTINUE
36    CONTINUE
C
C--------------CONCENTRATED LOAD NOT DIRECTLY ON NODAL POINTS-----------
      READ(5,*)NPATCH
C%%%%%
      IF(NPATCH .EQ.0)GO TO 77
64    FORMAT(I2)
      DO 76 NC=1,NPATCH
      READ(5,*) I,CG1,CG2,CG3,(XJN(J),J=1,NDF)
C%%%%%
66    FORMAT(I0,6F0.0)
      GE1(1)=CG1
      GE2(1)=CG2
      GE3(1)=CG3
      CALLISOP2(I,1,1,1,1,4)
C+++++
      DO 76 J=1,NNE1
      MJ=(MCODE(I,J)-1)*NDF
      DO 76 K=1,NDF
      MJ=MJ+1
76    P(MJ)=P(MJ)+ SP(J)*XJN(K)
77    CONTINUE
C----------------------------SELF WEIGHT OF THE MATERIAL----------------
C----------------------------------------------------------------------
C----------------------------------------------------------------------
82    FORMAT(5X,I5,8F10.4)
83    FORMAT(F3.1)
84    FORMAT(//,8X, 34HCOEFFICIENT OF THERMAL EXPANSION =, F12.9)
75    FORMAT(/,5X,7HELEMENT, 8X,17HNODAL TEMPRATURES)
      READ(5,*)CTE
C%%%%%
      IF(CTE .EQ. 0.0 ) GO TO 28
      WRITE(6,84) CTE
C#####
      WRITE(6,75)
C#####
      DO 62 I=1,NTE1
      DO 388 J=1,JP
388   TF(J)=0.0
      CALL DMAT(I)
C+++++
      IF(NNE1.EQ.20)GO TO 80
      READ(5,*)(TE(J),J=1,NNE1)
C%%%%%
      GO TO 81
80    READ(5,*)(TE(J),J=1,NNE1)
C%%%%%
81    CONTINUE
      WRITE(6,82) I,(TE(J),J=1,NNE1)
C#####
      CALL GAUSS
C+++++
      DO 55 J1=1,NG1
      DO 55 J2=1,NG1
      DO 55J3=1,NG1
      CALL ISOP2(I,J1,J2,J3,1,4)
```

```
C+++++
       TR=0.0
       DO 51 J=1,NNE1
       TE(J)=TE(J)-17.0
51     TR=TR+TE(J)*SP(J)
C                CALCULATE TEMPERATURE LOADS DUE TO TEMP. RISE
       SV(1,1)=TR*CTE
       SV(I,2)=SV(I,1)
       SV(I,3)=SV(I,1)
       DO 13 IJ=1,6
       SUM=0.0
       DO 14 JI=1,3
14     SUM=SUM+D1(IJ,JI)*SV(I,JI)
13     CET(IJ)=SUM
       CALL ISOP2(I,J1,J2,J3,3,4)
C+++++
       DOS=DETJ*WE(J1)*WE(J2)*WE(J3)
       DO 56 IS=1,JP
       SUM=0.0
       DO 57 J=1,6
57     SUM=SUM+H(J,IS)*CET(J)
56     TF(IS)=TF(IS)+ SUM *DOS
55     CONTINUE
       DO 63 N1=1,NNE1
       M1= MCODE(I,N1)
       M1=(M1-1)*NDF
       N2=(N1-1)*NDF
       DO 61 IN=1,NDF
       M1 = M1+1
       N2=N2+1
61     P(M1)=P(M1)+TF(N2)
63     CONTINUE
62     CONTINUE
28     CONTINUE
C...      DYN = .FALSE. STATIC LOADING
       IF(.NOT.DYN) GO TO 1
       GO TO 3
1      DO 2 K1 = 1,NEQ
2      PS(K1) = P(K1)
C...   DYN = .TRUE. DYNAMIC LOADING
3      IF(DYN) GO TO 49
       GO TO 47
49     DO 48 K1 = 1,NEQ
48     PIU(K1) = P(K1)
47     CONTINUE
       CALL CTIMEA(MTL2)
C+++++
       RTL = FLOAT((MTL2-MTL1)/100.)
       WRITE(6,2001) MTL2,MTL1,RTL
C#####
2001   FORMAT('CPU TIME AFTER ASSEMBLING LOAD VECTOR =',I10/
      1       'CPU TIME AT ENTRY TO LOAD ROUTINE      =',I10/
      2       'CPU TIME SPENT IN LOAD ROUTINE         =',F10.2/)
       WRITE(6,2000)((J ,P(J)),J=1,NEQ)
C#####
2000   FORMAT(5X,I5,5X,3F15.4)
C-------------------------------------------------------------------------
C
       RETURN
       END
Cffffffffffffffffffffff
       SUBROUTINE BCOND
Cffffffffffffffffffffffff
       IMPLICIT REAL*8(A-H,O-Z)
       COMMON/LID/ SK(366,165),SW(366,165),SKK(1,1)
       COMMON/BON/ NNODE, NEUB,NETB,NBLOK
       COMMON/AAA/ NEL,NNP,NEQ,NHBD,NBC,NTF1,NTE2,NTE3,NTE4,
      1 NNE1,NNE2,NNE3,NNE4,NDF,NRF,NRS,DETJ
       COMMON/CCC/ X(128),Y(128),Z(128),NZN(366) ,NFIX(366) ,
      1 AST(12),EST(12),DIA(12),ELINE(6,6),ELINK(6,6)
       DO 40 J=1, NEUB
       IF(NZN(J) .EQ. 0) GO TO 40
       SK(J,1)=1.0
       DO 30 IM = 2, NHBD
       SK(J,IM) = 0.0
30     CONTINUE
       IF(J .EQ. 1) GO TO 40
       IS = 1
       IM = J-1
       IF(J.GT.NHBD) IS=J-NHBD+1
```

```
         DO 35 IJ= IS, IM
         MS = J- IJ+ 1
         SK(IJ,MS) = 0.0
35       CONTINUE
40       CONTINUE
         IF(NBLOK .EQ. 1) RETURN
         IMIN=NEUB+1
         IMAX = NETB-1
         DO 50 J=IMIN,IMAX
         IF(NFIX(J) .EQ. 0) GO TO 50
         IS=J-NHBD+1
         DO 45 IJ = IS, NEUB
         MS= J-IJ+1
         SK(IJ,MS) = 0.0
45       CONTINUE
50       CONTINUE
         RETURN
         END
Cfffffffffffffffffff
         SUBROUTINE RESOLV
Cfffffffffffffffffff
         IMPLICIT REAL*8(A-H,O-Z)
         COMMON/CCC/ X(128),Y(128),Z(128),NZN(366) ,NFIX(366) ,
        1 AST(12),EST(12),DIA(12),ELINE(6,6),ELINK(6,6)
         COMMON/LID/ SK(366,165),SM(366,165),SKK(1,1)
         COMMON/REL/ U(366),P(366),PT(366),U1(366),U10(366),U2(366)
        1  ,U20(366),U0(366),P1(366),PS(366),PIU(366),PIT(366)
         COMMON/BON/ NNODE, NEUB,NETB,NBLOK
         COMMON/AAA/ NEL,NNP,NEQ,NHBD,NBC,NTE1,NTE2,NTE3,NTE4,
        1 NNE1,NNE2,NNE3,NNE4,NDF,NRF,NRS,DETJ
         MATER =0
         CALL TIMING(1)
C+++++
         DO 310 IJ=1,NEQ
         DO 305 IS=2,NHBD
         IF(SK(IJ,IS).EQ.0.0) GO TO 305
         II=IJ+IS-1
         P(II)=P(II)-SK(IJ,IS)*P(IJ)
305      CONTINUE
         P(IJ)=P(IJ)/SK(IJ,1)
310      CONTINUE
         KEUB=NEUB
         DO 85 IS=1, NEUB
         JL=NEUB+1-IS
         DO 82 KL=2, NHBD
         IF(SK(JL,KL) .EQ. 0.0) GO TO 82
         JJ= JL+KL-1
         P(JL) = P(JL) - SK(JL,KL)* P(JJ)
82       CONTINUE
85       CONTINUE
         DO 99 J=1,NEQ
99       U(J)=P(J)
118      CONTINUE
         WRITE(6,1000)
C#####
1000     FORMAT(*TIME TAKEN TO RESOLV = *)
         CALL TIMING(2)
C+++++
         WRITE(6,2002)
C#####
2002     FORMAT(1H1 , 5X,6H NODES, 8X, 10H X- DISPL., 8X,9H Y-DISPL. ,
        1 8X, 9H Z-DISPL.)
         DO 912 I=1,NNP
912      WRITE(6,412) I , U(3*I-2)   ,U(3*I-1) , U(3*I )
C#####
412      FORMAT(/,5X, I5, 6X, E16.8, 6X, E16.8, 6X, E16.8)
         RETURN
         END
         SUBROUTINE STRESS
Cfffffffffffffffffffff
         IMPLICIT REAL*8(A-H,O-Z)
         INTEGER*4 MTS1,MTS2
         DIMENSION TF(60),A(9),B(9)
         COMMON/TOR/ SV(4,3),TE(20),CET(6),CTE
         COMMON/REL/ U(366),P(366),PT(366),U1(366),U10(366),U2(366)
        1  ,U20(366),U0(366),P1(366),PS(366),PIU(366),PIT(366)
         COMMON/DLE/S(20,3),CC(3,20),C(3,3)
         COMMON/AAA/ NEL,NNP,NEQ,NHBD,NBC,NTE1,NTE2,NTE3,NTE4,
        1 NNE1,NNE2,NNE3,NNE4,NDF,NRF,NRS,DETJ
         COMMON/BBB/ D(6,6),D1(6,6),F(12,3),POIS(12,6),MCODE(12,20),
```

```
      1             EK(60,60)  ,H(6,60),LRF(12),IDENT(12),RAW(1),EM(60,60)
       COMMON/CCC/ X(128),Y(128),Z(128),NZN(366) ,NFIX(366) ,
      1 AST(12),EST(12),DIA(12),ELINE(6,6),ELINK(6,6)
        COMMON/GSS/ ZETA(27), ETA(27), ZI(27), W(27), NGP
         COMMON/FFF/ SIGG1(110)
         COMMON/GS/NG1
         COMMON/CAP/ GE1(27),GE2(27),GE3(27),WE(4)
         COMMON/ABC/ PS1(27),PS2(27),PS3(27),SIG(27,6),EC(27,6)
      1,DC1(27,3), DC2(27,3), DC3(27,3)
         CALL CTIMEA(MTS1)
C+++++
       WRITE(6,316)
C#####
316    FORMAT(1H1,43HELEMENT STRAINS STRESSES PRINCIPAL STRESSES,
      1 21HAND DIRECTION COSINES////)
         CALL GAUSS
C+++++
       WRITE(6,465)
C#####
465    FORMAT(///,5X, 7HELEMENT,5X,9HGAUSS PT., 8X,6H SIGMX, 8X,7H SIGMY
      1, 8X,6H SIGMZ, 9X, 7H SIGMXY,8X,7H SIGMYZ,8X,7H SIGMZX)
       JP=NNE1*NDF
       DO 18 I = 1 , NEL
       LET = IDENT(I)
       GO TO (111,211,222,333),LET
111    CONTINUE
       CALL DMAT(I)
C+++++
       DO 24 IS = 1, NGP
       DO 24 IM = 1, 6
       SIG(IS,IM)=0.0
       EC(IS,IM)=0.0
24     CONTINUE
       DO 114 J=1,NNE1
       JK= (J-1)*NDF
        MJ=(MCODE(I,J)-1)*NDF
       DO 114 K=1,NDF
       MJ=MJ+1
       JK=JK+1
114    TF(JK)=U(MJ)
312    FORMAT(5X,I5)
       WRITE(6,312)I
C#####
       IF(NGP .EQ. 14 ) GO TO 42
       M=0
       DO 115 J1=1,NG1
       DO 115 J2=1,NG1
       DO 115 J3=1,NG1
       M=M+1
        CALL ISOP2(I,J1,J2,J3,3,4 )
C+++++
C
C                         STRAINS IN CONCRETE
       DO 116 K=1,6
       DO 116 J=1,JP
116    EC(M,K)=EC(M,K)+H(K,J)*TF(J)
C
       DO 118 J=1,3
118    EC(M,J)=EC(M,J)-SV(I,J)
C
C                        CORRESPONDING STRESSES
C
       DO 122 J=1,6
       DO 122 K=1,6
122    SIG(M,J)=SIG(M,J)+D1(J,K)*EC(M,K)
115    CONTINUE
       GO TO 125
42     CONTINUE
       DO130 M=1,NGP
        CALL ISOP2(I,M,M,M,3,1)
C+++++
       DO 131 K=1,6
       DO 131 J=1,JP
131    EC(M,K)=EC(M,K)+H(K,J)*TF(J)
       DO 132 J=1,3
132    EC(M,J)=EC(M,J)-SV(I,J)
       DO 134 J=1,6
       DO 134 K=1,6
134    SIG(M,J)=SIG(M,J)+D1(J,K)*EC(M,K)
130    CONTINUE
```

```
125     CONTINUE
        DO 321 IS=1,NGP
321     WRITE(6,313) IS,( EC(IS,J),J=1,6)
C#####
        DO 322  IS=1,NGP
322     WRITE(6,314) IS,( SIG(IS,J),J=1,6)
C#####
313     FORMAT(12X,I5,9X,F10.8,4X,F10.8,4X,F10.8,4X,F10.8,4X,F10.8,4X,
        1 F10.8)
314     FORMAT(12X,I5,9X,F10.4,4X,F10.4,4X,F10.4,4X,F10.4,4X,F10.4,4X,
        1 F10.4)
        WRITE(6,323)
C#####
323     FORMAT(///)
        WRITE(6,324)
C#####
324     FORMAT(//,12X, 3HPT.,, 9X,31HPRINCL. STRESS AND DIRE.COSINES)
        DO 20  M=1,NGP
        G1 = SIG(M,1)
        G2 = SIG(M,2)
        G3 = SIG(M,3)
        G4 = SIG(M,4)
        G5 = SIG(M,5)
        G6 = SIG(M,6)
        ZNV1 = G1 + G2 + G3
        ZNV2 = G1 *G2 + G2*G3 + G3*G1 - G4*G4 - G5*G5- G6*G6
        ZNV3 = G1*G2*G3 + 2.0*G4*G5*G6 - G1*G5*G5
        1      - G2*G6*G6 - G3*G4*G4
        PS1(M) = 0.0
        PS2(M) = 0.0
        PS3(M) = 0.0
        BB = -ZNV1
        CW = ZNV2
        DD = - ZNV3
C...        FIND ALL ROOTS OF CUBIC EQUATION AA*X*3 + BB*X*2 + CC*X + DD
C...        FIRST ROOT (X5) IS FOUND BY NEWTON'S METHOD USING 0 AS FIRST
C...        APPROX. THEN SOLVE QUADRATIC BY STANDARD FORMULA. ERR IS THE
C...        ACCURACY REQUIRED FOR ROOT X5
        ERR = 1E-6
        X1 = 0.0
        CORR = 2.0*ERR
1000    B1 = BB + X1
        B2 = CW + X1*B1
        IF(DABS(CORR).LT.ERR) GO TO 2000
        B3 = DD+ X1*B2
        C3 = (X1+B1)*X1 + B2
        IF(DABS(C3) .LT . 1E-30) C3 = 1.0
        CORR = B3/C3
        X1 = X1 - CORR
        GO TO 1000
2000    X5 = X1
C...
C...        SECOND PART TO FIND ROOTS OF QUADRATIC
C...        X**2 + B1*X1 + B2 = 0.0
C...
        DIP = B1*B1 - 4.0*B2
        IF(DIP .LT . 0.0) GO TO 3000
        SD = DSQRT(DIP)
        X6 = (SD - B1) * 0.5
        X7 = -(SD + B1) * 0.5
        GO TO 336
3000    X6 = -0.5* B1
        X7 = 0.5*DSQRT(-DIP)
        WRITE(6,800) I,M
C#####
800     FORMAT(/,15X,'CONJUGATE',2I5)
336     CONTINUE
        IF(X5 .GE. X6 .AND. X6 .GE. X7) GO TO 430
        IF(X5 .GE. X7 .AND. X7 .GE. X6) GO TO 431
        IF(X6 .GE. X6 .AND. X5 .GE. X7) GO TO 432
        IF(X6 .GE. X7 .AND. X7 .GE. X5) GO TO 433
        IF(X7 .GE. X5 .AND. X5 .GE. X6) GO TO 434
        IF(X7 .GE. X6 .AND. X6 .GE. X5) GO TO 435
430     PS1(M) = X5
        PS2(M) = X6
        PS3(M) = X7
        GO TO 438
431     PS1(M) = X5
        PS2(M) = X7
        PS3(M) = X6
```

```
        GO TO 438
432     PS1(M) = X6
        PS2(M) = X5
        PS3(M) = X7
        GO TO 438
433     PS1(M) = X6
        PS2(M) = X7
        PS3(M) = X5
        GO TO 438
434     PS1(M) = X7
        PS2(M) = X5
        PS3(M) = X6
        GO TO 438
435     PS1(M) = X7
        PS2(M) = X6
        PS3(M) = X5
438     CONTINUE
17      CONTINUE
C...
C...        PRINCIPAL DIRECTIONS
C...        DC1,DC2,DC3 ARE THE DIRECTION COSINES OF
C...        PRINCIPAL STRESSES PS1,PS2,PS3
C...
        DO 440 IS = 1,3
        GO TO (443,445,447),IS
443     AS1 = G1 - PS1(M)
        AS2 = G2 -PS1(M)
        AS3 = G3 - PS1(M)
        GO TO 444
445     AS1 = G1 - PS2(M)
        AS2 = G2 - PS2(M)
        AS3 = G3 - PS2(M)
        GO TO 444
447     AS1 = G1 - PS3(M)
        AS2 = G2 - PS3(M)
        AS3 = G3 - PS3(M)
444     CONTINUE
        AK = G4
        BK = G5
        CK = G6
        YAP1 = AS2*CK -BK*AK
        YAP2 = AK*AK - AS1*AS2
        IF(YAP1 .EQ . 0.0) YAP1 = 1.0
        IF(YAP2 . EQ .0.0) YAP2 = 1.0
        BJM1 = (BK*BK - AS2*AS3)/YAP1
        BJM2 = (AS1*BK - AK*CK) / YAP2
        BJ1 = BJM1*BJM1
        BJ2 = BJM2*BJM2
        ZIP = DSQRT(BJ1 + BJ2 + 1.0)
        DC3(M,IS) = 1.0/ZIP
        DC2(M,IS) = BJM2*DC3(M,IS)
        DC1(M,IS) = BJM1*DC3(M,IS)
440     CONTINUE
20      CONTINUE
        DO 325 J = 1,NGP
        WRITE(6,317)J,PS1(J),PS2(J),PS3(J),(DC1(J,IJ),DC2(J,IJ),DC3(J,IJ)
C#####
1       ,IJ = 1,3)
325     CONTINUE
317     FORMAT(2X,I3,3F10.4,2X,9(F7.5,1X))
        GO TO 19
211     CONTINUE
        GO TO 19
222     CONTINUE
C
C    THERMAL STRESS  IN  STEEL
C
        N = LRF(I)
        MN1 = MCODE(I,1)
        MN2 = MCODE(I,2)
        EL    =DSQRT (( X(MN2)- X(MN1))**2 +(Y(MN2) - Y(MN1))**2 +
1           ( Z(MN2) - Z(MN1))**2)
        AST(N) =(3.14   * DIA(N)**2)/4
        AL    =  (X(MN2) - X(MN1))/EL
        AM    =  (Y(MN2) - Y(MN1))/EL
        AN    =  (Z(MN2) - Z(MN1))/ EL
        MN1= (MN1-1)*NDF+1
        MN2= (MN2-1)*NDF+1
        CR1 = AL * U(MN1) + AM*U(MN1+1)+AN*U(MN1+2)
        CR2=AL*U(MN2)+AM*U(MN2+1)+AN*U(MN2+2)
```

```
          SIGG1(I) = EST(N)*(CR2 - CR1) / EL
          GO TO 19
333       CONTINUE
C
C   CALL SUBR. BOND TO CALCULATR THE BOND STRESSES
C+++++
C
19        CONTINUE
18        CONTINUE
22        CONTINUE
          WRITE(6,311)
C#####
311       FORMAT(1H1,5X,13HSTFEL ELEMENT,10X,8HSTRESSES)
          LEN1=NTE1+NTE2+1
          LEN2=NTE1+NTE2+NTE3
          DO  491 JS=LEN1,LEN2
          WRITE(6,309)JS,SIGG1(JS)
C#####
491       CONTINUE
309       FORMAT(7X,I5,10X,F12.6)
          CALL CTIMFA(MTS2)
C+++++
          WRITE(6,1001) MTS2 ,MTS1 ,RTS
C#####
1001      FORMAT('CPUTIME AT EXIT FROM STRESS ROUTINE =',I10/
     1      'CPU TIME AT ENTRY TO STRESS ROUTINE =',I10/
     2      'CPU TIME SPENT IN STRESS ROUTINE    =',F10.2/)
          RETURN
          END
Cfffffffffffffffffffff
Cfffffffffffffffffffff
          SUBROUTINE ASSEMM
C...      THIS ROUTINE IS CODED BY **THIRU** (29/10/80)
C...      ROUTINE TO ASSEMBLE CONSISTENT MASS MATRIX IN
C...      BANDED FORM.
          IMPLICIT REAL*8(A-H,O-Z)
Cffffffffffffffffffffff
          COMMON/AAA/ NEL,NNP,NEQ,NHBD,NBC,NTE1,NTE2,NTE3,NTE4,
     1    NNE1,NNE2,NNE3,NNE4,NDF,NRF,NRS,DETJ
          COMMON/SEP/ NDI(366), JRC(3),XJN(12)
          COMMON/BBB/ D(6,6),D1(6,6),E(12,3),POIS(12,6),MCODE(12,20),
     1         EK(60,60) ,H(6,60),LRF(12),IDENT(12),RAW(1),EM(60,60)
          COMMON/LID/ SK(366,165),SM(366,165),SKK(1,1)
          COMMON/BON/ NNODE, NEUB,NETB,NBLOK
          CALL TIMING(1)
C+++++
          DO 1 J=1,NEQ
          DO 1 IJ=1,NHBD
          SM(J,IJ)=0.0
1         CONTINUE
          DO 2 I=1,NEL
          CALL MASS(I)
C+++++
          DO 3  IM=1,NNE1
          IND=(IM-1)*NDF
          JND=MCODE(I,IM)
          KND=(JND-1)*NDF
          DO 4 IS=1,NDF
          KND=KND+1
          NDI(IND+IS)=KND
4         CONTINUE
3         CONTINUE
          JP=NNE1*NDF
          DO 5 II=1,JP
          NR=NDI(II)
          DO 6 JJ=1,JP
          NCL=NDI(JJ)
          IF(NCL.LT.NR)GO TO 6
          NCL=NCL-NR+1
          SM(NR,NCL)=SM(NR,NCL)+EM(II,JJ)
6         CONTINUE
5         CONTINUE
2         CONTINUE
          WRITE(5,1000)
C#####
          CALL TIMING(2)
C+++++
1000      FORMAT('TIME TO ASSEMBLE CONSISTENT MATRIX = ')
C         DO 7 J=1,NEUB
C         NEQN=NEQN+1
```

```
C       WRITE(6,100)NEQN,(SM(J,IJ),IJ=1,NHBD)
C#####
C100     FORMAT(2X,I3,10E12.4,(/,4X,10E12.4))
C7       CONTINUE
         RETURN
         END
         SUBROUTINE MASS(I)
         IMPLICIT REAL*8(A-H,O-Z)
Cfffff:fffffffffffffff
         COMMON/GS/ NG1
         COMMON/MEM/ SP(20),SJ(3,3)
         COMMON/CAP/ GE1(27),GE2(27),GE3(27),WE(4)
          COMMON/DLE/S(20,3),CC(3,20),C(3,3)
         COMMON/AAA/ NEL,NNP,NEQ,NHBD,NBC,NTE1,NTE2,NTE3,NTE4,
     1  NNE1,NNE2,NNE3,NNE4,NDF,NRF,NRS,DETJ
         COMMON/SEP/ NDI(366), JRC(3),XJN(12)
         COMMON/BBB/ D(6,6),D1(6,6),E(12,3),POIS(12,6),MCODE(12,20),
     1           EK(60,60) ,H(6,60),LRF(12),IDENT(12),RAW(1),EM(60,60)
          COMMON/LID/ SK(366,165),SM(366,165),SKK(1,1)
         COMMON/BON/ NNODE, NEUR,NETR,NBLOK
         WRITE(6,6)
C#####
6        FORMAT('MASS')
         JP=NDF*NNE1
         N=LRF(I)
         DO 1 IS=1,60
         DO 1 JS=1,60
1        EM(IS,JS)=0.0
         DO 2 J1=1,NG1
         DO 2 J2=1,NG1
         DO 2 J3=1,NG1
         CALL ISOP2(I,J1,J2,J3,2,4)
C+++++
         DOS=WE(J1)*WE(J2)*WE(J3)*DETJ
         DO 3 II=1,NNE1
         DO 3 JJ=1,NNE1
         IF(II.GT.JJ) GO TO 10
         EIMJ=0.0
         EIMJ=EIMJ+RAW(N)*SP(II)*SP(JJ)*DOS
         I3=3*(II-1)
         J3=3*(JJ-1)
         DO 4 III=1,3
         EM(I3+III,J3+III)=EM(I3+III,J3+III)+EIMJ
10       CONTINUE
4        CONTINUE
3        CONTINUE
2        CONTINUE
         DO 5 II=1,JP
         DO 5 JJ=1,JP
5        EM(JJ,II)=EM(II,JJ)
         RETURN
         END
         SUBROUTINE EIG(A,R,N,MV)
         IMPLICIT REAL*8(A-H,O-Z)
Cffffffffffffffffffff
         DIMENSION A(1),R(1)
C        GENERATE IDENTITY MATRIX
         IF(MV-1) 10,25,10
10       IQ=-N
         DO 20 J=1,N
         IQ=IQ+N
         DO 20 I9=1,N
         IJ=IQ+I9
         R(IJ)=0.0
         IF(I9-J) 20,15,20
15       R(IJ)=1.0
20       CONTINUE
C        COMPUTE INITIAL AND FINAL NORM(ANORM AND ANORMX)
25       ANORM=0.0
         DO 35 I9=1,N
         DO 35 J=1,N
         IF(I9-J) 30,35,30
30       IA=I9+(J*J-J)/2
         ANORM=ANORM+A(IA)*A(IA)
35       CONTINUE
         IF(ANORM)165,165,40
40       ANORM=1.414*DSQRT(ANORM)
         ANRMX=ANORM*1.0E-6/FLOAT(N)
C        INITIALIZE INDICATORS AND COMPUTE THRESHOLD THR
         IND=0
```

```
          THR=ANORM
45        THR=THR/FLOAT(N)
50        L=1
55        M=L+1
C            COMPUTE SIN AND COS
60        MQ=(M*M-M)/2
          LQ=(L*L-L)/2
          LM=L+MQ
62        IF(DABS(A(LM))-THR)130,65,65
65        IND=1
          LL=L+LQ
          MM=M+MQ
          X=0.5*(A(LL))-A(MM)
68        Y=-A(LM)/DSQRT(A(LM)*A(LM)+X*X)
          IF(X) 70,75,75
70        Y=-Y
75        SINX=Y/DSQRT(2.0*(1.0+(DSQRT(1.0-Y*Y))))
          SINX2=SINX*SINX
78        COSX=DSQRT((1.0-SINX2))
          COSX2=COSX*COSX
          SINCS=SINX*COSX
          ILQ=N*(L-1)
          IMQ=N*(M-1)
          DO 125 I9=1,N
          IQ=(I9*I9-I9)/2
          IF(I9-L) 80,115,80
80        IF(I9-M) 85,115,90
85        IM=I9+MQ
          GO TO 95
90        IM=M+IQ
95        IF(I9-L)100,105,105
100       IL=I9+LQ
          GO TO 110
105       IL=L+LQ
110       X=A(IL)*COSX-A(IM)*SINX
          A(IM)=A(IL)*SINX+A(IM)*COSX
          A(IL)=X
115       IF(MV-1)120,125,120
120       ILR=ILQ+I9
          IMR=IMQ+I9
          X=R(ILR)*COSX-R(IMR)*SINX
          R(IMR)=R(ILR)*SINX+R(IMR)*COSX
          R(ILR)=X
125       CONTINUE
          X=2.0*A(LM)*SINCS
          Y=A(LL)*COSX2+A(MM)*SINX2-X
          X=A(LL)*SINX2+A(MM)*COSX2+X
          A(LM)=(A(LL)-A(MM))*SINCS+A(LM)*(COSX2-SINX2)
          A(LL)=Y
          A(MM)=X
C            TESTS FOR COMPLETION
C            TEST FOR M=LAST COLUMN
130       IF(M-N) 135,140,135
135       M=M+1
          GO TO 60
140       IF(L-(N-1))145,150,145
145       L=L+1
          GO TO 55
150       IF(IND-1)160,155,160
155       IND=0
          GO TO 50
160       IF(THR-ANRMX)165,165,45
165       IQ=-N
```

```
180     R(IMR)=X
185     CONTINUE
        RETURN
        END
Cfffffffffffffffffff
        SUBROUTINE PFORM(DT,TAW)
Cfffffffffffffffffff
        IMPLICIT REAL*8(A-H,O-Z)
        COMMON/REL/ U(366),P(366),PT(366),U1(366),U10(366),U2(366)
     1    ,U20(366),U0(366),P1(366),PS(366),PIU(366),PIT(366)
        COMMON/LID/ SK(366,165),SM(366,165),SKK(1,1)
        COMMON/AAA/ NEL,NNP,NEQ,NHBD,NBC,NTE1,NTE2,NTE3,NTE4,
     1 NNE1,NNE2,NNE3,NNE4,NDF,NRF,NRS,DETJ
        COMMON/CCC/ X(128),Y(128),Z(128),NZN(366) ,NFIX(366) ,
     1 AST(12),EST(12),DIA(12),ELINE(6,6),ELINK(6,6)
        CALL TIMING(1)
C+++++
        TAW1=6.0/TAW
        TAW2=TAW1/TAW
        K2=NEQ-NHBD
        DO 1 I1 = 1,NEQ
        P1(I1)=0.0
        IF(NZN(I1).EQ.1) GO TO 1
        K1=I1+NHBD-1
        IF(I1.GT.K2)K1=NEQ
        DO 2 I2 =I1,K1
        I4=I2-I1+1
        SMI=TAW2*U0(I2)
        SMI=SMI+TAW1*U10(I2)
        SMI=SMI+2.0*U20(I2)
        SMI=SMI*SM(I1,I4)
        P1(I1)=P1(I1)+SMI
2       CONTINUE
1       CONTINUE
        DO 3 I3=1,NEQ
        P(I3)=PS(I3)+PIT(I3)+P1(I3)
3       CONTINUE
        WRITE(6,1000)
C#####
1000    FORMAT(1X,'PFORM')
        WRITE(6,1001)
C#####
1001    FORMAT('TIME TO FORM LOAD VECTOR = ')
        CALL TIMING(2)
C+++++
        CALL WRITE1(PIT,NEQ,4HPT  ,2)
C+++++
        CALL WRITE1(PS,NEQ,4HP   ,2)
C+++++
        CALL WRITE1(P1,NEQ,4HP1  ,2)
C+++++
        CALL WRITE1(U0,NEQ,4HU0  ,2)
C+++++
        CALL WRITE1(U10,NEQ,4HU10 ,2)
C+++++
        CALL WRITE1(U20,NEQ,4HU20 ,2)
C+++++
        RETURN
        END
Cfffffffffffffffffff
        SUBROUTINE EFSTIF(DT,TAW,THET)
C...         THIS ROUTINE IS CODED BY THIRU 29/10/80 TO FORM
C...         THE EFFECTIVE STIFNESS BY ADDING A SCALAR MULTIPLE OF
C...         CONSISTENT MASS MATRIX TO THE  GLOBAL STIFFNESS MATRIX
        IMPLICIT REAL*8(A-H,O-Z)
        COMMON/LID/ SK(366,165),SM(366,165),SKK(1,1)
        COMMON/AAA/ NEL,NNP,NEQ,NHBD,NBC,NTE1,NTE2,NTE3,NTE4,
     1 NNE1,NNE2,NNE3,NNE4,NDF,NRF,NRS,DETJ
        CALL TIMING(1)
C+++++
        TAW=THET*DT
        TAW2=6.0/TAW**2
        WRITE(6,1000)DT,TAW,THET,TAW2
C#####
1000    FORMAT(1X,'DT= ',F5.2,'TAW =',F5.2,'THET =',F5.2,'TAW2=',F5.2)
        DO 1 I1=1,NEQ
        DO 1 I2 =1,NHBD
        SK(I1,I2)=TAW2*SM(I1,I2)+SK(I1,I2)
1       CONTINUE
        WRITE(6,1001)
```

```
C#####
1001   FORMAT(*TIME TO ASSEMBLE EFECTIVE STIFNESS = *)
       CALL TIMING(2)
C+++++
       CALL BCOND
C+++++
       CALL WRITE2(SK,NEQ,NHBD,4HSK  ,1)
C+++++
       CALL WRITE2(SM,NEQ,NHBD,4HSM  ,1)
C+++++
       RETURN
       END
Cffffffffffffffffff
       SUBROUTINE ACVEDI(TAW,THET)
C...       THIS ROUTINE IS CODED BY THIRU 29/10/80
C...       THIS ROUTINE IS CALLED IN TO CALCULATE THE DISPLACEMENT ,
C+++++
C...       VELOCITY AND ACCELERATION FOR EACH TIME STEP
C...       TAW    =THET*DT
C...       THET   >1.37 (B.REBORA)
       IMPLICIT REAL*8(A-H,O-Z)
       COMMON/REL/ U(366),P(366),PT(366),U1(366),U10(366),U2(366)
      1   ,U20(366),U0(366),P1(366),PS(366),PIU(366),PIT(366)
       COMMON/LID/ SK(366,165),SM(366,165),SKK(1,1)
       COMMON/AAA/ NEL,NNP,NEQ,NHBD,NBC,NTE1,NTE2,NTE3,NTE4,
      1 NNE1,NNE2,NNE3,NNE4,NDF,NRF,NRS,DETJ
C...       U...ON ENTRY DISP AT T...ON EXIT DISP AT T+DT
C...       U1 VELOCITY AT T+DT
C...       U10 VELOCITY AT T
C...       U2... ACCN AT T+DT
C...       U20 ACCN AT T
       CALL TIMING(1)
C+++++
       TAW1=6.0/(TAW*THET)
       TAW2=TAW1/TAW
       DT1=TAW1/TAW
       DT2=0.5*DT1
       DT3=DT1**2/6.0
       TAW3=1.0-3.0/THET
       DO 1 I1 =1,NEQ
       U2(I1)=TAW2*(U(I1)-U0(I1))
      2    -TAW1*U10(I1)
      2    +TAW3*U20(I1)
       U1(I1)=U10(I1)+DT2*(U20(I1)+U2(I1))
       U(I1)=U(I1)+DT1*U10(I1)
      1    +DT3*(2.0*U20(I1)+U2(I1))
1      CONTINUE
       CALL WRITE1(U,NEQ,4HU   ,1)
C+++++
       CALL WRITE1(U1,NEQ,4HU1  ,1)
C+++++
       CALL WRITE1(U2,NEQ,4HU2  ,1)
C+++++
       DO 2 I1=1,NEQ
       U0(I1)=U(I1)
       U10(I1)=U1(I1)
       U20(I1)=U2(I1)
2      CONTINUE
       WRITE(6,1000)
C#####
1000   FORMAT(*TIME SPENT IN ACVEDI = *)
       CALL TIMING(2)
C+++++
       RETURN
       END
Cffffffffffffffffffff
       SUBROUTINE WRITE1(A,N,NAME,MOD)
       IMPLICIT REAL*8(A-H,O-Z)
       DIMENSION A(N)
       IF(MOD.EQ.1) RETURN
       WRITE(6,1001) NAME,N
C#####
1001   FORMAT(1X,A4,* MATRIX *,I4)
       WRITE(6,1000) (A(J),J=1,N)
C#####
1000   FORMAT(5X,6F15.4)
       RETURN
       END
Cffffffffffffffffffff
       SUBROUTINE WRITE2(A2,M,N,NAME,MOD)
```

```
      IMPLICIT REAL*8(A-H,O-Z)
      DIMENSION A2(M,N)
      IF(MOD.EQ.1) RETURN
      WRITE(6,1001) NAME,M,N
C#####
1001  FORMAT(1X,A4, * MATRIX *,I3,1X,I3)
      K=0
      DO 1 J=1,M
      K=K+1
      WRITE(6,1000) K,(A2(J,IJ),IJ=1,N)
C#####
1000  FORMAT(2X,I3,10E12.4,(/,1X,10E12.4))
1     CONTINUE
      RETURN
      END
Cffffffffffffffffff
      LOGICAL FUNCTION PCOMP(A,B)
Cffffffffffffffffffff
      IMPLICIT REAL*8(A-H,O-Z)
      PCOMP=.FALSE.
      IF(A.EQ.B) PCOMP=.TRUE.
      RETURN
      END
Cffffffffffffffffffff
      SUBROUTINE MACRO
      IMPLICIT REAL*8(A-H,O-Z)
      LOGICAL DYN
      COMMON/LID/ SK(366,165),SM(366,165),SKK(1,1)
      COMMON/BBB/ D(6,6),D1(6,6),E(12,3),POIS(12,6)
     1            EK(60,60) ,H(6,60),LRF(12),IDENT(12
      COMMON/CCC/ X(128),Y(128),Z(128),NZN(366) ,NF
     1 AST(12),EST(12),DIA(12),ELINE(6,6),ELINK(6,6
      COMMON/REL/ U(366),P(366),PT(366),U1(366),U10
     1   ,U20(366),U0(366),P1(366),PS(366),PIU(366),
      COMMON/SEP/ NDI(366), JRC(3),XJN(12)
      COMMON/BON/ NNODE, NEUB,NETB,NBLOK
      COMMON/AAA/ NEL,NNP,NEQ,NH8D,NBC,NTE1,NTE2,NT
     1 NNE1,NNE2,NNE3,NNE4,NDF,NRF,NRS,DETJ
      LOGICAL PCOMP,AFL,AFR,BFL,BFR,CFL,CFR,DFL,DFR
      DIMENSION WD(21),CT(4,32),LVE(9),LVS(9)
      DATA WD/4HTOL ,4HDT  ,4HSTRE,4HPAVD,4HTANG,4H
     1         4HNEXT,4HPROP,4HDATA,4HTIME,4HCONV,4H
     2         4HCMAS,4HMESH,4HEIGE ,4HEXCD,4HACCN,4H
      DATA NWD/21/,ENDM/4HEND /
C...      SET INITIAL VALUES OF THE PARAMETERS
      DT=0.0
      PROP=1.0
      RNMAX=0.0
      TOL=1.E-9
      THET=1.4
      UN=0.0
      TIME = 0.0
      K1 = 0
      NPLD = 0
      AFL=.TRUE.
      AFR=.FALSE.
      BFL=.TRUE.
      BFR=.FALSE.
      CFL=.TRUE.
      CFR=.FALSE.
      DFL=.FALSE.
      EFL=.TRUE.
      GFL=.TRUE.
```

```
          NE=NEND
          JP=NDF*NNE1
          DO 30 I=1,NEQ
          U0(I)=0.0
          U10(I)=0.0
          U20(I)=0.0
30        CONTINUE
C...      READ MACRO CARDS
C%%%%
          LL=1
          LMAX=16
          CT(1,1)=WD(7)
          CT(3,1)=1.0
100       LL=LL+1
C         WRITE(6,4005)
C#####
4005      FORMAT(1X,'100+')
```

```
        IF(LL.LT.LMAX) GO TO 110
        LMAX=LMAX+16
110     READ(5,1000) (CT(J,LL),J=1,4)
C%%%%
1000    FORMAT(A4,1X,A4,1X,2F5.0)
        WRITE(6,2000) (CT(J,LL),J=1,4)
C#####
2000    FORMAT(10X,A4,1X,A4,1X,2G15.5)
        IF(.NOT.PCOMP(CT(1,LL),ENDM)) GO TO 100
200     CT(1,LL)=WD(8)
C...        SET LOOP MARKERS
        LX=LL-1
        DO 230 L=1,LX
        IF(.NOT.PCOMP(CT(1,L),WD(7))) GO TO 230
        J=1
        K=L+1
        DO 210 I2=K,LL
        IF(PCOMP(CT(1,I2),WD(7))) J=J+1
        IF(J.GT.9) GO TO 401
        IF(PCOMP(CT(1,I2),WD(8))) J=J-1
210     IF(J.EQ.0) GO TO 220
        GO TO 400
220     CT(4,I2)=L
        CT(4,L)=I2
230     CONTINUE
        J=0
        DO 240 L=1,LL
        IF(PCOMP(CT(1,L),WD(7))) J=J+1
240     IF(PCOMP(CT(1,L),WD(8))) J=J-1
        IF(J.NE.0) GO TO 400
C...        EXECUTE MACRO INSTRUCTION PROGRAM
        LV=0
        L=1
299     DO 300 J=1,NWD
300     IF(PCOMP(CT(1,L),WD(J))) GO TO 310
        GO TO  330
310     I2=L-1
        IF(L.NE.1.AND.L.NE.LL)
       1WRITE(6,2010) I2, (CT(K,L),K=1,4)
C#####
2010    FORMAT(2X,'MACRO INSTRUCTION',I4,2X,'EXECUTED',2X,
       12(A4,2X),'V1 =',G13.4,'V2 =',G13.4)
        GO TO (1,2,3,4,5,6,7,8,9,10,11,12,13,14,15,16,17,18,19,20,21),J
C...        SET SOLUTION TOLERENCE
1       TOL=CT(3,L)
        GO TO 330
C...        SET TIME INCREMENT
2       DT=CT(3,L)
        GO TO 330
C...        PRINT STRESS VALUES
3       CONTINUE
        CALL STRESS
C+++++
        GO TO  330
4       LX = LVE(LV)
        IF(DMOD(CT(3,LX),DMAX1(CT(3,L),1.)).EQ.0.0) CALL PAVD
        GO TO 330
C...        FORM TANGENT STIFFNESS
5       IF(J.EQ.5) CFR=.FALSE.
        CALL ASSEMB
C+++++
        AFR=.TRUE.
        GO TO 330
C...        FORM OUT OF BALANCE FORCE FOR TIME STEP
6       IF(NPLD.GT.0)CALL PROPL(TIME,0,PROP,DT,INT1,INT,TL)
C+++++
        CALL PLOAD(PROP)
C+++++
        CALL PFORM(DT,TAW)
C+++++
        GO TO  330
C...        SET LOOP START INDICATORS
7       LV=LV+1
        LX=CT(4,L)
        LVS(LV)=L
        LVE(LV)=LX
        CT(3,LX)=1.0
        GO TO 330
C...        SET LOOP TERMINATOR CONTROLS
8       N=CT(4,L)
```

```
        CT(3,L)=CT(3,L)+1.0
        IF(CT(3,L).GT.CT(3,N)) LV=LV-1
        IF(CT(3,L).LE.CT(3,N)) L=N
        GO TO  330
9       NPLD = CT(3,L)
        CALL PROPL(0.,NPLD,PROP,DT,INT1,INT,TL)
C+++++
        CT(3,L+1) = INT1
        GO TO 330
10      GO TO 330
11      K1 = K1 + 1
        IF(K1.GT.INT) GO TO 101
        TIME = TIME + DT
        GO TO 330
101     TIME = TIME + TL
        GO TO 330
12      GO TO 330
13      CALL DECOMP
C+++++
        GO TO 330
14      CALL RESOLV
C+++++
        GO TO 330
15      CALL ASSEMM
C+++++
        GO TO  330
16      GO TO  330
17      GO TO 330
18      CALL EFSTIF(DT,TAW,THET)
C+++++
        GO TO 330
19      CALL ACVEDI(TAW,THET)
C+++++
        GO TO 330
20      CONTINUE
        CALL STDISP
        GO TO 330
21      DYN = .TRUE.
        CALL LOAD(DYN)
C+++++
        GO TO 330
330     L=L+1
        IF(L.GT.LL) RETURN
        GO TO 299
400     WRITE(6,4000)
C#####
        RETURN
4000    FORMAT(5X,*FATAL ERROR 10 UNBALANCED LOOP NEXT MACROS*)
401     WRITE(6,4001)
C#####
        RETURN
4001    FORMAT(5X,*FATAL ERROR 11 LOOP NESTED DEEPER THAN 8*)
402     WRITE(6,4002)
C#####
        RETURN
4002    FORMAT(5X,*FATAL ERROR 12 MACRO LABEL MISMATCH ON A READ COMMAND*)
C%%%%%
403     WRITE(6,4003)
C#####
        RETURN
4003    FORMAT(5X,*FATAL ERROR 13 MACRO EXCD MUST BE PRECEEDED BY LMAS AND
       1FORM*)
        RETURN
404     WRITE(6,4004)
C#####
4004    FORMAT(5X,*FATAL ERROR 14 ATTEMPT TO CHANGE BOUNDARY RESTRAINT*)
        RETURN
        END
Cfffffffffffffff
Cfffffffffffffffff
        SUBROUTINE BAND
C...        THIS ROUTINE CALCULATES BANDWITH(SEMI).
C...        BANDWIDTH WILL DETERMINE THE SIZE OF THE *SK*
C...        AND *SM* MATRICES
Cfffffffffffffffff
        IMPLICIT REAL*8(A-H,O-Z)
        COMMON/SEP/ NDI(366), JRC(3),XJN(12)
        COMMON/AAA/ NEL,NNP,NEQ,NHBD,NBC,NTE1,NTE2,NTE3,NTE4,
       1 NNE1,NNE2,NNE3,NNE4,NDF,NRF,NRS,DETJ
        COMMON/BBB/ D(6,6),D1(6,6),E(12,3),POIS(12,6),MCODE(12,20),
```

```
      1              EK(60,60) ,H(6,60),LRF(12),IDENT(12),RAW(1),EM(60,60)
C
C             CALCULATE   HALF - BANDWIDTH
C
      JHBD = 1
      DO  266  I =  1, NEL
      LET =  IDENT(I)
      GO TO (256,257,258,260) ,LET
256   NER = NNE1
      GO TO 259
257   NER = NNE2
      GO TO  259
258   NER = NNE3
      GO TO 259
260   NER=NNE4
259   MET = 10000
      JET = 1
      DO  266 J = 1, NER
      IF (MCODE(I , J) .LT. MET)    MET = MCODE(I,J)
      IF (MCODE(I , J) .GT. JET)    JET = MCODE(I,J)
      IF ((JET - MET). GT. JHBD)    JHBD =(JET - MET )
266   CONTINUE
      NHBD = (JHBD+ 1 )*NDF
      WRITE(6,207) NHBD
C#####
207   FORMAT(8X,20HHALF BANDWIDTH IS  =,I5)
      RETURN
      END
C£££££££££££££££££££
      SUBROUTINE PLOAD(PR)
      IMPLICIT REAL*8(A-H,O-Z)
      COMMON/CCC/ X(128),Y(128),Z(128),NZN(366) ,NFIX(366) ,
     1 AST(12),EST(12),DIA(12),ELINE(6,6),ELINK(6,6)
      COMMON/AAA/ NEL,NNP,NEQ,NHBD,NBC,NTE1,NTE2,NTE3,NTE4,
     1 NNE1,NNE2,NNE3,NNE4,NDF,NRF,NRS,DETJ
      COMMON/REL/ U(366),P(366),PT(366),U1(366),U10(366),U2(366)
     1  ,U20(366),UO(366),P1(366),PS(366),PIU(366),PIT(366)
      DO 1 I = 1,NEQ
      J = NZN(I)
1     IF(J.EQ.0) PIT(I) = PIU(I) * PR
      RETURN
      END
      SUBROUTINE PROPL(T,J,PROP,DT,INT1,INT,TL)
      IMPLICIT REAL*8(A-H,O-Z)
C
C
C
      DIMENSION A(2)
      IF(J.GT.0) GO TO 200
C...       COMPUTE VALUE AT TIME T
      PROP = 0.0
      IF(T.LT.TMIN.OR.T.GT.TMAX) RETURN
      PROP = A(1) + A(2)*T
      RETURN
200   READ(5,*)K,L,TMIN,TMAX,A(1),A(2)
C%%%%%
      WRITE(6,2000) K,L,TMIN,TMAX,A(1),A(2)
C#####
2000  FORMAT(5X,*PROPORTIONAL LOAD TABLE*//*NUMBER TYPE.*,
     1      *MINIMUM TIME*,*MAXI TIME *,5X,*A1*,13X,*A2*
     2     /2I8,4G15.5)
      INT = (TMAX -TMIN)/DT
      TL = TMAX -(INT*DT + TMIN )
      IF(TL.GT.1.E-4) GO TO 1
      INT1 = INT
      RETURN
1     INT1= INT + 1
      RETURN
      END
      SUBROUTINE TIMING(NTIM)
      IMPLICIT REAL*8(A-H,O-Z)
      INTEGER*4 ICP,ITM1,ITM2
      DOUBLEPRECISION TIM
      CALL CTIM£A(ICP)
C+++++
      CALL TIME£A(TIM)
C+++++
      WRITE(6,101)NTIM,TIM,ICP
C##4##
101   FORMAT(I5,A8,I10)
      GO TO (1,2),NTIM
```

```
1       ITM1 = ICP
        RETURN
2       ITM2 = ICP
        RTM = FLOAT((ITM2 - ITM1)/100.0)
        WRITE(6,100) RTM
C#####
100     FORMAT(1H+,50X,F10.2,'SECS')
        RETURN
        END
        SUBROUTINE PAVD
        IMPLICIT REAL*8(A-H,O-Z)
        COMMON/AAA/ NEL,NNP,NEQ,NHBD,NBC,NTE1,NTE2,NTE3,NTE4,
     1 NNE1,NNE2,NNE3,NNE4,NDF,NRF,NRS,DETJ
        COMMON/REL/ U(366),P(366),PT(366),U1(366),U10(366),U2(366)
     1  ,U20(366),U0(366),P1(366),PS(366),PIU(366),PIT(366)
        CALL WRITE1(U,NEQ,4HU   ,2)
        CALL WRITE1(U1,NEQ,4HU1  ,2)
        CALL WRITE1(U2,NEQ,4HU2  ,2)
        RETURN
        END
        SUBROUTINE STDISP
        IMPLICIT REAL*8(A-H,O-Z)
        COMMON/AAA/ NEL,NNP,NEQ,NHBD,NBC,NTE1,NTE2,NTE3,NTE4,
     1 NNE1,NNE2,NNE3,NNE4,NDF,NRF,NRS,DETJ
        COMMON/REL/ U(366),P(366),PT(366),U1(366),U10(366),U2(366)
     1  ,U20(366),U0(366),P1(366),PS(366),PIU(366),PIT(366)
        WRITE(6,2002)
C#####
2002    FORMAT(1H1 , 5X,6H NODES, 8X, 10H X- DISPL., 8X,9H Y-DISPL. ,
     1 8X, 9H Z-DISPL.)
        DO 912 I=1,NNP
912     WRITE(6,412) I , U(3*I-2)    ,U(3*I-1) , U(3*I )
C#####
412     FORMAT(/,5X, I5, 6X, E16.8, 6X, E16.8, 6X, E16.8)
        RETURN
        END
```

INDEX

Index

Index compiled by INDEXING SPECIALISTS, 202 Church Road, Hove, East Sussex, BN3 2DJ. Telephone No.
01273 738299.